Life Safety Code® Handbook

Fifth Edition

Life Safety Code Handbook

Fifth Edition

Based on the 1991 Edition of the
Life Safety Code®

Edited by

James K. Lathrop

National Fire Protection Association, Inc.
Quincy, Massachusetts
NFPA®

This Fifth Edition of the *Life Safety Code Handbook* is based on the 1991 Edition of NFPA *101,*® *Life Safety Code.*® The nation's most authoritative and comprehensive document on safety to life in buildings, the *Code* addresses safety to life from fire in both new and existing structures. The *Code* is developed by the NFPA Committee on Safety to Life. This Committee, along with its twelve subcommittees, consists of a broad range of representatives from many building-related fields, including architects, engineers, building product manufacturers, code enforcers, building owners, and insurers.

Like other NFPA code handbooks, the *Life Safety Code Handbook* explains *Code* requirements, especially changes to the *Code* since the last edition. It also serves as a helpful quide in applying *Code* provisions. The *Handbook* contains the complete text of the *Code*, along with explanatory commentary, which is integrated between *Code* requirements.

All of the commentary material has been researched, written, and reviewed by recognized experts in the field of life safety who are also members of committees that have developed the *Life Safety Code*.

All NFPA codes and standards are processed in accordance with NFPA's *Regulations Governing Committee Projects*. The commentary in this *Handbook* is the opinion of the authors. The commentary is not processed in accordance with the NFPA *Regulations Governing Committee Projects* and, therefore, shall not be considered to be, nor relied upon as, a formal interpretation of the meaning or intent of any specific provision or provisions of NFPA *101*. The language contained in NFPA *101*, as opposed to this commentary, represents the official position of the Committee on Safety to Life and the NFPA.

This *Handbook* is a must for architects, engineers, building and fire officials, safety personnel, and all others whose responsibilities include fire and life safety.

Copyright © 1991
National Fire Protection Association, Inc.
All Rights Reserved

®Registered Trademark National Fire Protection Association, Inc.

NFPA No.: 101HB91
ISBN: 0-87765-379-8
Library of Congress No.: 89-642947
Printed in U.S.A.

Second Printing, January 1992

Contents

Foreword

For over 60 years, the National Fire Protection Association has been the developer and publisher of the *Life Safety Code*. Formerly known as the *Building Exits Code*, the *Code* is prepared by the NFPA Committee on Safety to Life, one of the more than 200 technical committees operating within the framework of the NFPA's standards-making system. The members of the Committee on Safety to Life are a group of highly qualified individuals who have demonstrated knowledge and competence in the design and construction of buildings and structures, in the manufacture and testing of building components and accessories, and in the enforcement of regulations pertaining to life safety from fire and other related hazards encountered in buildings and structures.

The *Life Safety Code* is a unique document; its contents address specific requirements that have a direct influence on safety to life in both new *and* existing structures — not new construction alone. Moreover, although the *Code's* paramount concern is life safety and not protection of property per se, there are also, by observance of the *Code's* requirements, ancillary benefits to property protection.

The impact that application of the *Code* may have on saving lives is difficult to measure; however, it is reasonable to assume that its influence is extremely significant. For example, of the many fatal building fires (other than those in one- and two-family dwellings) investigated by the NFPA, invariably one or more of the factors contributing to loss of life from fire were in violation of the requirements of the *Code*.

The NFPA recognizes that a code suitable for enforcement must, by the nature of its purpose, be concise and without explanatory text. In addition, a code cannot be written to cover every situation that will be encountered; thus, it must be applied with judgment and used with good sense and with an awareness of the rationale for the requirements to be enforced. A little help and counsel along the way can make the job a lot easier; hence, the NFPA has also developed this *Life Safety Code Handbook*.

This *Handbook* gives users of the *Life Safety Code* background information on the reasons for certain *Code* provisions, as recalled by members of the Committee on Safety to Life and by NFPA staff members. It also provides some suggestions, through its text and illustrations, on how some *Code* requirements can be implemented intelligently. With the availability of this kind of information, it is hoped that users of the *Code* will have a better understanding of, and appreciation for, the requirements contained in the *Code*. The net result should be buildings and structures that are increasingly more firesafe. The reader is cautioned, however, to look upon the commentary that appears in the *Handbook* simply as the views expressed by the contributors to the *Handbook*. The commentary does not necessarily reflect the official position of the NFPA or of the Committee on Safety to Life.

The editor welcomes critiques of the commentary on *Code* requirements appearing in this Fifth Edition as well as suggestions on other *Code* provisions that should be discussed. In the sense that the *Life Safety Code* reflects consensus of the best firesafety solutions developed by a balanced committee, the *Life Safety Code Handbook* represents, in turn, the best in thought by fire protection practitioners involved with the *Code* and its requirements. It is knowledge that must be shared.

ARTHUR E. COTE, P.E.
Assistant Vice President and Chief Engineer
National Fire Protection Association

Preface

The *Life Safety Code* had its origin in the work of the Committee on Safety to Life of the National Fire Protection Association, which was first appointed in 1913. For the first few years of its existence, the Committee devoted its attention to a study of notable fires involving loss of life and to analyzing the causes of that loss of life. This work led to the preparation of standards for the construction of stairways, fire escapes, and similar structures; for fire drills in various occupancies; and for the construction and arrangement of exit facilities for factories, schools, and other occupancies, which form the basis of the present *Code*. These reports were adopted by the National Fire Protection Association and published in pamphlet form as "Outside Stairs for Fire Exits" (1916) and "Safeguarding Factory Workers from Fire" (1918). A pamphlet, "Exit Drills in Factories, Schools, Department Stores and Theatres," was published in 1912 following its presentation by the late Committee member, R. H. Newbern, at the 1911 Annual Meeting of the Association. Although antedating the organization of the Committee, this pamphlet was considered to have the status of a Committee publication and subsequently became, with the other pamphlets, the groundwork for the present *Code*. Those pamphlets were widely circulated and put into general use.

In 1921, the Committee was enlarged to include representation of certain interested groups not previously participating, and work was started on the further development and integration of previous Committee publications in order to provide a comprehensive guide to exits and related features of life safety from fire in all classes of occupancy. Known as the *Building Exits Code*, various drafts were published, circulated, and discussed over a period of years, and the first edition of the *Building Exits Code* was published by the National Fire Protection Association in 1927. Thereafter, the Committee continued its deliberations, adding new material on issues not originally covered and revising various details in light of fire experience and practical experience in the use of the *Code*. New editions were published in 1929, 1934, 1936, 1938, 1942, and 1946 to incorporate the amendments adopted by the National Fire Protection Association.

The Cocoanut Grove Night Club fire in Boston in 1942, in which 492 lives were lost, focused national attention upon the importance of adequate exits and related firesafety features. Public attention to exit matters was further stimulated by a series of hotel fires in 1946 (the LaSalle, Chicago — 61 dead; the Canfield, Dubuque — 19 dead; and the Winecoff, Atlanta — 119 dead). Thereafter, the *Building Exits Code* was used to an increased extent for legal regulatory purposes. However, the *Code* was not in suitable form for adoption into law, because it had been drafted as a reference document containing many advisory provisions useful to designers of buildings but not appropriate for legal use. This led to a decision by the Committee to re-edit the entire *Code*, limiting the body of the text to requirements suitable for mandatory application and placing advisory and explanatory material in notes. The re-editing also involved adding to the *Code* provisions for many new features in order to produce a complete document. Preliminary work was carried on concurrently with development of the 1948, 1949, 1951, and 1952 Editions. The results were incorporated into the 1956 Edition and further refined in subsequent editions dated 1957, 1958, 1959, 1960, 1961, and 1963.

In 1955, separate documents, NFPA 101B and NFPA 101C, covering nursing homes and interior finish, respectively, were published. NFPA 101C was revised in 1956. These publications have since been withdrawn.

In 1963, the Committee on Safety to Life was reconstructed. The Committee was decreased in size to include only those individuals having very broad knowledge in fire matters while representing all interested factions. The Committee served as a review and correlating committee for seven sectional committees whose members included personnel having a special knowledge and interest in various parts of the *Code*.

Under the revised structure, the sectional committees, through the Safety to Life Committee, prepared the 1966 Edition of the *Code*, which was a complete revision of the 1963 Edition. The *Code* title was changed from *Building Exits Code* to *Code for Safety to Life from Fire in Buildings and Structures*. The text was put into "code language," and all explanatory notes were placed in an appendix. The *Code* was placed on a three-year revision schedule, with new editions published in 1967, 1970, 1973, and 1976.

In 1977, the Committee on Safety to Life was reorganized as a Technical Committee, with an Executive Committee and eleven standing subcommittees responsible for various chapters and sections. The 1981 Edition contained major editorial changes, including reorganization within the occupancy chapters to make them parallel to each other and separation of the requirements for new and existing buildings into individual chapters. New chapters on detention and correctional facilities were added, as well as new requirements for atria, apartments for the elderly, and ambulatory health care centers. The 1985 Edition contained major editorial and technical changes in Section 5-2 on means of egress components; a new Chapter 21 on residential board and care occupancies (with related Appendices F and G); deletion of special provisions for housing for the elderly and dormitories; a new Appendix D on alternative calculations for stair width; and Appendix E, a Firesafety Evaluation System (FSES) for detention and correctional facilities. The 1988 edition contained a major change in the method of determining egress capacity as a result of the deletion of the traditional units of exit width and the substitution of a straight linear approach to calculating egress capacity. Also, revisions to the method of measuring travel distance and specific requirements for remoteness of exits, as well as new provisions for amusement buildings and exhibit halls, were made. Appendices C through G were moved from NFPA *101* and published in a new document, NFPA 101M, *Manual on Alternative Approaches to Life Safety*.

Mandatory automatic sprinkler requirements constitute some of the major revisions to the 1991 Edition. New to this edition is the requirement for automatic sprinkler systems in health care, hotel, apartment, lodging and rooming, and residential board and care occupancies (most of which have some exceptions). Also, existing high rise apartments and hotels are now required to have automatic sprinkler systems throughout (also with some exceptions). Residential board and care requirements have been separated into one chapter for new facilities and one chapter for existing facilities (Chapters 22 and 23, respectively). Chapter 21 now covers one- and two-family dwellings.

In all of the work in developing the various sections of the *Code*, those groups concerned with specific issues have been given an opportunity to provide input and comment. All public proposals have been reviewed, and these proposals, along with Committee proposals and the Committee's response to all proposals, have been published by the NFPA for review by all concerned. Any comments received have been discussed, and many have been adopted by the Committee or at meetings of the NFPA. Records of the discussions and action taken by the NFPA can be found in the *Technical Committee Reports* and the *Technical Committee Documentation*.

The Committee on Safety to Life welcomes comments and suggestions on the *Life Safety Code*. Any reader may file a request for consideration of changes to the *Code*. Such requests should be filed in writing and should contain specific proposals and supporting data.

James K. Lathrop, Editor
Chief Life Safety Engineer
National Fire Protection Association

Revision and Use of the Life Safety Code

The *Life Safety Code* is revised approximately every three years. During each cycle, the Secretary of the Committee on Safety to Life accepts revision proposals from the public until an established deadline. These proposals are referred to appropriate subcommittees.

When the subcommittees meet, each proposal is considered, and some form of action is taken. A proposal may be accepted, accepted-in-part, accepted-in-principle, or rejected. This work is reviewed by the Committee on Safety to Life. Proposals and Committee actions are published in the *Technical Committee Reports* (TCR), which are distributed on request.

Following the publication of the TCR, a comment period of approximately sixty days is established. During this time, the public has the opportunity to respond to both the proposals and the Committee action. Comments must address TCR contents only; new concerns are not considered at this point in the cycle. At the closing of the comment period, the subcommittees reconvene to act on the public comments. Action on comments is similar to action on proposals and is published in the *Technical Committee Documentation* (TCD), which is distributed on request.

The contents of the TCR, as amended by the TCD, form the Committee's report to the NFPA membership. The membership votes to adopt, amend, or return the report (in whole or in part) to the Committee for further study. When the Committee report is adopted, the report of the association and the Committee input are reviewed by the NFPA Standards Council, which ultimately issues the document, and the new edition of the *Life Safety Code* is published.

During the revision cycle, *Tentative Interim Amendments* (TIAs) may be approved and released by the NFPA's Standards Council. TIAs are not subject to the standards-making procedure until the next successive edition of the *Code* is acted upon. Nevertheless, a TIA can have the force of a mandatory requirement if the local authority having jurisdiction adopts it.

The 1991 Edition of the *Life Safety Code* was adopted by the National Fire Protection Association, Inc. on November 14, 1990, at its 1990 Fall Meeting in Miami, Florida and was issued by the Standards Council on January 11, 1991, with an effective date of February 8, 1991. Major changes for this edition include but are not limited to: revisions to guard heights and locations of, as well as the opening sizes in, handrails and guards; modifications regarding the continuity of horizontal exits and duct penetration in horizontal exits; new provisions for areas of refuge; modifications to emergency lighting illumination levels; new material on egress requirements for mechanical equipment, boiler, and furnace rooms; a reorganization of the requirements for fire barriers; new provisions for mezzanines in Chapters 5 and 6; reorganization of the requirements for hazardous areas in Section 6-4 and rework of the hazardous area requirements in Chapters 14, 15, 16, 17, 18, and 19; revisions to aisle provisions in Chapters 8 and 9, for clarity as well as for including specific provisions for aisle accessways; revisions to the requirements of exhibit booths in Chapters 8 and 9; mandates for automatic sprinklers in all new health care facilities (including the use of quick response or residential sprinklers in patient sleeping zones); revisions to the door latching requirements in both new and existing health care occupancies; a mandate for automatic sprinklers in all new hotels and apartments as well as in all existing high rise hotels and apartments (with some exceptions); a mandate for all new board and care facilities to be sprinklered and for all new lodging and rooming houses to be sprinklered (with some exceptions); splitting the requirements for board and care facilities into one chapter for new structures and one chapter for existing structures and renumbering them as Chapters 22 and 23; moving one- and two-family dwellings from Chapter 22 to Chapter 21; completely revising the requirements for the means of escape in one- and two-family dwellings, as well as recognizing in hotels and apartment buildings that apartments and guest rooms must meet means of escape requirements rather than means of egress requirements; new provisions for combined mercantile and parking structures; revisions to shopping mall egress capacity figures; and complete revisions to the requirements for contents and furnishings in Chapter 31.

This 1991 Edition has been approved by the American National Standards Institute.

The following comments are offered to assist in the use of the *Life Safety Code*.

The *Code* consists essentially of five major parts. The first part comprises Chapters 1 through 7; these are often referred to as the base or fundamental chapters. The second part consists of Chapters 8 through 30, which are the occupancy chapters. The next part consists of Chapter 31, which covers operating features. The fourth part is Chapter 32, which covers mandatory referenced publications, and the fifth and last part consists of Appendices A and B, which contain useful additional information.

A thorough understanding of Chapters 1 through 7 is necessary before using the *Code*, since these chapters provide the "building blocks" upon which the occupancy chapters build their requirements. It should be noted that many of the provisions of Chapters 1 through 7 are mandatory for all occupancies. Some provisions are mandated only where referenced by a specific occupancy, while others are exempted for specific occupancies. Often, in one of the base chapters,

especially in Chapter 5, the term "where permitted by Chapters 8 through 30" appears. Where this does appear, that provision can be used only where specifically allowed by an occupancy chapter. For example, the provisions of 5-2.1.6 allow special locking devices only where permitted by Chapters 8 through 30. Permission to use such special locking devices is normally found in the "2.2" subsection of each occupancy chapter. For example, 8-2.2.2.4 specifically allows the use of these special locking arrangements in new assembly occupancies. If this permission is not found in an occupancy chapter, the special locking devices cannot be used. Similar types of restricted permission are found for such items as security grilles, double cylinder locks, special stairway reentry, revolving doors, atria, and other special features. At other points, in the base chapters, the term "unless prohibited by Chapters 8 through 30" is used. In this case, the provision is allowed in all occupancies unless specifically prohibited by an occupancy chapter.

Metric units of measurement in this *Code* are in accordance with the modernized metric system known as the International System of Units (SI). The unit "liter," which is not included in but nevertheless recognized by SI, is common usage and is used in this *Code*. In this *Code*, values for measurements are followed by an equivalent in SI units. The value that appears first shall be regarded as the requirement, because the given equivalent value may be approximate.

Acknowledgments

As editor of the Fifth Edition of the *Life Safety Code Handbook*, I offer my sincere gratitude and appreciation to those who have given so generously of their time, support, and knowledge in the preparation of this *Handbook*. The following persons deserve special acknowledgement for their extensive work in researching, writing, and reviewing the materials contained herein:

Donald W. Belles

William Koffel

Much of the material in this Fifth Edition is based on the First, Second, Third, and Fourth Editions. Contributors to the First Edition include: Donald W. Belles, Michael Slifka, Calvin Yuill, James Thompson, Harold Clar, Orville (Bud) Slye, and John A. Sharry (editor of the First Edition). Contributors to the Second Edition include: John A. Sharry, Donald W. Belles, Wayne G. (Chip) Carson, and David P. Demers. Contributors to the Third Edition include: John F. Behrens, Donald W. Belles, Wayne G. (Chip) Carson, Clifford S. Harvey, Alfred J. Longhitano, and John A. Sharry. Contributors to the Fourth Edition include: John F. Behrens, Donald W. Belles, Wayne G. (Chip) Carson, George Flach, Charles (Chuck) Kime, William Koffel, and Jake Pauls. It should be noted that Don Belles has contributed to every edition of the *Handbook*. The authors of new supplement material are identified in their by-lines, and their significant contribution is appreciated.

I sincerely appreciate the efforts of the NFPA staff members who attended to the countless details that went into the preparation of this *Handbook* and without whose efforts this book would never have gone to press. Included are:

Jennifer Evans, Project Manager

Pamela A. Nolan, Project Editor

Laurie A. Beaulieu, Art Coordinator

Kathleen Barber, Cathy Ray, Claire McRudin, and Nancy Maria, Composition

Donald McGonagle, Production

Cover Design: Cameron, Inc.

Interior Design: Joyce C. Weston

The NFPA Fire Analysis and Research Division under the leadership of Dr. John Hall, Assistant Vice President of the division, provided significant material regarding fire data.

Special appreciation is extended to Pamela A. Nolan, Joseph M. Jardin, and Ron Coté of the NFPA staff. Pamela's dedicated attention to detail in the proofreading and copy editing of the 1991 *Life Safety Code* contributed significantly to the quality of the document upon which this *Handbook* is based. Her tireless effort in editing also added to the quality of this *Handbook*. Ron and Joe not only contributed to many chapters of this *Handbook*, but in their staff positions as Senior Life Safety Engineer and Life Safety Engineer, they handled, along with Greg Cahanin, Senior Life Safety Specialist, much of the day-to-day workload of the Life Safety Field Service Department during the period in which this publication was being prepared.

Finally I would like to thank my children, Michael and Melissa, for their patience and understanding during the preparation of four editions of the *Life Safety Code* and four editions of the *Life Safety Code Handbook* over the last dozen years.

James K. Lathrop

Photograph Acknowledgments

Photograph, page 63, reproduced with permission of Won-Door Corp.

Photograph, page 75, reproduced with permission of Jake Pauls, Hughes Associates, Inc.

Photograph, pages 241 and 294, by Jake Pauls, NRC Canada. Reproduced with permission of Jake Pauls, Hughes Associates, Inc.

Photograph, pages 248 and 302, by L. Smith, NRC Canada. Reproduced with permission of Jake Pauls, Hughes Associates, Inc.

Photograph, pages 257 and 311, by Pauls/Swibold/Garsonnin. Reproduced from the documentary film, "The Stair Event," with permission of Jake Pauls, Hughes Associates, Inc.

Photograph, pages 258 and 311, by L. Smith, NRC Canada. Reproduced with permission of Jake Pauls, Hughes Associates, Inc.

Photograph, pages 258 and 312, by Jake Pauls, NRC Canada. Reproduced with permission of Jake Pauls, Hughes Associates, Inc.

Photograph, pages 260 and 313, by E. Garsonnin. Reproduced with permission of Jake Pauls, Hughes Associates, Inc.

Photograph, pages 262 and 315, NRC Canada. Reproduced with permission of Jake Pauls, Hughes Associates, Inc.

PART 1

1991 *Life Safety Code* and Commentary

The text and illustrations that make up the commentary on the various sections of the *Life Safety Code* are printed in black. The text of the *Code* itself is printed in green.

The Formal Interpretations included in this *Handbook* were issued as a result of questions raised on specific editions of the *Code*. They apply to all previous and subsequent editions in which the text remains substantially unchanged. Formal Interpretations are not part of the *Code* and therefore are printed in a shaded green box.

Paragraphs that begin with the letter "A" are extracted from Appendix A of the *Code*. Appendix A material is not mandatory. It is designed to help users apply the provisions of the *Code*. In this *Handbook*, material from Appendix A is integrated with the text, so that it follows the paragraph it explains. An asterisk (*) following a paragraph number indicates that explanatory material from Appendix A will follow.

1

Administration

1-1.1 This *Code* shall be known as the *Life Safety Code*, may be cited as such, and is referred to herein as "this *Code*" or "the *Code*."

As discussed in the Preface to this *Life Safety Code Handbook*, the name of the *Code* was changed from the *Building Exits Code* to the *Life Safety Code* in 1966. This is significant because the change in title expanded this document beyond a specification code for stairways, doors, and fire escapes into a performance and specification code addressing all factors that contribute to or center upon life safety in the event of fire.

SECTION 1-2   Purpose

1-2.1 The purpose of this *Code* is to establish minimum requirements that will provide a reasonable degree of safety from fire in buildings and structures.

This *Code* reflects what should be considered as MINIMUM requirements that endeavor to ensure the safety of occupants from fires and similar emergencies. However, nothing in this *Code* should be interpreted as restricting the user from doing better than the specified minimums. (*See 1-5.9.*)

It is intended that these requirements address the life safety of all occupants. It is recognized that a percentage of the population functions with disabilities, either physical, emotional, or mental. Although the *Code* does not specifically make mention, the Committee has given consideration to the disabled in developing these egress related requirements. However, the user of this *Code* should be aware that federal, state, and local laws regarding handicapped ingress may impact building design.

1-2.2 The *Code* endeavors to avoid requirements that might involve unreasonable hardships or unnecessary inconvenience or interference with the normal use and occupancy of a building, but insists upon compliance with a minimum standard for firesafety consistent with the public interest.

When a building or structure is built, there is normally a reason for its presence. The *Code* takes into consideration the normal occupancy of a building and attempts not to interfere with the normal use of a building or set requirements that would cause unreasonable hardships or unnecessary inconvenience. Therefore, the *Life Safety Code* tends to be "occupancy oriented" but, nevertheless, the *Code* still insists upon compliance with a minimum standard of firesafety that is necessary for the public interest.

SECTION 1-3   Scope

1-3.1* This *Code* addresses life safety from fire and similar emergencies.

A-1-3.1   Panic. The *Code* recognizes that panic in a burning building may be uncontrollable, but deals with the potential panic hazard through measures designed to prevent the development of panic. Experience indicates that panic seldom develops, even in the presence of potential danger, so long as occupants of buildings are moving toward exits that they can see within a reasonable distance with no obstructions or undue congestion in the path of travel. However, any uncertainty as to the location or adequacy of means of egress, the presence of smoke, or stoppage of exit travel, such as may occur when one person stumbles and falls on the stairs, may be conducive to panic. Panic danger is greatest when there are large numbers of people in a confined area.

Evaluation of recent fire situations confirm that, contrary to popular perception, panic is not a typical occurrence in fire situations. In fact, studies indicate that occupants typically exhibit altruistic behavior. Human behavior in a dangerous situation may follow one of many courses. The usual choices are: (1) investigate, (2) sound an alarm, (3) rescue, (4) seek help, and (5) flee. Any of these actions would be considered normal behavior, even when taken en masse. The objective uppermost in the minds of most people is to avoid direct contact with a fire in the course of action taken.

1-3.2 The *Code* addresses those construction, protection, and occupancy features necessary to minimize danger to life from fire, smoke, fumes, or panic.

As pointed out in 1-3.6, this *Code* is not intended to be either a building code, nor a fire prevention code. However, in the interest of public safety, the *Code* does contain provisions typically associated with either a fire prevention or building code. For example, Chapters 12 and 13 provide minimum construction requirements for buildings housing health care occupancies. While construction requirements are typically considered the domain of the building code, it is necessary to ensure the integrity of the structure over the period of time required for staff to evacuate those who are incapable of self-preservation.

1-3.3 The *Code* identifies the minimum criteria for the design of egress facilities so as to permit prompt escape of occupants from buildings or, where desirable, into safe areas within the building.

Evacuation into safe areas (areas of refuge) should not be overlooked as an important aspect in means of egress design. In some cases, it is not practical to consider total evacuation to the exterior. Evacuation to areas of refuge can also increase design flexibility.

1-3.4 The *Code* recognizes that life safety is more than a matter of egress and, accordingly, deals with other considerations that are essential to life safety.

There are numerous elements that impact on the ultimate level of life safety. The *Code* does address many of these items. There are, however, elements that are not addressed. An example would be public education related to firesafety.

1-3.5 Where in fixed locations and occupied as buildings, vehicles, vessels, or other mobile structures shall be treated as buildings.

It is not uncommon to find railroad cars being converted into lounges or restaurants; ships or barges converted into hotels, lounges, or restaurants; or trailer units of tractor semitrailer combinations being used for storage or even assembly purposes. Where these types of vehicles, vessels, or other mobile structures are in a fixed location and are being occupied as a building, the *Code* intends that they be regulated as a building under the *Code*. The fact that there are tires on a trailer or that a ship is still floating does not automatically mean that they are not fixed locations and occupied as buildings. The authority having jurisdiction should ensure that the vehicle or vessel is being regulated by some other agency, such as the Coast Guard or Department of Transportation, before exempting it from the requirements of the *Code*.

1-3.6 The *Code* does not attempt to address those general fire prevention or building construction features that are normally a function of fire prevention and building codes.

As stated, the *Code* is not intended to be a building or fire code. However, in the interest of life safety, the *Code* does contain requirements that may resemble provisions of each. Chapter 31, "Operating Features," contains requirements that limit the flammability of contents introduced into certain occupancies, regulate smoking, and require the training of facility employees. These maintenance items combined with occupancy chapter provisions ensure an appropriate life safety package.

The *Code* intentionally remains silent on traditional building code issues such as wind loads, seismic considerations, and exterior exposure protection.

1-3.7 The prevention of accidental personal injuries during the course of normal occupancy of buildings, personal injuries incurred by an individual's own negligence, and the preservation of property from loss by fire have not been considered as the basis for any of the provisions of this *Code*.

The scope of the *Code* indicates that the *Code* covers only those design elements that relate to life safety from fire; however, the benefits of accident prevention and the preservation of property may result from adherence to the provisions of the *Code*.

The *Code* clearly states that it cannot "save" everyone in an occupancy even if all the design and operational requirements of the *Code* are met. In particular, those people who accidentally or deliberately initiate a fire or who are close to the point of ignition are beyond the *Code's* capability to totally or, in some cases, partially protect.

SECTION 1-4 Objective

1-4.1* The objective of this *Code* is to provide a reasonable level of safety by reducing the probability of injury and loss of life from the effects of fire and other emergencies having the potential for similar consequences with due consideration for functional requirements. This objective is accomplished within the context of the physical facilities, type of activities undertaken, the provisions for the capabilities of the staff, and the needs of all occupants. The level of safety is defined by the combination of prevention, protection, egress, and other features enumerated in the individual occupancy chapters.

A-1-4.1 The level of life safety is defined through requirements directed at the:

(a) Prevention of ignition.
(b) Detection of fire.
(c) Control of fire development.
(d) Confinement of the effects of fire.
(e) Extinguishment of fire.
(f) Provision of refuge and/or evacuation facilities.
(g) Staff reaction.
(h) Provision of firesafety information to occupants.

New to the 1991 Edition of the *Life Safety Code*, this section reinforces the occupancy orientation of the *Code* to the extent that each chapter reflects a package of life safety selected in recognition of facility function and staffing. The degree or "level" of life safety afforded an occupancy is an interwoven combination of the features reflected in A-1-4.1. A reduction in any one feature affects the whole package. Those seeking equivalencies or *Code* alternatives must be cognizant of this cause and effect relationship.

SECTION 1-5 Application

1-5.1 The *Code* applies to both new construction and existing buildings. In various chapters there are specific provisions for existing buildings that may differ from those for new construction.

This concept is essential to understanding the intent of the *Code*, which is to achieve a minimal level of life safety in all structures and in all occupancies. To this end, there are provisions throughout the document that either specifically apply to existing buildings or that are specifically modified for existing buildings. This represents an attempt to limit the impact of *Code* provisions on existing buildings. If no special provisions are made for existing structures, the provisions for new construction apply, which is an approach quite different from that of a building code. Therefore, given the adoption of a more recent edition of the *Code*, it is the *Code's* intent that existing buildings be brought into compliance with the provisions for existing buildings found in the current edition.

The following applies to the entire text: Where life safety is involved, there is no reason for an existing structure to fail to conform to the *Code*. As a minimum, the *Code* will modify or will alter the new requirements as they are applied to existing buildings. Yet, in many instances, the *Code* will not alter a basic provision at the expense of life safety and will call for its application in both new and existing buildings. In recognition of the fact that the *Life Safety Code* is a general code that applies across the board to all structures and occupancies, the *Code* is designed to be flexible in the event of the extenuating circumstances that may exist in an individual case. Since only the individuals involved can properly assess these extenuating circumstances, the authority having jurisdiction is recognized as the best judge of the extent to which the *Code* may be further modified. However, the *Code* does establish the minimum provision so that reasonable life safety against the hazards of fire, explosion, and panic is provided and maintained.

Also see 1-5.2, 1-5.4, 1-5.6, Section 1-6, 1-7.2, and 3-2 Existing.

1-5.2 A limited but reasonable time shall be allowed for compliance with any part of this *Code* for existing buildings commensurate with the magnitude of expenditure, disruption of services, and degree of hazard.

In some cases, appreciable costs, in terms of actual monetary expenditures and disruption of daily activities, may be involved in bringing an existing occupancy into compliance with the requirements of the *Code*. Where this

is true, it would be appropriate for the owner of the facility to formulate a schedule, approved by the authority having jurisdiction, that allows suitable periods of time for correcting various deficiencies and gives due consideration to the ability of the owner to secure the necessary funding. However, the degree of hazard is an important consideration in this instance and, if the degree of hazard is serious enough, it may be necessary to close the building while renovations are made to bring the building into compliance.

1-5.3 The authority having jurisdiction shall determine the adequacy of means of egress and other measures for life safety from fire in accordance with the provisions of this *Code*.

This paragraph gives the authority having jurisdiction the final determination of whether adequate life safety is or is not provided in the building. This paragraph, in conjunction with the fundamental requirements of Chapter 2, can be used by the authority having jurisdiction where that authority determines that the *Code* has not contemplated a specific situation that might be encountered. Based upon this paragraph, the authority having jurisdiction could increase or decrease the requirements for the specific installation. This is an important paragraph since the *Code* cannot anticipate every type of building and occupancy configuration and, therefore, the authority having jurisdiction is given the final power to determine whether life safety is or is not adequately provided.

1-5.4* The requirements for existing buildings may be modified if their application clearly would be impractical in the judgment of the authority having jurisdiction, but only where it is clearly evident that a reasonable degree of safety is provided.

A-1-5.4 In existing buildings, it is not always practical to strictly apply the provisions of this *Code*. Physical limitations may require disproportionate effort or expense with little increase in life safety. In such cases, the authority having jurisdiction must be satisfied that reasonable life safety is assured.

In existing buildings it is intended that any condition that represents a serious threat to life be mitigated by application of appropriate safeguards. It is not intended to require modifications for conditions that do not represent a significant threat to life, even though such conditions are not literally in compliance with the *Code*.

This provides the authority having jurisdiction latitude where applying the *Code* to existing buildings. The *Code* recognizes that there may be situations where the requirements for existing buildings would not be practical and gives the authority having jurisdiction the ability to modify those requirements. However, the *Code* reemphasizes that a reasonable degree of safety still must be provided. In existing buildings, it is not always practical to strictly apply the provisions of this *Code*. Physical limitations may require disproportionate effort or expense with little increase in life safety. In such cases, the authority having jurisdiction should be satisfied that reasonable life safety is ensured. In existing buildings, it is intended that any condition that represents a serious threat to life be mitigated by application of appropriate safeguards. It is not intended to require modifications for conditions that do not represent a significant threat to life, even though the circumstances are not literally in compliance with the *Code*.

1-5.5 **Additions.** Additions shall conform to the provisions for new construction.

1-5.6* **Modernization or Renovation.** Any alteration or any installations of new equipment shall be accomplished as nearly as practical in conformance with the requirements for new construction. Alterations shall not diminish the level of life safety below that which exists prior to the alteration. In no case shall the resulting life safety be less than that required for existing buildings. Life safety features that do not meet the requirements for new buildings but exceed the requirements for existing buildings shall not be further diminished. Life safety features in excess of those required for new construction are not required to be maintained.

A-1-5.6 The following is an example of what is intended by 1-5.6. In a hospital that has 6-ft (183-cm) corridors, these corridors cannot be reduced in width even though the requirements for existing buildings do not require 6-ft (183-cm) wide corridors. However, if a hospital has 10-ft (3-m) wide corridors, they may be reduced to 8 ft (244 cm), which is the requirement for new construction. If the hospital corridor is 3 ft (91 cm) wide, it would have to be increased to 4 ft (122 cm). If alterations require replacement of a portion of a hospital corridor wall, this portion of the wall should have fire resistance increased to 1 hour in accordance with the requirements for new construction. However, it would not be required that the corridor width be increased to 8 ft (244 cm) unless it was practical to do so.

It should be recognized that all changes and alterations that are made must be in conformance with the minimum *Code* provisions for new construction. This may not be practical if the structure involved cannot accommodate the design provisions for new construction. For example, an existing hospital may have a corridor 6 ft (183 cm) wide that, if renovated, is required to be 8 ft (244 cm) wide. However, if the building's column spacing is 7 ft by 7 ft (213 cm by 213 cm), there is no way to achieve an 8-ft (244-cm) corridor width. Therefore, the authority having jurisdiction would have to decide if a 6-ft (183-cm) wide or even a 7-ft (213-cm) wide corridor is adequate or if additional provisions are required to accommodate a corridor less than 8 ft (244 cm) in width.

It is important to note that the occupancy chapters for existing buildings deal essentially with existing conditions and that where renovations or alterations are being made, they must comply with the requirements for new construction to the extent practical. For example, where installing new carpeting, it is very practical to install it using the requirements for new interior floor finish; or, where rebuilding a corridor wall, it may not be practical to move it to widen the corridor to meet the requirements for new corridor width, but most likely it will be practical to build it to the required fire resistance rating for new construction. Another example would be the installation of a new smoke barrier in an existing hospital. A smoke barrier can be made to meet all the requirements for a new smoke barrier; however, if the corridor through which the smoke barrier extends is not sufficiently wide to install two 44-in. (112-cm) doors, the requirement for two 44-in. (112-cm) doors would have to be modified by the authority having jurisdiction to become a set of doors or possibly a single door of sufficient width that the corridor could accommodate. The "nearly as practical" provision may seem arbitrary but is necessary in order to allow evaluation on a case-by-case basis.

Paragraph 1-5.6 does not specify the degree or magnitude of a change or alteration at which conformance with the provisions of the *Code* becomes mandatory. Both minor and major alterations and changes must comply. The authority having jurisdiction may still modify the *Code's* requirements or accept equivalent design options based on the special circumstances and the technical documentation presented.

1-5.7 Mixed Occupancies. Where two or more classes of occupancy occur in the same building or structure and are so intermingled that separate safeguards are impracticable, means of egress facilities, construction, protection, and other safeguards shall comply with the most restrictive life safety requirements of the occupancies involved.

Note that the *Code* does not automatically require that separate occupancies be provided with a fire resistance rated separation, as is often required by building codes. Some of the occupancies do require a specific fire resistance rated separation if the occupancies are to be considered individually, but, for the most part, the question of whether or not a fire resistance rated separation is needed and the extent to which it is needed is left to the authority having jurisdiction on a case-by-case basis. However, in the case where the occupancies are so intermingled that separate safeguards cannot be provided, ie, a mixed occupancy, the entire facility must meet the most restrictive life safety requirements for all the occupancies involved. It should also be noted that in many cases an occupancy requires a type of protection to be provided throughout the building, and this would be required throughout the structure regardless of fire separation, unless the structure was being built as "separate buildings." If the authority having jurisdiction accepts them as separate buildings, even though a single structure, the requirements could be applied to only the applicable side of the barrier. The authority having jurisdiction determines whether separate buildings are or are not, in fact, involved.

A fairly simple example, although quite common, is illustrated in Figure 1-1. As shown, this is not a mixed occupancy. Several factors should be considered by the authority having jurisdiction in determining the fire resistance rating and other requirements needed for the walls between occupancies. Some occupancies do establish a

specific fire resistance rating for these walls; [*see the 1.4 subsection of each occupancy chapter (e.g., 12-1.4)*]. If the occupancies involved do not require automatic sprinkler protection or fire alarm systems or do not involve sleeping or high hazards, the separation may be required to have little if any fire resistance (something one might find in older "strip shopping centers"). At the other end of the spectrum, if one of the occupancies involved requires automatic sprinkler protection or involves sleeping, then the authority may require a fire barrier of higher rating.

Formal Interpretation 81-25
Reference: 1-5.7, 8-1.6, 24-4.3.1

Given that, per 8-1.6, a 3-story shopping mall with a food park (restaurant) on the third level is required to be of fire-resistive construction under the criteria for a Class A assembly occupancy above grade level:

Question 1: Is it possible to construct an anchor store of a different construction type from the mall building by separating it from the mall building by a 3-hour fire wall?

Question 2: Are 3-hour fire doors required for openings in this 3-hour wall between the mall and the anchor store?

Question 3: If the answer to Question 2 is no, is any type of opening protection required for openings between the mall and anchor store?

Answer: With only a few exceptions, the *Life Safety Code* sets no specific occupancy separation requirements. The authority having jurisdiction determines what separation is needed, if any, based on 1-5.7 and the 1.2 subsection of each occupancy chapter. The local building code or the model building codes may be consulted by the authority having jurisdiction in making this determination, keeping life safety rather than property protection in mind.

Issue Edition: 1981
Reference: 1-4.5, 8-1.6, 24-4.3.1
Date: October 1982 ∎

In any case, the *Code* will allow the facility to be a mixed occupancy with no separation as long as the entire facility complies with the most stringent requirements of the occupancies involved.

An example of common mixed occupancy arrangement is illustrated in Figure 1-2. The commentary following 8-1.6 discusses in greater detail the problem of separating sprinklered and nonsprinklered occupancies. In general, for life safety purposes, nonsprinklered areas should not exist below sprinklered areas, regardless of separation. For example, an occupancy on the ground floor of a building with floors numbered B through 5 would require that at least floors B and 1 be sprinklered regardless of separation; a similar building with an occupancy that requires sprinkler protection on the top floor would result in the entire building being sprinklered. Again, 8-1.6 provides excellent guidance on this subject.

In some cases, an occupancy will require that the "building" be sprinklered throughout. Where this is required, the entire structure must be protected throughout regardless of the fire resistance of any separation. The model building codes do establish requirements for separate buildings and, if met, the authority having jurisdiction could (and should if a building code is mandated in addition to the *Life Safety Code*) rule that, although one structure is involved, it does consist of separate buildings.

Lastly, as indicated above, where the *Life Safety Code* is being used in conjunction with a building code, the authority having jurisdiction enforcing the *Life Safety Code* should work in conjunction with the authority enforcing the building code, especially on matters such as this.

For further information on mixed occupancies, see commentary on the 1.4 subsection of each occupancy chapter as well as commentary following 8-1.6 and 8-3.5.

1-5.8 Where specific requirements contained in Chapters 8 through 30 differ from general requirements contained in Chapters 1 through 7, the requirements of Chapters 8 through 30 shall govern.

Paragraph 1-5.8 indicates the general arrangement of the *Life Safety Code*. The first seven chapters contain administrative provisions and fundamental requirements establishing minimum acceptable criteria for all types of

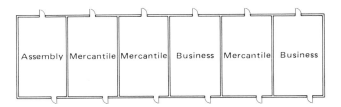

Figure 1-1. An Example of a Building That, Although it Contains More Than One Occupancy, Is Not a Mixed Occupancy. Each occupancy can be treated separately with regard to egress, interior finish, corridors, etc. Most occupancies do not establish specific fire resistance ratings for the wall between occupancies, and this would be determined by the authority having jurisdiction.

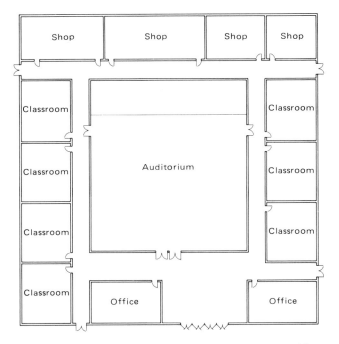

Figure 1-2. An Example of a Mixed Occupancy Building. Regardless of the fire separations provided, the egress system is mixed and, therefore, the most stringent requirements of the occupancies involved must be met.

occupancies. Chapters 8 through 30 of the *Code* establish criteria for life safety based upon specific occupancies. If conflicts between the general requirements and specific occupancy requirements occur, the requirements contained in the specific occupancy chapter apply.

It is interesting to note that the Committee on Safety to Life prohibits occupancy subcommittees from establishing provisions less stringent than those in Chapters 1 through 7 without an exception in Chapters 1 through 7, but since the term "stringent," whether more or less, could be subject to interpretation, the *Code* establishes that the more specific provisions, i.e., the occupancy chapters, rule where questions develop during the enforcement of the *Code*.

1-5.9 **Provisions in Excess of Code Requirements.** Nothing in this *Code* shall be construed to prohibit a better type of building construction, additional exits, or otherwise safer conditions than are specified by the minimum requirements of this *Code*.

Because the *Life Safety Code* is a minimum code, it never prohibits the use of a design that exceeds the provisions of the *Code*. In practice, however, economic considerations usually prevent the use of a design that exceeds the written provisions of the *Code*.

However, there have been situations in which, by exceeding the *Code* provisions, money was saved or generated. A specific example is a hotel project that was not required to have complete automatic sprinkler protection. By including sprinklers, a stairway was eliminated due to allowable increases in travel distance, and many revenue-producing guest rooms were put in the vacated space.

SECTION 1-6   Equivalency Concepts

Section 1-6 helps to establish one of the most sensitive and the most critical design criteria found in the *Code*. It takes the *Life Safety Code* beyond the scope of a typical general specification code into that of a goal-oriented performance code where state-of-the-art fire protection/egress design is permissible and even desirable.

1-6.1* Nothing in this *Code* is intended to prevent the use of systems, methods, or devices of equivalent or superior quality, strength, fire resistance, effectiveness, durability, and safety as alternatives to those prescribed by this *Code*, provided technical documentation is submitted to the authority having jurisdiction to demonstrate equivalency, and the system, method, or device is approved for the intended purpose.

A-1-6.1 It is the intent of the Committee on Safety to Life to recognize that future editions of this *Code* are a further refinement of this edition and earlier editions. The changes in future editions will reflect the continuing input of the fire protection/life safety community in its attempt to meet the goals stated in Chapter 2, "Fundamental Requirements."

As discussed in the commentary to 1-6, this *Code* has evolved from a specification code into what is intended to be a performance based document. Section 1-6.1 recognizes that, although the written specification language is required as a basis for enforcement, it should not limit one from using alternate or equivalent equipment or approaches in complying with the *Code*-specified performance. It is stipulated, however, that equivalency must be demonstrated by appropriate technical documentation. It is the responsibility of the authority having jurisdiction to evaluate and approve equivalencies.

The *Code* does contemplate several forms of equivalency:

Code-specified alternative – Through the use of *Code* language the *Code* sets a standard, and then provides an alternate method of obtaining the desired level of protection (i.e., via an exception). For example, Chapter 10, "New Educational Occupancies," requires that interior corridors be constructed of 1-hour rated assemblies; however, given the installation of an approved supervised automatic sprinkler system throughout the building, the *Code* allows the 1-hour rating requirement to be dropped to that of a smoke resistant assembly. This alternative has been judged to provide an "equivalent" level of life safety.

NFPA 101M – NFPA 101M,® *Alternative Approaches to Life Safety*,[1] provides a set of equivalency methodologies that may be used to assess *Code* equivalency. In addition to fire safety evaluation systems for health care occupancies, detention and correctional occupancies, board and care facilities, and business occupancies, NFPA 101M contains an alternate method of calculation for stair widths and a procedure for determining evacuation capabilities. It must be realized that this is not *Code*-specified and is therefore subject to the review and approval of the authority having jurisdiction.

More Recent Edition of the Code – As pointed out in A-1-6.1, future editions of the *Code* are considered refinements of earlier editions because they clarify Committee intent with respect to the revised topics. Therefore, they should be considered as equivalent to the earlier editions.

Caution must be exercised when applying this concept. One must recognize that specific provisions are part of a carefully crafted set of requirements that result in a desired level of life safety. A revision to one portion of the *Code* may be a part of, or the result of, changes to other *Code* sections. Therefore, it would be inappropriate to refer to a specific section of a more recent edition of the *Code* that might reflect a less stringent requirement in comparison to previous editions without taking into account the associated provisions that allowed the subject provision to be relaxed.

It is not the intent of the *Code* to limit the user to the three aforementioned methods of judging equivalency. It is the intent to allow emerging technology to be used to satisfy the prescribed performance requirements (i.e., fire testing, fire modeling, and other documented forms of engineering analysis).

1-6.2 The specific requirements of this *Code* may be modified by the authority having jurisdiction to allow alternative arrangements that will secure as nearly equivalent safety to life from fire as practical, but in no case shall the modification afford less safety to life than that which, in the judgment of the authority having jurisdiction, would be provided by compliance with the corresponding provisions contained in this *Code*.

This is a further enhancement of 1-6.1. To further the flexibility of the *Code* requirements in instances where new technology can be effectively incorporated into structures, 1-6.2 allows the authority having jurisdiction to modify the requirements of the *Code*. These modifications must result in a level of safety equal to or greater than that attained by a strict compliance with those *Code* provisions that would normally apply.

Paragraph 1-6.2 also allows the authority having jurisdiction to exercise some flexibility in dealing with historically preserved buildings. These buildings may have numerous design defects, such as open stair shafts or highly combustible interior finishes. To attain an equivalent level of safety, the authority having jurisdiction may

require the use of sprinkler systems, smoke detection systems, voice alarm systems for staged evacuation, smoke control systems, etc., to overcome the built-in design defects. This would be done in lieu of rebuilding the structure to the written *Code* requirements, which might mean totally destroying the historical character of the structure that is to be preserved. The design alternatives used in such an instance may actually raise the level of safety many times over that which is already found in the existing structure. They must, however, provide equivalent safety to life or greater safety to life than the written *Code* provisions.

1-6.3 Buildings with alternative fire protection features accepted by the authority having jurisdiction shall be considered as conforming with the *Code*.

This emphasizes the difference between accepted alternatives and waivers. When one presents an alternative approach to life safety, and that alternative is accepted by the authority having jurisdiction, the building is considered in compliance. This is different from a waiver that allows a noncomplying building to be continued in use.

SECTION 1-7   Occupancy

(See also Section 31-1.)

1-7.1 No new construction or existing building shall be occupied in whole or in part in violation of the provisions of this *Code*.

From an enforcement standpoint, this paragraph is probably one of the most important in the *Code*, since it says that no building, whether it be new or existing, may be occupied where the building is in violation of the provisions of the *Code*.

1-7.2 Existing buildings that are occupied at the time of adoption of the *Code* may remain in use provided:

(a) The occupancy classification remains the same.

(b) No serious life safety hazard exists that would constitute an imminent threat.

Because the *Code* is to be applied retroactively, 1-7.1 prohibits the use of existing nonconforming facilities. However, 1-7.2 goes on to modify this by saying that the building may be continued in use provided that the occupancy classification remains the same and there is no serious life safety hazard that would constitute an imminent threat. It should be noted that this does not exempt the building from compliance with the *Code* but only states that it can be continued in use. A plan, as described under 1-5.2, for bringing the building into compliance with the *Code* to the extent deemed necessary by the authority having jurisdiction under 1-5.4 and 1-6.2 must be established and its provisions met.

1-7.3* Buildings or portions of buildings may be occupied during construction, repair, alterations, or additions only if all means of egress and all fire protection features are in place and continuously maintained for the part occupied.

A-1-7.3 Fatal fires have occurred when a required stairway has been closed for repairs or removed for rebuilding, when a required automatic sprinkler system has been shut off to change piping, etc.

Paragraph 1-7.3 helps to control a now common practice: the occupation of a partially completed structure (usually done to obtain rent revenue). The *Code* first requires that all exit facilities for the part occupied be complete. In many cases the exit facilities, although completed, may be blocked with supplies and equipment needed for the ongoing construction, or the exits may be locked to limit access to parts of the building still under construction. If any of these conditions are found, occupancy should be absolutely prohibited. One must bear in mind that the incidence of fire is more frequent, and therefore more likely, during construction, alterations, repairs, etc. Extra caution and concern must be exercised to ensure adequate exit capacity and arrangement during periods of construction in any occupied building. In addition, all fire protection features must also be in place and continuously maintained for similar reasons.

1-7.4* **Changes of Occupancy.** In any building or structure, whether necessitating a physical alteration or not, a change from one occupancy classification to another, or from one occupancy subclassification to another subclassification of the same occupancy, shall be permitted only if such building or structure conforms with the requirements of this *Code* applying to new construction for the proposed new use.

A-1-7.4 Examples of changes from one occupancy subclassification to another subclassification of the same occupancy could include a change from a Class C to a Class B assembly occupancy or a change from a Class B to a Class A mercantile occupancy. Hospitals and nursing homes are both health care occupancies and are defined separately but are not established as separate suboccupancies; thus a change from one to the other does not constitute a change of occupancy subclassification.

Hotels and apartments, although both residential occupancies, are treated separately, and a change from one to the other constitutes a change of occupancy.

Formal Interpretation 81-12
Reference: 1-7

Question: A building was used as a hospital but has been closed for four years. It is again to be used as a hospital. Is the facility to be considered new or existing under the *Life Safety Code?*

Answer: As long as the building was not used as another occupancy during the time, it would be considered existing.

Issue Edition: 1981
Reference: 1-7
Date: January 1982 ■

SECTION 1-8   Maintenance

(See also Section 31-1.)

This section was new in the 1988 *Code.* Although maintenance has been addressed to some extent in Chapter 31 of previous editions, Section 1-8 helps emphasize the importance of maintenance of items required by the *Code*. It is useless to have a door that will not open or a closer that does not close the door or a sprinkler system with no water. See Chapter 31 for additional maintenance provisions.

1-8.1 **Maintenance.** Whenever or wherever any device, equipment, system, condition, arrangement, level of protection, or any other feature is required for compliance with the provisions of this *Code*, such device, equipment, system, condition, arrangement, level of protection, or other feature shall thereafter be permanently maintained unless the *Code* exempts such maintenance.

Reference Cited in Commentary

[1]NFPA 101M,® *Manual on Alternative Approaches to Life Safety*, National Fire Protection Association, Quincy, MA, 1988.

2
Fundamental Requirements

The goals toward which the provisions of this *Code* are aimed are specified in Chapter 2. The achievement of these goals ensures a reasonable level of life safety in building design and arrangement. Simply stated, they are:

1. To provide for adequate safety without dependence on any single safeguard,
2. To ensure that construction is sufficient to provide structural integrity during a fire while occupants are exiting,
3. To provide an appropriate degree of life safety considering the size, shape, and nature of the occupancy,
4. To ensure that the exits are clear, unobstructed, and unlocked,
5. To ensure that the exits and routes of escape are clearly marked so that there is no confusion in reaching an exit,
6. To provide adequate lighting,
7. To ensure prompt occupant response by providing early warning of fire,
8. To provide for back-up or redundant exit arrangements,
9. To ensure the suitable enclosure of vertical openings, and
10. To make allowances for those design criteria that go beyond the *Code* provisions and are tailored to the normal use and needs of the occupancy in question.

2-1* Every building or structure, new or old, designed for human occupancy shall be provided with exits and other safeguards sufficient to permit the prompt escape of occupants or furnish other means to provide a reasonable degree of safety for occupants in case of fire or other emergency. The design of exits and other safeguards shall be such that reliance for safety to life in case of fire or other emergency will not depend solely on any single safeguard; additional safeguards shall be provided for life safety in case any single safeguard is ineffective due to some human or mechanical failure.

A-2-1 It is not always necessary to completely evacuate the building or structure to escape from a fire or other emergency. An area of refuge formed by horizontal exits, smoke barriers, other floors, or like compartmentation often can serve as a place for the occupants to remain in relative safety until the emergency is over. In those occupancies where access to the exits is by way of enclosed corridors, particularly those occupancies with sleeping occupants, a single fire may block access to all exits, including horizontal exits and smoke barriers. In such cases, the occupants may achieve a greater degree of safety by remaining in their rooms.

2-2 Every building or structure shall be so constructed, arranged, equipped, maintained, and operated as to avoid undue danger to the lives and safety of its occupants from fire, smoke, fumes, or resulting panic during the period of time reasonably necessary for escape from the building or structure or for that period of time needed to defend in place in case of fire or other emergency.

2-3 Every building or structure shall be provided with exits and other safeguards of kinds, numbers, locations, and capacities appropriate to the individual building or structure, with due regard to the character of the occupancy, the capabilities of the occupants, the number of persons exposed, the fire protection available, the height and type of construction of the building or structure, and other factors necessary to provide all occupants with a reasonable degree of safety.

2-4 In every building or structure, exits shall be so arranged and maintained as to provide free and unobstructed egress from all parts of the building or structure at all times when it is occupied. No lock or fastening shall be installed to prevent free escape from the inside of any building. Exits shall be accessible to the extent necessary to assure reasonable safety for occupants having impaired mobility.

Exception: Locks shall be permitted in mental health, detention, or correctional facilities where supervisory personnel are continually on duty and effective provisions are made to remove occupants in case of fire or other emergency.

Problems with locking devices have consistently been a contributing factor in multiple-fatality fires in correctional facilities. Some of these problems include malfunction of locks, inability to locate keys in smoke or in the dark (frequently caused by smoke obscuration of lighting), locks jammed from toothpicks and chewing gum, and locks made inoperative due to pushing against the doors. All of these problems have shown up in the fire record. Many times, prior to a fire, it might have been assumed that, in the event of an emergency, there would

be effective provisions for unlocking locks and that personnel would be continually on duty. Extreme care must be exercised to ensure that locks can and will be unlocked or that alternate methods of providing life safety, other than total evacuation, are provided. (*See "Seminole County Jail Fire" and "Fire in Prisons."*)[1,2]

2-5 Every exit shall be clearly visible, or the route to reach every exit shall be conspicuously indicated in such a manner that every occupant of every building or structure who is physically and mentally capable will readily know the direction of escape from any point. Each means of egress, in its entirety, shall be so arranged or marked that the way to a place of safety is indicated in a clear manner. Any doorway or passageway that is not an exit or a way to reach an exit, but is capable of being confused with an exit, shall be so arranged or marked to prevent occupant confusion with acceptable exits. Every effort shall be taken to avoid occupants mistakenly traveling into dead-end spaces in a fire emergency.

2-6 Where artificial illumination is required in a building or structure, exit facilities shall be included in the lighting design in an adequate and reliable manner.

2-7 In every building or structure of such size, arrangement, or occupancy that a fire itself may not provide adequate occupant warning, fire alarm facilities shall be provided where necessary to warn occupants of the existence of fire. Fire alarms will alert occupants to initiate emergency procedures. Fire alarms facilitate the orderly conduct of fire exit drills.

Several multiple-fatality fire incidents in recent years, especially in hotels, have shown that fire alarm sounding devices were inadequate to alert building occupants. This was because occupants either could not hear the alarm or did not recognize the alarm as a fire alarm signal. Confusion with telephones or alarm clocks has been reported. Authorities having jurisdiction must ensure that sounding devices can be heard over ambient noise levels and can be recognized as fire alarm signals. (*See "Familiar Problems Cause 10 Deaths in Hotel Fire" and "Ten Die in Greece, New York Hotel Fire."*)[3,4]

2-8 Two means of egress, as a minimum, shall be provided in every building or structure, section, and area where their size, occupancy, and arrangement endanger occupants attempting to use a single means of egress that is blocked by fire or smoke. The two means of egress shall be arranged to minimize the possibility that both may be rendered impassable by the same fire or emergency condition.

2-9 Every vertical way of exit and other vertical opening between floors of a building shall be suitably enclosed or protected, as necessary, to afford reasonable safety to occupants while using exits and to prevent spread of fire, smoke, or fumes through vertical openings from floor to floor before occupants have entered exits.

Unprotected or improperly protected vertical openings have consistently shown up in NFPA fire records as a major contributing factor to multiple-death fires. Some recent multiple-death fires in which unprotected vertical openings have been identified as a significant factor in these deaths are:

November 20, 1980, Las Vegas, NV	85 dead[5]
January 9, 1981, Keansburgh, NJ	31 dead[6]
March 14, 1981, Chicago, IL	19 dead[7]
October 28, 1982, Pittsburgh, PA	5 dead[8]
April 19, 1983, Worcester, MA	7 dead[9]
June 14, 1983, Fort Worth, TX	5 dead[10]
August 31, 1983, Gwinnett, GA	8 dead[11]
December 31, 1986, San Juan, PR	97 dead[12]

Also see commentary under Section 6-2.

2-10* Compliance with this *Code* shall not be construed as eliminating or reducing the necessity for other provisions for safety of persons using a structure under normal occupancy conditions. Also, no provision of the *Code* shall be construed as requiring or permitting any condition that may be hazardous under normal occupancy conditions.

A-2-10 The provisions of this *Code* will not necessarily provide a building suitable for use by physically handicapped peo-

ple. Reference is made to ANSI A117.1, *Standard for Buildings and Facilities—Providing Accessibility and Usability for Physically Handicapped People. (See Appendix B.)*

References Cited in Commentary

[1]Richard Best, "The Seminole County Jail Fire," *Fire Journal*, Vol. 70, No. 1, January 1976, pp. 5-10, 17.

[2]David P. Demers, "Fire in Prisons," *Fire Journal*, Vol. 72, No. 2, March 1978, pp. 29-42.

[3]David P. Demers, "Familiar Problems Cause 10 Deaths in Hotel Fire," *Fire Journal*, Vol. 74, No. 1, January 1980, pp. 52-56.

[4]David P. Demers, "Ten Die in Greece, New York Hotel Fire," *Fire Journal*, Vol. 73, No. 4, July 1979, pp. 25-30.

[5]Richard Best and David P. Demers, "Fire at the MGM Grand," *Fire Journal*, Vol. 76, No. 1, January 1982, pp. 19-37.

[6]Richard Best and Steven W. Hill, "Fires in Two Boarding Facilities Kill 34 Residents," *Fire Journal*, Vol. 76, No. 4, July 1982, pp. 44-57, 106.

[7]Steven Hill, "19 Die in Chicago Hotel Fire," *Fire Journal*, Vol. 76, No. 2, March 1982, pp. 53-55, 60-61.

[8]James R. Bell, "Five Die in Pittsburgh Boarding Home Fire," *Fire Journal*, Vol. 77, No. 5, September 1983, pp. 68-71, 75.

[9]Richard Best, "Fire in Community Home Causes Seven Deaths," *Fire Journal*, Vol. 78, No. 2, March 1984, pp. 19-23, 79-80.

[10]Ron Coté, Thomas Klem, and William P. Walls, "Five Die in Fire at Texas Ramada Inn," *Fire Journal*, Vol. 78, No. 2, March 1984, pp. 55-57, 60-70.

[11]Tom Timoney, "Eight Mentally Handicapped Occupants Die in Georgia Fire," *Fire Journal*, Vol. 78, No. 3, May 1984, pp. 91-97, 134.

[12]Thomas J. Klem, Investigation Report on the Dupont Plaza Hotel Fire, NFPA LS-11, National Fire Protection Association, Quincy, MA, 1987.

3

Definitions

SECTION 3-1 General

3-1.1 The following terms, for the purposes of this *Code*, shall have the meanings given in this chapter, if not otherwise modified for a specific occupancy.

3-1.2 Words used in the present tense include the future; words used in the masculine gender include the feminine and neuter; the singular number includes the plural and the plural the singular.

3-1.3 Where terms are not defined in this chapter, they shall have their ordinarily accepted meanings or such as the context may imply.

SECTION 3-2 Definitions

Accessible Area of Refuge. (*See Section 5-1.*)

Accessible Means of Egress. Accessible means of egress is a path of travel that is usable by a person with a severe mobility impairment and that leads to a public way or an area of refuge.

Addition. An extension or increase in floor area or height of a building or structure.

Also see 1-5.5.

Aisle Accessway. (*See Section 8-1 or 9-1.*)

Ambulatory Health Care Centers. (*See Section 12-1 or 13-1.*)

Anchor Store. (*See Section 25-1.*)

Apartment Building. (*See Section 18-1 or 19-1.*)

Approved.* Means "acceptable to the authority having jurisdiction."

A-3-2 **Approved.** The National Fire Protection Association does not approve, inspect, or certify any installations, procedures, equipment or materials; nor does it approve or evaluate testing laboratories. In determining the acceptability of installations or procedures, equipment or materials, the authority having jurisdiction may base acceptance on compliance with NFPA or other appropriate standards. In the absence of such standards, said authority may require evidence of proper installation, procedure or use. The authority having jurisdiction may also refer to the listings or labeling practices of an organization concerned with product evaluations that is in a position to determine compliance with appropriate standards for the current production of listed items.

A common error is the assumption that "approved" means listed or labeled or similar designation. Although the authority having jurisdiction may use a listing or label to assist in approving an item, that does not mean that all approvals are based on listing or labeling and does not mean that listings and/or labels automatically mean approval.

Area.   See Floor Area.

Area of Refuge.*   An area of refuge is an accessible space protected from fire or smoke, separated from all other spaces in the same building or an adjacent building that permits a delay in egress travel from any level.

A-3-2   **Area of Refuge.**   An area of refuge has a temporary use during egress. It generally serves as a staging area that provides relative safety to its occupants while potential emergencies are assessed, decisions are made, and mitigating activities are begun. Refuge is thus a stage of the total egress process; a stage between egress from the immediately threatened floor area and egress by means of some route.

An area of refuge might be another building connected by a bridge or balcony, a compartment of a subdivided story, an elevator lobby, or an enlarged exit stair landing. Generally, it is accessible by means of horizontal travel or, as a minimum, it complies with the "accessible route" requirements of ANSI A117.1, *Standard for Buildings and Facilities—Providing Accessibility and Usability for Physically Handicapped People. (See Appendix B.)*

Horizontal exits are traditional examples of areas of refuge that provide substantial floor area and superior fire protection permitting a delay sufficient for a large number of people to move to the level of exit discharge. Other areas of refuge, intended for use by fewer people, may provide shorter delays by virtue of smoke separation without substantial, rated fire separation from adjoining areas. Such shorter delays might be appropriate for organizing assisted or supervised egress that requires movement from one level to another. (*See 5-2.4.*)

Although not new to the *Code*, the term "area of refuge" has been defined in the 1991 edition to clarify *Code* requirements concerning this concept. This term should not be perceived as applying only to the physically handicapped. See 5-2.12.

Arena Stage.   A stage or platform open on at least three sides to audience seating. It may be with or without overhead scene handling facilities.

Assembly Occupancy.   (*See Section 4-1 and Section 8-1 or 9-1.*)

Atrium.   A floor opening or series of floor openings connecting two or more stories that is covered at the top of the series of openings and is used for purposes other than an enclosed stairway; elevator hoistway; escalator opening; or utility shaft used for plumbing, electrical, air conditioning, or communication facilities.

Also see 6-2.4.6.

Authority Having Jurisdiction.*   The "authority having jurisdiction" is the organization, office, or individual responsible for "approving" equipment, an installation, or a procedure.

A-3-2   **Authority Having Jurisdiction.**   The phrase "authority having jurisdiction" is used in NFPA documents in a broad manner since jurisdictions and "approval" agencies vary, as do their responsibilities. Where public safety is primary, the "authority having jurisdiction" may be a federal, state, local, or other regional department or individual such as a fire chief, fire marshal, chief of a fire prevention bureau, labor department, health department, building official, electrical inspector, or others having statutory authority. For insurance purposes, an insurance inspection department rating bureau or other insurance company representative may be the "authority having jurisdiction." In many circumstances, the property owner or his designated agent assumes the role of the "authority having jurisdiction"; at government installations, the commanding officer or departmental official may be the "authority having jurisdiction."

In the simplest terms, the authority having jurisdiction (AHJ) is that person or office enforcing the *Code*. Commonly, the AHJ is a fire marshal or building official where enforcement is mandatory. It can also be a safety office, insurance engineer, accreditation service, or other agency, especially where enforced on a nongovernmental level. It is not uncommon to have multiple AHJs reviewing the same project, enforcing this and/or other codes (e.g., in a health care facility, it would not be uncommon to have several agencies doing inspections under the *Code* such as state and local fire marshal; federal, state, and local health care licensing agencies; JCAHO; insurance inspectors; and building inspectors.

Automatic. Providing a function without the necessity of human intervention.

Examples are an automatic sprinkler system or automatic fire detection system. An automatic-closing door is one that closes when necessary, usually by activation of a smoke detector, whereas a self-closing door closes each time it is opened.

Board and Care. *(See Section 22-1 or 23-1.)*

Building. Any structure used or intended for supporting or sheltering any use or occupancy. The term building shall be construed as if followed by the words "or portions thereof." *(See Structure.)*

Building, Existing. Any structure erected prior to the adoption of this *Code* or for which a permit for construction has been issued.

Also see definition of "existing."

Business Occupancy. *(See Section 4-1.)*

Combustible. Capable of undergoing combustion.

Combustion. A chemical process that involves oxidation sufficient to produce light or heat.

Common Atmosphere (Educational Occupancies). *(See Section 10-1 or 11-1.)*

Common Path of Travel. That portion of exit access that must be traversed before two separate and distinct paths of travel to two exits are available. Paths that merge are common paths of travel. Common path of travel is measured in the same manner as travel distance but terminates at that point where two separate and distinct routes become available.

See commentary on 5-5.1.2.

Complete Smoke Detection System. *(See 7-6.2.7.)*

Correctional Occupancies. *(See Section 4-1.)*

Court. An open, uncovered, unoccupied space, unobstructed to the sky, bounded on three or more sides by exterior building walls.

Court, Enclosed. A court bounded on all sides by the exterior walls of a building or exterior walls and lot lines on which walls are allowable.

Covered Mall. *(See Section 25-1.)*

Critical Radiant Flux. The level of incident radiant heat energy on a floor covering system at the most distant flameout point as determined by the test procedure of NFPA 253, *Standard Method of Test for Critical Radiant Flux of Floor Covering Systems Using a Radiant Heat Energy Source*. The unit of measurement of critical radiant flux is watts per square centimeter (W/cm²).

See commentary in Section 6-5.

Cyclorama. *(See Section 8-1 or 9-1.)*

Day-Care Centers. *(See Section 10-7 or 11-7.)*

Detention Occupancies. *(See Section 4-1.)*

Direct Exit. *(See Section 14-1 or 15-1.)*

Dormitories. *(See Section 16-1 or 17-1.)*

Draft Stop. A continuous membrane used to subdivide a concealed space to restrict the passage of smoke, heat, and flames.

Drop. *(See Section 8-1 or 9-1.)*

Educational Occupancies. *(See Section 10-1 or 11-1.)*

Evacuation Capability. *(See Section 22-1 or 23-1.)*

Exhibitor. *(See Section 8-1 or 9-1.)*

Exhibits.   (*See Section 8-1 or 9-1.*)

Existing.   That which is already in existence on the date when this *Code* goes into effect, such as existing buildings, structures, or exit facilities.

Formal Interpretation 76-118
Reference: 3-2

Question 1: The definition of "existing" in Section 3-2 states "that which is already in existence at the date when this *Code* goes into effect...." If a building was designed and construction began before adoption of the *Code*, but the construction was not finished until after the adoption, should the building be inspected under the "new" or "existing" criteria?

Answer: Existing.

Question 2: If a building was designed before adoption of the *Code*, but construction was not started until after adoption of the *Code*, should the building be inspected under the "new" or "existing" criteria?

Answer: The key is not when the building was designed or when construction started, but rather the date of plan approval. If permission (approval) was given prior to adoption, inspection should be based on the *Code* in effect at the time of approval. Subsequently, "existing" sections of newly adopted editions would be used.

Issue Edition: 1976
Reference: 3-2
Date: October 1979 ∎

Exit.   That portion of a means of egress that is separated from all other spaces of the building or structure by construction or equipment as required in 5-1.3.1 to provide a protected way of travel to the exit discharge. Exits include exterior exit doors, exit passageways, horizontal exits, and separated exit stairs or ramps.

Exit Access.   That portion of a means of egress that leads to an exit.

Exit Discharge.   That portion of a means of egress between the termination of an exit and a public way.

Exposition.   (*See Section 8-1 or 9-1.*)

Exposition Faciltiy.   (*See Section 8-1 or 9-1.*)

Family Day-Care Home.   (*See Section 10-9 or 11-9.*)

Fire Barrier.   A fire barrier is a continuous membrane, either vertical or horizontal, such as a wall or floor assembly that is designed and constructed with a specified fire resistance rating to limit the spread of fire and that will also restrict the movement of smoke. Such barriers may have protected openings. (*See 6-2.3.*)

Fire Compartment.*   A fire compartment is a space within a building that is enclosed by fire barriers on all sides, including the top and bottom. (*See 6-2.2.*)

A-3-2   **Fire Compartment.** In the provisions of fire compartments utilizing the outside walls of a building, it is not intended that the outside wall be specifically fire resistance rated unless required by other standards. Likewise it is not intended for outside windows or doors to be protected unless specifically required for exposure protection by another section of this *Code* or by other standards.

Fire Resistance Rating.   The time, in minutes or hours, that materials or assemblies have withstood a fire exposure as established in accordance with the test procedures of NFPA 251, *Standard Methods of Fire Tests of Building Construction and Materials.*

Flame Spread.   The propagation of flame over a surface. (*See Section 6-5.*)

Flexible Plan Educational Buildings.   (*See Section 10-1 or 11-1.*)

Floor Area, Gross.   Gross floor area shall be the floor area within the inside perimeter of the outside walls of the building under consideration with no deduction for hallways, stairs, closets, thickness of interior walls, columns, or other features. Where the term area is used elsewhere in this *Code*, it shall be understood to be gross area unless otherwise specified.

Floor Area, Net. Net floor area shall be the actual occupied area, not including accessory unoccupied areas or thickness of walls.

The net area is arrived at after deductions have been made for the space that structural features and fixed fixtures occupy. Deductions could be made for hallways, stairs, closets, interior walls, columns, fixed counters and display racks, fixed tables and bars, and other fixed items that take up space that might otherwise have been used for human occupancy.

Flow Time. (*See Section 8-1 or 9-1.*)

Fly. (*See Section 8-1 or 9-1.*)

Fly Gallery. (*See Section 8-1 or 9-1.*)

General Industrial Occupancies. (*See Section 28-1.*)

Gridiron. (*See Section 8-1 or 9-1.*)

Gross Leasable Area. (*See Section 25-1.*)

Group Day-Care Homes. (*See Section 10-8 or 11-8.*)

Guard. A vertical protective barrier erected along exposed edges of stairways, balconies, and similar areas.

Handrail. A bar, pipe, or similar member designed to furnish persons with a handhold. (A handrail, if of suitable design, may also serve as part of a guard.)

Hazardous Areas. Those areas of structures or buildings posing a degree of hazard greater than that normal to the general occupancy of the building or structure, such as those areas used for the storage or use of combustibles or flammables, toxic, noxious, or corrosive materials, or use of heat-producing appliances. (*Also see Section 22-1 or 23-1.*)

Health Care Occupancies. (*See Section 4-1.*)

High Hazard Areas. Those areas of structures or buildings used for purposes that involve highly combustible, highly flammable, or explosive products or materials that are likely to burn with extreme rapidity, or that may produce poisonous fumes or gases, including highly toxic or noxious alkalies, acids, or other liquids or chemicals that involve flame, fume, explosive, poisonous, or irritant hazards; also those uses that cause division of material into fine particles or dust subject to explosion or spontaneous combustion, and uses that constitute a high fire hazard because of the form, character, or volume of the material used.

High Hazard Industrial Occupancy. (*See Section 28-1.*)

High Rise Building.* A building more than 75 ft (23 m) in height. Building height shall be measured from the lowest level of fire department vehicle access to the floor of the highest occupiable story.

A-3-2 High Rise Building. It is the intent of this definition that in determining the level from which the highest occupiable floor is to be measured, the enforcing agency should exercise reasonable judgment, including consideration of overall accessibility to the building by fire department personnel and vehicular equipment. Where a building is situated on a sloping terrain and there is building access on more than one level, the enforcing agency may select the level that provides the most logical and adequate fire department access.

This definition was first added in the 1988 Edition of the *Code*. Prior to this time, each occupancy set its own criteria. Business and health care occupancies used similar provisions, while the residential occupancies used six stories as the criteria. This establishes one definition so the *Code* can use the term consistently throughout. The definition has been accepted fairly well throughout the United States, but some jurisdictions set a lower height at which the definition applies due to local conditions. The appendix note highlights the need for reasonable judgment in establishing the level from which to start the measurement.

The "Airlie House" Report[1] is considered to be one of the principal sources of this definition. Although most admit that the definition has flaws, it is widely acknowledged as an acceptable method used to determine if a building is high rise. One major flaw is the problem of lower height buildings that are set back over a large one-story section.

High rise buildings pose several problems:
1. Potential for significant stack effect
2. Difficulty in evacuation
3. Difficulty experienced by fire services in reaching fire.

Also see definition of "occupiable story."

Horizontal Exit. *(See Section 5-1.)*

Hospital. *(See Section 12-1 or 13-1.)*

Hotel. *(See Section 16-1 or 17-1.)*

Industrial Occupancy. *(See Section 4-1.)*

Interior Finish. *(See Section 6-5.)*

Interior Floor Finish. *(See Section 6-5.)*

Interior Room (Educational Occupancies). *(See Section 10-1 or 11-1.)*

Labeled. Equipment or materials to which has been attached a label, symbol or other identifying mark of an organization acceptable to the "authority having jurisdiction" and concerned with product evaluation, that maintains periodic inspection of production of labeled equipment or materials and by whose labeling the manufacturer indicates compliance with appropriate standards or performance in a specified manner.

Although NFPA publishes the *Life Safety Code*, it does not "list" or "label" any materials, products, or services.

Leg Drop. *(See Section 8-1 or 9-1.)*

Life Safety Evaluation. *(See Section 8-1 or 9-1.)*

Limited Care Facility. *(See Section 12-1 or 13-1.)*

Limited-Combustible.* As applied to a building construction material, other than interior finish, means a material not complying with the definition of noncombustible material that, in the form in which it is used, has a potential heat value not exceeding 3500 Btu/lb (8.14×10^6 J/kg) and complies with one of the following paragraphs (a) or (b).

Materials subject to increase in combustibility or flame spread rating beyond the limits herein established through the effects of age, moisture, or other atmospheric condition shall be considered combustible.

(a) Materials having a structural base of noncombustible material with a surfacing not exceeding a thickness of ⅛ in. (0.3 cm) that has a flame spread rating not greater than 50.

(b) Materials, in the form and thickness used, other than as described in (a), having neither a flame spread rating greater than 25 nor evidence of continued progressive combustion, and of such composition that surfaces that would be exposed by cutting through the material on any plane would have neither a flame spread rating greater than 25 nor evidence of continued progressive combustion.

A-3-2 **Limited-Combustible.** See NFPA 259, *Standard Test Method for Potential Heat of Building Materials* and NFPA 220, *Standard on Types of Building Construction*. *(See Appendix B.)*

Listed.* Equipment or materials included in a list published by an organization acceptable to the "authority having jurisdiction" and concerned with product evaluation, that maintains periodic inspection of production of listed equipment or materials and whose listing states either that the equipment or material meets appropriate standards or has been tested and found suitable for use in a specified manner.

A-3-2 **Listed.** The means for identifying listed equipment may vary for each organization concerned with product evaluation, some of which do not recognize equipment as listed unless it is also labeled. The "authority having jurisdiction" should utilize the system employed by the listing organization to identify a listed product.

Also see definition of "labeled."

Living Area. Any normally occupiable space in a residential occupancy, other than sleeping rooms or rooms that are intended for combination sleeping/living, bathrooms, toilet compartments, kitchens, closets, halls, storage or utility spaces, and similar areas.

This definition was added to the 1991 Edition of the *Code* for use in the various residential chapters. It is intended to include such rooms as living rooms, dens, family rooms, recreation rooms, libraries, dining rooms, lounges, and similar spaces.

Load, Live. The weight superimposed by the use and occupancy of the building, not including the wind load, earthquake load, or dead load.

Lodging Homes. (*See Section 20-1.*)

Means of Egress. (*See Section 5-1.*)

Means of Escape. A way out of a building or structure that does not conform to the strict definition of means of egress but does provide an alternate way out.

Mercantile Occupancies. (*See Section 4-1.*)

Mezzanine. An intermediate level between the floor and the ceiling of any room or space.

See commentary following 6-2.5.

Multipurpose Assembly Occupancy. (*See Section 8-1.*)

Noncombustible. A material that, in the form in which it is used and under the conditions anticipated, will not aid combustion or add appreciable heat to an ambient fire. Materials, where tested in accordance with ASTM E136, *Standard Test Method for Behavior of Materials in a Vertical Tube Furnace at 750°C*, and conforming to the criteria contained in Section 7 of the referenced standard shall be considered as noncombustible.

Nursing Homes. (*See Section 12-1 or 13-1.*)

Occupancy. The purpose for which a building or portion thereof is used or intended to be used.

Occupant Load. The total number of persons that may occupy a building or portion thereof at any one time.

Occupiable Story. A story occupied by people on a regular basis. Stories used exclusively for mechanical equipment rooms, elevator penthouses, and similar spaces are not occupiable stories.

Also see definition of "high rise."

One- and Two- Family Dwellings. (*See Section 21-1.*)

Open-Air Mercantile Operations. (*See Section 25-1.*)

Open Industrial Structures. (*See Section 28-1.*)

Open Plan Educational Buildings. (*See Section 10-1 or 11-1.*)

Outpatient (Ambulatory) Clinics. (*See Section 12-1 or 13-1.*)

Outside Stairs. Outside stairs include stairs where at least one side is open to the outer air. (*See 5-2.2.*)

Partial Smoke Detection System. (*See 7-6.2.8.*)

Personal Care. (*See Section 22-1 or 23-1.*)

Pinrail. (*See Section 8-1 or 9-1.*)

Place of Assembly. (*See Assembly Occupancy in Section 4-1.*)

Plastic, Cellular or Foamed. Cellular or foamed plastic material means a heterogeneous system comprised of at least two phases, one of which is a continuous polymeric organic material, and the second of which is deliberately introduced for the purpose of distributing gas in voids throughout the material, and foamed and unfoamed polymeric or monomeric precursors (prepolymer, if used) plasticizers, fillers, extenders, catalysts, blowing agents, colorants, stabilizers, lubricants, surfactants, pigments, reaction control agents, processing aids, and flame retardants.

Platform. (*See Section 8-1 or 9-1.*)

Platform, Permanent. (*See Section 8-1 or 9-1.*)

Platform, Temporary. (*See Section 8-1 or 9-1.*)

Plenum. An air compartment or chamber to which one or more ducts are connected and that forms part of an air distribution system.

Point of Safety. (*See Section 22-1 or 23-1.*)

Proscenium Wall. (*See Section 8-1 or 9-1.*)

Public Way. Any street, alley, or other similar parcel of land essentially open to the outside air, deeded, dedicated, or otherwise permanently appropriated to the public for public use and having a clear width and height of not less than 10 ft (3 m).

Ramp. An inclined floor surface. (*See Section 5-1 and 5-2.5.*)

Resident. (*See Section 22-1 or 23-1.*)

Residential Board and Care. (*See Section 22-1 or 23-1.*)

Residential Housing Area. (*See Section 14-1 or 15-1.*)

Residential Occupancies. (*See Section 4-1.*)

Room (Educational Occupancies). (*See Section 10-1 or 11-1.*)

Rooming House. (*See Section 20-1.*)

Sally Port (Security Vestibule). (*See Section 14-1 or 15-1.*)

Self-Closing. Equipped with an approved device that will ensure closing after having been opened.

This is different from automatic-closing in that automatic-closing means equipped with a device that will ensure closing when needed, usually upon activation of a smoke detector and/or power failure.

Separate Atmosphere (Educational Occupancies). (*See Section 10-1 or 11-1.*)

Separate Means of Egress (Educational Occupancies). (*See Section 10-1 or 11-1.*)

Separated Exit Ramp. (*See Section 5-1.*)

Separated Exit Stair. (*See Section 5-1.*)

Smoke Barrier. A smoke barrier is a continuous membrane, either vertical or horizontal, such as a wall, floor, or ceiling assembly, that is designed and constructed to restrict the movement of smoke. A smoke barrier may or may not have a fire resistance rating. Such barriers may have protected openings. (*See Section 6-3.*)

Smoke Compartment.* A smoke compartment is a space within a building enclosed by smoke barriers on all sides, including the top and bottom. (*See Section 6-3.*)

A-3-2 **Smoke Compartment.** In the provision of smoke compartments utilizing the outside walls or the roof of a building, it is not intended that outside walls or roofs or any openings therein be capable of resisting the passage of smoke.

Smoke Detector. A device that senses visible or invisible particles of combustion.

See Supplement 2 of this *Handbook* for additional information on smoke detectors.

Smoke Protected Assembly Seating. (*See Section 8-1 or 9-1.*)

Special Amusement Building. (*See Section 8-1 or 9-1.*)

Special Purpose Industrial Occupancies. (*See Section 28-1.*)

Special Structures. (*See Section 4-1.*)

Staff. (*See Section 22-1 or 23-1.*)

Stage. (*See Section 8-1 or 9-1.*)

Stage, Legitimate. (*See Section 8-1 or 9-1.*)

Stage, Regular. (*See Section 8-1 or 9-1.*)

Stage, Thrust. (*See Section 8-1 or 9-1.*)

Stage Properties. (*See Section 8-1 or 9-1.*)

Stage Scenery. (*See Section 8-1 or 9-1.*)

Storage Occupancy. (*See Section 4-1.*)

Stores. (*See Section 24-1 or 25-1.*)

Story. That portion of a building included between the upper surface of a floor and the upper surface of the floor or roof next above.

Note that this definition of story would include a usable basement. This is important since several requirements in the *Code* are based on a limit to the number of stories. Therefore, if a provision is permitted in a 3-story building and the building in question includes B-1-2-3, the provision would not be allowed.

Story of Exit Discharge. (*See Section 11-1.*)

Street. Any public thoroughfare (street, avenue, boulevard) 30 ft (9.1 m) or more in width that has been dedicated or deeded to the public for public use and is accessible for use by the fire department in fighting fire. Enclosed spaces and tunnels, even though used for vehicular and pedestrian traffic, are not considered as streets for the purposes of the *Code*.

Street Floor. Any story or floor level accessible from the street or from outside the building at ground level with floor level at the main entrance not more than three risers above or below ground level at these points, and so arranged and utilized as to qualify as the main floor. Where, due to differences in street levels, there are two or more stories accessible from the street, each is a street floor for the purposes of the *Code*. Where there is no floor level within the specified limits for a street floor above or below ground level, the building shall be considered as having no street floor.

Structure. That which is built or constructed. The term structure shall be construed as if followed by the words "or portion thereof." (*See Building*.)

Thermal Barrier. (*See Section 22-1 or 23-1.*)

Thrust Stage. (*See Section 8-1 or 9-1.*)

Tower. (*See Section 30-1.*)

Underground Structure. (*See Section 30-1.*)

Vehicle. (*See Section 30-1.*)

Vertical Opening. An opening through a floor or roof.

Vessel. (*See Section 30-1.*)

Yard. An open, unoccupied space other than a court, unobstructed from the ground to the sky, except where specifically provided by the *Code*, on the lot on which a building is situated.

Reference Cited in Commentary

[1]Public Buildings Service International Conference on Firesafety in High-Rise Buildings, April 12-16, Airlie House, Warrenton, VA, U.S. Government Printing Office 2204-0005, Washington, D.C., May 1971.

4

Classification of Occupancy and Hazard of Contents

SECTION 4-1   Classification of Occupancy

The occupancy groupings found in Chapter 4 are based upon design features and occupancy patterns that are particular to certain types of occupancies, the main concern being to achieve a certain level of life safety for each. It is of paramount importance that the correct occupancy classification is selected when evaluating *Code* compliance. Improper classification may result in an inadequate level of life safety or overspending on nonrequired items. These occupancy groupings are:

Assembly. These occupancies generally house large groups of people who are unfamiliar with the space and therefore subject to indecision regarding the best means of egress in an emergency.

Educational. Primarily, the *Code* is concerned with the large numbers of young people found in school buildings. In some cases (as with day-care and preschool age children), they may even have to be carried out.

Health Care. The overriding concern with these occupancies is that, regardless of how many exits are called for or provided, the occupants are not necessarily able or free to use them. They might be immobile, perhaps wired to monitoring equipment, debilitated, or recovering from surgery; or they might be in some way handicapped. The *Code*, in this instance, calls for a design that stresses horizontal movement and compartmentation. It recognizes that the occupants must be provided enough protection to enable them to survive the fire by remaining in the structure, at least temporarily, during the fire.

Detention and Correctional. Many of the concerns for life safety in detention and correctional facilities are similar to those in health care facilities; however, there are additional special problems. Among these problems are security, inmate population, ignition potential, and staff training.

The large number of multiple-fatality fires in correctional facilities during the mid-1970s led to the formation of a new subcommittee on correctional facilities, and in the 1981 Edition of the *Code*, new chapters for this type of occupancy were added.

Residential. The main concern is that the occupants will be asleep for a portion (sometimes the major portion) of the time they occupy the building. Thus, they will be unaware of an incipient fire and may be trapped before actions to exit can be taken. In the 1985 Edition of the *Code*, a new chapter was added on residential board and care facilities. The poor fire record in these facilities has been well documented.[1]

Mercantile. As with assembly occupancies, large numbers of people are gathered in a space relatively unfamiliar to them, sometimes in the presence of a sizable fuel load.

Business. A lower occupant density occurs here than in mercantile occupancies, and the occupants are generally more familiar with their surroundings. However, confusing and indirect egress patterns are often developed. The *Code* does recognize that visitors, guests, clients, etc., are occupants in this occupancy type. The problems associated with high rise office occupancies have been recognized. Provisions contained in the *Code* are based on the fact that a rapid evacuation (and possibly any evacuation at all) may not be physically possible in multistory office buildings. As in health care occupancies, occupants may have to survive a fire while located within the structure.

Industrial. Because of the special circumstances involved, the *Code* relates the hazard of the occupancy to its incipient fuel load and considers the hazard of sizable industrial processes (including their unique or unusual features) where determining the requirements for exiting.

Storage. As in the case of industrial occupancies, fuel load and fuel arrangement, as well as a relatively low human population, are the basis for the *Code* provisions.

4-1.1 A building or structure shall be classified as follows, subject to the ruling of the authority having jurisdiction in case of question as to proper classification in any individual case.

This paragraph includes an important provision. If there is doubt about the proper occupancy classification, the authority having jurisdiction makes the determination.

4-1.2* Assembly. *(For requirements, see Chapters 8 and 9.)* Assembly occupancies include, but are not limited to, all buildings or portions of buildings used for gathering together 50 or more persons for such purposes as deliberation, worship, entertainment, eating, drinking, amusement, or awaiting transportation. Assembly occupancies include:

Armories	Gymnasiums
Assembly halls	Libraries
Auditoriums	Mortuary chapels
Bowling lanes	Motion picture theaters
Churches	Museums
Club rooms	Passenger stations and
College and university	terminals of air, surface,
classrooms, 50 persons	underground and marine
and over	public transportation facil-
Conference rooms	ities
Courtrooms	Pool rooms
Dance halls	Recreation piers
Drinking	Restaurants
establishments	Skating rinks
Exhibition halls	Theaters

Occupancy of any room or space for assembly purposes by less than 50 persons in a building of other occupancy and incidental to such other occupancy shall be classed as part of the other occupancy be and subject to the provisions applicable thereto.

Formal Interpretation 76-119
Reference: 4-1.2

Question 1: Is it the intent of the Committee that those facilities that are occupied by 49 persons or fewer are in fact not considered as assembly occupancies and are not subject to the requirements specified in Chapter 8 (Assembly Occupancies)?

Answer: Yes.

Question 2: If the answer to Question 1 is yes, under what occupancy classification would such an eating and drinking establishment be properly placed?

Answer: Mercantile.

Issue Edition: 1976
Reference: 4-1.2
Date: October 1979 ■

A-4-1.2 Such occupancies are characterized by the presence or potential presence of crowds with attendant panic hazard in case of fire or other emergency. They are generally open to the public, or may on occasion be open to the public, and the occupants, present voluntarily, are not ordinarily subject to discipline or control. Such buildings are ordinarily occupied by able-bodied persons and are not used for sleeping purposes. The need for alternate exit routes for small commercial places of assembly, such as restaurants, lounges, theaters, etc., with capacities of as few as 50 persons, is specially treated in this method of classification. Special conference rooms, snack areas, etc., incidental to and under the control of the management of other occupancies, such as offices, fall under the 50-person limitation.

4-1.3* Educational.

(*For requirements, see Chapters 10 and 11.*) Educational occupancies include all buildings or portions of buildings used for educational purposes through the twelfth grade by six or more persons for four or more hours per day or more than twelve hours per week. Educational occupancies include:

Academies	Nursery schools
Kindergartens	Schools

Educational occupancies also include day-care facilities of any occupant load. (*See Sections 10-7, 10-8, 10-9; 11-7, 11-8, 11-9.*) Other occupancies associated with educational institutions shall be in accordance with the appropriate parts of this *Code.*

In cases where instruction is incidental to some other occupancy, the section of this *Code* governing such other occupancy shall apply.

A-4-1.3

Educational occupancy is distinguished from assembly in that the same occupants are regularly present and they are subject to discipline and control.

Educational occupancies include buildings or portions of buildings used for educational purposes through the twelfth grade. College classroom buildings are considered business occupancies. See 10-1.1.3 for further information on requirements beyond the twelfth grade.

4-1.4 Health Care.

(*For requirements, see Chapters 12 and 13.*) Health care occupancies are those used for purposes such as medical or other treatment or care of persons suffering from physical or mental illness, disease or infirmity; and for the care of infants, convalescents, or infirm aged persons. Health care occupancies provide sleeping facilities for four or more occupants and are occupied by persons who are mostly incapable of self-preservation because of age, physical or mental

disability, or because of security measures not under the occupants' control.

Health care occupancies include:

(a) Hospitals.
(b) Nursing homes.
(c) Limited care facilities.

Health care occupancies also include ambulatory health care centers. (*See Sections 12-6 and 13-6.*)

Chapters 12 and 13 provide detailed definitions for the terms hospital, nursing home, limited care facility, and ambulatory care facility. Each of these definitions carries a requirement that the facility handle four or more persons (Chapter 21 allows up to three outsiders in a one- or two-family dwelling).

4-1.5 Detention and Correctional Occupancies.

(*For requirements, see Chapters 14 and 15.*) Detention and correctional occupancies are those used to house individuals under varied degrees of restraint or security and, as such, are occupied by persons who are mostly incapable of self-preservation because security measures are not under the occupants' control.

Detention and correctional occupancies include:

Adult correctional institutions	Juvenile training schools
Adult local detention facilities	Juvenile community residential centers
Adult community residential centers	Adult and juvenile work camps
Juvenile detention facilities	Adult and juvenile substance abuse centers

Chapters 14 and 15 address the residential housing areas of the detention and correctional occupancy as defined by 14-1.3(d) and 15-1.3(d). Other uses within detention and correctional facilities, such as gymnasiums or industries, shall be in accordance with the appropriate chapter of the *Code.* (*See 14-1.2.1 and 15-1.2.1.*)

It is intended that Chapters 14 and 15 apply only to those areas of detention and correctional facilities used for occupant housing (i.e., sleeping and day areas). Other occupancy use spaces within the facility should be evaluated using the appropriate chapter but with due consideration to the special security needs. For example, cafeterias should be reviewed using the assembly occupancy chapter, and metal shops should be evaluated using the industrial occupancy chapter.

4-1.6 **Residential.** (*For requirements, see Chapters 16 through 23.*) Residential occupancies are those occupancies in which sleeping accommodations are provided for normal residential purposes and include all buildings designed to provide sleeping accommodations.

Exception: Those classified under health care or detention and correctional occupancies.

Residential occupancies are treated separately in this *Code* in the following groups:

(a) Hotels (*Chapters 16 and 17*).
    Motels.
    Dormitories.
(b) Apartments (*Chapters 18 and 19*).
(c) Lodging or rooming houses (*Chapter 20*).
(d) One- and two-family dwellings (*Chapter 21*).
(e) Board and care facilities (*Chapters 22 and 23*).

Each of the occupancies is specifically defined within the chapters that govern them.

4-1.7* **Mercantile.** (*For requirements, see Chapters 24 and 25.*) Mercantile occupancies include stores, markets, and other rooms, buildings, or structures for the display and sale of merchandise. Mercantile occupancies include:

Auction rooms   Supermarkets
Department stores   Shopping centers
Drug stores

Minor merchandising operations in buildings predominantly of other occupancies, such as a newsstand in an office building, shall be subject to the exit requirements of the predominant occupancy.

A-4-1.7 Office, storage, and service facilities incidental to the sale of merchandise and located in the same building are included with mercantile occupancy.

4-1.8* **Business.** (*For requirements, see Chapters 26 and 27.*) Business occupancies are those used for the transaction

of business (other than that covered under "Mercantile"), for the keeping of accounts and records, and for similar purposes. Business occupancies include:

City halls   General offices
College and university   Laboratories for basic
  instructional buildings,   or applied research
  classrooms under 50 persons,   not including
  and instructional laboratories   hazardous chemicals
Courthouses   Outpatient clinics,
Dentists' offices   ambulatory
Doctors' offices   Town halls

Minor office occupancy incidental to operations in another occupancy shall be considered as a part of the predominating occupancy and shall be subject to the provisions of this *Code* that apply to the predominant occupancy.

A-4-1.8 Doctors' and dentists' offices are included unless of such character as to be classified as health care occupancies. Service facilities common to city office buildings such as newsstands, lunch counters serving less than 50 persons, barber shops, and beauty parlors are included in this occupancy group.

City halls, town halls, and court houses are included in this occupancy group insofar as their principal function is the transaction of public business and the keeping of books and records. Insofar as they are used for assembly purposes, they are classed as assembly occupancies.

4-1.9 **Industrial** (*For requirements, see Chapter 28.*) Industrial occupancies include factories making products of all kinds and properties devoted to operations such as processing, assembling, mixing, packaging, finishing or decorating, and repairing. Industrial occupancies include:

Dry cleaning plants   Laundries
Factories of all kinds   Power plants
Food processing plants   Pumping stations
Gas plants   Refineries
Hangars (for servicing/main-   Sawmills
  tenance)   Telephone exchanges
Laboratories involving
  hazardous chemicals

4-1.10* **Storage.** (*For requirements, see Chapter 29.*) Storage occupancies include all buildings or structures utilized primarily for the storage or sheltering of goods, merchandise, products, vehicles, or animals. Storage occupancies include:

Barns
Bulk oil storage
Cold storage
Freight terminals
Grain elevators
Hangars (for storage only)

Parking structures
Stables
Truck and marine
  terminals
Warehouses

Minor storage incidental to another occupancy shall be treated as part of the predominant occupancy.

A-4-1.10 Storage properties are characterized by the presence of relatively small numbers of persons in proportion to the area; any new use that increases the number of occupants to a figure comparable with other classes of occupancy changes the classification of the building to that of the new use.

4-1.11 Special Structures. Special structures that house occupancies include the occupancies from the preceding groups that are in special structures or buildings including, among others, the following:

Open structures
Towers
Underground structures
Vehicles

Vessels
Water surrounded structures
Windowless buildings

Such special buildings and structures shall conform to the requirements of the specific occupancy Chapters 8 through 29 except as modified by Chapter 30.

In reality, special structures can be one of two types. The first type is a structure that houses an unusual occupancy, such as a railroad signal tower or forest fire tower. Another type is a structure that houses an occupancy regulated under one of the normal descriptions but in a special building, such as a restaurant on top of a tower, or an assembly or mercantile function on a pier. In either case, Chapter 30 should be referenced for specific requirements.

4-1.12 Mixed Occupancies. (*See 1-5.7.*)

SECTION 4-2 Hazard of Contents

4-2.1 General.

4-2.1.1 The hazard of contents, for the purpose of this *Code*, shall be the relative danger of the start and spread of fire, the danger of smoke or gases generated, and the danger of explosion or other occurrence potentially endangering the lives and safety of the occupants of the building or structure.

To understand the purpose of Section 4-2, one must recognize that the classification of hazard is based on the potential threat to life represented by the contents. A fuel load that might be considered as a "light" hazard in terms of its ease of extinguishment by a sprinkler system may, in fact, produce enough smoke and other toxic products of combustion to threaten the lives of the occupants; hence, the *Code* may classify the material as an "ordinary" hazard.

The *Code's* method of hazard classification is based on life safety. For this reason, its provisions are not readily incorporated into the design criteria of other codes where hazard classification is based on property preservation. Thus, for a material considered to be a "high hazard" by the *Life Safety Code*, there may be no constructive design or system arrangement to compensate for the potential threat to life short of total enclosure and isolation of the material involved. Further, many "light hazard" fuels (from an extinguishment point of view) may be treated as "ordinary" hazards under the *Life Safety Code*. For example, an office occupancy may have a "light hazard" classification under NFPA 13, *Standard for the Installation of Sprinkler Systems,*[2] but is considered "ordinary" hazard under the *Life Safety Code*.

As stated in 4-2.1, this *Code* classifies contents based on the threat of fire, explosions, and other similar occurrences. It does not specifically consider the danger posed by toxic chemical, etiological contamination, or similar hazards.

4-2.1.2 Hazard of contents shall be determined by the authority having jurisdiction on the basis of the character of the contents and the processes or operations conducted in the building or structure.

4-2.1.3* Where different degrees of hazard of contents exist in different parts of a building or structure, the most hazardous shall govern the classification for the purpose of this *Code*.

Exception: Where hazardous areas are separated or protected as specifed in Section 6-4 and the applicable sections of Chapters 8 through 30.

A-4-2.1.3   Under this provision, any violation of the requirements of Chapters 8 through 30 for separation or protection of hazardous operation or storage would inherently involve violation of the other sections of the *Code* unless additional exit facilities appropriate to high hazard contents were provided.

4-2.2   Classification of Hazard of Contents.

4-2.2.1*   The hazard of contents of any building or structure shall be classified as low, ordinary, or high in accordance with 4-2.2.2, 4-2.2.3, and 4-2.2.4.

A-4-2.2.1   These classifications do not apply to the application of sprinkler protection classifications. (*See NFPA 13, Standard for the Installation of Sprinkler Systems.*) (*See Appendix B.*)

4-2.2.2*   **Low Hazard.** Low hazard contents shall be classified as those of such low combustibility that no self-propagating fire therein can occur.

A-4-2.2.2   Chapter 29, Storage Occupancies, recognizes storage of noncombustible materials as low hazard. In other occupancies it is assumed that even where the actual contents hazard may normally be low, there is sufficient likelihood that some combustible material or hazardous operations will be introduced in connection with building repair or maintenance, or that some psychological factor might create conditions conducive to panic, so that the exit facilities cannot safely be reduced below those specified for ordinary hazard contents.

It should be noted that very few occupancies qualify as having low hazard contents.

4-2.2.3*   **Ordinary Hazard.** Ordinary hazard contents shall be classified as those that are likely to burn with moderate rapidity or to give off a considerable volume of smoke.

A-4-2.2.3   This classification represents the conditions found in most buildings and is the basis for the general requirements of this *Code.*

The fear of poisonous fumes or explosions is necessarily a relative matter to be determined on a judgment basis. All smoke contains some toxic fire gases, but under conditions of ordinary hazard there should be no unduly dangerous exposure during the period necessary to escape from the fire area, assuming there are proper exits.

4-2.2.4*   **High Hazard.** High hazard contents shall be classified as those that are likely to burn with extreme rapidity or from which explosions are likely. (*For means of egress requirements, see Section 5-11.*)

A-4-2.2.4   High hazard contents may include occupancies where gasoline and other flammable liquids are handled or used or are stored under conditions involving possible release of flammable vapors; where grain dust, wood flour or plastic dust, aluminum or magnesium dust, or other explosive dusts may be produced; where hazardous chemicals or explosives are manufactured, stored, or handled; where cotton or other combustible fibers are processed or handled under conditions producing flammable flyings; and other situations of similar hazard. Chapter 28, "Industrial Occupancies," and Chapter 29, "Storage Occupancies," include detailed provisions on high hazard contents.

As can be seen from the definitions, occupancies containing low hazard or high hazard contents are rare. As an aid to users of the *Code* in deciding which hazard classification applies, it is suggested that the users ask themselves the following questions: Do the contents qualify for a low hazard classification? Do the contents qualify for a high hazard classification? If the answer to both of these questions is "no," then the hazard of contents must be in the "ordinary" classification.

References Cited in Commentary

[1]NFPA SPP-76, *Firesafety in Boarding Homes*, National Fire Protection Association, Quincy, MA, 1982.

[2]NFPA 13, *Standard for the Installation of Sprinkler Systems*, National Fire Protection Association, Quincy, MA, 1991.

5

Means of Egress

(See also Chapter 31.)

The purpose of this chapter is to establish minimum requirements for the means of egress; requirements that can be applied to all classifications of occupancy. Those instances in which these requirements are not specific enough for the needs of a particular circumstance are noted in the exceptions.

Means of egress is a term defined in 5-1.2.9 as including the exit, the exit access, and the exit discharge. This chapter covers the type, width, number, and arrangement of exits; their lighting and identification; as well as such key factors as travel distances and exit capacity. It also contains detailed requirements for the various components that may be included in the means of egress.

SECTION 5-1   General

5-1.1 Application.

Means of egress must comply with this chapter. The occupancy chapters, Chapters 8 through 30, may not contain provisions or requirements less stringent than those in Chapter 5 unless expressly authorized by Chapter 5. This provision was adopted to standardize similar requirements as they apply to the various occupancies, to the greatest extent possible.

Since this was a shift in the prior organization of the *Code*, undetected discrepancies may arise. Therefore, for enforcement purposes, 1-5.8 continues to state that, where conflicts occur, the more specific requirements of the occupancy chapters prevail. Also see commentary following 1-5.8.

5-1.1.1* Means of egress for both new and existing buildings shall comply with this chapter. (*Also see Chapter 1 and Section 31-1.*)

A-5-1.1.1 Portable ladders, rope fire escapes, and similar emergency escape devices may have a useful function in facilitating escape from burning buildings lacking adequate exits of the stair or other standard type, but they are not the equivalent of standard exits, and their use is not in any way recognized by this *Code* as satisfying the requirements for means of egress. Furthermore, many such devices are of types quite unsuited to use by aged or infirm persons or by small children. Therefore, such devices may give a false sense of security and should not be used as an excuse for not providing standard exit facilities.

These requirements apply to both new construction and existing buildings. No change, in either the structure or the occupancy, that reduces the level of life safety is permitted. The objective is to provide an acceptable degree of safety in terms of not only the present but also the future use of a building.

Whenever a building is renovated or when additions are made to it, care must be taken not to reduce the means of egress below the level required by the *Code*. Even though a new addition in itself may meet all requirements, it is prohibited to add to an existing building if, by doing so, the means of egress in the existing portion is reduced to a level below that specified by the *Code*. Similarly, any change in building occupancy or occupancy subclassification requires a review of the means of egress to ensure that the requirements specified for the new occupancy classification are met. (*See 1-5.6 for additional information regarding application to alterations and 1-7.4 regarding application to changes of occupancy or occupancy subclassification.*)

5-1.2 Definitions.

5-1.2.1 Accessible Area of Refuge. An accessible area of refuge is an area of refuge that complies with the accessible route requirements of ANSI A117.1, *Buildings and Facilities—Providing Accessibility and Usability for Physically Handicapped People.*

5-1.2.2* Accessible Means of Egress. Accessible means of egress is a path of travel that is usable by a person with a severe mobility impairment and that leads to a public way or an area of refuge.

A-5-1.2.2 Accessible Means of Egress. Generally, an accessible means of egress complies with the "accessible route" requirements of ANSI A117.1, *Standard for Buildings and Facilities – Providing Usability and Accessibility for Physically Handicapped People (see appendix B)*. A "severe" mobility impairment means the ability to move to stairs but not the ability to use the stairs.

5-1.2.3* Area of Refuge. An area of refuge is a space protected from the effects of fire, either by means of separation from other spaces in the same building or by virtue of location in an adjacent building, thereby permitting a delay in egress travel from any level.

A-5-1.2.3 Area of Refuge. An area of refuge has a temporary use during egress. It generally serves as a staging area that provides relative safety to its occupants while potential emergencies are assessed, decisions are made, and mitigating activities are begun. Refuge is thus a stage of the total egress process; a stage between egress from the immediately threatened floor area and egress by means of some route.

An area of refuge might be another building connected by a bridge or balcony, a compartment of a subdivided story, an elevator lobby, or an enlarged exit stair landing. An area of refuge is accessible by means of horizontal travel or, as a minimum, it complies with the "accessible route" requirements of ANSI A117.1, *Standard for Buildings and Facilities — Providing Accessibility and Usability for Physically Handicapped People. (See Appendix B.)*

Horizontal exits are traditional examples of areas of refuge that provide substantial floor area and superior fire protection permitting a delay sufficient for a large number of people to move to the level of exit discharge. Other areas of refuge, intended for use by fewer people, may provide shorter delays by virtue of smoke separation without substantial, rated fire separation from adjoining areas. Such shorter delays might be appropriate for organizing assisted or supervised egress that requires movement from one level to another. (*See 5-2.4.*)

The three definitions contained in 5-1.2.1, 5-1.2.2, and 5.1.2.3 were added in this edition of the *Code* along with new subsection 5-2.12. Note that, by definition, an area of refuge is not necessarily accessible but that an accessible area of refuge must be "accessible" as defined in accordance with ANSI A117.1, *Buildings and Facilities – Providing Accessibility and Usability for Physically*

Handicapped People.[1] See the commentary in 5-2.12 for additional information.

5-1.2.4 **Common Path of Travel.** Common path of travel is that portion of exit access that must be traversed before two separate and distinct paths of travel to two exits are available. Paths that merge are common paths of travel. Common path of travel is measured in the same manner as travel distance but terminates at that point where two separate and distinct routes become available.

A definition of common path of travel was added in the 1988 *Code* to identify that part of the exit access to be considered in applying the common path provisions of certain occupancy chapters. For discussion of common path of travel, see 5-5.1.6.

5-1.2.5* **Exit.** Exit is that portion of a means of egress that is separated from all other spaces of the building or structure by construction or equipment as required in 5-1.3.1 to provide a protected way of travel to the exit discharge. Exits include exterior exit doors, exit passageways, horizontal exits, and separated exit stairs or ramps.

A-5-1.2.5 **Exit.** In the case of a stairway, the exit includes the door to the stairway enclosure, stairs and landings inside the enclosure, the door from the stairway enclosure to the street or open air, or any passageway and door necessary to provide a path of travel from the stairway enclosure to the street or open air. In the case of a door leading directly from the street floor to the street or open air, the exit comprises only the doorway.

Doors of small individual rooms, as in hotels, while constituting exit access from the room, are not referred to as exits except when they lead directly to the outside of the building or other place of safety.

The exit is that portion of the means of egress that is separated from other building spaces by enclosing it within construction having the minimum degree of fire resistance as specified in 5-1.3.1, with limited openings through the enclosing construction, and protection of such openings. The exit may include parts of corridors, stairs, smokeproof enclosures, outside balconies, ramps, and doors. In each case, the exit component must conform to the specifications for fire protection and the maximum or minimum dimensions established by the *Code*. In its simplest form, an exit is simply a door or doors opening directly to the exterior at grade.

In the case of a stairway, the exit includes the stair enclosure, the door to the stairway enclosure, the stairs and landings inside the enclosure, and the door from the enclosure to the street or open air.

The entrance to an exit (part of the exit) is a fire door that provides a protected entrance into a protected area. A fire door, however, does not always signal an entrance to an exit. A door or fire door between a hotel room and a corridor, or a fire door across a corridor or lobby, is not part of an exit unless the corridor or lobby and all other openings into the corridor or lobby are separated and protected as required for an exit in accordance with 5-1.3.1.

The important fact to remember is that an exit, other than a door opening directly to the outside, provides a protected path of travel.

The last sentence of 5-1.2.5 specifically identifies those building features that, where properly arranged and constructed, constitute an exit such as an exterior exit door, an exit passageway, a horizontal exit, and an enclosed exit stair or ramp.

Several types of exits, as they may actually occur in some buildings, are shown in Figure 5-1. For detailed requirements for a horizontal exit, see 5-2.4.

5-1.2.6 **Exit Access.** Exit access is that portion of a means of egress that leads to an exit.

The exit access includes the room or space in a building in which a person is located and the aisles, stairs, ramps, passageways, corridors, and doors that must be traversed on the way to an exit. Special protection may be required for corridor portions of the exit access beyond that which is normally required by building regulations for compartmentation within the building. (*See 5-1.3.4 and the applicable occupancy chapters.*) For maximum travel distances, see Section 5-6 and the occupancy chapters, Chapters 8 through 30. Some variations in arrangement of exit access are shown in Figure 5-2.

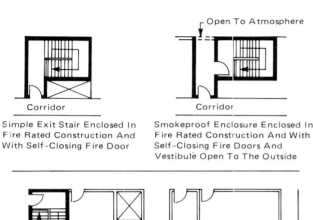

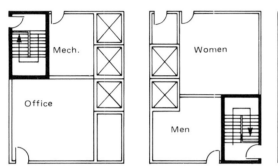

Core-Type Exits With Stairs Enclosed In Fire
Rated Construction And With Self-Closing
Fire Doors

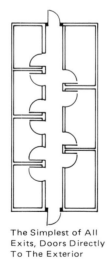

The Simplest of All
Exits, Doors Directly
To The Exterior

Figure 5-1.   Variations of Exits.

5-1.2.7 **Exit Discharge.** Exit discharge is that portion of a means of egress between the termination of an exit and a public way.

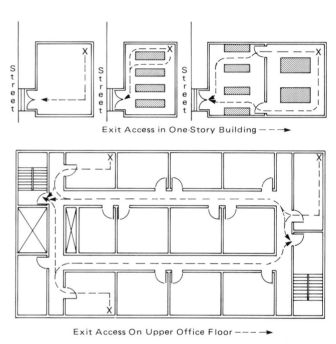

Figure 5-2.   Variations of Exit Access.

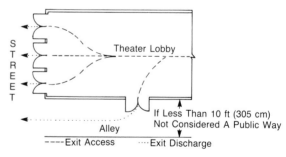

Figure 5-3.   Examples of Exit Discharge. If the alley is less than 10 ft (305 cm) wide, it will not meet the definition of a public way; thus, the exit discharge continues to the street.

Not all exits discharge directly into a public way. In such cases there remains some travel from the point where the occupant leaves the exit enclosure to the public way or other equivalent safe place. This travel may be inside the building, as permitted in 5-7.2, or outside. Where an exit opens onto an alley, court, or yard, a safe passageway must be provided to a public way or some equivalent safe area. In each case, this portion of the means of egress is the exit discharge. (*See also 5-7.1.*)

Typical plans of various forms of the exit discharge are shown in Figures 5-3, 5-4, and 5-5.

5-1.2.8*   **Horizontal Exit.** A horizontal exit is a way of passage from one building to an area of refuge in another building on approximately the same level, or a way of passage

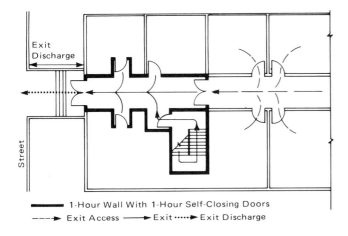

1-Hour Wall With 1-Hour Self-Closing Doors
- - - ▶ Exit Access ——▶ Exit ·····▶ Exit Discharge

Figure 5-4.   Example of Exit Discharge from an Exit That Uses an Exit Passageway. The exit discharge from a building of this configuration, which includes an enclosed stair and exit passageway, extends from the exterior door to the public way (street).

through or around a fire barrier to an area of refuge on approximately the same level in the same building that affords safety from fire and smoke originating from the area of incidence and areas communicating therewith. (*See 5-2.4.*)

A-5-1.2.8   **Horizontal Exit.** Horizontal exits should not be confused with egress through doors in smoke barriers. Doors in smoke barriers are designed only for temporary protection against smoke, whereas horizontal exits provide protection against serious fire for a relatively long period of time in addition to providing immediate protection from smoke.

A horizontal exit is a protected passage from one area of a building to another area in the same building or in an adjoining building on approximately the same level. Substantial fire separations are required, since the area to which exit is made is to serve as an area of refuge. The horizontal exit may be a fire door in a 2-hour fire resistance rated wall separating a building into two areas, or it may be a bridge or balcony leading to an adjoining building. Examples of horizontal exits are shown in Figure 5-6.

Horizontal exits may be useful in any occupancy. They are particularly useful in health care and in detention and correctional occupancies. They make it possible to move

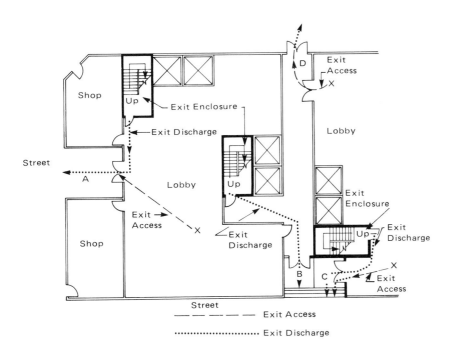

Street
—— —— —— —— —— Exit Access
····························· Exit Discharge

Figure 5-5.   Examples of Exit Discharge in a Multistory Building. To the occupants of the building at the discharge level, the doors at A, B, C, and D are exits, and the path denoted by long dash lines (– – –) is the exit access. To people emerging from the exit enclosure, the same doors and the paths denoted by dotted lines (. . . .) are the exit discharges. This arrangement must meet the requirements of 5-7.2.

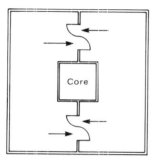

Two-Way Horizontal Exit In
An Open Plan Building. Self-
Closing Fire Doors Required
In Fire Separation.

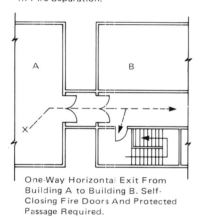

One-Way Horizontal Exit From
Building A to Building B. Self-
Closing Fire Doors And Protected
Passage Required.

Figure 5-6. Types of Horizontal Exits. See 5-2.4 for more details on horizontal exits.

bedridden patients horizontally to an area of refuge rather than vertically down stairs and to protect inmates without moving them to the outside. Horizontal exits are very effective in the defend-in-place concept. With their use, total evacuation can often be avoided. For complete details of horizontal exits, see 5-2.4.

5-1.2.9 **Means of Egress.** A means of egress is a continuous and unobstructed way of exit travel from any point in a building or structure to a public way and consists of three separate and distinct parts: (a) the exit access, (b) the exit, and (c) the exit discharge. A means of egress comprises the vertical and horizontal travel and shall include intervening room spaces, doorways, hallways, corridors, passageways, balconies, ramps, stairs, enclosures, lobbies, escalators, horizontal exits, courts, and yards.

A means of egress, by definition, leads to a public way. This is the most succinct way the *Code* can express the need to get a building occupant to a safe place. In many instances, such as in the case of university campuses, military bases, resorts, and other large complexes, there are numerous places where a building occupant would be safe from a building fire before reaching an actual public way. It is the basic intent of the *Code* that occupants be able to get to a safe place.

From every location in a building, there must be a means of egress, or path of travel, over which a person can move to gain access to the outside or gain access to a place of safety or refuge should the need arise. Any person who gains entrance to a building has available that same route by which to exit. Yet, one important consideration makes exiting more than just reversing one's route of entry, especially if emergency conditions exist. This reverse route, or any other route chosen for exiting, may consist of features that, though they were not obstacles upon entrance, prove to be such upon exit. For example, a door hinged to swing in the direction of entry can become an obstacle when one attempts to leave the building in the opposite direction. The door swings against the flow of traffic — a flow that in an emergency egress situation is greatly increased as compared with the leisurely flow of people entering a building. The path of travel must be one that is easily traversable and recognizable.

A basic principle of the *Code* is that every component of a means of egress be operable by and under the control of the occupant seeking egress. Where the *Code* makes any exception to this basic concept, it does so only by imposing conditions deemed adequate to maintain the desired level of life safety.

The occupant of a building must be protected from obstacles to safe egress. To achieve this goal, the protection of each component in the exiting process must be considered individually. Clear and concise definitions are needed, definitions that help point to the special needs for that component. The term "means of egress" has been used for many years, but it was not until the late 1950s that it took on a more meaningful definition, comprising three separate and distinct parts: (1) the exit access, (2) the exit, and (3) the exit discharge. Until the late 1950s, the term exit was used more often than not, a fact evidenced by the *Life Safety Code's* original title — the

Building Exits Code. At that time, the Sectional Committee on Means of Egress developed a proposed definition for "means of egress" and presented it for consideration to the NFPA Committee on Safety to Life. The original definition proposed contained the description of just two parts: an exit access and an exit. The Committee saw the need for a third part: the exit discharge. Currently, when reference is made to any of the three parts, there is a clear understanding of the part of a building being referenced and the function it serves in relation to the total means of egress.

Formal Interpretation 76-81
Reference: 5-1.2.9, 5-2.1.5.1

Question 1: Are doors that serve individual rooms, such as offices and classrooms, intended to be classified as a portion of a means of egress as defined in Paragraph 5-1.2.9?

Answer: Yes.

Question 2: If the answer to Question 1 is yes, are these doors then required to comply with Subparagraph 5-2.1.5.1, whereby locks requiring the use of a key from the side from which egress is to be made are prohibited?

Answer: Yes.

Issue Edition: 1976
Reference: 5-1.2.1
Date: September 1978 ∎

5-1.2.10   Ramp. A ramp is a walking surface in an accessible space that has a slope steeper than 1 in 20.

For requirements for ramps used in a means of egress, see 5-2.5.

5-1.3   Separation of Means of Egress. (*See also Section 6-2.*)

5-1.3.1   Exits. Where an exit is required by this *Code* to be protected by separation from other parts of the building, the separating construction shall meet the requirements of Section 6-2 and the following requirements:

(a) The separation shall have at least a 1-hour fire resistance rating where the exit connects three stories or less. This applies whether the stories counted are above or below the story where exit discharge begins.

Exception to (a): Existing apartment buildings in accordance with 19-2.2.1.2.

(b) The separation shall have at least a 2-hour fire resistance rating where the exit connects four or more stories, whether above or below the level of exit discharge. It shall be constructed of an assembly of noncombustible or limited-combustible materials and shall be supported by construction having at least a 2-hour fire resistance rating.

Exception to (b): Hotels in accordance with 16-2.2.1.2 and 17-2.2.1.2 and apartment buildings in accordance with 18-2.2.1.2 and 19-2.2.1.2.

(c) Any opening therein shall be protected by a fire door assembly equipped with a door closer complying with 5-2.1.8.

(d) Openings in exit enclosures shall be limited to those necessary for access to the enclosure from normally occupied spaces, from corridors, and for egress from the enclosure.

(e) Penetrations into and openings through an exit enclosure assembly are prohibited except for required exit doors; duct work and equipment necessary for independent stair pressurization; sprinkler piping; standpipes; and electrical conduit serving the stairway.

There shall be no penetrations or communicating openings between adjacent exit enclosures.

Exits must provide protection from fire throughout their entire length. This is accomplished by enclosure with construction having a designated degree of fire resistance, by the use of interior finish within the exit that meets the *Code's* requirements related to flame spread and smoke development, and by careful control of openings into the exit enclosure itself. (*For a discussion of interior finish, see Section 6-5 and the occupancy chapters, Chapters 8 through 30.*) The only openings permitted in the enclosure walls between the exit and the building spaces are those needed to enter the exit from any normally occupied space and those needed to leave the exit at the level of exit discharge; in other words, only openings necessary for an occupant to enter and leave the exit enclosure. The *Code* also prohibits the use of an exit enclosure for any purpose that could possibly interfere with the exit's ability to function as a protected path of travel. Every measure must be taken to preserve the integrity of that portion of the means of egress.

The degree of fire resistance required is dependent upon the number of stories or floor levels that the individual exit connects and not the height of the building. It is possible to have stairs in a high rise building connecting only three stories. In such a case, the enclosing construction need not be more than 1-hour fire resistance rated. (*See Figures 5-7 and 5-8.*)

The doors in walls of exit enclosures are to be 1-hour fire protection rated where used in 1-hour enclosures and 1½-hour fire protection rated where used in 2-hour enclosures. (*See 6-2.3.5.*)

If a pair of fire doors opening in the same direction without a mullion is to be used in an exit enclosure, the pair of doors should be listed for use without an astragal. The reason for this is the need for pairs of doors with an astragal to close in sequence. A coordinator is required to accomplish the sequential closing, and the record of coordinators functioning properly is poor.

Fire doors, if they are to function as intended, must not only be tightly closed, but also be held closed with positive latching. To avoid the possibility of doors improperly closing, the use of pairs of doors with an astragal in an exit enclosure should be avoided. However, without an astragal, considerable smoke could pass between the doors into the exit; therefore, the use of pairs of fire doors opening in the same direction into an exit enclosure is discouraged. Doors opening in opposite directions from each other, such as are often found in horizontal exits, are easily equipped with astragals, and as such, these doors and doors with mullions do not present this problem.

The only openings permitted into the exit enclosure are for access to the enclosure from normally occupied spaces and at the exit discharge. These are required to be self-closing fire doors, as described in 5-2.1.8. No opening through the enclosure walls is permitted from storage rooms, closets, maids' closets, boiler rooms, equipment spaces, utility rooms, electrical vaults, or similar spaces that are not normally occupied. Panels providing access

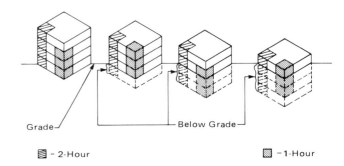

Figure 5-7. With Four Stories or More, Exit Stairs Must Be Enclosed in 2-Hour Fire Resistance Rated Noncombustible or Limited-Combustible Construction (Shaded Areas) and Supported by 2-Hour Construction.

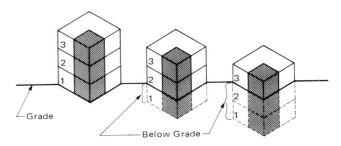

Figure 5-8. With Three Stories or Less, Exit Stairs Must Be Enclosed in 1-Hour Fire Resistance Rated Construction (Shaded Areas).

to building spaces cannot be installed in the walls of exit enclosures regardless of whether or not the panels have a fire resistance rating.

Openings for ductwork serving smokeproof enclosures may be permitted (*see 5-2.3*), but penetration by other ductwork is not allowed. Openings to the exterior are permitted provided there is no potential fire exposure from an adjacent source. They need not be protected with fire protection rated assemblies, since they are not separating the exit from other parts of the building. (*See 5-2.2.6.2.*)

Certain exit access corridors must also be separated from other building spaces in new construction. (*See 5-1.3.4.*) However, some of the occupancy chapters contain varying provisions.

5-1.3.2 The enclosing walls of exits shall be so arranged as to provide a continuous protected path of travel, including landings and passageways, to an exit discharge.

This extremely important paragraph emphasizes that exits, and the protection they afford the occupants, must be continuous. It is a fundamental premise that once an occupant has been provided the level of protection afforded by an exit, that level of protection shall not be thereafter reduced.

This paragraph prohibits a required exit stair or exit ramp design that requires a person to leave the exit enclosure, enter a floor, and then reenter the exit enclosure to continue down. Figure 5-9 shows an unacceptable arrangement.

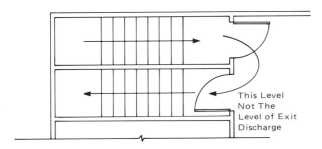

Figure 5-9. An Unacceptable Arrangement for Enclosing a Stairway Serving as a Required Exit.

5-1.3.3* No exit enclosure shall be used for any purpose that could interfere with its uses as an exit and, if so designated, as an area of refuge.

A-5-1.3.3 This provision prohibits the use of exit enclosures for storage or for installation of equipment not necessary for safety. Occupancy is prohibited other than for egress, refuge, and access. The intent is that the exit enclosure essentially be "sterile" with respect to firesafety hazards.

Paragraph 5-1.3.3 prohibits the use of an exit for any purpose that could potentially interfere with its use as an exit or as an area of refuge (*see 5-2.12 for a discussion on exits being used as an area of refuge*). For example, wiring, vending machines, copying machines, storage, and similar use or equipment are not permitted within an exit enclosure. Standpipes and emergency lighting that are part of the egress system are permitted, but only if arranged so as not to interfere with the passage of people. This paragraph is not limited to a mechanical obstruction of the egress path, but includes any use or item that could

interfere for any reason with the use of the exit. Paragraph 31-1.2.1 deals primarily with the physical or mechanical blockage issue. This paragraph was modified for the 1991 edition to add emphasis that any potential blockage was intended. The appendix note was added to further clarify the intent of the *Code.*

It should be noted that these prohibitions also apply to exit passageways since they are exits.

Also see 5-1.3.1(d), which would prohibit such spaces from having doors into an exit enclosure, 5-1.7.3, 5-2.2.6.5 and 31-1.2.1.

5-1.3.4* Exit Access Corridors. Corridors used as exit access and serving an area having an occupant load of more than 30 shall be separated from other parts of the building by a fire barrier having a 1-hour fire resistance rating in accordance with 6-2.3.

Exception No. 1: Existing buildings.

Exception No. 2: As otherwise provided in Chapters 8 through 30.

A-5-1.3.4 The purpose of a tight-fitting door is to control the flow of smoke. The tight fit can be achieved by close attention to tolerances or by supplemental means. In no case should the "crack dimensions" exceed the maximum tolerances allowed in NFPA 80, *Standard for Fire Doors and Windows.* (*See Appendix B. Also see NFPA 105, Recommended Practice for the Installation of Smoke-Control Door Assemblies.*)

Paragraph 5-1.3.4 establishes protection of certain exit access corridors in new buildings. It must be noted, however, that most of the occupancy chapters establish exit access corridor protection requirements that supersede these requirements. Also, many of the occupancy chapters establish corridor requirements for existing buildings. These special corridor provisions are usually in the 3.6 subsection of each occupancy chapter. For example, see 10-3.6 or 12-3.6. If no special requirements appear in the 3.6 subsection, then the provisions of 5-1.3.4 prevail.

Paragraph 5-1.3.4 does not require corridors, but does require that where corridors do exist and they serve an area having an occupant load of more than 30, they must be separated. The construction of the barrier forming the corridor walls as well as the opening protection is regulated by 6-2.3. Walls that serve both as a corridor wall and a wall protecting an exit enclosure or separating a hazardous area must meet the more stringent provisions required for exit enclosure and protection of hazardous areas. (*See Figure 5-10.*)

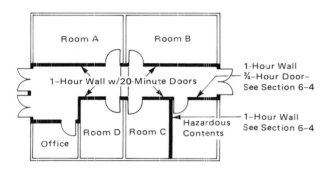

Figure 5-10. *Protection of Exit Access Corridors. This plan shows an example of the requirement for protection of exit access corridors required by 5-1.3.4. Note the difference for the protection from the hazardous area.*

5-1.4 **Interior Finish in Exits.** The flame spread of interior finish on walls and ceilings shall be limited to Class A or Class B in exit enclosures. Chapters 8 through 30 governing individual occupancies may impose further limitations.

Except as provided in Chapters 8 through 30, the interior finish in exits is required to be Class A (0-25 flame spread rate, 0-450 smoke development) or Class B (26-75 flame spread rate, 0-450 smoke development) as defined in Section 6-5. Obviously, the effort is to minimize the possibility of fire spreading into and within the exit.

5-1.5 **Headroom.** Means of egress shall be so designed and maintained as to provide adequate headroom as provided in other sections of this *Code* (*see 5-2.2.2.1*), but in no case shall the ceiling height be less than 7 ft 6 in. (229 cm) nor shall any projection from the ceiling be less than 6 ft 8 in. (203 cm) nominal height from the floor. Headroom on stairs is the vertical distance above a plane parallel to and tangent with the most forward projection of the stair tread.

Exception: In existing buildings, the ceiling height shall be not less than 7 ft (213 cm) from the floor with no projection below a 6 ft 8 in. (203 cm) nominal height from the floor.

The lowest projection of 6 ft 8 in. (203 cm) is identified as nominal height. It is the intent to recognize and permit standard door height. Note that 5-2.2.2.1 allows the 6 ft 8 in. (203 cm) height on stairways also. (*See Figure 5-11.*)

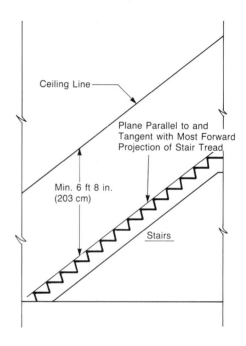

Figure 5-11. *The Method of Measuring Headroom on Stairs.*

5-1.6 **Changes in Level in Means of Egress.**

5-1.6 is a restatement, in more fundamental terms, of three separate requirements that were part of the *Code* prior to 1988. (These requirements were designated 5-1.6, 5-2.2.4.5, and 5-2.2.4.7 of the 1985 and previous editions). They dealt with both the elevation differences and the minimum number of risers that could be used with stairs as opposed to ramps. These previous rules have not been well respected in actual practice, and a major problem remained to be solved with regard to a more basic approach to stairs traversing small elevation differences. Starting with the 1988 Edition of the *Code* Paragraph 5-1.6 now permits stairs to have fewer than three risers. However, it should be emphasized that, if they are built, they must meet even more stringent requirements than those for other stairs because of the record of accidents on such limited-rise stairs. It should be made clear to designers that, as far as the *Code* is concerned, single risers and two-riser combinations are stairs and must meet all the requirements for stairs. Additionally, they must be designed more carefully, with particular attention to making their presence evident to all users and allowing for the larger walking stride that may occur in such situations [hence the requirement for a larger minimum tread size of 13 in. (33.0 cm)].

5-1.6.1 Changes in level in means of egress shall be by a ramp or a stair where the elevation difference is more than 21 in. (53.3 cm).

5-1.6.2* Changes in level in means of egress not more than 21 in. (53.3 cm) shall be either by a ramp or by a stair complying with the requirements of 5-2.2. The minimum tread depth of such stair shall be 13 in. (33.0 cm), and the location of each step shall be readily apparent.

A-5-1.6.2 Aside from the problems created for persons who are mobility impaired, small changes of elevations in floors are best avoided because of the increased occurrence of missteps where the presence of single steps or a series of steps is not readily apparent. A contrasting marking stripe on each stepping surface may be provided at the nosing or leading edge such that the location of each step is readily apparent, especially when viewed in descent. Such stripes should be at least 1 in. (2.5 cm) but not more than 2 in. (5.0 cm) in width. Other methods could include lighting of each tread, contrasting colors, contrasting textures, a combination thereof, or other similar means. The construction or application of marking stripes should be such that slip resistance is consistent over the walking surface and no tripping hazard is created (*see also A-5-2.2.3.4*). Depending on the distractions of the surroundings, the familiarity of users with a particular small change of level, and the number of people that might be in a group traversing the change of level (thereby reducing visibility of the level changes), additional warning measures might be needed to ensure that the attention of all individuals is drawn to such ramps, platforms, and steps, especially during descent. These measures include prominent handrails within reach of users, warning signs, and highlighting each step by illumination.

Editions of the *Code* prior to 1988 prohibited stairs where changes of elevation were less than 21 in. (53.3 cm). The Committee recognized a need to allow steps in these locations for functional reasons but noted that something needed to be done to avoid missteps. The minimum 13 in. tread (33.0 cm) was established to help reduce missteps. The appendix note provides information to further help reduce problems in these situations. (*Also see commentary following 5-1.6.*)

5-1.7 Workmanship, Impediments to Egress.

5-1.7.1 Doors, stairs, ramps, passageways, signs, and all other components of means of egress shall be of substantial, reliable construction and shall be built or installed in a workmanlike manner.

5-1.7.2 Any device or alarm installed to restrict the improper use of a means of egress shall be so designed and installed that it cannot, even in case of failure, impede or prevent emergency use of such means of egress.

Exception No. 1: As provided in 5-2.1.6.

Exception No. 2: In detention and correctional occupancies as provided in Chapters 14 and 15.

Formal Interpretation 76-83
Reference: 5-1.7.2

Question: Is it the intent of 5-1.7.2 to permit, under controlled conditions, the use of an electric locking device on an outside exit door equipped with panic hardware?

Answer: It is the intent of the Committee that the exits in a building be under the control of any individual occupant seeking egress.

Issue Edition: 1976
Reference: 5-1.6.2
Date: September 1978 ■

5-1.7.3* Means of egress shall be free of obstructions that would prevent its use, including the accumulation of snow and ice.

A-5-1.7.3   Means of egress must permit unobstructed travel at all times. Any type barrier including, but not limited to, the accumulations of snow and ice in those climates subject to such accumulations is an impediment to free movement in the means of egress.

Paragraph 5-1.7.3 is intended to prevent the obstruction or partial obstruction of any portion of the means of egress by construction features, furniture, fixtures, accumulations of ice and snow, or by any other condition. The reference to the accumulation of ice and snow was moved back into the main body of the *Code* for this edition, as enforcers of the *Code* felt that placement in the appendix did not properly emphasize this point. The method of controlling the accumulation could vary based on many factors and is left to the final approval of the authority having jurisdiction. This paragraph is not only a design requirement but also a maintenance requirement. It should be remembered that this provision applies to the entire means of egress, including the exit discharge, which usually includes sidewalks leading to the public way.

(Also see 5-1.3.3 and 31-1.2.1.)

SECTION 5-2   Means of Egress Components

While moving along any means of egress, many different components of the building or structure are encountered — components that make up the features of the means of egress. These components are items such as the doors, stairs, ramps, horizontal exits, exit passageways, hardware, handrails, guardrails, balconies, and other features. Their composition, properties, use, limits, and function relative to the total means of egress must be understood.

Portable ladders, rope ladders, and similar devices are not recognized by the *Code* as providing any portion of the required capacity of a means of egress. In addition, they should not be considered as in any way upgrading an inadequate means of egress in an existing building where the means of egress system is below minimum requirements. While on occasion such devices have been used and have provided a way to safety, they most definitely should not be relied upon and can lead to a false

sense of security. They are often unusable by small children, older people, the physically handicapped, or those who simply have not used them before.

The components of a means of egress must meet certain standards, be built in a prescribed manner, and perform at a level specified by the *Code*, depending upon whether they are part of the access to an exit, the exit itself, or the exit discharge. In most instances, the requirements are the same throughout the means of egress.

5-2.1   Doors.

5-2.1.1   General.

Doors serve three purposes related to the comfort and safety of building occupants. They provide protection from:
1. Weather, drafts, and noise and disturbance from adjoining areas;
2. Trespass by unauthorized persons; and,
3. Fire and smoke, with which this *Code* is concerned.

There are three broad categories of doors, each providing varying degrees of protection from fire. The first is the non-fire-rated door, such as is used in one- and two-family dwelling construction. While not fire-rated, such doors do, in fact, provide a limited degree of protection if closed. The second is the tested fire door that has passed the standard fire test for doors (NFPA 252, *Standard Methods of Fire Tests of Door Assemblies*).[2] These doors will withstand a severe fire and hose stream exposure for a definite period of time, as is required for various uses and occupancies. Finally, there is the smoke-stop door that is usually of lighter construction than the fire door. Its function is to provide a temporary barrier against the passage of heat, smoke, and gases.

None of these doors will perform satisfactorily if they are left open during a fire, thus allowing the entry of fire and combustion products into what should be a safer area. The history of fires is full of tragic examples of those who died because of an open door. There are also many examples of people saved because a door was closed. Less frequent, but nonetheless tragic, are those situations in which doors needed for escape were blocked or locked, resulting in dire consequences. Code requirements take these possibilities into consideration.

Some types of doors that are designed to prevent spread of fire through wall openings are not necessarily suitable for use in means of egress, and they pose the potential hazard of personal injury if they are so used. This category includes various rolling-shutter and sliding-doors. However, under limited conditions, certain horizontal sliding doors are permitted to be used in a means of egress. (*See 5-2.1.14.*)

5-2.1.1.1 A door assembly, including the doorway, frame, door, and necessary hardware, used as a component in a means of egress shall conform to the general requirements of Section 5-1 and to the special requirements of this subsection. Such an assembly is designated as a door.

Paragraph 5-2.1.1.1 alerts the *Code* user to the fact that the *Code* uses the term "door" to mean door assembly. Thus, wherever the *Code* refers to a rated door or fire door, it is referring to the entire door assembly. If any single component is not properly provided, installed, and functioning, the assembly is not a fire protection rated assembly.

5-2.1.1.2 Every door and every principal entrance that is required to serve as an exit shall be so designed and constructed that the way of exit travel is obvious and direct. Windows that, because of their physical configuration or design and the materials used in their construction, could be mistaken for doors shall be made inaccessible to the occupants by barriers or railings.

In prior editions of the *Code* it was required that the rails used to comply with this paragraph comply with the requirements for guard rails. This additional requirement was deleted for the 1991 Edition since the purpose of a guard is to prevent falls over an open side, and a rail designed to prevent one from walking through a window may not necessarily comply with the guard requirements.

5-2.1.1.3 For the purpose of Section 5-2, a building is considered to be occupied at any time it is open to or accessi-

ble to the public or at any other time it is occupied by more than 10 persons.

There are many industrial, storage, and business buildings that are never open to or accessible to the public, and, therefore, there are times or situations where the term "accessible to the public" should not be taken too literally but should be interpreted as "operating" or "functioning." Usually, the 10-person maximum will prevent abuse of this situation, but in smaller buildings or storage buildings, the authority having jurisdiction will have to broadly interpret the term "public." The intent of this provision is to allow small security or cleaning crews to be inside a building and yet not have the building considered occupied. This will allow doors to be locked and lights to be turned off without violating the *Code*. The intent is that such individuals will use lights as they need them and turn them off, or in the case of security personnel, carry their own lights and keys. [*See 5-2.1.5.1(d).*] It is not the intent to allow people, no matter how few the number, to be locked in a building without a ready means of escape.

5-2.1.2 **Egress Width.**

5-2.1.2.1* In determining the egress width for a doorway for purposes of calculating capacity, only the clear width of the doorway when the door is in the full open position shall be measured. Clear width shall be the net, unobstructed width of the door opening without projections into such width.

A-5-2.1.2.1 Figure A-5-2.1.2.1 illustrates the method of measuring the width of doorways.

In cases where an occupancy chapter requires a minimum door width, such as the minimum 44-in. (112-cm) cross-corridor or patient sleeping room door for new health care occupancy construction, this requirement can be met by a door leaf of the minimum specified width if the term "clear width" does not appear as part of the minimum width requirement. The pair of cross-corridor doors, as referenced above, which are often installed in a health care smoke barrier, would be judged under two sets of criteria:

1. Each door leaf must be a minimum of 44 in. (112 cm) in width, and

2. The pair of doors must provide sufficient, clear, unobstructed width (which will be less than the door leaf width measurement) to handle their assigned occupant load based on a calculation using the appropriate egress capacity factor (as found in 5-3.3.1.).

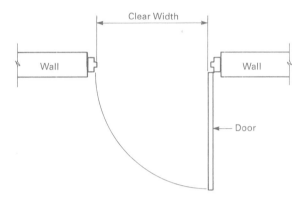

Figure A-5-2.1.2.1

Two important changes were made to this paragraph for the 1991 Edition of the *Code* in addition to significant changes made to the appendix note. First, it was clarified that this method of measuring door width only applies where determining the capacity of the door, not for minimum sizes of doors as specified elsewhere in the *Code*, unless clear width is specifically required. This is explained in the revised appendix note. Secondly, the exception previously provided for existing buildings has been deleted. This deletion recognizes that the change in the method of calculating capacity first introduced in the 1988 Edition of the *Code* made this exception unnecessary. The new method almost always results in larger capacities and more importantly is not subject to arbitrary increases that could significantly penalize the capacity of a door opening due to a door stop. For example, a 44-in. (112-cm) door leaf under the 1981 Edition of the *Code* would have been credited with 2 units of exit width, or 2 units × 100 people per unit, or 200 people. If clear width was required with no exception for existing buildings, the unit of exit width method of calculating capacity would only credit 1½ units of exit width [22 in. (55 cm) plus 12 in. (30 cm) since a 44-in. (112-cm) leaf door usually only provides 40-42 in. (100-107 cm) of clear opening, and only 22 in. (55 cm) whole units and

12 in. (30 cm) half units were recognized]. This would result in a decrease in exit capacity from 200 people to 150 people in an existing situation that could not be justified. However, in the 1988 Edition of the *Code* the unit of exit width method was dropped and the 40 in. (100 cm) clear opening existing door is now credited with $^{40}/_{0.2}$ in. ($^{100}/_{0.5}$ cm) per person or 200 people. Therefore, the exception is no longer needed, which is a significant simplification of the *Code* with no increased hardship and no decrease in safety.

5-2.1.3 Width and Floor Level.

5-2.1.3.1 No door opening in the means of egress shall be less than 32 in. (81 cm) in clear width. Where a pair of doors is provided, at least one of the doors shall provide a minimum 32 in. (81 cm) clear width opening.

Exception No. 1: Exit access doors serving a room not greater than 70 sq ft (6.5 sq m) and not required to be accessible to persons in wheelchairs shall be not less than 24 in. (61 cm) wide.

Exception No. 2: In existing buildings, the minimum door width shall be not less than 28 in. (71 cm).

Exception No. 3: In detention and correctional occupancies as provided in Chapters 14 and 15.

Exception No. 4: Interior doors within dwelling units as provided in Chapter 21.

Generally, there are doors of varying types along the entire route of a means of egress, and each door opening must be wide enough to accommodate the number of people expected to move through that doorway during an emergency. This width is based on the occupant load served and on the capacity factors in 5-3.3.1. A doorway is a level egress component. Therefore, its capacity is based on that specified for level components. In general, no door opening may be less than 32 in. (81 cm) wide. Note that this specifically requires clear width even though it is not for purposes of determining capacity. Where another particular *Code* section specifies a width greater than 32 in. (81 cm), that greater width must be used. However, this greater width is often not specified as a clear width and therefore would be a door leaf measurement. The minimum 32 in. clear width specified here would still apply unless one of the exceptions above applied.

It is the intent of the *Code* that the doorway not create a bottleneck in the means of egress. At times, another portion of the means of egress may be larger than required, creating the illusion of a bottleneck. However, the door opening width is determined by the occupant load served, and this specified width will be sufficient. A door serving a hallway need not be as wide as the hallway since hallway width requirements are determined by other factors in addition to the occupant load. (*See Figure 5-12.*) An example is a health care facility, where corridor and doorway widths are much wider than the occupant load would seem to dictate. In this instance, the sizes of the corridor and door opening are governed by the necessity to move patients along the means of egress route; therefore, their widths are sized accordingly.

Exception No. 1 was new to the 1988 *Code*. The intent of this exception is to allow a small room (probably occupied by only a couple of people) that is not required to be accessible to people in wheelchairs to use what may be considered to be an absolute minimum size door. This exception does not specify clear width, so door leaf width would be sufficient.

Previous editions of the *Code* specified that no single door in a doorway be less than 28 in. (71 cm) wide; therefore, an exception is provided for existing buildings. The new wider width permits the passage of wheelchairs. It should also be noted that the minimum width required may not be adequate for the normal usage of the doorway for purposes other than exiting.

For security and operations purposes, detention and correctional facilities are allowed to have doors of smaller width. (*See Chapters 14 and 15.*)

5-2.1.3.2 No single door in a doorway shall exceed 48 in. (122 cm) in width.

The *Code* places a maximum of 48 in. (122 cm) on any door leaf width. This requirement prevents the possible installation of doors of unwieldy size, a size that would make them difficult to handle, and thus unable to easily accommodate the occupant load to be served.

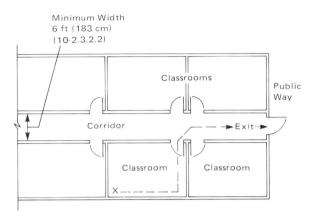

Figure 5-12. Exit Door Need Not Be as Wide as the Corridor Is Required to Be Because Operational Features of the Occupancy in Addition to the Occupant Load Are Used in Determining Required Corridor Width. In this example of a school, the corridor is required to be 6 ft (180 cm) wide while the occupant load served would dictate the size of the exit door.

5-2.1.3.3 The floor on both sides of a doorway shall be substantially level and shall have the same elevation on both sides of the doorway for a distance at least equal to the width of the widest leaf.

Exception: In one- and two-family dwellings and in existing buildings where the door discharges to the outside or to an exterior balcony, exterior exit, or exterior exit access, the floor level outside the door is permitted to be one step lower than the inside, but not more than 8 in. (20.3 cm) lower.

Previously, the *Code* permitted the floor level outside exterior doors to be one step but not more than 8 in. (20.3 cm) lower than the floor level inside the door. The reason was to avoid blocking the outward swing of the door by a buildup of snow or ice. The Committee changed the paragraph to prohibit the one exterior step based on the possible tripping hazard. The Committee also noted that other provisions of the *Code* require that the means of egress be maintained free of obstructions and be protected from the weather, thus providing for the removal of snow or ice accumulations. Existing buildings and one- and two-family dwellings are permitted to use the one exterior step as noted in the exception.

5-2.1.4 Swing and Force to Open.

5-2.1.4.1* Any door in a means of egress shall be of the side-hinged or pivoted-swinging type. The door shall be so designed and installed that it is capable of swinging from any position to the full use of the opening in which it is installed. Doors shall swing in the direction of exit travel where serving a room or area with an occupant load of 50 or more.

Exception No. 1: Sliding doors in detention and correctional occupancies as provided in Chapters 14 and 15, and doors for dwelling units as provided in Chapter 21.

Exception No. 2: Smoke barrier door swing in existing health care occupancies as provided in Chapter 13.

Exception No. 3: Where permitted by Chapters 8 through 30, horizontal sliding or vertical rolling security grilles or doors that are a part of the required means of egress shall conform to the following:

(a) They must remain secured in the full open position during the period of occupancy by the general public.

(b) On or adjacent to the door, there shall be a readily visible, durable sign that reads "THIS DOOR TO REMAIN OPEN WHEN THE BUILDING IS OCCUPIED." The sign shall be in letters not less than 1 in. (2.5 cm) high on a contrasting background.

(c) Doors or grilles shall not be brought to the closed position when the space is occupied.

(d) Doors or grilles shall be openable from within the space without the use of any special knowledge or effort.

(e) Where two or more means of egress are required, not more than half of the means of egress shall be permitted to be equipped with horizontal sliding or vertical rolling grilles or doors.

Exception No. 4: Horizontal sliding doors complying with 5-2.1.14.

Exception No. 5: Doors to private garages and industrial and storage areas with an occupant load of not more than 10 need not be side-hinged swinging doors where such garages and industrial and storage areas contain low or ordinary hazard contents.

Exception No. 6: Revolving doors complying with 5-2.1.10.

A-5-2.1.4.1 Where doors are subject to two-way traffic, or where their opening may interfere with pedestrian traffic, an appropriately located vision panel can reduce the chance of accidents.

The provisions for direction of door swing have been separated into two paragraphs for the 1991 *Code*. The requirement that doors located in an exit enclosure and serving high hazard areas swing in the direction of exit travel has been moved into a separate paragraph (5-2.4.2). The purpose of this is to assure that the exceptions shown in what is now 5-2.1.4.1 are not used for exit enclosures or high hazard areas.

Ideally, all doors in a means of egress would swing in the direction of exit travel. Doors located in the exit access are considered separately from doors in an exit enclosure, since there are cases where swing in the direction of travel is not necessary or even desirable. An example is a classroom door that provides passage into a corridor that serves as an exit access for several other classrooms. It is believed that, because a student is aware of and accustomed to a door opening into a room, it is preferable to have the door swing into the room. If the door opened into the corridor, it could open against another door or against the flow of people and possibly restrict or decrease the width of passage in that more critical element of the means of egress. The *Code* recognizes this danger and limits the occupant load of such a room to less than 50, thus limiting the number of people using a door that swings against traffic. The *Code* also recognizes similar constraints with regard to an exterior exit door, and even though it is an exit, does not require that it swing in direction of exit travel unless it serves 50 or more occupants. (*See Figure 5-13.*)

Paragraph 5-2.1.4.1 requires that doors be the side-hinged, swinging type. This is the type of door most familiar to the general public, and its operation is readily understood.

Some of the occupancy chapters provide exceptions to these requirements. For example, detention and correctional occupancies allow certain sliding doors. An exception is also allowed for horizontal sliding or vertical rolling security grilles or doors, provided the exception is specifically allowed by the applicable occupancy chapter. This exception permits the security doors and grilles normally found in a covered shopping mall. It should be noted that there is a difference between items (a) and (c) in Excep-

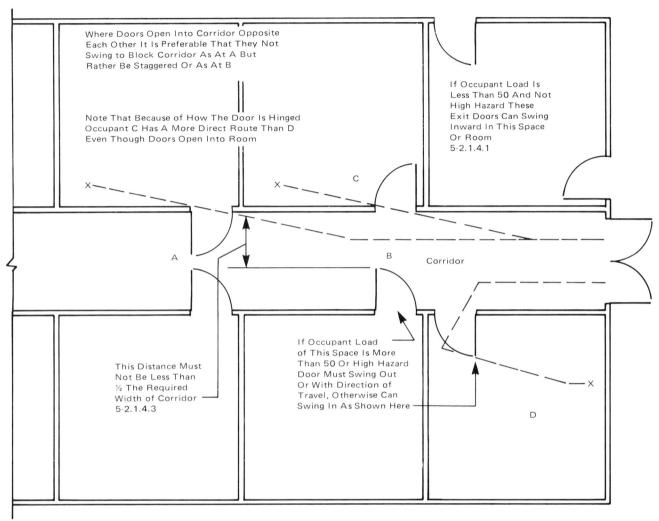

Where Doors Open Into Corridor Opposite
Each Other It Is Preferable That They Not
Swing to Block Corridor As At A But
Rather Be Staggered Or As At B

Note That Because of How The Door Is Hinged
Occupant C Has A More Direct Route Than D
Even Though Doors Open Into Room

If Occupant Load Is
Less Than 50 And Not
High Hazard These
Exit Doors Can Swing
Inward In This Space
Or Room
5-2.1.4.1

This Distance Must
Not Be Less Than
½ The Required
Width of Corridor
5-2.1.4.3

If Occupant Load
of This Space Is More
Than 50 Or High Hazard
Door Must Swing Out
Or With Direction of
Travel, Otherwise Can
Swing In As Shown Here

Corridor

A   B   C   D

Note: All Doors To Stairways Must Swing In Direction of Exit Travel (5-2.1.4.2)

Figure 5-13. *Door Swing Considerations. A diagrammatic representation of some of the considerations involved in evaluating the effect of various arrangements of door swing at entrances to corridors.*

tion No. 3. Item (a) requires that the door be fully open when the space is occupied by the public, while item (c) states that the door cannot be closed when the space is occupied. This allows the common practice of the door being partially closed during inventory, closing, and at other times when restricting entry by the general public is desired.

The following occupancies allow the use of the horizontal sliding or vertical rolling doors complying with Exception No. 3. Check the referenced paragraphs for

additional restrictions that may be imposed by the occupancy chapter:

Assembly — 8-2.2.2.2, 9-2.2.2.2

Mercantile — 24-2.2.2.5, 25-2.2.2.5

Business — 26-2.2.2.5, 27-2.2.2.5

Exception 4 is new in the 1991 *Code* and is a consolidation of four exceptions that were in the 1988 *Code*. This recognizes the use of certain sliding doors under limited conditions. (*See 5-2.1.14 for further information.*)

5-2.1.4.2   Doors shall swing in the direction of exit travel where used in an exit enclosure or where serving a high hazard area.

Exception: Doors from individual living units that open directly into an exit enclosure need not swing in the direction of egress travel.

This is a new paragraph in the 1991 *Code*. The requirements were contained in 5-2.1.4.1 in prior editions. The exception, however, is new. These provisions were moved to clarify that it was not the intent to allow the exceptions of 5-2.1.4.1 to be used where the door is in an exit enclosure or where the door serves a high hazard area. The exception was needed since apartment doors normally swing into the unit, and in many designs the main door into an apartment opens directly into the exit enclosure (This is very common in three-story single exit "garden" apartment designs). The swing of the door in this arrangement is not a significant concern. Another situation that often arises is the existence of hotel room doors that open directly into an exit enclosure where the intent is to enclose a formerly open stair, since it is often necessary to take part of a corridor and make it a stair landing.

A conflict sometimes arises between the requirement of the *Life Safety Code* that doors to hazardous areas swing in the direction of travel and the desire of those responsible for explosion control that doors to areas subject to explosion swing inward. In new construction, this apparent conflict can usually be resolved if the hazardous area can be located on an outside wall of the main building; then, required egress doors could open directly to the outside. This is not only desirable for life safety considerations but also easily allows the doors to swing outward, as this is also favorable for explosion relief. Subsequently, convenience doors between the hazardous area

and the remainder of the building are not required for egress and can swing toward the hazardous area to assist in containing the explosion if so desired. In existing situations or where the hazardous area must be internal to a building, the conflict is not easily resolved if a serious explosion exposure is involved. The authority having jurisdiction will have to work with the building owner, insurer, and other experts to determine how best to reduce the exposure while adequately protecting those who work in the hazardous area. (*Also see Section 5-11.*)

5-2.1.4.3*   During its swing, any door in a means of egress shall leave unobstructed at least one-half of the required width of an aisle, corridor, passageway, or landing. When fully open, the door shall not project more than 7 in. (17.8 cm) into the required width of an aisle, corridor, passageway, or landing.

Exception: In existing buildings, a door providing access to a stair shall neither reduce the unobstructed width of a stair or landing to less than 22 in. (55.9 cm) nor, when open, project more than 7 in. (17.8 cm) into the required width of a stair or landing.

A-5-2.1.4.3   This paragraph is not intended to apply to the swing of cross corridor doors such as smoke barrier doors and horizontal exits.

Doors that open 180 degrees have a greater utility than those that open only 90 degrees. As shown in Figure 5-14, the former can open into a corridor without blocking the passageway. The 90-degree door, however, must either open into an unusually wide corridor or be set into an alcove as shown, or must otherwise be recessed. (*See Figure 5-14.*)

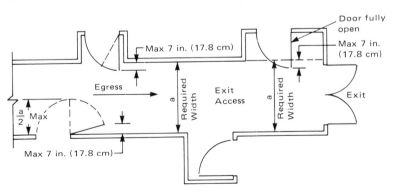

Figure 5-14. Door Swing into a Corridor. Doors that swing 180 degrees to come to rest against a wall provide the best arrangement for clear passage in an exit access corridor. A door swinging 90 degrees into the path of travel is considered to partially block an exit access if more than 7 in. (17.8 cm) of the required width of the corridor remains obstructed.

Doors serving as an entrance to an exit stairway should not unduly block the stair landing or the stairs. It is preferred that the door not reduce the required width either during its swing or while at rest. However, the *Code* does allow arrangements similar to Figure 5-15. An acceptable arrangement for a door opening onto a stair landing in an existing building is shown in Figure 5-16.

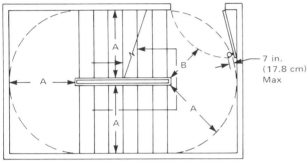

A-Required Width
B-At Least ½ A

Figure 5-15.   A Typical Interior Stairway Showing Clearances that Must Be Observed in New Buildings. For example, if the stairway is required to be 66 in. (168 cm) in width, Dimension "B" must be at least 33 in. (84 cm).

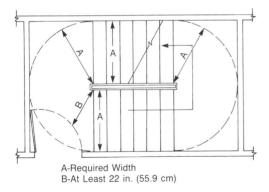

A-Required Width
B-At Least 22 in. (55.9 cm)

Figure 5-16.   A Typical Interior Stairway Showing Clearances that Must Be Observed in Existing Buildings. Stair widths and landing radii (A) are equal; clearance (B) between opening door and stair newel post must be at least 22 in. (55.9 cm).

5-2.1.4.4   The forces required to fully open any door manually in a means of egress shall not exceed 15 lbf (67 N) to release the latch, 30 lbf (133 N) to set the door in motion, and 15 lbf (67 N) to open the door to the minimum required width. These forces shall be applied at the latch stile.

Exception No. 1:   The opening force for doors in existing buildings shall not exceed 50 lbf (222 N) applied to the latch stile.

Exception No. 2:   Horizontal sliding doors in detention and correctional occupancies as provided by Chapters 14 and 15.

Exception No. 3:   Power-operated doors as provided in 5-2.1.9.

The *Code* recognizes that, in the operation of any door, there are several movements necessary and identifies each of the movements and its required force. As a result, the force required to unlatch the door is limited to 15 lbf (67 N); that force necessary to start the door in motion, or to overcome its inertia, cannot exceed 30 lbf (133 N); and that force necessary to fully open the door can be no more than 15 lbf (67 N). The Committee concluded that many people may not be capable of exerting 50 lbf (222 N) horizontally under some rather common circumstances. (*Also see 5-2.1.9 for power-operated doors.*)

Care must be taken to ensure that the 30 lbf (133 N) needed to overcome the inertia of a door in a means of egress is not exceeded for doors opening into pressurized stairs. Many times the pressure necessary to protect the stair may be such that a 30 lbf (133 N) will not be sufficient to open the door. The use of barometric relief dampers or other pressure regulating methods may be required.

5-2.1.4.5   Screen and Storm Doors. No screen door or storm door used in a means of egress shall swing against the direction of exit travel where doors are required to swing in the direction of exit travel.

There are various methods by which the function of screen or storm doors may be provided without having any door swing against the exit travel. A screen or storm door may be used in the same doorway with an ordinary door by means of a vestibule of sufficient size as to permit the inner door to swing outwardly without interfering with the operation of the door at the other end of the vestibule. (*See Figure 5-17.*)

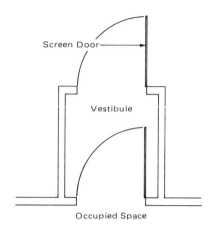

Figure 5-17. A Possible Arrangement of a Vestibule Leading to a Screen Door that Complies with 5-2.1.4.5.

A jalousie door with a screen or storm sash panel provides the function of both a regular door and screen or storm sash, in a single unit.

5-2.1.5 Locks, Latches, and Alarm Devices.

The increase in theft, molestations, and similar crimes has led, in some instances, to the practice of providing extra security on exit doors and doors leading to them. Such practices, particularly where the doors to exit stairs and exit discharges are involved, are open invitations to tragedy in the event of fire or other emergency. Paragraph 5-2.1.5 is aimed at preventing locked doors in means of egress or any other unnecessary interference with the orderly movement of people in the event of fire. The Committee on Safety to Life has attempted to accomplish this objective while maintaining those features essential to security within the building.

A special study of 1981-85 structural fires reported to U.S. fire departments found that 117 fire deaths a year involved locks or gates that prevented escape.[3] Most such deaths occurred in fires at residential properties. This report also described a number of incidents, including the following:

In a Texas dwelling fire, 7 people died when a space heater ignited a sofa. Two of the adults who died were overcome while they struggled to unlock the dead bolt lock on the front door and the security bars.

In another Texas dwelling fire, 3 people died when a bedridden woman accidentally ignited her bedding with a cigarette. The other two victims died while trying to escape past burglar bars, double-cylinder dead bolt locks, and a security bar on a sliding glass door.

The report also found that makeshift security arrangements, such as windows that had been nailed shut, were factors in more multiple-fatality fires than in cases where more expensive security devices such as security bars and gates had been used. The conflict between some security provisions and sound firesafety practices takes many forms. Also see Supplement 1 of this *Handbook*.

Consistent with the concept that all components in the means of egress must be under the control of the occupant is the requirement that doors must be easily openable from the egress side, even in complete darkness. This prohibits the use of key locks or hard-to-use devices, such as door handles or latches covered with glass that has to be broken. Where panic hardware is used, no device that might interfere with its operation can be used; however, this does not prevent the use of alarm connections that indicate that the door is in use.

Requirements for doors leading to exits apply also to doors opening to roofs where exit stairs terminate at a recognized roof exit and to exit discharge doors leading to the street or other public way.

5-2.1.5.1 Doors shall be arranged to be readily opened from the egress side whenever the building is occupied. Locks, if provided, shall not require the use of a key, tool, special knowledge, or effort for operation from the inside of the building.

Exception No. 1: In health care occupancies as provided in Chapters 12 and 13, and in detention and correctional occupancies as provided in Chapters 14 and 15.

Exception No. 2: Exterior doors shall be permitted to have key-operated locks from the egress side provided:

(a) That on the egress side, on or adjacent to the door, there is a readily visible, durable sign that reads "THIS DOOR TO REMAIN UNLOCKED WHEN THE BUILDING IS OCCUPIED." The sign shall be in letters not less than 1 in. (2.5 cm) high on a contrasting background, and

(b) The locking device is of a type that is readily distinguishable as locked, and

(c) This exception is specifically permitted by Chapters 8 through 30 for the specific occupancy.

(d) A key shall be immediately available to any occupant inside the building when it is locked.

(e) This exception may be revoked by the authority having jurisdiction for cause.

Exception No. 3: Where permitted by Chapters 8 through 30, key operation is allowed provided the key cannot be removed when the door is locked from the side from which egress is to be made.

Formal Interpretation 76-81
Reference: 5-1.2.9, 5-2.1.5.1

Question 1: Are doors that serve individual rooms, such as offices and classrooms, intended to be classified as a portion of a means of egress as defined in Paragraph 5-1.2.9?

Answer: Yes.

Question 2: If the answer to Question 1 is yes, are these doors then required to comply with Subparagraph 5-2.1.5.1, whereby locks requiring the use of a key from the side from which egress is to be made are prohibited?

Answer: Yes.

Issue Edition: 1976
Reference: 5-1.2.1
Date: September 1978 ∎

Paragraph 5-2.1.5.1 establishes the principle that doors must be readily openable from the side from which egress is to be made. It prohibits the installation of locks that require the use of a key to open the door from the inside. Paragraph 5-2.1.1.3 defines "occupied" for the purpose of this requirement. It should be noted that the *Code* prohibits the installation of such a lock as well as its use when the building is occupied.

Exception No. 2 is provided for key-operated locks under five conditions, one of which is that the appropriate occupancy chapter must specifically allow the excep-

tion. In permitting up to 10 persons in a locked building, the *Code* is not writing off those persons as unimportant. It is recognizing that there are instances where a building must be occupied by security personnel or by janitorial crews when it is locked. Such persons are generally familiar with the premises, and the *Code* requires that they have keys available for egress when necessary. (*Also see commentary following 5-2.1.1.3.*) The following occupancies allow the use of a key-operated lock in Exception No. 2. Check the referenced paragraphs for additional restrictions that may be imposed by the occupancy chapter:

    Assembly — 8-2.2.2.3 Exception No. 1, 9-2.2.2.3 Exception No. 1
    Mercantile — 24-2.2.2.2, 25-2.2.2.2
    Business — 26-2.2.2.2, 27-2.2.2.2

In addition, there is an exception to allow special provisions in the occupancy chapters to override these requirements for detention and correctional occupancies as well as special health care occupancies.

Exception No. 3, allowing the "captive key" hardware, is permitted in lodging and rooming houses in 20-2.8.

5-2.1.5.2* Every stair enclosure door shall allow reentry from the stair enclosure to the interior of the building, or an automatic release shall be provided to unlock all stair enclosure doors to allow reentry. Such automatic release shall be actuated with the initiation of the building fire alarm system.

Exception No. 1: Selected doors on stair enclosures shall be permitted to be equipped with hardware that prevents reentry into the interior of the building provided that:

(a) Such arrangement is specifically permitted by Chapters 8 through 30, and

(b) There are at least two levels where it is possible to leave the stair enclosure, and

(c) There shall be not more than four floors intervening between floors where it is possible to leave the stair enclosure, and

(d) Reentry is possible on the top or next to top floor permitting access to another exit, and

(e) Doors permitting reentry are identified as such on the stair side of the door.

Exception No. 2: In new health care occupancies as provided in Chapter 12, and in new detention and correctional occupancies as provided in Chapter 14.

Exception No. 3: Existing installations as permitted by Chapters 8 through 30.

Exception No. 4: Stair enclosures serving a building permitted to have a single exit in accordance with Chapters 8 through 30.

Exception No. 5: Stairs serving not more than four stories.

A-5-2.1.5.2 This arrangement makes it possible to leave the stairway at such floor should the fire render the lower part of the stair unusable during egress or should the occupants seek refuge on another floor.

Every stairway door must be arranged to permit reentry into the building. However, the *Code* recognizes the need for varying degrees of security and does allow some equivalent alternatives. Stairway doors may be arranged to unlock automatically upon initiation of the fire alarm system. In addition, certain stairway doors may be arranged to prevent reentry where such arrangement is permitted by the appropriate occupancy chapter. In such instances, there must be at least two levels providing a way out of the stairway, one of which must be the top or next to top floor, and there may not be more than four floors between those levels providing a way out of the stairway. Note that this does not require that every fifth floor must allow reentry, but ensures that one does not have to travel more than two floors up or down to reenter the building. This provides flexibility, especially in office buildings, which may require that entry be prevented on certain floors, but at the same time ensures that one can reenter the building without having to travel too many flights of stairs. Any door providing a way out of the stairwell must be identified as such on the stairwell side. (*See Figure 5-18.*)

Two new exceptions were added to the 1991 *Code*. Exception No. 4 recognizes that reentry in buildings permitted to have a single exit would not be particularly beneficial. In most single exit buildings, the doors from the stairway enter directly into the occupant space, such as the typical three-story "garden" apartment building. Most

occupancies restrict single exit situations to very low buildings, usually a maximum of three stories. Therefore, Exception No. 4 will probably not be as commonly used as the new Exception No. 5, which exempts stairs serving not more than four stories. Stairs serving so few floors can be exited to the outside almost as quickly as reentering the building. Therefore, the exception was added.

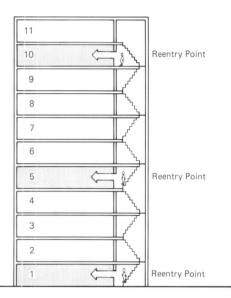

Figure 5-18.   Stairway Reentry Option. This diagram illustrates Exception No. 1 to 5-2.1.5.2. The arrangement can be very beneficial in office buildings which may need to secure certain floors.

5-2.1.5.3* A latch or other fastening device on a door shall be provided with a knob, handle, panic bar, or other simple type of releasing device having an obvious method of operation under all lighting conditions. Doors shall be openable with no more than one releasing operation.

Exception: Egress doors from individual living units and guest rooms of residential occupancies shall be permitted to be provided with devices that require not more than one additional releasing operation, such as a night latch, dead bolt, or security chain, provided such device is operable from the inside without the use of a key or tool and is mounted at a height not to exceed 48 in. (122 cm) above the finished floor. Existing security devices shall be permitted to have two additional releasing operations. Existing security devices other than automatic latching devices shall not be located more than 60 in.

(152 cm) in height above the finished floor. Automatic latching devices shall not be located more than 48 in. (122 cm) above the finished floor.

A-5-2.1.5.3   This requirement may be satisfied by the use of conventional types of hardware, whereby the door is released by turning a knob or handle or pushing against a panic bar, but not by unfamiliar methods of operation such as a blow to break glass.

This paragraph requires that, where a latch or other similar device is provided, its releasing device must be such that the method of operation is obvious even in the dark. This requires that the method of release be one that is familiar to the average person. Generally, a two-step release, such as a knob and an independent slide bolt, is not acceptable. In most occupancies, it is important that a single function unlatch the door. However, in living units and guest rooms, one additional device is permitted in new construction and two are permitted in existing situations.

This provision allows an existing condition to continue in which a hotel room door has hardware in which one operation releases the latch, another operation releases the lock, and a third operation releases the security device (chain or bar). However, in new installations, if a security device (chain or bar) is used, then one operation would have to release both the latch and lock.

An important revision for the 1991 *Code* prohibits automatic latching devices from being located more than 48 in. (122 cm) above the floor, even in existing buildings. This is intended to prevent children and wheelchair users from being trapped in a space when a door that is equipped with an automatic latching device closes behind them.

5-2.1.5.4   Where pairs of doors are required in a means of egress, each leaf of the pair shall be provided with its own releasing device. Devices that depend upon the release of one door before the other shall not be used.

Exception: Where exit doors are used in pairs and approved automatic flush bolts are used, the door leaf having the automatic flush bolts shall have no doorknob or surface-mounted hardware. The unlatching of any leaf shall not require more than one operation.

This applies only to pairs of doors that are required for means of egress. If the second leaf is provided for other reasons and not for egress, the provision does not apply. In a situation where a second leaf is provided for reasons other than egress, the second leaf must be arranged so as not to be mistaken for the exit door.

5-2.1.5.5   No lock, padlock, hasp, bar, chain, or other device, or combination thereof shall be installed or maintained on or in connection with any door on which panic hardware or fire exit hardware is required by this *Code* if such device prevents or is intended to prevent the free use of the door for purposes of egress.

Exception: As otherwise provided in 5-2.1.6.

It is not the intent of 5-2.1.5.5 to require panic hardware. That requirement is made by the various occupancy chapters. It is the intent, however, that where panic hardware is installed, no device or arrangement interfere with its function.

5-2.1.6   **Special Locking Arrangements.**

5-2.1.6.1   In buildings protected throughout by an approved supervised automatic fire detection system or approved supervised automatic sprinkler system, and where permitted by Chapters 8 through 30, doors in low and ordinary hazard areas as defined by 4-2.2 may be equipped with approved, listed, locking devices that shall:

(a) Unlock upon actuation of an approved supervised automatic sprinkler system installed in accordance with Section 7-7, or upon the actuation of any heat detector or not more than two smoke detectors of an approved supervised automatic fire detection system in accordance with Section 7-6, and

(b) Unlock upon loss of power controlling the lock or locking mechanism, and

(c) Initiate an irreversible process that will release the lock within 15 seconds whenever a force of not more than 15 lbf (67 N) is continuously applied to the release device required in 5-2.1.5.3 for a period of not more than 3 seconds. Relocking of such doors shall be by manual means only. Operation of the release device shall activate a signal in the vicinity of the door to assure those attempting to exit that the system is functional.

Exception to (c): The authority having jurisdiction may approve a delay not to exceed 30 seconds provided that reasonable life safety is assured.

5-2.1.6.2* On the door adjacent to the release device, a sign shall be provided that reads:

"PUSH UNTIL ALARM SOUNDS.
DOOR CAN BE OPENED IN 15 SECONDS."

Sign letters shall be at least 1 in. (2.5 cm) high and ⅛ in. (0.3 cm) wide stroke.

A-5-2.1.6.2 In the event that the authority having jurisdiction has allowed increased operation time, the sign should reflect the appropriate time.

5-2.1.6.3 Emergency lighting in accordance with Section 5-9 shall be provided at the door.

This special locking arrangement is allowed only where specifically permitted by the appropriate occupancy chapter. Paragraph 5-2.1.6.1 requires that the building be protected throughout with either a supervised automatic fire detection system or a supervised automatic sprinkler system, and item (a) requires that the locking devices unlock immediately upon activation of that system. Item (c) requires that, once the release device is activated manually, the door must unlock within 15 seconds. This action must be irreversible and cannot require that the user maintain pressure on the release device for more than 3 seconds. Once opened, the door may be relocked by manual means only.

It should be pointed out that the operations described do not automatically open the door. They simply unlock it, making it immediately openable by anyone seeking to exit. Security is not sacrificed. Of course, any exterior exit door may be locked against entry at any time.

The following occupancies allow the use of delay release hardware in accordance with 5-2.1.6. Check the referenced paragraphs for additional restrictions that may be imposed by the occupancy chapter:

Assembly — 8-2.2.2.4, 9-2.2.2.4

Educational — 10-2.2.2.3, 11-2.2.2.3

Day-Care Centers — 10-7.2.2.2(e), 11-7.2.2.2(e)

Health Care — 12-2.2.2.4 Exception No. 2, 13-2.2.2.4 Exception No. 2

Hotels — 16-2.2.2.2 Exception, 17-2.2.2.2 Exception

Apartment Buildings — 18-2.2.2.2 Exception, 19-2.2.2.2 Exception

Lodging and Rooming Houses — 20-2.7 Exception

Board and Care Facilities — 22-3.2.2.2(b) Exception, 23-3.2.2.2(b) Exception

Mercantile — 24-2.2.2.4, 25-2.2.2.4

Business — 26-2.2.2.4, 27-2.2.2.4

Industrial — 28-2.2.2.2

Storage — 29-2.2.2.2, 29-8.2.2.2(b).

5-2.1.7 Panic Hardware and Fire Exit Hardware.

The difference between panic hardware and fire exit hardware is that fire exit hardware is tested for use on fire-rated doors; panic hardware is not. (*See 5-2.1.7.1 and 5-2.1.7.3.*)

Paragraph 5-2.1.7 does not require panic hardware but sets the requirements for such hardware where called for by the applicable occupancy chapter.

The following occupancies require the use of panic hardware or fire exit hardware (check the referenced paragraphs for where such hardware is required):

Assembly — 8-2.2.2.3, 9-2.2.2.3

Educational — 10-2.2.2.2, 11-2.2.2.2

Day-Care Centers — 10-7.2.2.2(b), 11-7.2.2.2(b).

Although not required by the other occupancy chapters, panic hardware or fire exit hardware is often used either due to an assembly occupancy being located within another occupancy or as a means of complying with 5-2.1.5.3.

5-2.1.7.1 Panic hardware and fire exit hardware consist of a door latching assembly incorporating a device that releases the latch upon the application of a force in the direction of exit travel. Fire exit hardware additionally provides fire protection where used as part of a fire door assembly.

Note the clear distinction between panic hardware and fire exit hardware.

As the name implies, panic hardware and fire exit hardware should be designed for utility, serviceability, and reliability under conditions that range from the orderly evacuation of building spaces to the hurried egress that can accompany fast-moving fires; hence, the emphasis on ease of operation under extreme conditions.

5-2.1.7.2 Where a door is required to be equipped with panic hardware or fire exit hardware by some other provision of this *Code*, such releasing device shall:

(a) Consist of bars or panels, the actuating portion of which shall extend across not less than one-half of the width of the door leaf, not less than 30 in. (76 cm) nor more than 44 in. (112 cm) above the floor, and

(b) Cause the door latch to release when a force not to exceed 15 lbf (67 N) is applied.

Panic hardware and fire exit hardware, as specified in 5-2.1.7, must be able to be instantly and easily released. Panic hardware and fire exit hardware are to be located at a convenient height above the floor — 30 to 44 in. (76 to 112 cm) — and the actuating portion is to extend at least one-half the width of the door leaf. A force no greater than 15 lbf (67 N) shall be needed to operate the device. This is the force needed to release the latching device only. The force needed to open the door itself is governed by 5-2.1.4.4. Nothing is permitted that could interfere with the proper operation of the panic hardware.

5-2.1.7.3 Only approved panic hardware shall be used on doors that are not fire doors. Only approved fire exit hardware shall be used on fire doors.

It is not the intent of this paragraph to require the use of panic hardware or fire exit hardware. The two requirements of this paragraph are (1) that only approved hardware is to be used, and (2) that where such devices are used on fire-rated doors, they must be tested for use on fire-rated doors. Panic hardware is not tested for use on fire-rated doors; fire exit hardware is tested for use on fire-rated doors.

5-2.1.7.4 Required panic hardware and fire exit hardware shall not be equipped with any locking device, set screw, or other arrangement that can be used to prevent the release of the latch when pressure is applied to the releasing device. Devices that hold the latch in the retracted position are prohibited on fire exit hardware unless listed and approved for such use.

Exception: In detention and correctional occupancies as provided in Chapters 14 and 15.

It is the intent of the *Code* to allow the use of the special locking arrangement described by 5-2.1.6 where panic hardware is required, if permitted by the occupancy chapters, Chapters 8 through 30.

5-2.1.8 Self-Closing Devices. A door designed to normally be kept closed in a means of egress, such as a door to a stair enclosure or horizontal exit, shall be a self-closing door and shall not at any time be secured in the open position.

Exception: In any building of low or ordinary hazard contents, as defined in 4-2.2.2 and 4-2.2.3, or where permitted by the authority having jurisdiction, doors shall be permitted to be automatic-closing where:

(a) Upon release of the hold-open mechanism, the door becomes self-closing; and

(b) The release device is so designed that the door may be instantly released manually and upon release become self-closing, or the door may be closed by some simple or readily obvious operation; and

(c) The automatic releasing mechanism or medium is activated by (1) the operation of an approved automatic smoke detection system installed to protect the entire building, so designed and installed as to provide for actuation of the system so promptly as to preclude the generation of heat or smoke sufficient to interfere with egress before the system operates, or (2) the operation of approved smoke detectors installed in such a way as to detect smoke on either side of the door opening, as detailed in Chapter 9 of NFPA 72E, Standard on Automatic Fire Detectors. The above systems may be zoned as approved by the authority having jurisdiction; and

(d) Any fire detection system or smoke detector is provided with such supervision and safeguards as are necessary to assure complete reliability of operation in case of fire (see also Section 7-6); and

(e) Upon loss of power to the hold-open device, the hold-open mechanism is released and the door becomes self-closing; and

(f) The release by means of smoke detection of one door in a stair enclosure results in closing all doors serving that stair.

Fire doors in a means of egress route should be kept in the closed position, particularly those in the entrance to a stair enclosure or in a horizontal exit; however, it is in these latter two locations that doors so often are held open by some type of door-stopping chock. The simple requirement that these doors be self-closing is not sufficient, since this feature works only when the door can move freely. Often a door is held open to aid in the free flow of normal traffic. This sets the stage for the easy and rapid spread of fire, smoke, and heat throughout the building — the very situation that the stringent design requirements for the exit enclosure are intended to prevent.

Recognizing that tampering with the self-closing feature may occur, and in an effort to encourage the use of positive measures rather than the use of a printed prohibition unlikely to be followed, the *Code* makes an exception for doors located in buildings that house contents of low or ordinary hazard or where the authority having jurisdiction has given approval. There are some paragraphs in the *Code* where automatic closing doors are required. The Exception to 5-2.1.8 allows for doors to be held open by an automatic releasing device. The triggering of the automatic release is done through the operation of an automatic smoke detection system protecting the entire building or through the operation of smoke detectors designed to detect smoke on either side of the door opening (*see NFPA 72E, Standard on Automatic Fire Detectors, Section 9-2*).[4] Fusible links are not an acceptable trigger in this system, because untenable smoke conditions could very easily render an exit enclosure unusable long before the heat has built up to a point high enough to operate the fusible link. Any detection system or detector is to be supervised to the extent necessary to ensure its reliability.

The doors can be arranged to close throughout the building or only in the affected zones. Zoning is generally better. If protecting a room, that room may be considered a zone. If protecting a stair, the entire stair is a

zone, and the signal to close one door in a stair must close all doors in that stair.

With the exception of certain hazardous areas where flash fires or explosions could occur, the use of automatic closers in accordance with these provisions is widely accepted and, in fact, encouraged to prevent doors from being held open.

5-2.1.9 Power-Operated Doors.
Where required doors are operated by power, such as doors actuated by sensing devices upon the approach of a person or doors with power-assisted manual operation, the design shall be such that in the event of power failure, the door may be opened manually to permit exit travel or closed where necessary to safeguard means of egress. The forces required to open these doors manually shall not exceed those specified in 5-2.1.4.4 except that the force required to set the door in motion shall not exceed 50 lbf (222 N). The door shall be so designed and installed that when a force is applied to the door on the side from which egress is made, it shall be capable of swinging from any position to the full use of the required width of the opening in which it is installed. (*See 5-2.1.4.*)

Exception No. 1: Doors complying with 5-2.1.14.

Exception No. 2: In detention and correctional occupancies as provided in Chapters 14 and 15.

Power-operated sliding doors activated by some automatic mechanism are permitted, provided their movement can be manually overpowered and the door made to swing in the direction of travel while still providing the exit capacity for which it has been given credit. The feature for manual operation must work at all times, even when other features of the door's mechanism (such as the treadle, the electric eye, or sliding rail) have failed. Such door must be arranged so that it can be made to swing manually from any position, fully closed or partially closed. Care must be taken to ensure that the enclosing construction of any door pocket does not defeat its ability to swing. Note that the breakaway feature cannot require a force in excess of 50 lbf (222 N).

5-2.1.10 Revolving Doors.

Note that 5-2.1.10.1 and 5-2.1.10.3 apply to all revolving doors, not just those in the means of egress.

5-2.1.10.1 All revolving doors shall comply with the following:

(a) Revolving doors shall be capable of being collapsed into a book-fold position.

Exception to (a): Existing revolving doors where approved by the authority having jurisdiction.

(b) When in the book-fold position, the parallel egress paths formed shall provide an aggregate width of 36 in. (91 cm).

Exception to (b): Existing revolving doors where approved by the authority having jurisdiction.

(c) Revolving doors shall not be used within 10 ft (3 m) of the foot of or top of stairs or escalators. Under all conditions, there shall be a dispersal area acceptable to the authority having jurisdiction between the stairs or escalators and the revolving door.

(d) The revolutions per minute (rpm) of revolving doors shall not exceed the following:

Inside Diameter	Power Driven-type Speed Control (rpm)	Manual-type Speed Control (rpm)
6 ft 6 in. (198 cm)	11	12
7 ft 0 in. (213 cm)	10	11
7 ft 6 in. (229 cm)	9	11
8 ft 0 in. (244 cm)	9	10
8 ft 6 in. (259 cm)	8	9
9 ft 0 in. (274 cm)	8	9
9 ft 6 in. (290 cm)	7	8
10 ft 0 in. (305 cm)	7	8

(e) Each revolving door shall have a conforming side-hinged swinging door in the same wall as the revolving door and within 10 ft (3 m) of the revolving door.

Exception No. 1 to (e): Revolving doors shall be permitted without adjacent swinging doors for street floor elevator lobbies if no stairways or doors from other parts of the building discharge through the lobby and the lobby has no occupancy other than as a means of travel between elevators and street.

Exception No. 2 to (e): Existing revolving doors where the number of revolving doors does not exceed the number of swing doors within 20 ft (6.1 m).

These regulations governing revolving doors were completely rewritten for the 1985 *Code*. Until then, defini-

tive requirements were lacking. With the assistance of the revolving door industry, specifications were developed to assist the designer and the authority having jurisdiction in determining what is meant by an "approved" revolving door. These *Code* provisions deal with collapsibility, width of egress path, location, speed of rotation, credit for required egress capacity, and force to collapse.

5-2.1.10.2 Where permitted by Chapters 8 through 30, revolving doors shall be permitted as a component in a means of egress under the following conditions:

(a) Revolving doors shall not be given credit for more than 50 percent of the required exit capacity.

(b) Each revolving door shall be credited with no more than 50 persons capacity.

(c) Revolving doors shall be capable of being collapsed into a book-fold position when a force of not more than 130 lbf (578 N) is applied to wings within 3 in. (7.6 cm) of the outer edge.

The following occupancies allow the use of a revolving door in a means of egress. Check the referenced paragraphs for additional restrictions that may be imposed by the occupancy chapter:

Assembly — 8-2.2.2.5, 9-2.2.2.5

Hotels — 16-2.2.2.4, 17-2.2.2.4

Apartments — 18-2.2.2.3, 19-2.2.2.3

Board and Care Facilities — 22-3.2.2.2(d), 23-3.2.2.2(d)

Mercantile — 24-2.2.2.7, 25-2.2.2.7

Business — 26-2.2.2.6, 27-2.2.2.6.

Anyone who has used a revolving door can easily understand the problems encountered when too many people try to use it in too short a period of time. The congestion created is one reason why their use is prohibited at the foot or top of stairs. Because of the potential danger such doors present, they are not permitted to be used in numbers that would have them providing more than 50 percent of the required exit capacity. Where they are used, they each receive credit for a maximum of 50 persons, regardless of the width of the revolving panel.

Satisfying the 50-percent credit provision in item 5-2.1.10.2(a) does not automatically satisfy the 50-person maximum limit in (b) and vice versa.

5-2.1.10.3 Revolving doors not used as a component of a means of egress shall have a collapsing force of not more than 180 lbf (800 N).

Exception: Revolving doors may have a collapsing force set in excess of 180 lbf (800 N) if the collapsing force is reduced to not more than 130 lbf (578 N) when:

(a) There is a power failure or power is removed to the device holding the wings in position.

(b) There is an actuation of the automatic sprinkler system where such system is provided.

(c) There is actuation of a smoke detection system that is installed to provide coverage in all areas within the building that are within 75 ft (23 m) of the revolving doors.

(d) There is the actuation of a manual control switch that reduces the holding force to below the 130 lbf (578 N) level. Such switch shall be in an approved location and shall be clearly identified.

Note that 5-2.1.10.1 and 5-2.1.10.3 apply even if the door is not part of the required means of egress. The exception to 5-2.1.10.3 does not have to be complied with unless the collapsing force is otherwise in excess of 180 lbf (800 N).

5-2.1.11 Turnstiles.

The intent of 5-2.1.11 is to provide as much guidance as possible on how best to place turnstiles in a building, and to describe the circumstances under which they are permitted, with the intent that this will reduce the probability of their improper use during an emergency.

5-2.1.11.1 No turnstile or similar device to restrict travel to one direction or to collect fares or admission charges shall be so placed as to obstruct any required means of egress.

Exception No. 1: Approved turnstiles not over 39 in. (99 cm) high that turn freely in the direction of exit travel shall be permitted in any occupancy where revolving doors are permitted by Chapters 8 through 30.

Exception No. 2: Where permitted by the authority having jurisdiction and Chapters 8 through 30, turnstiles may be used for

exiting and each turnstile credited for 50 persons capacity provided such turnstiles:

(a) Freewheel in the exit direction when primary power is lost, and freewheel in the direction of exit travel upon the manual release by an employee assigned in the area, and

(b) Shall not be given credit for more than 50 percent of the required exit width, and

(c) Shall not be over 39 in. (99 cm) high nor have a clear width less than 16½ in. (41.9 cm).

5-2.1.11.2 Turnstiles over 39 in. (99 cm) high shall be subject to the requirements for revolving doors.

5-2.1.11.3 Turnstiles in or furnishing access to required exits shall be of such design as to provide at least 16½ in. (41.9 cm) clear width at and below a height of 39 in. (99 cm) and at least 22 in. (55.9 cm) clear width at heights above 39 in. (99 cm).

Generally, turnstiles are installed to prevent or control entry. As such, they are not always suitable for installation in a means of egress. Certain turnstiles are permitted where revolving doors are permitted, although they are used in some occupancies where revolving doors are generally not found. This is not meant to imply that there is a relationship between revolving doors and turnstiles insofar as their purpose is concerned. The revolving door is not meant to restrict traffic in either direction, while the turnstile is often used to do just that, with the restriction or obstruction to traffic movement usually in the direction of entry. Yet, if a turnstile does not restrict egress, it may be looked upon as being the equivalent of a revolving door.

While some turnstiles will not turn in the direction of entry until coin operated, there are those that are used simply to count numbers of people. Perhaps the most dangerous are those that do not bar entry but specifically bar egress. An example would be in large stores where turnstiles turn freely for entering but will not turn in the direction of egress, thereby causing patrons to go through a checkout slot. It is possible that the patrons of places using one-way turnstiles are quite aware of this limitation and will know the correct path to be taken in order to leave; however, this cannot be relied upon, especially if the turnstiles are placed near the exit doors. In emergencies, people do not always stop to think clearly and could head for what appears to be the shortest means of escape only to find the route blocked by a "wrong way" turnstile.

In some locations of certain occupancies, an approved turnstile is acceptable for providing a portion of the required exit capacity. Therefore, where the occupancy chapter specifically allows turnstiles, they may be installed provided they are in strict compliance with the dimensional criteria and performance requirements of 5-2.1.11.1 Exception No. 2. In no case may turnstiles be allowed to provide more than 50 percent of the required exit capacity, and no single turnstile can be rated at more than 50 persons.

Turnstiles not over 39 in. (99 cm) in height that allow free egress can be used anywhere a revolving door is allowed, subject to 5-2.1.11.3, and all turnstiles over 39 in. (99 cm) in height must meet all requirements for revolving doors.

5-2.1.12   **Doors in Folding Partitions.** Where permanently mounted folding or movable partitions are used to divide a room into smaller spaces, a swinging door or open doorway shall be provided as an exit access from each such space.

Exception No. 1: Under the following conditions, the swinging door is not required, and the partition may be used to enclose the space completely:

(a) The subdivided space shall not be used by more than 20 persons at any time.

(b) The use of the space shall be under adult supervision.

(c) The partitions shall be so arranged that they do not extend across any aisle or corridor used as an exit access to the required exits from the floor.

(d) The partitions shall conform to the interior finish and other applicable requirements of this Code.

(e) The partitions shall be an approved type, shall have a simple method of release, and shall be capable of being opened quickly and easily by inexperienced persons in case of emergency.

Exception No. 2: Where a subdivided space is provided with at least two means of egress, the swinging door in the fold-

ing partition is not required, and one such means of egress may be equipped with a horizontal sliding door complying with 5-2.1.14.

Although item (c) to Exception No. 1 may appear to be contradictory to the intent of the exception, it is referring to exit access for the rest of the floor, not exit access for the small space created by the closing of the partition.

5-2.1.13   **Balanced Doors.** If panic hardware is installed on balanced doors, the panic hardware shall be of the push-pad type, and the pad shall not extend more than approximately one-half the width of the door measured from the latch side.

In the case of balanced doors, where the hinge or pivot point is set in from the edge of the door leaf, care must be taken to position the panic hardware device to the latch side of the pivot point; otherwise, pushing on the bar may actually hold the door closed. Figure 5-19 illustrates a balanced door, and Figure 5-20 illustrates the difference between traditional panic hardware and pushpad panic hardware.

5-2.1.14   **Horizontal Sliding Doors.**

The 1985 *Code* included new provisions for the installation, operation, and fire protection rating requirements for horizontal sliding doors. It should be noted that these are not typical sliding doors. All the requirements of 5-2.1.14.2 must be met. In the 1991 Edition of the *Code*, a new 5-2.1.14.1 was added using provisions that were previously contained in three exceptions to 5-2.1.4.1 and incorporating them here so that all requirements for these special doors are in one location.

5-2.1.14.1   Horizontal sliding doors complying with 5-2.1.14.2 shall be permitted under the following conditions:

(a) Where serving elevator lobbies,

(b) In a means of egress serving an occupant load of less than 50,

(c) In horizontal exits or smoke barriers where permitted by Chapters 8 through 30.

Horizontal sliding doors are permitted only in the locations specified in 5-2.1.14.1. Note particularly those

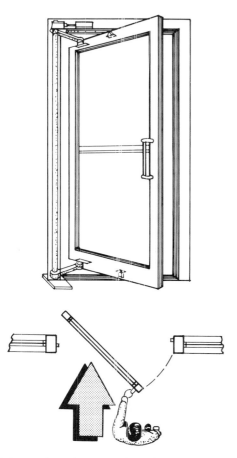

Figure 5-19.   Balanced Door. Balanced doors do not have side hinges but have a pivot point set in a small distance to reduce opening force.

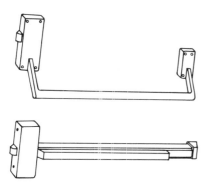

Figure 5-20.   Pushpad Panic Hardware. This figure illustrates the difference between "traditional" panic hardware (on the left) and "pushpad" panic hardware (on the right).

instances where specific authorization to use horizontal sliding doors must be given by the particular occupancy chapter. In addition, several occupancies put further location restrictions on such doors, and some occupancies impose additional operating requirements. If an occupancy chapter requirement is more stringent than that found in Chapter 5, the occupancy chapter requirements prevail.

Check the references for those locations where horizontal sliding doors may be used, and for additional restrictions that may be imposed by the referencing chapter:

5-2.1.12, Exception No. 2

Educational — 10-2.2.2.6, 10-2.2.2.7, 11-2.2.2.6, 11-2.2.2.7

Health Care — 12-2.2.2.9, 12-2.2.5, 12-3.7.5, 13-2.2.2.9, 13-2.2.5, 13-3.7.7

Hotels and Dormitories — 16-2.2.2.5, 17-2.2.2.5

Apartment Buildings — 18-2.2.2.4, 19-2.2.2.4

Board and Care Facilities — 22-3.2.2.2(e), 23-3.2.2.2(e)

Industrial — 28-2.2.2.3, 28-2.2.2.4

Storage — 29-2.2.2.3, 29-2.2.2.4, 29-8.2.2.2(c)

Unusual — 30-2.2.2.2, 30-2.2.2.3.

5-2.1.14.2   Horizontal sliding doors shall comply with the following:

(a) The door shall be operable by a simple method from either side without special knowledge or effort, and

(b) The force required to operate the door shall not exceed 30 lbf (133 N) to set the door in motion, and 15 lbf (67 N) to close the door or open it to the minimum required width, and

(c) The door shall be operable with a force not to exceed 50 lbf (222 N) when a force of 250 lbf (1,110 N) is applied perpendicularly to the door adjacent to the operating device, and

(d) The door assembly shall comply with the applicable fire protection rating and, when rated, shall be self-closing or automatic-closing by smoke detection in accordance with 5-2.1.8 and shall be installed in accordance with NFPA 80, *Standard for Fire Doors and Windows.*

(e) The door shall be operable by force not to exceed 15 lbf (67 N) applied to the operating device in the direction of egress.

The provisions for the installation of horizontal sliding doors include typical door requirements for simple method of operation, from either side, without special

Photo courtesy of Won-Door Corp.

Figure 5-21. *Horizontal Sliding Door. This illustrates the horizontal sliding doors permitted by 5-2.1.14.*

knowledge or effort; for forces necessary to operate the door; for fire protection ratings applicable to their location and use; and for self-closing or automatic-closing by smoke detection installation. It is the forces in (c) and (e) that make this door special.

Typical sliding doors cannot comply with these requirements. It is important that sliding doors be evaluated for compliance with all the requirements of 5-2.1.14.2.

An example of the types of doors being discussed in 5-2.1.14 is shown in Figure 5-21.

5-2.2 Stairs.

Stairs, whether interior or outside, serve three functions: they are a means of normal circulation between the floors and different levels of a building; they serve as an emergency exit in case of fire; and they are essential for the rescue and fire-control operations conducted by fire fighters.

Stairs are part of the most critical component of a means of egress system: the exit. In addition, they are one of the most commonly used elements of buildings on a day-to-day, nonemergency basis. Stairs have also been identified by extensive statistics as one of the most common scenes of accidents, costing hundreds of millions of dollars annually, not to mention personal suffering. For

all of these reasons, it is of the utmost importance that extremely careful attention be given to the design, construction, and maintenance of stairs. Starting with the 1988 Edition of the *Code*, both interior and outside stairs are covered under "Stairs." Some requirements apply specifically to only one or the other.

5-2.2.1 **General.** Stairs, either interior or exterior, used as a component in the means of egress shall conform to the general requirements of Section 5-1 and to the special requirements of this subsection.

Exception No. 1: Aisle steps in assembly occupancies as provided in Chapters 8 and 9.

Aisle steps are detailed in 8-2.5.8 and 9-2.5.8.

Exception No. 2: Existing noncomplying stairs may continue to be used subject to the approval of the authority having jurisdiction.

Stairs can be any one of the three means of egress components. They are most often thought of as an exit, but to be considered an exit they must be enclosed in accordance with 5-1.3.1. (Outside stairs need to be separated from the building in accordance with 5-2.2.6.3.) Open stairs are normally exit access rather than exits. (*See* 5-6.3.*) Where an interior stairway connects two or more stories, it is a vertical opening and must comply with the requirements for vertical openings regardless of its egress status.

It is sometimes more difficult to determine whether outside stairs are exit access, exit, or exit discharge. If they are protected in accordance with 5-2.2.6.3, the stairway would normally be considered an exit. Outside stairs adjacent to the building and not protected would normally be considered part of the exit access, with the exit being the discharge of the stairs. (*See* 5-6.5.*) The *Code* is not clear with regard to where a stairway is part of an exit discharge. Where a set of stairs occurs in a sidewalk that connects an exit door to a public way, there is some unspecified distance away from the building where the stairs are no longer considered an exit but part of the exit discharge. Where the stairway is more than 10 ft (3 m) (*see* 5-6.5 *or* 5-2.2.6.3) from the building, it may easily be considered exit discharge. Distances shorter than 10 ft (3 m) require considerable judgment on the part of the authority having jurisdiction.

5-2.2.2 Types of Stairs.

5-2.2.2.1* Dimensional Criteria.
Stairs shall be in accordance with the following table:

New Stairs	
Minimum width clear of all obstructions, except projections not exceeding 3½ in. (8.9 cm) at or below handrail height on each side	44 in. (112 cm) 36 in. (91 cm), where total occupant load of all floors served by stairways is less than 50.
Maximum height of risers	7 in. (17.8 cm)
Minimum height of risers	4 in. (10.2 cm)
Minimum tread depth	11 in. (27.9 cm)
Minimum headroom	6 ft 8 in. (203 cm)
Maximum height between landings	12 ft (3.7 m)
Doors opening immediately onto stairs without a landing that is at least the width of door	No

Exception: Existing stairs in existing buildings shall be permitted to remain in use or be rebuilt if they meet the requirements shown in the table for existing stairs.

Existing Stairs	Class A	Class B
Minimum width clear of all obstructions, except projections not exceeding 3½ in. (8.9 cm) at or below handrail height on each side	44 in. (112 cm)	44 in. (112 cm)
	36 in. (91 cm), where total occupant load of all floors served by stairways is less than 50.	
Maximum height of risers	7½ in. (19.1 cm)	8 in. (20.3 cm)
Minimum tread depth	10 in. (25.4 cm)	9 in. (22.9 cm)
Minimum headroom	6 ft 8 in. (203 cm)	6 ft 8 in. (203 cm)
Maximum height between landings	12 ft (3.7 m)	12 ft (3.7 m)
Doors opening immediately onto stairs without a landing that is at least the width of door	No	No

A-5-2.2.2.1 It is the intent of 5-2.2.2.1 to use the table for "Existing Stairs," in existing buildings even where there is a change in occupancy per 1-7.4.

Paragraph 5-2.2.2.1 presents complete information on required stair geometry for both new and existing stairs. The *Code* requires that all new stairs comply with the first table.

Editions of the *Code* prior to 1981 contained a requirement that "the height of every riser and the width of every tread shall be so proportioned that the sum of two risers and a tread, exclusive of its nosing or projection, is not less than 24 in. (61 cm) nor more than 25 in. (64 cm)." This requirement was deleted since it was based on a 300-year-old French formula in which the inch was a slightly larger unit of measure. Moreover, people's feet and stride length — the basis for the rule — were somewhat smaller at that time, and the rule was originally intended only for stairs of moderate steepness or pitch. For these reasons, as well as extensive research on the subject, experts in people movement urged that this rule not be used. Its use does not guarantee a good step geometry, and some of the better stair geometries do not comply with the old rule.

Due to the potential impact of these dimensions, the *Code* permits existing stairs in existing buildings to comply with previous requirements. It also allows existing stairs to be rebuilt to previous requirements, since a new stairway may not fit in an existing stairwell. Existing stairs are divided into two classes: Class A and Class B. Actually, there is little difference between the two. As shown in Figure 5-22, the difference lies in the tread depth and riser height. If the total occupant load of all floors served is less than 50, the minimum width can be reduced from 44 in. (112 cm) to 36 in. (91 cm). The occupancy chapters specify which class of stair may be used. If an existing occupancy chapter does not specify which class of existing stair can be used, then either A or B is allowed. A change of occupancy does not require that stairways be rebuilt to meet the requirements for new construction.

Note that 5-2.12.2.3 requires that stairs used to egress an area of refuge as required by 5-2.12 must be 48 in. (122 cm) clear between handrails. See the commentary in 5-2.12.

Also see 5-1.6 for special requirements where changes in elevation involve fewer than three risers.

5-2.2.2.2* Tread Slope.
Tread slope shall not exceed ¼ in./ft (2.1 cm/m) (1 in 48).

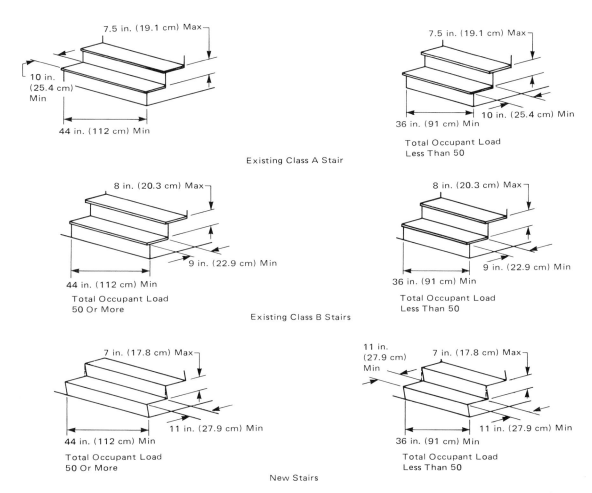

Figure 5-22. *Stair Specifications. Stair specifications are illustrated for both new and existing stairs. Note existing Class* A and B stairs showing maximum and minimum dimensions for each class.

A-5-2.2.2.2 A small drainage slope for stair treads subject to wetting may improve tread slip resistance (*see also A-5-2.2.3.4*). A consistent slope to a side of the stair, where drainage is possible, may be preferable to a front-to-back slope of the treads.

Sloping treads are traditionally used in order to shed water. They might also occur, without planning, when the treads erode unevenly through usage or when differential settlement occurs. Limiting permitted tread slope was new to the 1988 *Code.* The limit is appropriate to reduce dimensional nonuniformity of the effective riser heights and to reduce the chance of slipping on sloping treads.

5-2.2.2.3* **Riser Height and Tread Depth.** Riser height shall be measured as the vertical distance between tread nosings. Tread depth shall be measured horizontally between the vertical planes of the foremost projection of adjacent treads and at a right angle to the tread's leading edge but shall not include bevelled or rounded tread surfaces that slope more than 20 degrees (a slope of 1 in 2.75). At tread nosings, such bevelling or rounding shall not exceed ½ in. (1.3 cm) in horizontal dimension.

A-5-2.2.2.3 Figures A-5-2.2.2.3(a), (b), (c), and (d) illustrate the method for measuring riser height and tread depth. Stairs that will be covered with resilient floor coverings may need additional tread depth beyond the minimum specified in the

Code. Any horizontal projection of resilient covering materials beyond the tread nosing and riser, such as carpet and underlayment, can interfere with users' feet and thereby reduce usable tread depth. At the tread nosing, such resilient covering materials may not be capable of providing stable support for users' feet. Generally, effective tread depth is reduced by the uncompressed thickness of such resilient coverings and might be further reduced over time if coverings are not well secured and consequently move forward at the nosings. [*See Figure A-5-2.2.2.3(e).*]

RISER MEASUREMENTS:

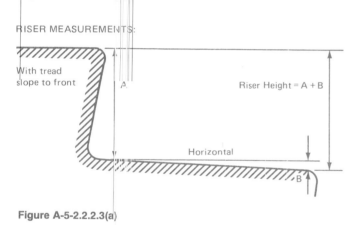

Figure A-5-2.2.2.3(a)

Figure A-5-2.2.2.3(b)

Figure A-5-2.2.2.3(c)

TREAD MEASUREMENTS:

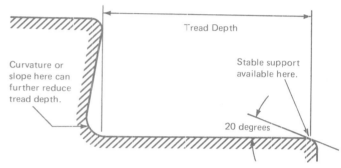

Figure A-5-2.2.2.3(d)

CARPETED STAIR:

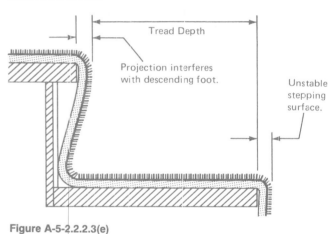

Figure A-5-2.2.2.3(e)

It will be noted that the detail on measurement of riser and tread dimensions (first introduced in this detail in the 1988 *Code*) specifies that the measurement be consistent with how people actually experience the dimensions when walking up or down the stairs. Moreover, the tread dimension does not include any part of the tread that is not functional for normal foot placement, especially where the tread slopes mores than 20 degrees from the horizontal. Normal foot placement, when stepping down onto the step nosing, results in an initial contact angle of less than 20 degrees. Therefore, any part of the nosing sloping more than this angle is simply not effective, and furthermore, it might create a tripping hazard. Related to this is the limitation of 1/2-in. (1.3-cm) horizontal dimension for bevelling or rounding of the step nosings. Keeping the nosing bevelling or rounding under this limit will

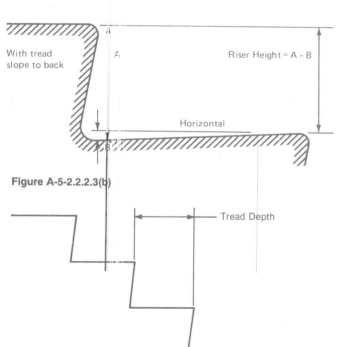

also reduce the chance of a slip occurring when the foot initially contacts the nosing during descent of the stair. By following this rule, the designer will also achieve acceptable step dimensions while keeping the space used for the stair to a minimum.

Stair designers should keep in mind the possibility that a stair originally designed without a resilient covering may someday be carpeted, thereby possibly reducing significantly the effective tread depth of the steps. Designing such stairs to provide slightly more than the minimum required tread depths is especially prudent in these cases. In addition, those responsible for maintaining stairs should keep in mind that the addition of resilient coverings may reduce the steps' tread dimensions to below the standard, and the dimensions will be further reduced if the coverings are not installed and maintained to be tight to the underlying steps.

5-2.2.2.4 There shall be no variation exceeding $\frac{3}{16}$ in. (.5 cm) in the depth of adjacent treads or in the height of adjacent risers, and the tolerance between the largest and smallest riser or between the largest and smallest tread shall not exceed $\frac{3}{8}$ in. (1.0 cm) in any flight.

Exception: Where the bottom riser adjoins a sloping public way, walk, or driveway having an established grade and serving as a landing, a variation in height of the bottom riser of not more than 3 in. (7.6 cm) in every 3 ft (91 cm) of stairway width is permitted.

Many accidents have resulted from irregularities in stairs. There should be no design irregularities. Variations due to construction are permitted provided the variation between adjacent treads or adjacent risers does not exceed $\frac{3}{16}$ in. (.5 cm) and that the difference between the largest and smallest riser, as well as the largest and smallest tread, in any flight of stairs does not exceed $\frac{3}{8}$ in. (1.0 cm). (*See Figure 5-23.*)

Figure 5-23 illustrates a stair that has various non-uniformities or irregularities. Note that the treads are not all uniformly horizontal and the risers are not all vertical. This situation, illustrating construction errors, is sometimes encountered with cast-in-place concrete stairs. Here there are unacceptable nonuniformities of the dimensions measured in accordance with 5-2.2.2.3. The nonuniformities measured at the backs of the treads and along the risers (that is, not the effective dimensions referred to in 5-2.2.2.3) might be greater or smaller depending on how the treads and risers slope.

Where a stair lands on sloping public property, such as a public sidewalk, the building owner usually has no right to alter the public property. Therefore, the *Code* accepts a certain minimum across-the-stair slope not in excess of 1 in 12. If reasonably possible, any such variation in riser height should be avoided. Figure 5-24 illustrates the exception.

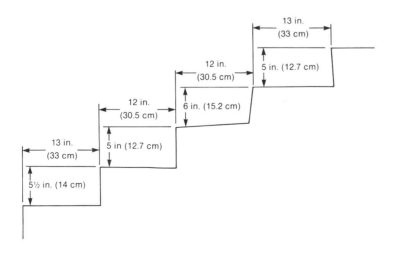

Figure 5-23. Variations in Tread and Riser Dimensions Invite Accidents. In this arrangement, the variations are excessive and are prohibited.

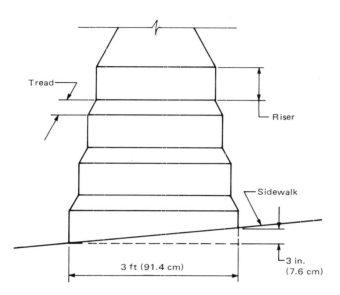

Figure 5-24. *This figure illustrates the Exception to 5-2.2.2.4.*

5-2.2.2.5 Monumental Stairs. Monumental stairs, either inside or outside, shall be permitted as a component in a means of egress if in compliance with all the requirements for stairs.

5-2.2.2.6 Curved Stairs. Curved stairs shall be permitted as a component in a means of egress provided the minimum depth of tread is 11 in. (27.9 cm) measured 12 in. (30.5 cm) from the narrower end of the tread, and the smallest radius is not less than twice the stair width.

Exception: Existing curved stairs shall be permitted to be continued in use provided the minimum depth of tread is 10 in. (25.4 cm) and the smallest radius is not less than twice the stair width.

Paragraph 5-2.2.2.6 relates the degree of curvature to the width of the stair, as shown in Figure 5-25. This relationship of smallest radius to stair width should be based on the actual width of the stair rather than just the required width. Otherwise, some unsafe conditions could be created toward the outside of wide-curved stairs. The 11-in. (27.9-cm) tread depth is measured at the so-called "inner walking line" where feet land when walking on the inner part of the stair.

The *Code* specifies the measurement method for curved stairs in a manner that is more closely related to how such stairs are used — with reference to a minimum 11-in.

(27.9-cm) tread depth at the so-called "inner walking line." This is a concept that has been employed in the *Code's* requirement for winders for some time. With the minimum tread depth stated as a dimension similar to that of other stairs usable as a required means of egress, it is more evident that curved stairs are acceptable as a component in a required means of egress, without restriction of occupancy.

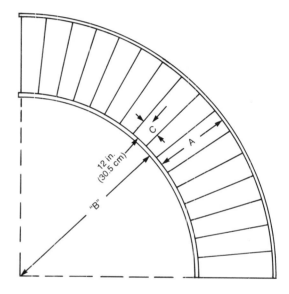

Figure 5-25. *Curved Stairs. Dimension B must be at least twice A. Dimension C must be at least 11 in. (27.9 cm).*

5-2.2.2.7 Spiral Stairs. Where permitted for individual occupancies by Chapters 8 through 30, spiral stairs shall be permitted as a component in a means of egress provided:

(a) The clear width of the stairs is not less than 26 in. (66 cm).

(b) The height of risers shall not exceed 9½ in. (24.1 cm).

(c) Headroom shall be not less than 6 ft 6 in. (198 cm).

(d) Treads shall have a minimum depth of 7½ in. (19.1 cm) at a point 12 in. (30.5 cm) from the narrower edge.

(e) All treads shall be identical.

(f) The occupant load served is not more than 5.

In addition to setting the specifications for spiral stairs, 5-2.2.2.7 states that they may serve as required means of egress for an occupant load of not more than five.

However, they can be used only where expressly allowed by the appropriate occupancy chapter. (*See Figure 5-26.*)

These applications make it very unlikely that there will be simultaneous use of the stair by a person ascending and another descending. A single user descending the spiral stair is able to use the best part of the small treads — the part closer to the outside of the stair.

The following occupancies allow the use of spiral stairs (check the referenced paragraphs for additional requirements that may be imposed by the occupancy chapter):

Detention and Correctional — 14-2.2.3.2, 15-2.2.3.2
Apartments — 18-2.2.3.3, 19-2.2.3.3
One- and Two-Family Dwellings — 21-2.5.1
Mercantile — 24-2.2.3.2, 25-2.2.3.2
Business — 26-2.2.3.2, 27-2.2.3.2
Industrial — 28-2.2.3.2
Storage — 29-2.2.3.2
Unusual Occupancies — 30-2.2.3.2

5-2.2.2.8 **Winders.** Where permitted for individual occupancies by Chapters 8 through 30, winders are allowed in stairs. Such winders shall have a minimum depth of tread of 6 in. (15.2 cm), and a minimum depth of tread of 9 in. (22.9 cm) at a point 12 in. (30.5 cm) from the narrowest edge.

A winder is a tapered tread used to change the direction of the stairway. Because they introduce a variation in the stair geometry, and their effective tread dimensions are less than 11 in. (27.9 cm), winder stairs are suited to limited applications. At one time, the *Code* prohibited winders. Chapter 5 now sets criteria for winders if the appropriate occupancy chapter permits their use. Other than within dwelling unit type settings, the *Code* restricts winders to existing situations. (*See Figure 5-27.*)

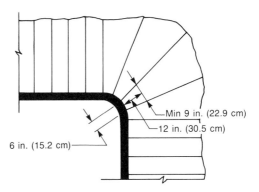

Figure 5-27. Acceptable Winders. Where allowed by the occupancy chapter, winders that comply with 5-2.2.2.8 are acceptable in a required means of egress.

The following occupancies allow the use of winders (check the referenced paragraphs for additional requirements that may be imposed by the occupancy chapter):

Apartments — 18-2.2.3.4
Existing Apartment Buildings — 19-2.2.3.4
Lodging and Rooming Houses — 20-2.6
One- and Two-Family Dwellings — 21-2.5.1
Board and Care Facilities — 22-2.2.7, 23-2.2.7
Existing Mercantile — 25-2.2.3.3
Existing Business — 27-2.2.3.3
Existing Industrial — 28-2.2.3.3
Existing Storage — 29-2.2.3.3 and 29-8.2.2.3
Existing Unusual Structures — 30-2.2.3.3.

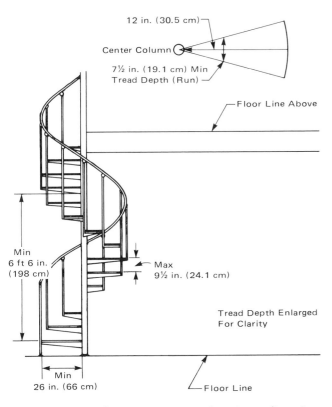

Figure 5-26. Spiral Stairs. Minimum and maximum dimensions for spiral stairs as given in 5-2.2.2.7. All treads must be identical, and the stair can serve a maximum occupant load of five.

5-2.2.3 Stair Details.

5-2.2.3.1 All stairs serving as required means of egress shall be of permanent fixed construction.

5-2.2.3.2 Each new stair, platform, and landing used in buildings more than three stories in height and in new buildings required by this *Code* to be of Type I or Type II construction shall be of noncombustible material throughout.

Exception: Handrails.

Paragraph 5-2.2.3.2 covers the combustibility of materials used in the construction of stairs. Stairs serving up to and including three stories may be of combustible construction, unless the structure is otherwise required to be of Type I or Type II construction (noncombustible) as described in NFPA 220, *Standard on Types of Building Construction.*[5] In the latter case, the materials used for the stair construction must be noncombustible. In all buildings of more than three stories, the stairway construction must be of noncombustible materials.

5-2.2.3.3 Stairs and intermediate landings shall continue with no decrease in width along the direction of exit travel. In new buildings, every landing shall have a dimension measured in direction of travel equal to the width of the stair. Such dimension need not exceed 4 ft (122 cm) where the stair has a straight run.

Figure 5-28 illustrates the intent of 5-2.2.3.3.

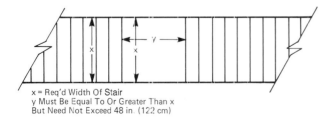

x = Req'd Width Of Stair
y Must Be Equal To Or Greater Than x
But Need Not Exceed 48 in. (122 cm)

Figure 5-28.   Width of Stairs and Intermediate Landings.

5-2.2.3.4* Stair treads shall be uniformly slip resistant and shall be free of projections or lips that could trip stair users.

A-5-2.2.3.4 The tripping hazard referred to in 5-2.2.3.4 occurs especially during descent, where the tread walking surface has projections such as strips of high friction materials or lips from metal pan stairs that are not completely filled with concrete or other material. Tread nosings that project over adjacent treads can also be a tripping hazard. ANSI A117.1, *Standard for Buildings and Facilities — Providing Accessibility and Usability for Physically Handicapped People* (*see Appendix B*), illustrates projecting nosing configurations that minimize the hazard.

Regarding the slip resistance of treads, it should be recognized that when walking up or down stairs a person's foot exerts a smaller horizontal force against treads than achieved when walking on level floors. Therefore, materials used for floors that are acceptable as slip resistant (as described by ASTM) provide adequate slip resistance where used for stair treads, including the important leading edges of treads — the part of the tread that the foot first contacts during descent, the most critical direction of travel. If stair treads are wet, there may be an increased danger of slipping, just as there may be an increased danger of slipping on wet floors of similar materials. A small wash or drainage slope on exterior stair treads is therefore recommended to shed water (*see NBS BSS 120*). Where environmental conditions (such as illumination levels and directionality or a complex visual field drawing a person's attention away from stair treads) lead to a hazardous reduction in one's ability to perceive stair treads, they should be made of a material that permits ready discrimination of the number and position of treads. In all cases, the leading edges of all treads should be readily visible during both ascent and descent. A major factor in injury-producing stair accidents and in the ability to use stairs efficiently in conditions such as egress is the clarity of the stair treads as separate stepping surfaces.

Relatively little information is available on slip resistance. There is an ASTM Committee E-17 on Skid Resistance that published results of a symposium STP 649, "Walking Surfaces: Measurement of Skid Resistance," a symposium sponsored by ASTM Subcommittee E-17.26, Denver, Colorado, June 30, 1977, published 1978.

5-2.2.3.5 Treads of stairs and landing floors shall be solid.

Exception: Industrial occupancies as provided in Chapter 28.

5-2.2.3.6 Stairs shall be so arranged as to make clear the direction of egress to a public way. Stairs that continue beyond the level of exit discharge shall be interrupted at the level of exit discharge by partitions, doors, or other effective means.

Exception: Stairs that continue one-half story beyond the level of exit discharge need not be so interrupted where the exit discharge is obvious.

Figure 5-29 illustrates an important stair detail designed to minimize the possibility of a person inadvertently passing through the exit discharge level into a basement or some level below that of the exit discharge. This can be accomplished by the use of a partition or other physical barrier that effectively interrupts the flow of travel, causing a person to perform a conscious act to overcome the barrier. The use of railings, gates, or grilles to create this barrier is acceptable. (*Also see 5-7.3.*)

5-2.2.4 **Guards and Handrails.**

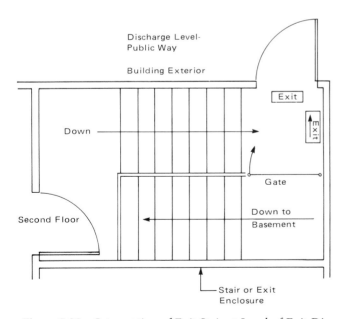

Figure 5-29. Interruption of Exit Stair at Level of Exit Discharge. This can be done by placing a physical barrier to prevent continuation below the level of exit discharge into the basement. This helps to warn occupants in the stair enclosure that they are on the level of exit discharge.

5-2.2.4.1 **Guards.** Means of egress such as stairs, landings, balconies, corridors, passageways, floor or roof openings, ramps, aisles, porches, or mezzanines that are more than 30 in. (76 cm) above the floor or grade below shall be provided with guards to prevent falls over the open side.

Exception: Existing handrails meeting the requirements of 5-2.2.4.5 shall be permitted to serve as guards.

A significant change to this paragraph for the 1991 *Code* is that stairs will require guards on the open side. This requirement was in previous editions of the *Code* but had been deleted. It was reinstituted in the *Code* since approximately 25 percent of those who fall on stairs do strike the side and the 95 percentile male needs a 42-in. (107-cm) high guard. Although there is no firm data, there are sufficient anecdotal incidents to show the need for this requirement. An exception was added for existing stairs to recognize that this was not previously required.

5-2.2.4.2* **Handrails.** Each new stair and each new ramp with a slope exceeding 1 in 15 shall have handrails on both sides. In addition, handrails shall be provided within 30 in. (76 cm) of all portions of the required egress width of stairs. The required egress width shall be along the natural path of travel. Existing stairs and stairs within dwelling units and within guest rooms shall have a handrail on at least one side. (*See also 5-2.2.4.5.*)

Exception: On existing stairs, handrails shall be provided within 44 in. (112 cm) of all portions of the required egress width of stairs.

A-5-2.2.4.2 The intent of this provision is to place handrails for the required exit width of stairs only regardless of the actual width of the stairs. The required exit width is along the natural path of travel to and from the building. Examples of this requirement are shown in Figure A-5-2.2.4.2. The reduced intermediate handrail spacing of 60 in. (152 cm) along with a handrail height within the permissible height limits permits everyone to reach and grasp one handrail. Except as noted in 5-2.2.4.3 and 5-2.2.4.5, handrails are not required on stair landings.

Handrails are required on each side of new stairs and ramps, but they are not required on landings except as

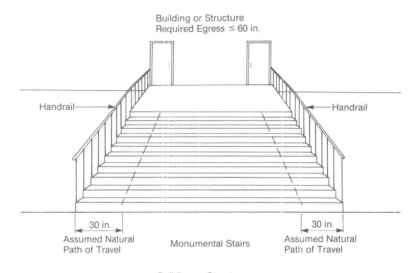

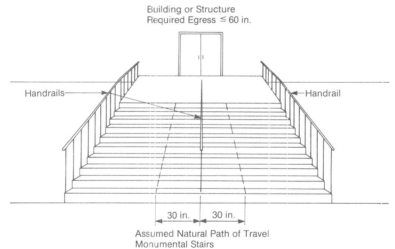

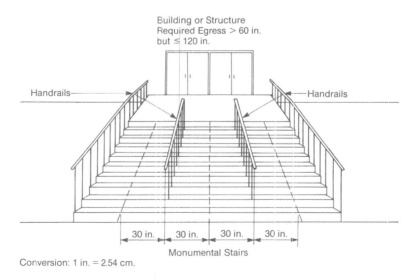

Conversion: 1 in. = 2.54 cm.

Figure A-5-2.2.4.2

noted in 5-2.2.4.3 and 5-2.2.4.5. Handrails are also required on at least one side of existing stairs and stairs within dwelling units. They provide support for people using stairs and can serve as a guide when smoke enters the stairway in a quantity sufficient to interfere with one's vision or when the stair lighting system fails. Thus, it is important to have railings within reach of each file of people.

Superficially, the design details for guards and handrails may appear to be relatively unimportant. Yet, even in normal use, poorly designed and constructed guards and handrails can cause accidents. Lack of guards and handrails on stairs, ramps, landings, and balconies can be even more hazardous.

On monumental stairs, the required handrails should be located along the normal path of travel to and from the building.

Figure A-5-2.2.4.2 illustrates the required provision of handrails on wide, monumental stairs. Handrails are provided along the natural paths of travel from the exit doors. (Note that where the doors are separated and are close to the two sides of the wide stair, the maximum stair egress width includes two of the 3½-in. (8.9-cm) projections permitted by 5-3.2.1, and, thus, the maximum width is actually 67 in. (170 cm), not 60 in. (152 cm). This does not occur with handrails that are used by people on both sides.

The 30-in. (76-cm) figure, applying to stairs, is a significant change from earlier Codes. It comes from the realization that people can only reach about 24 in. (60 cm) to the side to grasp a handrail. The 6 in. (15 cm) added to this reach distance accounts for the overlapping configuration of people in a crowd as illustrated in Figure 5-30. The arrangement of stair and people, seen in overhead plan view, is typical of what is observed in evacuation conditions where movement, speed, density, and flow are near optimum for safe, comfortable crowd movement.

5-2.2.4.3 Required guards and handrails shall continue for the full length of each flight of stairs. At turns of stairs, inside handrails shall be continuous between flights at landings.

Exception: On existing stairs, the handrails are not required to be continuous between flights of stairs at landings.

It is not the intent of this *Code* to require handrails on stair landings. However, the interior handrail on stairs

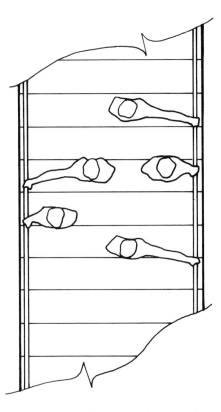

Figure 5-30. Overhead, Plan View of Stair with Handrails at the Maximum 60-in. (152-cm) Spacing Permitted by the Code for New Stairs. Crowd configuration shown is near optimum for efficient, safe and comfortable movement.

that change direction at a landing shall be continuous. (*See Figure A-5-2.2.4.5.*)

5-2.2.4.4 The design of guards and handrails and the hardware for attaching handrails to guards, balusters, or walls shall be such that there are no projections that may engage loose clothing. Openings in guards shall be designed to prevent loose clothing from becoming wedged in such openings.

5-2.2.4.5* Handrail Details.

(a) Handrails on stairs shall be not less than 34 in. (86 cm) nor more than 38 in. (96 cm) above the surface of the tread, measured vertically to the top of the rail from the leading edge of the tread.

Exception No. 1 to (a): Required handrails that form part of a guard shall be permitted to have a maximum height of 42 in. (107 cm) measured vertically to the top of the rail from the leading edge of the tread.

Exception No. 2 to (a): Existing required handrails shall not be less than 30 in. (76 cm) nor more than 38 in. (97 cm) above the upper surface of the tread, measured vertically to the top of the rail from the leading edge of the tread.

Exception No. 3 to (a)*: Additional handrails that are lower or higher than the main handrail shall be permitted.

A-5-2.2.4.5(a)   Exception No. 3. Additional handrails, beyond those required by the *Code*, are permitted at heights other than those stipulated. For example, where children under the age of 5 are major users of a facility, an additional handrail at a height in the range of 28 to 32 in. (71 to 81 cm) might be useful. Generally, children apparently prefer to use, and can effectively use, handrails that are located at shoulder to head height. This is because of their developmental characteristics and their less developed balance and walking abilities.

Provision of the higher handrail height was the subject of extensive research by the National Research Council of Canada.

Very high handrails have been tested in field and laboratory conditions. Heights up to about 42 in. (107 cm) are very effective in helping people to stabilize themselves to help arrest a fall. Therefore, a guard-height railing that also meets the graspability criteria for handrails [5-2.2.4.5(c)] should serve well as a handrail also. This explains why Exception No. 1 now accepts the rail on top of a 42-in. (107-cm) high guard to serve as a handrail. Three different types of studies of handrail height for stairs all led to the same conclusion: handrail heights previously required by the *Code* were suboptimum. The studies included anthropometric analyses (such as illustrated in Figure 5-31), field studies of the use of various handrails, and laboratory studies where functional capability of users to grasp a handrail as if arresting a fall could be accurately measured and compared for a range of handrail conditions. These studies included a wide range of ages and sizes of people, from young children to those in their seventies. Most functional heights, even for elderly persons tested, were in the range of 36 in. (91 cm) to 38 in. (97 cm), and the average height most preferred by elderly persons tested was about 37 in. (94 cm).

(These studies were reported in the scientific journal, Ergonomics, Vol. 28, No. 7, 1985, pp. 999-1010, "Review of Stair-Safety Research with an Emphasis on Canadian Studies," by Jake Pauls.) The recommendation for lower handrails for young children is particularly important for family dwellings and for children's day-care facilities.

This frame (Figure 5-32) from the documentary film, "The Stair Event," shows field testing of an adjustable-height handrail in an aisle stair in Edmonton's Commonwealth Stadium. Evidence from such field testing, from anthropometric analyses, and from laboratory testing with a range of younger and older adults, has led to the higher handrail heights first introduced in the 1988 *Code*. The upper handrail is located 37 in. (94 cm) above tread nosings, which, in the laboratory testing, was the average preferred height for elderly people and an especially effective height for arresting a fall in descent. The lower railing, provided for children, is approximately 24 in. (60 cm) above the tread nosings. Note that even in this case of ascent, one of the children has chosen to use the higher railing, located at about his shoulder height, in preference to the lower one. Note also that, a moment after this frame was taken, even the smaller of the two boys chose to use the upper handrail, which was located at about the height of his head. This behavior has been observed in other studies of young children; when given a choice of handrail heights, they often select one between shoulder and head height. For a variety of reasons, including use by children, the lower handrail is required on aisle stairs. Also, as indicated in the appendix notes to Chapters 10 and 11, a second lower handrail is recommended for stairs that will be used extensively by very young children.

(b)* New handrails shall provide a clearance of at least 1½ in. (3.8 cm) between the handrail and the wall to which they are fastened.

A-5-2.2.4.5(b)   This 1½-in. (3.8-cm) clearance assures that the wall adjacent to the handrail is a smooth surface. Where rough wall surfaces are used, greater clearances are recommended.

(c)* Handrails shall have a circular cross-section with an outside diameter of at least 1.25 in. (3.2 cm) and not greater

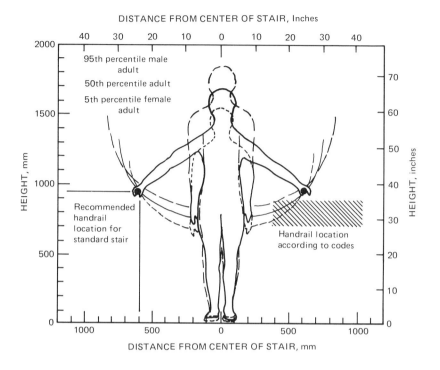

DISTANCE FROM CENTER OF STAIR, Inches

95th percentile male adult

50th percentile adult

5th percentile female adult

HEIGHT, mm

Recommended handrail location for standard stair

HEIGHT, inches

Handrail location according to codes

DISTANCE FROM CENTER OF STAIR, mm

Figure 5-31. *One of the Studies Leading to the Code's Requirement for Higher Handrails and Closer Lateral Spacing Included this Anthropometric Analysis of User's Capability to Reach a Handrail to the Side. On the left side is shown the recommended height and spacing of handrails; on the right is the location of handrails formerly permitted by the Code for new stairs. It is evident that people in the middle of a wide stair will be unable to reach the lower, more distant handrails; therefore, this condition is not desirable when a stair is crowded, as in an egress situation.*

than 2.0 in. (5 cm). New handrails shall be continuously graspable along the entire length.

Exception to (c): Any other shape with a perimeter dimension of at least 4 in. (10.2 cm), but not greater than 6.25 in. (15.9 cm), and with the largest cross-sectional dimension not exceeding 2.25 in. (5.7 cm).

A-5-2.2.4.5(c) Handrails should be designed so they can be grasped firmly with a comfortable grip and so the hand can be slid along the rail without encountering obstructions. The profile of the rail should comfortably match the hand grips. For example, a round profile such as is provided by the simplest round tubing or pipe having an outside diameter of 1½ to 2 in. (3.8 to 5 cm) provides good graspability for adults. Factors such as the use of a handrail by small children and the wall-fixing details should be taken into account in assessing handrail graspability. The most functional as well as the most preferred handrail shape and size is circular with a 1.5-in. (3.8-cm) outside diameter (according to research conducted using adults). Handrails used predominantly by children should be designed at the lower end of the permitted dimensional range.

Photo Courtesy of Jake Pauls, Hughes Associates, Inc.

Figure 5-32. *Field Testing of an Adjustable-Height Handrail.*

It should be noted that handrails are one of the most important components of a stair; therefore, design excesses such as oversized wood handrail sections should be avoided unless there is a readily perceived and easily grasped handhold provided. In handrail design, it is useful to remember at all times the effectiveness of a simple round profile that permits some locking action by fingers as they curl around the handrail.

Item (c) introduces a subtle but important requirement for handrails: graspability. People are incapable of exerting sufficient finger pressure to adequately grasp a handrail using only a "pinch grip" as opposed to a "power grip," where fingers curl around and under a properly shaped and sized railing. This would prohibit the use of rectangular lumber for handrails. Figure 5-33 shows examples of acceptable and unacceptable handrails. It also shows how an unacceptable rail can be retrofitted to create a handrail that complies with the *Code*.

Figure 5-34 illustrates acceptable, unacceptable, and marginal handrail shapes and sizes based on a Canadian study, using younger and older adults, testing functional capability as well as user preference. The traditional residential handrail section, shown at the bottom center, did not perform well in the functional testing, and it was not a comfortable shape to grasp in comparison with other sections. A key difference between the acceptable and unacceptable handrail sections is the ability to wrap one's fingers completely around the handrail to achieve a "power grip." Unacceptable sections permit only a "pinch

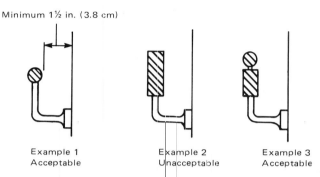

Figure 5-33. Handrails. Example 1 shows a typical handrail that is acceptable for graspability. Example 2 shows a handrail that is unacceptable from a graspability standpoint. Example 3 shows how to modify the handrail in Example 2 to comply with the graspability criteria and also increase the handrail height.

grip," which provides for little opportunity to help arrest a fall, even for people with ordinary hand dexterity and strength. Figure 5-33 shows how an ungraspable, oversized railing can be easily retrofitted with a proper handrail section on top of the railing to improve graspability as well as to bring the handrail into closer conformity with new height requirements.

(d) New handrail ends shall be returned to the wall or floor or shall terminate at newel posts.

Figure 5-34. Acceptable, Unacceptable, and Marginal Handrail Sections.

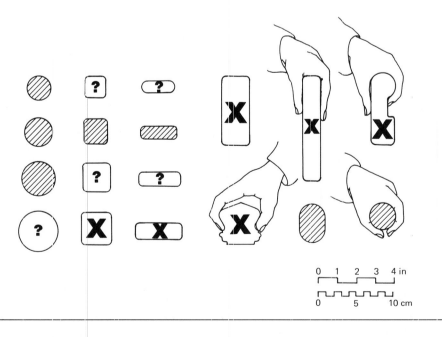

(e) New handrails that are not continuous between flights shall be extended horizontally a minimum of 12 in. (30.5 cm) at the required height at landings where a guard or wall exists.

(f)* New handrails on open sides of stairs shall have intermediate rails or an ornamental pattern such that a sphere 4 in. (10.1 cm) in diameter cannot pass through any openings in such handrail.

Exception No. 1 to (f): The triangular openings formed by the riser, tread, and bottom element of a guardrail at the open side of the stair shall be of such a size that a sphere 6 in. (15.2 cm) in diameter cannot pass through.

Exception No. 2 to (f): In detention and correctional occupancies, in industrial occupancies, and in storage occupancies, the clear distance between intermediate rails measured at right angles to the rails shall not exceed 21 in. (53.3 cm).

A-5-2.2.4.5(f) Vertical intermediate rails are preferred to reduce climbability.

The change from a 6-in. (15.2-cm) sphere to a 4-in. (10.1-cm) sphere is one of the major changes in the 1991 *Code*. This change was made based on the submission of a proposal that received the backing of the American Academy of Pediatrics. Approximately 950 out of 1000 children under age 10 can pass through a 6-inch (15.2-cm) wide opening. In order to prevent small children from falling through guards or handrails and to prevent them from being caught in openings, the configuration and construction of a guard or handrail must meet certain minimum requirements. Rather than detailed specifications for intermediate rails, the *Code* sets a performance criterion that allows alternative solutions.

A-5-2.2.4.5 Figure A-5-2.2.4.5 illustrates some of the requirements of 5-2.2.4.5.

See 8-2.5.8.6 for requirements for handrails on aisle stairs.

5-2.2.4.6 Guard Details.

(a) The height of guards required by 5-2.2.4.1 shall be measured vertically to the top of the guard from the surface adjacent thereto.

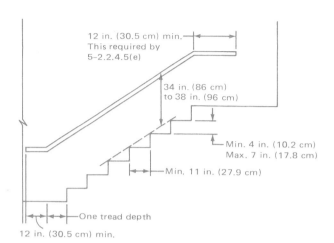

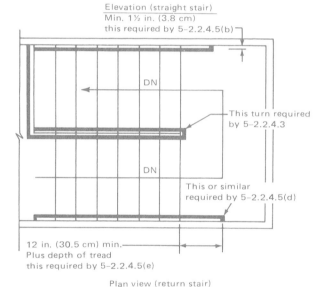

Figure A-5-2.2.4.5

(b) Guards shall be not less than 42 in. (107 cm) high.

Exception No. 1 to (b): Existing guards within dwelling units shall be not less than 36 in. (91 cm) high.

Exception No. 2 to (b): In assembly occupancies as provided in Chapters 8 and 9.

(c)* Open guards shall have intermediate rails or an ornamental pattern such that a sphere 4 in. (10.1 cm) in diameter cannot pass through any opening.

Exception No. 1 to (c): The triangular openings formed by the riser, tread, and bottom element of the guardrail at the open side of a stair shall be of such size that a sphere 6 in. (15.2 cm) in diameter cannot pass through.

Exception No. 2 to (c): In detention and correctional occupancies, in industrial occupancies, and in storage occupancies, the clear distance between intermediate rails measured at right angles to the rails shall not exceed 21 in. (53.3 cm).

Exception No. 3 to (c): Approved existing open guards.

A-5-2.2.4.6(c)   Vertical intermediate rails are preferred to reduce climbability.

Several major changes were made to the guard requirements for the 1991 Edition of the *Code*. First, 5-2.2.4.1 now requires that guards be installed on the open sides of stairs. Next, the openings in the guard have been revised from restricting a 6-in. (15.2-cm) sphere from passing through to restricting a 4-in. (10.1-cm) sphere. This change was made for the same reason as the change to 5-2.2.4.5(f). Another change is that guards within dwelling units will no longer be able to use the lower 36-in. (91-cm) height, although an exception will continue for existing guards within a dwelling unit. This change was made since neither the center of gravity nor a person's anatomical measurements change within a dwelling unit, and data indicates that the 95th percentile male needs a 42-in. (107-cm) guard to resist falls.

5-2.2.5   Special Provisions for Outside Stairs.

5-2.2.5.1   **Balconies.** Balconies to which access doors lead shall be approximately level with the floor of the building.

Exception: In existing buildings located in climates where balconies may be subject to accumulation of snow or ice, one step, not to exceed 8 in. (20.3 cm), shall be permitted below the level of the inside floor.

Where snow and ice are a possibility, protection must be provided against accumulations that could block the free swing of the access doors leading to balconies or prevent full use of the stairs. The 8-in. (20.3-cm) clearance

provided in the Exception to 5-2.2.5.1 provides some of that protection; however, protection of the walking surfaces is also required.

5-2.2.5.2*   **Visual Protection.** Outside stairs shall be so arranged as to avoid any handicap to the use of the stairs by persons having a fear of high places. For stairs more than three stories in height, any arrangement intended to meet this requirement shall be at least 4 ft (122 cm) in height.

A-5-2.2.5.2   The guards that are required by 5-2.2.4 will usually meet this requirement where the stair is not more than three stories high. Special architectural treatment, including application of such devices as metal or masonry screens and grilles, will usually be necessary to comply with the intent of the requirements for stairs over three stories in height.

Outside stairs frequently have an open side that must be protected by a railing or guard. On high buildings, the fear of height may interfere with use of such stairs, and so 5-2.2.5.2 calls for a 4-ft (122-cm) high guard construction to protect against this possibility.

5-2.2.5.3   Subject to the approval of the authority having jurisdiction, outside stairs may be accepted where leading to roofs of other sections of the building or adjoining building, where the construction is fire resistive, where there is a continuous and safe means of egress from the roof, and where all other reasonable requirements for life safety are maintained. (*Also see 5-7.5.*)

Outside stairs leading to the roofs of other sections of the building or onto the roofs of adjoining buildings are acceptable as part of the means of egress, but only upon approval of the authority having jurisdiction. The conditions and settings of such paths of travel are likely to be so varied that it is virtually impossible to cover them by written provisions. Each situation is best judged individually by the authority having jurisdiction. (*Also see 5-7.5.*)

5-2.2.6   Enclosure and Protection of Stairs.

5-2.2.6.1   **Enclosures.** All interior stairs serving as an exit or exit component shall be enclosed in accordance with 5-1.3.1. All other interior stairs shall be protected in accordance with 6-2.4.

Formal Interpretation: 85-16
Reference: 5-2.2.6.1

Question 1: Given a stair, from the second floor of an assembly occupancy, which discharges directly to the outside at the first (ground) floor and which is separated by one hour fire resistance construction from the first floor but open to the second floor (i.e., stair not fully enclosed but separated from the first floor), if the stair is called exit access and meets the associated requirements is it the intent of 5-2.2.6.1 to require full enclosure?

Answer: No.

Question 2: If the intent of 5-2.2.6.1, under the conditions stated in Question 1, is to allow the stair to be open to the second floor, will an opening in the floor between the first and second stories meeting all the requirements of 6-2.4.5 still allow the stair to be called exit access, permitting the stair to be open to the second floor?

Answer: Yes.

Issue Edition: 1985
Reference: 5-2.2.3.1
Date: August 1987 ■

Paragraph 5-2.2.6.1 was rewritten for the 1985 Edition of the *Code* to emphasize the two different features of interior stairs that the *Code* addresses: protection of vertical openings and enclosure of exits. Most interior stairs serve as exits and are vertical openings; they therefore must meet the requirements of 5-1.3.1 and, as vertical openings, must comply with 6-2.4. Stairs that are not being used as exits but are vertical openings must be protected in accordance with 6-2.4. This is an important distinction since it is possible to comply with 6-2.4 and not comply with 5-1.3.1. It should also be noted that there are some stairs that are neither exits nor vertical openings, such as a stair to a platform or stage or those running between two different floor levels on the same story.

5-2.2.6.2* Where nonrated walls or unprotected openings are used to enclose the exterior of a stairway and the walls

or openings are exposed by other parts of the building at an angle of less than 180 degrees, the building enclosure walls within 10 ft (3 m) horizontally of the nonrated wall or unprotected opening shall be constructed as required for stairway enclosures including opening protectives, but need not have greater than a 1-hour fire resistance rating with 45-minute fire protection rated opening protectives. This construction shall extend vertically from the ground to a point 10 ft (3 m) above the topmost landing of the stairway or to the roofline, whichever is lower.

Exception: Existing stairways.

A-5-2.2.6.2   The purpose of this provision is to protect the exterior wall of a stairway from fires in other portions of the building. If the exterior wall of the stair is flush with the building exterior wall, the fire would need to travel around 180 degrees in order to impact the stair. This has not been a problem in existing buildings, so no protection is required. However, if the angle of exposure is less than 180 degrees, protection of either the stair wall or building wall is required.

Figures A-5-2.2.6.2 (a), (b), and (c) illustrate the requirement (assuming nonrated glass on exterior wall of stair is used).

This paragraph only applies where the stair is required to be enclosed either as an exit or as a vertical opening.

5-2.2.6.3   **Separation and Protection of Outside Stairs.** Outside stairs shall be separated from the interior of the building by walls with the fire resistance rating required for enclosed stairs with fixed or self-closing opening protectives. This construction shall extend vertically from the ground to a point 10 ft (3 m) above the topmost landing of the stairs or to the roofline, whichever is lower, and at least 10 ft (3 m) horizontally.

Exception No. 1: Outside stairs serving an exterior exit access balcony that has two remote outside stairways or ramps.

Exception No. 2: Outside stairs serving not more than two stories, including the story of exit discharge, shall be permitted to be unprotected where there is a remotely located second exit.

Exception No. 3: In existing buildings, outside stairs serving not more than three stories, including the story of exit discharge, shall be permitted to be unprotected where there is a remotely located second exit.

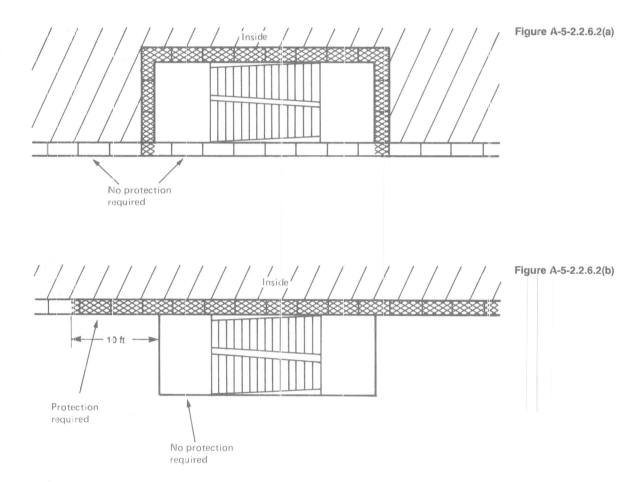

Figure A-5-2.2.6.2(a)

Figure A-5-2.2.6.2(b)

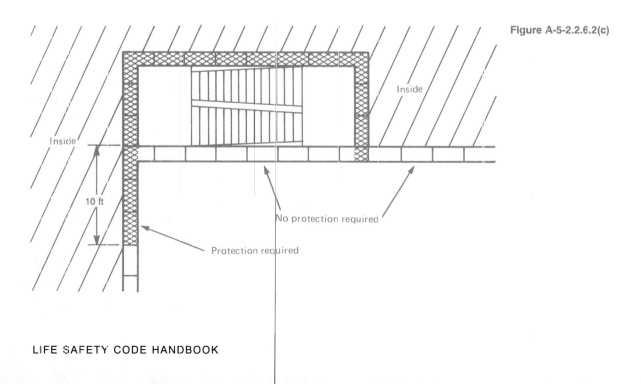

Figure A-5-2.2.6.2(c)

Exception No. 4: The fire resistance rating of the portion of the separation extending 10 ft (3 m) from the stairs need not exceed 1 hour with openings protected by ¾-hour fire protection rated assemblies.

This paragraph only applies where the outside stair serves as an exit. See the commentary following 5-2.2.1 Exception No. 2.

Most important in the consideration of outside stairs is their proximity to openings in the wall of the building, openings through which fire emerging from the building could render stairs useless as a means of egress. Protection against this kind of occurrence takes two forms: (1) protection from openings, which is accom-

plished by distance separation; and (2) protection of openings, which must be done if the openings occur or are placed in a wall in such a way that the separation distances are less than required. The example of the old fire escape arrangement, in which a window access immediately below the fire escape landing leads to fire exposure of the fire escape, is the type of situation that must be avoided. The separation and protection provisions in 5-2.2.6.3 (outside stairs) can more easily be understood by studying Figures 5-35 to 5-37.

5-2.2.6.4 All openings below an outside stair shall be protected with an assembly having a ¾-hour fire protection rating:

(a) Where located in a court, the smallest dimension of which is less than one-third its height, or

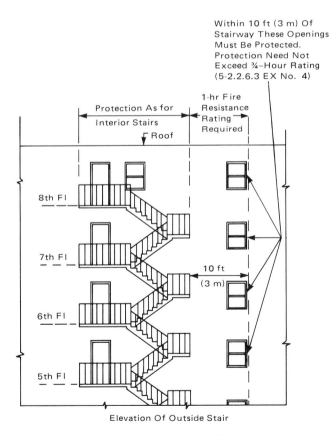

Figure 5-35. Protection of Openings for Outside Stairs — Example 1. If openings are within 10 ft (3 cm) of the outside stairs, they must be protected. (See 5-2.2.6.3.) However, the fire resistance ratings in the 10-ft (3-m) "extension" need not exceed 1 hour, and fire protection rating for the opening need not exceed ¾ hour.

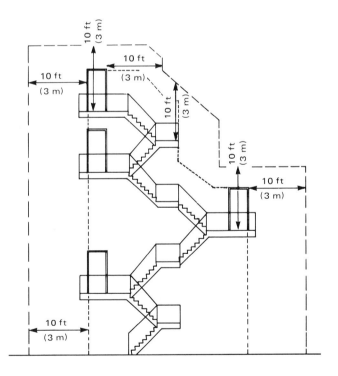

Figure 5-36. Protection of Outside Stairs — Example 2. Fire resistance rating for the walls of the 10 ft (3 m) extension is a minimum of 1 hr. Fire resistance rating for the walls within the short dashed lines is based on the number of stories served by the outside stair, the same as for interior stairs.

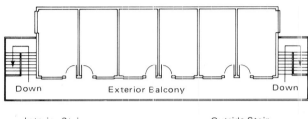

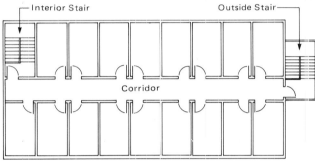

Figures 5-37 a and b. *Protection of Openings for Outside Stairs — Examples 3 and 4. Exception No. 1 to 5-2.2.6.3 is illustrated in the top figure. Exception No. 2, which is restricted to stairways serving no more that two stories, is illustrated in the bottom figure. This same figure illustrates Exception No. 3, but this is permitted to serve up to three stories and is restricted to existing buildings.*

(b) Where located in an alcove having a width less than one-third its height and a depth greater than one-fourth its height.

Figure 5-38 illustrates the provisions of 5-2.2.6.4.

5-2.2.6.5   There shall be no enclosed usable space within an exit enclosure, including under stairs, nor shall any open space within the enclosure including stairs and landings, be used for any purpose such as storage or similar use that could interfere with egress. Where there is enclosed usable space, under stairs, the walls and soffits of the enclosed space shall be protected the same as the stair enclosure. (*Also see 5-1.3.3.*)

Although this paragraph may, at first, seem to contradict itself, it does not. First, the paragraph states that *within* an exit enclosure there shall be no enclosed usable space nor shall any open space be used for any purpose that could interfere with the use of the exit enclosure. An enclosed usable space under a stair can be considered to

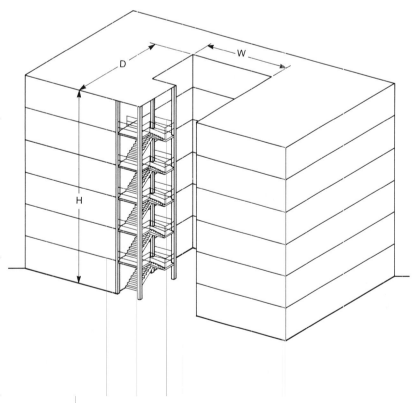

Figure 5-38. The Basis for Required Protection of Openings Below Open, Outside Stairs Discharging to a Courtyard.
1. If D or W is less than one-third of H, all openings within the courtyard below the open, outside stairs must be protected.
2. If D is greater than one-fourth of H and W is less than one-third of H, protection is required at openings.
*   Example 1*
H = 60 ft (18.3m)
D or W <20 ft (610 cm)
Special Protection Required
*   Example 2*
H = 60 ft (18.3 m)
D >15 ft (457.2 cm) and
W <20 ft (610 cm)
Special Protection Required

be outside the exit enclosure if the walls and soffits of the enclosed space are protected the same as required for the stair enclosure, thereby separating the space from the exit enclosure. The door to the space cannot open into the exit enclosure, per 5-1.3.1(d). (*See Figure 5-39.*) (*Also see 5-1.3.3 and 31-1.2.1.*)

5-2.2.6.6 **Signs.** Stairs serving four or more stories shall be provided with a sign within the enclosure at each floor landing. The sign shall indicate the floor level, the terminus of the top and bottom of the stair enclosure, and the identification of the stair. The sign shall also state the floor level of, and the direction to, exit discharge. The sign shall be inside the enclosure located approximately 5 ft (152 cm) above the floor landing in a position that is readily visible when the door is in the open or closed position.

The provisions of 5-2.2.6.6, added in the 1985 *Code* and revised for the 1988 and 1991 Editions, require the posting of important information at each floor landing in each stairwell if the stair serves four or more stories in height. The sign shall identify the stair, indicate the floor level of the landing and where the stairwell terminates at top and bottom, and show the direction to the exit discharge. While primarily intended as advice for fire fighting personnel in an emergency, the information is often useful to other building users. The requirement that the sign indicate the direction to the level of exit discharge can be extremely useful to occupants of a building, especially if they are located below the level of exit discharge, since the natural tendency would be to exit by traveling downward in a stair, a direction that would be counter-productive where the exit discharge is located above. Also, many buildings that have multiple levels of entrance create confusion as to which way to go in which stair. The requirements of this paragraph are not exempted for existing buildings, as the *Code* is not looking for an expensive nor illuminated sign, only a reasonable sign to provide the requested information.

5-2.3 **Smokeproof Enclosures.**

5-2.3.1 Where smokeproof enclosures are required by other sections of this *Code*, they shall comply with 5-2.3.

Exception: Existing smokeproof enclosures subject to the approval of the authority having jurisdiction.

A smokeproof enclosure is a stair enclosure designed to limit the infiltration of heat, smoke, and fire gases from a fire in any part of a building. It is designed to provide improved protection against the products of combustion entering the actual stairway enclosure.

5-2.3.2* A smokeproof enclosure shall be a stair enclosure so designed that the movement into the smokeproof enclosure of products of combustion produced by a fire occurring in any part of the building shall be limited.

A-5-2.3.2 For further guidance see:

ASHRAE *Handbook and Product Directory*—Fundamentals. (*See Appendix B.*)

Design of Smoke Control Systems for Buildings, by Klote and Fothergill. (*See Appendix B.*)

NFPA 105, *Recommended Practice for the Installation of Smoke-Control Door Assemblies*. (*See Appendix B.*)

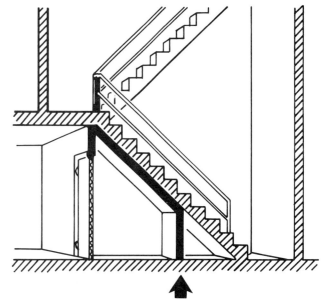

Wall Rated Same as Stairway

Figure 5-39.   Enclosed Usable Space Under Last Flight of Stairs.

5-2.3.3 The appropriate design method shall be any system that meets the performance level stipulated in 5-2.3.2 above. The smokeproof enclosure may be created by using natural ventilation, by using mechanical ventilation incorporating a vestibule, or by pressurizing the stair enclosure.

Paragraph 5-2.3.3 requires that smokeproof enclosures meet the "performance criteria" of 5-2.3.2. It goes on to specify three different means of creating smokeproof enclosures: (1) by the use of natural ventilation as detailed in 5-2.3.7; (2) by mechanical ventilation in accordance with 5-2.3.8; and (3) by pressurizing the stair enclosure as provided in 5-2.3.9. However, the *Code* does not limit the design to one of these if the design meets the requirements of 5-2.3.2 and is acceptable to the authority having jurisdiction. This is especially important for existing smokeproof enclosures, since they often do not meet all the specifications that follow.

See Figure 5-40 for examples of smokeproof enclosures that meet the specific *Code* criteria that follow.

5-2.3.4 Enclosure. A smokeproof enclosure shall consist of a continuous stair enclosed from the highest point to the lowest point by fire barriers having a 2-hour fire resistance rating. Where a vestibule is used, it shall be within the 2-hour rated enclosure and shall be considered part of the smokeproof enclosure.

Paragraph 5-2.3.4 requires that the smokeproof enclosure and all of its components be within the required 2-hour fire-resistant enclosure with openings therein protected by a door having a 1½-hour fire protection rating. This enclosure protects the smokeproof enclosure from the direct attack of fire. However, the door from the vestibule into the actual stairway need have only a 20-minute fire protection rating since the purpose at this point is to minimize air or smoke leakage.

5-2.3.5 Discharge. Every smokeproof enclosure shall discharge into a public way, into a yard or court having direct access to a public way, or into an exit passageway. Such exit passageways shall be without other openings and shall be separated from the remainder of the building by fire barriers having a 2-hour fire resistance rating.

Note that 5-2.3.5 prohibits smokeproof enclosures from discharging through the level of exit discharge. It emphasizes the need for continuity to a public way, the exit discharge, or an exit passageway. As an exit, such exit passageway may have only those openings required for exiting building occupants.

5-2.3.6 Access. Access to the stair shall be by way of a vestibule or by way of an exterior balcony.

Exception: Smokeproof enclosures consisting of a pressurized stair enclosure complying with 5-2.3.9.

5-2.3.7 Natural Ventilation. Smokeproof enclosures using natural ventilation shall comply with all the following:

(a) Where a vestibule is provided, the doorway into the vestibule shall be protected with an approved fire door assembly having a 1½-hour fire protection rating, and the fire door assembly from the vestibule to the stair shall have not less than a 20-minute fire protection rating. Doors shall be designed to minimize air leakage and shall be self-closing or shall be automatic-closing by actuation of a smoke detector within 10 ft (3 m) of the vestibule door. Where access to the stair is by means of an open exterior balcony, the door assembly to the stair shall have a 1½-hour fire protection rating and shall be self-closing or shall be automatic-closing by actuation of a smoke detector. Openings adjacent to such exterior balconies shall be protected as required in 5-2.2.6.3.

(b) Every vestibule shall have a minimum net area of 16 sq ft (1.5 sq m) of opening in an exterior wall facing an exterior court, yard, or public space at least 20 ft (6.1 m) in width.

(c) Every vestibule shall have a minimum dimension not less than the required width of the corridor leading to it and a minimum dimension of 72 in. (183 cm) in the direction of travel.

5-2.3.8 Mechanical Ventilation. Smokeproof enclosures by mechanical ventilation shall comply with all of the following:

(a) The door assembly from the building into the vestibule shall have a 1½-hour fire protection rating, and the door assembly from the vestibule to the stairway shall have not less than a 20-minute fire protection rating. The door to the stairway shall be designed and installed to minimize air leakage. The doors shall be self-closing or shall be automatic-closing by actuation of a smoke detector located within 10 ft (3 m) of the vestibule door.

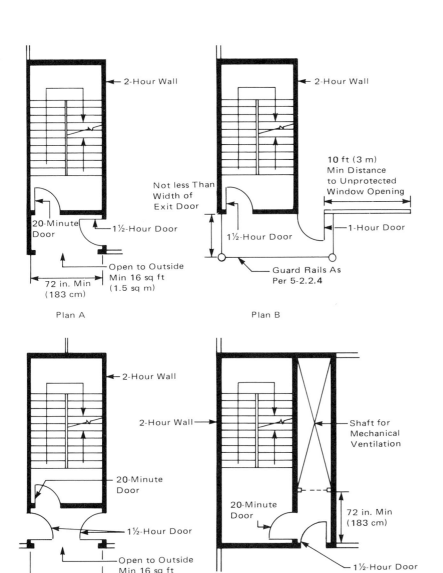

Figure 5-40. *Four Variations of Smokeproof Enclosures Conforming to Code Criteria. Plan A utilizes an open air vestibule. Plan B shows an entrance by way of an outside balcony. Plan C could provide a stair enclosure entrance common to two buildings. In Plan D, smoke and gases entering the vestibule would be exhausted by mechanical ventilation. In each case, a double entrance to the stair enclosure with at least one side open or vented is characteristic of this type of construction. Pressurization of the stair enclosure in the event of fire provides an attractive alternative to sprinklered buildings and is a means of eliminating the entrance vestibule.*

(b) Vestibules shall have a minimum dimension of 44 in. (112 cm) in width and 72 in. (183 cm) in direction of exit travel.

(c) The vestibule shall be provided with not less than one air change per minute, and the exhaust shall be 150 percent of the supply. Supply air shall enter and exhaust air shall discharge from the vestibule through separate tightly constructed ducts used only for that purpose. Supply air shall enter the vestibule within 6 in. (15.2 cm) of the floor level. The top of the

exhaust register shall be located not more than 6 in. (15.2 cm) down from the top of the trap and shall be entirely within the smoke trap area. Doors, when in the open position, shall not obstruct duct openings. Controlling dampers are permitted in duct openings if needed to meet the design requirements but are not otherwise required.

(d) To serve as a smoke and heat trap and to provide an upward moving air column, the vestibule ceiling shall be at least 20 in. (50.8 cm) higher than the door opening into the vestibule. The height may be decreased where justified by engineering design and field testing.

(e) The stair shall be provided with a dampered relief opening at the top and supplied mechanically with sufficient air to discharge a minimum of 2500 cu ft/min (70.8 cu m/min) through the relief opening while maintaining a minimum positive pressure of 0.10 in. water column (25 Pa) in the stair relative to the vestibule with all doors closed.

Figure 5-41 illustrates an elevation view of a vestibule using mechanical ventilation.

5-2.3.9 Stair Pressurization.

5-2.3.9.1 Smokeproof enclosures by stair pressurization shall comply with all of the following:

(a) The building shall be protected throughout by an approved supervised automatic sprinkler system in accordance with Section 7-7.

(b) There shall be an engineered system to pressurize the stair enclosure capable of developing 0.05 in. water column (12.5 Pa) in addition to the maximum anticipated stack pressure relative to other parts of the building measured with all

the enclosure doors closed. The combined positive pressure shall not exceed 0.35 in. water column (87.5 Pa).

5-2.3.9.2 Equipment and ductwork for stair pressurization shall be located:

(a) Exterior to the building and be directly connected to the stairway by ductwork enclosed in noncombustible construction, or

(b) Within the stair enclosure with intake and exhaust air directly to the outside or through ductwork enclosed in 2-hour construction, or

(c) Within the building if separated from the remainder of the building, including other mechanical equipment, with 2-hour construction.

In each case, openings into the required 2-hour construction shall be limited to those needed for maintenance and operation and shall be protected by self-closing 1½-hour fire protection rated devices.

Exception to (c): Where the building, including the stairway enclosure, is protected throughout by an approved supervised automatic sprinkler system in accordance with Section 7-7, fire-rated construction shall be a minimum of 1-hour construction.

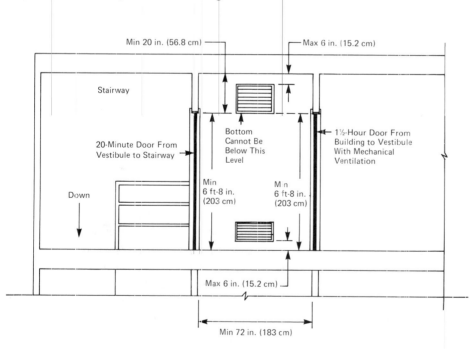

Figure 5-41.   Elevation View of Vestibule Using Mechanical Ventilation.

Note that to accept pressurized stairs as smokeproof enclosures, the building must be sprinklered. Figure 5-42 illustrates some potential arrangements complying with 5-2.3.9.2.

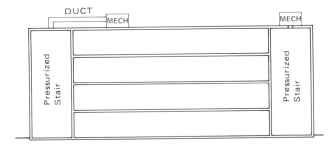

Figure 5-42(a). Mechanical Equipment and Ductwork Complying with 5-2.3.9.2(a).

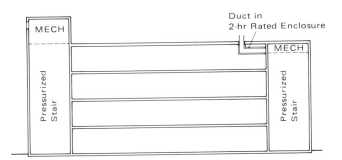

Figure 5-42(b). Mechanical Equipment and Ductwork Complying with 5-2.3.9.2(b).

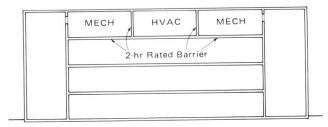

Figure 5-42(c). Mechanical Equipment and Ductwork Complying with 5-2.3.9.2(c).

5-2.3.10 Activation of Mechanical Ventilation Systems.

5-2.3.10.1 For both mechanical ventilation and pressurized stair enclosure systems, the activation of the systems shall be initiated by a smoke detector installed in an approved location within 10 ft (3 m) of the entrance to the smokeproof enclosure.

5-2.3.10.2 The required mechanical systems shall operate at the activation of the smoke detectors in 5-2.3.10.1 and by manual controls accessible to the fire department. The required system shall also be initiated by the following, if provided:

(a) Water flow signal from a complete automatic sprinkler system.
(b) General evacuation alarm signal. (*See 7-6.3.5.*)

5-2.3.11 Door Closers. The activation of an automatic closing device on any door in the smokeproof enclosure shall activate all other automatic closing devices on doors in the smokeproof enclosure.

5-2.3.12 Standby Power. Standby power for mechanical ventilation equipment shall be provided by an approved self-contained generator set to operate whenever there is a loss of power in the normal house current. The generator shall be located in a separate room having a minimum 1-hour fire-resistive occupancy separation and shall have a minimum fuel supply adequate to operate the equipment for 2 hours.

5-2.3.13 Testing. Before the mechanical equipment is accepted by the authority having jurisdiction, it shall be tested to confirm that the mechanical equipment is operating in compliance with these requirements.

5-2.3.14 Emergency Lighting. The stair shaft and vestibule shall be provided with emergency lighting. A standby generator that is installed for the smokeproof enclosure mechanical ventilation equipment shall be permitted to be used for such stair shaft and vestibule power supply.

5-2.4 Horizontal Exits.

5-2.4.1* Application. Horizontal exits shall be permitted to be substituted for other exits to the extent that the total exit capacity of the other exits (stairs, ramps, doors leading outside the building) will not be reduced below half that required for the entire area of the building or connected buildings if no horizontal exits existed.

Exception: In health care occupancies as provided in Chapters 12 and 13, and in detention and correctional occupancies as provided in Chapters 14 and 15.

A-5-2.4.1 Example: One way to provide the required exit capacity from the upper floor of a department store building 350 ft by 200 ft (107 m by 60 m) (occupant load 1166 per floor) would be to furnish eight 44-in. (112-cm) stairs. [*See Figure A-5-2.4.1(a)*.]

Assume that this building is divided into two sections by a fire wall meeting the requirements for a horizontal exit, one 130 ft by 200 ft (40 m by 60 m) and the other 220 ft by 200 ft (67 m by 60 m), with two pairs of 44-in. (112-cm) double egress doors, with each door providing 44 in. (112cm) of egress width [*see Figure A-5-2.4.1(b)*]. The smaller section, considered separately, will require the equivalent of three 44-in. (112-cm) stairs and the larger section will require five such exits. The horizontal exits will serve as one of the three exits required for the smaller section and two of the five exits required for the larger section. Therefore, only two 44-in. (112-cm) stairs from the smaller section and three 44-in. (112-cm) stairs from the larger section will be required, if the exits can be arranged to meet the requirements for the 150-ft (45-m) travel distance allowed from any point in a sprinklered building. Thus, the total number of stairs required for the building will be five, as compared with eight if no horizontal exit had been provided.

Another option would be the use of two 56-in. (142-cm) stairs from the larger section, which would reduce the total number of stairways required from the floor to four [*see Figure A-5-2.4.1(c)*]. However, if the building were further subdivided by a second fire wall meeting the requirements for a horizontal exit, no further reduction in stairways would be permitted in order to keep from exceeding the maximum one-half of exiting via horizontal exits.

A horizontal exit is a passage from one building area into another building area, each separated from the other by a fire barrier, space, or other form of protection of such a character that it enables each area to serve as an area of refuge from a fire in the other area. A horizontal exit, however, need not be confined to one building. It can be a bridge from one building to another. Just as with other types of exits, the horizontal exit has components consisting of doors and enclosure walls and often

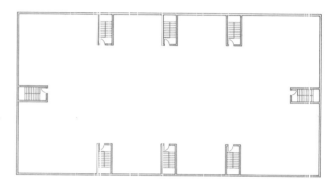

Figure A-5-2.4.1(a) Eight Exits, None Via Horizontal Exit, Required to Provide the Necessary Egress Capacity.

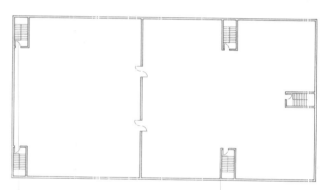

Figure A-5-2.4.1(b) Number of Stairs Reduced by Three Through Use of Two Horizontal Exits; Same Egress Capacity Provided.

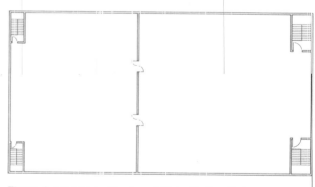

Figure A-5-2.4.1(c) Number of Stairs Further Reduced by Widening Stairs in Larger Compartment, but Not to Less Than One-Half the Required Number and Capacity of Exits from that Compartment.

includes structural features, such as bridges and balconies, used in the passage from one area to the other. Because the horizontal exit is usually located on the same level as the area from which escape is desired, there are no stairs or ramps involved.

Although horizontal exits can provide as fast and as safe a means of reaching an area of refuge as any other exit, they cannot be given credit for providing more than one-half the required exits or exit capacity of the building or buildings connected, except in health care and detention and correctional occupancies where special exceptions apply.

Before any space can be used as an area of refuge in a horizontal exit, it must itself satisfy certain criteria. Such space, although separated with 2-hour fire barriers (*see 5-2.4.3 for details on the fire barrier*), cannot be used as an area of refuge unless there is at least one standard type of exit (not another horizontal exit) leading from it and unless the space is large enough to accommodate the occupants of both the fire area and area of refuge, allowing 3 sq ft (.28 sq m) of floor space per person. This area figure is modified in health care occupancies and in detention and correctional occupancies. The nature of a horizontal exit is such that the psychological feeling of being in another area or building, away from the fire, can do much to protect the occupants and prevent the disorderly movement of people.

Figure 5-43 illustrates how to apply the requirement allowing the substitution of horizontal exits for other exits. Figure 5-44 illustrates how that requirement is violated.

5-2.4.2 Fire Compartments.

5-2.4.2.1 Every fire compartment for which credit is allowed in connection with a horizontal exit shall have, in addition to the horizontal exit or exits, at least one stairway or doorway leading outside or other exit that is not a horizontal exit. Any fire compartment not having a stairway or doorway leading outside shall be considered as part of an adjoining compartment with stairway.

Exception: In detention and correctional occupancies as provided in Chapters 14 and 15.

5-2.4.2.2 Every horizontal exit for which credit is given shall be so arranged that there are continuously available paths of travel leading from each side of the exit to stairways or other means of egress leading to outside the building.

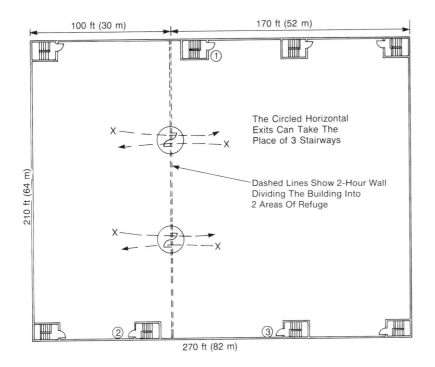

Figure 5-43. An Example of Substituting Horizontal Exits for Other Exits. Note that the horizontal exits (circled) take the place of stair enclosures as paths of escape for the occupants on either side of the 2-hour wall (shown as a dashed line) dividing the area into two sections. This would permit the elimination of the three stair enclosures closest to the horizontal exits, stair enclosures that would be required if the entire area were to be considered as one.

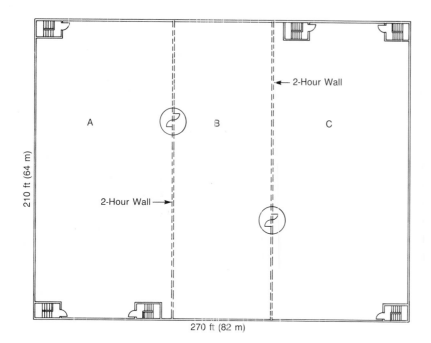

210 ft (64 m)

A   B   C

2-Hour Wall →

2-Hour Wall →

270 ft (82 m)

Figure 5-44.   An Example of How Horizontal Exits (Circled) Cannot Be Used. The two horizontal exits from area B violate 5-2.4.1 in that at least one-half of the required exits and exit capacity must be other than horizontal exits. Area B also does not provide a continuous path of travel by stairway or other type of exit for occupants evacuating either area A or C as required by 5-2.4.2.

5-2.4.2.3 Whenever either side of the horizontal exit is occupied, the doors used in connection with the horizontal exit shall be unlocked from the egress side.

Exception: In health care occupancies as provided in Chapters 12 and 13, and in detention and correctional occupancies as provided in Chapters 14 and 15.

5-2.4.2.4 The floor area on either side of a horizontal exit shall be sufficient to hold the occupants of both floor areas, allowing not less than 3 sq ft (.28 sq m) clear floor area per person.

Exception: Special floor area requirements in health care occupancies as provided in Chapters 12 and 13, and in detention and correctional occupancies as provided in Chapters 14 and 15.

The design or incorporation of a horizontal exit into a building is not complicated. For proper arrangement of the total means of egress system, it is simply a matter of designing each separated portion, or compartment, as if it were a completely separate building. The point of passage through the horizontal exit is treated as if it were, in fact, an exterior exit door. In determining the required exit capacities from each separated portion, or compartment, the occupant loads are not to be combined.

It must be kept in mind that exiting is a dynamic process. While each compartment must contain sufficient available floor area, allowing at least 3 sq ft (.28 sq m) per person for the total occupant load of both compartments, exiting from the area of refuge continues through its "other" exits. The 2-hour fire resistant separation from the compartment of fire origin provides the additional time for exiting from the compartment of refuge.

5-2.4.3 Walls for Horizontal Exits.

5-2.4.3.1 Fire barriers separating buildings or areas between which there are horizontal exits shall be an assembly of non-combustible or limited-combustible material having a 2-hour fire resistance rating. They shall provide a separation continuous to ground. (*See also 6-2.3.*)

Exception No. 1: Where a fire barrier is used to provide a horizontal exit in any story of a building, such fire barrier is not required on other stories under the following conditions:

(a) The stories on which the fire barrier is omitted shall be separated from the story with the horizontal exit by construction having a fire resistance rating at least equal to that of the horizontal exit fire barrier.

(b) Vertical openings between the story with the horizontal exit and the open fire area story shall be enclosed with construction having a fire resistance rating at least equal to that of the horizontal exit fire barrier.

(c) All required exits, other than horizontal exits, shall discharge directly to the outside.

Exception No. 2: One-hour fire rated barriers as permitted in detention and correctional occupancies in accordance with Chapters 14 and 15.

Figure 5-45 illustrates how separation walls can be eliminated from the lower floors of a multistory building and still conform to the basic requirements of 5-2.4.3.

For the 1991 *Code*, revisions have been made to Exception No. 1 to reflect the fact that Exception No. 2 has been added to allow detention and correctional occupancies to have horizontal exits with less than a 2-hour rating. A review of Chapters 14 and 15 will reveal that the use of this exception is not yet authorized by Chapters 14 and 15. It is the intent of the Subcommittee on Detention and Correctional Occupancies to add a provision allowing facilities up to three stories in height to take advantage of this exception.

5-2.4.3.2 Where fire barriers serving horizontal exits terminate at outside walls and the outside walls for a distance of 10 ft (3 m) on each side of the horizontal exit are at an angle of less than 180 degrees, the outside walls shall be 1-hour fire-resistance rated fire barriers with ¾-hour fire protection rated opening protectives for a distance of 10 ft (3 m) on each side of the horizontal exit.

Exception: Existing horizontal exits.

This paragraph is new to the 1991 Edition of the *Code*. It provides for the protection of the end of the horizontal exit wall where the building walls on each side of the horizontal exit expose each other at an angle of less than 180 degrees. The concept for protection follows the same intent as 5-2.2.6.2 for the protection of nonrated walls of enclosed stairs. Since this is a new provision, existing buildings are exempted. (*See Figure 5-46.*)

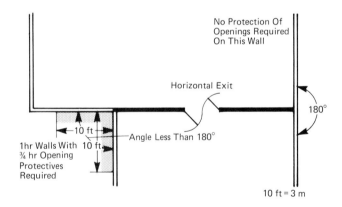

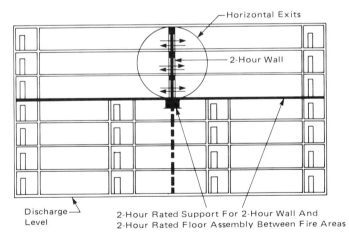

Figure 5-45. A Multistory Building Illustrating How a 2-Hour Rated Division Wall for Horizontal Exits Can Be Stopped at any Lower Floor Rather than Extended to the Ground Floor (as Shown by the Dashed Line), as Required by 5-2.4.3.1. The same arrangement can be provided for basement areas.

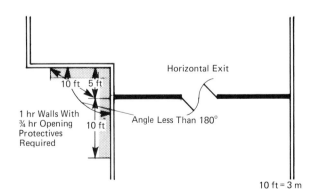

Figure 5-46. Protecting Horizontal Exit Walls Where the Building Walls on each Side Expose Each Other at an Angle of Less than 180 degrees.

5-2.4.3.3 Fire barriers forming horizontal exits shall not be penetrated by ducts.

Exception No. 1: Existing penetrations protected by approved and listed fire dampers.

Exception No. 2: In buildings protected throughout by an approved supervised automatic sprinkler system in accordance with Section 7-7.

Exception No. 3: Duct penetrations in detention and correctional occupancies as allowed by Chapters 14 and 15 that are protected by combination fire dampers/smoke leakage-rated dampers that meet the smoke damper actuation requirements of 6-3.5.

This new paragraph addresses a question that has recently arisen regarding penetrations of horizontal exits. Since horizontal exits often subdivide floor spaces, it is not uncommon to encounter the problem of what to do with HVAC ductwork. Many have argued that a horizontal exit is an exit and should not be allowed to be penetrated by ducts (*see 5-1.3.1*), while others have argued that this was impractical. The *Code* now specifically prohibits duct penetrations except under three conditions. It should be noted that, although Exception No. 2 allows ductwork to penetrate horizontal exit walls in buildings protected throughout by sprinklers, this penetration still requires an approved fire damper since it is a 2-hour fire rated barrier.

5-2.4.3.4 Any opening in such fire barriers, whether or not such opening serves as an exit, shall be protected as provided in 6-2.3.5.

5-2.4.3.5 Doors in horizontal exits shall comply with 5-2.1.4.

Exception: Sliding doors in industrial occupancies as provided in Chapter 28, and in storage occupancies as provided in Chapter 29.

An exception is provided in Chapters 28 and 29, industrial and storage occupancies, for those locations where a fire rated door may be required for insurance or building code reasons on both sides of the wall. (*See 28-2.2.5.2 and 29-2.2.5.2.*)

5-2.4.3.6 Where swinging fire doors are used in horizontal exits, they shall comply with the following:

(a) They shall swing in the direction of exit travel, and

(b) Where a horizontal exit serves areas on both sides of a fire barrier, there shall be adjacent openings with swinging doors at each, opening in opposite directions, with signs on each side of the fire barrier indicating the door that swings with the travel from that side, or

Exception to (b): Sleeping room areas in detention and correctional occupancies are exempt from the sign requirement.

(c) They shall be of any other approved arrangement provided that doors always swing with any possible exit travel.

Exception: Door swing in existing health care occupancies as provided in Chapter 13.

Also see 5-2.4.4.3, 5-2.4.4.4 and 2-2.4.4.5.

5-2.4.3.7* Doors in horizontal exits shall be designed and installed to minimize air leakage.

A-5-2.4.3.7 For further information, see NFPA 105, *Recommended Practice for the Installation of Smoke-Control Door Assemblies.* (*See Appendix B.*)

5-2.4.3.8* All fire doors in horizontal exits shall be self-closing or automatic-closing in accordance with 5-2.1.8. All opening protectives in horizontal exits are to be consistent with the fire resistance rating of the wall. Horizontal exit doors located across a corridor shall be automatic-closing in accordance with 5-2.1.8.

Exception: Where approved by the authority having jurisdiction, existing doors in horizontal exits may be self-closing.

A-5-2.4.3.8 Fusible link actuated automatic-closing doors do not qualify as horizontal exits under these provisions, as smoke might pass through the opening before there is sufficient time to release the hold open device.

Such doors are also objectionable because, once closed, they are difficult to open and would inhibit orderly egress.

Since cross-corridor doors are so commonly wedged open, the *Code* does not offer the option of using self-closing doors but mandates the use of automatic-closing doors in these locations. In existing installations, the authority having jurisdiction has the capability to observe if the wedging open of doors has been a problem, and therefore, the exception gives the enforcing agency the authority to allow self-closing doors to be continued in use.

5-2.4.4 Bridges and Balconies.

5-2.4.4.1 Each bridge or balcony utilized in conjunction with horizontal exits shall have guards and handrails in conformity with the requirements of 5-2.2.

5-2.4.4.2 Every bridge or balcony shall be at least as wide as the door leading to it and not less than 44 in. (112 cm) for new construction.

5-2.4.4.3 Every door leading to a bridge or balcony serving as a horizontal exit shall swing in the direction of exit travel.

Exception: In existing health care occupancies as provided in Chapter 13.

5-2.4.4.4 Where the bridge or balcony serves as a horizontal exit in one direction, only the door leading from the bridge or balcony into the area of refuge need swing in the direction of travel.

5-2.4.4.5 Where the bridge or balcony serves as a horizontal exit in both directions, doors shall be provided in pairs, swinging in opposite directions. Only the door swinging with the exit travel shall be counted in determination of exit width.

Exception No. 1: If the bridge or balcony has sufficient floor area to accommodate the occupant load of either connected building or fire area on the basis of 3 sq ft (.28 sq m) per person.

Exception No. 2: In existing buildings, doors on both ends of the bridge or balcony may swing out from the building subject to the approval of the authority having jurisdiction.

5-2.4.4.6 The bridge or balcony floor shall be approximately level with the building floor and, in climates subject to the accumulation of snow and ice, shall be protected to prevent the accumulation of snow and ice.

Exception: In existing buildings in climates where balconies may be subject to the accumulation of snow or ice, one step, not to exceed 8 in. (20.3 cm), is permitted below the level of the inside floor.

5-2.4.4.7 All wall openings, in both of the connected buildings or fire areas, any part of which is within 10 ft (3 m) of any bridge or balcony as measured horizontally or below, shall be protected with fire doors or fixed fire window assemblies having a ³/₄-hour fire protection rating.

Exception: Where bridges have solid sides not less than 6 ft (183 cm) in height, such protection of wall openings is not required.

5-2.5 Ramps.

Ramps are permitted as a part of a means of egress and, in fact, are to be preferred over stairs under some circumstances. To quote from an earlier reference: "One can consider ramps and steps simply as prosthetic devices for assisting the human organism in climbing from floor to floor.... When one must consider the energy cost of both horizontal and vertical movement, one finds that a ramp with a gradient of less than about eight degrees is more economical than any stairway that is likely to be encountered in normal activity."[6] The National Bureau of Standards study states in part: "For certain occupancies, such as schools and institutions, they (ramps) are believed to be more satisfactory and their use in these buildings is recommended.... Ramps have a rate of discharge between that of stairways and level passageways."[7]

The National Safety Council[8] has suggested the following criteria as a basis for the selection of a straight run of steps, a combination of steps and landings, or ramps:

Grade	Preference
20° - 50°	Stairway
7° - 20°	Stairway and landings
under 7°	Ramps

5-2.5.1 General. A ramp, either interior or outside, used as a component in a means of egress shall conform to the general requirements of Section 5-1 and to the special requirements of this subsection.

5-2.5.2 Classification. A ramp shall be designated as Class A or Class B in accordance with the following table:

	Class A	Class B
Minimum width	44 in. (112 cm)	30 in. (76 cm)
Maximum slope	1 in 10	1 in 8
Maximum height between landings	12 ft (3.7 m)	12 ft (3.7 m)

Exception No. 1: Existing Class B ramps with slopes of 1³/₁₆ to 2 in 12 (10 to 17 cm in 1 m) are permitted subject to the approval of the authority having jurisdiction.

Exception No. 2: All existing Class A ramps and new ramps not steeper than 1 in 15 need not be provided with landings.

Paragraph 5-2.5.2 establishes two classes of ramps: Class A and Class B. Class A ramps are required to be at least 44 in. (112 cm) wide with a maximum slope of 1 in 10. Class B ramps are to be at least 30 in. (76 cm) wide, with a maximum slope of 1 in 8. Where a reference is made to ramps and no class is specified, then either can be used. Considerable latitude is given the authority having jurisdiction with regard to the use of Class B ramps in existing buildings. Most new ramps must be of a lesser slope than either of these due to requirements for the use of ramps by the mobility impaired. (*See ANSI A117.1, Standard for Buildings and Facilities – Providing Accessibility and Usability for Physically Handicapped People.*)[1]

5-2.5.3 Ramp Details.

5-2.5.3.1 All ramps serving as required means of egress shall be of permanent fixed construction.

5-2.5.3.2 A ramp used as a means of egress in a building more than three stories in height or in a building of any height of noncombustible or fire-resistive construction shall be constructed of an assembly of noncombustible or limited-combustible material. The ramp floor and landings shall be solid and without perforations.

5-2.5.3.3 Ramps and intermediate landings shall continue with no decrease in width along the direction of exit travel. Every landing shall have a dimension measured in the direction of travel equal to the width of the ramp. Such dimension need not exceed 4 ft (122 cm) where the ramp has a straight run.

5-2.5.3.4 A ramp shall have a slip-resistant surface.

5-2.5.3.5 The slope of a ramp shall not vary between landings. Landings shall be level, and changes in direction of travel, if any, shall be made only at landings.

5-2.5.4 Guards and Handrails. Guards complying with 5-2.2.4 shall be provided for ramps. Handrails complying with 5-2.2.4 shall be provided for ramps with a slope exceeding 1 in 15. The height of handrails and guards shall be measured vertically to the top of the guard or rail from the walking surface adjacent thereto.

5-2.5.5 Special Provision for Outside Ramps.

Paragraph 5-2.5.5 sets the same requirements for outside ramps as 5-2.2.5 does for outside stairs. (*See 5-2.2.5 for a discussion of the requirements for outside stairs.*)

5-2.5.5.1 Balconies or landings to which doors lead shall be approximately level with the floor of the building.

Exception: In existing buildings located in climates where balconies or landings may be subject to accumulation of snow or ice, one step, not to exceed 8 in. (20.3 cm), is permitted below the level of the inside floor.

5-2.5.5.2* Visual Protection. Outside ramps shall be so arranged as to avoid any handicap to their use by persons having a fear of high places. For ramps more than three stories in height, any arrangement intended to meet this requirement shall be at least 4 ft (122 cm) in height.

A-5-2.5.5.2 The guards required by 5-2.2.4 for the unenclosed sides of ramps will usually meet this requirement where the ramp is not more than three stories high. Special architectural treatment, including application of such devices as metal or masonry screens and grilles, will usually be necessary to comply with the intent of the requirements for ramps over three stories in height.

5-2.5.6 Enclosure and Protection of Ramps.

Outside ramps may serve as part of a means of egress subject to the regulations governing exits, exit access, and exit discharge. Where used as exits, ramps must afford the occupant a protected passage from the point of entrance to the point of discharge. This applies to outside ramps as well as inside ramps.

The 1991 *Code* has greatly simplified the enclosure and protection of ramps by requiring ramps to be protected the same as stairs. See 5-2.2.6 for requirements and commentary.

5-2.5.6.1 Ramps shall be enclosed or protected as a stair in accordance with 5-2.2.6.

5-2.6* Exit Passageways.

A-5-2.6 An exit passageway serves as a horizontal means of exit travel that is protected from fire in a manner similar to an enclosed interior exit stair. Where it is desired to offset exit stairs in a multistory building, an exit passageway can be used to preserve the continuity of the protected exit by connecting the bottom of one stair to the top of the other stair that continues to the street floor. Probably the most important use of an exit passageway is to satisfy the requirement that exit stairs shall discharge directly outside from multistory buildings. Thus, if it is impractical to locate the stair on an exterior wall, an exit passageway can be connected to the bottom of the stair to convey the occupants safely to an outside exit door. In buildings of extremely large area, such as shopping malls and some factories, the exit passageway can be used to advantage where the distance of travel to reach an exit would otherwise be excessive.

The fact that the word "exit" is used in the expression "exit passageway" distinguishes it from an ordinary passageway or corridor. It is a path of travel providing the same level of protection and safety that is required of any exit. It is a very versatile feature because it can be used to extend an exit, or, as is done in many cases, it can be used to bring an exit closer. As shown in Figure 5-47a, by simply extending the protecting enclosure as required for an exit passageway along what would otherwise be

the corridor and then relocating the exit door, the exit is, in effect, extended. Since it is an exit, an exit passageway qualifies as an end point for measuring travel distance.

The proper use of an exit passageway can often solve what may seem to be insurmountable problems and very costly alternatives in the design of the means of egress. Figures 5-47a, b, and c illustrate some typical uses of exit passageways.

Formal Interpretation 81-39
Reference 5-2.6

Question: Is it the *Code's* intent to allow an exit passageway in an apartment building, which connects a discontinuous interior exit stair, to serve as a corridor with apartment entrance doors penetrating the walls of the exit passageway if: 1) the exit passageway enclosure meets the applicable requirements of Chapter 5, including the separation requirements for exits of 5-1.3, and 2) the apartment door assemblies, complete with door closures, meet the required fire protection rating associated with the required fire resistance rated enclosures?

Answer: Yes.

Issue Edition: 1981
Reference: 5-2.7
Date: February 1984 ■

5-2.6.1 **General.** Exit passageways such as hallways, corridors, passages, tunnels, underfloor passageways, or overhead passageways used as exit components shall conform to the general requirements of Section 5-1 and to the special requirements of this subsection.

5-2.6.2 **Enclosure.** An exit passageway shall be separated from other parts of the building as specified in 5-1.3.1.

Exception No. 1: Fire windows in accordance with 6-2.3.4 shall be permitted to be installed in such a separation in a building protected throughout by an approved supervised automatic sprinkler system in accordance with Section 7-7.

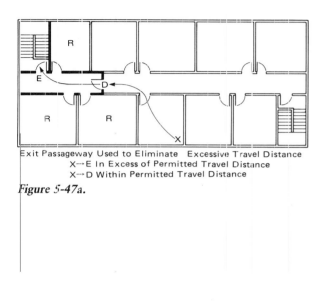

Exit Passageway Used to Eliminate   Excessive Travel Distance
X→E In Excess of Permitted Travel Distance
X→D Within Permitted Travel Distance

Figure 5-47a.

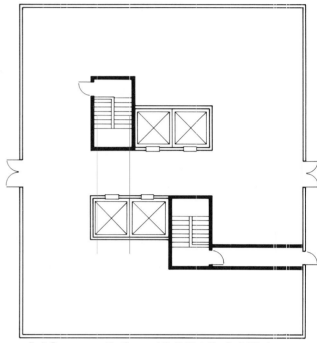

Exit Passageway To Connect Exit Stair To Exit Discharge
(Also See 5-7.2)

Figure 5-47b.

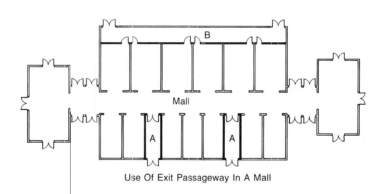

Use Of Exit Passageway In A Mall

Figure 5-47c.

Figures 5-47a, b, and c.   *Typical Uses of Exit Passageways. Note that in Figure 5-47a, rooms labeled "R" must be "normally occupied" spaces and cannot be storage rooms, boiler rooms, trash rooms, or similar spaces. In Figure 5-47b, the exit passageways are marked "A" and "B." Note that storage rooms cannot open directly into passageway "B," since it is an exit.*

Exception No. 2: Existing fixed wired glass panels in steel sash shall be permitted to be continued in use in such a separation in a building protected throughout by an approved sprinkler system in accordance with Section 7-7.

An important point here is not only the hourly fire resistance and fire protection ratings required by 5-1.3.1 but also the limitation on openings into the enclosure.

5-2.6.3 **Stair Discharge.** An exit passageway that serves as a discharge from a stair enclosure shall have the same fire resistance rating and opening protective fire protection rating as that required for the stair enclosure.

While an exit passageway is a horizontal means of travel, it must be considered in light of the entire exit of which it is a part. Paragraph 5-1.3 details separation requirements. A simple way to determine the protection requirements for exit passageways is to employ the protection requirements for exit stairs, which are the same. An exit passageway serving only one floor, such as is illustrated in Figure 5-47b, would be required to have a 1-hour fire resistance rating with 1-hour fire protection rated doors. An exit passageway serving the termination of an enclosed exit stair, as illustrated in Figure 5-47c, must have the same rating as the stair. This fact is emphasized by the new 5-2.6.3. An exit passageway serving the entrance of an enclosed exit stair, as is illustrated in Figure 5-47a, serves only the one floor and is, therefore, required to have only a 1-hour fire resistance rating regardless of the required rating for the stair enclosure. However, if in this case the stair is required to have a 2-hour fire resistance rating, then the exit passageway and the stair would be required to be separated from each other by a wall with a 2-hour fire resistance rating and a door with a 1½-hour fire protection rating.

5-2.6.4 **Width.** The width of an exit passageway shall be adequate to accommodate the aggregate required capacity of all exits discharging through it.

Exception: As allowed by Chapters 24 and 25, an exit passageway in a covered mall building may independently accommodate occupant loads from the covered mall and the tenant spaces. (See 24-2.2.7 Exception and 25-2.2.7 Exception.)

See the appendix note and commentary on the Exception to 24-2.2.7 for an explanation of the Exception to 5-2.6.4.

5-2.6.5 **Floor.** The floor shall be solid and without perforations.

5-2.7 **Escalators and Moving Walks.**

5-2.7.1 Escalators and moving walks shall not constitute a part of the required means of egress.

Exception: Previously approved escalators and moving walks in existing buildings.

Older editions of the *Code* allowed some credit for escalators serving as required exit capacity under certain circumstances. However, it has been determined that such devices should not be relied upon for required means of egress. Existing, previously approved escalators and moving walks may continue to be used as part of the means of egress if permitted by the occupancy chapter. Although not permitted as part of the required means of egress in new construction, escalators and moving walks, where installed, must comply with ASME/ANSI A17.1, *Safety Code for Elevators and Escalators.*[9]

It should be noted that, even in existing buildings, escalators are acceptable as an egress component only in the following occupancies:

Existing Assembly — 9-2.2.8
Existing Hotels — 17-2.2.8
Existing Apartment Buildings — 19-2.2.8
Existing Mercantile — 25-2.2.8
Existing Business — 27-2.2.8.
Existing Industrial — 28-2.2.8
Existing Unusual Structures — 30-2.2.8

When evaluating escalators in existing buildings, the following should be considered:

1. The escalator should comply with the applicable requirements for stairs in 5-2.2. It is assumed that, where escalators serve as required means of egress, they will continue in operation in case of fire, but if they stop due to electric current failure or other cause, they may be used as ordinary stairs.

2. Escalators constituting a means of egress should operate only in the direction of egress. Usually escalators are provided in pairs, with one separate stair moving up and another moving down; however, should the electricity fail and both stop, there would actually be two stairs available for downward movement. In this situation, one might propose that both stairways be accepted as constituting a means of egress, since the current could be turned off intentionally. The problem is that in an emergency the current might not get turned off, and one stair would continue to move against traffic. For this reason, only those escalators moving in the direction of egress should be allowed to be part of a means of egress.

3. Escalators should be of the horizontal tread type and, with the exception of step tread surfaces, handrails, and step wheels, should be of noncombustible construction throughout.

4. A single escalator 32 in. (81 cm) wide should be given credit for 75 people. An escalator 48 in. (122 cm) wide should be given credit for 150 people. Even though a person does not have to exert any energy or do any moving while on an escalator, there are many people who are frightened by them and many who are extremely cautious in approaching them. These are factors that could contribute to a bottleneck. Thus, it is recognized that an escalator would have to be wider than a stair to effectively move the same number of people.

5. There should be unobstructed spaces of at least 4 in. (10.2 cm) outside the handrail and above the handrail for the full length of the escalator.

6. No single escalator should have an uninterrupted vertical travel of more than one story.

The above guidelines were taken from older editions of the *Code* and were required when escalators were given credit in new construction. Therefore, they are offered here as guidance for existing buildings.

It should be noted that, even in an existing building, an escalator cannot be counted as an exit unless it is enclosed as an exit in accordance with 5-1.3.1, which is rarely seen.

Most of the same principles that apply to the design and operation of escalators also apply when evaluating existing moving walkways. The major difference is that the moving walkway — moving in the direction of exit travel — can be evaluated in terms of the usual exit capacities rather than the larger dimensions specified for escalators in item 4 above. (*See ASME/ANSI A17.1, Safety Code for Elevators and Escalators.*)[9]

5-2.8   Fire Escape Stairs.

Fire escape stairs and ladders have fallen into disfavor for a variety of reasons. These include:
1. Unsightly appearance;
2. Possible icing in winter weather;
3. Expense of maintenance (the metal is subject to corrosion);
4. Possibility of users being trapped by a fire below; and
5. Fear of height, and hence an objection to using them.

On the other hand, well-maintained fire escape stairs can and have saved many lives when smoke-filled exit stairs have become impassable. A classic example of this is the June 5, 1946 fire in the 22-story LaSalle Hotel in Chicago. Hundreds of people made their escape from the building on outside fire escape stairs.[10] Other similar examples could be quoted.

There have been times when fire fighters have been able to use outside fire escape stairs to advantage. However, instances could be cited where rusted fire escapes have collapsed or where people have been fatally burned because fire broke out of windows or doors at a lower level. The Committee has consistently held that the goal of safety from fire can best be served by the proper internal design of means of egress and the gradual phasing out of fire escape stairs as new buildings replace old ones.

Fire escape stairs can, however, help correct serious means of egress deficiencies in existing buildings and are helpful to fire department rescue and fire fighting efforts.

In summary, the provisions of 5-2.8 on fire escape stairs should be looked upon in this light: if fire escape stairs must be put on an existing building or are found on an existing building, they must adhere to provisions of the *Code* in order to provide as high a level of safety as possible.

5-2.8.1 General.

5-2.8.1.1 Fire escape stairs shall comply with the provisions of 5-2.8.

Exception: Existing noncomplying fire escape stairs may be continued to be used subject to the approval of the authority having jurisdiction.

Fire escape stairs as specified in this section of the *Code* should not be confused with the outside stairs covered in 5-2.2.

The fire escape stairs specified by this *Code* should not be confused with the inferior fire escapes that are commonly found on old buildings. These inadequate, flimsy, precipitous fire escapes, unshielded against fire in the structure to which they are attached, give an occupant a false sense of security. Such escape stairs are not recognized by this *Code*.

Even the fire escape stairs constructed in accordance with this *Code* have limitations that may prevent their effective use in time of fire. Even where window protection is provided, conditions may be such that fire (or the smoke from fire) on lower floors may render the stairs impassable before the occupants of the upper floors have had time to use them. Fire escape stairs may be blocked by snow, ice, or sleet at the time when they are most needed. People using fire escape stairs at a considerable height are likely to be timid and to descend the stairs, if at all, at a rate much slower than that used for inside stairs. This is true even when the solid tread stairs that are specified by the *Code* are used in place of the ordinary slatted-tread construction. Fire escape stairs are not the usual means of egress. Occupants of buildings will not so readily use them in case of fire as they will the more common means of exit, the inside stairway. Because they are an emergency device and not ordinarily used, their proper upkeep is often neglected.

5-2.8.1.2 Fire escape stairs shall not constitute any of the required means of egress in new buildings.

Fire escape stairs comprise an unfamiliar means of egress to most occupants of a building. Persons using fire escape stairs from a considerable height can be timid and

seriously slow the rate of descent for themselves and those behind them. Since these stairs are used only in emergencies, maintenance is often neglected, and they should be inspected on a regular basis.

At best, fire escape stairs are regarded only as an expedient in remedying the deficiencies in exits of existing buildings where it may not be practicable to provide outside stairs or additional inside stairways that are properly enclosed and that conform to all other provisions of this *Code*.

5-2.8.1.3 New fire escape stairs for existing buildings may be erected only where it has been determined that outside stairs (*see 5-2.2*) are not practical. New fire escape stairs shall not incorporate ladders or access windows, regardless of occupancy classification or load.

In most cases, outside stairs complying with 5-2.2 must be used rather than fire escape stairs. However, the *Code* recognizes that there are situations in the case of some existing buildings that make stairs complying with 5-2.2 impractical. For example, a building may be too narrow to accommodate the space needed by a conforming stair, or it may be necessary to have the stair located over a sidewalk, alley, or similar space.

Authorities having jurisdiction may wish to impose additional requirements because of climate. In conditions such as snow and ice, the effective use of fire escape stairs may be seriously impaired. In such a case, for example, exit capacity credit for the fire escape stairs could be reduced.

5-2.8.1.4 Fire escape stairs shall be permitted in existing buildings as permitted in the applicable existing occupancy chapters but shall not constitute more than 50 percent of the required exit capacity.

The basic principles of the *Code* regarding fire escape stairs are contained in 5-2.8.1.1 to 5-2.8.1.4. Absolutely no recognition is given to the use of fire escape stairs in new buildings for any of the three parts of a means of egress. Only a token recognition of 50 percent is given for their use in existing buildings, and this is simply because the fire escape stairs have already been installed or because they may be the only feasible manner of upgrading a means of egress in an existing building.

5-2.8.1.5 Fire escape stairs shall provide a continuous, unobstructed, safe path of travel to the exit discharge or a safe area of refuge.

5-2.8.1.6 Fire escape stairs of the return platform type with superimposed runs or the straight run type with platform that continues in the same direction shall be permitted.

5-2.8.1.7 Either type shall be permitted to be parallel to or at right angles to buildings. Either type shall be permitted to be attached to buildings or erected independently of buildings and connected by walkways.

5-2.8.2 **Protection of Openings.** Fire escape stairs shall be exposed to the smallest possible number of window and door openings. Each opening shall be protected with approved fire door or window assemblies where the opening or any portion of the opening is located as follows:

(a) *Horizontally.* If within 15 ft (4.5 m) of any balcony, platform, or stairway constituting a component of the fire escape stair.

(b) *Below.* If within three stories or 35 ft (10 m) of any balcony, platform, walkway, or stairway constituting a component of the fire escape stair or within two stories or 20 ft (6 m) of a platform or walkway leading from any story to the fire escape stair.

(c) *Above.* If within 10 ft (3 m) of any balcony, platform, or walkway as measured vertically or of any stair tread surface as measured vertically.

(d) *Top Story.* Protection for wall openings shall not be required where stairs do not lead to the roof.

(e) *Court.* Any wall facing a court served by a fire escape stair where the least dimension of the court is less than one-third of the height to the uppermost platform of the fire escape stair measured from the ground.

(f) *Alcove.* Any wall facing an alcove served by a fire escape stair where the width of the alcove is less than one-third or the depth greater than one-fourth of the height to the uppermost platform of the fire escape stair measured from the ground.

Exception: The provisions of 5-2.8.2 may be modified by the authority having jurisdiction in consideration of automatic sprinkler protection, low hazard occupancy, or other special conditions.

5-2.8.3 **Access.**

5-2.8.3.1 Access to fire escape stairs shall be in accordance with 5-2.8.4 and 5-5.1.2.

Exception: Where permitted by the existing occupancy chapters of this Code, access to fire escape stairs shall be permitted by way of windows. No screening or storm windows may be used if they impair free access to the fire escape stair. Windows shall be arranged and so maintained as to be easily opened with a minimum of physical effort.

5-2.8.3.2 Fire escape stairs shall extend to the roof in all cases where the roof is subject to occupancy or provides an area of safe refuge. In other cases, if the roof has a pitch of 1 to 6 or less, fire escape ladders in accordance with 5-2.9 shall be provided for access to the roof.

5-2.8.3.3 Access to a fire escape stair shall be directly to a balcony, landing, or platform. These shall be no higher than the floor or windowsill level and no lower than 8 in. (20.3 cm) below the floor level or 18 in. (45.7 cm) below the windowsill.

The height requirements of 5-2.8.3.3 establish the maximum distance, on the *outside* of the building, down to the balcony, landing, or platform of the fire escape stair measured from the windowsill level or from the floor level.

Figure 5-48 indicates the measurements for windows opening onto fire escape stairs and the maximum *interior* measurements from the floor to the windowsill. (*See Table 5-2.8.4.*)

5-2.8.4 **Stair Details.** Fire escape stairs shall comply with the requirements of Table 5-2.8.4 A and subsequent sections. Replacement of fire escape stairs shall comply with the requirements of Table 5-2.8.4 B.

Generally, the requirements for fire escape stairs are similar to those specified for outside stairs. The major difference between the two types of stairways lies in the

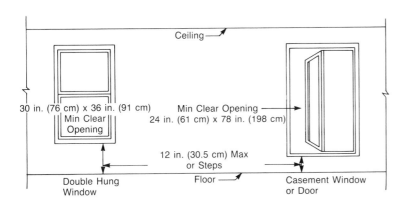

Figure 5-48. Window Openings for Fire Escape Exits.

Ceiling

30 in. (76 cm) x 36 in. (91 cm)
Min Clear Opening

Min Clear Opening
24 in. (61 cm) x 78 in. (198 cm)

12 in. (30.5 cm) Max
or Steps

Double Hung Window

Floor

Casement Window or Door

dimensions for fire escape stairs, as shown in Table 5-1. Also shown are the differences between the generally accepted fire escape stair of existing buildings and the lighter fire escape stair acceptable for existing "very small" buildings serving ten or fewer occupants.

The existing stair with a minimum width of 22 in. (55.9 cm) is a type that may be acceptable for buildings of small or moderate size. Depending upon local conditions, these existing fire escape stairs may generally be accepted.

The existing stair with a minimum width of 18 in. (45.7 cm) represents the absolute minimum that may be accepted in an existing fire escape stairway. Because of access over windowsills, steep pitch, and a narrow width, travel down such stairs will necessarily be slow and may be dangerous. Stairs with spiral stair treads or stairs that terminate at a balcony above ground level with a fixed or movable ladder extending downward from that point are even worse. These stairs are suitable only in situations where a very small number of people is involved.

5-2.8.5 Guards, Handrails, and Visual Enclosures.

5-2.8.5.1 All fire escape stairs shall have walls or guards and handrails on both sides in accordance with 5-2.2.4.

Exception: Existing handrails on existing fire escape stairs shall be permitted to continue to be used if the height does not exceed 42 in. (107 cm).

Table 5-1. Differences Between Outside Stairs and Fire Escape Stairs.

Design Factor	New Outside Stair	Existing Outside Stair		Fire Escape Stair	
		Class A	B	Normal	Small Buildings
Accepted as Exit	Yes	Yes	Yes	Existing buildings	
Width	44 in.*	44 in.*	44 in.*	22 in.	18 in.
Maximum rise	7 in.	7½ in.	8 in.	9 in.	12 in.
Minimum tread	11 in.	10 in.	9 in.	9 in.	6 in.
Tread construction	solid	solid	solid	solid	metal bars
Access by windows	No	No	No	Yes	Yes
Swinging Stair accepted	No	No	No	Yes	Yes
Ladder accepted	No	No	No	No	Yes

Conversion 1 in. = 2.54 cm.
Note: The capacity of normal fire escape stairs is 45 persons for doors and 20 for windows where necessary to climb over a sill. On small buildings, the capacity is 10 persons; 5 if winders or a ladder from bottom landing; or 1 if both winders and a ladder from bottom landing.
*36 in. where serving occupant load of 50 or less.

5-2.8.5.2 Replacement fire escape stairs in occupancies serving more than 10 occupants shall have visual enclosures to avoid any handicap to stair use by persons having a fear of high places. For stairs more than three stories in height, any arrangement intended to meet this requirement shall be at least 42 in. (107 cm) in height.

Table 5-2.8.4 A

	Fire Escape Stairs (Serving more than 10 occupants)	Fire Escape Stairs (Serving 10 or fewer occupants)
Minimum Widths	22 in. (55.9 cm) clear between rails	18 in. (45.7 cm) clear between rails
Minimum horizontal dimension of any landing or platform	22 in. (55.9 cm) clear	18 in. (45.7 cm) clear
Maximum riser height	9 in. (22.9 cm)	12 in. (30.5 cm)
Minimum tread, exclusive of nosing	9 in. (22.9 cm)	6 in. (15.3 cm)
Minimum nosing or projection	1 in. (2.5 cm)	No requirement
Tread construction	Solid ½-in. (1.3-cm) dia. perforations permitted	Flat metal bars on edge or sq. bars secured against turning, spaced 1¼ in. (3.2 cm) max. on centers
Winders	None	Permitted subject to capacity penalty
Risers	None	No requirement
Spiral	None	Permitted subject to capacity penalty
Maximum height between landings	12 ft (3.7 m)	No requirement
Headroom, minimum	6 ft 8 in. (203 cm)	Same
Handrail height	42 in. (107 cm)	Same
Access to escape	Door or casement windows 24 in. × 6 ft 6 in. (61 cm × 198 cm) or double hung windows 30 in. × 36 in. (76 cm × 91 cm) clear opening	Windows
Level of access opening	Not over 12 in. (30.5 cm) above floor; steps if higher	Same
Discharge to ground	Swinging stair section permitted if approved by authority having jurisdiction	Swinging stair, or ladder if approved by authority having jurisdiction
Capacity, number of persons	0.5 in. (1.3 cm) per person, if access by door; 1.0 in. (2.5 cm) per person if access by climbing over windowsill	10; if winders or ladder from bottom balcony, 5; if both, 1

5-2.8.6 Materials and Strength.

5-2.8.6.1 Noncombustible materials shall be used for the construction of all components of fire escape stairs.

5-2.8.6.2 The authority having jurisdiction may approve any existing fire escape stair that has been shown by load test or other satisfactory evidence to have adequate strength.

5-2.8.7* Swinging Stairs.

A-5-2.8.7 Swinging stairs, although superior to fire escape ladders, are generally unsatisfactory for even emergency use. Although they are permitted by this *Code*, they should not be used where it is reasonably possible to terminate the fire escape stair at the ground.

Where a fire escape stair would block a sidewalk or other public way or provide ready access for intruders, the discharge may be counterweighted and the unlocked swinging stair designed so that a 150-lb (68-kg) weight applied at one-quarter of the length of the stair from the pivot point will cause the stair to drop into the usable position.

5-2.8.7.1 A single swinging stair section shall be permitted to terminate fire escape stairs over sidewalks, alleys, or driveways where it is impractical to make the termination with fire escape stairs.

5-2.8.7.2 Swinging stair sections shall not be located over doors, over the path of travel from any other exit, or in any locations where there are likely to be obstructions.

Table 5-2.8.4 B

	Replacement Fire Escape Stairs (Serving more than 10 occupants)	Replacement Fire Escape Stairs (Serving 10 or fewer occupants)
Minimum widths	22 in. (55.9 cm) clear between rails	Same
Minimum horizontal dimension of any landing or platform	22 in. (55.9 cm)	Same
Maximum riser height	9 in. (22.9 cm)	Same
Minimum tread, exclusive of nosing	10 in. (25.4 cm)	Same
Tread construction	Solid, $1/2$-in. (1.3-cm) dia. perforations permitted	Same
Winders	None	Permitted subject to 5-2.2.2.8
Spiral	None	Permitted subject to 5-2.2.2.7
Risers	None	None
Maximum height between landings	12 ft (3.7 m)	Same
Headroom, minimum	6 ft 8 in. (203 cm)	Same
Access to escape	Door or casement windows 24 in. × 6 ft 6 in. (61 cm × 198 cm) or double hung windows 30 in. × 36 in. (76 cm × 91 cm) clear opening	Windows
Level of access opening	Not over 12 in. (30.5 cm) above floor; steps if higher	Same
Discharge to ground	Swinging stair section permitted if approved by authority having jurisdiction	Same
Capacity, number of persons	0.5 in. (1.3 cm) per person, if access by door; 1.0 in. (2.5 cm) per person if access by climbing over windowsill	10

5-2.8.7.3 Width of swinging stair sections shall be no less than that of the fire escape stairs above.

5-2.8.7.4 Pitch of swinging stair sections shall be no steeper than that of the fire escape stairs above.

5-2.8.7.5 Guards and handrails, in accordance with 5-2.2.4, shall be provided and shall be similar in height and construction to those used with the fire escape stairs above. Guards and handrails shall be designed to prevent any possibility of injury to persons where stairs swing downward. Minimum clearance between moving sections and any other portion of the stair system where hands might be caught shall be 4 in. (10.2 cm).

5-2.8.7.6 If the distance from the lowest platform to ground exceeds 12 ft (3.7 m), an intermediate balcony not more than 12 ft (3.7 m) from the ground or less than 7 ft (213 cm) in the clear underneath shall be provided, with width not less than that of the stairs and length not less than 4 ft (122 cm).

5-2.8.7.7 Swinging stairs shall be counterbalanced about a pivot, and cables shall not be used. A weight of 150 lb (68 kg) located one step from the pivot shall not cause the stairs to swing downward, and a weight of 150 lb (68 kg) located one-quarter of the length of the swinging stairs from the pivot will positively cause the stairs to swing down.

5-2.8.7.8 The pivot for swinging stairs shall be of a corrosion-resistant assembly or have clearances to prevent sticking due to corrosion.

5-2.8.7.9* No device to lock a swinging stair section in the up position shall be installed.

A-5-2.8.7.9 A latch is desirable to hold swinging stairs down after they have swung to the ground.

5-2.8.8 Intervening Spaces.

5-2.8.8.1 Where approved by the authority having jurisdiction, fire escape stairs may lead to an adjoining roof that must be crossed before continuing downward travel. The direction of travel shall be clearly marked, and walkways with guards and handrails complying with 5-2.2.4 shall be provided.

5-2.8.8.2 Where approved by the authority having jurisdiction, fire escape stairs may be used in combination with interior or outside stairs complying with 5-2.2, provided a continuous safe path of travel is maintained.

5-2.9 Fire Escape Ladders.

5-2.9.1 General. Fire escape ladders shall be permitted to be used only under the following conditions:

(a) To provide access to unoccupied roof spaces as permitted by 5-2.8.3.2;

(b) To provide a second means of escape from storage elevators as permitted by Chapter 29;

(c) To provide a means of egress from towers and elevated platforms around machinery or similar spaces subject to occupancy only by able-bodied adults, totaling no more than three in number; or

(d) To provide a secondary means of egress from boiler rooms or similar spaces subject to occupancy only by able-bodied adults, totaling no more than three in number; or

(e) To provide access to the ground from the lowest balcony or landing of a fire escape stair for very small buildings as permitted by 5-2.8.4 where approved by the authority having jurisdiction.

Although the *Code* contains provisions for fire escape ladders, it does not recommend their use. These ladders are used because they are one of the only means of moving from one space to another along what might be a path of escape from spaces not normally occupied. The intent of the *Code* is not to encourage the use of ladders but to provide access to an exit from any regularly occupied

area. The provisions of 5-2.9.1 and those contained in Chapters 29 and 30, which address storage occupancies and unusual structures, constitute the very minimal recognition given fire escape ladders by this *Code*. The *Code* does specify requirements for ladder construction and installation to ensure their structural integrity and ease of use if they must be installed. (*Also see 5-2.11.*)

5-2.9.2 Construction and Installation. Fire escape ladders shall comply with the requirements of ANSI A14.3, *Safety Code for Fixed Ladders*.

Exception No. 1: Existing ladders complying with the edition of this Code that was in effect when the ladders were installed may continue to be used subject to the approval of the authority having jurisdiction.

Exception No. 2: Ladders installed with pitch less than 75 degrees shall not be permitted.

Exception No. 3: Combustible ladders shall not be permitted.

5-2.9.3 The lowest rung of any ladder shall be not more than 12 in. (30.5 cm) above the level of the surface beneath it.

5-2.10 Slide Escapes.

5-2.10.1 General.

5-2.10.1.1 A slide escape shall be permitted as a component in a means of egress where specifically authorized by Chapters 8 through 30.

5-2.10.1.2 Each slide escape shall be of an approved type.

5-2.10.1.3 Slide escapes used as exits shall comply with the applicable requirements of Chapter 5 for other types of exits subject to the approval of the authority having jurisdiction.

Slide escapes are permitted in specified locations as a component in a means of egress and can even be considered as exits. Customarily, one thinks of entering a slide escape through a window or special opening in an exterior wall, and from that point on, it functions as an exit discharge. Should the slide escape be entered from within the building, and thus be considered as an exit, it must be protected as an exit enclosure as required by 5-1.3; that is, until it passes through the exterior wall. It is the *Code's* intent that slide escapes have the same separation or protection from openings in the exterior walls as do outside stairs and ramps.

Where provided, slide escapes should be regularly used in drills or for normal exit so that occupants are, through practice, familiar with their use.

A slide pole, of the type found in fire stations, is not considered as a slide escape.

Slide escapes are now permitted only in high hazard industrial occupancies (28-2.2) and where existing in storage occupancies (29-2.2).

5-2.10.2 Capacity.

5-2.10.2.1 Slide escapes, where permitted as required exits, shall be rated at a capacity of 60 persons.

5-2.10.2.2 Slide escapes shall not constitute more than 25 percent of the required exit capacity from any building or structure or any individual story or floor thereof.

Exception: As permitted for high hazard manufacturing buildings or structures.

The 25 percent limitation on slide escapes as a required exit prohibits designating a slide escape as one of two exits where two exits are required.

5-2.11* Alternating Tread Devices.

A-5-2.11 Special consideration should be given prior to the application of such devices where children, the elderly, or physically disabled persons may have to utilize such devices. These devices present obstacles in ascent and descent that differ from stairs and ladders.

Alternating tread device is the term used in the *Code* for a form of climbing implement that is intermediate between a ladder and a stair. It consists of a steep succession of treads that alternate, one riser-height apart from the left side to the right side. A person using the device is constrained to place only one foot on each tread. This alternating tread design, now generally developed as a series of treads supported by a central spine, permits stairlike half treads to be used with ladderlike slopes. Use of such devices, while perhaps awkward due to initial lack of familiarity or infrequent usage, may be acceptable for some occupancy situations where the alternative means of changing levels are ladders or ships ladders; that is, devices that are generally in the range of 50 to 75 degrees in pitch. This is approximately twice the pitch of stairs permitted by the *Code*. A benefit of alternating tread devices is that one can descend with one's back to the device, unlike a ladder, where one can only descend safely while facing the ladder because of the more limited surface area and depth of ladder rungs. A further benefit of the device is that objects can be carried more easily while ascending or descending because the handrails provide support under the arms, which are left free. The *Code*, unlike some building codes, limits the use of alternating tread devices to those situations where a ladder is acceptable. Figure 5-49 illustrates an alternating tread device.

5-2.11.1 Alternating tread devices complying with 5-2.11.2 shall be permitted to be used only as follows:

(a) To provide access to unoccupied roof spaces as permitted by 5-2.8.3.2;

(b) To provide a second means of egress from storage elevators as permitted by Chapter 29;

(c) To provide a means of egress from towers and elevated platforms around machinery or similar spaces subject to occupancy only by able-bodied adults, totaling no more than three in number; or

(d) To provide a secondary means of egress from boiler rooms or similar spaces subject to occupancy only by able-bodied adults, totaling no more than three in number.

5-2.11.2 Alternating tread devices shall comply with the following:

(a) Handrails shall be provided on both sides of alternating tread devices in accordance with 5-2.2.4.5; and

(b) The clear width between handrails shall be a minimum of 17 in. (43.2 cm) and shall not exceed 24 in. (61 cm); and

(c) Head room shall not be less than 6 ft 8 in. (203 cm); and

Photograph Courtesy of LID Group

Figure 5-49. *An Example of an Alternating Tread Device Discussed in 5-2.11.*

(d) The angle of the device shall be between 50 and 68 degrees to horizontal; and

(e) The height of the riser shall not exceed 9.5 in. (24.1 cm); and

(f) Treads shall have a minimum projected tread depth of 5.8 in. (14.7 cm) measured in accordance with 5-2.2 with each tread providing 9.5 in. (24.1 cm) of depth including tread overlap; and

(g) A minimum distance of 6 in. (15.2 cm) shall be provided between the stair handrail and any other object; and

(h) The initial tread of the stair shall begin at the same elevation as the platform, landing, or floor surface; and

(i) The alternating treads shall not be laterally separated by more than 2 in (5.0 cm); and

(j) The occupant load served shall not be more than three.

5-2.12 Areas of Refuge.

This subsection is new to the *Code*. In conjunction, see the new definitions for: Accessible Area of Refuge, 5-1.2.1; Accessible Means of Egress, 5-1.2.2; and Area of Refuge, 5-1.2.3. The purpose of this subsection is to provide the occupancy chapters with a basic standard that can be referenced if areas of refuge are considered necessary in certain situations. It can be especially useful for the protection of persons who for reasons of health, capability, confinement, building height, or other reasons cannot be expected to achieve safety by normal egress systems.

Although not limited to the mobility impaired, this new subsection provides a viable method for the protection of the mobility impaired.

It is *not* the intent of the *Code* to mandate that the areas of refuge created by horizontal exits comply with 5-2.12, but only those areas of refuge specifically mandated by the occupancy chapters. (*See 5-2.12.1.1.*)

The material in this new subsection was heavily based on a report by Jake Pauls, "Review of Standards and Codes Plus Recommendations for Accessible Means of Egress,"[11] and on the work of the Board for the Coordination of Model Codes, a board of the Council of American Building Officials.

5-2.12.1* **Application.**

A-5-2.12.1 Areas of refuge may serve two functions. The first function, which might be required in certain situations, is to improve the usability of means of egress for some occupants of the building. This function might also have the effect of making "fire fighter service" elevators usable for egress. The second function, which is permitted in certain situations, is to provide greater flexibility in the provision of means of egress as illustrated by the example in A-5-2.4.1

5-2.12.1.1 Areas of refuge shall be provided where required by Chapters 8 through 30.

At the present time, the areas of refuge described in this subsection are mandated only in New Assembly Occupancies (8-2.5.2) and New Educational Occupancies (10-2.11.2). In both cases, the facility is exempted if the building is protected throughout by an automatic sprinkler system. Many of the remaining chapters now mandate automatic sprinklers in all or almost all new construction (health care, board and care, hotels, apartment buildings, lodging and rooming houses, and large mercantile). Of the remaining occupancies, detention and correctional does mandate subdivision by smoke barriers, business occupancies have an extraordinarily good record with regard to life safety from fire, and new industrial and storage occupancies tend to be of one-story design, but this is not always true.

It should be anticipated that, as these provisions become more refined and understood, more occupancies may begin to require their use, and eventually they may be applied to existing buildings in some form.

5-2.12.2 **General Requirements for Areas of Refuge.**

5-2.12.2.1 Every required portion of an area of refuge shall be accessible from the space it serves by an accessible means of egress.

Since one of the primary reasons for 5-2.12 is to provide an area of refuge for the mobility impaired, it stands to reason that the area must be accessible by a route that can be used by the mobility impaired. (*See definition of Accessible Means of Egress in 5-1.2.2.*)

5-2.12.2.2* Every area of refuge shall be sufficient in size to provide at least two accessible, level, floor areas each 30 in. by 48 in. (76 cm m⁻ 122 cm) in area. These minimum areas shall not reduce the required width of the means of egress. For any area of refuge less than 1000 sq ft (93 sq m) in size, it shall be demonstrated by calculation or test that the refuge area can maintain tenable conditions when exposed to the maximum expected fire conditions for a period of 15 minutes, unless determined otherwise by the authority having jurisdiction.

A-5-2.12.2.2 Figure A-5-2.12.2.2 illustrates the application of this minimum space requirement to an area of refuge located within an exit stair. Note that each of the two required spaces is sufficient to permit the parking of a standard wheelchair. Preferably, such spaces should be provided adjacent to each other in a location where the presence of people making temporary shelter in an area of refuge will be immediately apparent to rescue personnel or other evacuees.

The method of meeting the required performance of a refuge area may involve control of the exposing fire (as with sprinkler protection), provision of tight-fitting smoke doors (*see NFPA 105, Recommended Practice for the Installation of Smoke-Control Door Assemblies*), the provision of smoke control to prevent or limit smoke migration through cracks or other leakage paths that exist (*see NFPA 92A, Recommended Practice for Smoke Control Systems*), or a combination of these or other means.

Calculations, if used, need to be based on established engineering relationships and equations. Such calculational procedures are described in NFPA 92A, *Recommended Practice for Smoke Control Systems*, the ASHRAE publication, *Design of Smoke Control Systems for Buildings* by Klote and Fothergill, and the SFPE *Handbook of Fire Protection Engineering*. Tenable conditions are those that maintain the temperature of any smoke in the refuge area at less than 200°F (93°C) if the smoke is more than 5 ft. (153 cm) above the floor level and 120°F (49°C) if the smoke descends below the 5-ft (153-cm) level in the refuge area. Also, if the smoke descends below the 5-ft (153-cm) level, tenable conditions require at least 16 percent oxygen and no more than 30,000 ppm-min exposure to carbon monoxide. The exposing conditions used in such calculations should be in accordance with the following:

(a) *Exposing space is sprinkler protected.* The temperature of the exposing smoke is 200°F (93°C), the smoke layer extends to the floor, the oxygen content is 16 percent, and the carbon monoxide concentration is 2000 ppm (0.2 percent).

(b) Exposing space is a nonsprinklered corridor finished with Class A interior finish. The temperature of the exposing smoke is 600°F (315°C), the smoke layer extends to a level 2 ft (61 cm) above the floor, the oxygen content is 3 percent, and the carbon monoxide concentration is 50,000 ppm (5 percent).

(c) *Exposing space is either not a corridor or, if a corridor, corridor is not finished with a Class A interior finish.* The temperature of the exposing smoke is 1,500°F (815°C), the smoke layer extends to a level 2 ft (61 cm) above the floor, the oxygen content is 3 percent, and the carbon monoxide concentration is 50,000 ppm (5 percent).

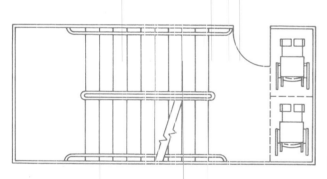

Figure A-5-2.12.2.2   Exit Stair Used as an Area of Refuge.

Examples of typical areas of refuge are subdivided floors, elevator lobbies, entrance ways to stairs, or an oversized landing of an exit stair enclosure, as illustrated in Figure A-5-2.12.2.2. Since smaller areas of refuge can go "sour" quickly, the *Code* requires an analysis of the area to ensure tenability. The appendix note provides considerable guidance on this.

5-2.12.2.3*   Every area of refuge shall provide access to an exit or to a fire fighter service elevator. Such access shall not require returning to the building space from which egress was begun. Where this required exit includes steps, the minimum clear width of landings and stair flights measured between handrails shall be 48 in. (122 cm).

Exception: For stairs where egress is in the descending direction, the minimum clear width shall be 44 in. (112 cm) if approved alternative measures are provided that do not require carrying occupied wheelchairs on the stairs.

A-5-2.12.2.3   The 48-in. (122-cm) clear width is needed for a three-person carry of an occupied wheelchair up or down a stair. This procedure, as well as the more dangerous two-person wheelchair carry or roll, requires training and experience. Safer, alternative stair descent measures for transporting a person who normally requires a wheelchair include evacuation chairs and self-braking stair descent devices. In addition to having such devices available where needed, it is important to have people trained and experienced in wheelchair transfer techniques as well as in the operation of the devices.

In view of the logistical difficulties as well as the dangers inherent in carrying occupied wheelchairs or otherwise transporting their occupants on stairs, the preferred means of egress from an area of refuge consists of facilities normally employed by people using wheelchairs. Foremost among these options are "fire fighter service" elevators. (*See 5-2.12.2.4.*)

Only elevators meeting the requirement of fire fighter service in ANSI/ASME A17.1, *Safety Code for Elevators and Escalators*, should be utilized for egress from areas of refuge with fire service supervision during emergencies.

Areas of refuge in which the only way out is to return through the area from where it was entered, the area of origin, are not permitted. Every area of refuge must have a way out other than the way it was entered. In this case, an elevator that has "firefighter service" per ASME/ANSI A17.1[9] is acceptable, and, in fact, probably preferable. Note that, if stairs are involved, they must be wider than the "standard 44 in. stair," since not only are they required to be 48 in.(122 cm), but the measurement is made as the clear distance between handrails. The allowance of 5-2.2.2.1 for handrails [3½ in.(8.9 cm) on each side] is not permitted here.

Figure 5-50 illustrates several methods of complying with 5-2.12.2.3.

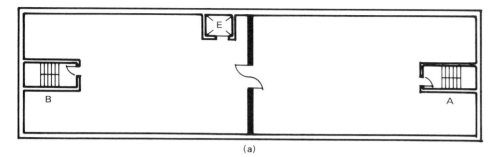

(a)

Figure 5-50(a) (top). Area of Refuge by Subdividing the Building. Stairway A must provide 48 in.(122 cm) clear width between handrails (or comply with 5-2.12.2.3 Exception) and the elevator must have "firefighter service" and must comply with 5-2.12.2.5. The size of the area of refuge is not of concern here.

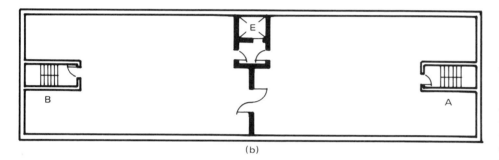

(b)

Figure 5-50(b) (below). Area of Refuge by Subdividing the Building. In this instance neither stair needs to comply with 5-2.12.2.3 since the elevator can be considered part of either compartment. The elevator must have "firefighter service" and must comply with 5-.12.2.5. Although it would first appear that the size of the area of refuge would be of concern, it must be remembered that the lobby can be considered part of each larger area of refuge.

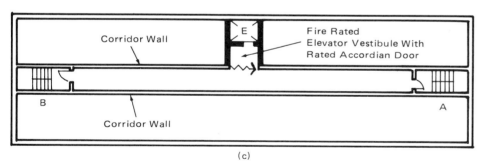

Corridor Wall

Fire Rated Elevator Vestibule With Rated Accordian Door

Corridor Wall

(c)

Figure 5-50(c) (top). Area of Refuge Using the Elevator Lobby. In this case, the size of the area of refuge is important since the elevator lobby by itself is one area of refuge and 5-2.12.2.2 becomes critical. The elevator must have "firefighter service," and either stair A or stair B must meet 5-2.12.2.3.

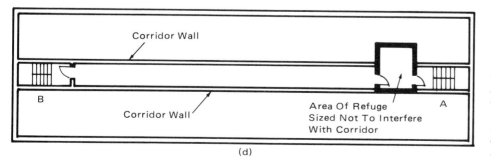

Corridor Wall

Corridor Wall

Area Of Refuge Sized Not To Interfere With Corridor

(d)

Figure 5-50(d) (below). Area of Refuge Using Area Near Entrance to Exit Stair. In this case, as in Figure 5-50(c), the size of the area of refuge is again important. The stairs must meet the width requirements of 5-2.12.4.2. Although not required, in large buildings consideration should be given to providing a protected area near stair B. Although stair B serves the large area of refuge, almost the entire rest of the floor, it is easy to predict a fire that would block the entrance to the area of refuge at A.

5-2.12.2.4* Elevators intended for use from areas of refuge shall be approved for fire fighter service as provided in ASME/ANSI A17.1, *Safety Code for Elevators and Escalators*, and shall be operated by fire service personnel. Such elevators and the areas of refuge serving them shall be identified. Information on alternative egress routes shall be posted. Every area of refuge using a fire fighter service elevator for egress shall be provided with a two-way communication system between the area of refuge and a central control point used for emergency management of the elevator.

A-5-2.12.2.4 The use of elevators for egress, especially during an emergency such as a fire, is not an approach to be taken without considerable planning, ongoing effort, and a high degree of understanding on the part of everyone involved. Due in part to their limited capacity, as well as the conflicting demands of elevator use for fire fighting activities, even these special elevators cannot be considered as satisfying any of the *Code's* requirements for egress capacity, number of exits, or travel distance to exits.

5-2.12.2.5* A barrier shall be provided between every area of refuge and the adjoining building spaces from which egress is begun. Such barriers, and any openings in them, shall be designed and installed to minimize air leakage and retard the passage of smoke. Unless the area of refuge is a required horizontal exit, the barrier shall consist of an assembly having at least a 1-hour fire resistance rating.

Exception No. 1: For separations other than those for exits, no fire-resistance rating is required if the building is protected throughout by an approved supervised automatic sprinkler system in accordance with Section 7-7.

Exception No. 2: One-half hour fire resistance rating for existing barriers.

A-5-2.12.2.5 For further information on smoke barriers, see NFPA 105, *Recommended Practice for the Installation of Smoke-Control Door Assemblies. (See Appendix B.)*

Generally, the provision of one barrier subdividing a floor area in some fashion creates two areas of refuge. This geometric fact, plus the possibility of creating areas with compartmented elevator lobbies or enlarged exit stair landings, make less onerous any requirement for a story to have a minimum number of areas of refuge.

Also see Section 6-2 and Section 6-3.

5-2.12.2.6 Any opening in required barriers for areas of refuge shall be protected according to 6-2.3.5.

SECTION 5-3   Capacity of Means of Egress

5-3.1   Occupant Load.

5-3.1.1 The capacity of means of egress for any floor, balcony, tier, or other occupied space shall be sufficient for the occupant load thereof.

It is a basic concept of the *Code* that a safe means of egress system be provided for all people occupying a building, however many that may be.

The geometry of a building, its occupancy and related occupant load, and the travel distance to exits dictate in large measure the appropriate location of exits, number of exits, capacity of exits, and access thereto. As a consequence, the exits themselves profoundly influence the plan and layout of the entire system of means of egress. The ability of the means of egress to accommodate a given volume of people is proportionately related to the ability of each component within the means of egress to accommodate that particular volume. It is beyond the scope of this chapter to do more than simply provide the basic steps toward designing a safe and satisfactory system of means of egress from a building, while keeping economic considerations in mind.

The number of people or occupant load for which the means of egress must provide a path of travel must be determined first. The occupant load is based on the maximum number of people that can be anticipated to occupy the building rooms or spaces at any given time, under all situations or unusual circumstances. It must not be based only upon the normal occupancy. In no case may the means of egress system be based on an occupant load less than that specified in 5-3.1.2.

While occupant load distribution in buildings may vary, it is important that exit capacity distribution among the exits provided is not significantly unbalanced. The reason for requiring multiple exits is the assumption that in a fire event one of the exits will be obstructed by the fire and unavailable to the occupants. Even though the exit with the greatest share of the total required exit capacity may be the one nearest to the majority of the occupants, it may also be the one that is lost in a fire; as a consequence, a disproportionate amount of the total exit capacity will be lost.

5-3.1.2* The occupant load in any building or portion thereof shall not be assumed to be less than the number determined by dividing the floor area assigned to that use by the occupant load factor as specified in Chapters 8 through 30 for individual occupancies. Where both gross and net area figures are given for the same occupancy, calculations shall be made applying the gross area figure to the building as a whole and the net area figure to the net area of the specific use.

A-5.3.1.2 The normal occupant load is not necessarily a suitable criterion, as the greatest hazard may occur when an unusual crowd is present, a condition often difficult for authorities having jurisdiction to control by regulatory measures. The principle of this *Code* is to provide exits for the maximum probable number of occupants rather than to attempt to limit occupants to a number commensurate with available exits. There are, however, limits of occupancy specified in certain special cases for other reasons.

The following table represents a compilation of the occupant load factors specified by the individual occupancies of Chapters 8 through 30.

Occupant load is determined by the nature of the use of a building or space and the amount of space available for that use. Since different generic uses will be characterized by different occupant densities, the occupancy chapters have established appropriate density factors for each occupancy and use. The occupant load factor, being a density factor, indicates that the presence of at least one person for each specified unit of area must be assumed. The table following A-5.3.1.2 provides these occupant

load factors as specified by the individual occupancy chapters, Chapters 8 through 30. Note that some values are for net area, while others are based on gross area. The gross area figure applies to the building as a whole (the area within the exterior confines of the building), while the net area figure applies to actual occupied spaces, such as classroom spaces, and does not include the corridors, the area occupied by walls, or other unoccupied areas. None of the occupancy chapters specifies values for both the net and gross areas of a building; however, there may be cases of mixed occupancy where, for example, a place of assembly having an occupant load based on net floor area may be located in an office or mercantile building, where the occupant load is based on gross area. In such instances, net and gross areas are used for the separate occupancies as appropriate.

Occupant Load Factors

Use	Sq Ft	Sq M
Assembly		
Less concentrated use without fixed seating	15 net	1.4
Concentrated use without fixed seating	7 net	.65
Waiting space	3 net	.28
Library—stack areas	100 gross	9.3
Library—reading areas	50 net	4.6
Mercantile		
Street floor and sales basement	30 gross	2.6
Multiple street floors—each	40 gross	3.7
Other floors	60 gross	5.6
Storage, shipping	300 gross	27.9
Malls	See 24-1.7.1	
Educational		
Classroom area	20 net	1.9
Shops and other vocational areas	50 net	4.6
Day-care centers	35 net	3.3
Business (offices), industrial	100 gross	9.3
Hotel and apartment	200 gross	18.6
Health care		
Sleeping departments	120 gross	11.1
Inpatient treatment departments	240 gross	22.3
Detention and correctional	120 gross	11.1

These figures, based on counts of typical buildings, represent the average maximum density of occupancy.

Note, too, that 5-3.1 requires that exit capacity must be provided for at least the occupant load as determined by dividing the area of the space (gross or net) by the appropriate occupant load factor.

The table uses the term "use" rather than "occupancy" for an important reason, since the generic use of an area may be different from its occupancy classification. For example, a meeting room for fewer than 50 people in an office building is not an assembly occupancy; it is a business occupancy, but its occupant load is based on an assembly use. The same concept applies to a classroom in a university, which although classified as business occupancy, would have its occupant load based on educational (if of traditional classroom style) or assembly (if of lecture style).

5-3.1.3 The occupant load permitted in any building or portion thereof shall be permitted to be increased from that number established for the given use as specified in 5-3.1.2, where all other requirements of this *Code* are also met, based on such increased number. The authority having jurisdiction may require an approved aisle, seating, or fixed equipment diagram to substantiate any increase in occupant load and may require that such diagram be posted in an approved location.

The concept expressed in 5-3.1.3 is very important. The *Code* is not attempting to restrict the occupant load of a building on the basis of area. An occupant load is established for later use in determining exit capacity, numbers of exits, aisle and corridor widths, and similar values. If all *Code* provisions are met using a higher occupant load, the higher occupant load may be permitted provided the authority having jurisdiction is satisfied that all corridors, aisles, stairs, and other means of egress components can accommodate the higher occupant load based on the specified criteria for each component.

For example, an office area of 20,000 sq ft (1,900 sq m) would usually be assigned an occupant load of 200. However, that number could be increased if all provisions of the *Code* for aisles, corridors, exits, stairs, ramps,

doors, exit capacity, discharge, and every means of egress component were to be met for the increased number.

Assembly occupancies have special but similar provisions for increasing occupant load.

Densities greater than one person for each 5 sq ft (.46 sq m) should be avoided since travel speeds are reduced to a crawl where an occupancy exceeds one person for each 3 sq ft (.65 m) density. This density is approaching the jam point.

5-3.1.4 Where exits serve more than one floor, only the occupant load of each floor considered individually need be used in computing the capacity of the exits at that floor, provided that exit capacity shall not be decreased in the direction of exit travel.

Paragraph 5-3.1.4 states another principle of the *Code*. It provides that, once a maximum required exit capacity is determined, such required maximum capacity must be maintained throughout the remainder of the egress system.

Stair size is determined by the required exit capacity for each floor. It is not necessary to accumulate occupant loads from floor to floor to determine stair width. Each story or floor level is considered separately when calculating the occupant load to be served by the exits from that floor. The size or width of the exits at a floor level need be only that required to accommodate the floor served. However, in a multistory building, the floor requiring the greatest exit capacity dictates the minimum width of exits from that point on in the direction of exit travel. It is not permissible to reduce the stair width for the floors below; that is, in the direction of exit travel. The exit must be capable of accommodating that exit capacity all along its path from the entrance point. Exits serving the stories above that critical floor may be equal or less in width as long as their occupant load does not require more capacity.

5-3.1.5 Where means of egress from floors above and below converge at an intermediate floor, the capacity of the means of egress from the point of convergence shall be not less than the sum of the two.

Figure 5-51 illustrates the intent of 5-3.1.5.

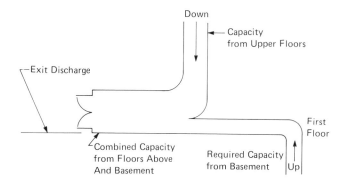

Figure 5-51. *Schematic Illustration of Requirements Contained in 5-3.1.5.*

5-3.1.6 Where any required egress capacity from a balcony or mezzanine passes through the room below, that required capacity shall be added to the required egress capacity of the room in which it is located.

This paragraph is new to the 1991 Edition of the *Code*. A series of changes have been made to this edition of the *Code* to clarify requirements for mezzanines and balconies. While mezzanines and balconies provide the benefit of being counted as part of the room in which they are located, conversely, they are subject to the penalty of having their occupant load added to that of the room or space in which they are located if their egress passes through that room or space. For example, in the case of a room with an occupant load of 300 and a balcony with an occupant load of 75; if the required egress from the balcony passes through the room, then the egress capacity for the room must be at least 375. In the past, this has been a concept specifically stated in many of the occupancies, but it now applies throughout the *Code*.

5-3.2* **Measurement of Means of Egress.** Width of means of egress shall be measured in the clear at the narrowest point of the exit component under consideration.

Exception: Projections not to exceed 3½ in. (8.9 cm) on each side are permitted at and below handrail height.

A-5-3.2 For further information on stair capacity, see Chapter 2 of NFPA 101M, *Alternative Approaches to Life Safety.* (*See Appendix B.*)

Projections at or below handrail height do not actually restrict the effective width of exits, since the human body is usually widest at shoulder level. Other projections, however, may very well constitute obstructions and cause impediments to the free flow of pedestrian travel. The *Code*, therefore, bases the measurements of widths of means of egress on the clear, net, usable, available, unobstructed width. Only those projections specifically permitted may encroach on the required widths. Note that the minimum widths required by 5-2.12.2.3 do not allow for the handrail projection.

5-3.3 **Egress Capacity.**

5-3.3.1 Egress capacity for approved components of means of egress shall be based on the following:

Use	Stairways (inch per person) [cm per person]	Level Components and Class A Ramps (inch per person) [cm per person]
Board and Care	0.4 [1.0]	0.2 [0.5]
Health Care Sprinklered	0.3 [0.8]	0.2 [0.5]
Health Care Nonsprinklered	0.6 [1.5]	0.5 [1.3]
High Hazard	0.7 [1.8]	0.4 [1.0]
All Others	0.3 [0.8]	0.2 [0.5]

For Class B ramps used for ascent, the width per person shall be increased by 10 percent beyond what is required for Class A ramps. Widths for Class B ramps used for descent shall be calculated the same as for Class A ramps.

A significant change in the calculation method was introduced in the 1988 *Code*. The unit of exit width formerly widely used as a measure of egress capacity was replaced by a system of smaller increments of egress width and capacity. For egress widths that were close to, and no smaller than, the previously used units [22 in. (55.9 cm)] and half units [12 in. (30.5 cm)], there was little change in the egress capacities that are calculated. For other widths, as with doors and nonstandard stairs, the new method of using small increments (approximating a linear formula) provides significantly greater egress capacity. The following examples demonstrate this:

Example 1

The common combination of a 34-in. (86-cm) clear width doorway, providing access to a stair 44 in. wide with a 34-in. (86-cm) clear width discharge doorway, has its capacity based on the capacity of its least efficient element. Individual capacities of the elements are simply calculated by dividing the widths by the appropriate inch-per-person figure found in 5-3.3.1. The doorways have a capacity of 36 ÷ 0.2 = 180 persons. The stair has a capacity of 44 ÷ 0.3 = 147 persons. The capacity of the exit is, therefore, 147. Under the previously used unit width method, the capacities were 150 for the 1½-unit doorways and 150 for the 2-unit stair.

Example 2

If the entry doorway is 32 in. (81 cm) clear width, the discharge doorway is 36 in. (91 cm) clear width, and the stair is 54 in. (137 cm), the individual capacities are, respectively:

32 in. ÷ 0.2 = 160 persons for the entry doorway,

36 in. ÷ 0.2 = 180 persons for the discharge doorway, and

54 in. ÷ 0.3 = 180 persons for the stair.

Therefore, the capacity of the overall combination is the smallest of the three capacities, or 160 persons. Under the previous unit width method, the capacities would have been as follows:

1 unit for the entry doorway × 100 = 100 persons,

1.5 units for the discharge doorway × 100 = 150 persons, and

2 units for the stair × 75 = 150 persons.

Therefore, the capacity for the combination as previously calculated would have been only 100 persons.

The low width per person figures specified in 5-3.3.1 are based on previously used values credited for full units. The chief difference is that small increments are now considered to add to capacity. Although relatively recent Canadian research studies of egress movement in tall office buildings and in larger assembly occupancy buildings have demonstrated the validity of the small increment approach, there had been evidence for this approach even in some significant early studies of egress and exit design. Excerpts from two very influential reports (dating from 1935 in the USA[7] and 1952 in Britain[12]) are provided in a discussion of the issue of exit unit size that was published in Fire Technology,[13] May 1984. These excerpts clearly show that this was an unsettled issue even in those reports that were thought to support only the unit width method. The weight of more recent evidence relating egress facility width and crowd flow capacity, along with clear documentation that crowds do not move in regular files or lanes, especially on stairs where side-to-side body sway almost prevents people from walking shoulder to shoulder, has led to the change to the more linear, small increment method. Further information about the nature of crowd movement was published in the 1985 Edition of the *Code* as Appendix D, which described an even more sophisticated approach to crediting egress capacity for stairs: the effective width method. The new methods, whether in the simplified form found in 5-3.3.1 or the more complex alternative for the effective width method (formerly Appendix D) now included in NFPA 101M, *Alternative Approaches to Life Safety*,[14] lead to more cost-effective design of egress facilities with a better match of performance among different facilities. The nominal performance to be expected where using the newer methods, for most occupancies, is a flow time of about 3½ minutes; i.e., there will be sustained crowd flow past one point in the system (such as a doorway) for 3½ minutes when the width and egress population are related as set out in 5-3.3.1. Notably, the newer methods are very useful in assessing the capacity of existing facilities that may fall slightly short of the integral unit width and half-unit width sizes credited under previous Codes.

The capacity figures found in 5-3.3.1 are simply derived from previously used combinations of egress component width and capacity, such as 75 persons per 22 in. (55.8 cm) unit of exit width for stairs; 22 ÷ 75 = 0.293 which, when rounded off to the closest single digit value, is 0.3. Similarly, for level and ramped components, the derivation is simply 22 ÷ 100, which is rounded off to 0.2.

The differences in the width figures specified in 5-3.3.1 arise from the following factors:

Stairs entail a totally different type of movement, by both individuals and crowds, than do level and moderately ramped components. These are differences in biomechanics as well as in the difficulty of seeing (or otherwise detecting) the next stepping surface in order to avoid misstepping and suffering a serious fall and resulting injury. The approximate ratio of 3 to 2, relating the required widths of these respective components, is based on previous ratios and on empirical observations. The difference of 10 percent between Class A and Class B ramps reflects the decreased speed on steeper ramps along with the greater concern that people in a crowd might have with the danger of misstepping or slipping.

The greater range of width requirements for different occupancies reflects two factors: the need for a much more rapid egress time in the case of high hazard occupancies, and the slower movement and greater need for assistance from others during evacuations in health care and related institutional and semi-institutional occupancies.

In summary, given the designer's knowledge of the occupancy, the occupant load of the floor level, and the type of egress component, the required minimum width for each component can be determined by simple multiplication (that is, multiply the occupant load figure by the appropriate width per person figure found in the table in 5-3.3.1 to obtain the minimum width of the component under consideration). If the width of the component under consideration is known, divide that width by the appropriate width per person figure to obtain the number of people it can handle. These calculated minimum widths are then considered along with other *Code* requirements, including minimum widths based on other factors, in order to design a system in which performance will be closely matched from one part of the system to another.

5-3.3.2 The required capacity of a corridor is the occupant load utilizing the corridor for exit access divided by the required number of exits to which the corridor connects but shall not be less than the required capacity of the exit to which the corridor leads.

For example, if a corridor system serves a floor with 400 people that has two exits, the required capacity of the corridor is 200. Another example is a floor with 900 people that has three exits, in which case the required capacity of the corridor is 300. In the first case, the corridor would be required to be 200 × .2 or 40 in. wide. (Note: Some occupancies have wider minimum corridor widths.) In the second case, the corridor would be required to be 300 × .2 or 60 in. wide. If the required capacity of the corridor for some unusual arrangement ends up being smaller than the required capacity of the exit to which it leads, the *Code* states that the corridor required capacity can never be less than that of the exit to which it leads.

5-3.4 Minimum Width.

5-3.4.1 The minimum width of any exit access shall be as specified for individual occupancies by Chapters 8 through 30, but in no case shall such width be less than 36 in. (91 cm).

Exception No. 1: Doors as provided for in 5-2.1.3.

Exception No. 2: In existing buildings, the minimum width shall not be less than 28 in. (71 cm).

Exception No. 3: Aisles in assembly occupancies as provided in Chapters 8 and 9.

5-3.4.2 Where a single exit access leads to an exit, its capacity in terms of width shall be at least equal to the required capacity of the exit to which it leads. Where more than one exit access leads to an exit, each shall have a width adequate for the number of persons it must accommodate.

The physical makeup of the ways of access to exits is dependent on the occupancy. The minimum width needed is specified in the *Code* chapters for individual occupancies. The widths are based on experience and on observations of the manner in which people move along paths used for exit access purposes. The minimum width permitted for any passageway used as an exit access is 36 in. (91 cm), but most occupancies require more. Educational occupancies require a corridor width of not less than 6 ft (183 cm). Health care occupancies require a corridor width of not less than 8 ft (244 cm), which reflects the need to have the ability to move bedridden patients along the path to an exit. Hotels, apartment buildings, and business occupancies generally require 44 in. (112 cm). Other occupancies rely on the provisions in Chapter 5, which set the following standard: where an exit has only a single way of access, the access width cannot be less than that of the exit itself. Under no circumstances, even in one- and two-family dwellings, is the exit access to be less than 36 in. (91 cm). The exception for existing buildings is in recognition of the previous minimum width of 28 in. (71 cm).

The thrust of 5-3.4.2 is to balance the flow of persons from the exit access to the exit to avoid a bottleneck and to assure that the occupants to be served by the exit can, in fact, reach it.

SECTION 5-4   Number of Means of Egress

5-4.1 General.

5-4.1.1 The minimum number of means of egress from any balcony, mezzanine, story, or portion thereof shall be two.

Exception No. 1: Where a single means of egress is permitted by Chapters 8 through 30.

Exception No. 2: A mezzanine or balcony shall be permitted to have a single means of egress provided the common path of travel limitations of Chapters 8 through 30 are not exceeded.

In most occupancies, the principle of redundancy requires at least two means of egress. Some occupancies will identify minimal situations where only a single means of egress is needed. Where large numbers of occupants are to be served, additional means of egress must be provided as required in 5-4.1.2.

Changes made to 5-4.1.1 for the 1991 *Code* regarding mezzanines are part of a series of changes to the *Code* meant to comprehensively cover mezzanines. Mezzanines are required to have the same number of means of egress as any other story unless one can reach either the single exit or the bottom of a single open stair within the allowable common path of travel permitted by each occupancy. Figure 5-52 illustrates the balcony provisions of 5-4.1.1.

(Also see Section 5-5 with regard to remoteness of exits and common paths of travel; 5-6.3 with regard to travel distance on open stairs; and 6-2.5 on Mezzanines.)

5-4.1.2 The minimum number of separate and remote means of egress from all floors or portions thereof shall be as follows:

Occupant load more than 500 but not more than 1,000: 3

Occupant load more than 1,000: 4

Exception: Existing buildings as permitted by Chapters 8 through 30.

Chapter 5 requires a minimum number of means of egress unless otherwise specified by the occupancy chapters. Several occupancies establish not only the minimum

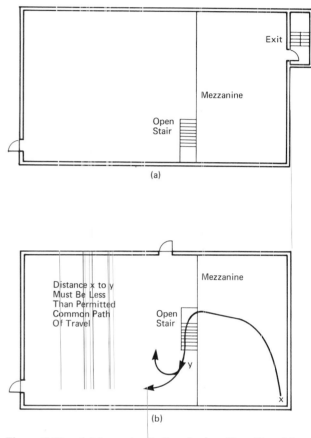

Figure 5-52. A Mezzanine Is Required to Have Two Means of Egress. In this case, (a), one means of egress is an open stair to the floor below and the other is an exit. Both could be open stairs to the floor below. If the common path of travel is within the limits specified by the occupancy involved, then a single means of egress, (c), is permitted.

number of means of egress but also the minimum number of actual exits on each floor. In most occupancies, by the time exit capacities and travel distances are complied with, the minimum numbers will automatically have been met. However, in assembly occupancies, educational occupancies, and mercantile occupancies, this may require additional attention.

5-4.1.3 Where exits serve more than one story, only the occupant load of each story considered individually need be used in computing the number of exits at that story, provided that the required number of exits shall not be decreased in the direction of exit travel.

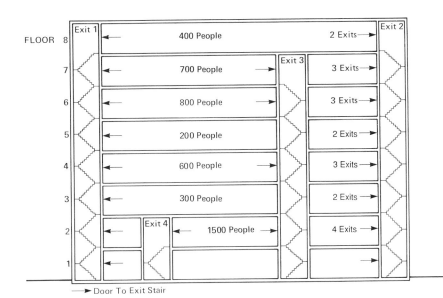

Figure 5-53. Illustrates Minimum Number of Exits Based on Occupant Load of Each Floor. The 3rd, 5th, and 8th floors do not require access to the third exit, whereas the 2nd floor requires four exits.

Similar to exit capacity (*see 5-3.1.4*), the number of exits is based on a floor by floor consideration rather than the accumulation of floors. However, the number of exits cannot decrease as one proceeds along the egress path. For example, if the sixth floor (800 people) requires three exits, and the seventh floor (700 people) requires three exits, only three exits are required, not six, regardless of the fact that the two floors together hold 1500 people. The three exits cannot be merged into two exits on the lower floors even though the lower floors may require only two exits. If a lower floor requires only two exits, one of the three exits could be left unaccessible (blind) on that floor. (*See Figure 5-53.*)

5-4.1.4 Doors other than the hoistway door and the elevator car door shall be prohibited at the point of access to an elevator car.

Exception: Doors that are readily openable from the car side without a key, tool, special knowledge, or effort.

This is a new paragraph in the 1991 *Code*. It prohibits the installation of a door at the entrance to an elevator unless that door is readily operable by those in the elevator. This prevents entrapment between the elevator and the door, which is unsafe for many reasons Of primary concern to the *Life Safety Code* is the fact that one could enter this small space and become trapped during a fire.

There have also been nonfire situations where children have been stuck in this space and crushed by the elevator.

5-4.1.5 Elevator lobbies shall have access to at least one exit. Such exit access shall not require the use of a key, tool, special knowledge, or effort.

This paragraph is also new to the 1991 *Code* and is similar in intent to 5-4.1.4 but addresses a more common situation than the arrangement in 5-4.1.4. The purpose of this provision is to ensure that someone who has gained access to an elevator lobby can get out of the lobby without the use of tool or key. It is not uncommon, especially in office buildings where a tenant occupies an entire floor, for the elevator lobby to be locked after hours. This new paragraph requires that the lobby have access to at least one exit.

SECTION 5-5 Arrangement of Means of Egress

5-5.1 General.

5-5.1.1 Exits shall be so located and exit access shall be so arranged that exits are readily accessible at all times.

5-5.1.2* Where exits are not immediately accessible from an open floor area, safe and continuous passageways, aisles, or corridors leading directly to every exit shall be maintained and shall be so arranged as to provide access for each occupant to at least two exits by separate ways of travel.

Exception No. 1: Where a single exit is permitted by Chapters 8 through 30.

Exception No. 2: Where common paths of travel are permitted for an occupancy by Chapters 8 through 30, such common path of travel shall be permitted but shall not exceed the limit specified.

A-5-5.1.2 See A-5-5.1.6.

5-5.1.3 Where more than one exit is required from a building or portion thereof, such exits shall be remotely located from each other and so arranged and constructed as to minimize any possibility that more than one may be blocked by any one fire or other emergency condition.

It is a precept of life safety in buildings, repeated many times in the *Code*, that if multiple exits are required, they should be not only separate but also remote from one another. While the objective of this requirement is clear — if one exit is blocked by smoke or fire, the other will be available — the term "remote" cannot always be sharply defined.

Where exits are located at each end of a long corridor or at each end or side of a building, they qualify as remotely located exits. However, core-type buildings with elevators, service shafts, and stairs in one central or side core introduce some challenging problems with respect to remote exits. Figure 5-54 shows two core-type buildings that illustrate this problem. The upper sketch shows the plan of the Rault Center Building in New Orleans where five women were trapped by fire on the 15th floor. Both exit stairways were blocked, and the women finally jumped to the roof of an adjacent eight-story building. Four of the five died.[15]

The lower sketch in Figure 5-54 shows the plan of the 20th floor of a New York City office building. An incendiary device evidently was set off somewhere near the lobby reception area. One of fifteen people on the floor at the time made it to the stair exit, but the other four-

teen were trapped and removed by fire fighters. One of the fourteen died.[16] With more attention given to life safety during the design stage, a much better solution might have been devised for these buildings. Figure 5-55 was reproduced from a discussion of core-type building designs in the NFPA *Fire Journal*.[17] It illustrates how, with a little thought and imagination and little, if any, added expense, a poor design can be greatly improved.

(*See also discussion under 5-5.1.4.*)

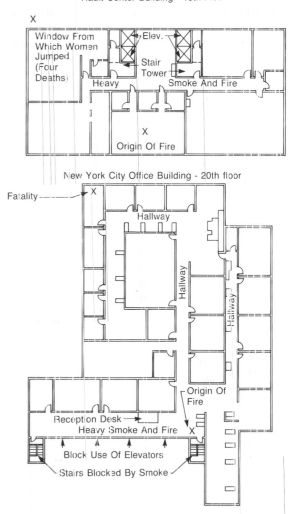

Figure 5-54. *Plan Views of Upper Floors of Two Core-Type High Rise Buildings where Fires Occurred. Exit stairs were located in the core areas, which became heavily involved in smoke and fire, blocking paths of escape.*

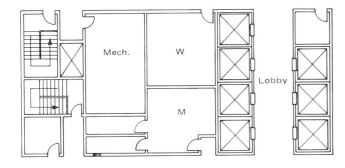

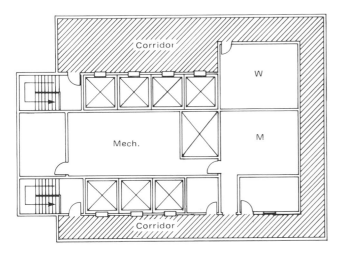

Figure 5-55.   An Example of Poor Planning and Good Planning of Exits in a Core-Type Multitenant Building. In the upper plan view, the exit stairs are not as remote from each other as practicable; they are both located on the same end of the core, a detriment when tenants, current and future, lay out their own partition arrangements to suit their needs. By removing the elevator lobby from the core, as shown in the lower plan, and adding a corridor around three sides of the core, the designer can ensure that tenants will have access to two remote exits. This solution also assists in providing two ways out of each tenant space.

5-5.1.4*   In new construction, if two exits or exit access doors are required, they shall be placed at a distance from one another equal to not less than one-half the length of the maximum overall diagonal dimension of the building or area to be served, measured in a straight line between exits. Where exit enclosures are provided as the required exits and are interconnected by a corridor conforming to the requirements of 5-1.3.4, exit separation shall be permitted to be measured along the line of travel within the corridor.

In new construction, where more than two exits or exit access doors are required, at least two of the required exits or exit access doors shall be so arranged to comply with the above. The other exits or exit access doors shall be so located that if one becomes blocked, the others will be available.

Exception: In buildings protected throughout by an approved supervised automatic sprinkler system in accordance with Section 7-7, the minimum separation distance between two exits or exit access doors shall be not less than one-third the length of the maximum overall diagonal dimension of the building or area to be served.

A-5-5.1.4   Figures A-5-5.1.4(a) through (e) illustrate the method of measurement intended by 5-5.1.4.

The Subcommittee on Means of Egress and the Committee on Safety to Life concluded that it has become necessary to quantify remoteness in order to make certain that exits are, in fact, sufficiently remote to reasonably ensure that multiple exits will not be obstructed by the same fire incident. This need is demonstrated in part by the building configurations shown in Figure 5-54.

Since 1988 the *Code* has contained a remoteness formula that has been used for years by the Uniform Building Code[18] and more recently has been recommended by the Board for the Coordination of the Model Codes (BCMC) of the Council of American Building Officials (CABO).

The formula is referred to as the "one-half diagonal rule" and was contained in A-5-5.1.4 of the 1985 *Life Safety Code.* This rule is stated in full in the first paragraph of 5-5.1.4. Figures A-5-5.1.4(a) through (e) detail the application of the rule.

In adopting the rule, however, an amendment was added to allow the exit separation to be reduced to one-third the maximum overall diagonal in fully sprinklered buildings.

Although existing buildings are exempt from this rule, they still must meet the performance requirement of 5-5.1.3.

5-5.1.5*   Interlocking or scissor stairs shall be permitted to be considered separate exits if enclosed in accordance with 5-1.3.1 and separated from each other by 2-hour fire resis-

Arrangement of Exits

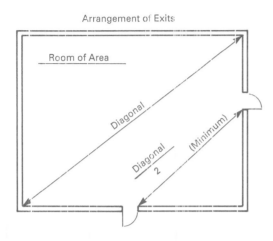

Minimum Distance = One-Half of Diagonal

Figure A-5-5.1.4(a)

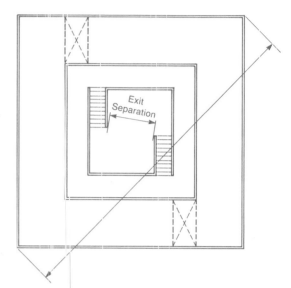

Figure A-5-5.1.4(c)

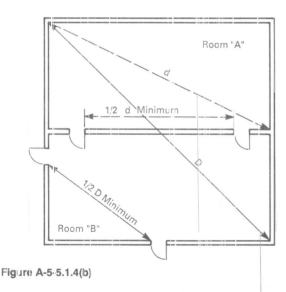

Figure A-5-5.1.4(b)

tance rated noncombustible construction. There shall be no penetrations or communicating openings, whether protected or not, between the stair enclosures.

A-5-5.1.5 Attention is called to the fact that it is difficult in actual practice to construct scissor stairs so that products of combustion that have entered one stairway do not penetrate into the other. Use as separate required exits is discouraged. The term "limited-combustible" is intentionally not included in this paragraph. The user's attention is directed to the definitions of "noncombustible" and "limited-combustible" in Chapter 3.

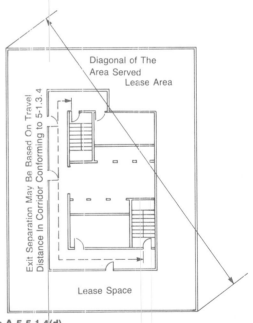

Figure A-5-5.1.4(d)

Scissor-type stairs (*see Figure 5-56*) must be addressed, since they are used and are a highly controversial subject. Some believe they are hazardous and should not be permitted; others believe just the opposite. Generally, the principal objection seems to be that they cannot be reliably built to create an absolute barrier to the passage of

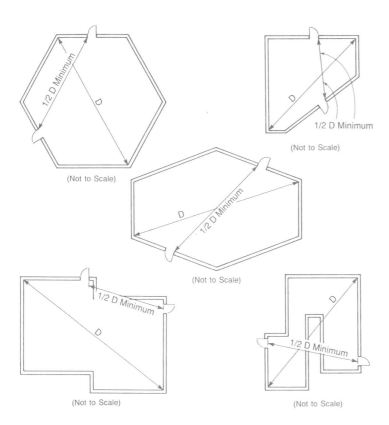

Figure A-5-5.1.4(e)

smoke and toxic gases between the stairs. Even if this can be done, there is still concern that settling of the building or exposure to fire conditions might result in the cracking of the separating wall, which could permit smoke and gases to pass into one exit stairway from the other. On the other hand, those who feel that scissor stairs do not present these problems see advantages because they reduce construction costs and save space. The *Code* requires separating construction to be noncombustible and 2-hour fire resistance rated. Note the definition of Noncombustible in Chapter 3. This definition normally will require some form of masonry or poured concrete wall. Even though, side by side, scissor stairs can be located with their entrances remote from one another and their discharges also remotely placed, it must be emphasized that the remoteness requirements are applicable to scissor stairs if they are to be considered as separate exits. Where not sufficiently remote, scissor stairs cannot be used as separate exits but can be used to increase the capacity of the single exit. These points are illustrated in Figures 5-56 and 5-57.

5-5.1.6* Exit access shall be so arranged that there are no dead-end pockets, hallways, corridors, passageways, and courts.

Exception: Where dead ends are permitted for an occupancy by Chapters 8 through 30, such dead ends shall be permitted but shall not exceed the limit specified.

A-5-5.1.6 The terms dead end and common path of travel are commonly used interchangeably. While the concepts of each are similar in practice, they are two different concepts.

A common path of travel exists where a space is arranged so that occupants within that space are able to travel in only one direction to reach any of the exits or to reach the point at which the occupants have the choice of two paths of travel to remote exits. Part (a) of Figure A-5-5.1.6 is an example of a common path of travel.

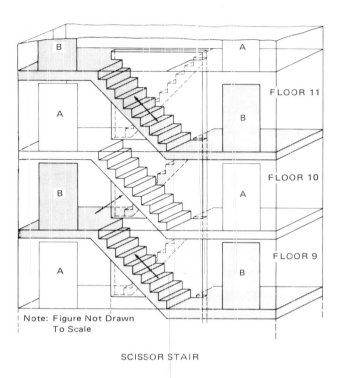

Note: Figure Not Drawn
To Scale

SCISSOR STAIR

Figure 5-56. *Scissor Stairs. Two stairways in the same enclosure but completely separated from each other are called scissor stairs. This result in space saving is that two stairways are provided in one enclosure. With this arrangement, two entirely independent escape paths are possible, even though they may not qualify as separate exits. Note the continuity of all walls, providing a complete separation at all points. Follow arrows for path of travel.*

While a dead end is similar, a dead end may occur where there is no path of travel from an occupied space, but where an occupant may enter a corridor or space thinking there is an exit at the end and, finding none, must retrace his or her path to again reach a choice of exits. Part (b) of Figure A-5-5.1.6 is an example of such a dead-end arrangement.

Combining the two concepts, Part (c) of Figure A-5-5.1.6 is an example of a combined dead-end common path of travel problem.

Common paths of travel and dead-end travel are measured using the same principles used to measure travel distance as described in Section 5-6 of the *Code.* Starting in the room in Part (d) of Figure A-5-5.1.6, measurement is made 1 ft (30.5 cm) from the most remote point in the room along the natural path of travel, and through the doorway along the centerline of the corridor to Point C, located at the centerline of the cor-

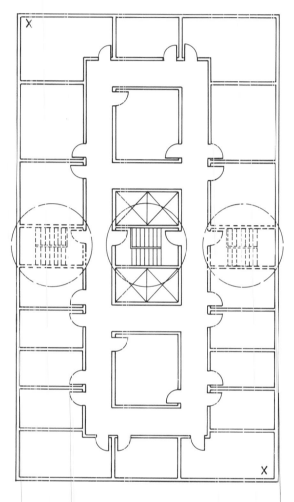

Figure 5-57. *Scissor Stairs Versus Conventional Exit Stairs — Advantages and Disadvantages. This set of scissor stairs provides the same degree of remoteness as the stairs shown by dotted lines. Travel distance for all occupants is the same, even if the dotted exit stairs were located at opposite corners denoted by the cross mark. Space is saved. However, the integrity of the separation of the 2 scissored stairs may remain in question.*

ridor, which then provides the choice of two different paths to remote exits; this is common path of travel. The space between Point B and Point C is a dead end. (*See 5-1.2.4 for a definition of common path of travel.*)

A dead end occurs where a hallway or other space is so arranged that a person is able to travel in only one direction in order to reach any of the exits. Although relatively short dead ends are permitted by the *Code,* it is better practice to avoid them as much as possible, for they

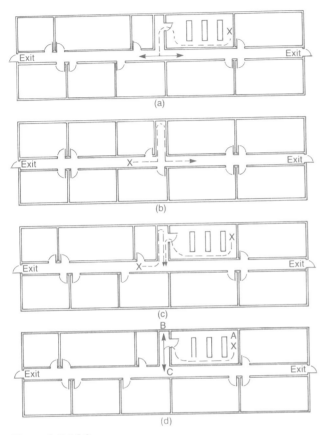

Figure A-5-5.1.6

increase the danger of people being trapped in case of fire. Compliance with the limits on dead ends does not necessarily mean that the requirements for remoteness of exits have been met. This is particularly true in small buildings or buildings with short public hallways.

Figure 5-58 illustrates examples of two types of dead-end corridors. The one serving the occupied rooms is far more dangerous than the one adjoining the bank of elevators or elevator lobby. The occupants of the rooms off the dead-end hall do not have a choice of two directions to an exit until they reach Point A. They could very easily be cut off altogether should a fire originate and break through a door, such as at Point B. The elevator lobby, Point C, does not pose the same problem because there are no doors to occupied rooms from the lobby. However, people heading toward exits could very easily turn into the dead-end corridors and become confused, as neither of the corridors leads to an exit. Sometimes it is very difficult to avoid dead ends, but there are some little-used

spaces that can be conveniently located in a dead end without undue hazard to those who must frequent these spaces. A dead end is never a desirable feature.

Excessive dead ends can be a factor in large losses of life because they increase the time required to exit and could result in fire coming between an individual and an exit. The effects of this deficiency were especially evident in a 1977 Rhode Island dormitory fire that killed 10 people: "Dead-end corridors approximately 61 feet long existed at each end of the dormitory. These dead-ends were allowed by the Rhode Island Building Code in effect at the time when the building renovations were made in 1972. ... A factor contributing to four of the ... deaths and several of the injuries was the long, dead-end corridor. Residents who left their rooms in this dead-end were forced away from their only exit."[19]

In those limited situations where only one means of egress is required, travel in the opposite direction is not considered to be a dead end for that reason alone.

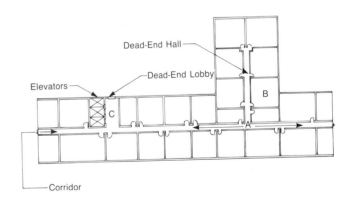

Figure 5-58. Examples of Two Types of Dead-End Corridors. See commentary for 5-5.1.6.

5-5.1.7 Egress from rooms or spaces shall be permitted to open into adjoining or intervening rooms or areas, provided such adjoining rooms are accessory to the area served and provide a direct means of egress to an exit. Foyers, lobbies, and reception rooms constructed as required for corridors shall not be construed as intervening rooms. Exit access shall be so arranged that it will not be necessary to pass through any area identified under Protection from Hazards in Chapters 8 through 30.

Paragraph 5-5.1.7 prohibits the exit access from passing through any area identified under "Protection from Hazards" (generally in the -3.2 sections such as 18-3.2 or 24-3.2) in the appropriate occupancy chapter.

This underscores a fundamental principle regarding occupant safety. The principle is that, once an occupant is brought to a certain level of safety in the egress system, that level of safety is not to be reduced. Therefore, leading an occupant into an area of relatively greater hazard is prohibited.

5-5.2 Impediments to Egress. *(See also 5-1.7 and 5-2.1.5.)*

5-5.2.1 In no case shall access to an exit be through kitchens, storerooms, restrooms, workrooms, closets, bedrooms or similar spaces, or other rooms subject to locking.

Exception No. 1: Where the exit is required to serve only the bedroom or other room subject to locking, or adjoining rooms constituting part of the same dwelling or apartment used for single-family occupancy.

Exception No. 2: Exit access in detention and correctional occupancies shall be permitted to pass through rooms or spaces subject to locking as provided in Chapters 14 and 15.

Exception No. 3: Exit access in mercantile occupancies shall be permitted to pass through storerooms as provided in Chapters 24 and 25.

Paragraph 5-5.2.1 in combination with 5-5.1.7 prevents exit access from passing through certain rooms due either to increased relative hazard or to potential blockage or locking.

5-5.2.2* Exit access and the doors to exits to which they lead shall be so designed and arranged as to be clearly recognizable. Hangings or draperies shall not be placed over exit doors or otherwise located so as to conceal or obscure any exit. Mirrors shall not be placed on exit doors. Mirrors shall not be placed in or adjacent to any exit in such a manner as to confuse the direction of exit.

A-5-5.2.2 Doors that lead through wall paneling and that harmonize in appearance with the rest of the wall so as to avoid detracting from some desired aesthetic or decorative effect are

not acceptable, as casual occupants may not be aware of such exits even though actually visible.

Also see 31-1.2.

5-5.3 Exterior Ways of Exit Access.

These provisions are for exit access in the typical "motel" arrangement where exit access is provided via an open-air exit access balcony to an open stair. This is also common for apartment buildings and office buildings in warm climates. These provisions play an increasingly important role in the 1991 *Code*, as many of the exceptions for mandatory sprinklers in the various residential occupancies are based on exterior exit access.

5-5.3.1 Exit access shall be permitted to be by means of any exterior balcony, porch, gallery, or roof that conforms to the requirements of this chapter.

5-5.3.2 Exterior exit access balconies shall be separated from the interior of the building by walls and opening protectives as required for corridors.

Exception: Where the exterior exit access balcony is served by at least two stairs and has no dead ends, or where dead ends occur, travel past an unprotected opening is not necessary to reach a stair.

Paragraph 5-5.3.2 states that exterior exit access is to be protected the same as a corridor. However, the exception to this paragraph is very important as the exception is more commonly used than the requirement. Figure 5-59 illustrates different arrangements using the Exception to 5-5.3.2.

5-5.3.3 A permanent, reasonably straight path of travel shall be maintained over the required exterior exit access.

5-5.3.4 There shall be no obstruction by railings, barriers, or gates that divide the open space into sections appurtenant to individual rooms, apartments, or other subdivisions.

5-5.3.5 An exterior exit access shall be so arranged that there are no dead ends in excess of 20 ft (6.1 m).

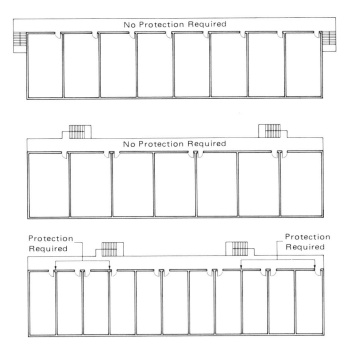

Figure 5-59. In Figures 5-59(a) and (b), no protection is required. Although a limited dead end occurs in (b), travel past an unprotected depending does not occur. In (c), protection is required; otherwise, it would be necessary to travel past an unprotected opening.

5-5.3.6 Any gallery, balcony, bridge, porch, or other exterior exit access that projects beyond the outside wall of the building shall comply with the requirements of this chapter as to width and arrangement.

5-5.3.7 Exterior exit access shall have smooth, solid, substantially level floors and shall have guards on the unenclosed sides at least equivalent to those specified in 5-2.2.4.

5-5.3.8 Where accumulation of snow or ice is likely because of the climate, the exterior exit access shall be protected by a roof.

The intent of the *Code* is to prevent the accumulation of ice and snow to the extent that they prevent the use of the exit access. Any method that accomplishes this goal and is acceptable to the local authority would be satisfactory. Examples of alternative methods are snow melting cables, pipes within the floor, or radiant heaters.

5-5.3.9 The materials of construction shall be as permitted for the building served.

SECTION 5-6 Measurement of Travel Distance to Exits

The *Life Safety Code* specifies the maximum distance that individuals should have to travel from their position in a building to the nearest exit. There is no formula by which this distance can be established.

The factors upon which the Committee on Safety to Life bases maximum travel distances are:

1. The number, age, and physical condition of building occupants and the rate at which they can be expected to move;
2. The type and number of obstructions (e.g., display cases, seating, heavy machinery) that must be negotiated;
3. The number of people in any room or space and the distance from the farthest point in that room to the door;
4. The amount and nature of combustibles expected in a particular occupancy; and
5. The rapidity with which fire might spread, which is a function of the type of construction, the materials used, the degree of compartmentation, and the presence or absence of automatic fire detection and extinguishing systems.

It is obvious that travel distances will vary with the type and size of occupancy and the degree of hazard present. As shown in Table A-5-6.1, maximum travel distances in nonsprinklered buildings can vary from 75 ft (23 m) in high hazard locations to 300 ft (75 m). This figure may be increased by as much as 100 percent, in some cases, if complete sprinkler systems have been installed.

Where the occupant has been provided with at least two paths of travel to an exit, it becomes important that the time needed to travel those paths should not be so great as to place the occupant in further danger. Many factors have been considered and weighed in establishing the maximum permitted travel distances. Because there are no formulae or exact criteria for determining these distances, they are the result of the observation of people in motion, good judgment, and many years of studying the results of fires in which the prefire conditions of a building were known.

Excessive travel distances can be a factor in large losses of life because they increase the time required to exit. There is some evidence that excessive travel distances played a role in a number of the fatalities on the casino floor at the MGM Grand Hotel Fire in Las Vegas in 1980[20]. Of the 85 fatalities, 18 victims were locted on the casino level and some apparently were overrun by the flame front.

5-6.1* The maximum travel distance in any occupied space to at least one exit, measured in accordance with the following requirements, shall not exceed the limits specified in 5-6.4.

A-5-6.1 Table A-5-6.1 is a compilation of the requirements of the individual occupancy chapters (Chapters 8 through 30) for length of dead-end corridors and permissible travel distance to at least one of the required exits.

A dead end occurs where a hallway or other space is so arranged that a person therein is able to travel in one direction only in order to reach any of the exits. Although relatively short dead ends are permitted by this *Code*, it is better practice to eliminate them wherever possible, as they increase the danger of persons being trapped in case of fire. Compliance with the dead-end limits does not necessarily mean that the requirements for remoteness of exits have been met. This is particularly true in small buildings or buildings with short public hallways. Adequate remoteness can be obtained in such cases by further reducing the length of dead ends. (*Also see A-5-5.1.6.*)

It must be kept in mind that the maximum travel distance is that which must not be exceeded to reach the *nearest* exit as defined by 5-1.2.3.

5-6.2* The travel distance to an exit shall be measured on the floor or other walking surface along the centerline of the natural path of travel starting 1 ft (30.5 cm) from the most remote point subject to occupancy, curving around any corners or obstructions with a 1-ft (30.5-cm) clearance therefrom, and ending at the center of the doorway or other point at which

the exit begins. Where measurement includes stairs, the measurement shall be taken in the plane of the tread nosing.

Exception: Travel distance measurement shall be permitted to terminate at a smoke barrier in existing detention and correctional occupancies as provided in Chapter 15.

A-5-6.2 The natural exit access (path of travel) will be influenced by the contents and occupancy of the building. Furniture, fixtures, machinery, or storage may serve to increase the length of travel. It is good practice in building design to recognize this by spacing exits at closer intervals than would be needed for a completely open floor area, thus reducing the hazard of excessive travel distances due to introduction of furniture, fixtures, machinery, or storage, and minimizing the danger of violation of the travel distance requirements of this *Code*.

Figures 5-60a and b illustrate the path along which travel distance to an exit is measured.

Travel distance is that length of travel to an exterior exit door (as shown in Figure 5-60b), an enclosed stair (as shown in Figure 5-60a), an exit passageway, or a horizontal exit. It includes all travel within the occupied space and its atmosphere until an occupant reaches that level of protection afforded by an exit. Therefore, where stairs form part of an exit access rather than an exit, they are to be included in the travel distance (as shown in Figure 5-60b). The measurement, in such cases, would be taken in the plane of the tread nosings. (*See Figure 5-61.*)

Travel distance is always measured from the most remote point, subject to occupancy. (*See Figure 5-62.*)

In the 1988 Edition of the *Code*, the maximum permitted travel distances were increased by 50 ft in most occupancies, since the exception for excluding small rooms or spaces from the measurement of travel distance was deleted at that time. This former provision exempted rooms that contained six or fewer people and that had a travel distance within them of less than 50 ft (15 m) from being included in the overall travel distance measurement. It was deleted since the provision had little validity and was easily and often abused.

5-6.3 Where open stairways or ramps are permitted as a path of travel to required exits, such as between mezzanines or bal-

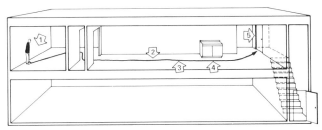

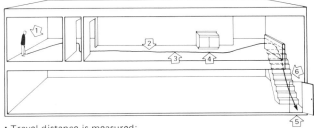

Figures 5-60a and b.   Measuring Travel Distance to an Exit. In Figure 5-60a the stair is enclosed to meet the requirements of an exit enclosure, whereas in Figure 5-53b the stair is not enclosed.

• Travel distance is measured:
1 - starting 1 foot from the most remote point,
2 - along the center line of the natural path of travel,
3 - on the floor or other walking surface,
4 - curving around corners/obstructions with a clearance of 1 foot,
5 - ending where exit begins

• Travel distance is measured:
1 - starting 1 foot from the most remote point,
2 - along the center line of the natural path of travel,
3 - on the floor or other walking surface,
4 - curving around corners/obstructions with a clearance of 1 foot,
5 - ending where exit begins
6 - travel distance includes travel over open stairs and ramps; stairs are measured in the plane of the tread nosing

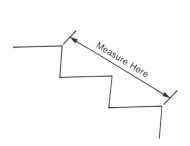

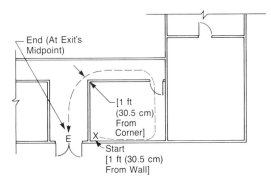

Figure 5-61.   Method for Measuring Distance on Stairs.

Figure 5-62.   Measuring Travel Distance to an Exit. Measurement is always started 1 ft (30.5 cm) from the most remote point, subject to occupancy.

Table A-5.6.1   Exit Travel Distance and Dead-End Limits (By Occupancy)

Type of Occupancy	Dead-End Limit	Travel Limit to an Exit	
		Unsprinklered (ft)	Sprinklered (ft)
ASSEMBLY			
NEW	20[a](6.1 m)	150 (45m)	200 (60 m)
EXISTING	20[a] (6.1 m)	150 (45 m)	200 (60 m)
EDUCATIONAL			
NEW	20 (6.1 m)	150 (45 m)	200 (60 m)
EXISTING	20 (6.1 m)	150 (45 m)	200 (60 m)
NEW DAY-CARE CENTER	20 (6.1 m)	150[c] (45 m)	200[c] (60 m)
EXISTING DAY-CARE CENTER	20 (6.1 m)	150[c] (45 m)	200[c] (60 m)
HEALTH CARE			
NEW	30 (9.1 m)	N.A.[b]	200[c] (60 m)
EXISTING	N.R.[b]	150[c] (45 m)	200[c] (60 m)
NEW AMBULATORY CENTER	20[d] (6.1 m)	150[c] (45 m)	200[c] (60 m)
EXISTING AMBULATORY CENTER	50 (15m)	150[c] (45 m)	200[c] (60 m)
DETENTION AND CORRECTION			
NEW			
Use Conditions			
II, III, IV	50 (15 m)	150[c] (45 m)	200[c] (60 m)
V	20 (6.1 m)	150[c] (45 m)	200[c] (60 m)
EXISTING			
Use Conditions			
II, III, IV, V	N.R.[b]	150[c] (45 m)	200[c] (60 m)
RESIDENTIAL			
A. Hotels and Dormitories			
NEW	35[d] (10.7 m)	100[e] (30 m)	200[e] (60 m)
EXISTING	50 (15 m)	100[e] (30 m)	200[e] (60 m)
B. Apartments			
NEW	35[d] (10.7 m)	100[f] (30 m)	200[f] (60 m)
EXISTING	50 (15 m)	100[f] (30 m)	200[f] (60 m)
C. Board and Care	[g]	[g]	[g]
D. Lodging or Rooming Houses, 1– and 2–Family Dwellings	N.R.[b]	N.R.[b]	N.R.[b]
MERCANTILE			
Class A, B and C			
NEW	20[d] (6.1 m)	100 (30 m)	200 (60 m)
EXISTING	50 (15 m)	150 (45 m)	200 (60 m)
Open Air	0	N.R.[b]	N.R.[b]
Covered Mall			
NEW	20[d] (6.1 m)	100 (30 m)	400[h] (120 m)
EXISTING	50 (15 m)	150 (45 m)	400[h] (120 m)
BUSINESS			
NEW	20[d] (6.1 m)	200 (60 m)	300 (91 m)
EXISTING	50 (15 m)	200 (60 m)	300 (91 m)

(continued)

Table A-5-6.1 Exit Travel Distance and Dead–End Limits (By Occupancy) (continued)

Type of Occupancy	Dead–End Limit (ft)	Travel Limit to an Exit	
		Unsprinklered (ft)	Sprinklered (ft)
INDUSTRIAL			
General	50 (15 m)	200 (60 m)	250[i] (75 m)
Special Purpose (Low or Ordinary Hazard)	50 (15 m)	300 (91 m)	400 (122 m)
High Hazard	0	75 (23 m)	75 (23 m)
Open Structures	N.R.[b]	N.R.[b]	N.R.[b]
STORAGE			
Low Hazard	N.R.[b]	N.R.[b]	N.R.[b]
Ordinary Hazard	50[j] (15 m)	200 (60 m)	400 (122 m)
High Hazard	0	75 (23 m)	100 (30 m)
Parking Garages, Open	50 (15 m)	200 (60 m)	300 (91 m)
Parking Garages, Enclosed	50 (15 m)	150 (45 m)	200 (60 m)
Aircraft Hangars, Ground Floor	50[j] (15 m)	Varies[j]	Varies[j]
Aircraft Hangars, Mezzanine Floor	50[j] (15 m)	75 (23 m)	75 (23 m)
Grain Elevators	[j]	200[j] (60 m)	400[j] (122 m)
Miscellaneous Occupancies, Towers, Piers, and Water Surrounded Structures,Vehicles, and Vessels, and Emergency Shelters	50 (15 m)	100 (30 m)	150 (45 m)

[a] See Chapters 8 and 9 for aisles and mezzanines.
[b] No requirement or not applicable.
[c] This dimension is for total travel distance, for travel distance within the room, and from the room exit access door to the exit. See the appropriate occupancy chapter.
[d] In sprinklered facilities 50 ft (15 m).
[e] This dimension is from the room exit access door to the exit. See Chapters 16 and 17 for exceptions and limitations within the room/suite.
[f] This dimension is from the room exit access door to the exit. See Chapters 18 and 19 for exceptions and limitations within the room/suite.
[g] See Chapters 22 and 23.
[h] See Chapters 24 and 25 for exceptions and special considerations.
[i] See Chapter 28 for special considerations.
[j] See Chapters 28 and 29 for special requirements.

conies and the floor below, the distance shall include the travel on the stairway or ramp and the travel from the end of the stairway or ramp to an outside door or other exit in addition to the distance traveled to reach the stairway or ramp.

5-6.4 Travel Distance Limitations. Travel distance to at least one exit shall not exceed 200 ft (60 m) in buildings not sprinklered or exceed 250 ft (76 m) in buildings protected throughout by an approved supervised sprinkler system in accordance with Section 7-7.

Exception No. 1: Where other travel distance limitations are specified in Chapters 8 through 30.

Exception No. 2: Travel distance for areas having high hazard contents as specified in Section 5-11.

Although Chapter 5 establishes general travel distance limitations, almost all occupancy chapters establish their own limits, and therefore Exception No. 1 is very important.

5-6.5 Where any part of an exterior exit is within 10 ft (3 m) horizontal distance of any unprotected building opening, as permitted by 5-2.2.6.3 for outside stairs, the travel distance to the exit shall include the length of travel to ground level.

The intent of this paragraph is to clarify that, if the exterior stair is exposed by unprotected building openings, it is not considered as an exit but as an exit access, and the travel distance is measured down the stair. (*Also see commentary in 5-2.2.1.*)

SECTION 5-7   Discharge from Exits

5-7.1* All exits shall terminate directly at a public way or at an exit discharge. Yards, courts, open spaces, or other portions of the exit discharge shall be of required width and size to provide all occupants with a safe access to a public way.

Exception No. 1: As permitted by 5-7.2 and 5-7.5.

Exception No. 2: Means of egress may terminate in an exterior area of refuge in detention and correctional occupancies as provided in Chapters 14 and 15.

A-5-7.1 An exit from the upper stories, in which the direction of exit travel is generally downward, should not be arranged so that it is necessary to change over to travel in an upward direction at any point before discharging to the outside. A similar prohibition of reversal of the vertical component of travel should be applied to exits from stories below the floor of exit discharge. However, an exception is permissible in the case of stairs used in connection with overhead or underfloor exit passageways that serve the street floor only.

It is important that ample roadways be available from buildings in which there are large numbers of occupants so that exits will not be blocked by persons already outside. Two or more avenues of departure should be available for all but very small places. Location of a larger theater, for example, on a narrow dead-end street, may properly be prohibited by the authority having jurisdiction under this rule unless some alternate way of travel to another street is available.

The principle addressed in this section is that once a building occupant is brought into the protected portion of the means of egress, the level of protection cannot be reduced or eliminated. Therefore, except as noted, all exits must be continuous to a public way or other safe place or to an exit discharge that must, in turn, be continuous to the public way.

It is not sufficient to require that exits terminate at the outside of a building, because there may not be a space affording sufficient protection to provide safe movement away from the building involved. Also, the terminus cannot be to the outside in a closed court from which some sort of travel back through the building may be neces-

sary in order to get away from the building. In such a case, an exit passageway at least as wide as the exit itself and constructed as specified for exits is required to provide travel from the courtyard to the safe place.

(Also see commentary on exit passageways in 5-2.6.)

Formal Interpretation 81-33
Reference: 5-7.1

Question 1: In a health care occupancy, are sidewalks required between the exit door and the public way in order to qualify as an exit discharge as stated in Paragraph 5-7.1?

Answer: No.

Question 2: If the answer to Question 1 is "no," then is an open and unobstructed yard large enough to provide all occupants with a safe access to a public way acceptable as an exit discharge?

Answer: Yes, however, the path of safe access to the public way must also meet 5-1.6 with respect to changes in elevation and 5-1.7.3 with respect to maintaining the means of egress free of obstructions that would prevent its use, such as snow in some climates and the need for its removal.

Issue Edition: 1981
Reference: 5-7.1
Date: July 1983 ■

5-7.2 A maximum of 50 percent of the required number of exits and 50 percent of the required exit capacity shall be permitted to discharge through areas on the level of discharge provided all of the following are met:

(a) Such exits discharge to a free and unobstructed way to the exterior of the building, which way is readily visible and identifiable from the point of discharge from the exit.

(b) The entire area on the level of discharge is separated from areas below by construction having a fire resistance rating not less than that for the exit enclosure.

(c) The level of discharge is protected throughout by an approved automatic sprinkler system, and any other portion of the level of discharge with access to the discharge area is protected throughout by an approved automatic sprinkler system or separated from it in accordance with the requirements for the enclosure of exits. (*See 5-1.3.1.*)

Exception to (c): If the discharge area is a vestibule or foyer meeting all of the following:

1. The depth from the exterior of the building is not greater than 10 ft (3 m) and the length is not greater than 30 ft (9.1 m).

2. The foyer is separated from the remainder of the level of discharge by construction providing protection at least the equivalent of wired glass in steel frames.

3. The foyer serves only for means of egress including exits directly to the outside.

Exception: One hundred percent of the exits shall be permitted to discharge through areas on the level of exit discharge in detention and correctional occupancies as provided in Chapters 14 and 15.

The intent of 5-7.2 is to provide an equivalent level of protection for exits discharging through the level of exit discharge. Probably the most often asked question concerning this section involves the requirements of item (c). The intent of item (c) is to require that the entire level of exit discharge and any area connected to the level of discharge with access to the discharge area be protected by automatic sprinklers. As an alternative, the sprinklered area must be separated from the rest of the level of discharge by construction as required for exits (*see 5-1.3.1*). An exception to the sprinkler requirement is the 10-ft (3-m) maximum by 30-ft (9.1-m) maximum wired glass foyer.

The use of the 50 percent rule for discharge through the level of exit discharge is allowed in all occupancies. It is not allowed in conjunction with smokeproof enclosures and is limited in use with horizontal exits. Note, however, that detention and correctional occupancies (14-2.7.2 and 15-2.7.2) and mercantile occupancies (24-2.7 and 25-2.7) have special requirements for discharging through the level of exit discharge.

Figures 5-63 and 5-64 illustrate alternate arrangements for the exit discharge required by 5-7.2.

5-7.3 The exit discharge shall be so arranged and marked as to make clear the direction of egress to a public way. Stairs that continue beyond the level of exit discharge shall be interrupted at the level of exit discharge by partitions, doors, or other effective means.

Exception: Stairs that continue one-half story beyond the level of exit discharge need not be so interrupted where the exit discharge is obvious.

See also 5-2.2.3.6 on stair details.

The Exception to 5-7.3 is most commonly used in "garden-type" apartment buildings.

5-7.4 Stairs, ramps, bridges, balconies, escalators, moving walks, and other components of an exit discharge shall comply with the detailed requirements of this chapter for such components.

Section 5-2 details the requirements.

5-7.5 Subject to the approval of the authority having jurisdiction, exits may be accepted where:

(a) They discharge to the roof or other sections of the building or adjoining buildings, and

(b) The roof has a fire resistance rating at least the equivalent of that required for the exit enclosure, and

(c) There is a continuous and safe means of egress from the roof, and

(d) All other reasonable requirements for life safety are maintained.

An exit discharge to a roof is not acceptable unless there is another continuous and safe means of egress from the roof and the roof construction affords protection against fire at least equivalent to that of the stair enclosure. Helicopter rescue from roofs is not dependable enough to be given credit as an exit; many factors are too unpredictable for this to be a consideration.

In addition, exits over roofs must be protected against the accumulation of snow or ice and other impediments to their free use as exits.

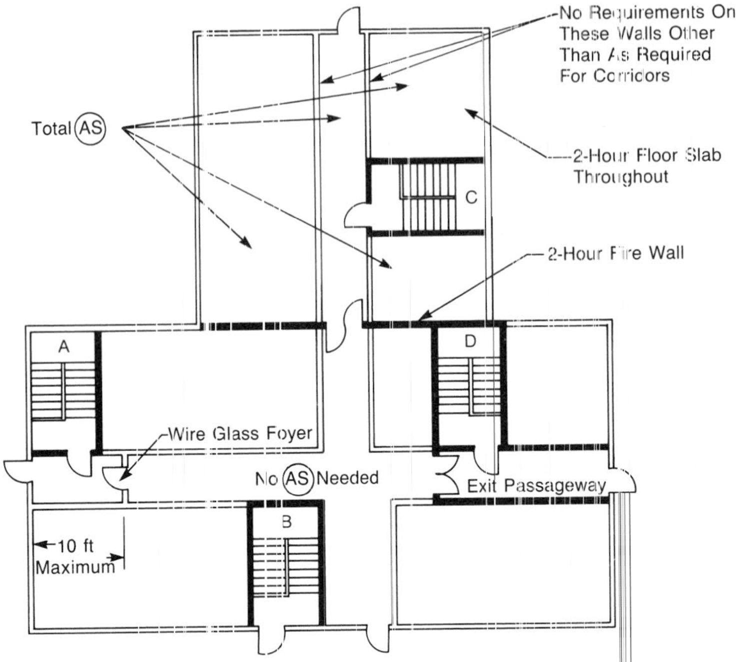

No Requirements On
These Walls Other
Than As Required
For Corridors

Total (AS)

2-Hour Floor Slab
Throughout

C

2-Hour Fire Wall

A

Wire Glass Foyer

No (AS) Needed

Exit Passageway

D

10 ft
Maximum

B

Figure 5-63. *Exit Discharge. The stairs provide four required exits for the upper floors. Two of these exits (B & D) exit directly outside (an exit passageway is part of the exit) and 50 percent discharge across the first floor (one using the wired glass foyer option). The rating of the floor slab and the fire wall are based on the required rating of the stair enclosure.*

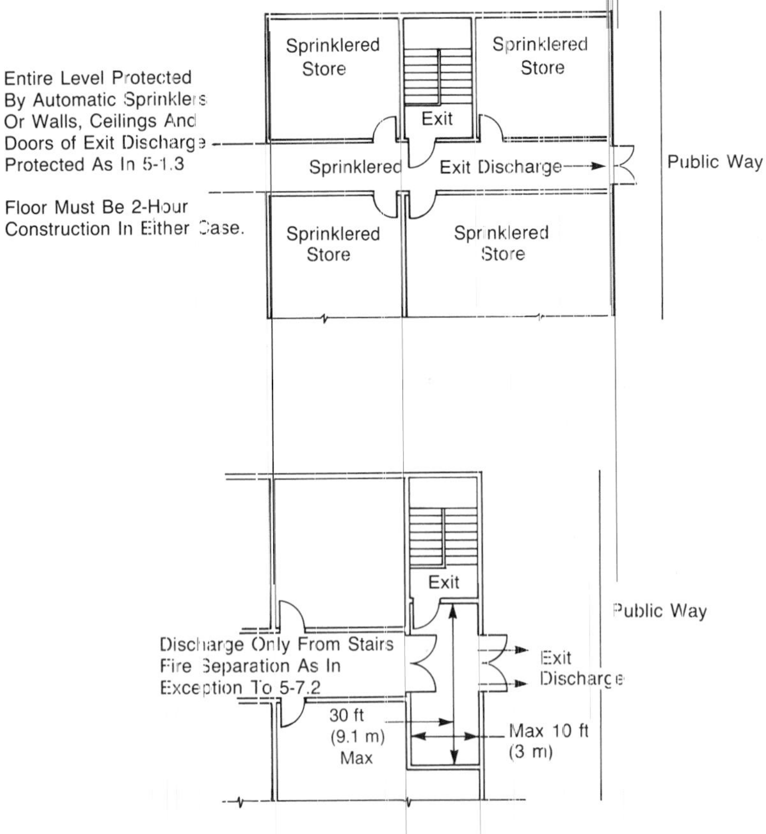

Entire Level Protected
By Automatic Sprinklers
Or Walls, Ceilings And
Doors of Exit Discharge
Protected As In 5-1.3

Floor Must Be 2-Hour
Construction In Either Case.

Sprinklered
Store

Sprinklered
Store

Exit

Sprinklered

Exit Discharge

Public Way

Sprinklered
Store

Sprinklered
Store

Figure 5-64. *Alternate Arrangements for Exit Discharge. Two ways to comply with 5-7.2(c) are illustrated.*

Exit

Public Way

Discharge Only From Stairs
Fire Separation As In
Exception To 5-7.2

30 ft
(9.1 m)
Max

Exit
Discharge

Max 10 ft
(3 m)

SECTION 5-8 Illumination of Means of Egress

When fire occurs in a building, the degree of visibility in corridors, stairs, and passageways may mean the difference between orderly evacuation and chaos — possibly between life and death. A brief glance at the history of fires reveals several famous fires in which the failure of normal or emergency lighting was a major factor in the casualties incurred. Some of these fires are listed below.

Iroquois Theater, Chicago, 1903 — 602 deaths[21]
Cocoanut Grove Night Club, Boston, 1942 — 492 deaths[21]
Baltimore Oyster Roast, 1956 — 11 deaths[21]
Apartment House, Boston, 1971 — 8 deaths[22]
Summerland, Isle of Man, 1973 — 50 deaths[23]
Mental Hospital, Mississippi, 1978 — 15 deaths[24]

The report on the 1971 Massachusetts apartment fire where 8 people died stated, "Among the conditions contributing to the ... loss of life were ... the lack of emergency lighting and the lack of illuminated exit signs."

The report on the 1973 fire in the amusement complex on the Isle of Man in Great Britain, where 50 people died, stated, "the problems with the evacuation are...(5) an insufficient number of exit signs and directional signs. ...(7) The emergency lighting did not come on when the main power was shut off by a staff member in an act of misguided zeal."

The report on the 1978 mental hospital fire in Mississippi, which killed 15 people, stated "Heat and flame ... impinged directly on the emergency lighting conduit, causing ... a short circuit to occur. The short tripped the circuit breaker ... leaving the north end of the building without emergency lighting. However, in this fire, the emergency lighting circuits on the first floor were not used. The dual-function lighting circuits were switched in the 'off' position in both wards. The attendant entering Ward 1 to evacuate the residents did not turn the lights on. In Ward 2, the switch could not be reached by the attendants, and the circuit shorted out soon after the discovery of the fire. The darkness contributed to the difficulty in evacuating both wards." A lack of illuminated exit signs in several key places was also noted in the report.

5-8.1 General.

5-8.1.1 Illumination of means of egress shall be provided in accordance with this section for every building and structure where required in Chapters 8 through 30. For the purposes of this requirement, exit access shall include only designated stairs, aisles, corridors, ramps, escalators, and passageways leading to an exit.

The *Code* requires that there be at least 1 footcandle (10 lx) of illumination at floor level in all three elements of a means of egress: the exit access, the exit, and the exit discharge. For the purposes of this section only, the *Code* limits exit access to designated stairs, aisles, corridors, and passageways leading to an exit. Such components should include those portions of the exit access serving occupied spaces. It is not necessary to keep the lights on in all rooms if the rooms are not occupied. The stairs, aisles, and corridors should be designated by the authority having jurisdiction. While motion pictures, slides, and the like are being shown in theaters, auditoriums, and other assembly occupancies, the level of illumination can be reduced to one-fifth of a footcandle.

5-8.1.2 Illumination of means of egress shall be continuous during the time that the conditions of occupancy require that the means of egress be available for use. Artificial lighting shall be employed at such places and for such periods of time as required to maintain the illumination to the minimum footcandle [Lux (lx)] values herein specified.

5-8.1.3* The floors of means of egress shall be illuminated at all points including angles and intersections of corridors and passageways, stairways, landings of stairs, and exit doors to values of not less than 1 footcandle (10 lx) measured at the floor.

Exception: In assembly occupancies, the illumination of the floors of exit access shall be not less than 1/5 footcandle (2 lx) during periods of performances or projections involving directed light.

Formal Interpretation 76-91
Reference: 5-8.1.2

Question 1: Is it the intent of 5-8.1.2 that all means of egress be continuously illuminated?

Answer: Yes, when occupied.

Question 2: Does 5-8.1.2 permit illumination of the means of egress to be shut off at times when the entire building is unoccupied?

Answer: Yes.

Question 3: Does 5-8.1.2 permit shutting off the illumination of the means of egress on an area-by-area basis, as the occupants of these areas leave the building?

Answer: Yes, as long as there are no required means of egress serving occupied areas through the nonilluminated areas.

Issue Edition: 1976
Reference: 5-8.1.2
Date: March 1979 ■

A-5-8.1.3 A desirable form of means of egress lighting is by lights recessed in walls about a foot (30 cm) above the floor. Such lights are not likely to be obscured by smoke.

5-8.1.4 Any required illumination shall be so arranged that the failure of any single lighting unit, such as the burning out of an electric bulb, will not leave any area in darkness.

All arrangements of lights, circuits, or auxiliary power must be such that continuity of egress lighting will be ensured. This can be accomplished in a number of ways: duplicate light bulbs in fixtures, overlapping light patterns, or overlapping dual circuits.

5-8.1.5 The equipment or units installed to meet the requirements of Section 5-10 shall be permitted also to serve the function of illumination of means of egress, provided that all applicable requirements of this section for such illumination are also met.

5-8.2 Sources of Illumination.

5-8.2.1 Illumination of means of egress shall be from a source of reasonably assured reliability, such as public utility electric service.

5-8.2.2 No battery-operated electric light nor any type of portable lamp or lantern shall be used for primary illumination of means of egress. Battery-operated electric lights shall be permitted to be used as an emergency source to the extent permitted under Section 5-9, "Emergency Lighting."

Where batteries are used for emergency power, they shall be the type that will automatically be kept charged and shall perform at the specified levels for 1½ hours when needed.

SECTION 5-9   Emergency Lighting

Also see commentary following Section 5-8.

Note that emergency lighting is not required unless specifically called for in the appropriate occupancy chapter. Most occupancy chapters require emergency lighting in medium to large buildings. See the -2.9 subsection (for example, 8-2.9 or 24-2.9) of each occupancy chapter.

Formal Interpretation 76-135
Reference: Section 5-9

Question: When an occupancy chapter requires emergency lighting, is it the intent of Section 5-9 to require emergency lighting in the exit discharge?

Answer: Yes. However, the authority having jurisdiction may modify this requirement if he believes that conditions are such that emergency lighting is not warranted based on other factors.

Issue Edition: 1976
Reference: Section 5-9
Date: May 1980 ■

5-9.1 General.

5-9.1.1 Emergency lighting facilities for means of egress shall be provided in accordance with this section for every building or structure where required in Chapters 8 through 30. For the purposes of this requirement, exit access shall include only designated stairs, aisles, corridors, ramps, escalators, and passageways leading to an exit.

5-9.1.2 Where maintenance of illumination depends upon changing from one energy source to another, there shall be no appreciable interruption of illumination during the changeover. Where emergency lighting is provided by a prime mover-operated electric generator, a delay of not more than 10 seconds shall be permitted.

An on-site generator driven by a prime mover must be automatically started and capable of picking up the emergency lighting load within ten seconds. Where the generator set is not able to supply power within this time frame, an auxiliary power source must be provided.

Some turbine driven emergency generators take longer than ten-seconds to reach operating speed. A backup battery pack, such as an uninterruptible power supply (UPS), capable of delivering emergency power for a few minutes must be used in conjunction with any on-site generator that cannot meet the ten-second requirement.

Section 700-5 of NFPA 70, the *National Electrical Code®*,[25] allows use of an emergency generator for load shedding and peak load shaving provided that these loads can be disconnected when normal power to the emergency lighting system is lost.

Although not required by the National Electrical Code, the use of bypass-isolation transfer switches should be considered. These devices allow maintenance and repair of the transfer switch mechanism without interruption of power to the emergency loads. Bypass switches are interlocked to prevent simultaneous interconnection of the two power sources, and isolation of the transfer switch is usually accomplished by operation of a drawout handle. This type of construction should be used where continuity of electrical service to the emergency system is essential. (*See Figure 5-65.*)

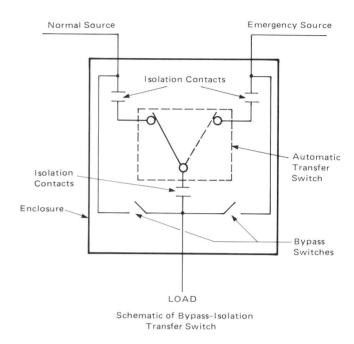

Figure 5-65. *Schematic of Bypass-Isolation Transfer Switch.*

5-9.2 Performance of System.

5-9.2.1* Emergency illumination shall be provided for a period of 1½ hours in the event of failure of normal lighting. Emergency lighting facilities shall be arranged to provide initial illumination that is no less than an average of 1 footcandle (10 lx) and a minimum at any point of .1 footcandle (1 lx) measured along the path of egress at floor level. Illumination levels may decline to .6 footcandle (6 lx) average and a minimum at any point of .06 footcandle (.6 lx) at the end of the emergency lighting time duration. A maximum to minimum illumination uniformity ratio of 40 to 1 shall not be exceeded.

A-5-9.2.1 The illumination uniformity ratio is determined by the following formula:

$$\frac{\text{Maximum illumination at any point}}{\text{Minimum illumination at any point}}$$

This paragraph was significantly revised for the 1991 Edition of the *Code*. Instead of a 1 footcandle (10 lx) minimum, the *Code* now requires a 1 footcandle (10 lx) *average* and establishes a .1 footcandle (1 lx) *minimum*, with a uniformity ratio maximum of 40 to 1 to prevent excessively bright and dark spots. Testimony on this change indicated that the former requirements were simply not being met, especially when using unit lighting. Research by the Illuminating Engineering Society's (IES) Emergency Lighting Committee showed that significantly lower levels were very satisfactory and were, in fact, used in Europe. The committee concurred with the material submitted but felt that the reduction to .5 footcandles (5 lx) and .05 footcandles (.5 lx) was too drastic a reduction, and the new figures were agreed upon. This will still provide an adequate safety factor based on the research conducted.

5-9.2.2* The emergency lighting system shall be so arranged as to provide the required illumination automatically in the event of any interruption of normal lighting, such as any failure of public utility or other outside electrical power supply, opening of a circuit breaker or fuse, or any manual act(s), including accidental opening of a switch controlling normal lighting facilities.

A-5-9.2.2 Where approved by the authority having jurisdiction, this requirement may be met by means such as:

(a) Two separate electric lighting systems with independent wiring, each adequate alone to provide the specified lighting, one supplied from an outside source such as a public utility service and the other from an electric generator on the premises driven by an independent source of power, both sources of illumination being in regular simultaneous operation whenever the building is occupied during periods of darkness.

(b) An electric circuit or circuits used only for means of egress illumination with two independent electric sources so arranged that on the failure of one the other will come automatically and immediately into operation. One such source by a connection from a public utility or similar outside power source and the other an approved storage battery with suitable provision to keep it automatically charged. Such battery being provided with automatic controls that after the battery comes into operation, due to failure of the primary power source or to turning off the primary electric source for the lights, it will be shut off after its specified period of operation and will be automatically recharged and ready for further service when the primary current source is again turned on.

(c) Electric battery-operated emergency lighting systems, where permitted, complying with the provisions of 5-9.2.2, and operating on a separate circuit and at a voltage different from that of the primary light. Refer to NFPA 70, *National Electrical Code*. (See *Appendix B*.)

These requirements are not intended to prohibit the connection of a feeder serving exit lighting and similar emergency functions ahead of the service disconnecting means, but such provision does not constitute an acceptable alternate source of power. It furnishes only supplementary protection for emergency electrical functions, particularly where intended to permit the fire department to open the main disconnect without hampering exit activities. Provision should be made to alert the fire department that certain power and lighting is fed by an emergency generator and will continue operation after the service disconnect is opened.

> **Formal Interpretation 76-94**
> Reference: Section 5-9
>
> *Question:* Where emergency lighting is provided by automatic transfer between normal power service and an emergency diesel generator, does Section 5-9 permit installation of a single switch that can interrupt both energy sources for reasons of repair and maintenance?
>
> *Answer:* No.
>
> *Issue Edition:* 1976
> *Reference:* Section 5-9
> *Date:* March 1979 ∎

Six methods of providing emergency power are recognized in NFPA 70, the *National Electrical Code*;[25] however, some of these sources do not meet the requirements for emergency lighting under the *Life Safety Code*.

Storage batteries are an acceptable emergency source and may be used to continuously supply required emergency lighting. For this arrangement, two separate lighting systems with independent wiring are employed. One system may be supplied from a public utility and the other from storage batteries. Either supply source must have

Formal Interpretation 76-50
Reference: 5-9.2.2

Question No. 1: Does a second "source of power" fed from a second substation (i.e., other than the normal feed), supplied by a second tie line fed by two public utilities, and requiring no automatic switch operation, if properly maintained, comply with the literal meaning of 5-9.2.2?

Answer: No.

Question No. 2: Does the design given in Question 1 comply with the intent of 5-9.2.2 regarding sources of emergency lighting system power?

Answer: No.

NOTE: Emergency lighting is to be designed to provide lighting for the emergency evacuation of building occupants regardless of the reason for power failure. However, it is not the intent of the *Code* that the emergency lighting system be capable of withstanding building structure damage as may be present in earthquakes or tornadoes.

Issue Edition: 1976
Reference: 5-9.2.3
Date: May 1978 ■

Formal Interpretation 76-93
Reference: 5-9.2.2

Question: In a building with an independent emergency lighting system, is it the intent of 5-9.2.2 that the emergency lights automatically turn on when corridor lights are manually turned off during periods of adequate daylight, or when the building is unoccupied?

Answer: No.

Issue Edition: 1976
Reference: 5-9.2.3
Date: March 1979 ■

sufficient capacity, and emergency lighting must be designed so that adequate light for a specified time is available should one system fail.

Instead of installing two separate wiring systems, a single emergency system connected to an automatic transfer switch is often used. The two sources of power — normal and emergency — are connected to the transfer switch, which automatically switches the emergency lighting load from the normal source to the emergency source upon loss of normal power. When normal power is restored, the emergency load is transferred to the normal source.

Batteries that are used for the emergency source must be suitable for the application. Automotive-type batteries are not acceptable.

Where an on-site generator is the emergency power source, it is generally controlled by a transfer switch. Upon loss of normal emergency power, a signal is sent to start the generator. When the generator is running at rated speed and its output voltage is correct, the emergency load is connected to this source by operation of the automatic transfer switch. This transfer must take place in ten seconds or less. (*See Figure 5-66.*)

Figure 5-67 shows two methods of obtaining an emergency power supply by connection ahead of the service disconnecting means. Although not prohibited by NFPA 70, this method does not comply with the requirements for emergency lighting of NFPA 101 and may not be acceptable to the authority having jurisdiction. Before considering this method to supply emergency power for other than emergency lighting, the reliability of the utility system in the area must be evaluated, and the risk to occupants of the building must be carefully thought out. Since this arrangement only provides protection from electrical failures in the occupancy, such as blown fuses; tripped circuit breakers; a localized fire at the electrical service, distribution panels, etc., availability of the emergency source is dependent on the reliability of the public utility.

Connecting the emergency lighting circuit to the main power line on the "live" side of the main disconnect has the advantage of service continuity should the main switch be thrown by employees or fire fighters as a precautionary measure. The *Code* does not prohibit this practice;

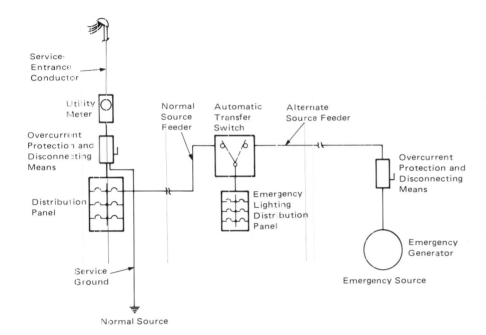

Figure 5-66. Arrangement of Normal and Alternate Sources Where Emergency Power is Supplied from an On-Site Generator.

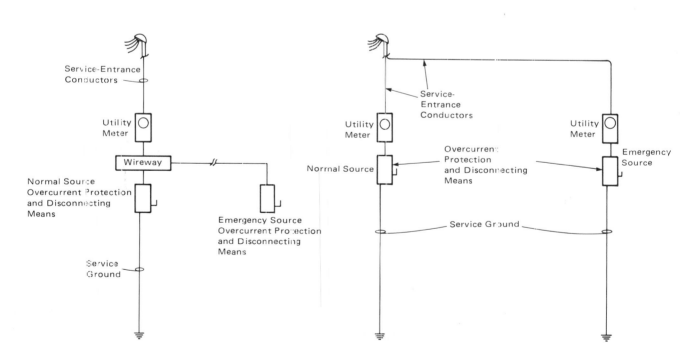

Figure 5-67. Two Methods of Obtaining an Emergency Source by Connection Ahead of the Service Disconnecting Means. [See Section 700-12(e) of NFPA 70, National Electrical Code.] This does not meet the requirements for emergency lighting in the Life Safety Code.

however, it should be noted that this method does not meet the requirements for emergency lighting.

Two separate services — one for normal power and the other for emergency power — are also recognized by NFPA 70, *National Electrical Code*, subject to approval by the authority having jurisdiction but, again, not acceptable by the *Life Safety Code* for emergency lighting. Usually this method provides a higher degree of reliability than the "connection ahead of the service disconnecting means" but does not satisfy the requirements of 5-9.2.3. However, underground loop systems in downtown areas of large cities are quite reliable. Many public utilities have not experienced an outage on their loop systems for many years, but there is no protection from any electrical failures that might occur outside of the occupancy. To reduce the possibility of simultaneous loss of both power sources, consideration should be given to the use of different voltages for the normal and emergency systems, taking power for each system from separate manholes or employing other schemes that provide both electrical and physical separation between the normal and emergency source. (*See Figure 5-68.*)

Individual battery operated lights can also be used for emergency lighting. Specific rules in NFPA 70, *National Electrical Code*, govern installation. These products are referred to in the *National Electrical Code* as unit equipment.

To qualify for emergency lighting, each unit equipment must have a rechargeable battery, a battery charging means, provision for one or more lamps, and a relay to energize the lamps automatically upon failure of the normal supply. Unit equipment must be connected to the same branch circuit that supplies normal lighting to the area in which it is located. Connection to this branch circuit must be ahead of, or on the line side of, any switches controlling the normal lighting. An exception in the *NEC*® allows connection of unit equipment directly to a branch circuit from a panelboard that also supplies a minimum of three normal lighting circuits to the area in which the unit equipment is installed. The overcurrent device protecting this unit equipment circuit must be provided with a lock-on feature that will prevent accidental disconnection.

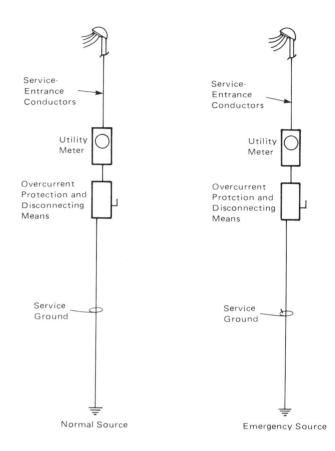

Figure 5-68. *Two Separate Services to the Same Building as Permitted by Section 700-12(d) of NFPA 70, National Electrical Code. This is not recognized by the Life Safety Code for emergency lighting.*

5-9.2.3 Emergency generators used to provide power to emergency lighting systems shall be installed, tested, and maintained in accordance with NFPA 110, *Emergency and Standby Power Systems*.

5-9.2.4* Battery-operated emergency lights shall use only reliable types of rechargeable batteries provided with suitable facilities for maintaining them in properly charged condition. Batteries used in such lights or units shall be approved for their intended use and shall comply with NFPA 70, *National Electrical Code*.®

A-5-9.2.4 Automobile-type lead storage batteries are not suitable by reason of their relatively short life when not subject to frequent discharge and recharge as occurs in automobile operation.

For proper selection and maintenance of appropriate batteries, refer to NFPA 70, *National Electrical Code*. (*See Appendix B.*)

5-9.2.5 The emergency lighting system shall be either continuously in operation or capable of repeated automatic operation without manual intervention.

5-9.3 Testing and Maintenance. (*See Section 31-1.*)

SECTION 5-10   Marking of Means of Egress

In the fatal Westchase Hilton Hotel fire, which occurred in Houston, Texas, March 1982,[26] "several people were confused by the exit markings or the similarity of exit doors and adjacent storage room doors. The directional exit signs within the exit foyers at the ends of the hotel corridors indicated that the exit path from this point would be perpendicular to the exit access corridor. Some of the occupants moved toward the locked storage room doors and away from the exits."

Also see commentary on Sections 5-8 and 5-9.

5-10.1 General.

5-10.1.1 Means of egress shall be marked in accordance with this section where required in Chapters 8 through 30.

Marking of means of egress is not required unless specifically called for by the appropriate occupancy chapter. See the -2.10 section (for example, 8-2.10) of each chapter to find out where marking is required.

5-10.1.2* Exits shall be marked by an approved sign readily visible from any direction of exit access.

Exception: Main exterior exit doors that obviously and clearly are identifiable as exits.

A-5-10.1.2 Where a main entrance serves also as an exit, it will usually be sufficiently obvious to occupants so that no exit sign is needed.

The character of the occupancy has a practical effect upon the need for signs. In any place of assembly, hotel, department store, or other building subject to transient occupancy, the need for signs will be greater than in a building subject to permanent or semipermanent occupancy by the same people, such as an apartment house where the residents may be presumed to be familiar with exit facilities by reason of regular use thereof. Even in a permanent residence type of building, however, there is need for signs to identify exit facilities such as outside stairs that are not subject to regular use during the normal occupancy of the building.

There are many types of situations where the actual need for signs may be debatable. In cases of doubt, however, it is desirable to be on the safe side by providing signs, particularly as the placing of signs does not ordinarily involve any material expense or inconvenience.

The requirement for the locations of exit signs visible from any direction of exit access may be illustrated as shown in Figure A-5-10.1.2.

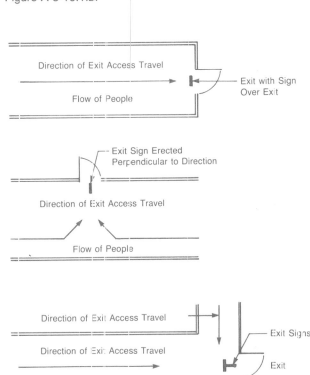

Figure A-5-10.1.2

5-10.1.3   Access to exits shall be marked by approved readily visible signs in all cases where the exit or way to reach it is not readily apparent to the occupants. Sign placement shall be such that no point in the exit access is more than 100 ft (30 m) from the nearest visible sign.

Exception: Signs in existing buildings need not meet the 100-ft (30-m) distance requirement.

The 100-ft (30-m) distance requirement has been established since sign size and illumination levels are based on visibility from 100 ft (30 m).

5-10.1.4*   Where floor proximity exit signs are specifically required by Chapters 8 through 30, exit signs shall be placed near the floor level in addition to those signs required for doors or corridors by 5-10.1.2 and 5-10.1.3. These signs shall be sized and illuminated in accordance with the requirements of 5-10.2 and 5-10.3. The bottom of the sign shall be not less than 6 in. (15.2 cm) nor more than 8 in. (20.3 cm) above the floor. For exit doors, the sign shall be mounted on the door or adjacent to the door with the closest edge of the sign within 4 in. (10.2 cm) of the door frame.

A-5-10.1.4   (*See A-5-10.2.*)

Since locations near the ceiling may be the first to become obstructed by smoke, this provision makes it possible for the occupancy chapters to specify low level signs to supplement the regular exit signs that are usually placed over the exits. Such supplemental signs may be approved luminescent, self-luminous, or self-illuminated types. They are not intended to replace standard exit signs but are designed as an extra asset to a building occupant seeking egress in a smoke-filled environment at a location that is the last to become obscured.

The provisions of 5-10.1.3 can be used as guidance where it is desired to install low level signs even though they may not be required.

At the present time, none of the occupancy chapters mandates low level exit signs other than for special amusement buildings in 8-4.6 and 9-4.6.

5-10.1.5*   Every sign required by Section 5-10 shall be so located and of such size, distinctive color, and design as to

be readily visible and shall provide contrast with decorations, interior finish, or other signs. No decorations, furnishings, or equipment that impair visibility of an exit sign shall be permitted, nor shall there be any brightly illuminated sign (for other than exit purposes), display, or object in or near the line of vision of the required exit sign of such a character as to so detract attention from the exit sign.

A-5-10.1.5   In stores, for example, an otherwise adequate exit sign may be made inconspicuous by some high-intensity illuminated advertising sign in the immediate vicinity.

Red is the traditional color for exit signs and is required by law in many places. However, at an early stage in the development of the *Code*, a provision was made that green be the color for exit signs, following the idea of traffic lights where green indicates safety and red is the signal to stop. During the period when green signs were specified by the *Code*, many such signs were installed, but the traditional red signs also persisted. In 1949, the Fire Marshals Association of North America voted to request that red be restored as the required exit sign color, as they found that the provision for green involved difficulties in law enactment out of proportion to the importance of the subject. The 10th Edition of the *Code* accordingly specified red where not otherwise required by law. The present text avoids any specific requirement for color on the assumption that either red or green will be used in most cases, and that there may be some situations where some color other than red or green may actually provide better visibility.

In some locations, an otherwise adequate exit sign might be rendered inconspicuous by a high-intensity illuminated advertising sign in the immediate vicinity. For this reason, such distractions are not allowed near the line of vision to an exit sign.

The location of exit signs is not specified. Usually they are placed over the exit near the ceiling. There are those who argue, with reason, that smoke builds up more rapidly at higher levels and exit signs a foot or so above the floor would be visible for a much longer period in a fire situation. However, when several people are moving toward an exit, those in the rear might not be able to see signs located at a low level. Also, in the absence of careful housekeeping, such signs might be damaged or blocked. Thus, the *Code* simply states that exit signs be located to be readily visible and provide contrast with the surroundings.

As indicated in the appendix note, the issue of sign color has been the subject of considerable debate. The *Building Exits Code* required since its first edition in 1927 through 1947 that exit signs have white letters on a green field unless such color was contrary to local law. The appendix note describes the development of events since 1949.

5-10.1.6   Where floor proximity egress path marking is specifically required by Chapters 8 through 30, a listed and approved floor proximity egress path marking system that is internally illuminated shall be installed within 8 in. (20.3 cm) of the floor. The system shall provide a visible delineation of the path of travel along the designated exit access and shall be essentially continuous, except as interrupted by doorways, hallways, corridors, or other such architectural features. The system shall operate continuously or at any time the building fire alarm system is activated. The activation, duration, and continuity of operation of the system shall be in accordance with 5-9.2.

This is a new paragraph in the 1991 Edition of the *Code*. It provides a standard for floor proximity egress path marking for use by the occupancy chapters or for use by one wishing to use such a system. This type of marking has been mandatory on aircraft for several years. It is not mandatory for any occupancy under the *Code*. However, it could be used to comply with the provisions for special amusement buildings in Chapters 8 and 9.

5-10.2*   **Size of Signs.** Every sign required by Section 5-10 shall have the word EXIT or other appropriate wording in plainly legible letters not less than 6 in. (15.2 cm) high with the principal strokes of letters not less than ¾ in. (1.9 cm) wide. The word EXIT shall have letters of a width not less than 2 in. (5 cm) except the letter "I," and the minimum spacing between letters shall be not less than ⅜ in. (1 cm). Signs larger than the minimum established in this paragraph shall have letter widths, strokes, and spacing in proportion to their height.

Exception No. 1: Existing approved signs.

Exception No. 2: Existing signs having the required wording in plainly legible letters not less than 4 in. (10.2 cm) high.

Exception No. 3: Marking required by 5-10.1.6.

A-5-10.2   Where graphics are used, the symbols of NFPA 170, *Standard Firesafety Symbols* (*see Appendix B*), should be utilized. Such sign needs to provide equal visibility and illumination and comply with the other requirements of Section 5-10.

Traditionally, the letters in an exit sign have been required to be 6 in. (15.2 cm) in height with the principal strokes not less than ¾ in. (1.9 cm) wide. In an effort to increase visibility, the *Code* requires that the letters, other than the "I," be at least 2 in. (5 cm) wide and have a minimum spacing between letters of ⅜ in. (1.0 cm).

5-10.3   **Illumination of Signs.**

5-10.3.1*   Every sign required by 5-10.1.2 or 5-10.1.3 shall be suitably illuminated by a reliable light source. Externally and internally illuminated signs shall be visible in both the normal and emergency lighting mode.

A-5-10.3.1   It is not the intent of this paragraph to require emergency lighting but only to have the sign illuminated by emergency lighting if emergency lighting is required and provided.

Exit signs may be internally or externally illuminated. Internally illuminated signs are usually provided in occupancies where reduction of normal illumination is permitted, such as in motion picture theaters, but may be used anywhere.

5-10.3.2*   Externally illuminated signs shall be illuminated by not less than 5 footcandles (54 lx) and shall employ a contrast ratio of not less than 0.5.

A-5-10.3.2   Colors providing a good contrast are red or green letters on matte white background. Glossy background and glossy letter colors should be avoided.

5-10.3.3*   The visibility of an internally illuminated sign shall be the equivalent of an externally illuminated sign that complies with 5-10.3.2.

Formal Interpretation 85-12
Reference: 5-10.3

Question 1: Is it the intent of 5-10.3 that all exit signs be continuously illuminated?

Answer: Yes, when occupied.

Question 2: Does 5-10.3 permit exit sign illumination to be shut off at times when the entire building is unoccupied?

Answer: Yes.

Question 3: Does 5-10.3 permit shutting off the illumination of exit signs on an area-by-area basis as the occupants of these areas leave the building?

Answer: Yes, as long as there are no required means of egress serving occupied areas through the nonilluminated areas.

Question 4: Is general area lighting subject to control by an ordinary, freely accessible light switch, permitted by 5-10.3 to serve as the required illumination of an externally illuminated exit sign?

Answer: No.

Question 5: Does 5-10.3 permit a freely accessible light switch to control the illumination of either an internally or externally illuminated exit sign?

Answer: No.

Issue Edition: 1985
Reference: 5-10.3
Date: September 1986 ■

Formal Interpretation 88-15
Reference: 5-10.3.1

Question 1: Given that marking of means of egress in accordance with Section 5-10 is required by a section of the *Code*, is it the intent of 5-10.3.1 to require that the entire stroke width and entire stroke height of all letters comprising the word EXIT be visible per the requirements of 5-10.3.2 or 5-10.3.3 under normal, i.e., nonemergency lighting, operation?

Answer: No. However, the sign must be visible and legible at a 100-ft distance under all room illumination conditions.

Question 2: Given that the marking of means of egress in accordance with Section 5-10 and emergency lighting in accordance with Section 5-9 are required by a section of the *Code*, is it the intent of 5-10.3.1 to require that the entire stroke width and entire stroke height of all letters comprising the word EXIT be visible per the requirements of 5-10.3.2 or 5-10.3.3 under emergency lighting operation?

Answer: No. However, the sign must be visible and legible at a 100-ft distance under all room illumination conditions.

Issue Edition: 1988
Reference: 5-10.3.1
Issue Date: August 21, 1990
Effective Date: September 10, 1990 ■

Exception No. 1: Approved existing signs.

Exception No. 2*: Approved self-luminous or electroluminescent signs that provide evenly illuminated letters shall have a minimum luminance of 0.06 footlamberts (0.21 cd/sq m) as measured by a color-corrected photometer.

A-5-10.3.3 The average luminance of the letters and background shall each be measured in footlamberts. The contrast ratio shall be computed from these measurements by the following formula:

$$\text{Contrast} = \frac{\text{Lg} - \text{Le}}{\text{Lg}}$$

Where Lg is the greater luminance and Le is the lesser luminance, either the variable Lg or Le may represent the letters, and the remaining variable will represent the background. The average luminance of the letters and background may be computed by measuring the luminance at the positions indicated in the diagram by numbered spots.

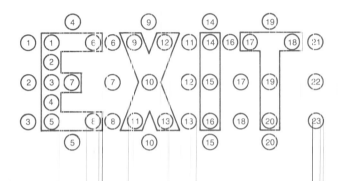

A-5-10.3.3 Exception No. 2. The luminance of these signs is determined by measuring the luminance of circular areas, no greater than ⅜ in. (1.0 cm) in diameter, at the positions indicated in the diagram by Xs.

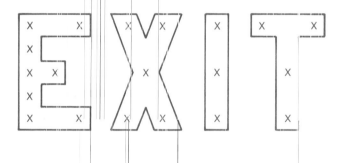

Self-luminous signs are illuminated by self-contained power sources and operate independently of external power sources. Batteries do not qualify as a self-contained power source under this definition.

The requirements for internally illuminated exit signs were greatly simplified in the 1985 Edition of the *Code*. The requirements are now stated on a performance basis. They must provide luminance and contrast ratios equivalent to an externally illuminated sign. Self-luminous and electroluminescent signs with evenly illuminated letters and a minimum luminance of 0.06 footlambert (0.21 cd/sq m) are permitted.

5-10.3.4 Every sign required by 5-10.1.4 shall provide evenly illuminated letters having a minimum luminance of 0.06 footlamberts (0.21 cd/sq m).

Exception: Signs complying with the requirements of 5-10.3.3 are acceptable.

5-10.3.5 Every sign required to be illuminated by 5-10.3 shall be continuously illuminated as required under the provisions of Section 5-8.

Exception: Illumination for signs shall be permitted to flash on and off upon activation of the fire alarm system.*

A-5-10.3.5 Exception. The flashing repetition rate should be approximately one cycle per second, and the duration of the off-time should not exceed one quarter second per cycle. During on-time, the illumination levels must be provided in accordance with 5-10.3.2 or 5-10.3.3. Flashing signs, when activated with the fire alarm system, may be of assistance.

5-10.3.6 Where emergency lighting facilities are required by the applicable provisions of Chapters 8 through 30 for individual occupancies, the exit signs, except approved self-luminous signs, shall be illuminated by the emergency lighting facilities. The level of illumination of the exit sign shall be at the levels provided in accordance with 5-10.3.2 or 5-10.3.3 for the required emergency lighting time duration as specified in 5-9.2.1 but shall be permitted to decline to 60 percent of the illumination level at the end of the emergency lighting time duration.

5-10.4 Specific Requirements.

5-10.4.1 Directional Signs.

5-10.4.1.1* A sign complying with 5-10.2 reading "EXIT" or a similar designation with a directional indicator showing the direction of travel shall be placed in every location where the direction of travel to reach the nearest exit is not apparent. Directional signs shall be listed.

A-5-10.4.1.1 Escalators, Moving Walks. A sign complying with 5-10.4.1.1 indicating the direction of the nearest approved exit should be placed at the point of entrance to any escalator or moving walk. (*See A-5-10.2.*)

5-10.4.1.2* Directional Indicator. The directional indicator shall be located outside of the EXIT legend, not less than ⅜ in. (1 cm) from any letter, and may be integral to or separate from the sign body. The directional indicator shall be of a chevron type as shown in Figure 5-10.4.1.2 and shall be identifiable as a directional indicator at a minimum distance of 100 ft (30 m) under all space illumination conditions. The directional indicators shall not be located at the end of the sign opposite the direction indicated.

Exception: Existing approved signs.

Figure 5-10.4.1.2

A-5-10.4.1.2 Following are examples of acceptable locations of directional indicators with regard to left and right orientation.

EXIT>
<EXIT
<EXIT>

In order to improve the directional indicators on directional exit signs, the Subcommittee on Means of Egress along with its Task Force on Marking and Illumination of Means of Egress has spent considerable effort over the last several years reviewing dozens of reports. In the 1988 *Code*, two requirements were added: 1) the directional indicator cannot be within the letters in the word EXIT, and 2) the directional indicator must be of such size, character, and location to be identifiable as an arrow. In the

1991 *Code*, three changes were made: (1) the term "arrow" was changed to "directional indicator," since research showed that a chevron type indicator was more effective than the symbol that the term arrow conjures in users' minds, (2) a chevron indicator was mandated, and (3) performance criteria were specified to ensure that the chevron would be of adequate size, contrast, and illumination. A specific size was avoided, since size is dependent on color, contrast, illumination, etc., and therefore 5-10.4.1.1 was changed to require that signs be listed to ensure that the performance criteria are met. Where symbols are used instead of the word EXIT, the *Code* (A-5-10.2) recommends use of NFPA 170, *Standard for Firesafety Symbols.*[27]

5-10.4.2* Special Signs. Any door, passage, or stairway that is neither an exit nor a way of exit access and that is so located or arranged that it is likely to be mistaken for an exit shall be identified by a sign reading "NO EXIT." Such sign shall have the word "NO" in letters 2 in. (5 cm) high with stroke width of ⅜ in. (1 cm) and the word EXIT in letters 1 in. (2.5 cm) high, with the word EXIT below the word NO.

Exception: Approved existing signs.

A-5-10.4.2 The likelihood of mistaking for exit doors passageways or stairways that lead to dead-end spaces where occupants might be trapped depends upon the same considerations as govern the need for exit signs. Thus, such areas should be marked with a sign reading "NO EXIT." Supplementary identification indicating the character of the area such as "TO BASEMENT," "STOREROOM," "LINEN CLOSET," or the like may be provided. (*See A-5-10.2.*)

SECTION 5-11   Special Provisions for Occupancies with High Hazard Contents

(See Section 4-2.)

Attention is called to the definition of High Hazard Areas in Chapter 3, which reads:

"High Hazard Areas. Those areas of structures or buildings used for purposes that involve highly combustible, highly flammable, or explosive products or materials that are likely to burn with extreme rapidity, or that may produce poisonous fumes or gases, including highly toxic or noxious alkalies, acids, or other liquids or chemicals that involve flame, fume, explosive, poisonous or irritant hazards; also uses that cause division of material into fine particles or dust subject to explosion or spontaneous combustion, and uses that constitute a high fire hazard because of the form, character, or volume of the material used."

Also note the definition of High Hazard Contents from 4-2.2.4, which reads:

"4-2.2.4 High hazard contents shall be classified as those that are likely to burn with extreme rapidity or from which explosions are to be feared. (For means of egress requirements, see Section 5-11.)'

5-11.1* In all cases where the contents are classified as high hazard, exits shall be provided of such types and numbers and so arranged as to permit all occupants to escape from the building or structure or from the hazardous area thereof to the outside or to a place of safety with a travel distance of not over 75 ft (23 m), measured as specified in 5-6.2.

A-5-11.1 Seventy-five ft (23 m) can be traversed in approximately 10 to 15 seconds, even when allowing for a momentary delay for making a decision as to which way to go, during which it may be assumed that a normal individual can hold his or her breath.

Paragraph 5-11.1 does not specify a 75-ft (23-m) travel distance, but 75 ft (23 m) to escape from the building or structure or from the hazardous area thereof.

5-11.2 Capacity of means of egress provided in accordance with 5-11.1 shall be as specified in the applicable section of Chapters 8 through 30 but not less than such as to provide 0.7 in./person (1.8 cm/person) where exit is by inside or outside stairs or 0.4 in. (1.0 cm) per person where exit is by doors at grade level, by horizontal exits, or by Class A ramps.

5-11.3 At least two means of egress shall be provided from each building or hazardous area thereof.

Exception: Rooms or spaces not greater than 200 sq ft (18.6 sq m) and having an occupant load of not greater than three persons and having a maximum travel distance to the room door of 25 ft (7.6 m).

The exception indicates that it is not always necessary or feasible to provide two ways out of a very small high hazard space.

5-11.4 Means of egress shall be so arranged that there are no dead-end pockets, hallways, corridors, passageways, or courts.

It is not the intent of the *Code* to apply the provisions of this section to hazardous areas as defined in each occupancy chapter, but to apply them to an area of high hazard contents. Small areas of high hazard are considered incidental to the main occupancy of the building. The decision as to when an area becomes sufficiently hazardous to warrant application of this section is left to the authority having jurisdiction.

SECTION 5-12   Mechanical Equipment Rooms, Boiler Rooms, and Furnace Rooms

This is a new section in the 1991 *Code* and applies to mechanical equipment rooms, boiler rooms, and furnace rooms in all buildings. It is the intent of the *Code* that this should answer the numerous questions received on this subject. The number of exits and common path of travel limitations in these spaces are independent of the occupancy in which they are located. The presence of these rooms does not result in a facility being called a mixed occupancy.

5-12.1 Mechanical equipment rooms, boiler rooms, furnace rooms, and similar spaces shall be arranged to limit common path of travel to a maximum of 50 ft (15 m).

Regardless of the occupancy that houses the room, common path of travel within the boiler room, mechanical equipment room, or furnace room is limited to 50 ft (15 m).

5-12.2 Stories used exclusively for mechanical equipment, furnaces, or boilers shall be permitted to have a single exit where the travel distance on that story does not exceed the common path of travel limitations.

This paragraph is especially useful in equipment penthouses and for basement furnace and boiler rooms. As long as the 50-ft (15-m) common path of travel is not exceeded, the story *used exclusively* for mechanical equipment, boilers, or furnaces may be served by a single exit. It should be emphasized that 5-1.3.1 prohibits doors from such spaces from opening directly into an exit enclosure and, therefore, a small hall or vestibule would be required.

References Cited in Commentary

[1] ANSI A117.1, *Standard for Buildings and Facilities — Providing Accessibility and Usability for Physically Handicapped People.*

[2] NFPA 252, *Standard Methods of Fire Tests of Door Assemblies*, National Fire Protection Association, Quincy, MA, 1990.

[3] Alison Norton, "When Security Provisions Threaten Fire Safety," *Fire Journal*, Vol. 82, No. 6, Nov./Dec. 1988, pp. 40, 42, 45, 76-77.

[4] NFPA 72E, *Standard on Automatic Fire Detectors*, National Fire Protection Association, Quincy, MA, 1990.

[5] NFPA 220, *Standard on Types of Building Construction*, National Fire Protection Association, Quincy, MA, 1985.

[6] Fitch, Templar, Corcoran, "The Dimensions of Stairs," *Scientific American*, October, 1974.

[7] *Design and Construction of Building Exits*, Miscellaneous Publication M 51, October 10, 1935, National Bureau of Standards, Washington, DC (out of print).

[8] National Safety Council Safe Practices, Pamphlet No. 2, National Safety Council, 425 N. Michigan Avenue, Chicago, IL 60611, 1934.

[9] ASME/ANSI A17.1, *Safety Code for Elevators and Escalators*, American Society of Mechanical Engineers, 345 East 47th Street, New York, NY 10017, 1990.

[10] Paul Robert Lyons, *Fire in America*, NFPA SPP-33, National Fire Protection Association, Quincy, MA, 1976, p. 190.

[11] Jake Pauls, Review of Standards and Codes Plus Recommendations for Accessible Means of Egress, one of a series of reports prepared in part of the study, "Egress Procedures and Technologies for People with Disabilities," by Hughes Associates, Inc. for the U.S. Architectural and Transportation Compliance Board, Washington, D.C., Nov. 1988, 57 pp.

[12] London Transit Board Research, "Second Report of the Operational Research Team on the Capacity of Footways," Research Report No. 95, London, August, 1958.

[13] Jake Pauls, "Development of Knowledge about Means of Egress," *Fire Technology*, Vol. 20, No. 2, May, 1984, pp. 28-40.

[14] NFPA 101M, *Alternative Approaches to Life Safety*, National Fire Protection Association, Quincy, MA, 1988.

[15] Laurence D. Watrous, "High-Rise Fire in New Orleans," *Fire Journal*, Vol. 67, No. 3, May, 1973, pp. 6-9.

[16] Robert F. Mendes, *Fighting High-Rise Building Fires — Tactics and Logistics*, NFPA FSP-44, National Fire Protection Association, Quincy, MA, 1975.

[17] Richard E. Stevens, "Exits in Core-Type Office Buildings," *Fire Journal*, Vol. 64, No. 3, May, 1970, pp. 68-70.

[18] *Uniform Building Code*, International Conference of Building Officials, Whittier, CA.

[19] David P. Demers, "Ten Students Die in Providence College Dormitory Fire," *Fire Journal*, Vol. 72, No. 4, July, 1978, pp. 59-63, 103.

[20] Investigation Report on the MGM Grand Hotel Fire, Las Vegas, NV, Nov. 21, 1980, NFPA LS-4, 1982.

[21] R. S. Moulton, "Emergency Lighting for Fire Safety," *NFPA Quarterly*, Vol. 50, No. 2, October, 1956, pp. 93-96.

[22] A. Elwood Willey, "Unsafe Existing Conditions! Apartment House Fire, Boston, Massachusetts," *Fire Journal*, Vol. 65, No. 4, July 1971, pp. 16-23.

[23] James K. Lathrop, "The Summerland Fire: 50 Die on Isle of Man," *Fire Journal*, Vol. 69, No. 2, March 1975, pp. 5-12.

[24] James Bell, "Fifteen Residents Die in Mental Hospital Fire", *Fire Journal*, Vol. 73, No. 4, July 1979, pp. 68-76.

[25] NFPA 70, *National Electrical Code*, National Fire Protection Association, Quincy, MA, 1990.

[26] NFPA Investigation Report: Westchase Hilton Hotel Fire, Houston, Texas, March 6, 1982, 12 Fatalities.

[27] NFPA 170, *Standard for Firesafety Symbols*, National Fire Protection Association, Quincy, MA, 1991.

6

Features of Fire Protection

SECTION 6-1   General

This chapter establishes basic requirements for features of fire protection, which include such items as construction, compartmentation through use of fire barriers, protection of vertical openings, protection of concealed spaces, subdivision of building space through use of smoke barriers, protection from hazards, and interior finish. For the most part, this chapter specifies a menu of protection options, which is then mandated by specific occupancy chapters. However, some of the provisions of this chapter apply as requirements to all occupancies.

6-1.1 Application.

6-1.1.1 The features of fire protection set forth in this chapter apply to both new construction and existing buildings.

Lack of compartmentation and rapid fire development have been found to be primary factors in numerous multiple-fatality fires, especially in residential occupancies. In many fire reports, the factors of unprotected vertical openings and highly combustible interior finish appear repeatedly, indicating the need to apply requirements to both new construction and existing buildings.

SECTION 6-2   Construction and Compartmentation

The purpose of Section 6-2 is to set forth, in general terms, how those using exits and other "safe" areas in buildings are to be protected from fire in adjoining areas. Protection is achieved by providing wall, ceiling, and floor construction that will be reasonably free from penetration by fire and smoke for a safe period. Because requirements vary for different occupancies, specific requirements for construction and compartmentation are included in Chapters 8 through 30 of the *Code*.

To be consistent and to preserve the integrity of the "compartment" or safe area, all openings for doors, ducts, and building services, i.e., electric power, telephone, water supply, and waste lines, must also be effectively closed or fitted with automatic closures. Equally important, and sometimes overlooked, are concealed spaces, particularly those above suspended ceilings, that can be, and frequently have been, the means of spreading fire into otherwise protected areas.[1] In some instances, these interstitial spaces may be 8 ft (244 cm) or more in height; in others, they may serve as supply or return air plenum chambers for air conditioning systems. Proper protection of concealed spaces can include firestopping, draftstopping, automatic extinguishment, area limitations, and other limitations on the combustibility of contents, interior linings, and construction materials. For specific protection details, see 6-2.6.

In this section and throughout the *Code*, a distinction is made between smoke barriers and fire barriers. The function of the former is to restrict the passage of smoke, including fire gases. As such, a smoke barrier needs to be reasonably airtight even under an increase in air pressure on the fire side due to the expansion of the heated air. The fire barrier, on the other hand, must prevent passage of heat and flame for a designated period of time. In other words, it must be capable of withstanding direct impingement of the fire as determined by large-scale tests conducted in accordance with NFPA 251, *Standard Methods of Fire Tests of Building Construction and Materials,*[2] and NFPA 252, *Standard Methods of Fire Tests of Door Assemblies.*[3]

6-2.1* **Construction.** Buildings or structures occupied or used according to the individual occupancy chapters (Chapters 8 through 30) shall meet the minimum construction requirements of those chapters. NFPA 220, *Standard on Types of Building Construction,* shall be used to determine the requirements for the construction classification.

A-6-2.1 Table A-6-2.1 on page 151 is a reprint of Table 3 from NFPA 220, *Standard on Types of Building Construction* (*see Appendix B*). This is included for the convenience of users of the *Life Safety Code.*

In general, the *Life Safety Code* is not a building code. However, in certain occupancies, minimum construction requirements are established to help maintain structural integrity for the time period needed for evacuation, or, as in the case of health care occupancies where evacua-

tion does not assure the safety of sick occupants, for an even longer period of time so as to establish a safe area of refuge within the building but away from the zone of fire origin.

Paragraph 6-2.1 does not set minimum construction requirements but rather provides the reference to the detailed NFPA 220, *Standard on Types of Building Construction,*[4] so that where construction types are specified in other sections of the *Code,* particularly in the occupancy Chapters 8 through 30, a shorthand notation, such as "Type I (332)," can be used without additional expansive detail. The user should then go to NFPA 220 for the necessary details.

Appendix A provides the user of the *Life Safety Code* with a reprint of Table 3 from NFPA 220. The table summarizes the verbiage of the document. Note that the shorthand notation, such as "Type I (332)," provides the minimum hourly fire resistance ratings required to meet the definition of that construction type for only three components of the building: exterior bearing walls, structural frame/columns/girders, and floor construction. In order to meet the definition fully, other building components, such as roof construction and interior bearing walls, need to have certain minimum fire resistance ratings. Thus, the shorthand notation alone does not provide all the needed information. NFPA 220 should be consulted as necessary.

At times, the minimum construction requirements of other sections of the *Code* may establish criteria in addition to those of NFPA 220 for use in judging compliance with the definition of a specific building construction type. Chapter 12 for new health care occupancies, which provides an overall package of life safety to a population that is incapable of self-preservation and thus difficult to protect, requires that, for a building to be classified as either Type I or Type II construction, it must meet the requirements of NFPA 220 and additionally have noncombustible or limited-combustible interior nonbearing walls. Interior nonbearing walls are not addressed by NFPA 220.

Table 6-1 matches the various NFPA 220 construction types with their approximate equivalent construction types as contained in the three major model building codes: the *Uniform Building Code* (UBC),[5] the *BOCA/National Building Code* (NBC),[6] and the *Standard Building Code* (SBC)[7]. For example, a building that NFPA 220 would consider Type I (332), the *Uniform Building Code* (UBC) considers Type I FR, the *BOCA/National Building Code* (B/NBC) considers Type 1B, and the *Standard Building Code* (SBC) considers Type II. When using the *Life Safety Code* in conjunction with one of these codes, the authority having jurisdiction may wish to consider (per Section 1-6) "equivalent" construction types by utilizing Table 6-1.

Table A-6-2.1 Fire Resistance Requirements for Type I Through Type V Construction.

	Type I		Type II			Type III		Type IV	Type V	
	443	332	222	111	000	211	200	2HH	111	000
EXTERIOR BEARING WALLS—										
Supporting more than one floor, columns or other bearing walls	4	3	2	1	0¹	2	2	2	1	0¹
Supporting one floor only	4	3	2	1	0¹	2	2	2	1	0¹
Supporting a roof only	4	3	1	1	0¹	2	2	2	1	0¹
INTERIOR BEARING WALLS—										
Supporting more than one floor, columns or other bearing walls	4	3	2	1	0	1	0	2	1	0
Supporting one floor only	3	2	2	1	0	1	0	1	1	0
Supporting a roof only	3	2	1	1	0	1	0	1	1	0
COLUMNS—										
Supporting more than one floor, bearing walls or other columns	4	3	2	1	0	1	0	H²	1	0
Supporting one floor only	3	2	2	1	0	1	0	H²	1	0
Supporting a roof only	3	2	1	1	0	1	0	H²	1	0
BEAMS, GIRDERS, TRUSSES, and ARCHES—										
Supporting more than one floor, bearing walls or columns	4	3	2	1	0	1	0	H²	1	0
Supporting one floor only	3	2	2	1	0	1	0	H²	1	0
Supporting a roof only	3	2	1	1	0	1	0	H²	1	0
FLOOR CONSTRUCTION	3	2	2	1	0	1	0	H²	1	0
ROOF CONSTRUCTION	2	1½	1	1	0	1	0	H²	1	0
EXTERIOR NONBEARING WALLS	0¹	0¹	0¹	0¹	0¹	0¹	0¹	0¹	0¹	0¹

Those members listed that are permitted to be of approved combustible material.
¹ Requirements for fire resistance of exterior walls, the provision of spandrel wall sections, and the limitation or protection of wall openings are not related to construction type. They need to be specified in other standards and codes, where appropriate, and may be required in addition to the requirements of this Standard for the construction type.
² "H" indicates heavy timber members; see text for requirements.

Table 6-1 Cross-Reference of Building Construction Types.

NFPA 220	I (443)	I (332)	II (222)	II (111)	II (000)	III (211)	III (200)	IV (2HH)	V (111)	V (000)
UBC	—	I FR	II FR	II-1 hr	II N	III-1 hr	III N	IV HT	V 1-hr	V-N
B/NBC	1A	1B	2A	2B	2C	3A	3B	4	5A	5B
SBC	I	II	—	IV 1 hr	IV unp	V 1 hr	V unp	III	VI 1 hr	VI unp

6-2.2 Compartmentation.

6-2.2.1 Where required by Chapters 8 through 30, every building shall be divided into compartments to limit the spread of fire and restrict the movement of smoke.

6-2.2.2* Fire compartments shall be formed with fire barriers that are continuous from outside wall to outside wall, from one fire barrier to another, or a combination thereof; including continuity through all concealed spaces, such as those found above a ceiling, including interstitial spaces.

Exception: A fire barrier required for an occupied space below an interstitial space is not required to extend through the interstitial space provided the construction assembly forming the bottom of the interstitial space has a fire resistance rating equal to that of the fire barrier.

A-6-2.2.2 To ensure that a fire barrier is continuous, it is necessary to completely seal all openings where the fire barrier abuts other fire barriers, exterior walls, the floor below, and the floor or ceiling above. In the Exception to 6-2.2.2, the fire resistance rating of the bottom of the interstitial space must be provided by that membrane in and of itself. Ceilings of rated floor/ceiling and roof/ceiling assemblies do not necessarily provide the required fire resistance.

In Figure 6-1, the bold, solidly-colored lines designate a variety of fire barriers that meet the requirement of horizontal continuity. Fire barrier A divides the building into two distinct fire compartments by running continuously from an outside wall to an outside wall. This barrier could, but does not, have door openings that would be protected by fire rated door assemblies meeting the requirements of 6-2.3.5. Fire barrier B further subdivides the building into a third fire compartment and achieves its required continuity by running from an outside wall to a fire barrier, i.e., barrier A. The door opening is allowed if protected by an appropriately rated fire door assembly.

The fire barriers surrounding room C meet the continuity requirement by running from one fire barrier, to another fire barrier, to another so as to envelop the room. This would commonly be done to isolate and thus meet

the protection requirements associated with protecting a hazardous area such as a storage room.

Fire barriers are often used to meet the protection and isolation requirements associated with corridors. Corridor D consists of fire barriers meeting the horizontal continuity requirements by running from an outside wall to a fire barrier, to another fire barrier, to an outside wall.

In addition to horizontal continuity, fire barriers are required to be continuous vertically through all interstitial spaces.

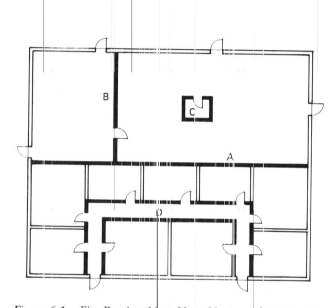

Figure 6-1.   Fire Barriers Must Have Horizontal Continuity.

Interstitial spaces in some cases contain a considerable fuel load and are readily accessible by people. Over the life of a building, the possibility that an interstitial space will be used for storage should not be overlooked. These factors must be considered to determine whether or not an interstitial space is in fact another floor.

Normally, ceilings are not tested alone but are tested as part of a floor/ceiling or roof/ceiling assembly. This test does not indicate the performance of the ceiling, but of the total assembly. For example, the ceiling of a 1-hour floor/ceiling assembly may fail after 20 minutes, but the overall assembly passes the 1-hour test. Often an architect or contractor will refer to a 1- or 2-hour ceiling and request permission to terminate a fire barrier at the ceiling, but in reality the ceiling is part of a 1-hour or 2-hour floor/ceiling or roof/ceiling assembly. Because the ceiling itself does not provide the appropriately rated fire barrier against which the wall assembly can be terminated, the fire barrier must extend from slab to slab.

There are tests reported by the Gypsum Association in the *Fire Resistance Design Manual*[8] that indicate that two layers of ⅝-in. (1.6-cm) fire-rated Type X gypsum wallboard applied at right angles to the underside of nominal 2 in. × 10 in. (nominal 5 cm × 25 cm) wood joists, spaced 24 in. (61 cm) on centers with the face layer of the gypsum board offset by 24 in. (61 cm) from the base layer joints, will provide 1-hour fire resistance protection for the wood framing. Using this information, the authority having jurisdiction could judge that such a ceiling meets the intent of the Exception to 6-2.2.2 and allow for a 1-hour fire resistance rated wall assembly to terminate tightly against the underside of the ceiling.

Figure 6-2 shows a 1-hour fire resistance rated wall assembly continuing up through the ceiling and void space of a 1-hour fire resistance rated floor/ceiling assembly so as to terminate tightly against the underside of floor slab so as to achieve the required vertical continuity. At the right side of Figure 6-2, the Exception to 6-2.2.2 is utilized to allow for the 1-hour rated wall assembly to terminate at a ceiling that provides the required 1-hour of fire resistance rating by itself.

Some occupancies do allow the fire barrier to terminate at the underside (i.e., ceiling) of a fire protection rated floor/ceiling assembly. However, caution must be exercised, since ceilings of these assemblies are often improperly installed or, once installed, have been violated during routine maintenance.

6-2.3 Fire Barriers.

6-2.3.1 Floor-ceiling assemblies; bearing and nonbearing wall or partition assemblies used as fire barriers to form fire compartments; and columns, beams, girders, or trusses supporting such assemblies shall be of a design that has been tested to meet the conditions of acceptance of NFPA 251, *Standard Methods of Fire Tests of Building Construction and Materials.* Fire barriers shall be continuous in accordance with 6-2.2.2.

The fire resistance of a fire barrier is determined by the test method described in NFPA 251, *Standard Methods*

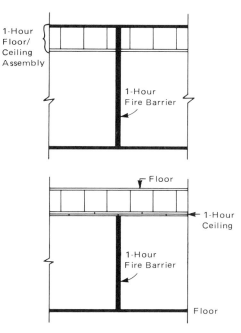

Figure 6-2. *Fire Barriers Must Extend Through Ceiling Spaces Unless the Ceiling Is Itself a Fire Barrier.*

of Fire Tests of Building Construction and Materials.[2] The test is also commonly known by its ASTM designation, ASTM E119 (same title).[9] The NFPA 251 / ASTM E119 test standard provides for the construction of the particular assembly to be rated and the actual testing of the assembly in the test furnace. The test is conducted under very rigid conditions so that test results on the same assembly are reproducible, and tests of different assemblies are comparable. Temperatures in the furnace are generated in strict accordance with the standard time-temperature curve and reach levels of 1000°F, 1300°F, 1550°F, 1700°F, and 1850°F (538°C, 704°C, 843°C, 927°C, and 1010°C) at time periods of 5, 10, 30, 60, and 120 minutes into the test. Temperatures both in the furnace and on the unexposed side of the assembly being tested are monitored closely at specified intervals and locations. During the course of the test, cotton waste is placed against the unexposed surface and observed for flaming. During the test, the assembly being tested is also loaded the same way that it would be expected to be loaded when in place in a building.

Acceptance criteria for an assembly to complete the fire test successfully for a specified time period include the following:

1. Cotton waste on unexposed side does not ignite;
2. Temperature rise on the unexposed side does not exceed 325°F (180°C) at any point or an average of 250°F (139°C);
3. The assembly must continue to support design loads.

The above criteria apply to floor, roof, wall, and partition assemblies. In addition, wall and partition assemblies to be rated at 1 hour or more are subjected to the hose stream test. A duplicate specimen of the assembly to be rated is tested in the furnace for one-half the time period indicated as the fire resistance rating in the fire endurance test. This specimen is then removed from the furnace and immediately subjected to the hose stream test. If there is any projection of water beyond the unexposed surface, the assembly is considered to have failed.

NFPA 251 testing is commonly done by testing laboratories, which normally issue a report of the test and then list the assembly. Listings of tested fire resistance rated assemblies may be found in any of the model building codes (*see commentary following A-6-2.1*) or in publications of the laboratories that conduct fire testing, such as the Underwriters Laboratories *Fire Resistance Directory*[10] or the *Factory Mutual Specification Tested Products Guide*.[11] It is important that the assembly in the field be the same as that listed. For example, if a floor/ceiling assembly calls for clips on the ceiling tiles, these must be installed and maintained. Another example is the special treatment often required for lights or air ducts in suspended ceilings. A common problem in walls is the installation of an untested material between the wallboard and the studs or the installation of recessed wall fixtures, which requires the removal of wallboard.

Exception No. 1: Structural elements need only have the fire resistance rating required for the construction classification of the building where supporting nonbearing wall or partition assemblies having a required fire resistance rating of 1 hour or less and that do not serve as exit enclosures or protection of vertical openings.

If Exception No. 1 to 6-2.3.1 was not included in the *Code*, a two-story building, for example, used for an occupancy that would both (1) allow Type II (000) construction to be occupied and (2) require the presence of 1-hour

fire resistance rated corridor walls would be required to upgrade all construction supporting the nonbearing second floor corridor walls (i.e., the columns, beams, and girders supporting the second floor) to 1-hour fire resistance ratings. Because such 1-hour rated corridor walls are not intended to provide structural integrity but rather to serve as barriers that create fire compartments on the floor on which they are installed, the exception provides the necessary relief to allow the unprotected, noncombustible Type II (000) building to be occupied as allowed by the -1.6 subsection of the applicable occupancy chapter.

Figure 6-3 further illustrates the use of Exception No. 1 to 6-2.3.1. The floor shown is the second of a two-story building that, based on the occupancy, is allowed to be placed in a building of Type II (000) construction as defined by NFPA 220, *Standard for Types of Building Construction*[4] (*see A-6.2.1 and its associated commentary*). In addition, the occupancy in question requires (1) corridor walls with a 1-hour fire resistance rating, and (2) enclosure of hazardous area rooms, enclosure of interior exit stairs, and enclosure of vertical openings such as elevator shafts by 1-hour fire resistance rated barriers. The exception allows for the building construction that supports the second floor corridor walls (A) and the walls enclosing the hazardous storage room (B) to remain unprotected but noncombustible as defined by building construction Type II (000). However, the second floor 1-hour rated fire barriers enclosing the exit stairs (C and D) and the elevator shaft (E), as well as other vertical openings (F), must be supported by 1-hour rated construction.

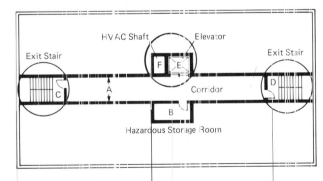

Figure 6-3. *Circled Fire-Rated Barriers on Second Floor Must Be Supported By 1-Hour Rated First Floor Construction.*

Exception No. 2*: Assemblies calculated to have equivalent fire resistance provided that the calculations are based on the conditions of acceptance and the fire exposure specified in NFPA 251, Standard Methods of Fire Tests of Building Construction and Materials.

A-6-2.3.1 **Exception No. 2** Methods for calculating the fire endurance of assemblies may be found in the following publications:

(a) Concrete and Masonry.

1. ACI 2/6R, *Guide for Determining the Fire Endurance of Concrete Elements*

2. Concrete and Masonry Industry Firesafety Committee, *Analytical Methods of Determining Fire Endurance of Concrete and Masonry Members — Model Code Approved Procedures*

3. CRSI, *Reinforced Concrete Fire Resistance*

4. PCI, *Design for Fire Resistance of Precast Prestressed Concrete*

(b) Steel.

1. AISI, *Designing Fire Protection for Steel Columns*

2. AISI, *Designing Fire Protection for Steel Beams*

3. AISI, *Designing Fire Protection for Steel Trusses*

(c) Wood.

1. National Forest Products Assn., *Design of Fire-Resistive Exposed Wood Members*

2. UBC, *Methods for Calculating Fire Resistance of Wood-Framed Walls, Floors and Roofs*

The following illustrates the use of calculating fire resistance as allowed by Exception No. 2 to 6-2.3.1.

A designer who wants to provide a 2-hour fire resistance rating for a W14 × 233 steel column by boxing the column with gypsum wallboard can not find such an assembly in the *Underwriters Laboratories Fire Resistance Directory*.[10] Designs No. X520 and No. X521 come very close to providing the needed information but deal with W14 × 228 steel columns and show that, with one layer of ¹/₂-in. (1.3-cm) thick gypsum wallboard, the assembly will provide a 2-hour fire resistance rating. The UL Directory further explains that most structural steel producers began rolling a new series of structural shapes in

accordance with ASTM A6, *Standard Specification for General Requirements for Rolled Steel Plates, Shapes, Sheet Piling, and Bars for Structural Use*, in 1978 and that some of the column sizes specified for individual designs may have been discontinued. Rather than make a judgment call as to whether the W14 × 233 column will provide the same rating as the discontinued W14 × 228 shape by comparing flange and web thicknesses, the designer chooses to calculate the fire resistance rating of a W14 × 233 steel column with a single layer of ¹/₂-in. (1.3-cm) gypsum wallboard built around the column in a box profile using criteria from the AISI *Designing Fire Protection for Steel Columns*.

Based on results from accumulated fire-test data, the AISI manual presents the following formula for calculating fire endurance of steel columns protected by gypsum wallboard:

$$R = 130 \left(h(W'/D) / 2 \right)^{0.75}$$

Where R = fire resistance (minutes)
W' = weight of steel column and gypsum wallboard protection (lb/ft)
h = thickness of gypsum wallboard (in.)
D = heated perimeter of steel column (in.), which, for the box profile, is the inside perimeter of the gypsum wallboard material and is calculated as D = 2(a+b) per Figure 6-4.

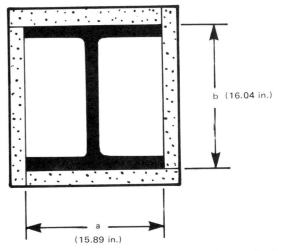

Figure 6-4. *Box Profile of Gypsum Wallboard Around a Steel Column.*

The total weight (W') of both the column and its gypsum wallboard protection is calculated using the following formula:

$$W' = W + [(50 \ h \ D) / 144]$$

where W = weight of steel column (lb/ft)

Performing the calculations:

$$
\begin{aligned}
D &= 2(a+b) \\
&= 2(15.89 + 16.04) \\
&= 63.86 \text{ in.} \\
W' &= W + [(50 \ h \ D) / 144] \\
&= 233 + [(50 \times 0.5 \times 63.86) / 144] \\
&= 244.09 \text{ lb/ft} \\
W'/D &= 244.09 / 63.86 = 3.82 \\
R &= 130 \ [h(W'/D) / 2]^{0.75} \\
&= 130 \ [(0.50 \times 3.82) / 2]^{0.75} \\
&= 125.6 \text{ min. (approximately 2 hours)}
\end{aligned}
$$

Based on the above calculation, the designer specifies with a degree of comfort that the 2-hour fire resistance rating for the assembly consisting of the W14 × 233 steel column and gypsum board box profile enclosure be achieved using a single layer of 1/2-in. (1.3-cm) gypsum wallboard.

6-2.3.2 Fire barriers used to provide enclosure of floor openings or used for subdivision of stories shall be classified in accordance with their fire resistance rating as follows:

(a) 2-hour fire resistance rating.

(b) 1-hour fire resistance rating.

(c) 3/4-hour fire resistance rating.

(d) 1/2-hour fire resistance rating.

(e) 20-minute fire resistance rating.

Fire resistance testing of building construction per NFPA 251/ASTM E119 allows for assemblies to receive fire resistance ratings up through the category of "8 hours and over." Ratings of more than 2 hours are used primarily in protecting property. The *Life Safety Code*, which addresses life safety as opposed to property protection, requires no more than 2-hour fire resistance rating, even in the occupancy chapters such as health care and detection and correctional, which promote a defend-in-place concept. Thus, in the -1.6 subsections of the health care

and detention/correctional occupancy chapters, i.e., Chapters 12 through 15, the construction Types I (443), I (332), and II (222) are grouped so as to be treated as equals. A design professional is free to specify that material assemblies with 3- or 4-hour fire resistance rating be used but receive no reduction in other requirements other than those offered to construction with a 2-hour fire resistance rating.

6-2.3.3 Door assemblies in fire barriers shall be of an approved type with appropriate rating for the location in which installed and shall comply with the following:

(a) Fire doors shall be installed in accordance with NFPA 80, *Standard for Fire Doors and Windows*. Fire doors shall be of a design that has been tested to meet the conditions of acceptance of NFPA 252, *Standard Methods of Fire Tests of Door Assemblies*.

Exception to (a): As permitted in 6-2.3.5.

(b) Fire doors shall be self-closing or automatic-closing in accordance with 5-2.1.8 and, where used within the means of egress, shall comply with the provisions of 5-2.1.

Fire protection rated door assemblies are tested in accordance with NFPA 252, *Standard Methods of Fire Tests of Door Assemblies*,[1] which is also commonly known as ASTM E152 (same title),[12] and must be installed in accordance with the requirements of NFPA 80, *Standard for Fire Doors and Windows*.[11] Where the *Life Safety Code* uses the term "door," it includes not only the door proper, but also the doorway, frame, and necessary hardware, including hinges. Where describing a fire door, the applicable standards similarly define a fire protection rated assembly as including all of the above components as well as a listed door closer and positive latching.

Fire doors, if they are to be effective, must not only be closed but also be held closed. Building fires are capable of generating pressures sufficient to force fire doors open if they are not held closed with positive latching, thereby rendering the doors incapable of protecting the opening in which they are installed.

The acceptance criteria for fire protection rated assemblies, such as fire doors, differ from those for fire resistance rated construction, such as a wall or floor/ceiling assembly. The limitation of temperature rise through the fire door is not normally a measure of acceptance, whereas this is so for a fire resistance rated assembly. In addition, during the course of the fire test, fire doors will expand on the exposed side and, as a result, will warp, sometimes expanding through the door opening at the top of the door. This will, of course, result in some flaming through the top of the door openings. The test standard recognizes this phenomenon, and a certain amount of such flaming is permitted under the acceptance criteria. This does not adversely affect safety, given that fire protection rated assemblies are intended to protect relatively small openings in larger fire resistance rated barriers. (*Also see the commentary following 6-2.3.1 and 6-2.3.5.*)

6-2.3.4 Fire window assemblies shall be permitted in fire barriers having a required fire resistance rating of 1 hour or less and shall be of an approved type with appropriate rating for the location in which installed. Fire windows shall be installed in accordance with NFPA 80, *Standard for Fire Doors and Windows*, and shall comply with the following:

(a) Fire windows used in fire barriers shall be of a design that has been tested to meet the conditions of acceptance of NFPA 257, *Standard for Fire Tests of Window Assemblies*.

(b) Fire windows used in fire barriers shall not exceed 25 percent of the area of the fire barrier in which they are used.

Exception No. 1: Existing installations of wired glass in approved metal frames.

Exception No. 2: Fire rated glazing material may be installed in approved existing frames.

The provisions of 6-2.3.4 provide guidelines for fire window assemblies that are parallel to those covered by 6-2.3.3 for fire door assemblies. Here, and throughout the *Code* for consistency, new glazing for use in fire barriers and fire doors will be regulated by performance-oriented criteria, which refer to fire rated glazing, in lieu of the more traditional but prescriptive requirements previously applicable to "wired glass." Although the requirements are new and limit the installation of fire windows used in fire barriers to not more than 25 percent of the area of the fire barrier in which they are used, exceptions were adopted to continue to recognize current practice

for existing fire windows and vision panels in fire doors, namely that of using wired glass.

6-2.3.5* Every opening in a fire barrier shall be protected to limit the spread of fire and restrict the movement of smoke from one side of the fire barrier to the other. The fire protection rating for opening protectives shall be as follows:

(a) 2-hour fire barrier — 1½-hour fire protection rating.

(b) 1-hour fire barrier — 1-hour fire protection rating where used for vertical openings or exit enclosures or ¾-hour fire protection rating where used for other than vertical openings or exit enclosures.

Exception No. 1 to (b): Where a lesser fire protection rating is specified by Chapter 5 or Chapters 8 through 30.

Exception No. 2 to (b): Where the fire barrier is provided as a result of a requirement that corridor walls or smoke barriers be of 1-hour fire resistance rated construction, the opening protectives shall have a fire protection rating of not less than 20 minutes when tested in accordance with NFPA 252, Standard Methods of Fire Tests of Door Assemblies, without the hose stream test.

Exception No. 3 to (b): Where special requirements for doors in 1-hour fire resistance rated corridor walls and 1-hour fire resistance rated smoke barriers are specified in Chapters 12 and 13.

(c) ¾-hour fire barrier — 20-minute fire protection rating.

(d) ½-hour fire barrier — 20-minute fire protection rating.

(e) 20-minute fire barrier — 20-minute fire protection rating.

A-6-2.3.5 Longer ratings may be required where doors are provided for property protection as well as life safety.

NFPA 80, *Standard for Fire Doors and Windows* (*see Appendix B*), may be consulted for standard practice in the selection and installation of fire doors.

In existing installations only, a 1¾-in. (4.4-cm) thick solid bonded wood core door has been considered a satisfactory substitute for a door with a 20-minute fire protection rating.

Whereas 6-2.3.2 discussed the fire resistance rating of fire barriers, 6-2.3.5 addresses the fire protection rating of opening protectives. Fire barriers have fire resistance ratings; opening protectives, such as fire doors, have fire protection ratings. For a better understanding of the difference in test methods used for rating fire barriers and fire doors, compare the commentaries following 6-2.3.1 and 6-2.3.3.

In general, 1-hour fire barriers for vertical openings require doors with a 1-hour fire protection rating, and 1-hour fire barriers for other than vertical openings require doors with a ¾-hour fire protection rating.

Exception No. 1 to item (b) allows Chapter 5 and the occupancy chapters to alter this general rule. For the most part, though, this is usually done only with regard to the requirement that corridor walls be of a 1-hour fire resistance rating. Exception No. 2 to item (b) specifically deals with this subject and introduces an allowance for a corridor door with a 20-minute fire protection rating.

Exception No. 3 to item (b) recognizes the special requirements contained in Chapters 12 and 13 for health care occupancies, which, for example, allow the omission of the self-closing device. This means that a true fire protection rated patient room door assembly is not required in recognition of the functional needs of these facilities.

Note that the fire protection ratings of the opening protectives are, in some cases, allowed to be of a lower time rating than the fire resistance rating of the fire barrier whose openings are to be protected. For example, a 2-hour fire resistance rated fire barrier is allowed to have its openings protected by 1½-hour fire protection rated door assemblies. The perceived mismatch of ratings actually accomplishes a reasonable, practical match because:

1. The test procedures on which the ratings are based, i.e., NFPA 251/ASTM E119 for fire barriers and NFPA 252/E152 (see commentary following 6-2.3.3) for fire doors are different, and

2. It is thought that, whereas combustibles may be placed against a fire resistance rated wall and expose the wall to a considerable fire challenge, a fire protection rated door assembly will not have similar combustibles placed against it because the opening must be maintained clear to allow passage through the door. Such a scenario suggests that, if a door is not to be used and combustible storage is to be placed at the door opening, the door should be removed and the opening filled with material to restore the wall to its required fire resistance rating.

6-2.3.6   **Penetrations and Miscellaneous Openings in Fire Barriers.**

6-2.3.6.1*   Openings in fire barriers for air-handling ductwork or air movement shall be protected in accordance with 7-2.1.

The *Code*, in referencing 7-2.1 for protection of openings in fire barriers for air-handling ductwork or air movement, mandates that the requirements of NFPA 90A, *Standard for the Installation of Air Conditioning and Ventilating Systems*,[14] and not the usual *Life Safety Code* requirements for opening protectives (i.e., 6-2.3.5), apply to HVAC penetrations of fire barriers. NFPA 90A requires that approved fire dampers be provided in all air transfer openings in partitions required to have a fire resistance rating. It requires that approved fire dampers be provided where ducts or air grilles penetrate partitions required to have a fire resistance rating of 2 hours or more. Thus, although any air transfer opening would have to be fire dampered in a required fire barrier of any rating, penetrations by ducts or air grilles would not have to be fire dampered if the required rating of the fire barrier is less than 2 hours. These requirements are depicted in Figure 6-5.

A-6-2.3.6.1   In engineered smoke management systems, the designer should consider the use of high temperature links on fire dampers where air-handling ducts penetrate fire barriers.

Formal Interpretation 81-6
Reference: A-6-2.3.6.1

Question: Is it the intent of paragraph A-6-2.3.6.1 of NFPA 101 to recommend to designers of engineered smoke control systems that they consider the use of high temperature fusible links that exceed the 285°F (141°C) maximum temperature for operation of all fire dampers required by UL 555, Fire Dampers and Ceiling Dampers, Conditions of Acceptance?

Answer: No, the intent of the Committee was to encourage the consideration of higher temperature fusible links, but not to exceed the maximums set in UL 555.

Issue Edition: 1981
Reference: A-6.2.2.7
Date: April 1982 ■

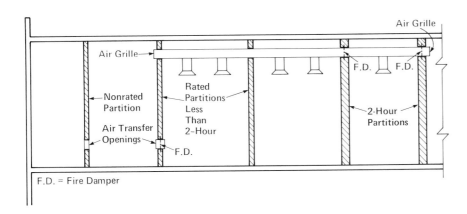

Figure 6-5. *Fire Damper Requirements of NFPA 90A for HVAC Penetrations of Partitions.*

F.D. = Fire Damper

6-2.3.6.2* Pipes, conduits, bus ducts, cables, wires, air ducts, pneumatic tubes and ducts, and similar building service equipment that pass through fire barriers shall be protected as follows:

(a) The space between the penetrating item and the fire barrier shall:

1. Be filled with a material capable of maintaining the fire resistance of the fire barrier, or

2. Be protected by an approved device designed for the specific purpose.

(b) Where the penetrating item uses a sleeve to penetrate the fire barrier, the sleeve shall be solidly set in the fire barrier, and the space between the item and the sleeve shall:

1. Be filled with a material capable of maintaining the fire resistance of the fire barrier, or

2. Be protected by an approved device designed for the specific purpose.

(c)* Insulation and coverings for pipes and ducts shall not pass through the fire barrier unless:

1. The material is capable of maintaining the fire resistance of the fire barrier, or

2. Protected by an approved device designed for the specific purpose.

(d) Where designs take transmission of vibration into consideration, any vibration isolation shall:

1. Be made on either side of the fire barrier, or

2. Be made by an approved device designed for the specific purpose.

A-6-2.3.6.2 Penetrations through fire barriers should meet the following criteria. Cables, wires, pipes, tubes, conduits, vents, and other penetrating items as well as insulation and coverings on penetrating items should be:

(a) Tested in accordance with NFPA 251, *Standard Methods of Fire Tests of Building Construction and Materials*, as part of a rated assembly, or

(b) Protected by an approved, through-penetration system that has been tested in accordance with ASTM E814, *Methods for Fire Tests of Through-Penetration Fire Stops*.

In lieu of the above, the annular space around the penetrating item may be protected where the penetrating item is a cable or wire without a combustible jacket or a noncombustible cable, wire, pipe, tube, conduit, or vent. The material used to fill the annular space, i.e., spaces between a sleeve and penetrating item and sleeve and fire barrier, should prevent the passage of flame and hot gases that are sufficient to ignite cotton waste when subjected to the time temperature fire conditions of NFPA 251, *Standard Methods of Fire Tests of Building Construction and Materials*, under a minimum positive pressure differential of 0.01 in. of water column (2.5 Pa) at the location of the penetration for the time period equivalent to the required fire resistance rating of the assembly penetrated. Where sleeves are used, the sleeves should be noncombustible and should be securely fastened to the fire barrier.

Openings for steel electrical outlet boxes not exceeding 16 sq in. (.01 sq m) in area and that are not listed for use in fire resistance rated assemblies should be permitted provided the area of such openings does not exceed 100 sq in. (.065 sq m) for any 100 sq ft (9.3 sq m) of enclosure wall area. Outlet boxes on opposite sides of the enclosure should be separated by a horizontal distance of not less than 24 in. (61 cm).

A-6-2.3.6.2(c)   See NFPA 90A, *Standard for the Installation of Air Conditioning and Ventilating Systems (see Appendix B),* for additional information on air-handling ducts passing through fire barriers.

One source of information on tested materials, devices, and systems for protecting through-penetrations of fire resistance rated barriers is the Underwriters Laboratories *Building Materials Directory*[15] in the categories of Through-Penetration Firestop Devices and Through-Penetration Firestop Systems. Such devices and systems are designed to resist the spread of fire through openings made in fire resistance rated floor or wall barriers to accommodate penetrating items, such as electrical cables, cable trays, conduits, and pipes. Such devices and systems are classified by UL with respect to installation in a wall only, installation in a floor only, or suitability for installation in a wall or floor. The basic standard used by Underwriters Laboratories to investigate products in this category is UL 1479, *Fire Tests of Through-Penetration Firestops*[16] *(similar to ASTM E814; see A-6-2.3.6.2).* A sampling of the currently classified devices includes the use of ceramic fibers, foamed silicones, mineral wool batts, intumescent sheets, sealing blankets and plugs, fittings and couplings, various caulks, putties and mastics, and even spring-loaded guillotine blades.

Over the life of a building, it is important to maintain the integrity of barriers to fire spread. Renovations or any changes to building utilities will tend to violate the compartmentation provided when a building is first occupied.

Figure 6-6 illustrates some of the typical fire barrier penetrations, which are covered in 6-2.3.5 and 6-2.3.6.

6-2.4   Vertical Openings.

Unprotected or improperly protected vertical openings have consistently shown up as major contributing factors to multiple-death fires. This is particularly well illustrated

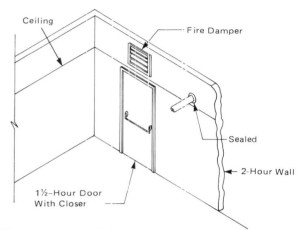

Figure 6-6.   Typical Penetrations of a Fire Barrier.

by the two deadliest hotel fires in recent decades in the U.S. and its possessions:[17]

Under the *Life Safety Code,* the unprotected vertical opening between the ballroom level (where fire originated in the 1986 DuPont Plaza Hotel fire that killed 97 people in San Juan, PR)[18] and the casino level (where nearly all deaths occurred), would not have been allowed, given the lack of other fire protection design features of that area.

In the 1980 MGM Grand Hotel fire (85 killed in Las Vegas, NV),[19] smoke spread occurred via unprotected vertical openings (concealed spaces, elevator shafts) and insufficiently protected stairways. Contributing to the vertical smoke spread were unprotected seismic joint shafts and elevator hoistways; insufficient fire-resistance rating used in interior stairway construction; exposure of stairway and exit passageway spaces to casino level plenum air; and heating, venting, and air conditioning systems with fire dampers that did not activate.

Most of the hotel and motel fires of recent decades that have resulted in 10 or more fatalities have involved unprotected vertical openings, typically open interior stairways.

6-2.4.1   Every floor that separates stories in a building shall be constructed as a smoke barrier to provide a basic degree of compartmentation. *(See Section 3-2 for definition of smoke barrier.)*

Exception No. 1:   As permitted by 6-2.4.5.

Exception No. 2:   As permitted by 6-2.4.6.

Exception No. 3:   As permitted by Chapters 8 through 30.

Although the *Code* states that every floor should be constructed as a smoke barrier, the requirement is tempered to stress that it intends that a "basic degree" of compartmentation is provided. The reference to the definition of smoke barrier in Section 3-2 provides the user with the statement that such barriers may have protected openings. Thus, it is not the *Code's* intent that every floor must restrict the passage of smoke to the same degree as that of a required smoke barrier in accordance with the provisions of Section 6-3. Even required smoke barriers, which are required to comply with Section 6-3, are afforded the use of 6-3.5.1 Exception No. 4, which allows smoke dampers to be omitted where ducts penetrate floors that serve as smoke barriers. See the commentary associated with 6-3.5.1 Exception No. 4.

6-2.4.2* Openings through floors, such as stairways, hoistways for elevators, dumbwaiters, inclined and vertical conveyors; shaftways used for light, ventilation, or building services; or expansion joints and seismic joints used to allow structural movements shall be enclosed with fire barriers (vertical), such as wall or partition assemblies. Such enclosures shall be continuous from floor to floor. Openings shall be protected as appropriate for the fire resistance rating of the barrier.

Exception No. 1: As permitted by 6-2.4.5.

Exception No. 2: As permitted by 6-2.4.6.

Exception No. 3: As permitted by Chapters 8 through 30.

Exception No. 4: Escalators and moving walks protected in accordance with 6-2.4.7.

Exception No. 5: Expansion or seismic joints designed to prevent the penetration of fire for a time period not less than the required fire resistance rating of the floor.

Exception No. 6: Enclosure is not reuqired for pneumatic tube conveyors protected in accordance with 6-2.3.6.2.

A-6-2.4.2 **Floor, Roof, and Ceiling Penetrations.** Penetrations through floor/ceiling and roof/ceiling assemblies should be protected using the methods specified below.

METHOD A   2-hour fire resistance rated shaft enclosure.
METHOD B   1-hour fire resistance rated shaft enclosure.
METHOD C   Protection of the annular space around the penetrating item.
    C1 = Protection at the ceiling line.
    C2 = Protection at the floor line.

METHOD D   Installation of an approved fire damper in a duct penetration in accordance with its listing.
    D1 = Ceiling damper at the ceiling line.
    D2 = Fire damper at the floor line.

METHOD E   Use of an approved, through-penetration protection system tested in accordance with ASTM E814, *Methods for Fire Tests of Through- Penetration Fire Stops,* at a positive pressure differential between the exposed and unexposed surfaces of the test assembly of not less than 0.01 in. water gauge (2.5 Pa).

Systems should have an F rating of at least 1 hour but not less than the required fire resistance rating of the assembly being penetrated. Systems protecting floor penetrations should have a T rating of at least 1 hour but not less than the required fire resistance rating of the floor being penetrated. Floor penetrations contained within the cavity of a wall at the location of the floor penetration do not require a T rating.

METHOD F   No requirements.
METHOD G   Penetrations permitted only when tested in accordance with NFPA 251, *Standard Methods of Fire Tests of Building Construction and Materials,* as a part of the rated assembly.

Penetrations of nonrated assemblies should be protected as required by Table A-6-2.4.2(a) as shown on next page. Penetrations of rated assemblies should be protected as required by Table A-6-2.4.2(b) as shown on the following page.

Expansion joints are usually found only in large buildings [i.e., at least 200 ft (60 m) in length and/or width] of steel or concrete construction. They are provided to permit the separate portions of the structural frame to expand and contract with temperature and moisture changes without adversely affecting the building's structural integrity or serviceability. Expansion joints can usually be identified by the following characteristics: 1) a double row of columns; 2) a width of 1 to 3 in. (2.5 to 7.6 cm); and 3) a steel plate cover that is attached to the floor on one side of the joint and free to slide on the other side. Expansion joints should not be confused with control or construction joints.

Control joints are normally found in concrete or masonry walls and concrete slabs-on-grade. They are provided to: 1) prevent cracking of the wall or slab due to excessive tensile forces in the concrete or masonry caused by shrinkage upon drying; or 2) induce cracking due to excessive tensile forces caused by drying shrinkage to occur at a predetermined location; hence the term "control" joint.

Table A-6-2.4.2(a)

	Nonrated Floor and Roof Assemblies						
	Conduits, Pipes,[1] and Tubes		Ducts		Factory-Built Appliance Vents and Chimneys		Cables and Wires
	Penetrating Material Classification						
	Non-Comb.	Comb.	Non-Comb.	Comb.	Non-Comb.	Comb.	All
Penetration through 3 floors or more (connecting 4 stories or more)	A or E		A				A or E
Penetration through 2 floors maximum (connecting 3 stories maximum)	A, B, C2, or E	A, B, or E	A, B, or D2	A or B	A, B, or C2	A or B	A, B, or E
Penetration through 1 floor maximum (connecting 2 stories maximum)	A, B, C2, or E		A, B, C2, or D2		A, B, or C2		A, B, C2, or E
Penetration through roof/ceiling assembly	F						
Penetration through roof membrane only							

[1] Pipes and tubes carrying hazardous materials may require additional protection.

Table A-6-2.4.2(b)

			Rated Floor and Roof Assemblies						
			Conduits, Pipes, and Tubes[1]		Ducts		Factory-Built Appliance Vents and Chimneys		Cables and Wires
			Penetrating Material Classification						
			Non-Comb.	Comb.	Non-Comb.	Comb.	Non-Comb.	Comb.	All
Penetration through 3 floors or more (connecting 4 stories or more)			A, E, or G	A or E	A				A or E
Penetration through 2 floors maximum (connecting 3 stories maximum)			A, B, E, or G		A or B		A or B		A, B, E, or G
Penetration through 1 floor maximum (connecting 2 stories maximum)	Monolithic Fire rated assembly		A, B, C2, E, or G	A, B, E or G	A, B, or D2[3]		A, B, or C2	A or B	A, B, C2, E, or G
	Fire rated assembly with membrane protection	Ceiling membrane penetrated	A, B, C1,[2] E, or G		A, B, D1,[2] or G		A, B, or C1[2]		A, B, C1,[2] E, or G
		Floor membrane penetrated	A, B, C2, E, or G		A, B, or D2[3]		A, B, or C2		A, B, C2, E, or G
Penetration through roof/ceiling assembly	Ceiling membrane		A, B, C1,[2] E, or G		A, B, D1,[2] or G		A, B, or C1[2]		A, B, C1,[2] E, or G
	Roof membrane		F						
Penetration through roof membrane only									

[1] Pipes and tubes carrying hazardous materials may require additional protection.
[2] Aggregate area of openings not to exceed 100 sq in. (.065 sq m)/100 sq ft (9.3 sq m).
[3] Duct must be part of fully ducted system (transfer grilles not permitted).

Construction joints are used as a stopping and starting point for two successive concrete placements (pours) in walls, floors, and beams. Since a construction joint must be designed to transfer load across the joints, separation due to thermal or moisture induced movements is not anticipated.

Seismic joints may be found in buildings other than those that are rectangular in plan (e.g., L- and T-shaped buildings) in areas where the risk of an earthquake is moderate to high. Such joints in multistory buildings can be as much as 12 in. (30.5 cm) in width. They are provided to allow the separated portions of the building to act independently of each other to undergo differential lateral displacements when an earthquake occurs.

With expansion or seismic joints, consideration should be given to the ability of the protecting system to remain in place and perform its intended function after repeated movements of the joint, and with the width of the joint varying from its maximum to minimum width. In the case of seismic joints, the protection system may be damaged during an earthquake that otherwise is not strong enough to cause major structural damage to the building. Therefore, it is necessary to conduct an inspection of those buildings after an earthquake.

Note that 6-2.4.1 and 6-2.4.2 apply to all occupancies unless the specific occupancy provides an exception. Protection of vertical openings is normally covered in the -3.1 subsection of each occupancy chapter.

Protection of vertical openings is of extreme importance if fire casualties are to be reduced. In report after report of fires involving fatalities, the major factors that contributed to loss of life included unprotected vertical openings.

A correlation frequently exists between loss of life from fire and monetary loss from fire, in that vertical fire spread is a major factor contributing to the extensive property damage characteristic of large loss building fires. This relates directly to the lack of protection for vertical openings, because the principal structural weakness responsible for vertical spread of fire is the absence of the fire cutoffs at openings between floors.

Figure 6-7 illustrates some typical floor openings.

Based on lessons learned from the Las Vegas MGM Grand Hotel fire,[19] the list of floor openings was expanded in the 1988 Code to include expansion joints and seismic joints that allow structural movements. Excep-

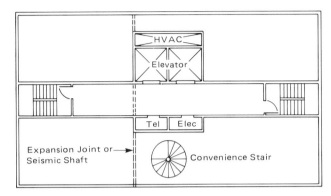

Figure 6-7. *Typical Floor Openings in a Building that Result in Vertical Openings.*

tion No. 5 specifically recognizes the use of fire protection rated expansion or seismic joints, with a minimum rating not less than the required fire resistance rating of the floor, in lieu of full enclosure from floor to floor. Without appropriately rated joints, the enclosure requirements might be satisfied by an arrangement of walls and doors as shown in Figure 6-8.

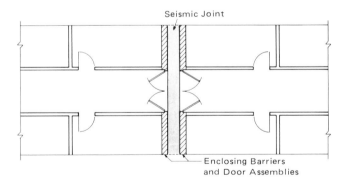

Figure 6-8. *Enclosure of Seismic Joint Accomplished by Back-to-Back Fire Resistance Rated Barriers and Cross-Corridor Fire-Protection Rated Door Assemblies.*

6-2.4.3 Enclosure of vertical openings (shafts) that do not extend to the bottom or the top of the building or structure shall be enclosed at the lowest and/or highest level of the shaft, respectively, with construction in accordance with 6-2.4.4.

Exception: Shafts may terminate in a room or space having a use related to the purpose of the shaft provided that the room or space is separated from the remainder of the building by construction having a fire resistance rating and opening protectives in accordance with 6-2.4.4 and 6-2.3.5.

Some shafts commonly found in buildings do not extend through the entire height of the building. For example, in a high rise building, a percentage of the overall number of elevator shafts will service only the lower rise portion of the building. Such shafts may run from street level through the twentieth floor of a 40-story building. In a typical hotel that devotes the first couple of stories to assembly occupancy uses and positions guest rooms above in the hotel occupancy tower, the shafts associated with guest room bathroom exhaust may begin at the third floor and continue to the roof. In such cases, although the shaft walls are constructed of fire resistance rated assemblies, an unprotected shaft ceiling/top or unprotected shaft floor/bottom would allow fire and other products of combustion to travel vertically to some other part of the building. Because of this concern, 6-2.4.3 requires that those shaft ceilings or floors be protected by construction as required for the shaft walls.

Figure 6-9 illustrates various shaft arrangements. Shaft A runs vertically for the full height of the building and requires only vertical fire barriers to separate the shaft from the remainder of the interior of the building. Because neither shaft B nor shaft C extends the full height of the building, horizontal fire barriers must be provided to complete the shaft envelope with a floor for shaft B and a ceiling for shaft C. Shaft D, which is used for heating, ventilating, and air conditioning (HVAC), extends vertically from floor two to the roof and makes use of the Exception to 6-2.4.3 so as not to have to install a rated floor barrier between it and mechanical equipment room E. In this case, the ceiling and walls of the mechanical equipment room, which is used for purposes related to the use of the HVAC shaft, must be of construction of at least the same hourly rating as required for shaft D. The room enclosure thus becomes an extension of the shaft. Access to room E from within the building would be gained through appropriately rated fire door assemblies.

6-2.4.4* The minimum fire resistance rating for the enclosure of floor openings shall be as follows (*see 5-1.3.1 for enclosure of exits*):

(a) Enclosures connecting four stories or more in new construction — 2-hour fire barriers.

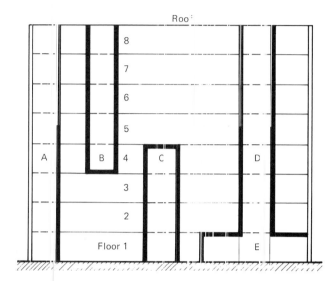

Figure 6-9. *Shafts That Do Not Run Full Height of Building Must Be Capped by Floors or Ceilings.*

(b) Other enclosures in new construction — 1-hour fire barriers.

(c) Enclosures in existing buildings — 1/2-hour fire barriers.

(d) As specified in Chapter 16 for new hotels, Chapter 18 for new apartment buildings, and in Chapter 20 for lodging and rooming houses.

A-6-2.4.4   The application of the 2-hour rule in buildings not divided into stories may be based on the number of levels of platforms or walkways served by the stairs.

The key to understanding 6-2.4.4 is the fact that the *Code's* concern is with the number of stories connected, not the height of the building. For example, if there is a vertical opening between the second, third, and fourth stories of an eight-story building, the enclosure of the opening must be of 1-hour and not 2-hour fire resistance rated construction.

Where addressing vertical openings, the *Code* does not use the height of buildings or a designated number of floors above ground as the basis for its requirements. Rather, it refers to the total number of floors connected by the vertical opening. Where a vertical opening connects any total of four stories or more, whether they are all above the exit discharge level, all below the exit discharge level, or any combination thereof, the protection afforded must have at least a 2-hour fire resistance rating (*see Figure 6-10*). Where three stories or less are connected by the vertical opening, the rating must be at least 1-hour. (*See Figures 6-11, 6-12, and 6-13.*)

Experience shows that, under some circumstances, each of the 1- and 2-hour rating levels provides a more-than-comfortable period of time for the occupants of a building to evacuate. On the other hand, there are times when the integrity of the construction will be taxed to its limit, e.g., during a situation in which a fire that has gone undetected for a long period generates heavy smoke and toxic gases, complicating evacuation by blocking the exit access.

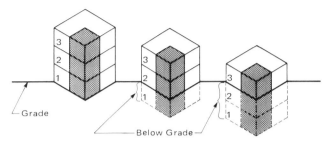

Figure 6-11. *Connecting Three Stories or Less, Vertical Openings Must Be Enclosed in 1-Hour Construction (Shaded Areas).*

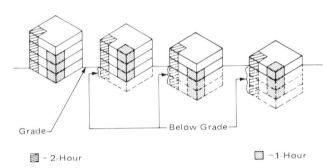

Figure 6-10. *Connecting Four Stories or More, Vertical Openings Must Be Enclosed in 2-Hour Construction.*

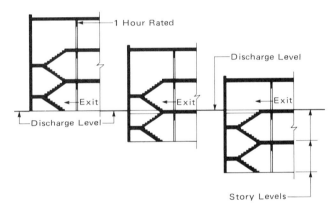

Figure 6-12. *No Matter Where the Discharge Level Is Located, There Are Three Stories Connected in Each of the Arrangements Illustrated; Thus, the Enclosure Must Have at Least a 1-Hour Fire Resistance Rating. If more than three stories are involved, a 2-hour fire resistance rating is required.*

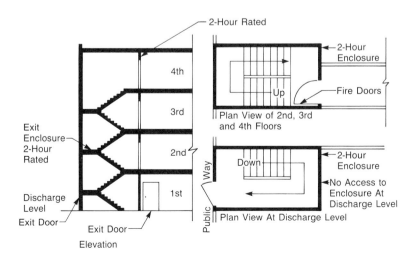

Figure 6-13. *While the Stairway Serves Three Stories, the Stairway Is a Vertical Opening Among Four Stories; Thus, According to 6-2.4.3, the Enclosure Must Have at Least a 2-Hour Fire Resistance Rating.*

An interior exit stair by definition (*see 5-1.2.5*), in order to be separated from other building spaces and to provide a protected way of travel to the exit discharge, must be enclosed. If not properly enclosed, it not only fails to meet the definition of an exit but also creates an unprotected vertical opening. Thus, an exit stair must meet both the requirements for enclosure of exit (*see 5-1.3.1*) and those for protection of vertical openings in accordance with this paragraph. Given that the requirements for enclosure of exits are more stringent than the requirements for protection of vertical openings, once the more stringent requirements have been met, the other requirements are usually met automatically.

Paragraph 6-2.4.4(d) references the hotel, apartment, and lodging and rooming house occupancy chapters which, under certain conditions, allow exceptions to the requirements of 6-2.4.4. Unlike the occupancy chapters that use exceptions to provide more leniency with respect to the enclosure of vertical openings than the basic Chapter 6 requirements, it is possible for a specific occupancy to be more stringent.

6-2.4.5   Where permitted by Chapters 8 through 30, unenclosed floor openings forming a communicating space between floor levels shall be permitted, provided that the following conditions are met:

(a) The communicating space does not connect more than three contiguous stories.

(b) The lowest or next to lowest story within the communicating space is a street floor.

(c) The entire floor area of the communicating space is open and unobstructed such that a fire in any part of the space will be readily obvious to the occupants of the space prior to the time it becomes a hazard to them.

(d) The communicating space is separated from the remainder of the building by fire barriers with at least a 1-hour fire resistance rating.

Exception No. 1 to (d): In buildings protected throughout by an approved automatic sprinkler system in accordance with Section 7-7, a smoke barrier in accordance with Section 6-3 shall be permitted to serve as the required separation.

Exception No. 2 to (d): Fully sprinklered residential housing units of detention and correctional occupancies in accordance with 14-3.1.1 Exception No. 3 and 15-3.1.1 Exception No. 3.

(e) The communicating space has ordinary hazard contents protected throughout by an approved automatic sprinkler system in accordance with Section 7-6 or has only low hazard contents. (*See 4-2.2.*)

(f) Exit capacity is sufficient to provide for all the occupants of all levels within the communicating space to simultaneously egress the communicating space by considering it as single floor area in determining the required exit capacity.

(g)* Each occupant within the communicating space shall have access to at least one exit without having to traverse another story within the communicating space.

A-6-2.4.5(g)   Given that a mezzanine meeting the maximum $\frac{1}{3}$ area definition of mezzanines per Chapter 3 is not a "story," it can therefore have 100 percent of its exit access within the communicating area run back through the story below.

(h) Each occupant not in the communicating space shall have access to at least one exit without having to enter the communicating space.

Paragraph 6-2.4.5 recognizes a vertical opening that is exempt from the normal enclosure requirements of 6-2.4.4 if such recognition is specifically permitted by the pertinent occupancy chapter for the occupancy type in question, and if all the alternative protection provisions (a) through (h) of 6-2.4.5, as explained and illustrated below, are met:

(a) The vertical space cannot connect or communicate among more than three stories, and all connected stories are required to be contiguous to each other. The building itself, which houses the vertical opening in question, may be more than three stories in height. For example, the vertical opening might communicate among floors one through three of a six-story building. (*See Figure 6-14.*)

The provisions of 6-2.4.5 are often referred to as the "mini-atrium" requirements. The requirements, because they are limited to a maximum three-story vertical opening, are not as stringent as those of 6-2.4.6, applicable to atria that can involve vertical openings that communicate among 50 or 100 stories or more. A two- or three-story atrium can adequately be protected by the requirements of 6-2.4.5 without having to resort to the requirements of 6-2.4.6. The fact that a two- or three-story space is labeled as an atrium on building plans does not necessarily mean that it must be protected by the requirements of 6-2.4.6. A two- or three-story vertical opening, whether or not called an atrium, should be allowed to be protected per the requirements of 6-2.4.5 as long as the occupancy chapter(s) involved permits its use and the requirements of subparts (a) through (h) are met.

(b) The lowest of the maximum three communicating floor levels is at, or not more than one level below, the street level. In other words, the vertical opening can communicate among only the first, second, and third floors or among the basement, first, and second floors (*see Figure 6-14*). As mentioned above, additional building floor levels may be present either above or below the floors involving the vertical opening, but these additional floors cannot be left open to the vertical opening. If it is necessary or desirable either to have more than three levels open or to locate the communicating levels such that the lowest level does not meet the placement requirement with respect to street level, the more stringent set of provisions for atriums per 6-2.4.6 should be considered. Again, the occupancy chapter applicable to the occupancy in question must specifically recognize the use of the atrium provisions of 6-2.4.6.

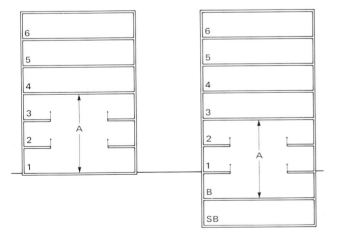

Figure 6-14. *Lowest Level of Maximum Three-Story Vertical Opening (A) Must Be at, or Not More Than One Level Below, the Street Floor.*

(c) The communicating space, meaning all areas within the vertical opening itself and all adjoining areas left open to the vertical opening (i.e., not separated by minimum 1-hour fire resistance rated barriers) must be open and unobstructed so as to make occupants of the space aware of fire and smoke conditions that might emanate from any part of the communicating space prior to the time that such conditions become a hazard.

The provisions of 6-2.4.5 were written originally as an exception to the enclosure requirements for vertical openings in recognition of typical mercantile occupancy construction practices, which left partial, mezzanine-like floors open to the main street-level shopping floor below. Such arrangements were sufficiently open that, where coupled with the other provisions of the exception, they allowed for the necessary awareness of emergency conditions in sufficient time to make use of the egress system. It was not the intent to recognize use of the exception for something like an unenclosed stairway. The small opening created by an unenclosed stairway is insufficient in size to provide the needed degree of awareness by occupants.

Between the two extremes of vast amounts of openness, as in the case of the mezzanine-like floors described above, and little or no openness, as depicted above by the unenclosed stair, judging sufficient openness becomes difficult. Through use of the equivalency concept addressed in Section 1-6 of the *Code*, some authorities having jurisdiction have allowed complete automatic smoke detection systems with proper occupant notification features to be substituted for the openness and unobstructedness required by the *Code* for awareness and early warning purposes.

(d) The communicating space must be separated from the remainder of the building by fire barriers with minimum 1-hour fire resistance rating. Once the boundaries of the communicating space are established, based, for example, on determining how much area is open enough per requirement (c) above to permit awareness and early warning, areas outside these boundaries must be separated from the communicating space associated with the vertical opening by barriers with a minimum 1-hour fire resistance rating. If the building is fully sprinklered, the barriers may be reduced to zero fire resistance rating but must resist the passage of smoke and meet the other smoke barrier requirements of Section 6-3. It is thought that the sprinkler system will control the fire and obviate the need for fire resistance rated barriers. The smoke barriers will control the limited smoke, under sprinklered conditions, and help maintain a tenable means of egress route.

In the case, for example, of a hotel building with fingerlike guest room wings fanning out from the vertical opening, it can be assumed that the guest room wing corridors will need separation from the vertical opening because persons in the corridor on the second or third floor will not be readily aware of a fire on the first floor before the fire becomes a hazard to them. The required 1-hour separation can be provided while the perception of openness is maintained by isolating the guest room wings from the vertical opening through the use of pairs of cross-corridor doors held open with automatic release devices. (See Figure 6-15.)

(e) If the communicating space, meaning the vertical opening itself and all adjoining areas open to it as described in (c) above, has ordinary hazard contents, per the definition of Section 4-2 of this Code, as opposed to the NFPA 13, *Standard for the Installation of Sprinkler Systems,*[20] definition of ordinary hazard occupancies, all areas within the confines of the communicating space must be sprinklered. If the contents are low hazard, again as defined by Section 4-2 of this Code, as opposed to the definition of light hazard occupancies from the sprinkler installation standard, no sprinklering is required by 6-2.4.5 itself. However, as stated and intended by Chapter 4, Classification of Occupancy and Hazard of Contents, of this Code, most occupancies are ordinary hazard. Given that only low hazard and ordinary hazard contents are addressed in 6-2.4.5(e), high hazard contents therefore are prohibited from any vertical openings recognized by 6-2.4.5.

Although sprinklering is required with ordinary hazard contents, only the communicating area, as defined above, needs to be sprinklered by the provisions of 6-2.4.5. The sprinkler system should cover all areas within the boundaries established by the 1-hour fire barriers required by (d) above. (See Figure 6-15.)

(f) Because all occupants within the communicating area might be exposed within a short period of time to the effects of a fire within the area, simultaneous evacuation capability needs to be provided. Thus, the combined occupant load for all spaces, on all levels, within

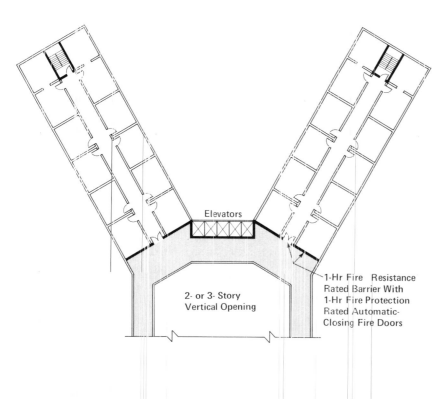

Elevators

1-Hr Fire Resistance Rated Barrier With 1-Hr Fire Protection Rated Automatic-Closing Fire Doors

2- or 3- Story Vertical Opening

Figure 6-15. With Cross-Corridor Fire Doors Held Open by Automatic Release Devices, Corridor Appears to Be Open to the Communicating Area of the Vertical Opening. Sprinkler protection must be provided for the vertical opening and the shaded adjoining areas up to the 1-hour barriers.

the boundaries of the communicating area needs to be used to size the means of egress for the communicating area. This represents an exception to the guidelines of 5-3.1.4, which normally exempt the accumulation of occupant loads from various floors.

(g) Per the requirements of (c) and (d), the communicating space is that space that is sufficiently open to the vertical opening so as to allow ready awareness of fire conditions on that and other levels within the communicating space. Areas sufficiently remote from the vertical opening so as to lose the requisite awareness are then located on the other side of 1-hour fire resistance rated fire barriers and considered as being outside the communicating space. Thus, in a typical office building making use of the provisions of 6-2.4.5, for example, some occupants will work and be normally positioned within the communicating space while others will work and be stationed outside the communicating space. This arrangement is shown in Figure 6-16.

Subpart (g) requires that occupants of the communicating space have access to at least one exit without having to traverse another story within the communicating space. The communicating space shown in Figure 6-16

would meet this requirement by having occupants travel horizontally across the communicating space, pass through the fire doors in the fire rated barrier into one of the building wings designated as "floor area outside the communicating space," and continue to that wing's enclosed exit stair. In other words, the occupants of the communicating space cannot be forced to use the open stairs exclusively to travel to another level of the communicating space in order to reach the required exits.

In the above example, assume that some occupants of the communicating space are farther from either of the enclosed exit stairs, located at each end of the building, than the distance allowed by other *Code* requirements as travel distance. Further, assume that those same occupants of the communicating space can travel down the open stair and across the bottom floor of the vertical opening to an exterior exit door within the allowable travel distance limitation. The open stair, although it is not an exit, could be considered as exit access, and the door to the outside at the lowest level of the vertical opening could then be regarded as the nearest *Code*-complying exit for those occupants. Either of the enclosed exit stairs at the end of the building could then serve as the second exit for those occupants of the communicating space. The

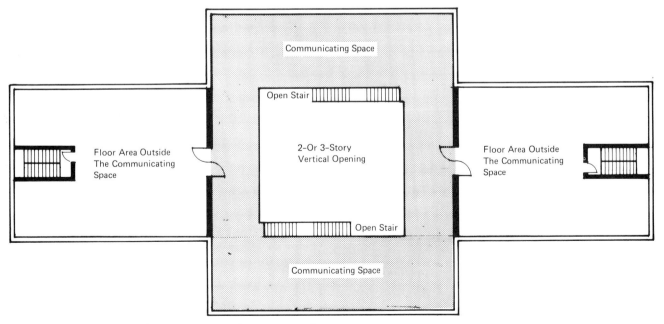

Figure 6-16. Maximum Three-Story Vertical Opening with Occupants of Communicating Space Having Access to an Exit Without Traversing to Another Story.

enclosed exit stairs would then serve three purposes, none being the primary exit for those occupants of the communicating space:

1. They would satisfy the business occupancy chapters' requirements that each floor be provided with two separate exits,
2. Either would satisfy the 6-2.4.5(g) requirement that the occupants of the communicating space have access to at least one exit without having to traverse another story within the communicating space, and
3. Each would satisfy the requirement of subpart (h) of 6-2.4.5, which will be discussed in the commentary below, that each occupant not in the communicating space have access to at least one exit without having to enter the communicating space.

(h) Although all occupants must have access to two separate exits, the occupants who are on any of the maximum three floors that communicate with the vertical opening but who are not within the communicating space, as shown in Figure 6-16 by the wings at each end of the building, must be able to reach one of their two required exits without entering the communicating space. This requirement is satisfied by the enclosed exit stair positioned within each of the floor areas outside the communicating space.

The following occupancies permit the use of the provisions of 6-2.4.5. Check the referenced paragraphs for any limitations or additional requirements. For example, Chapters 10 and 11 for educational occupancies recognize 6-2.4.5 only if the entire building is protected by a supervised automatic sprinkler system.

Assembly — 8-3.1 Exception No. 1, 9-3.1 Exception No. 1

Educational — 10-3.1.1 Exception, 11-3.1.1 Exception

Detention and Correctional — 14-3.1.1 Exception No. 3, 15-3.1.1 Exception No. 3

Hotels — 16-3.1.1 Exception No. 1, 17-3.1.1 Exception No. 1

Apartments — 19-3.1.1 Exception No. 4

Residential Board and Care — 22-3.3.1.1 Exception No. 1, 23-3.3.1.1 Exception No. 1

Mercantile — 24-3.1 Exception No. 1(c), 25-3.1 Exception No. 2(c)

Business — 26-3.1.1 Exception No. 1, 27-3.1.1 Exception No. 1

Industrial — 28-3.1.1 Exception No. 1

Storage — 29-3.1.1 Exception No. 1.

6-2.4.6* Atriums. Where permitted by Chapters 8 through 30, an atrium shall be permitted provided the following conditions are met:

(a)* No horizontal dimension between opposite edges of the floor opening is less than 20 ft (6.1 m), and the opening is a minimum of 1,000 sq ft (93 sq m).

A-6-2.4.6(a) As some atriums may be of other than square or rectangular shape, the 20-ft (6.1-m) measurement obviously cannot be applied where the corners exist. This would necessitate that the designer and the authority having jurisdiction work out equivalent life safety.

(b) The exits are separately enclosed from the atrium in accordance with 6-2.3.5. Access to exits is permitted to be within the atrium. Exit discharge in accordance with 5-7.2 is permitted to be within the atrium.

(c) The occupancy within the space meets the specifications for classification as low or ordinary hazard contents. (See 4-2.2.)

(d) The entire building is protected throughout by an approved supervised automatic sprinkler system in accordance with Section 7-7.

Exception to (d)*: Where the ceiling of the atrium is more than 55 ft (17 m) above the floor, the authority having jurisdiction may permit the omission of sprinklers at the top of the atrium.

A-6-2.4.6 Exception to (d) Automatic sprinklers have been successfully tested at ceiling heights up to 50 ft (15 m). Permission is granted the authority having jurisdiction to omit sprinklers at higher ceiling heights, since it has not been demonstrated that sprinklers directly over the fire will effectively respond to the fire in a timely manner.

(e)* In new construction, an engineered smoke control system acceptable to the authority having jurisdiction shall be provided. Factors such as means of egress and smoke control of adjacent spaces shall be considered.

A-6-2.4.6   Where atriums are used, there is an added degree of safety to occupants because of the large volume of space into which smoke can be dissipated. However, there is a need to ensure that dangerous concentrations of smoke are promptly removed from the atrium, and the exhaust system needs careful design.

A-6-2.4.6(e)   See A-7-3.1.

(f)* In new construction, if a mechanical system is installed to meet the requirements of (e) above, the mechanical system shall be independently activated by each of the following:

A-6-2.4.6(f)   Activation of the ventilation system by manual fire alarms, extinguishing systems, and detection systems can cause unwanted operation of the system, and it is suggested that consideration be given to zoning of the activation functions so the ventilation system operates only when actually needed.

1.* Approved smoke detectors located to detect smoke above the highest floor level of the atrium and at return air intakes from the atrium, and

A-6-2.4.6(f)1   Projected beam smoke detectors have been demonstrated as an effective method for detection of smoke, accessibility for testing and maintenance, and ability to overcome problems associated with smoke stratification within the height of the atrium. If stratification is a potential problem, use of projected beam smoke detectors at different levels is recommended.

2. The required automatic sprinkler system, and
3. Manual controls that are readily accessible to the fire department.

(g) In new construction, atriums shall be separated from the adjacent spaces by fire barriers with at least a 1-hour fire resistance rating with opening protectives as for corridor walls. [*See 6-2.3.5(b) Exception No. 2.*]

Exception No. 1 to (g): Any three levels of the building shall be permitted to open directly to the atrium without enclosure.

Exception No. 2 to (g): Glass walls shall be permitted in lieu of the fire barriers where automatic sprinklers are spaced 6 ft (183 cm) apart or less along both sides of the glass wall,* not more than 1 ft (30.5 cm) from the glass, and with the automatic sprinklers located so that the entire surface of the glass is wet upon operation of the sprinklers. The glass shall be tempered, wired, or laminated glass held in place by a gasket system that permits the glass framing system to deflect without breaking (loading) the glass before the sprinklers operate. Automatic sprinklers are not required on the atrium side of the glass wall where there is no walkway or other floor area on the atrium side above the main floor level. Doors in such walls shall be glass or other material that will resist the passage of smoke. Doors shall be self-closing or automatic-closing upon detection of smoke.*

A-6-2.4.6   **Exception No. 2 to (g)**   The intent of the requirement for closely spaced sprinklers to wet the atrium glass wall is to ensure that the surface of the glass is wet upon operation of the sprinklers with a maximum spacing of sprinklers of 6 ft (183 cm) on centers. Provided that it can be shown that the glass can be wet by the sprinklers using a given discharge rate and that the 6-ft (183-cm) spacing is not exceeded, the intent of the requirement is met.

The concept of wetting the glass that is exposed to a fire, without specifying a water application rate, is similar to boiling water in a Pyrex® container over an open flame. As long as there is some water present to absorb the heat, the glass itself does not reach excessive temperatures that would cause failure. To ensure that water will reach the surface of the glass, window blinds and draperies must not be placed between the line of closely spaced sprinklers and the glass. Careful design will allow for the sprinklers to be placed close enough to the glass to allow blinds and draperies to be installed within normal installation distances from the glass.

The following occupancies permit the use of atriums in accordance with 6-2.4.6. Check the referenced paragraphs for any additional limitations or restrictions:

Assembly — 8-3.1 Exception No. 2, 9-3.1 Exception No. 2

Educational — 10-3.1.1 Exception No. 2, 11-3.1.1 Exception No. 2

Health Care — 12-3.1.1 Exception No. 4, 13-3.1.1 Exception No. 4

Detention and Correctional — 14-3.1.1 Exception No. 4, 15-3.1.1 Exception No. 4

Hotels — 16-3.1.1 Exception No. 2, 17-3.1.1 Exception No. 2

Apartment Buildings — 18-3.1.1 Exception No. 2, 19-3.1.1 Exception No. 2

Residential Board and Care — 22-3.3.1.1 Exception No. 2, 23-3.3.1.1 Exception No. 2

Mercantile — 24-3.1 Exception No. 3, 25-3.1 Exception No. 4

Business — 26-3.1.1 Exception No. 3, 27-3.1.1 Exception No. 3

Industrial — 28-3.1.1 Exception No. 2

Storage — 29-3.1.1 Exception No. 2.

Figures 6-17a and b, which follow, illustrate a typical atrium.

Paragraph 6-2.4.6 recognizes a vertical opening that communicates among more than the three floors allowed by the "mini-atrium" provision of 6-2.4.5 if the occupancy chapter(s) involved specifically allow use of the atrium provisions of 6-2.4.6. Although the provisions are not prohibited from being used for two- or three- story atria-like vertical openings, the design professional should be allowed to protect such areas in accordance with the less stringent provisions of 6-2.4.5 if the occupancy chapter(s) in question allows for use of 6-2.4.5. Use of the provisions of 6-2.4.5, if allowed by the specific occupancy, should adequately protect a two- or three-story atrium. Health care occupancy Chapters 12 and 13, in their -3.1 subsections dealing with protection of vertical openings, recognize the use of the atrium provisions of 6-2.4.6 but not the use of the mini-atrium provisions of 6-2.4.5. Thus, in health care occupancies, a two- or three-story atrium-like vertical opening is allowed only if it meets all criteria of 6-2.4.6 applicable to large atria. For certain designs 6-2.4.5 is not desirable due to its restriction on exit access within the vertical opening. For example, a three-story hotel would prefer to use the more stringent provisions of 6-2.4.6 since this would permit the guests rooms to have exit access through the "atrium," whereas 6-2.4.5 would not allow exit access to be solely through the "mini-atrium."

The protection provisions of (a) through (g) of 6-2.4.6 are explained and illustrated below:

(a) The requirements of 6-2.4.6(a) specifying a minimum 20-ft (6.1-m) dimension between opposite edges of the floor opening and an overall minimum area of 1000 sq ft (93 sq m) for that same floor opening are shown in Figures 6-17a and 6-17b. These requirements are aimed at forcing the atrium designer into creating a large smoke accumulation chamber, which works as an asset in managing the smoke concentrations early in the fire before the building sprinkler system achieves control of the fire and before the required smoke control system begins to control smoke concentrations. The geometry specified by minimum area and dimensional criteria help to keep the atrium opening from becoming a flue or chimney in lieu of an initial smoke accumulation chamber. The 20-ft (6.1-m) and 1000-sq ft (93-sq m) specifications are not magic numbers founded in physics nor are they based on any specific research program. Rather, they represent the best aggregated thinking of experts who comprise the Committee on Safety to Life and its Subcommittee on Fire Protection Features. The requirements appeared first in the 1981 Edition of the *Life Safety Code* and have served well as reasonable approaches to an overall atrium package that includes the numerous provisions of subparts (a) through (g).

The verbiage of appendix material A-6-2.4.6(a) recognizes that some atria are designed and built to be of some shape other than square or rectangular. Applying the minimum 20-ft (6.1-m) cross-atrium provision becomes complex and will involve reaching an understanding with the authority having jurisdiction as to whether the intent of the provision is being met.

(b) The exit stairs, although allowed to be within the communicating space and so located as to require building occupants to walk through the communicating space of the atrium in order to gain access to the stairs, must be enclosed in accordance with the exit enclosure requirements of 5-1.3.1. Figure 6-17a shows three such exit stair enclosures located within the communicating space, with all occupants of the floor required to walk within the communicating space across the interior exit access balcony of that floor in order to gain access to the stairs. On the level of exit discharge, up to 50 percent of those three exits may discharge occupants from upper or lower

Plan View

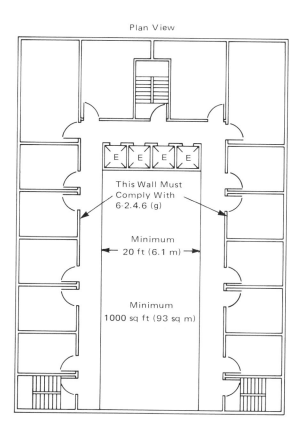

Figure 6-17a. *Plan View of a Typical Atrium.*

Elevation View

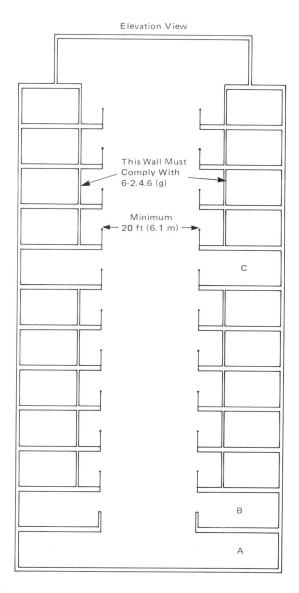

Figure 6-17b. *Elevation View of a Typical Atrium.*

floors in accordance with the provisions of 5-7.2, thus forcing those occupants to walk across the floor of the atrium to reach a door to the outside. Given the stringent requirements that must be met by subparts (a) through (g), an adequate overall package of life safety is afforded to allow for the exit access and exit discharge to be within the atrium.

(c) The occupancy within the communicating space [i.e., the vertical opening and all floor areas left open to the vertical opening such as balcony-like walking surfaces and the three levels allowed to be left completely open via the provisions of Exception No. 1 to subpart (g)] is limited to low or ordinary hazard contents as defined in 4-2.2. High hazard contents are thus prohibited from being placed within the communicating space but could be within hazardous area rooms surrounded by fire resistance rated walls in accordance with the provisions of Section 6-4. Because the provisions of 6-2.4.6(d) require that the building be completely protected by a supervised auto-

matic sprinkler system, the presence of only low hazard contents within the communicating space does not exempt the sprinkler requirement, whereas with the mini-artium provisions of 6-2.4.5 such an exemption would be allowed.

(d) The entire building, rather than just the communicating space involving the atrium opening, must be protected by a supervised automatic sprinkler system meeting the requirements of Section 7-7. Assuming that the atrium is in a hotel building of five or more stories, for example, the provisions of Section 7-7 would lead to mandatory use of NFPA 13, *Standard for the Installation of Sprinkler Systems*.[20] Although NFPA 13 generally would consider the sprinkler system to be complete and complying only if installed throughout all portions of the building, the Exception to (d) recognizes that sprinklers installed at the ceiling of an atrium that is more than 55 ft (17 m) in height may not respond effectively to a fire directly beneath the sprinklers in a timely manner. The exception thus allows the authority having jurisdiction to permit the system designer to omit sprinklers from such high ceilings and still be considered as meeting the requirements for full sprinklering.

(e) Since the atrium provisions were first introduced into the *Life Safety Code* in the 1981 Edition, an engineered smoke control or smoke removal system acceptable to the authority having jurisdiction has been required. As advisory but nonmandatory information, the appendix suggested that, depending on atrium height and volume, either four or six air changes per hour could provide the smoke exhaust rate needed to meet the tenability conditions intended by the requirement for atrium smoke control.

The "six air changes per hour" guideline came to be considered law by many authorities having jurisdiction and was thus accepted as the norm by many system designers. Authorities having jurisdiction then subjected such systems to acceptance testing using smoke bombs that produce cold smoke, which does not have the heat, bouyancy, and entrainment of smoke from a real fire. The acceptance criteria were further complicated by those who mistakenly believed that the intent of the smoke control requirement was to have no smoke visible within the atrium at the end of a ten-minute test, for example. Designers found that, in order to ensure that the acceptance test could be passed, the system should provide approximately ten to twelve air changes per hour. In effect, atrium smoke control systems typically were designed to pass the acceptance test with no assurance of effective smoke control under fire conditions. The new document NFPA 92B, *Guide for Smoke Management Systems in Malls, Atria, and Large Areas*,[21] warns that a system designed in accordance with NFPA 92B and capable of providing the intended smoke management might not pass smoke bomb tests. Conversely, it is possible for a system that is incapable of providing the intended smoke management to pass smoke bomb tests. Because of the impracticality of conducting real fire tests within an atrium, the acceptance tests described in NFPA 92B are directed at those aspects of smoke management systems that can be verified.

With the recent publication of NFPA 92B, *Guide for Smoke Management Systems in Malls, Atria, and Large Areas*, the physics associated with atrium smoke control have been quantified and methodologies for system design presented in an understandable and useful format. The guidelines of NFPA 92B allow the system designer to design a system and prepare the associated documentation that the authority having jurisdiction can judge to be adequate to meet the intent of 6-2.4.6(e). For example, the authority having jurisdiction might approve a design that provides for the level of smoke filling to be maintained for a minimum of 10 minutes after actuation of the fire alarm system to a point at least 5 ft (152 cm) above the highest floor level open to the atrium and the highest floor level used for exit access within the atrium.

The following example makes use of the guidelines of NFPA 92B in designing a smoke management system that meets the "10-minute/5-ft" criteria judged acceptable by the authority having jurisdiction in the above commentary:

The proposed atrium building is to be twelve stories in height with the third floor as the highest level open to the atrium and the ninth floor as the highest walking level within the atrium as shown in Figure 6-18. Further, the atrium ceiling is to be 120 ft (36.6 m) above the floor; the atrium opening is to be rectangular with horizontal dimensions of 100 ft × 200 ft (30.4 m × 61 m); the HVAC system will be designed to maintain the normal temperature difference from floor to ceiling within the atrium to no more than 50°F (28°C); and the atrium will be furnished with upholstered furniture and wood and plastic tables characteristic of the fire loading typically associated with a business occupancy.

Note: The following example and analysis have been done using the formulae from those portions of NFPA 92B that utilize the conventional "British" units of feet—

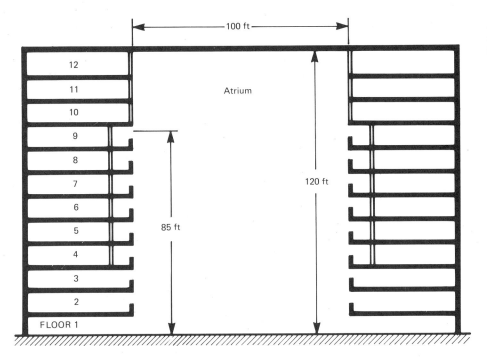

Figure 6-18. Twelve-Story Atrium for Which Smoke Control Is To Be Provided.

square feet, Btus per second, pounds per cubic foot, cubic feet per minute, etc. Although it is standard practice within this *Handbook* to provide metric or SI units where applicable, as parenthetically enclosed equivalents, this will not be done below. Rather, the reader is referred to Appendix D of NFPA 92B, where SI unit forms of all twenty-eight equations used in the Guide are shown.

Given that the designer would prefer to install smoke detectors, for activation of the smoke control system and initiation of the building fire alarm, at the top of the atrium only, the designer uses the guidelines of NFPA 92B to see if smoke will reach the ceiling or stratify at some distance below the ceiling. Stratification occurs when air containing smoke particles is heated by burning material and, becoming less dense than surrounding cooler air, rises until it reaches a level at which there is no longer a difference in temperature between it and the surrounding air. As specified above, the maximum difference in normal temperature between the floor and ceiling of the atrium will be maintained to be no more than a 50°F (28°C) difference. Having equated the furniture arrange-

ment as typical of the combustible loading associated with a business occupancy, the designer feels comfortable assuming a typical heat release rate per unit floor area of 20 Btu/ft²-sec, which realistically translates to a design fire heat release rate from steady fire of 5000 Btu/sec. Using Equation 8 from Section 3-4 of NFPA 92B:

$$H_{max} = 74 \, Q_c^{2/5} \Delta T_o^{-3/5}$$

where:

H_{max} = maximum height to which a plume of strength Q_c can rise for a given ΔT_o(ft)

Q_c = convective portion of the heat release rate (Btu/sec)

ΔT_o = difference between ambient temperature at the ceiling and ambient temperature at the level of the fire surface, i.e., the floor of the atrium, (°F)

In this case:

Q_c = 70% of 5000 = 3500 Btu/sec
ΔT_o = 50°F

Substituting:

$$H_{max} = 74 \ (3500)^{2/5} \ (50)^{-3/5}$$
$$H_{max} = 74 \ (26.2) \ (0.096)$$
$$H_{max} = 186 \ \text{ft}$$

Since H_{max} is greater than the ceiling height, the smoke is likely to reach the ceiling and not stratify prematurely.

Next, the designer checks to see if ceiling mounted spot-type smoke detectors will activate early enough to initiate a building alarm and notify occupants to evacuate while the exit access balconies are still usable. Using Equation 9 from 3-5.2 of NFPA 92B for steady fires, the depth of the smoke layer at time of ceiling smoke detector activation can be predicted:

$$z/H = 0.67 - 0.28 \ \ln[(tQ^{1/3}/H^{4/3})/(A/H^2)]$$

where:

  z = height of the smoke layer interface above the fire surface (ft)
  H = ceiling height above the fire surface (ft)
  t = time (sec)
  Q = heat release rate from steady fire (Btu/sec)
  A = cross-sectional area of the space being filled with smoke (ft²)

In this case:

  H = 120 ft
  t = 517 sec for smoke detector located at ceiling of previously described atrium. Value calculated using Equation 3 of 3-3.4 of NFPA 92B for steady fires. For detailed calculation, see Appendix E of NFPA 92B.
  Q = 5000 Btu/sec
  A = 100 ft × 200 ft = 20,000 ft²

Substituting:

$$z/H = 0.67 - 0.28 \ \ln \ [(517 \times 5000^{1/3}/120^{4/3})/(20,000/120^2)]$$
$$z/H = 0.67 - 0.28 \ \ln \ (10.75)$$
$$z/H = 0.0055$$

Therefore, $z = 0.66$ ft and, thus, the smoke layer will have descended almost to floor level at the time of ceiling smoke detector activation. Ceiling smoke detection will not be adequate to ensure that the smoke control system will actuate prior to the onset of hazardous condi-

tions within the atrium. Thus, the system designer substitutes projected beam detectors, including some at approximately the 30-ft height level, reducing the t-value used in the above equation to less than 1 minute. Additional calculations determine that, for the remainder of the exercise, it can be assumed that detection will occur before any of the exit access balcony walkways lose tenability. Furthermore, it can be assumed that occupant notification occurs by means of the activation of the building alarm almost immediately, and the 10-minute performance criteria approved by the authority having jurisdiction commences.

The designer next calculates the volumetric exhaust rate required to keep smoke 5 ft above the highest walking level in the atrium, i.e., the ninth floor balcony whose floor is at the 80 ft elevation. From the guidance offered in NFPA 92B, the designer locates the design fire in the center of the floor of the atrium so as to keep the fire away from the walls and thus create the worst case condition. With the fire at the center of the atrium floor, an axisymmetric fire plume is expected for which air is entrained from all sides and along the entire height of the plume until the plume becomes submerged in the smoke layer (see Figure 6-19). This leads the designer to the use of Equation 13 of 3-6.1 in order to determine the flame height:

$$z_1 = 0.533 \ Q_c^{2/5}$$

where:

  z_1 = limiting elevation (ft)
  Q_c = convective portion of heat release rate (Btu/sec), established above as 70% of the heat release rate, Q

In this case:

  Q_c = 3500 Btu/sec

Substituting:

$$z_1 = 0.533 \ (3500)^{2/5}$$
$$z_1 = 13.9 \ \text{ft}$$

With the design interface of the smoke layer at 85 ft above the floor level, the flame height is less than the design smoke layer height. Thus, Equation 14 of 3-6.1.2 can be used to determine the smoke production rate at the height of the smoke layer interface:

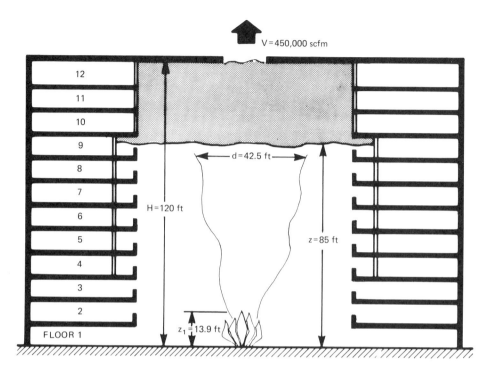

Figure 6-19. *Axisymmetric Fire Plume and Associated Smoke Interface.*

$$m = 0.022\ Q_c^{1/3}\ z^{5/3} + 0.0042\ Q_c \qquad (z \geq z_1)$$

where:

 Q_c = convective portion of heat release rate (Btu/sec)
 z = height above the fuel (ft)

In this case:

 Q_c = 3500 Btu/sec, as developed above
 z = 85 ft, as explained above

Substituting:

 $m = 0.022\ (3500)^{1/3}(85)^{5/3} + 0.0042\ (3500)$
 $m = 564$ lb/sec

If the smoke exhaust rate is equal to the smoke production rate, the smoke layer depth will be stabilized at the design height, i.e., the 85 ft elevation, and thus all balconies and areas open to the atrium will remain tenable as the fire continues to burn. The smoke production rate can be converted to a volumetric flow rate using Equation 16 from 3-6.1 of NFPA 92B:

$$V = 60\ m/\rho$$

where:

 m = smoke production rate, lb/sec

 ρ = density of smoke (lb/ft³), i.e., 0.075 lb/ft³

Substituting:

 V = 564 / 0.075
 V = 7521 ft³/sec or approximately 450,000 scfm

The above calculations assume that the smoke plume has not widened to contact the walls of the atrium prior to reaching the design interface height, i.e., the 85-ft elevation in this example. As a plume rises, it also widens. If the plume were to contact all of the walls of the atrium prior to reaching the ceiling, the smoke interface would be considered as occurring at the height of contact with all of the surrounding walls. No additional smoke generation can be assumed to occur above that point, because entrainment of additional air into the plume is considered to be negligible above the point of contact. In order to check if the widening plume has contacted the walls of the atrium, Equation 23 from Section 3-7 of NFPA 92B can be used to predict the total plume diameter, d, at the interface height, z:

 d = 0.5 z
 d = 0.5 (85)
 d = 42.5 ft

Thus, in this 100 ft × 200 ft atrium area, the smoke does not contact the walls prior to reaching the design interface height of 85 ft. Mechanical systems capable of extracting 450,000 scfm are then designed. The substantiation package is submitted to the authority having jurisdiction for approval.

(f) The provisions of subpart (f) address the activation of mechanical systems that achieve the smoke management requirements of subpart (e). They apply only if the needed smoke management is provided by a mechanical system. In some buildings with large atrium openings but no upper floors open to the atrium and no exit access on those upper floors through the atrium, it may be possible to meet smoke control criteria without any mechanical systems by allowing the large atrium to accumulate smoke above the heads of all atrium occupants. In that case, there is no mechanical system, and these activation requirements would not apply.

As addressed by appendix note A-6-2.4.6(f), automatic activation of the atrium smoke management system, especially upon initiation of the building alarm system via a manual pull station operation, could result in the wrong mode of smoke control being implemented. For example, a building occupant walking along the sixth floor exit access balcony within the atrium may see flames and smoke on the third floor, which is open to the atrium. The occupant walks to the exit stair enclosure on the sixth floor and operates the manual pull station. The building fire alarm system, if it were arranged to activate the smoke management system, might incorrectly assume that the fire is on the sixth level. The actual fire floor, the third, would incorrectly be identified as a nonfire floor. The smoke management system might positively pressurize the third floor and exhaust large volumes of air across the third floor opening into the atrium in an effort to keep smoke from entering the third floor communicating area. In reality, the smoke management system would accomplish just the opposite of what it was designed to do; it would spread the effects of the third floor fire into the atrium. The sixth floor would mistakenly be negatively pressurized and would receive the smoke and gases from the third floor fire via the atrium.

The projected beam smoke detectors addressed by appendix note A-6-2.4.6(f)1 were utilized in the detailed example on atrium smoke management discussed above in the commentary related to subpart (e).

The manual controls required by 6-2.4.6(f)3 must be readily accessible to the responding fire department personnel so that the smoke management system's mode of operation can be overridden and tailored to the specific needs of the emergency. These and other concepts on effective smoke management are covered in NFPA 92A, *Recommended Practice for Smoke Control Systems,*[22] and NFPA 92B, *Guide for Smoke Management Systems in Malls, Atria, and Large Areas.*

(g) Although a vertical opening of four or more stories in new construction generally must be separated from the rest of the building by an enclosure of 2-hour fire resistance rated construction in accordance with the requirements of 6-2.4.4(a), the atrium provisions work together as an overall package in allowing the construction that separates other areas of the building from the atrium to be reduced to a 1-hour fire resistance rating. Further, the doors in the 1-hour atrium fire barrier may be 20-minute fire protection rated assemblies as allowed for corridor doors. Thus, the intent of the 1-hour separation requirement mainly is to provide a carefully constructed smoke resistant barrier.

Per Exception No. 1 to (g), any three levels may be left open to the atrium. In Figure 6-20, levels 2, 3, and 9 have been left open to the atrium. In Figure 6-17b, the three open levels occur at the first, second, and eighth floors. The open levels could have been contiguous, such as the top three floors or bottom three floors, but any combination of three levels is allowed. The occupancy chapters that recognize the use of the 6-2.4.6 atrium provisions modify the requirements as needed to afford the users of those occupancies the level of life safety needed. For example, for health care occupancies, Chapters 12 and 13 allow the atrium but limit the location of the three open levels allowed by Exception No. 1 to (g) so that patient treatment and sleeping rooms are not left open to the atrium.

In order to allow other than the three open floors to have visual contact with the atrium but still provide at least a smoke resisting separation between those additional floors and the atrium, Exception No. 2 to (g) recognizes the use of glass walls, vision panels, and windows in lieu of actual 1-hour fire resistance rated construction. Appendix note A-6-2.4.6 Exception No. 2 to (g) explains the intent of the requirement for directing closely spaced sprinklers at the glass walls.

The allowance for omitting the lines of closely spaced sprinklers on the atrium side of glass walls, used in lieu of 1-hour fire resistance rated barriers, is intended to apply to the floor levels above the atrium main floor level. In other words, if glass walls are used on the main floor level in lieu of 1-hour enclosure, sprinklers must be installed on both sides of the glass at that level, because combustibles may be placed on the floor on the atrium side of the glass. (*See Figure 6-20.*)

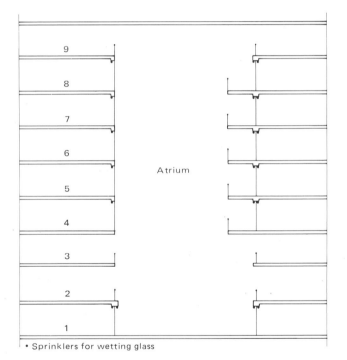

Figure 6-20. Levels 2, 3, and 9 Open to Atrium; Levels 1 and 4 Through 8 Enclosed by Glass Walls. Sprinklers required on non-atrium side of all glass walls, on atrium side at base of atrium, and on atrium side on other levels with walkways.

6-2.4.7 Any escalators or moving walks serving as a required exit in existing buildings shall be enclosed in the same manner as exit stairways. (*Also see 5-2.7.*)

Where used as an exit, an escalator must be completely enclosed with fire-rated construction, including entrance and discharge doors. It is rare to find an escalator enclosed in such a manner as to qualify as an exit. Escalators in existing buildings located within the required means of

egress that maintain compliance with the *Code* usually make use of one of the exceptions to 6-2.4.8 to avoid creating an unprotected vertical opening, and thereby qualify as exit access. Note that 5-2.7 prohibits escalators from constituting any part of the required means of egress in new buildings. Thus, in new construction, an escalator can be installed but is not recognized as satisfying the requirements for exit access, exit, or exit discharge.

6-2.4.8 Escalators or moving walks not constituting an exit shall have their floor openings enclosed or protected as required for other vertical openings.

Exception No. 1: *In buildings protected throughout by an approved automatic sprinkler system in accordance with Section 7-7, escalator or moving walk openings shall be permitted to be protected in accordance with the method detailed in NFPA 13, Standard for the Installation of Sprinkler Systems, or in accordance with a method as approved by the authority having jurisdiction.*

A-6-2.4.8 Exception No. 1 The intent of the exception is that a limitation be placed on the size of the opening to which the protection applies. The total floor opening should not exceed twice the projected area of the escalator or moving walk at the floor. Also, the arrangement of the opening is not intended to circumvent the requirements of 6-2.4.6.

As with any opening through a floor, the openings around the outer perimeter of the escalators should be considered as vertical openings. The sprinkler, draft stop installation is intended to provide adequate protection for these openings, provided that the criteria of NFPA 13, *Standard for the Installation of Sprinkler Systems* (*see Appendix B*), as well as the area criteria described above are met.

An important exception contained in 6-2.4.8 provides that new escalators, which cannot be part of the means of egress, and existing escalators not serving as exits (*see 6-2.4.7*) need not be enclosed if certain provisions are met.

The sprinkler-draft curtain method is detailed in NFPA 13, *Standard for the Installation of Sprinkler Systems.*[20] It consists of surrounding the escalator opening, in an otherwise fully sprinklered building, with an 18-in. (45.7-cm) deep draft stop located on the underside of the floor to which the escalator ascends. This would serve to delay the heat, smoke, and combustion gases devel-

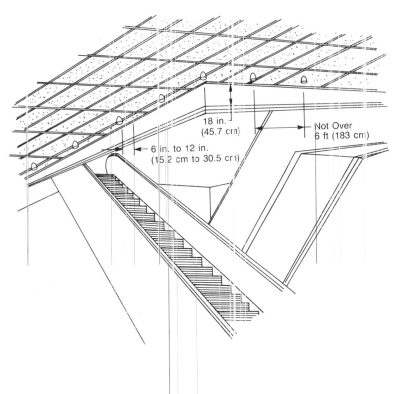

Figure 6-21. Sprinklers Around an Escalator.

oped in the early stages of a fire on that floor from entering into the escalator well. A row of closely spaced automatic sprinklers located outside of the draft stop also surrounds the escalator well. When activated by heat, the sprinklers provide a water curtain. A typical installation is shown in Figure 6-21. In combination with the sprinkler system in the building, this system should be effective in delaying fire spread and allowing time for evacuation.

Several methods were detailed in prior editions of this *Code* to permit the use of unenclosed escalators in completely sprinklered buildings, where the escalators are not used as exits. In addition to the sprinkler-draft curtain or rolling shutter methods, the authority having jurisdiction may consider one of the following when evaluating existing buildings:

(a) A sprinkler-vent method;

(b) A spray nozzle method; and

(c) A partial enclosure method.

The following discussion details these three methods.

(a) Sprinkler-Vent Method. Under the conditions specified, escalator or moving walk openings may be protected by the sprinkler-vent method, consisting of a combination of an automatic fire or smoke detection system, automatic exhaust system, and an automatic water curtain meeting the following requirements and of a design meeting the approval of the authority having jurisdiction:

1. The exhaust system should be of such capacity as to create a downdraft through the escalator or moving walk floor opening. The downdraft should have an average velocity of not less than 300 ft/min (1.5 m/s) under normal conditions for a period of not less than 30 minutes.

This requirement can be met by the provisions of an air intake from the outside of the building above the floor opening. The test of the system under "normal" conditions requires that the velocity of the downdraft be developed when windows or doors on the several stories normally used for ventilation are open. The size of the exhaust fan and exhaust ducts must be sufficient to meet such ventilation conditions. Experience indicates that fan capacity should be based on a rating of not less than 500 cfm/sq ft (8.3 cu m/s/sq m) of moving stairway opening to obtain the 300-ft/min (1.5-m/s) velocity required. If the building is provided with an air conditioning system arranged to be automatically shut down in the event of fire, the test conditions should be met with the air conditioning system shut down. The 300-ft/min (1.5-m/s) downdraft through the opening provides for the testing of the exhaust system without requiring an expansion of air present under actual fire conditions.

2. Operation of the exhaust system for any floor opening should be initiated by an approved device in the story involved and should use one of the following means in addition to a manual means for operating and testing the system:

  (a) Thermostats — fixed temperature, rate-of-rise, or a combination of both.

  (b) Water flow in the sprinkler system.

  (c) Approved supervised smoke detection. Smoke detection devices, if used, should be so located that the presence of smoke is detected before it enters the stairway.

3. Electric power supply to all parts of the exhaust system and its control devices should be designed and installed for maximum reliability. The electric power supply provision of NFPA 20, *Standard for the Installation of Centrifugal Fire Pumps*,[23] may be referred to as a guide to design and installation features to ensure maximum reliability.

4. Any fan or duct used in connection with an automatic exhaust system should be of the approved type and should be installed in accordance with the applicable standards listed in Chapter 32 and Appendix B.

5. Periodic tests, no less frequent than quarterly, should be made of the automatic exhaust system to maintain the system and the control devices in good working condition.

6. The water curtain should be formed by open sprinklers or spray nozzles so located and spaced as to form a complete and continuous barrier along all exposed sides of the floor opening and reaching from the ceiling to the floor. Water intensity for the water curtain should be not less than approximately 3 gal/min/lineal ft (0.6 L/sec/m) of water curtain, measured horizontally around the opening.

7. The water curtain should operate automatically from thermal-responsive elements of fixed temperature type so placed with respect to the ceiling (floor) opening that the water curtain actuates upon the advance of heat toward the escalator or moving walk opening.

8. Every automatic exhaust system, including all motors, controls, and automatic water curtain system, should be supervised in an approved manner, similar to that specified for automatic sprinkler system supervision.

  (b) Spray Nozzle Method. Under the conditions specified, escalator openings may be protected by the spray nozzle method, consisting of a combination of an automatic fire or smoke detection system and a system of high velocity water spray nozzles, meeting the following requirements and of a design meeting the approval of the authority having jurisdiction.

1. Spray nozzles should be of the open type and should have a solid conical spray pattern with discharge angles between 45 and 90 degrees. The number of nozzles, their discharge angles, and their location should be such that the escalator or moving walk opening between the top of the wellway housing and the treadway will be completely filled with dense spray on operation of the system.

2. The number and size of nozzles and water supply should be sufficient to deliver a discharge of 2 gal of water/sq ft/min (1.4 L/sq m/sec) through the wellway, with the area to be figured perpendicularly to treadway. (*See Figure 6-22.*)

3. Spray nozzles should be so located as to effectively utilize the full advantage of the cooling and counterdraft effect. They should be so positioned that the centerline of spray discharge is as closely in line as possible with the slope of the escalator or moving walk, not more than an angle of 30 degrees with the top slope of the wellway housing. Nozzles should also be positioned so that the centerline of discharge is at an angle of not more than 30 degrees from the vertical sides of the wellway housing.

4. Spray nozzles should discharge at a minimum pressure of at least 25 lb/sq in. (172 kPa). Water supply piping may be taken from the sprinkler system, provided that an adequate supply of water will be available for

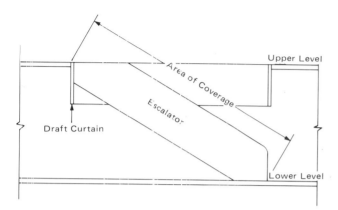

Figure 6-22. *Area of Coverage for the Spray Nozzle Method of Protecting Vertical Openings.*

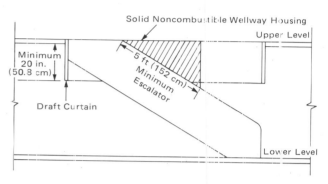

Figure 6-23. *The Draft Curtain and Wellway Housing Method of Protecting Vertical Openings.*

the spray nozzles and the water pressure at the sprinkler farthest from the supply riser is not reduced beyond the required minimum. Supply taken from the sprinkler system is designed to provide protection to the wellway opening for life hazard during the exit period but may not be relied upon to provide an effective floor cutoff.

5. Control valves should be readily accessible to minimize water damage.

6. A noncombustible or limited-combustible draft curtain should be provided that extends at least 20 in. (50.8 cm) below and around the opening, and a solid noncombustible wellway housing at least 5 ft (152 cm) long, measured parallel to the handrail and extending from the top of the handrail enclosure to the soffit of the stairway or ceiling above, should also be provided at each escalator floor opening. Where necessary, spray nozzles should be protected against mechanical injury or tampering that might interfere with proper discharge. (See Figure 6-23.)

7. The spray nozzle system should operate automatically from thermal response elements of the fixed temperature type, so placed with respect to the ceiling (floor) opening that the spray nozzle system actuates upon the advance of heat towards the escalator opening. Supervised smoke detection located in or near the esca-

lator opening may be used to sound an alarm. The spray nozzle system should also be provided with manual means of operation. Smoke detection devices are not desirable for action of the spray nozzles, as accidental discharge must be safeguarded against from both a panic hazard as well as a property damage standpoint.

8. Control valves for the spray nozzle system and approved smoke detection or thermostatic devices should be supervised in accordance with the applicable provisions of Section 7-6.

(c) Partial Enclosure Method. Under the conditions specified, escalator or moving walk openings may be protected by a partial enclosure, or so-called kiosk, so designed as to provide an effective barrier to the spread of smoke from floor to floor.

1. Partial enclosures should be of construction providing fire resistance equivalent to that specified for stairway enclosures in the same building, with openings therein protected by approved self-closing fire doors, or may be of approved wired glass and metal frame construction with wired glass panel doors.

2. Such doors may be equipped with an electric opening mechanism to open the door automatically upon the approach of a person. The mechanism should be such as to return the door to its closed position upon any interruption of electric current supply, and the adjustment should be such that the pressures generated by a fire will not cause opening of the door.

Exception No. 2: Escalators in large open areas such as atriums and enclosed shopping malls.

Exception No. 3: In buildings protected throughout by an approved automatic sprinkler system in accordance with Section 7-7, escalators or moving walk openings shall be permitted to be protected by rolling steel shutters appropriate for the fire resistance rating of the vertical opening protected. The shutters shall close automatically upon smoke detection and sprinkler operation, independently of each other. There shall be a manual means of operating and testing the operation of the shutter. The shutters shall be operated at least once a week to ensure that they remain in proper operating condition. The shutters shall operate at a speed of not more than 30 ft/min (.15 m/s) and shall be equipped with a sensitive leading edge. The leading edge shall arrest the progress of a moving shutter and cause it to retract a distance of approximately 6 in. (15.2 cm) upon the application of a force not in excess of 20 lbf (90 N) applied to the surface of the leading edge. The shutter, following this retraction, shall continue to close. The operating mechanism for the rolling shutter shall be provided with standby power complying with the provisions of NFPA 70, National Electrical Code.

6-2.5 Mezzanines.

6-2.5.1 **General.** A mezzanine shall not be counted as a story for the purpose of determining the allowable number of stories.

6-2.5.2 **Area Limitations.**

6-2.5.2.1 The aggregate area of mezzanines within a room shall not exceed one-third the open area of the room in which the mezzanines are located. Enclosed space shall not be included in a determination of the size of the room in which the mezzanine is located.

Exception No. 1: Special purpose industrial occupancies.

Exception No. 2: Multilevel residential housing areas in detention and correctional occupancies in accordance with Chapters 14 and 15 are exempt from the provisions of 6-2.5.2 and 6-2.5.3.

6-2.5.2.2 There is no limit on the number of mezzanines in a room.

6-2.5.2.3 For purposes of determining the allowable mezzanine area, the area of mezzanines shall not be included in the area of the room.

6-2.5.3 **Openess.** All portions of a mezzanine shall be open to and unobstructed from the room in which the mezzanine is located with the exception of walls not more than 42 in. (107 cm) high, columns, and posts.

Exception No. 1: Mezzanines or portions thereof need not be open to the room in which they are located, provided the occupant load of the aggregate area of the enclosed space does not exceed 10.

Exception No. 2: A mezzanine having two or more means of egress need not open into the room in which it is located if at least one of the means of egress provides direct access to an exit at the mezzanine level.

The mezzanine provisions of 6-2.5 are new in the 1991 Edition of the *Life Safety Code*. They are based on a report prepared by the Board for the Coordination of the Model Codes (BCMC) in an attempt to standardize the treatment of mezzanines among the three United States model building code organizations (*see the commentary prior to Table 6-1*) and NFPA.

A mezzanine within a room is limited to an aggregate area not to exceed one-third the open area, i.e., unenclosed space, of the room in which the mezzanine is located. The area of the mezzanine is not considered as part of the total open area of the room for the purposes of this calculation. For other purposes, the area of the mezzanine is considered part of the area of the room. Having been defined as limited to such size, the mezzanine is exempted from being counted as a building story, thus affecting the applicability of *Code* requirements based on the number of building stories or floors. The partially enclosed mezzanine shown in Figure 6-24a and the enclosed mezzanine of Figure 6-24b have an area less than one-third the area of the room above which each mezzanine is located. If each mezzanine can meet the other provisions of 6-2.5, then each can be considered as a part of the floor below and not considered as a separate story.

The openness requirements of 6-2.5.3 are intended to provide the occupants of the mezzanine with an equivalent degree of awareness of fire conditions on the floor below as would be afforded that floor's occupants. Because the mezzanine sits above the floor of which the mezzanine is considered a part, untenable smoke concentrations and the associated loss of visibility due to smoke obscuration may affect the mezzanine level before similarly affecting the floor below. In the same way that openness and awareness are required via the mini-atrium provisions of 6-2.4.5(c), the occupants of the mezzanine should be alerted to a fire in any part of the two-level space prior to the time that the fire becomes a hazard to them.

In recognition of the openness, the *Code* considers the mezzanine no differently than an area or room on the level below the mezzanine. If the mezzanine depicted in Figure 6-24a were in a business occupancy, for example, it would be required to follow the same exit access arrangement rules of any other room on the floor below. Thus, if all occupants could travel across the mezzanine, down the open stair to the room below, and as far across the floor of that room as necessary to reach a point where they had access to two different egress paths, and that total distance did not exceed the allowable common path of travel [i.e., 75 ft (23 m), or 100 ft (30 m) if sprinklered, for the business occupancy in this example], a single exit access from the mezzanine to the floor below would be allowed. If the allowable common path of travel were exceeded, the mezzanine would require a second, remote exit access.

Exception No. 1 to 6-2.5.3 permits a limited amount of enclosed space on the mezzanine to allow for toilet rooms, limited storage, small offices, and similar areas normally required to be separated from the open area of the mezzanine. In Figure 6-24a, the mezzanine is partially enclosed so that the total occupant load of all enclosed rooms does not exceed 10 persons.

Exception No. 2 exempts a mezzanine from being open to the room in which it is located if the occupants of the mezzanine are provided with at least two means of egress and one of those means of egress provides direct access to an exit at the mezzanine level. The mezzanine in Figure 6-24b can thus be enclosed because, as one of its two means of egress, it has been provided with access from the mezzanine directly into an exit stair enclosure that discharges to the outside. Those occupants are then judged

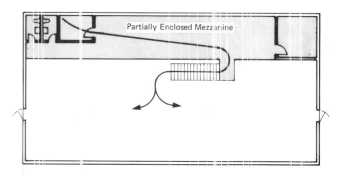

Figure 6-24a. Enclosed Portions of Mezzanine Have Occupant Load of Not More Than 10 to Satisfy Openness Requirement; Single Exit Access Allowed if Within Common Path of Travel Limitations.

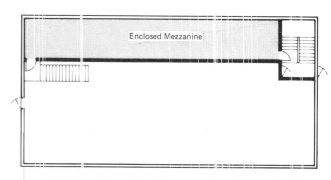

Figure 6-24b. Mezzanine Allowed to Be Enclosed and Considered Part of Floor Below if Within ⅓ Area Limitation, Minimum Two Means of Egress, and Direct Access to Exit on Mezzanine Level.

as being adequately safe from a fire on the level below, even if they learn about that fire later than they would have had there been openness, since one of their means of egress does not require occupants to return through the room below.

The above provisions clarify *Code* intent and answer numerous questions that were not previously addressed by *Code* wording.

6-2.6 Concealed Spaces.

6-2.6.1* In new Type III, Type IV, or Type V construction, any concealed space in which materials having a flame-spread rating greater than Class A (as defined in Section 6-5) are exposed shall be effectively firestopped or draftstopped as provided below:

(a) Every exterior and interior wall and partition shall be firestopped at each floor level, at the top-story ceiling level, and at the level of support for roofs.

(b) Every unoccupied attic space shall be subdivided by draftstops into areas not to exceed 3,000 sq ft (280 sq m).

(c) Any concealed space between the ceiling and the floor or roof above shall be draftstopped for the full depth of the space along the line of support for the floor or roof structural members and, if necessary, at other locations to form areas not to exceed 1,000 sq ft (93 sq m) for any space between the ceiling and floor and 3,000 sq ft (280 sq m) for any space between the ceiling and roof.

Exception No. 1: If the space is protected throughout by an approved automatic sprinkler system in accordance with Section 7-7.

Exception No. 2: Concealed spaces serving as plenums. (See NFPA 90A, Standard for the Installation of Air Conditioning and Ventilating Systems.)

A-6-2.6.1 The area limitations are based on life safety considerations and are not intended to suggest that changes should be made in local building codes having similar or more restrictive requirements that are based on other reasons. Building codes generally contain detailed information on the proper selection and installation of firestopping materials.

The vertical spread of fire through shafts, chases, and hollow wall construction, and the horizontal spread of fire through plenums and open attics are phenomena common to many serious fires. Where such spaces are protected with automatic sprinklers, the risk of unseen fires is minimized. Where this protection is not installed in new buildings of other than Type I or II construction as defined by NFPA 220, *Standard on Types of Building Construction,*[4] and the commentary following 6-2.1, and the materials used have a flame spread rating of more than 25 (i.e., not Class A), certain additional precautions are required.

Draftstopping of attic spaces is particularly important in "one-story and attic" shopping centers and in two-story apartment buildings or row houses. Experience has shown that fires starting in one of these occupancy units fre-

quently breaks into the attic space, spreads through the attic, and travels down into adjoining units.

Numerous fires in garden apartments have demonstrated two common weaknesses relating to the lack of adequate firestopping and draftstopping. The areas frequently not firestopped either are between the underside of the roof deck and the top of fire barriers that do not extend above the roofline or are in the pipe chase that contains the plumbing vent stack. The vent stack is of particular concern because it frequently is located between two mirror-image apartment units and interconnects all the floors of the apartment building. A fire that travels into this concealed space can spread to the attic and soon involve the entire structure.

Chapter 3 defines draft stop as follows: "A continuous membrane to subdivide a concealed space to restrict the passage of smoke, heat, and flames."

6-2.6.2 In every existing building, firestopping and draftstopping shall be provided as required by the provisions of Chapters 8 through 30.

An example of an occupancy chapter requiring firestopping appears in 13-1.6.5 for existing health care occupancies where firestopping is required between the basement and first floor.

SECTION 6-3 Smoke Barriers

6-3.1* Where required by Chapters 8 through 30, smoke barriers shall be provided to subdivide building spaces for the purpose of restricting the movement of smoke.

A-6-3.1 Wherever smoke barriers and doors therein require a degree of fire resistance as may be specified by requirements in the various occupancy chapters (Chapters 8 through 30), the construction is more appropriately a fire barrier that has been defined: "to limit the spread of fire and restrict the movement of smoke." (*See 6-2.3.2 and 6-2.3.3.*)

It is a misnomer to refer to a "1-hour rated smoke barrier." It is more accurate to refer to a "smoke barrier that additionally has a 1-hour fire resistance rating." A barrier with only a fire resistance rating does not necessarily make an effective smoke barrier. For example, the fire barrier, if rated at less than 2 hours, would not be required to have either a fire damper or smoke damper where ductwork penetrates the barrier. A smoke barrier, in accordance with Section 6-3, would have ducted penetrations protected by smoke dampers per 6-3.5.1. For additional information on fire barrier testing, rating, and installation, see the commentaries following 6-2.3.1 and 6-2.3.6.

6-3.2* Smoke barriers required by this *Code* shall be continuous from outside wall to outside wall, from a floor to a floor, from a smoke barrier to a smoke barrier, or a combination thereof; this includes continuity through all concealed spaces such as those found above a ceiling, including interstitial spaces.

Exception: A smoke barrier required for an occupied space below an interstitial space is not required to extend through the interstitial space, provided the construction assembly forming the bottom of the interstitial space provides resistance to the passage of smoke equal to that provided by the smoke barrier.

A-6-3.2 To ensure that a smoke barrier is continuous, it is necessary to seal completely all openings where the smoke barrier abuts other smoke barriers, fire barriers, exterior walls, the floor below, and the floor or ceiling above.

It is not the intent to prohibit a smoke barrier from stopping at a fire barrier if the fire barrier meets the requirements of a smoke barrier (i.e., the fire barrier is a combination smoke barrier/fire barrier).

In occupancies where evacuation is a last resort or is expected to be otherwise delayed, smoke barriers and doors therein will require a degree of fire resistance as specified by the requirements found in the occupancy chapters (Chapters 8 through 30) of the *Code*.

Other openings in smoke and fire barriers must be protected as well. Heating, air conditioning, and ventilation ducts provide a ready path for smoke and fire to travel from one area to another unless carefully protected. Penetrations in walls and ceiling construction for utility lines

and other building services must be firestopped to prevent fire spread. The hidden spaces behind suspended ceilings and attic spaces are out of sight and easily overlooked.

The Exception to 6-3.2 must be used with extreme care for several reasons. First, several chapters require the smoke barrier to have some fire resistance rating and, therefore, could terminate at the ceiling only if the ceiling could also obtain this rating (*see commentary on 6-2.2.2*). Also, even if no fire resistance were required, it is difficult to ensure that a ceiling is smoketight unless it is of monolithic construction without air-handling penetrations. However, this kind of construction is often found in apartment buildings, hotels, and dormitories and, consequently, the exception can be useful.

6-3.3 A fire barrier shall be permitted to be used as a smoke barrier if it meets the requirements of 6-3.4 through 6-3.6.

6-3.4 Doors.

6-3.4.1* Doors in smoke barriers shall close the opening with only a minimum clearance necessary for proper operation and shall be without undercuts, louvers, or grilles.

A-6-3.4.1 The clearance for proper operation of smoke doors has been defined as $\frac{1}{8}$ in. (0.3 cm). For additional information on the installation of smoke-control door assemblies, see NFPA 105, *Recommended Practice for the Installation of Smoke-Control Door Assemblies*. (*See Appendix B.*)

NFPA 105, *Recommended Practice for the Installation of Smoke-Control Door Assemblies*,[24] acknowledges that a nationally recognized test for the measurement of smoke leakage does not exist. However, that document suggests that Underwriters Laboratories, UL 1784, *Air Leakage Tests of Door Assemblies*,[25] can be used to measure ambient and warm air leakage rates of door assemblies.

UL 1784 should give satisfactory performance if, additionally, recognized design features are taken into account, such as close-fitting assemblies, limited deflections, and the use of gasketing and sealing materials. The document then provides performance criteria suggesting maximum air leakage rates expressed in air volume per time per area of door opening.

6-3.4.2* Where a fire resistance rating for smoke barriers is specified elsewhere in the *Code*, openings shall be protected as follows:

(a) Door opening protectives shall have a fire protection rating of not less than 20 minutes where tested in accordance with NFPA 252, *Standard Methods of Fire Tests of Door Assemblies*, without the hose stream test.

(b) Fire windows shall comply with 6-2.3.4.

Exception No. 1: If a different fire protection rating for smoke barrier doors is specified by Chapters 8 through 30.

Exception No. 2: Latching hardware is not required on doors in smoke barriers where so indicated by Chapters 8 through 30.

A-6-3.4.2 In existing installations only, a 1¾-in. (4.4-cm) thick solid bonded wood core door has been considered a satisfactory substitute for a door with a 20-minute fire protection rating.

Doors in smoke barriers are not required to have a fire protection rating unless the occupancy chapter requires the smoke barrier to have a fire resistance rating. Therefore, any door that resists the passage of smoke, even a hollow core wood door or glass door, would be acceptable provided it is tight-fitting. Stops at the head and sides of the door will help resist the passage of smoke. Where a pair of doors is used, it is recommended (*required* for cross-corridor door assemblies in new health care occupancies) that they open in opposite directions from each other so that rabbets, bevels, or astragals can be provided at the meeting edges without the use of coordinators. (*Also see 12-3.7.8.*)

Doors in smoke barriers, while not the equivalent of fire doors and not completely smoketight, are effective in restricting the spread of smoke and reducing drafts, which might otherwise spread fire rapidly. Where the smoke barrier is required to have a fire resistance rating by an occupancy chapter, a 20-minute fire protection rated door assembly in a smoke partition has been accepted by the Committee on Safety to Life as a reasonable barrier. It has been shown through tests that the commonly used 1¾-in. (4.4-cm) thick solid wood core door assembly can be expected to fail in 22 to 24 minutes but has performed well in actual fires when closed.[26] The use of the 20-minute designation replaces a specification standard with a performance standard. The same reference emphasizes that even fully rated fire doors will not keep out smoke because of the clearances needed to have the door work properly. Gasketing will help, but a tight-fitting door should keep out enough smoke so that orderly exiting may proceed.

6-3.4.3* Doors in smoke barriers shall be self-closing or automatic-closing in accordance with 5-2.1.8 and shall comply with the provisions of 5-2.1.

A-6-3.4.3 Where, because of operational necessity, it is desired to have smoke barrier doors that are usually open, such doors should be provided with hold-open devices that are activated to close the doors by the operation of smoke detectors and other alarm functions.

Doors in a fire separation, horizontal exit, or smoke barrier should be closed at all times to impede the travel of smoke and fire gases. Functionally, however, this involves decreased efficiency and, for example, limits patient observation by the professional staff of a health care occupancy. To accommodate these necessities, it is practical to presume that the door will be kept open even to the extent of employing wood chocks and other makeshift devices. Where, because of operational necessity, it is desired to have smoke barrier doors normally open, such doors should be provided with hold-open devices that are activated to close the doors by the operation of smoke detectors. For additional information on the use of smoke detectors for releasing service, see the commentary associated with 7-6.3.2 Exceptions No. 3 and 4.

6-3.5 Smoke Dampers.

6-3.5.1 An approved damper designed to resist the passage of smoke shall be provided at each air-transfer opening or duct penetration of a required smoke barrier.

Exception No. 1: Ducts or air-transfer openings that are part of an engineered smoke control system in accordance with Section 7-3.

Exception No. 2: Ducts where the air continues to move and the air-handling system installed is arranged to prevent recirculation of exhaust or return air under fire emergency conditions.

Exception No. 3: Where the air inlet or outlet openings in ducts are limited to a single smoke compartment.

Exception No. 4: Where ducts penetrate floors that serve as smoke barriers.

Exception No. 5: Where specifically permitted by Chapters 8 through 30.

Exception No. 1 to 6-3.5.1 addresses the omission of dampers in ducts that must remain open so that the smoke control system can operate. Exception No. 2 to 6-3.5.1 is applicable only in very limited cases. It can be used only on small ventilation systems, since NFPA 90A, *Standard for the Installation of Air Conditioning and Ventilating Systems,*[14] requires that systems over 15,000 cfm (7.1 cu m/sec) that are not part of a smoke control system shut down upon detection of smoke (*see NFPA 90A*). Even without the restriction of NFPA 90A, it is difficult to ensure that the air-handling system will be in continuous operation. Because of increased awareness of energy conservation, many systems are cycled or shut down during parts of the day. The cycling or shut-down feature might be added later without recognizing its potential detriment to building life safety. However, the exception can be useful for ductwork for small ventilation systems, such as for bathrooms or small suites.

Exception No. 3 to 6-3.5.1 covers situations where an "express" duct has no openings other than in a single smoke compartment. It can reasonably be extended to situations as illustrated in Figures 6-25a and b.

Exception No. 4 to 6-3.5.1, in recognition that 6-2.4.1 requires every floor that separates stories in a building to be constructed as a smoke barrier to provide a basic degree of compartmentation, differentiates between (1) a true smoke barrier in accordance with Section 6-3, which is provided via vertical barriers, and (2) a smoke-resisting horizontal barrier consisting of a floor not subject to the requirements of Section 6-3.

The occupancy chapters, such as Chapters 12 and 13 for health care, that mandate the installation of smoke barriers complying with the requirements of Section 6-3 do so to divide a floor into two or more smoke compartments. They impose no further subdivision using smoke barriers that would separate one floor from another so as to create different smoke compartments stacked upon each other. Rather, they rely on the vertical opening pro-

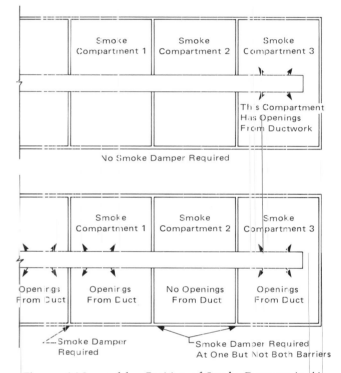

Figures 6-25 a and b.   Position of Smoke Dampers in Air-Handling Ductwork Utilizing Exception No. 3 to 6-3.5.1.

tection requirements of Chapter 6 to keep fire from spreading from floor to floor. In combination with 6-2.4.1, the vertical opening protection rules do an adequate job but do not elevate the floor construction to the stringent smoke barrier standards required of vertical barriers complying with Section 6-3. Ducts penetrating floors are thus exempt from the smoke damper requirements of 6-3.5.1.

Per the requirements of NFPA 90A, *Standard for the Installation of Air Conditioning and Ventilating Systems,* only a single floor can be penetrated by ductwork, and such an installation requires a fire damper at the plane of the floor where the penetration occurs. Ducts penetrating more than one floor must be enclosed within an appropriately fire rated shaft. Thus, where a smoke damper is exempted by Exception No. 4, the resulting openings have the potential to act as a minor route for smoke migration from one floor to another prior to the actuation of a fire damper. The floor, as a whole, serves as an adequate smoke barrier in accordance with the requirements of 6-2.4.1.

6-3.5.2 Required smoke dampers in ducts penetrating smoke barriers shall close upon detection of smoke by:

(a) Approved smoke detectors installed in accordance with Chapter 9 of NFPA 72E, *Standard on Automatic Fire Detectors*, or

(b) Approved local smoke detectors on either side of the smoke barrier door opening where ducts penetrate smoke barriers above the smoke barrier doors, or

(c) Approved smoke detectors located within the ducts in existing installations.

6-3.5.3 Required smoke dampers in air transfer openings shall close upon detection of smoke by approved smoke detectors installed in accordance with Chapter 9 of NFPA 72E, *Standard on Automatic Fire Detectors*.

Exception: Where a duct is provided on one side of the smoke barrier, the smoke detectors on the duct side shall be in accordance with 6-3.5.2.

NFPA 72E, *Standard on Automatic Fire Detectors*,[27] provides information on the installation of smoke detectors for closing smoke dampers. In addition, the *Code* continues to allow the damper to be closed by the same detector that closes the door in a smoke barrier if the duct penetrates the wall above the door. Existing installations of in-duct detectors, which may not be totally in compliance with NFPA 72E, continue to be recognized.

Item (c) of 6-3.5.2 does not prohibit the use of in-duct detectors in new construction provided that the installation complies with NFPA 72E as required in item (a) of that paragraph.

6-3.6 Penetrations and Miscellaneous Openings in Floors and Smoke Barriers.

6-3.6.1 Pipes, conduits, bus ducts, cables, wires, air ducts, pneumatic tubes and ducts, and similar building service equipment that pass through floors and smoke barriers shall be protected as follows:

(a) The space between the penetrating item and the smoke barrier shall:

1. Be filled with a material capable of maintaining the smoke resistance of the smoke barrier, or

2. Be protected by an approved device designed for the specific purpose.

(b) Where the penetrating item uses a sleeve to penetrate the smoke barrier, the sleeve shall be solidly set in the smoke barrier, and the space between the item and the sleeve shall:

1. Be filled with a material capable of maintaining the smoke resistance of the smoke barrier, or

2. Be protected by an approved device designed for the specific purpose.

(c) Where designs take transmission of vibration into consideration, any vibration isolation shall:

1. Be made on either side of the smoke barrier, or

2. Be made by an approved device designed for the specific purpose.

6-3.6.2 Openings occurring at points where floors or smoke barriers meet the outside walls, other smoke barriers, or fire barriers of a building shall:

(a) Be filled with a material capable of maintaining the smoke resistance of the floor or smoke barrier, or

(b) Be protected by an approved device designed for the specific purpose.

As with fire barriers, it is important to maintain the integrity of smoke barriers over the life of a building.

Figure 6-26 illustrates some of the key items regarding smoke barrier penetrations discussed in 6-3.4 through 6-3.6.

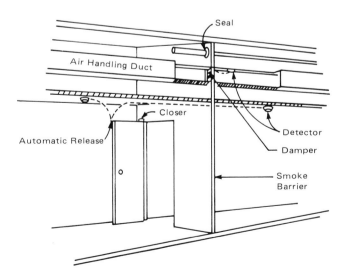

Figure 6-26. Typical Penetrations of a Smoke Barrier.

SECTION 6-4   Special Hazard Protection

6-4.1   General.

6-4.1.1* Protection from any area having a degree of hazard greater than that normal to the general occupancy of the building or structure shall be provided as follows:

(a) Enclose the area with a fire barrier having a 1-hour fire resistance rating in accordance with Section 6-2, without windows, or

(b) Protect the area with automatic extinguishing systems in accordance with Section 7-7, or

(c) Apply both (a) and (b) above where the hazard is severe or where otherwise specified by Chapters 8 through 30.

A-6-4.1.1 Areas requiring special hazard protection may include but are not limited to areas such as those used for storage of combustibles or flammables, areas housing heat-producing appliances, or areas used for maintenance purposes.

Here, the *Code* attempts to minimize the effects of fire originating in hazardous areas by isolating those areas that have a high potential for fire or a high fuel load. The Committees responsible for the occupancy chapters identify the particular hazards against which protection is to be provided and generally address them in the -3.2 subsection of each occupancy chapter. With each new edition of the *Code*, additional occupancy chapters reformat their -3.2 subsection to include a list of typical hazardous areas and the required level of associated protection. For example, see 14-3.2.1. This represents the fundamental fire protection concept of either protecting against known hazards via automatic extinguishment systems or isolating known hazards by means of construction. The authority having jurisdiction is responsible for the final determination of what constitutes a hazardous area.

6-4.1.2 In new construction where protection is provided with automatic extinguishing systems without fire-resistive separation, the space so protected shall be enclosed to resist the passage of smoke, and doors shall be self-closing or automatic-closing and resist the passage of smoke.

Exception No. 1: Mercantile occupancy general storage areas and stock rooms protected by automatic sprinklers in accordance with Section 7-7.

Exception No. 2: Hazardous areas in industrial occupancies protected by automatic extinguishing systems in accordance with 28-3.2.

The provisions of 6-4.1.2 are new in this edition of the *Code*. They introduce to 6-4.1 requirements that have long been a part of the -3.2 subsection of some occupancy chapters in the *Code*. The requirement is for a smoke resisting enclosure, including both surrounding wall barriers and opening protectives such as self-closing doors, where the 6-4.1.1(b) allowance is used to protect the hazardous area with automatic sprinkler protection in lieu of a fire rated enclosure. The smoke resisting enclosure, although lacking any mandated fire resistance rating, will help to contain the smoke generated prior to sprinkler activation and subsequent fire control.

Exception No. 1 allows omission of the additional smoke resisting enclosure or separation for general storage areas in mercantile occupancies protected by automatic sprinklers. For example, in a shoe store, a sprinklered shoe storage area could be left open to the sales area. The clerk may go behind a partial-height partition without going through a door opening to get shoes. Similarly, in a department store, which usually positions its general storage rooms behind floor-to-ceiling wall barriers at the rear of the store along exterior walls, double-acting doors (i.e., those that can swing both into and out of the storage room) that might not adequately resist the passage of smoke as required by 6-4.1.2 could be used if the storage area were sprinklered.

Exception No. 2 applies to hazardous areas in industrial occupancies and exempts them from the additional smoke-resisting enclosure requirement if the hazardous area is protected by an automatic extinguishing system. This allows for the necessary function of the industrial occupancy if each individual hazardous area is provided with automatic extinguishing. The nonhazardous areas might not be sprinklered but the protected hazardous areas can be left open to the nonhazardous areas.

6-4.1.3 Doors in barriers required to have a fire resistance rating shall have a ¾-hour fire protection rating and shall be self-closing or automatic-closing in accordance with 5-2.1.8.

6-4.2* **Explosion Protection.** Where hazardous processes or storage are of such a character as to introduce an explosion potential, an explosion venting or an explosion suppression system specifically designed for the hazard involved shall be provided.

A-6-4.2 For details, see NFPA 68, *Guide for Venting of Deflagrations*. (*See Appendix B.*)

If the potential hazard is of an explosive nature, explosion venting or explosion suppression systems are required safeguards. NFPA 68, *Guide for Venting of Deflagrations*,[28] contains details of acceptable venting systems, and NFPA 69, *Standard on Explosion Prevention Systems*,[29] covers suppression systems. NFPA 654, *Standard for the Prevention of Fire and Dust Explosions in the Chemical, Dye, Pharmaceutical, and Plastic Industries*,[30] is useful where explosive dusts are encountered.

6-4.3 **Flammable Liquids.** Flammable liquids shall be protected in accordance with NFPA 30, *Flammable and Combustible Liquids Code*.

6-4.4 **Laboratories.** Laboratories that use chemicals shall comply with NFPA 45, *Standard on Fire Protection for Laboratories Using Chemicals*, unless otherwise modified by other provisions of this *Code*.

Exception: Laboratories in health care occupancies and medical and dental offices shall comply with NFPA 99, Standard for Health Care Facilities.

SECTION 6-5   Interior Finish

Interior finish has been a significant factor in rapid flame spread for many of the deadliest U.S. fires of recent decades. A few examples are as follows:

In June 1989, five people died on the floor of origin of an "intense, rapidly developing fire on the sixth floor of an office building" in Atlanta, Georgia.[31] "...the fire spread was so fast that the blaze in the corridor had burned itself out by the time fire fighters entered the sixth floor about seven minutes after the initial alarm... This is not the first time that multiple layers of wall coverings have been identified as a contributing factor in a fire... It is evident that this condition existed in the Atlanta building, that the materials in those layers contributed to the total load in the corridor, and that it is likely they contributed to the rate of fire spread."

Regarding the 1986 DuPont Plaza Hotel fire where 96 died: "under the NFPA *Life Safety Code*, interior finish in all ballrooms, including the room of origin, should have been Class A or Class B. The wall finish of the room of origin contributed to the rapid fire growth."[18]

In the 1981 Las Vegas Hilton Hotel fire, combustible carpeting on the walls and ceilings of elevator lobbies contributed to horizontal fire spread on the floor of origin and vertical spread involving 22 floors. Eight people died in this fire.[47]

In a 1978 Holiday Inn fire that killed 10 people, "lightweight plywood paneling in stairway did not meet *Life Safety Code*, was involved early in fire, and produced rapid growth and spread." In a 1979 Holiday Inn fire that also killed 10 people, "carpeting and some wall covering in corridors had excessively high flame-spread properties."[17]

In a 1972 Springfield, Illinois convalescent nursing home fire that killed 10 of the 41 patients, "the wood-panel finish accelerated fire spread.... Combustible interior finish – especially interior finish such as the wood paneling in this facility – should not be allowed where infirm people are housed. ...The paneling on the stairway had completely burned away, permitting fire spread into the first floor through holes in the plaster."[32]

In the 1970 Pioneer International Hotel fire where 28 died: "Under the NFPA *Life Safety Code*, interior finish in all ballrooms, including the room of origin, corridors and stairs were carpeted (100% acrylic), with two layers of padding under carpet in corridors and carpeting extending 22 inches up the walls. Above the carpeted areas of the wall were sections of wood, wallpaper, and plastic-laminated plywood. Interior finish contributed to fire."[17]

6-5.1 **General.**

6-5.1.1* Interior finish includes interior wall and ceiling finish and interior floor finish.

A-6-5.1.1 The requirements pertaining to interior finish are intended to restrict the spread of fire over the continuous surface forming the interior portions of a building. Furnishings, which in some cases may be secured in place for functional reasons, should not be considered as interior finish.

The faster a fire develops, the greater a threat it represents to the occupants of a building and the more difficult it will be to control. Wall and ceiling surfaces of a building have a major influence on how fast a fire develops. In establishing restrictions for the use of interior finish materials, the *Code's* intention is preferably to prevent entirely or, as a minimum, to limit the spread of fire across the interior surfaces of a building.

Any large fire within a building represents a threat to occupants. A successful fire protection strategy requires that fires be limited in size. Any interior finish that acts as a "fuse" to spread flame to involve objects remote from the point of origin or that contributes "fuel" to the early growth of a fire, causing a large fire, is considered undesirable. The restrictions found in the *Code* for wall and ceiling finishes vary, depending on occupancy characteristics. Where occupants are immobile or have security measures allowed that restrict freedom of movement (as in health care facilities or detention and correctional facilities), conservative interior finish limits are set. In contrast, more relaxed limits are allowed in industrial or storage occupancies where occupants are assumed to be alert and mobile.

Interior finishes are the interior surfaces of a building that are generally secured in place. Thus, wall, ceiling, and column coverings may be considered interior wall and ceiling finishes. The surfaces of movable walls or folding partitions would also be treated as interior wall and ceiling finishes. However, this section uses the expression "but not limited to," which allows the authority having jurisdiction to exercise judgment in determining what constitutes interior finish. For example, a tapestry would not normally be considered as interior finish. However, a large tapestry that is secured to and covers a major portion of a wall could promote the rapid growth of fire and may warrant regulation. (*See the commentary following A-6-5.3.1.*)

Furnishings, including high-backed, plastic-upholstered restaurant booths, are not normally considered as interior finish, even in the case where the furnishings are fixed in place. However, if the furnishings are judged to represent a hazard, they could be regulated as interior finish by the authority having jurisdiction. (*See the commentary associated with Formal Interpretation 88-10 on 6-5.2.3.*)

6-5.1.2 Interior wall and ceiling finish means the exposed interior surfaces of buildings including, but not limited to, fixed or movable walls and partitions, columns, and ceilings.

6-5.1.3 Interior floor finish means the exposed floor surfaces of buildings including coverings that may be applied over a normal finished floor or stair, including risers.

Interior floor finish includes both exposed surfaces of "structural" floor systems and decorative floor treatments, such as carpet or imitation wood flooring. Coverings on stair risers and treads are regulated as interior floor finish, even though risers involve vertical applications. This provision recognizes that floor coverings on risers and treads will perform similarly to other floor surfaces during a fire.

6-5.1.4 Classification of interior finish materials shall be in accordance with tests made under conditions simulating actual installations, provided that the authority having jurisdiction may by rule establish the classification of any material on which a rating by standard test is not available.

For proper evaluation and classification, assemblies of materials must be tested as they will actually be installed. For example, thermally thin coverings will have their performance altered by the nature of the substrate over which they are installed.[33] Adhesives may also be an important factor. In the case of composites, such as textile wall coverings over gypsum board, the adhesive should be sufficient to maintain a bond between the "finish" and the substrate. However, excess adhesive may result in the adhesive contributing to the fire. Tests of textile wall coverings[34] have shown that changing adhesives, or simply changing the application rate for the same adhesive, may significantly alter product performance. Tests to qualify assemblies should use adhesives and application rates similar to actual installations.

Similarly, a product that is tested in intimate contact with a mineral board should be installed in contact with a mineral board or like substrate. In the case where products are tested in intimate contact with a substrate, performance may also be altered by installation of the product with air space behind the covering.

6-5.2* Use of Interior Finishes.

A-6-5.2 Table A-6-5.2 on page 193 gives a compilation of the interior finish requirements of the occupancy chapters of the *Code.*

Table A-6-5.2

Occupancy	Exits	Access to Exits	Other Spaces
Assembly — New			
Class A or B	A	A or B	A or B
Class C	A	A or B	A, B, or C
Assembly — Existing			
Class A or B	A	A or B	A or B
Class C	A	A or B	A, B, or C
Educational — New	A	A or B	A or B
			C on low partitions†
Educational — Existing	A	A or B	A, B, or C
Day–Care Centers — New	A	A	A or B
	I or II	I or II	N.R.
Day–Care Centers — Existing	A or B	A or B	A or B
Group Day-Care Homes — New	A or B	A or B	A, B, or C
Group Day–Care Homes — Existing	A or B	A, B, or C	A, B, or C
Family Day–Care Homes	A or B	A, B, or C	A, B, or C
Health Care — New A.S. Mandatory	A or B	A or B	A or B
		C lower portion	C in small individual
		of corridor wall†	rooms†
Health Care — Existing	A or B	A or B	A or B
Detention and Correctional — New	A†	A†	A, B, or C
	I	I	
Detention and Correctional — Existing	A or B†	A or B†	A, B, or C
	I or II	I or II	
Residential, Hotels and Dormitories — New	A	A or B	A, B, or C
	I or II	I or II	
Residential, Hotels and Dormitories — Existing	A or B	A or B	A, B, or C
	I or II†	I or II†	
Residential, Apartment Buildings — New	A	A or B	A, B, or C
	I or II†	I or II†	
Residential, Apartment Buildings — Existing	A or B	A or B	A, B, or C
	I or II†	I or II†	
Residential, 1– and 2–family, Lodging or	A, B, or C	A, B, or C	A, B, or C
Rooming Houses			
Residential, Board and Care — See Chapters 22			
and 23			
Mercantile — New	A or B	A or B	A or B
Mercantile — Existing Class A or B	A or B	A or B	ceilings — A or B
			existing on walls—
			A, B, or C
Mercantile — Existing Class C	A, B, or C	A, B, or C	A, B, or C
Office — New	A or B	A or B	A, B, or C
	I or II	I or II	
Office — Existing	A or B	A or B	A, B, or C
Industrial	A or B	A, B, or C	A, B, or C
Storage	A or B	A, B, or C	A, B, or C
Unusual Structures††	A or B	A, B, or C	A, B, or C

†See Chapters for details.
††See Section 30–1 for occupancy classification.
Notes:
Class A Interior Wall and Ceiling Finish — flame spread 0–25, smoke developed 0–450.
Class B Interior Wall and Ceiling Finish — flame spread 26–75, smoke developed 0–450.
Class C Interior Wall and Ceiling Finish — flame spread 76–200, smoke developed 0–450.
Class I Interior Floor Finish — minimum 0.45 watts per sq cm.
Class II Interior Floor Finish — minimum 0.22 watts per sq cm.
Automatic Sprinklers — where a complete standard system of automatic sprinklers is installed, interior wall and ceiling finish with flame spread rating not over Class C may be used in any location where Class B is required and with rating of Class B in any location where Class A is required; similarly, Class II interior floor finish may be used in any location where Class I is required and no critical radiant flux rating is required where Class II is required. This does not apply to new health care facilties.
Exposed portions of structural members complying with the requirements for heavy timber construction may be permitted.

6-5.2.1 Requirements for interior wall and ceiling finish shall apply as specified elsewhere in this *Code* for specific occupancies. (*See Chapter 5 and Chapters 8 through 30.*)

6-5.2.2* Requirements for interior floor finish shall apply only where (1) there is a floor finish of unusual hazard; or (2) where floor finish requirements are specified elsewhere in this *Code* for specific occupancies. (*See Chapters 8 through 30 for specific occupancy requirements.*)

A-6-5.2.2 This paragraph recognizes that traditional finish floors and floor coverings such as wood flooring and resilient floor coverings have not proved to present an unusual hazard.

Experience has shown that traditional floor coverings, such as wood flooring and resilient tile, do not contribute to the early growth of fire. Paragraph 6-5.2.2 acknowledges the satisfactory performance of traditional floor coverings and exempts such materials from the restrictions that would otherwise be applicable. However, the authority having jurisdiction is empowered to require substantiation of the performance of any unfamiliar floor covering. For example, "plastic" imitation wood floors, artificial turf, artificial surfaces of athletic fields, and carpeting are types of products that may merit substantiation. Where the authority having jurisdiction judges that a floor covering warrants testing and substantiation or where an occupancy chapter imposes restrictions — as is the case in Chapters 10 and 11, dealing with day-care centers; Chapter 13, dealing with existing health care occupancies; Chapters 14 and 15, dealing with detention and correctional occupancies; Chapters 16, 17, 18, and 19, dealing with residential occupancies; and others — the floor covering would be treated as interior floor finish and would be regulated on the basis of tests conducted in accordance with the Flooring Radiant Panel Test as required in 6-5.4.

6-5.2.3* Textile materials having a napped, tufted, looped, woven, nonwoven, or similar surface shall not be applied to walls or ceilings.

Exception No. 1: Such materials may be permitted on the basis of room/corner fire tests acceptable to the authority having jurisdiction that demonstrate that the product, using a product mounting system including adhesive, representative of

actual use, will not spread fire to the edges of the test sample or cause flashover in the test room.

Exception No. 2: Such materials having a Class A rating shall be permitted in rooms or areas protected by an approved automatic sprinkler system.

Exception No. 3: Previously approved, existing, Class A installations.

A-6-5.2.3 Previous editions of the *Code* have regulated textile materials on walls and ceilings using NFPA 255, *Standard Method of Test of Surface Burning Characteristics of Building Materials*. Full scale room/corner fire test research has shown that flame spread indices produced by NFPA 255 may not reliably predict all aspects of the fire behavior of textile wall and ceiling coverings.

Textile materials should be evaluated using a reasonable sized ignition source to show the material will not spread fire to involve objects remote from the area of origin, nor should the textile product generate sufficient energy to cause the room of origin to flashover. Acceptance of textile wall covering materials should be contingent upon qualification tests in which a specific textile/adhesive pair has been evaluated. One means of testing has been developed at the University of California and involved a gas diffusion burner, creating a wastebasket-sized fire exposure (40 kW) for 5 minutes followed by an upholstered chair-sized fire exposure (150 kW) for an additional ten minutes. Results of the research at the University of California have been described in a report entitled, "Room Fire Experiments of Textile Wall Coverings." (*See Appendix B.*)

Research is continuing to determine if correlation can be achieved between full scale tests and other test methods more suitable for regulatory purposes such as the cone calorimeter, the vertical flame spread apparatus (NBS), and the IMO flame spread test (NBS).

Prior to the 1988 Edition of this *Code*, the danger of carpetlike textile coverings used on walls and ceilings was recognized and regulated by a requirement that only Class A tufted or napped, carpetlike materials be used, even in a sprinklered building. In 1981, a fire at the Las Vegas Hilton Hotel, which resulted in eight deaths, began in an elevator lobby and was fueled by carpetlike interior wall and ceiling finishes that did not meet the qualifications for Class A interior finish.[35] Other than the interior finish materials and a cushioned seat pad on a metal bench, there was little other combustible material to fuel the fire in the elevator lobby. Yet, the lobby went to flashover; the fire broke out the windows and climbed to a nearly identical elevator lobby on the floor above; and the events repeated themselves in a leap frog fashion from the eighth floor through the twenty-fourth floor.

Research sponsored by the American Textile Manufacturer's Institute (ATMI), conducted by the Fire Research Laboratory of the University of California at Berkeley between March 1985 and January 1986, and described in the report "Room Fire Experiments of Textile Wall Coverings"[34] has shown that consideration of only the flame spread rating, as measured by NFPA 255, *Standard Method of Test of Surface Burning Characteristics of Building Materials*[38] *(see commentary following 6-5.3.1)*, may not reliably predict the fire behavior of textile wall and ceiling coverings. Test results indicate that some Class A textile wall coverings can produce room flashover when subjected to an ignition source scenario that models a small fuel item, such as a wastebasket, igniting a chair or similar furnishing. However, other Class A textile wall coverings did not produce room flashover when subjected to the same ignition source scenario. Thus, not all Class A textile wall coverings are alike with respect to potential for producing room flashover. Simply requiring textile wall coverings to be Class A interior wall and ceiling finishes does not ensure the level of life safety intended by the *Code*. Exceptions No. 1 and 2 to 6-5-2.3 first appeared in the 1988 Edition and reflect more stringent requirements where textile wall coverings are to be used.

The testing at the University of California was conducted in an $8 \times 12 \times 8$ ft ($2.4 \times 3.7 \times 2.4$ m) high room using a gas diffusion burner as an ignition source.[34] Products undergoing evaluation were applied to the walls of the room. The gas diffusion burner and ignition source were placed in the corner of the room to evaluate various textile wall coverings. Two of the sixteen products tested — one a tufted wall covering, the other a woven wall covering — were known to have flame spread ratings of 25 or less when tested in accordance with NFPA 255. When tested in the room/corner procedure, these two products readily spread flame and caused the fire in the test room to grow quickly to large size, causing full room involvement — flashover. Concerns relative to performance of these low flame spread textile wall coverings led to the requirement for full scale room/corner testing to qualify products for use in nonsprinklered buildings.

Tests revealed that the method of mounting, including adhesive and application rate, can be critically important. Changing the application rate of the same adhesive or changing the adhesive can cause a "safe" product to exhibit unsatisfactory performance.

The testing conducted at the University of California included only wall coverings. Caution should be exercised relative to the use of combinations of textile wall and ceiling coverings. Experience has shown that combinations of textile wall/ceiling coverings may result in intense burning.[35] Research conducted at the Illinois Institute of Technology Research[36] indicates that flame spread is more likely to occur with combinations of combustible wall and ceiling coverings than in those situations involving only combustible wall coverings or only combustible ceiling coverings. Therefore, full scale room/corner testing, using an appropriately sized ignition source, should be conducted to substantiate the performance of textile wall and ceiling coverings.

In Exception No. 1, the authority having jurisdiction can accept test results on textile wall coverings tested by a room/corner fire test. Although there is no nationally recognized room/corner fire test specifically for textile wall coverings, the test protocol developed at the University of California at Berkeley for ATMI and described in the report referenced above is one test method worthy of consideration.

The protocol allows for a screening test to evaluate materials in a full scale environment without the need for lining the entire wall surface area of the room. The test results indicate that materials that produce a peak rate of heat release (RHR) of less than 300 kW and do not spread flame to the perimeter of the test material are not expected to lead to full room involvement, or flashover, when tested in a fully lined room. Materials producing a peak RHR in the 300 – 450 kW range may cause room flashover and thus need to be evaluated in a fully lined room in order to determine their firesafety. This is also true for materials that produce flaming droplets that fall to the floor and continue to burn. Materials that produce a peak RHR in excess of 450 kW during the screening test have a high probability of causing flashover when tested in a fully lined room.

In view of the fact that there is no recognized room/corner test for textile wall coverings, Exception No. 2 to 6-5.2.3 allows such materials if they are Class A and the areas in which they are installed are sprinklered. Exception No. 3 continues to recognize existing, previously approved Class A textile wall coverings without requiring sprinklering of the area because, prior to the 1988 Edition of the *Code*, this condition would have met the exception to the basic requirement of 6-5.2.3.

Formal Interpretation 88-12
Reference: 6-5.2.3

Question 1: Given that 6-5.1.2 defines interior wall finish as being the exposed interior surfaces of buildings including, but not limited to, fixed or movable walls and partitions and that 6-5.2.3 prohibits textile materials from being applied to walls, is it the *Code's* intent that the provisions of 6-5.2.3 apply to less-than-ceiling height movable prefabricated panel furniture systems when a space so divided remains a single room?

Answer: No.

Question 2: Given that 6-5.1.2 defines interior wall finish as being the exposed interior surfaces of buildings including, but not limited to, fixed or movable walls and partitions and that 6-5.2.3 prohibits textile materials from being applied to walls, is it the *Code's* intent that the provisions of 6-5.2.3 apply to less-than-ceiling height movable prefabricated panel furniture systems when the space so divided becomes multiple rooms?

Answer: Yes.

Question 3: Given that 6-5.1.2 defines interior wall finish as being the exposed interior surfaces of buildings including, but not limited to, fixed or movable walls and partitions and that 6-5.2.3 prohibits textile materials from being applied to walls, is it the *Code's* intent that the provisions of 6-5.2.3 apply to ceiling-height relocatable partitions?

Answer: Yes.

Issue Edition: 1988
Reference: 6-5.2.3
Issue Date: July 18, 1990 ∎

The first two questions in this Formal Interpretation address prefabricated panel furniture systems, such as those prevalent in business occupancies, that are at least partially covered by textile materials. The third question addresses ceiling-height movable partitions.

Movable prefabricated panel furniture systems of less-than-ceiling height used to divide a space that remains a single room are treated as furniture. The textile materials covering all or part of such panels are exempt from interior wall finish requirements in the same way that the upholstery fabrics on a chair or sofa are exempt. Although the exposed surfaces of such panels may spread flame, the panels, due to their limited height, will help prevent flames from quickly reaching the ceiling and thus help avoid room flashover.

Where prefabricated panel furniture systems of less-than-ceiling height become of sufficient height so as to create the equivalent of separate rooms, the panel furniture system is treated as the equivalent of walls. The textile materials covering the panels would be regulated as textile wall coverings in accordance with 6-5.2.3 and its exceptions. A partition of sufficient height to create separate rooms from a single room must comply with 6-5.2.3 in order to prevent flames from spreading vertically to the ceiling.

Ceiling-height partitions, although movable, present the same interior wall finish fire challenges associated with a permanent wall assembly. Textile coverings on such partitions would be subject to the textile wall covering requirements of 6-5.2.3 and its exceptions.

Although the Committee on Safety to Life was unable to quantify the height at which a panel becomes the equivalent of a wall, particularly with respect to the associated danger of vertical fire spread to a ceiling, the user is asked to make a judgment as to whether the panels are high enough to create separate rooms. A 6-ft (1.8-m) high partition in a room with a 20-ft. (6.1-m) high ceiling might be judged as not creating separate rooms. The same 6-ft (1.8-m) high partition installed in a room with a 7.5-ft (2.3-m) high ceiling would be judged by the majority of *Code* users as creating separate rooms.

6-5.2.4   Cellular or foamed plastic materials shall not be used as interior wall and ceiling finish.

Exception No. 1: Cellular or foamed plastic materials may be permitted on the basis of fire tests that substantiate on a reasonable basis their combustibility characteristics for the use intended under actual fire conditions.

Exception No. 2: Cellular or foamed plastic shall be permitted for trim not in excess of 10 percent of the wall or ceiling area, provided it is not less than 20 lb/cu ft (320 kg/m³) in density, is limited to ½ in. (1.3 cm) in thickness and 4 in. (10.2 cm) in width, and complies with the requirements for Class A or B interior wall and ceiling finish as described in 6-5.3; however, the smoke rating is not limited.

The prohibition on the use of foamed plastics within buildings is based upon actual fire experience in which foamed plastics have contributed to very rapid fire development.[37] It is also acknowledged that tunnel testing per NFPA 255/ASTM E84 (*see 6-5.3.1*) may not accurately assess the potential hazard of plastics in general. Therefore, if cellular or foamed plastics are to be used within a building, their use should be substantiated on the basis of full-scale fire tests or fire testing that simulates conditions of actual use.

Exception No. 2 permits the limited use of plastics as a substitute for traditional wood trim. The exception allows foamed or cellular plastic materials to be be used as trim, assuming the performance under fire exposure will be comparable to that of wood. In establishing a minimum density of 20 lb/cu ft (320 kg/cu m), it is intended to prohibit the use of light [1 to 3 lb/cu ft (16 to 48 kg/cu m)] foamed plastics as trim. To control the mass of the material that can be used, limits have been established on width and thickness.

Limiting plastic trim to Class A or B materials, in combination with the 10 percent limit in area for walls and ceilings, imposes a greater restriction than would be applicable to wood. This limitation ensures that the performance of the plastic trim will be equivalent or superior to that of traditional materials.

In establishing the 10 percent limit, it is intended that the trim will be used around doors and windows or at the junction of walls and ceilings. Therefore, the trim will be uniformly distributed throughout the room. There would be a significant difference in the probable performance of wall and ceiling finish if the 10 percent were concentrated in one area, and this exception intends to prohibit such a situation.

6-5.2.5 For requirements on decorations and furnishings not meeting the definition of interior finish, see 31-1.2 and 31-1.4.

6-5.3 Interior Wall and Ceiling Finish Classification.

6-5.3.1* Interior wall and ceiling finish shall be classified in accordance with 6-5.3.2 based on test results from NFPA 255, *Standard Method of Test of Surface Burning Characteristics of Building Materials.*

Flame spread and smoke development are both recorded in the results of a test conducted in accordance with NFPA 255, *Standard Method of Test of Surface Burning Characteristics of Building Materials,*[38] also know as ASTM E84, *Standard Test Method for Surface Burning Characteristics of Building Materials.*[39] Fuel-contributed values are no longer recorded as a required part of the test procedure. (*See A-6-5.3.2.*)

Interior wall and ceiling finish classifications in accordance with 6-5.3.2 are based mainly on flame spread ratings with an additional requirement that smoke development not exceed a common value of 450, regardless of the class into which the material falls based on flame spread. Flame spread ratings offer a general indication of the speed with which fire may spread across the surface of a material. In assessing the hazard posed by a material on the basis of flame spread, it is assumed that a person may be in close proximity to the fire and would be directly exposed to the energy associated with the actual flames. By contrast, the purpose of smoke developed ratings is to address obscuration of the egress path by smoke. Given that the smoke development value is a cumulative measurement over the prescribed test duration, it is based on both quantity and rate of smoke liberation. Thus, an interior wall and ceiling finish material with a low smoke development value should provide better visibility in a given egress route than a material with a high smoke development value.

The *Code* requires the use of specific classes of interior wall and ceiling finish materials, which are differentiated by their allowable flame spread rating, based on consideration of installed location within the building, its egress paths, and the occupancy in question. Different classes of interior finish materials are specified for an office area, for example, as opposed to an exit stair enclosure or exit access corridor. The different classes recognize that, in escaping a building, people must move away from the flames while traveling through the means of egress toward an exit. The classes of interior finishes that are considered acceptable within an open office are, therefore, different from those that are required for exit enclosures. Similarly, occupancies used by those who are mobility impaired have stricter interior finish requirements than occupancies used by fully ambulatory occupants. For example, although both hospitals and hotels provide sleeping accommodations, the interior finish requirements are more stringent for hospitals due to the greater incapability of hospital patients for self-preservation.

The same smoke developed limit is used for all three flame spread classifications. This limit recognizes that smoke generated during a fire may affect visibility both in the vicinity of and remote from the fire. Large buildings can be quickly filled with smoke as a result of a fire. An upper limit has been established, therefore, that applies to interior finish materials regardless of where the materials are located.

There is an exception for existing buildings. In existing buildings, interior finish materials are restricted only on the basis of flame spread. Editions of the *Life Safety Code* prior to 1976 did not regulate interior finish materials based upon smoke development. As a general rule, the replacement of existing materials that previously received approval exclusively on the basis of flame spread is not warranted.

The smoke developed limit of 450 was determined on the basis of research conducted by Underwriters Laboratories Inc.[40] A 5,000-cu ft (140-cu m) room was filled with smoke from the tunnel test chamber. The room was equipped with illuminated exit signs. The time required to reach various stages of exit sign obscuration was recorded and compared to the smoke developed rating for the different materials involved. The report states that "materials having smoke developed ratings above 325 showed 'good' to 'marginal' visibility (scale readings of 3–4.8) in a few cases; other materials produced conditions of 'marginal' to obscuration in the six minute period."

Considering both time and smoke levels, the 450 limit on smoke ratings as used in the *Code* has been judged to be a "reasonable" limit. In considering flame spread and smoke development, it should be emphasized that there is no direct relationship between the two factors.

In the report referenced above, for example, one material had a flame spread rating of 490 and a smoke developed factor of 57, while another had a flame spread rating of 44 and a smoke developed factor of 1,387.

The 450 smoke developed limit is based solely on the level of obscuration. Although not addressed by the requirements on interior finishes, other important factors used in evaluating materials based on smoke generation are the effects of irritability and toxicity caused by gases. Smoke may also act as an irritant, further reducing visibility, and may in addition have a debilitating physiological effect on people attempting to escape from a building. These effects are not evaluated by the current smoke developed limit. Previous editions of the *Code* allowed the authority having jurisdiction to regulate products that present an "unreasonable life hazard due to the character of the products of decomposition." This provision was deleted in the 1988 Edition of the *Code* due to the unenforceable nature of the requirement. The adverse physiological effects on the human body caused by exposure to heat and the effects of inhaling hot gases should also be considered as part of an overall hazard risk assessment and should be considered separately from the interior finish requirements of Section 6-5.

A-6-5.3.1 It has been shown that the method of mounting interior finish materials may affect actual performance. Where materials are tested in intimate contact with a substrate to determine a classification, such materials should be installed in intimate contact with a similar substrate. Such details are especially important for "thermally thin" materials. For further information, refer to NFPA 255, *Standard Method of Test of Surface Burning Characteristics of Building Materials*. (*See Appendix B.*)

Some interior wall and ceiling finish materials, such as fabrics not applied to a solid backing, may not lend themselves to a test made in accordance with NFPA 255, *Standard Method of Test of Surface Burning Characteristics of Building Materials* (see Appendix B). In these cases, the large-scale test outlined in NFPA 701, *Standard Methods of Fire Tests for Flame-Resistant Textiles and Films* (*see Appendix B*), may be used.

Samples are tested in accordance with NFPA 255, *Standard Method of Test of Surface Burning Characteristics of Building Materials*,[38] using a noncombustible backing. Specimens are tested with adhesives, joints, and under other conditions that would simulate the actual installation of a product in a building. NFPA 255 will provide a general indication of product performance only if the product is installed in a fashion similar to that which has been tested. Data is available that demonstrates that the performance of interior finish materials varies depending upon mounting conditions.[33] For example, a product installed over a combustible substrate will tend to propagate fire more readily than would be typical of the same product installed over a noncombustible substrate. Further, a wall covering installed with air space behind the covering would tend to spread flame more readily than one installed in contact with a noncombustible substrate. Therefore, mounting techniques must be carefully considered in the evaluation of probable product performance. (*Also see commentary following 6-5.1.4.*)

For example, where decorative fabric is hung in front of a wall surface, and it covers a significant portion of that wall, the loosely hanging fabric creates a continuous surface that can spread flame and, thus, should comply with the requirements for interior finish. Testing in accordance with NFPA 255, which reports a flame spread rating and smoke development value that can be used to classify interior finish per 6-5.3.2, would not provide meaningful information for this specific use. Thus, testing per NFPA 701, *Standard Methods of Fire Tests for Flame-Resistant Textiles and Films*,[41] may be useful to the authority having jurisdiction in judging the safety of hanging fabrics that constitute interior finish.

NFPA 701 describes procedures for a small-scale and large-scale test, which both involve applying a flame to a vertically positioned sample for a specified time period. Upon removal of the flame-producing burner, the sample must self-extinguish and must not have charred beyond a specified distance in order to pass the test. This NFPA 701 test should help in evaluating the installation, although a strict Class A, B, or C determination of interior finish classification, per 6-5.3.2, cannot be made.

6-5.3.2* Interior wall and ceiling finishes shall be grouped in the following classes in accordance with their flame spread and smoke development:

Class A Interior Wall and Ceiling Finish. Flame spread 0-25, smoke developed 0-450. Includes any material classified at 25 or less on the flame spread test scale and 450 or

less on the smoke test scale described in 6-5.3.1. Any element thereof when so tested shall not continue to propagate fire.

Class B Interior Wall and Ceiling Finish. Flame spread 26-75, smoke developed 0-450. Includes any material classified at more than 25 but not more than 75 on the flame spread test scale and 450 or less on the smoke test scale described in 6-5.3.1.

Class C Interior Wall and Ceiling Finish. Flame spread 76-200, smoke developed 0-450. Includes any material classified at more than 75 but not more than 200 on the flame spread test scale and 450 or less on the smoke test scale described in 6-5.3.1.

Exception: Existing interior finishes complying with the above flame spread ratings only may continue to be used.

A-6-5.3.2 Prior to 1978, the test report described by NFPA 255, *Standard Method of Test of Surface Burning Characteristics of Building Materials*, included an evaluation of the fuel contribution as well as the flame spread rating and the smoke development value. However, it is now recognized that the measurement on which the fuel contribution is based does not provide a valid measure. Therefore, although the data are recorded during the test, the information is no longer normally reported. Classification of interior wall and ceiling finish thus relies only on flame spread index and smoke development value. The 450 smoke development value limit is based solely on obscuration.

The Class A, B, or C designations used by the *Life Safety Code* and the *Standard Building Code*[7] correlate directly with the Class I, II, or III designations used in the *BOCA/National Building Code*[6] and the *Uniform Building Code*.[5]

6-5.3.3 Wherever the use of Class C interior wall and ceiling finish is required, Class A or B shall be permitted. Where Class B interior wall and ceiling finish is required, Class A shall be permitted.

This section recognizes that the *Code* sets minimum criteria. One may always use an interior finish that performs better than that specifically prescribed by *Code*.

6-5.3.4 The classification of interior finish specified in 6-5.3.2 shall be that of the basic material used by itself or in combination with other materials.

Exception No. 1: Subsequently applied paint or wall covering not exceeding ¹/₂₈ in. (.09 cm) in thickness unless of such character or thickness or so applied as to affect materially the flame spread or smoke development characteristics.

Exception No. 2: Exposed portions of structural members complying with the requirements for Type IV (2HH) construction per NFPA 220, Standard on Types of Building Construction.

Interior finish classifications apply to the basic materials used, such as wood, gypsum board, plaster, or any combination of the materials. Exception No. 1 notes that thin coverings — those not exceeding ¹/₂₈ in. (.09 cm) in thickness — will not significantly affect the performance of the basic wall or ceiling material. Thermally thin coverings such as paint and wallpaper coverings, where secured to a noncombustible substrate, will not significantly alter the performance of the substrate during a fire. However, thicker coverings, such as multiple layers of wallpaper, can and have contributed to rapid fire growth in actual fires. For example, multiple layers of wall coverings contributed to rapid fire growth in the multiple-death fire in the Holiday Inn in Cambridge, Ohio, which occurred on July 31, 1979.[42] Exception No. 1 requires any wall or ceiling covering in excess of ¹/₂₈ in. (.09 cm) in thickness to be treated as interior finish.

Exception No. 2 recognizes that exposed surfaces of heavy timber structural members, such as wood columns, beams, and girders, although they often have flame spread ratings in the range of 76 to 200 and, therefore, are classified as Class C interior finish, can be safely used where Class A and B interior finish is required. This is because the structural members are located at intervals and do not constitute a continuous surface that allows flame to spread, for example, across a ceiling.

6-5.4 Interior Floor Finish Classification.

Experience and full-scale fire test data have shown that floor coverings of modest resistance to flame spread are unlikely to become involved in the early growth of a fire. Regulation of flooring materials based upon flammability considerations should, therefore, only be undertaken where required by the *Code* or where a need is clearly recognized. Regulation of flooring materials in general use areas of a building, except those that are judged to represent an unusual hazard, is usually not warranted.

When the judgment is made to regulate floor coverings, the evaluation is to be made based upon tests conducted in accordance with NFPA 253, *Standard Method of Test for Critical Radiant Flux of Floor Covering Systems Using a Radiant Heat Energy Source,*[43] also known as ASTM E648, *Standard Test Method for Critical Radiant Flux of Floor-Covering Systems Using a Radiant Heat Energy Source.*[44] The Flooring Radiant Panel Test was specifically developed to evaluate the tendency of a floor covering material to propagate flame.

Fire tests have been conducted by the National Bureau of Standards (*see NBSIR 76-1013, "Flame Spread of Carpet Systems Involved in Room Fires"*)[45] to demonstrate that carpet that passes the *Federal Flammability Standard FF-1-70 Pill Test*[46] is not likely to become involved in a fire until a room reaches or approaches flashover. Since all carpet manufactured for sale in the United States has been required since April 1971 to meet the Pill Test, no further regulation is necessary for carpet located within rooms.

On the other hand, it has been shown that floor coverings may propagate flame under the influence of a sizable exposure fire. For example, it has been shown that carpet located in a corridor may spread flame when subjected to the energy emanating from the doorway of a room fully developed in fire. The fire discharges flame and hot gases into the corridor causing a radiant heat energy exposure to the floor. It has been shown that the level of energy radiating onto the floor is a significant factor in determining whether or not progressive flaming will occur. NFPA 253, *Standard Method of Test for Critical Radiant Flux of Floor Covering Systems Using a Radiant Heat Energy Source,*[43] measures the minimum energy required on the floor covering to sustain flame in W/sq cm. This minimum value is termed the critical radiant flux. The Flooring Radiant Panel Test, therefore, measures a floor covering's tendency to spread flames where located in a corridor and exposed to the flame and hot gases from a room fire.

In summary, the Flooring Radiant Panel Test is to be used as a basis for estimating the fire performance of a floor covering installed in building corridor or exit. Floor coverings in open building spaces and in rooms within buildings merit no further regulation, provided the floor covering is at least as resistant to flame spread as a material that will meet the *Federal Flammability Standard FF-1-70 Pill Test.*[46]

Interior floor finishes should be tested as proposed for use. For example, where a carpet is to be used with a separate underlayment, the carpet should be tested with a separate underlayment. The Flooring Radiant Panel Test specifies that a carpet may be tested using either the "standard" underlayment as defined in NFPA 253, *Standard Method of Test for Critical Radiant Flux of Floor Covering Systems Using a Radiant Heat Energy Source,*[43] or the carpet may be tested with the actual underlayment proposed for use. Data generated using the standard underlayment is intended to allow the carpet tested to be used over any other underlayment. Where assembly tests are conducted with other than the standard underlayment, the results of such tests are valid only for the specific combination tested.

Floor coverings are not regulated on the basis of smoke generation. Smoke development limits are not believed to be practical or necessary because, as indicated in the previous commentary, floor coverings generally will not contribute to a fire until the fire has grown to large proportions. The minimal benefits achieved by imposing smoke development limits does not usually warrant such regulation. In addition, it is not considered practical to regulate on the basis of smoke development, because no regulatory test method that exists has been shown to be capable of producing data that correlates with the performance of products in actual fires.

6-5.4.1* Interior floor finish shall be classified in accordance with 6-5.4.2 based on test results from NFPA 253, *Standard Method of Test for Critical Radiant Flux of Floor Covering Systems Using a Radiant Heat Energy Source.*

A-6-5.4.1 The flooring radiant panel provides a measure of a floor covering's tendency to spread flames when located in a corridor and exposed to the flame and hot gases from a room fire. The Flooring Radiant Panel Test method is to be used as a basis for estimating the fire performance of a floor covering installed in the building corridor. Floor coverings in open building spaces and in rooms within buildings merit no

further regulation, providing it can be shown that the floor covering is at least as resistant to spread of flame as a material that will meet the federal flammability standard, FF1-70, Standard for the Surface Flammability of Carpets and Rugs (Pill Test). All carpeting sold in the U.S. since 1971 is required to meet this standard and therefore is not likely to become involved in a fire until a room reaches or approaches flashover. Therefore, no further regulations are necessary for carpet other than carpet in exitways and corridors.

It has not been found necessary or practical to regulate interior floor finishes on the basis of smoke development.

6-5.4.2 Interior floor finishes shall be grouped in the following classes in accordance with the critical radiant flux ratings:

Class I Interior Floor Finish. Critical radiant flux, minimum of 0.45 W/sq cm as determined by the test described in 6-5.4.1.

Class II Interior Floor Finish. Critical radiant flux, minimum of 0.22 W/sq cm as determined by the test described in 6-5.4.1.

Note that the greater the critical radiant flux value, expressed in W/sq cm, the greater the resistance of the floor finish to flame propagation. Thus, a Class I interior floor finish with a critical radiant flux of 0.45 W/sq cm or greater should perform better under fire conditions than a Class II interior floor finish material with its lesser critical radiant flux value range of 0.22 up to but not including 0.45 W/sq cm. Contrast this concept with the classification of interior wall and ceiling interior finish materials in 6-5.3.2 for which higher flame spread ratings generally denote the poorer performance under fire conditions.

6-5.4.3 Wherever the use of Class II interior floor finish is required, Class I interior floor finish shall be permitted.

6-5.5 **Trim and Incidental Finish.** Interior wall and ceiling finish not in excess of 10 percent of the aggregate wall and ceiling areas of any room or space shall be permitted to be Class C materials in occupancies where interior wall and ceiling finish of Class A or Class B is required.

This paragraph is intended to allow the use of wood trim around doors and windows as a decoration or functional molding, such as chair rails. Wood trim (*see 6-5.2.4 Exception No. 2 for restrictions applicable to plastic* trim) must meet the criteria for Class C materials. Where such trim is used in rooms or spaces requiring the use of Class A or B materials, the trim may constitute not more than 10 percent of the aggregate wall or ceiling area. The intent of the 10 percent area limit is that the trim will be more or less uniformly distributed throughout the room or space. If the trim is concentrated in one sizable, continuous pattern (for example, on one wall of a room), the materials could contribute to rapid fire growth, and application of this paragraph as substantiation for such a practice would be in error.

6-5.6 Fire Retardant Coatings.

6-5.6.1 The required flame spread or smoke developed classification of surfaces of walls, partitions, columns, and ceilings shall be permitted to be secured by applying approved fire retardant coatings to surfaces having higher flame spread ratings than permitted. Such treatments shall comply with the requirements of Chapter 3, NFPA 703, *Standard for Fire Retardant Impregnated Wood and Fire Retardant Coatings for Building Materials.*

6-5.6.2 Fire retardant coatings shall possess the desired degree of permanency and shall be maintained so as to retain the effectiveness of the treatment under the service conditions encountered in actual use.

Fire retardant paints, coatings, and penetrants are sometimes used to improve the flame spread ratings of materials or assemblies used as interior finishes within buildings. Fire retardant treatments may be used to satisfy the flame spread requirements for materials both in new construction and within existing buildings. Fire retardants are generally a surface treatment that, through intumescence or other chemical reaction, will delay ignition of a material and slow flame spread. The basic nature of the material to which the treatment has been applied is not changed. Fire exposures of sufficient duration or intensity can ultimately cause a treated material to burn. Therefore, as a rule, materials with favorable intrinsic performance characteristics are preferred over those that achieve a satisfactory level of performance through the use of externally applied treatments. However, external treatments, where properly applied and maintained, can be effective in achieving reasonable fire performance.

Fire retardant paints, coatings, and penetrants must be applied in strict accordance with the manufacturer's instructions and in conformance with the results of fire tests performed on appropriate specimens. Most fire retardant paints and coatings require an application rate three to four times greater than that of ordinary paints. Application is usually done by brush, spray, immersion, or pressure treatment. The treatment should be reapplied or renewed at periodic intervals. Treatments that may be removed by regular maintenance, washing, or cleaning procedures will require periodic examination and reapplication to maintain the required level of performance.

The use of fire retardants can improve the performance of some materials from Class C to Class B, and similarly, Class B materials can, in some cases, be upgraded to Class A. Likewise, materials having flame spread ratings in excess of 200 can sometimes be upgraded to Class C.

In approving fire retardant treatments, the authority having jurisdiction should give consideration to any increase in smoke generation likely to be caused by the treatment during a fire given that, in reducing flame spread, some fire retardant treatments increase the capacity for smoke generation by a material. In new construction, the material is required to have a smoke developed value of 450 or less.

6-5.7 Automatic Sprinklers.

6-5.7.1 Where an approved automatic sprinkler system is installed in accordance with Section 7-7, Class C interior wall and ceiling finish shall be permitted in any location where Class B is required, and Class B interior wall and ceiling finish materials shall be permitted in any location where Class A is required.

Exception: Unless specifically prohibited elsewhere in this Code.

6-5.7.2 Where an approved automatic sprinkler system is installed in accordance with Section 7-7, Class II interior floor finish shall be permitted in any location where Class I interior floor finish is required, and where Class II is required, no critical radiant flux rating is required.

Fire testing and actual fire experience have shown that automatic sprinklers prevent flame spread across the surface of a wall, ceiling, or floor covering. Flame spread limits, which are applicable to interior wall and ceiling finishes, and critical radiant flux limits, which are applicable to interior floor finishes, are reduced in areas protected by an automatic sprinkler system. However, there is a value beyond which the potential for flame spread becomes unacceptably high. For example, in occupancy types with the most lenient interior finish requirements, including fully sprinklered buildings, interior wall and ceiling finishes must meet the criteria for Class C materials.

Although Exception No. 3 to 6-5.2.3 does not specifically prohibit the application of the requirements of 6-5.7.1, the intent of the exception, which applies to previously approved, existing Class A installations of carpet-like textile materials used as interior wall and ceiling finish, is to recognize only Class A and not to recognize Class B textile materials, even if the area is sprinklered.

References Cited in Commentary

[1]*Designing Buildings for Fire Safety*, NFPA SPP-24, National Fire Protection Association, Boston, MA, 1975, pp. 72-74.

[2]NFPA 251, *Standard Methods of Fire Tests of Building Construction and Materials*, National Fire Protection Association, Quincy, MA, 1990.

[3]NFPA 252, *Standard Methods of Fire Tests of Door Assemblies*, National Fire Protection Association, Quincy, MA, 1990.

[4]NFPA 220, *Standard on Types of Building Construction*, National Fire Protection Association, Quincy, MA, 1985.

[5]*Uniform Building Code*, International Conference of Building Officials, Whittier, CA.

[6]*BOCA/National Building Code*, Building Officials and Code Administrators International, Inc., Country Club Hills, IL.

[7]*Standard Building Code*, Southern Building Code Congress International, Inc., Birmingham, AL.

[8]*Fire Resistance Design Manual*, 12th Edition, Gypsum Association, Evanston, IL, 1988.

[9]ASTM E119-88, *Standard Methods of Fire Tests of Building Construction and Materials*, American Society for Testing and Materials, Philadelphia, PA.

[10]*UL Fire Resistance Directory*, Underwriters Laboratories, Northbrook, IL.

[11]*Factory Mutual Specification Tested Products Guide*, Factory Mutual Research Corp., Norwood, MA.

[12]ASTM E152-81, *Standard Method of Fire Tests of Door Assemblies*, American Society for Testing and Materials, Philadelphia, PA.

[13]NFPA 80, *Standard for Fire Doors and Windows*, National Fire Protection Association, Quincy, MA, 1990.

[14]NFPA 90A, *Standard for the Installation of Air Conditioning and Ventilating Systems*, National Fire Protection Association, Quincy, MA, 1989.

[15]*UL Building Materials Directory*, Underwriters Laboratories, Northbrook, IL.

[16]UL 1479-83 (rev. 1984), *Fire Tests of Through-Penetration Firestops*, Underwriters Laboratories, Northbrook, IL.

[17]John R. Hall, Jr., "Report Prepared for the House Subcommittee on Science, Research, and Technology on H.R. 94, The Hotel and Motel Fire Safety Act of 1989," Quincy, MA: NFPA Fire Analysis and Research Division, National Fire Protection Association, Quincy, MA, March 2, 1989.

[18]Thomas Klem, "Investigation Report on the DuPont Plaza Hotel Fire," National Fire Protection Association, Quincy, MA, 1987.

[19]Richard Best and David Demers, "Investigation Report on the MGM Grand Hotel Fire," National Fire Protection Association, Quincy, MA, 1980.

[20]NFPA 13, *Standard for the Installation of Sprinkler Systems*, National Fire Protection Association, Quincy, MA, 1991.

[21]NFPA 92B, *Guide for Smoke Management Systems in Malls, Atria, and Large Areas*, National Fire Protection Association, Quincy, MA, 1991.

[22]NFPA 92A, *Recommended Practice for Smoke Control Systems*, National Fire Protection Association, Quincy, MA, 1988.

[23]NFPA 20, *Standard for the Installation of Centrifugal Fire Pumps*, National Fire Protection Association, Quincy, MA, 1990.

[24]NFPA 105, *Recommended Practice for the Installation of Smoke-Control Door Assemblies*, National Fire Protection Association, Quincy, MA, 1989.

[25]UL 1784-90, *Air Leakage Tests of Door Assemblies*, Underwriters Laboratories, Northbrook, IL.

[26]J. Degenkolb, "The 20-Minute Door and Other Considerations," *Building Standards*, Vol. XLV, No. 1, January-February 1976.

[27]NFPA 72E, *Standard on Automatic Fire Detectors*, National Fire Protection Association, Quincy, MA, 1990.

[28]NFPA 68, *Guide for Venting of Deflagrations*, National Fire Protection Association, Quincy, MA, 1988.

[29]NFPA 69, *Standard on Explosion Prevention Systems*, National Fire Protection Association, Quincy, MA, 1986.

[30]NFPA 654, *Standard for the Prevention of Fire and Dust Explosions in the Chemical, Dye, Pharmaceutical, and Plastics Industries*, National Fire Protection Association, Quincy, MA, 1988.

[31]Michael S. Isner, "Five Die in High-Rise Office Building Fire," *Fire Journal*, Vol. 84, No. 4, July/August 1990, pp. 50-57, 59.

[32]Laurence D. Watrous, "Ten Die in Convalescent Home Fire," *Fire Journal*, Vol. 66, No. 5, September 1972, pp. 16-20.

[33]David Waksman, and John B. Ferguson, "Fire Tests of Building Interior Covering Systems," *Fire Technology*, Vol. 10, No. 3, pp. 211-220.

[34]Fred Fisher, et al., "Room Fire Experiments of Textile Wall Coverings," Fire Research Laboratory, University of California, Berkeley, CA, March 1986.

[35]National Fire Protection Association, "Investigation Report on the Las Vegas Hilton Hotel Fire," *Fire Journal*, Vol. 76, No. 1, January 1982, pp. 52-63.

[36]W.J. Christian, and T.E. Waterman, "Flame Spread in Corridors: Effects of Location and Area of Wall Finish," *Fire Journal*, Vol. 65, No. 4, July 1971, pp. 25-32.

[37]John A. Sharry, "Foamed Plastic Fire: Fire Spreads 430 Feet in Eight Minutes," *Fire Journal*, Vol. 69, No. 1, January 1975, pp. 5-6, 56.

[38]NFPA 255, *Standard Method of Test of Surface Burning Characteristics of Building Materials*, National Fire Protection Association, Quincy, MA, 1990.

[39]ASTM E84-87, *Standard Test Method for Surface Burning Characteristics of Building Materials*, American Society for Testing and Materials, Philadelphia, PA.

[40]Underwriters Laboratories Inc., "Study of Smoke Ratings Developed in Standard Fire Tests in Relation to Visual Observations," Bulletin of Research, No. 56, April 1965.

[41]NFPA 701, *Standard Methods of Fire Tests for Flame-Resistant Textiles and Films*, National Fire Protection Association, Quincy, MA, 1989.

[42]David D. Demers, "Familiar Problems Cause 10 Deaths in Hotel Fire," *Fire Journal*, Vol. 74, No. 1, January 1980, pp. 52-56.

[43]NFPA 253, *Standard Method of Test for Critical Radiant Flux of Floor Coverings Systems Using a Radiant Heat Energy Source*, National Fire Protection Association, Quincy, MA, 1990.

[44]ASTM E648-88, *Standard Test Method for Ciritcal Radiant Flux of Floor-Covering Systems Using a Radiant Heat Energy Source*, American Society for Testing and Materials, Philadelphia, PA.

[45]Tu King-Mon and Sanford Davis, "Flame Spread of Carpet Systems Involved in Room Fires," NBSIR 76-1013, June 1976.

[46]Federal Flammability Standard FF-1-70, *Standard for the Surface Flammability of Carpets and Rugs (Pill Test)*.

[47]National Fire Protection Association, "Investigation Report on the Las Vegas Hilton Hotel Fire," *Fire Journal*, Vol. 76, No. 4, Quincy, MA, July, 1982.

7

Building Service and Fire Protection Equipment

SECTION 7-1 Utilities

Primarily, Chapter 7 serves to provide the user of the *Code* with cross-references to other codes and standards that provide design guidance for building service equipment. The provisions of these various codes and standards must be followed in order for the facility to comply with the *Life Safety Code*. Referencing within the main body of the *Code* is meant to reinforce the fact that compliance with these codes is mandatory. Sections 7-6 and 7-7, which provide menus of the various options for detection, alarm, and communications systems or automatic extinguishing systems, are mandated only where referenced by another section of the *Code*.

7-1.1 Equipment utilizing gas and related gas piping shall be installed in accordance with NFPA 54, *National Fuel Gas Code*, or NFPA 58, *Standard for Storage and Handling of Liquefied Petroleum Gases*.

Exception: Existing installations may be continued in service, subject to approval by the authority having jurisdiction.

Although the referenced documents do not specify whether or not gas piping is allowed to pass through an exit enclosure, such as an enclosed stair, other provisions of the *Life Safety Code* apply. For example, see the provisions of 5-1.3.1 (d) and (e) and the commentary following 5-1.3.1, which stress that the only openings permitted in the enclosure walls between an exit and the other building spaces are those needed to provide access into the exit from any normally occupied space and those needed to provide access out of the exit at the level of exit discharge; in other words, openings used only for an occupant to get into and out of the exit enclosure. Gas piping cannot pass through exit enclosure walls. Thus, the reference to another document is not intended to negate related requirements of the *Life Safety Code*.

7-1.2 Electrical wiring and equipment installed shall be in accordance with NFPA 70, *National Electrical Code*.

Exception: Existing installations may be continued in service subject to approval by the authority having jurisdiction.

Because the installation of natural gas piping or electrical wiring may require a complicated system or array involving many specifications and design details, the *Life Safety Code* does not repeat them; rather, it provides a reference to the appropriate code or standard in which the necessary design and installation guidance can be found.

The *Life Safety Code* requirements applicable to emergency lighting, as addressed by Section 5-9 and in particular by 5-9.2.2 with respect to independence of the emergency lighting source and distribution network, go beyond the more general guidelines of NFPA 70, *National Electrical Code*.[1] See the detailed commentary interspersed among the Section 5-9 emergency lighting requirements.

SECTION 7-2   Heating, Ventilating, and Air Conditioning

7-2.1   Air conditioning, heating, ventilating ductwork, and related equipment shall be installed in accordance with NFPA 90A, *Standard for the Installation of Air Conditioning and Ventilating Systems*, or NFPA 90B, *Standard for the Installation of Warm Air Heating and Air Conditioning Systems*, as applicable.

Exception: Existing installations may be continued in service, subject to approval by the authority having jurisdiction.

For the proper installation of HVAC systems, 7-2.1 refers *Code* users to either NFPA 90A, *Standard for the Installation of Air Conditioning and Ventilating Systems*,[2] or, for occupancies with small overall volumes such as one- and two-family dwellings, NFPA 90B, *Standard for the Installation of Warm Air Heating and Air Conditioning Systems*.[3]

For example, NFPA 90A addresses fire damper requirements for both ductwork and air transfer grilles that penetrate fire resistance rated barriers. NFPA 90A also prohibits means of egress corridors in health care, detention and correctional, and residential occupancies from being used as a portion of a supply, return, or exhaust air system serving adjoining areas.

7-2.2   Ventilating or heat-producing equipment shall be installed in accordance with: NFPA 91, *Standard for the Installation of Blower and Exhaust Systems for Dust, Stock, and Vapor Removal or Conveying*; NFPA 211, *Standard for Chimneys, Fireplaces, Vents, and Solid Fuel Burning Appliances*; NFPA 31, *Standard for the Installation of Oil Burning Equipment*; NFPA 54, *National Fuel Gas Code*; NFPA 70, *National Electrical Code*, as applicable.

Exception: Existing installations may be continued in service, subject to approval by the authority having jurisdiction.

7-2.3   Commercial cooking equipment shall be installed in accordance with NFPA 96, *Standard for the Installation of Equipment for the Removal of Smoke and Grease-Laden Vapors from Commercial Cooking Equipment*.

Exception: Existing installations may be continued in service, subject to approval by the authority having jurisdiction.

NFPA 96, *Standard for the Installation of Equipment for the Removal of Smoke and Grease-Laden Vapors from Commercial Cooking Equipment*,[4] by title and scope statement, is limited to commercial cooking equipment and should not automatically be applied to all food heating equipment simply because the equipment is present in other than a residential dwelling unit. In determining if NFPA 96 protection is needed, consideration should first be given to the quantities of smoke and grease-laden vapors that will be produced by operation of the equipment in question.

It is not the *Code's* intent, for example, to require NFPA 96 protection of a residential cooking top surface located in the snack preparation room on a hospital patient room floor, with the equipment used for heating foods or boiling water. Rather, the authority having jurisdiction may determine either that no special protection is needed or that the food heating device creates a hazardous area requiring protection under the provisions of 12-3.2 or 13-3.2. If judged to be hazardous, the area may be protected or isolated by either automatic sprinkler protection or by 1-hour fire resistance rated construction. In some cases, voluntary compliance with NFPA 96 may be judged by the authority having jurisdiction as a substitute for, and thus the equivalent of, full sprinklering of the room in which the equipment is located.

NFPA 96 also provides design guidance on the safe arrangement of hoods, ducting, and exhaust systems.

7-2.4 Ventilating systems in laboratories using chemicals shall be installed in accordance with NFPA 45, *Standard on Fire Protection for Laboratories Using Chemicals,*or NFPA 99, *Standard for Health Care Facilities,* as appropriate.

The mandatory references to NFPA 45, *Standard on Fire Protection for Laboratories Using Chemicals,* and NFPA 99, *Standard for Health Care Facilities,* were added to this chapter for consistency in the treatment of laboratories using chemicals. In prior editions of the *Code,* some occupancy chapters referenced NFPA 45 while others did not. An educational occupancy, which by definition includes educational uses up through grade twelve only, was required to protect its laboratories using chemicals in accordance with the requirements of NFPA 45. A similar college laboratory using chemicals would be classified as either an industrial occupancy or a business occupancy for which neither Chapter 28, Industrial Occupancies, nor Chapters 26 and 27, Business Occupancies, required the use of NFPA 45. The creation of 7-2.4 allows *Code* users some consistency in protection of laboratories using chemicals.

SECTION 7-3 Smoke Control

7-3.1* Smoke control systems shall be permitted in lieu of other specific requirements in accordance with the provisions of Chapters 8 through 30. The purpose of such smoke control systems is to confine smoke to the general area of fire origin and maintain the means of egress system usable.

A-7-3.1 For guidance on designing, installing, acceptance testing, periodic testing, and maintaining engineered smoke control systems see:

NFPA 92A, *Recommended Practice for Smoke Control Systems.* (*See Appendix B.*)

NFPA 92B, *Guide for Smoke Control Systems for Atria, Covered Malls, and Large Covered Spaces.* (*See Appendix B.*)

NFPA SPP-53, *Smoke Control in Fire Safety Design,* by Butcher and Parnell. (*See Appendix B.*)

ASHRAE *Handbook and Product Directory* — Fundamentals. (*See Appendix B.*)

See A-15-3.1.3 for existing detention and correctional occupancies.

This provision does not itself require smoke control systems but highlights the fact that some *Code* requirements, such as those applicable to atria, mandate smoke control systems or allow exceptions where smoke control is provided. Appendix references are provided to inform users of material that is presently available to assist in the design of smoke control systems.

NFPA 92A, *Recommended Practice for Smoke Control Systems,*[5] addresses smoke control utilizing barriers, airflows, and pressure differentials so as to confine the smoke of a fire to the zone of fire origin and thus maintain a tenable environment in other zones. The guidelines of NFPA 92A can be used to create a smokeproof enclosure using the stair pressurization method described in 5-2.3.9. The document also covers smoke control for elevator hoistways by employing, either singly or in combination, fire floor exhaust, elevator lobby pressurization, smoketight elevator lobby construction, and elevator hoistway pressurization.

NFPA 92A also addresses in detail zoned smoke control under which a building can be divided into a number of smoke control zones. Each zone is separated from the others by partitions, floors, and doors that can be closed to inhibit the movement of smoke. A smoke control zone can consist of one or more floors, or a floor can consist of more than one smoke control zone. Some arrangements of smoke control zones are illustrated in Figure 7-1 in which the smoke zones are indicated by minus signs and pressurized spaces are indicated by plus signs. All nonsmoke zones may be pressurized as in Figures 7-1(a) and (c), or only nonsmoke zones adjacent to the smoke zone may be pressurized as in Figure 7-1(b) and (d). In Figure 7-1(e), the smoke zone has been limited to a portion of a floor.

The subject of maintaining tenable conditions within large zones of fire origin, such as atria and shopping malls, is addressed by NFPA 92B, *Guide for Smoke Management Systems in Malls, Atria, and Large Areas.*[6] NFPA 92B provides technical data relevant to the design, installation, testing, operation, and maintenance of smoke management systems in buildings having large-volume spaces for the management of smoke within the space where the

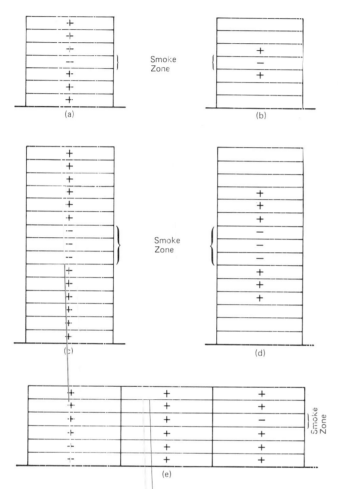

Figure 7-1. *Some Arrangements of Smoke Control Zones. Zoned smoke control is addressed by NFPA 92A.*

fire exists or between spaces not separated by smoke barriers. The guidelines of NFPA 92B can be used to implement smoke management systems that help to maintain a tenable environment in the means of egress from large-volume building spaces during the time required for evacuation. The guide also addresses the control and reduction of the migration of smoke between the fire area and adjacent spaces. The commentary in this handbook associated with 6-2.4.6(e) on the subject of atrium smoke control draws extensively from the theories and applications presented in NFPA 92B. In the example cited in that commentary, a volumetric exhaust rate was calculated following a detailed analysis of the physics associated with fire growth and smoke generation for a particular atrium building configuration that would keep smoke from

descending from the ceiling level to a level lower than head height of persons on the highest floor of the building open to the atrium. The summation of the exercise is detailed in Figure 6-19 and generalized in Figure 7-2.

A recommended practice or guide cannot be referenced mandatorily by the *Code*, but NFPA 92A and 92B should be used in the design, installation, testing, operation, and maintenance of smoke control systems covered by their scope statements.

7-3.2 Maintenance and Testing. To assure operational integrity, the smoke control system shall have an approved maintenance and testing program.

A smoke control system dedicated to emergency use only will not receive the daily use of a combination public adddress system and emergency occupant notification system. Therefore, maintenance and testing are necessary to ensure operational integrity. Although the general maintenance provisions of Section 1-8 do apply, the maintenance and testing requirements of 7-3.2 were added to Section 7-3 to remind the user of the importance of proper maintenance and testing.

SECTION 7-4   Elevators, Escalators, and Conveyors

7-4.1* An elevator shall not be considered a component in a required means of egress.

A-7-4.1 Under certain limited conditions, elevators have been recognized as required exits by prior editions of this *Code*. No such credit is given in this edition due to some characteristics that make them unsuitable for emergency exit use.

The use of elevators for emergency evacuation purposes where operated by trained emergency service personnel (building personnel, fire personnel, etc.) should be utilized in the building evacuation program. Elevators are normally capable of manual, in-car fire fighter's operation (Phase II) after elevator recall (Phase I). In addition, there usually are two or more shafts wherever there are more than three elevators, which further enhances the possibilities for elevator use during a fire emergency when operated by trained personnel.

In high rise buildings, towers, or in deep underground spaces where travel over considerable vertical distance on stairs may

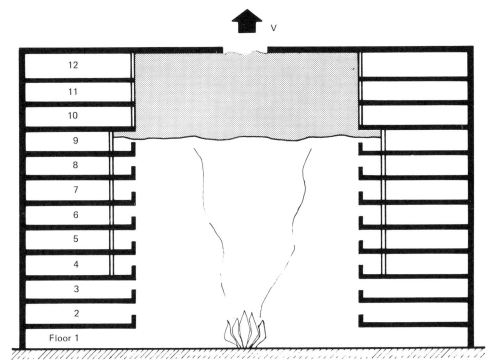

Figure 7-2. *Smoke Control in Large-Volume Building Spaces. NFPA 92B can be used to control smoke so as to keep the means of egress tenable within an atrium.*

cause persons incapable of such physical effort to collapse before they reach the street exit, stairways may be used for initial escape from the immediate area of danger, and elevators may be used to complete the travel to the street.

It may be reasonably assumed that in all buildings of sufficient height to indicate the need for elevators, elevators will be provided for normal use; and for this reason, no requirements for mandatory installation of elevators are included in the *Code*.

For additional information on elevators, see ASME/ANSI A17.1, *Safety Code for Elevators and Escalators* (*see Appendix B*), and ASME/ANSI A17.3, *Safety Code for Existing Elevators and Escalators.* (*See Appendix B*.)

In the past, the exit capacity of elevators *was* figured on the basis of three average elevators being roughly equivalent to the formerly used single unit of stairway exit width. In this way, elevators have been accepted as required exits under certain limited conditions by prior editions of the *Code*. No such credit has been given since 1956 because of some inherent characteristics that may make elevators unsuitable for emergency exit use. These characteristics are accentuated in modern automatic ele-

vators where no operator is available to exercise judgment in the control of the elevator in case of fire or other emergency. A summary of reasons for why elevators are not credited as part of the required means of egress follows:

1. People seeking to escape from a fire by means of an elevator may have to wait at the elevator door for some time, during which they may be exposed to fire or smoke or may become panicky.

2. Automatic elevators travel to floors by responding to pressed buttons, both in the elevator car and in elevator lobbies. Because this operation cannot be cancelled once a button is pressed, it is possible for an elevator descending from floors above a fire to stop automatically at the floor of the fire. The doors will then open automatically, thus exposing occupants to fire and smoke.

A further consideration is that an elevator shaft will act as a built-in "chimney" in a high rise building. Unless positively pressurized with respect to the fire floor, the shaft will carry heat and smoke from a fire and expose passengers to toxic levels of both, even if the elevator does not stop at the floor of the fire and continues to function. An elevator moving within its shaft enclosure may act similarly to a piston within a cylinder and push the smoke and gases of a fire to floors not initially involved.

3. Modern elevators will not operate until the doors are fully closed. In an emergency, a large number of people may try to crowd into an elevator, preventing the doors from closing and the elevator from operating.

4. Any power failure, such as the burnout of electric supply cables during a fire, may render the elevators inoperative or may cause people to become trapped in elevators stopped between floors. Under fire conditions, there may not be time to permit rescue of the trapped occupants through emergency escape hatches or doors.

Notwithstanding the dangers of using elevators for emergency exit purposes, they may serve an important function as a supplemental facility, particularly in occupancies such as hospitals, where under the controlled operation of trained emergency forces personnel. Elevators are also an important consideration in exiting from high rise buildings or from deep underground spaces, where travel over considerable vertical distance on stairs might cause people unaccustomed to such physical effort to tire and slow down or collapse before reaching the street. In these instances, required exits, such as stairs or horizontal exits, may be used for the initial escape from the area of immediate fire and smoke danger, and the elevators, under fire department control, may be used to complete the travel to the level of exit discharge.

An example of the *Code* requiring an elevator for use under emergency conditions can be found in 8-4.1.3(b), applicable to underground assembly occupancies. Each level of a new assembly occupancy with a floor level more than 30 ft (9.1 m) below the level of exit discharge, in addition to being required to meet the provisions of Section 30-7, "Special Provisions for Underground Structures and Windowless Buildings," must be divided into at least two smoke compartments, and each compartment must be provided with a mechanical means of moving people vertically, such as an elevator or escalator. In Figure 7-3, an escalator is used in smoke zone A and an elevator is

used in smoke zone B to provide the mechanical people mover required by 8-4.1.3(b).

Also, 5-2.12, which addresses areas of refuge, new to the 1991 Edition of the *Code*, recognizes an elevator approved for fire fighter service as a way out of an area of refuge. (*See commentary in 5-2.12.*)

7-4.2 Except as modified herein, new elevators, escalators, dumbwaiters, and moving walks shall be installed in accordance with the requirements of ASME/ANSI A17.1, *Safety Code for Elevators and Escalators*.

7-4.3 Except as modified herein, existing elevators, escalators, dumbwaiters, and moving walks shall conform to the requirements of ASME/ANSI A17.3, *Safety Code for Existing Elevators and Escalators*.

The *Life Safety Code* references ASME/ANSI A17.1, *Safety Code for Elevators and Escalators*,[7] and ASME/ANSI A17.3, *Safety Code for Existing Elevators and Escalators*,[8] because of the automatic recall provisions and the fire fighters' override provisions that these documents contain. These provisions make possible the recall of elevators to the ground floor or other predesignated floor during a fire, thus taking them out of service, or permit fire fighters to override the controls manually and use the elevators as necessary.

These documents are also referenced because the *Code* recognizes the use of elevators and escalators under limited conditions as discussed above and due to the fact that fire fighters may need to use the elevators during fire suppression efforts.

For elevator installations, the *Life Safety Code* requires compliance with ASME/ANSI A17.1 or A17.3, and the *Code* additionally requires that a sprinkler system, if installed, meet the requirements of NFPA 13, *Standard for the Installation of Sprinkler Systems*.[9] Prior to the issuance of an ASME/ANSI A17.1 official interpretation, it appeared that the elevator code and the sprinkler installation standard were in conflict. ASME/ANSI A17.1 severely restricted the installation of sprinklers in elevator machine rooms, and NFPA 13 states that a complete automatic sprinkler system includes the installation of sprinklers in all rooms and spaces.

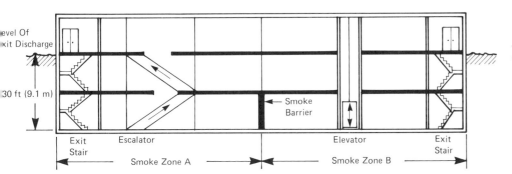

Figure 7-3 Use of Elevators and Escalators to Assist in Emergency Egress from Underground Assembly Occupancies per the Requirements of Chapter 8.

The ASME/ANSI A17.1 interpretation says that the intent of the elevator code, with respect to the sprinklering of machine rooms, is met if rate-of-rise/fixed temperature heat detectors, arranged to disconnect automatically the main line power supply, are provided in the elevator machine room, and

1. A detector is near each sprinkler;
2. The sprinkler rating exceeds the detector ratings; and
3. The detector is independent of the sprinkler system.

7-4.4 All new elevators having a travel of 25 ft (7.6 m) or more shall conform to the Fire Fighters Service Requirements of ASME/ANSI A17.1, *Safety Code for Elevators and Escalators.*

7-4.5 All existing elevators having a travel of 25 ft (7.6 m) or more above or below the level that best serves the needs of emergency personnel for fire fighting or rescue purposes shall conform to the Fire Fighters Service Requirements of ASME/ANSI A17.3, *Safety Code for Existing Elevators and Escalators.*

Due to the extreme hazard of elevators stopping at a fire floor, either intentionally or unintentionally, the *Code* mandates that the fire fighters' service requirements of ASME/ANSI A17.1 and A17.3 be complied with in both new and existing buildings. The fire fighters' service requirements establish elevator recall activated by smoke detection in each elevator lobby and in associated machine rooms. This recall function is controlled by a 3-position key-operated switch normally located in the main lobby

at the elevators. The requirements mandate specific functions for the "on," "off," and "by-pass" positions of this switch. The requirements also provide for "emergency in-car operations" or what is often referred to as fire fighters' service. This rule requires a 3-position key-operated switch in each elevator car. The functions of the "on," "off," and "hold" positions are specified in the elevator code. For specific details, refer to ASME/ANSI A17.1. Commentary on these rules is available in the ASME *Handbook A17.1.*[9]

Supplement 4 of this *Life Safety Code Handbook* contains extracts from ASME/ANSI A17.1 regarding this issue as well as commentary from the ASME *Handbook A17.1.*

7-4.6 Where there are three or fewer elevator cars in a building, they shall be permitted to be located within the same hoistway enclosure. Where there are four elevator cars, they shall be divided in such a manner that at least two separate hoistway enclosures are provided. Where there are more than four elevators, not more than four elevator cars shall be located within a single hoistway enclosure.

Exception: Existing buildings.

The new requirements addressed by 7-4.6 help to ensure that smoke and fire in an elevator hoistway will not prevent the use of all elevators in any building that has four or more elevators. If a building has four elevators, a maximum of three of those elevators are allowed within the same elevator hoistway or shaft. If the building has more than four elevators, no more than four elevators can be in one shaft. If smoke and fire prevent the use of the elevators within one hoistway, an elevator in another hoistway may be usable. Because of the maximum limit of four elevators per hoistway, a building with nine to twelve elevators must have a minimum of three hoistways.

The requirements of 7-4.6 mesh well with the high rise building requirements of 30-8.4.2, applicable to standby power. The required standby power system must be connected to at least one elevator serving all floors of the building. Additionally, elevator standby power must be transferable to any elevator. If the hoistway containing the elevator initally powered by the standby power system becomes untenable, the switching requirement will allow for an elevator in a different hoistway to be placed back into service.

7-4.7 Conveyors, elevators, dumbwaiters, and pneumatic conveyors serving various stories of a building shall not open to an exit. Service openings, where required to be open on more than one story at the same time for purposes of operation of the conveyor, shall be provided with closing devices in accordance with 5-2.1.8.

Openings in exit enclosures are strictly limited by the provisions of 5-1.3.1 to doors necessary for access to the exit from normally occupied spaces and for leaving the exit enclosure. Elevators and other conveyors are not considered normally occupied areas. Additionally, an elevator with its associated cables, controls, and mechanical equipment would introduce into an exit enclosure a degree of combustibles in conflict with the attempt to make the exit enclosure a sterile, safe place with little or no combustibles present.

SECTION 7-5   Rubbish Chutes, Incinerators, and Laundry Chutes

7-5.1 Rubbish chutes and laundry chutes shall be separately enclosed by walls or partitions in accordance with the provisions of Section 6-2. Inlet openings serving chutes shall be protected in accordance with Section 6-2. Doors of such chutes shall open only to a room that is designed and used exclusively for that purpose. The room shall be separated from other spaces in accordance with Section 6-4.

Exception No. 1: Existing installations having properly enclosed service chutes and properly installed and maintained service openings shall be permitted to have inlets open to a corridor or normally occupied space.

Exception No. 2: Rubbish chutes and laundry chutes shall be permitted to open into rooms not exceeding 400 sq ft (37 sq m) in area used for storage provided the room is protected by automatic sprinklers.

According to the provisions of 7-5.1 and those of Chapter 6, rubbish chutes and laundry chutes must be enclosed in fire-rated shafts, and the openings to the chutes must be located in enclosed fire-rated room constructions as a backup design feature. This redundant design prevents the possibility of an open incinerator or laundry chute directly exposing an exit access corridor to fire. Further, it prevents a fire in an incinerator or laundry chute from blocking exit access corridors with either smoke or flames before evacuation or corrective action can be taken. This arrangement also recognizes that occupants frequently pile rubbish in front of the incinerator chute door rather than placing it into the chute.

Paragraph 7-5.1 has been revised for this edition of the *Code* to address both rubbish chutes and laundry chutes with a common set of requirements. Whereas the former provision required that chutes open into a room designed for that purpose, the new requirement states that the room needs to be both designed and used exclusively for that purpose. Because laundry chutes are usually associated with a laundry/storage room, Exception No. 2 has been added to allow chutes to open into such rooms not exceeding 400 sq ft (37 sq m) in area. Without the new exception, the user could have interpreted the words "used exclusively" as limiting the use of that room to serving the chute only.

Standard good practice for the installation and maintenance of incinerator flues is included in NFPA 82, *Standard on Incinerators, Waste, and Linen Handling Systems and Equipment,*[11] referenced in 7-5.2, which covers rubbish chutes and linen or laundry chutes.

7-5.2 Rubbish chutes, laundry chutes, and incinerators shall be installed and maintained in accordance with NFPA 82, *Stan-*

dard on Incinerators, Waste and Linen Handling Systems and Equipment.

Exception: Existing installations may be continued in service, subject to approval by the authority having jurisdiction.

SECTION 7-6   Fire Detection, Alarm, and Communications Systems

Supplement 2 of this *Handbook* provides additional information regarding fire detection, alarm, and communications systems.

7-6.1   General.

7-6.1.1   The provisions of Section 7-6 shall apply only where specifically required by another section of this *Code.*

The intent of this section of the *Code* is to present a menu of general provisions related to protective signaling systems, not to indicate where any particular type is required. The actual requirements for providing detection, alarm, and communications systems appear in other parts of the *Code,* with emphasis in the various occupancy chapters. Thus, any or all of the signaling systems' menu of options, as suggested but not mandated by Section 7-6, can be required by other *Code* sections.

7-6.1.2   Fire detection, alarm, and communication systems installed in order to make use of an alternative allowed by this *Code* shall be considered "required" systems and shall meet the provisions of this *Code* applicable to required systems.

The provisions of 7-6.1.2 were added to this edition of the *Code* to remind the user that a fire detection, alarm, or associated communications system voluntarily installed as a *Code* alternative then becomes a required system subject to the same requirements, including maintenance, applicable to a detection, alarm, and communications system specifically mandated by the *Code.* For example, if an occupancy that does not require a detection system does allow the use of the delayed release door lock addressed by 5-2.1.6, "Special Locking Arrangements," and the designer/building operator meets one of the

unlocking provisions of 5-2.1.6 via the installation of an approved supervised automatic fire detection system, the fire detection system becomes a required system. Therefore, it must meet all the requirements applicable to a similar system installed to comply with the *Code* in addition to those of one installed to make use of an alternative provision, such as delayed release door locking.

7-6.1.3*   The provisions of this section cover the basic functions of a complete protective signaling and control system including fire detection, alarm, and communication. These systems are primarily intended to provide the indication and warning of abnormal conditions, the summoning of appropriate aid, and the control of occupancy facilities to enhance protection of life.

A-7-6.1.3   Some of the provisions of this section are excerpted from NFPA 72, *Standard for the Installation, Maintenance, and Use of Protective Signaling Systems (see Appendix B).* For purposes of this *Code,* some provisions of this section are more stringent than those of NFPA 72. NFPA 72 should be consulted for additional details.

The provision for early warning of fire accompanied by notification of appropriate authorities is a key element of a fire protection program. Where people are involved, protective signaling carries even greater importance.

The "Firewatch," included in each issue of the *NFPA Journal,* emphasizes the need for protective signaling equipment and the sometimes tragic consequences in situations where it was lacking. Among the more common problems encountered have been:

1. Fire had burned or smoldered for some time before discovery (the security guard passed by "twenty minutes" before);
2. Fire was observed, but it was assumed that someone had turned in the alarm;
3. People didn't know who to notify, were confused, gave the wrong address;
4. People present were asleep, bedridden, or otherwise unable to act;
5. Worker had attempted extinguishment rather than notifying others, thereby admitting that a careless act had started the fire; or
6. Person in position of responsibility had gone or sent someone to investigate before sounding an alarm.

In educational, mercantile, and business occupancies, there are usually enough people present, at least during a part of the day, to discover an incipient fire. Such circumstances are recognized by the *Code* by imposing less rigid requirements for protective signaling systems than would be mandated in some other occupancies. The installation of an automatic extinguishing system with an integral alarm can obviate the need for an independent signaling system or may allow some portion of the signaling system to be omitted, such as manual pull stations for system initiation, as permitted by the mercantile and business occupancies chapters of the *Code*.

Fire detection without warning is not sufficient. People must be alerted to the existence of an emergency in order to take appropriate action.

7-6.1.4* A fire alarm system required for life safety shall be installed, tested, and maintained in accordance with applicable requirements of the following:

NFPA 70, *National Electrical Code*;

NFPA 71, *Standard for the Installation, Maintenance, and Use of Signaling Systems for Central Station Service*;

NFPA 72, *Standard for the Installation, Maintenance, and Use of Protective Signaling Systems*;

NFPA 72E, *Standard on Automatic Fire Detectors*;

NFPA 74, *Standard for the Installation, Maintenance, and Use of Household Fire Warning Equipment*; and

NFPA 1221, *Standard for the Installation, Maintenance, and Use of Public Fire Service Communication Systems*.

Exception: Existing installations may be continued in use, subject to the approval of the authority having jurisdiction.

A-7-6.1.4 For additional information on the installation, testing, and maintenance of alarm systems, see NFPA 72G, *Guide for the Installation, Maintenance, and Use of Notification Appliances for Protective Signaling Systems*, and NFPA 72H, *Guide for Testing Procedures for Local, Auxiliary, Remote Station, and Proprietary Protective Signaling Systems*. (See Appendix B.)

7-6.1.5 All systems and components shall be approved for the purpose for which installed.

Approval of both the system as a whole and its individual components is required. Such approval is granted by the authority having jurisdiction. (*See the definition of "approved" in Section 3-2.*) Substantiating data could be in the form of test reports, listings issued by such organizations as the Factory Mutual System or Underwriters Laboratories Inc., or testing or evaluation by another recognized source.

7-6.1.6 Fire alarm system installation wiring or other transmission paths shall be monitored for integrity in accordance with 7-6.1.4.

A broken or short-circuited wire between a fire alarm system initiating device, e.g., a smoke detector, and the central control equipment will render the device inoperative without necessarily providing notification of the malfunction. Monitoring of the system installation wiring will result in an audible trouble signal indicating a circuit break or ground and allow for corrective action to be taken. It is not the intent of this paragraph to override the provisions for supervision in the standards referenced in 7-6.1.4, but only to highlight those requirements or to mandate them where the referenced standards may make such supervision optional.

7-6.1.7* **Maintenance and Testing.** To assure operational integrity, the fire alarm system shall have an approved maintenance and testing program complying with the requirements of the applicable documents specified in 7-6.1.4.

A-7-6.1.7 Records of conducted maintenance and testing and a copy of the certificate of compliance should be maintained. For information in addition to the standards referenced in the body of the *Code*, see NFPA 72G, *Guide for the Installation, Maintenance, and Use of Notification Appliances for Protective Signaling Systems* (see Appendix B), and NFPA 72H, *Guide for Testing Procedures for Local, Auxiliary, Remote Station, and Proprietary Protective Signaling Systems*. (See Appendix B.)

The operational integrity of a fire alarm system cannot be ensured without proper maintenance and testing. Thus, the *Code* requires that an approved (meaning acceptable to the authority having jurisdiction) maintenance and testing program be operational on an ongoing basis.

7-6.1.8   For the purposes of this *Code*, a protective signaling and control system is used for initiation, notification, and control.

(a) *Initiation.* The initiation function provides the input signal to the system.

Both automatic and manual signal initiation is considered. (*See 7-6.2.*)

(b) *Notification.* The notification function is the means by which the system advises that human action is required in response to a particular condition.

This covers all forms of notification, whether audible alone or both audible and visual. It includes notification of both occupants (*see 7-6.3*) and the fire department (*see 7-6.4*) where required.

(c) *Control.* The control function provides outputs to control building equipment to enhance protection of life.

This covers functions that the system may actuate to make the building safer, such as release of hold-open devices for self-closing doors or pressurization of stair enclosures. (*See 7-6.5.*)

7-6.2   Signal Initiation.

7-6.2.1   Where required by another section of this *Code*, actuation of the protective signaling and control system shall occur by any or all of the following means of initiation, but not limited thereto:

(a) Manual fire alarm initiation.

(b) Automatic detection.

(c) Extinguishing system operation.

The location of detector system components is of prime importance. If they are too close to a wall/ceiling intersection, particularly over a door, air currents may cause heat and smoke to bypass the unit completely. Likewise, location with respect to a dropped beam or other construction can have a similar nullifying effect. This can pose problems where partitions are moved without regard to the location of detector units. The problem is illustrated in Figure 7-4. NFPA 72E, *Standard on Automatic Fire Detectors,* [12] provides extensive guidance in this area.

Where both manual and automatic systems are in use, they should be complementary. If, due to poor maintenance, abuse, or mechanical failure, one system becomes inoperative, the second will provide backup support.

Any automatic fire detection system for life safety from fire should have a degree of reliability. This means that serious consideration should be given to providing such features as:

1. An electric current supply independent of the electric power source for the building;
2. Trouble signals to give warning in case of short circuits or breaks in wires, or other conditions that might interfere with the proper operation of the system;
3. Alarm indicating appliances located so as to ensure warning even to those sleeping; and
4. Above all, a regular maintenance program.

There is considerable diversity in the types of automatic fire detection and alarm equipment commercially available, and selection of types suitable for any given situation requires the exercise of judgment based upon experience. See Supplement 2 of this *Handbook* for additional information.

Figure 7-4.   Problems to Avoid in Detector Location.

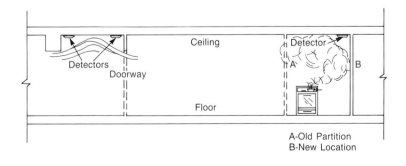

A-Old Partition
B-New Location

7-6.2.2 Manual fire alarm stations shall be approved for the particular application and shall be used only for fire protective signaling purposes. Combination fire alarm and guard's tour stations are acceptable.

7-6.2.3 A manual fire alarm station shall be provided in the natural path of escape near each required exit from an area, unless modified by another section of this *Code*.

Where manual fire alarm station boxes are required by Chapters 8 through 30 of the *Code*, they are required to be located near an exit, in the natural path of escape, and in a position of maximum visibility. The purpose is to expedite the occupant initiation of an alarm in a time of stress and to reduce the possibility of the person involved being caught by the fire between a remotely located alarm station and an exit. While the designer may not wish to detract from some special design effect at the end of a corridor, the advantage of proper placement, from the life safety point of view, is obvious, as shown in Figure 7-5.

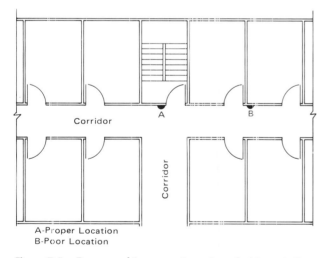

A-Proper Location
B-Poor Location

Figure 7-5. Proper and Improper Location of a Manual Alarm Station.

7-6.2.4 Additional manual fire alarm stations shall be so located that, from any part of the building, not more than 200 ft (60 m) horizontal distance on the same floor shall be traversed in order to reach a manual fire alarm station.

7-6.2.5 Each manual fire alarm station on a system shall be accessible, unobstructed, visible, and of the same general type.

7-6.2.6 Where a sprinkler system provides automatic detection and alarm system initiation, it shall be provided with an approved alarm initiation device that will operate when the flow of water is equal to or greater than that from a single automatic sprinkler.

7-6.2.7 Where a "complete smoke detection system" is required by another section of this *Code*, automatic detection of smoke in accordance with NFPA 72E, *Standard on Automatic Fire Detectors*, shall be provided in all occupiable areas, common areas, and work spaces in those environments suitable for proper smoke detector operation.

7-6.2.8 Where a "partial smoke detection system" is required by another section of this *Code*, automatic detection of smoke in accordance with NFPA 72E, *Standard on Automatic Fire Detectors*, shall be provided in all common areas and work spaces, such as corridors, lobbies, equipment rooms, and other tenantless spaces in those environments suitable for proper smoke detector operation. Selective smoke detection unique to other sections of this *Code* shall be provided as required by those sections.

Paragraphs 7-6.2.7 and 7-6.2.8 define the terms "complete smoke detection system" and "partial smoke detection system" to provide a self-contained reference for other Code paragraphs to use where requiring these systems. Selective smoke detection fits neither definition and relies on some other provision of the *Code* to detail what is intended. For example, new nursing homes and new and existing limited care facilities are required to provide a corridor smoke detection system. The extent of such a system, which meets neither the definition of "complete" nor "partial" as addressed by 7-6.2.7 or 7-6.2.8 and is unique to new nursing homes and new and existing limited care facilities, is explained in Chapters 12 and 13.

7-6.2.9* Where required by another section of this *Code*, single station smoke detectors shall be installed in accordance with NFPA 74, *Standard for the Installation, Maintenance, and Use of Household Fire Warning Equipment*. Smoke detectors shall receive their operating power from the building electrical system. In new construction, where two or more smoke detectors are required within a living unit, they shall be arranged so that the activation of any detector causes the operation of an alarm that shall be clearly audible throughout the living unit over background noise levels with all intervening doors closed. The detectors shall sound an alarm only within an individual living unit or similar area and shall not actuate the building protective signaling and control system. Remote annunciation shall be permitted.

Exception No. 1: Battery-operated devices as permitted by other sections of this Code.

Exception No. 2: Battery-operated devices complying with the appropriate documents specified in 7-6.1.4 that achieve indication of missing battery or low battery power condition at a remote location.

Exception No. 3: Multiple station or system smoke detectors arranged to function in the same manner shall be permitted.

A-7-6.2.9 A living unit is that structure, area, room, or combination of rooms, including hotel rooms/suites, in which a family or individual lives. This is meant to cover living areas only and not common usage areas in multifamily buildings such as corridors, lobbies, basements, etc.

This provision allows the use of single station or multiple station smoke detectors that are not part of a fire alarm system to be used within a dwelling or living unit, such as within a one- or two-family dwelling, within an apartment, or within a hotel or dormitory room, provided that certain performance oriented criteria can be met. Audibility over background noises, such as running water, home appliances, and audio systems, with intervening doors closed between the occupants and the detector sounding device is of key importance. In multistory or large-area living units, multiple detectors will probably need to be interconnected so that the sensing of smoke by one sounds the alarms of all detectors within that living unit.

The intent behind requiring smoke detection within an individual living unit without requiring connection to the overall building alarm system is to provide notification of a smoke condition within a living unit to occupants of that particular living unit. Once the occupants egress their unit to the building's common areas, they can use the manual pull stations to sound the building alarm to notify occupants of other living units of the emergency.

Mandatory interconnection of living unit smoke detectors to the building alarm system often results in numerous nuisance alarms due to the detection of cooking or bathroom shower vapors. Nuisance alarms lead to the deliberate disablement of the system and the resulting lack of early warning. Thus, a complete fire detection (versus smoke detection) system usually includes system smoke detection within building common areas and system heat detection within individual living units. Single station smoke detectors are then still necessary within each living unit to afford the occupants of each unit early warning of smoke conditions within their unit.

The term "single station" is often confused with the term "multiple station." Single station means that the detector that senses smoke also sounds an integral sounding device and does not ring a general alarm. Multiple station means the interconnection of single station devices such that, when one sounds, all those interconnected also sound.

The second sentence of 7-6.2.9 is new to this edition of the *Code*. In prior editions, 7-6.2.9 was silent on intended power source, i.e., battery-operated versus hardwired to the electrical system. Rather, specific occupancy chapters that require the installation of single station smoke detectors specified their intended power source. Most required that the detectors be continuously powered by the house electrical service. Exemptions were then made by the occupancy chapters for battery-operated units in existing one- and two-family dwellings, existing lodging and rooming houses, and under certain conditions in board and care facilities.

With the recent addition of the operating requirement in the new second sentence of 7-6.2.9, single station smoke detectors, unless exempted by either Exception No. 1 or Exception No. 2, must receive their operating power from the electrical system. This provision is based on the experience that battery-operated detectors do not provide the reliability with respect to uninterrupted power supply that building electrical system power provides; batteries are often removed to avoid nuisance alarms caused by kitchen or bathroom vapors or for use in other devices such as radios and electronic toys; and dead batteries are often times not replaced. Exception No. 1, however, permits the occupancies mentioned above to continue to allow battery-operated single station smoke detectors.

Exception No. 2 to 7-6.2.9 was added to clarify that it is not the *Code's* intent to prohibit the new wireless technology, in which a battery-operated detector reports by radio transmission to an alarm panel, if such devices

(a) comply with the appropriate standards referenced in 7-6.1.4, and

(b) indicate a missing battery or low battery power condition at the remotely located alarm system panel.

Compliance with (a) and (b) above increases the power source reliability to a level comparable to that provided by connection to the building electrical service.

7-6.3 Occupant Notification.

7-6.3.1 Occupant notification shall provide signal notification to alert occupants of fire or other emergency as required by another section of this *Code*.

7-6.3.2* Notification shall be a general audible alarm-type complying with 7-6.3.3 through 7-6.3.10.

Exception No. 1: Except where prohibited by an occupancy chapter, a presignal system shall be permitted when the initial fire alarm signal is automatically transmitted without delay to a municipal fire department, a fire brigade, or a staff person trained to respond to a fire emergency. (See 7-6.1.4.)

A presignal system, rather than immediately and automatically sounding a general alarm throughout the building, delays the general alarm by sounding alarm devices initially in only an approved and constantly attended area, such as a fire brigade station, guard station, or similar location with trained staff who then investigate the signal's origin and may subsequently sound a general alarm. If a presignal system is not intentionally aborted within a predetermined period of time, an audible general building alarm is sounded.

Because the delay in sounding the general alarm, which is inherent in a presignal system, may do more harm than good in those occupancies with populations that are difficult to evacuate or protect, the *Code* allows occupancy chapters to prohibit presignal systems specifically. For example, the health care occupancies chapters and the chapter applicable to new apartments specificially pro-

hibit presignal systems. The occupancy chapter applicable to new hotels allows a presignal system to be used only in a building protected throughout by an approved automatic sprinkler system, and then only with specific permission of the authority having jurisdiction. Existing hotels, even if not sprinklered, are allowed presignal systems, if permitted by the authority having jurisdiction. Many of the occupancy chapters are silent on the subject of presignal systems, in which case such systems would be allowed in accordance with the provisions of Exception No. 1 to 7-6.3.2.

A presignal system used in accordance with the provisions of Exception No. 1 to 7-6.3.2 is allowed to delay only the general occupant notification and must, at time of initiation, achieve immediate and automatic notification of emergency forces per the guidelines of 7-6.4.

Exception No. 2: Except where prohibited by an occupancy chapter, occupant notification from a smoke detector alarm shall be permitted to be delayed up to 180 seconds, provided:

(a) The building is protected throughout by an approved automatic sprinkler system installed in accordance with Section 7-7, and

(b) The alarm signal shall be received at a constantly attended location on the premises, and

(c) Staff persons shall be trained to respond and investigate, and

(d) The system automatically notifies occupants at the end of the time period unless it is reset.

Given that smoke detector sensitivity should result in alarm system initiation sooner than that achieved by either heat detection or manual discovery and use of a pull station, Exception No. 2 to 7-6.3.2 was added to this edition of the *Code* in an effort to offer relief from nuisance alarms in buildings equipped with a newer detection technology by allowing a delay in occupant notification. In a fully sprinklered building, the detector that senses smoke, automatically and without delay sends an alarm signal to a constantly attended location so that trained staff can investigate the origin of the signal. During this time, the smoke detector and the sophisticated alarm panel continue to communicate. If the smoke detector chamber clears of smoke prior to three minutes from initial detection, it so notifies the alarm panel and the pending general audible alarm-type notification is cancelled. If the smoke detector is still in alarm at the end of the three-minute period, audible alarm-type occupant notification must then immediately and automatically be sounded.

Exception No. 3: Elevator lobby and associated machine room detectors used for elevator recall are not required to sound the building evacuation alarm if the power supply and installation wiring to these detectors are monitored by the building fire alarm system, and activation of these detectors results in an audible supervisory signal.*

A-7-6.3.2 Exception No. 3 The concept addressed by the exception is that detectors used for "releasing service" for elevator recall need not sound the building evacuation alarm, provided that an alarm condition is indicated by an audible supervisory signal.

Exception No. 4: Duct detectors used for closing dampers or heating/ventilating/air conditioning system shutdown are not required to sound the building alarm.*

Exception No. 5: Detectors at doors for the operation of automatic door release are not required to sound the building alarm.*

A-7-6.3.2 Exceptions No. 4. and 5 The concept addressed by the exceptions is that detectors used for "releasing service," such as door or damper closing and fan shutdown, need not sound the building alarm.

Exceptions No. 4 and 5 reaffirm that not all detectors, simply because they are installed on the premises, are required to sound the building alarm. Detectors used for "releasing service," such as for the release of an automatic door hold-open device that allows a door to be self-closing under the presence of smoke, need only perform their intended function. In areas where smoke detection, complete with occupant notification via the building alarm system, is needed to provide the intended level of life safety, the *Code* will specifically require either a complete or partial smoke detection system. Interconnection with the building alarm should not be mandated in hope of receiving additional detection coverage simply because a detector may have been installed for another purpose, such as releasing service.

Although Exceptions No. 4 and 5 exempt detectors used for releasing service from initiating the building alarm system, an occupancy chapter can choose to be more stringent than Chapter 7. For example, paragraphs 12-3.4.2 and 13-3.4.2 mandate that all required detection devices initiate the required fire alarm system. Thus, in a health care occupancy where subdivision of building space via the use of smoke barriers is required, the smoke detectors associated with the release of automatic hold-open devices installed on cross-corridor smoke barrier doors must also initiate the building alarm system.

A-7-6.3.2 Where coded stations are used and more than one station is operated, at least three complete rounds of a clear coded signal should be transmitted.

7-6.3.3 Where a standard evacuation signal is required by another section of this *Code*, the evacuation signal shall be the standard fire alarm evacuation signal described in NFPA 72, *Standard for the Installation, Maintenance, and Use of Protective Signaling Systems.*

See commentary following 7-6.3.7.

7-6.3.4 Notification signals for occupants to evacuate shall be by audible and visible signals.

Exception No. 1: Buildings not subject to occupancy by persons who are hearing impaired need not comply with the provisions for visible signals.

Visible alarm devices, in addition to the audible alarms, are needed in buildings occupied by persons who are hearing impaired. Exception No. 1 recognizes that not all buildings are subject to occupancy by those who are hearing impaired. For example, in a special hazard industrial occupancy where, due to employee safety concerns, an adequate hearing level is a condition of employment, there should be no life safety need for visible signals in addition to the normal audible signals.

Exception No. 2: Existing buildings need not comply with the provisions for visible signals.

Exception No. 3: Visible signals need not be installed in each unit of a hotel or apartment building provided that those units designed for the hearing impaired are equipped with visible signals.

Exception No. 3 recognizes that hotel and apartment residential occupancies, unlike large open assembly spaces, are characterized by numerous small compartments such as bedrooms separated from corridors and common spaces by fire barriers and self-closing doors. If visible signals were required in all areas, almost every individual room would need an alarm strobe or similar visible device. Yet, only some minor percentage of the overall number of rooms would be occupied by persons who are hearing impaired at any given time. As long as some portion, acceptable to the authority having jurisdiction, of the total number of rooms is equipped with visible devices and those rooms are identified as available for those who are hearing impaired, the other rooms are exempted from having visible signal devices.

Exception No. 4: Other means of notification acceptable to the authority having jurisdiction may serve in lieu of visible signals.

7-6.3.5 The general evacuation alarm signal shall operate throughout the entire building.

Exception No. 1: Where total evacuation of occupants is not practical due to building configuration, only the occupants in the affected zones shall be initially notified. Provisions shall be made to selectively notify occupants in other zones to afford orderly evacuation of the entire building.

Exception No. 2: Where occupants are incapable of evacuating themselves because of age, physical/mental disabilities, or physical restraint, only the attendants and other personnel required to evacuate occupants from a zone, area, floor, or building are required to be notified. This notification shall include means to readily identify the zone, area, floor, or building in need of evacuation.

Exception No. 3: Notification within the covered mall per 24-4.4.3.3 and 25-4.4.3.3.

Exception No. 1 to 7-6.3.5 normally applies to high rise buildings. It makes provisions for zoned, staged evacuation. This exception anticipates that the portions of the building that do not receive the initial alarm are separated from the areas of immediate emergency by adequate fire

resistance rated construction, such as the 2-hour fire separation that is usually provided between floors of high rise buildings.

Exception No. 2 commonly applies to health care and detention and correctional occupancies. It is a common application in these occupancies to use coded chimes or a similar method to announce throughout the facility the location of the fire emergency. This allows all members of the emergency response team, regardless of current location within a potentially sprawling facility, to respond to their assigned emergency duties. For example, an engineer who may be working on a plumbing problem in the facility's adjacent original building at the time the coded alarm is chimed throughout the facility will receive the proper notification to carry out the previously assigned task of checking the fire pump to ensure that it is ready to operate if needed.

Exception No. 3 is new in this edition of the *Code* and emphasizes that the Chapter 24 and 25 provisions applicable to covered malls require an alarm system for the covered mall, i.e., the covered pedestrian walkway, rather than for the entire covered mall building which includes both the covered mall and all attached tenant spaces. The individual tenant spaces that are themselves Class A mercantile occupancies must also have an alarm system. Smaller tenant spaces are not required to have alarm systems. The alarm system required in the covered mall must sound throughout the covered mall but need not sound within the tenant spaces. The alarm system required in each Class A mercantile occupancy tenant space must sound within that tenant space, but is not required to sound either in the smaller tenant spaces that are exempt from the alarm system requirement or in the covered mall.

7-6.3.6 Audible alarm indicating appliances shall be of such character and so distributed as to be effectively heard above the average ambient sound level occurring under normal conditions of occupancy.

The authority having jurisdiction needs to review carefully the types and locations of alarm indicating appliances. Given that audibility above ambient sound level is of primary importance and that each additional sounding device adds cost to a system, a balance should be engineered so that excessive costs are not incurred while the installation of sufficient devices for adequate audibility is ensured. This is extremely important in hotels and apartment buildings. Sounding devices located in corridors may not be audible within units, especially in new construction, due to increased levels of acoustical insulation.

In new hotels it has become common to install alarm indicators within each guest room in order to meet the audibility requirement. With water running in the bathroom, the television operating on high volume, and the air conditioning system in use, the horn or speaker within the room achieves the required occupant notification that a similar device located in the corridor might not. Additionally, the alarm device often used is a speaker that can produce an alarm tone or deliver a specific voice message. This is particularly useful in a high rise building where, although it is important to get an initial message to all rooms, different messages will also need to be sent to different parts of the building as part of a zoned evacuation plan.

7-6.3.7 Audible alarm indicating appliances shall produce signals that are distinctive from audible signals used for other purposes in the same building.

Where the provisions of Chapters 8 through 30 require an evacuation alarm signal, the standard fire alarm evacuation signal described in NFPA 72, *Standard for the Installation, Maintenance, and Use of Protective Signaling Systems,*[13] should be used.

The manner of sounding alarms should be standardized with a view to obtaining uniformity throughout as large a geographic area as practicable. In this way, people moving from one locality to another will not be misled and confused by differences in the manner of sounding alarms.

Two multiple-fatality fires in hotel occupancies that occurred in late 1978 and 1979 illustrate the need for standardized fire alarm signals with adequate audibility. In both incidents, which occurred in the middle of the night, many survivors reported not hearing any alarm device or mistaking the alarm for telephones or alarm clocks. An additional multiple-fatality fire in a hotel in 1978 illustrated the special problems with alarm notification where occupants' hearing is impaired. In this fire, several elderly occupants removed hearing aids before going to bed, thus challenging the adequacy of the alarm's audibility.

7-6.3.8 Automatically transmitted or live voice evacuation or relocation instructions to occupants shall be permitted and shall be in accordance with NFPA 72, *Standard for the Installation, Maintenance, and Use of Protective Signaling Systems.*

Rather than specify additional requirements for recorded or live voice evacuation or relocation instructions, the *Code* mandatorily references NFPA 72, *Standard for the Installation, Maintenance, and Use of Protective Signaling Systems,*[13] which contains the necessary requirements.

7-6.3.9 Audible and visible fire alarm indicating appliances shall be used only for fire alarm system or other emergency purposes.

Exception No. 1: Voice communication systems may be used for other purposes, subject to the approval of the authority having jurisdiction, if the fire alarm system takes precedence over all other signals.

Permitting a voice communication system to be used for some other purpose requires that approval of the authority having jurisdiction be secured for such use. The system designer or building operator and the authority having jurisdiction should determine how susceptible the system is to deliberate tampering. For example, in a business occupancy where a combination emergency voice communication and day-to-day background music system is installed with a speaker located in the ceiling directly over an employee's desk, it should be predicted that the supposedly innocuous, but constant, background music may irritate the employee to the point that the speaker will be muffled or otherwise disabled. Therefore, the feature requiring that the fire alarm system take precedence over all other signals becomes futile, because a disabled speaker cannot deliver the required emergency message.

Exception No. 2: Where otherwise permitted by another section of this Code.

An example of this exception's use by another section of the *Code* appears in 10-3.4.3.2 for educational occupancies, where the fire alarm system is permitted to be used to designate class change provided that the fire alarm signal is distinctively different from the class change signal and overrides all other use.

7-6.3.10 Alarm notification signals shall take precedence over all other signals.

7-6.4* **Emergency Forces Notification.** Where required by another section of this *Code*, emergency forces notification shall be provided to alert the local fire brigade or municipal fire department of fire or other emergency.

Where fire department notification is required by another section of this *Code*, the fire alarm system shall be arranged to transmit the alarm automatically via any of the following means:

(a) An auxiliary alarm system in accordance with NFPA 72, *Standard for the Installation, Maintenance, and Use of Protective Signaling Systems,* or

(b) A central station connection in accordance with NFPA 71, *Standard for the Installation, Maintenance, and Use of Signaling Systems for Central Station Service,* or

(c) A proprietary system in accordance with NFPA 72, *Standard for the Installation, Maintenance, and Use of Protective Signaling Systems,* or

(d) A remote station connection in accordance with NFPA 72, *Standard for the Installation, Maintenance, and Use of Protective Signaling Systems.*

Exception: Where none of the above means of notification is available, a plan for notification of the municipal fire department, acceptable to the authority having jurisdiction, shall be provided.

The following definitions are provided to help in differentiating among the above four alarm transmission methods for fire department notification:

Auxiliary Alarm System. A connection to the municipal fire alarm system to transmit an alarm of fire to the municipal communication center. Fire alarms from an auxiliary alarm system are received at the municipal communication center on the same equipment and by the same alerting methods as alarms transmitted from municipal fire alarm boxes located on streets.

Central Station. An office to which remote alarm and supervisory signaling devices are connected, and where personnel are in attendance at all times to supervise the circuits and investigate signals.

Central Station System. A system, or group of systems, in which the operations of circuits and devices are sig-

naled automatically to, recorded in, and maintained and supervised from an approved central station having competent and experienced observers and operators who, upon receipt of a signal, take such action as required. Such systems are controlled and operated by a person, firm, or corporation whose principal business is the furnishing and maintaining of supervised signaling service.

Proprietary Protective Signaling System. An installation of protective signaling systems that serve contiguous and noncontiguous properties under one ownership from a central supervising station located at the protected property, where trained, competent personnel are in constant attendance. This includes the central supervising station; power supplies; signal-initiating devices; initiating device circuits; signal notification appliances; equipment for the automatic, permanent, visual recording of signals; and equipment for the operation of emergency building control services.

Remote Station Protective Signaling System. An installation using supervised dedicated circuits to transmit alarm, supervisory, and trouble signals from one or more protected premises to a remote location at which appropriate action is taken.

A-7-6.4 The selection of the means of fire department notification should be the most reliable depending on local conditions and should be determined in consultation with the authority having jurisdiction.

Fire alarm equipment installed for the notification of occupants of a building, in localities under the protection of a regularly organized fire department or private fire brigade, can be arranged to give automatic transmission of alarms (either directly or through an approved central station office) to the fire department or fire brigade upon operation of an alarm-sending station or system. Where no such connection is provided, a fire alarm box arranged to signal the fire department could be installed at the main entrance to the building, at the telephone switchboard, or somewhere outside the building, plainly visible during day or night, and conveniently accessible from the main entrance. While this arrangement is desirable, it is not required by 7-6.4 unless the occupancy chapter specifically requires this feature.

7-6.5 Emergency Control.

7-6.5.1 A protective signaling and control system shall, where required by another section of this *Code*, be arranged to actuate automatically control functions necessary to make the protected premises safer for building occupants.

7-6.5.2 Where required by another section of this *Code*, the following functions shall be actuated by the protective signaling and control system:

(a) Release of hold-open devices for doors or other opening protectives.

The Exception to 5-2.1.8, "Self-Closing Devices," allows for doors to be automatic-closing if, among other requirements, the detection of smoke automatically releases the device holding the door open, thus allowing the door to become self-closing. Those provisions do not require that the building alarm system release the doors. The health care chapters in 12-2.2.2.6 and 13-2.2.2.6 are more stringent on the subject and require that the automatic closing of doors also occur upon initiation of the building's required fire alarm system. This is an example of an occupancy chapter mandating the provisions of 7-6.5.2(a) as an extra requirement needed in addition to a Chapter 5 provision; i.e., the provision of Chapter 5 allowing the automatic closing of doors that normally would be required to be self-closing.

(b) Stairwell or elevator shaft pressurization.

(c) Smoke management or smoke control systems.

Manual fire alarm pull stations generally should not be used to activate smoke control systems other than stair tower pressurization systems due to the likelihood of a person signaling an alarm from a station outside the smoke zone of fire origin. For additional guidance on the subject, see NFPA 92A, *Recommended Practice for Smoke Control Systems,*[5] and NFPA 92B, *Guide for Smoke Management Systems in Malls, Atria, and Large Areas.*[6]

(d) Emergency lighting control.

New special amusement buildings are addressed in 8-4.6. Those that operate in reduced lighting levels, such as a haunted house amusement, must, upon actuation of the required automatic smoke detection system or the required automatic sprinkler system, increase illumination in the means of egress to at least the minimum level required by Section 5-8. The requirements applicable to special amusement buildings augment the concept of using the alarm system to initiate an emergency control function by mandating that conflicting or confusing sounds and visuals stop upon actuation of the required automatic smoke detection system or the required automatic sprinkler system. Thus, in the haunted house amusement addressed in the above example, all audible and visual special effects would cease upon alarm so as not to confuse the patrons. A fire alarm horn or strobe would not be recognized if forced to compete with the background special effects common to such an occupancy.

(e) Unlocking of doors.

For an example of the *Code* requiring the activation of the alarm system to unlock a door, see the provisions for delayed release door locking addressed by 5-2.1.6, "Special Locking Arrangements."

7-6.5.3 The functions specified in 7-6.5.2 shall be permitted to be actuated by any protective signaling and control system where otherwise not required by this *Code*. Additionally, the protective signaling and control system may recall elevators, as required by Section 7-4, if the activation of the system for this purpose comes only from elevator lobby or associated machine room detectors, or if otherwise permitted by the authority having jurisdiction.

ASME/ANSI A17.1, *Safety Code for Elevators and Escalators*[7] and ASME/ANSI A17.3, *Safety Code for Existing Elevators and Escalators,*[8] which are referenced mandatorily for elevators by Section 7-4, prohibit the recall of elevators by any detectors other than those installed in the elevator lobbies, hoistways, and associated elevator machine room. Recall by other detectors leads to numerous nuisance recalls under conditions where it would be safe to operate elevators. To avoid having elevators taken out of service every time any building system detector senses smoke, the recall feature is often deliberately disabled. In an attempt to keep the recall feature operational, ASME/ANSI A17.1 and A17.3 impose the above restriction. Given that there may be situations under which elevator recall by additional detection devices would be desirable, 7-6.5.3 allows the authority having jurisdiction to make such a judgment. The *Life Safety Code* reserves this right to differ from ASME/ANSI A17.1 and A17.3 via the introductory wording to 7-4.2, which reads: "Except as modified herein . . ."

7-6.5.4 The performance of emergency control functions shall not, in any way, impair the effective response of all required alarm notification functions.

7-6.5.5* An auxiliary fire alarm relay used to control an emergency control device that provides any of the functions of 7-6.5.2 or elevator capture per 7-6.5.3, e.g., motor controller for HVAC system fan, shall be located within 3 ft (91 cm) of the emergency control device. The installation wiring between the protective signaling and control system panel and the auxiliary fire alarm relay shall be monitored for integrity.

A-7-6.5.5 Control devices that operate on loss of power to the actuator may be considered self-monitoring for integrity.

The concept of monitoring installation wiring for integrity is explained in the commentary following paragraph

---

Formal Interpretation 88-13
Reference: 7-6.5.5

Question 1: Is it the Committee's intent that control devices (fire alarm relays) that operate on loss of power or by a fault on any lines(s) would mean that the relay could be located at a motor control center which would be floors away from the device to be activated, i.e., air handling units and exhaust fans located on the roof?

Answer: Yes.

Question 2: Is it the Committee's intent that control devices (fire alarm relays) requiring power to operate would require the relay to be located to within 3 ft of the device to be actuated, i.e., air handling units and exhaust fans located on the roof?

Answer: No, it must be within 3 ft of the emergency control device.

Issue Edition: 1988
Reference: 7-6.5.5
Issue Date: July 20, 1990 ∎

7-6.1.6. The requirements of 7-6.5.5 explain that the monitoring needs to be done to within 3 ft (91 cm) of the control associated with the fan motor or similar unit being controlled. The 3-ft (91-cm) dimension reasonably recognizes that different contractors are responsible for the building mechanical systems and the building protective signaling and control system. To require monitoring right to the actual motor or similar unit could create jurisdictional problems among the building trades, with the alarm contractor being asked to enter and modify the equipment installed by another party. Formal Interpretation 88-13 further explains this concept.

7-6.6 Location of Controls.

7-6.6.1 Operator controls, alarm indicators, and manual communications capability shall be installed in a control center at a convenient location acceptable to the authority having jurisdiction.

At times it is not practical physically or from a security standpoint to locate control centers adjacent to an entrance. For example, control centers for proprietary protective signaling systems designed in accordance with NFPA 72, *Standard for the Installation, Maintenance, and Use of Protective Signaling Systems,*[13] for reasons of security, often need to be located away from public areas. Thus, the *Code* no longer requires that control centers be located adjacent to an entrance but, because the controls are intended to be used by the fire department, they need to be located in a position approved by the authority having jurisdiction.

7-6.7 Annunciation.

7-6.7.1 Where alarm annunciation is required by another section of this *Code*, it shall comply with the following provisions.

Subsection 7-6.7 establishes provisions applicable to alarm annunciation to be referenced by another section of the *Code* as part of the overall life safety package needed for a specific occupancy or situation. Alarm annunciation allows trained individuals such as building engineers, security and safety officers, and responding fire service personnel to read the indicator lamps or alphanumeric displays of an annunciator unit to identify circuits, associated building locations, and conditions that warrant attention or investigation.

7-6.7.2 Alarm annunciation at the control center shall be by means of audible and visible indicators.

Alarm annunciation at the control center is required to be by audible indication as well as visible indication in order to capture the attention of the trained attendant who may have numerous job functions within or near the control center that might distract attention from the annunciator unit.

7-6.7.3 For the purposes of alarm annunciation, each floor of the building shall be considered, as a minimum, one zone.

Exception No. 1: Where otherwise permitted by another section of this Code.

Exception No. 2: Existing buildings.

7-6.7.4 If a floor area exceeds 20,000 sq ft (1,860 sq m), additional zoning shall be provided. The length of any zone shall not exceed 300 ft (91 m) in any direction.

Exception No. 1: Where the building is provided with automatic sprinklers throughout, installed in accordance with Section 7-7, the area of the alarm zone shall be permitted to coincide with the allowable area of the sprinkler zone.

Exception No. 2: Where otherwise permitted by another section of this Code.

Paragraphs 7-6.7.3 and 7-6.7.4 address the choice of zone locations and zone sizes for meaningful annunciation. In a new multiple story building required to have alarm annunciation by another section of the *Code*, 7-6.7.3 would not allow two or more floors to be considered as a single zone, because an alarm condition would be annunciated as originating in a zone that includes multiple floors and thus would not identify the specific area with the emergency. Such a situation would delay the investigation and associated emergency response effort. Exception No. 2 to 7-6.7.3 exempts existing alarm annunciation systems so as not to unfairly render *Code*-complying existing installations abruptly noncompliant, thus avoiding the need for major alterations or a complete replacement of the alarm system.

Paragraph 7-6.7.4 further specifies that no one zone for alarm annunciation purposes, even if located entirely on one floor of the building, should become so large as to delay identification of the exact location from which the alarm was initiated. The maximum zone area and zone dimensional criteria are waived by Exception No. 1 to 7-6.7.4 for fully sprinklered buildings to allow the alarm zoning to coincide with the area of the sprinkler system zone. This helps to achieve consistency in reporting alarms from signaling system devices and from sprinkler system water flow to the annunciator unit. Although a sprinkler system may be designed and installed by parties different from those who design and install signaling systems, coordination of these two systems is needed during the design phase in order to have systems that complement each other.

7-6.7.5 A system trouble signal shall be annunciated at the control center by means of an audible and visible indicator.

7-6.7.6 A system supervisory signal shall be annunciated at the control center by means of audible and visible indicators.

Paragraphs 7-6.7.5 and 7-6.7.6 require that trouble signals and supervisory signals from the alarm system be annunciated at the control center by both audible indication and visible indication to help ensure that personnel in attendance will pay attention to the indication and act appropriately. Trouble signals indicate such conditions as a circuit break or ground occurring in the protective signaling system wiring. Supervisory signals indicate a problem with the supervision of sprinkler systems, such as a shut valve. Supervisory signals can also be associated with the supervision of other extinguishing systems and equipment or the maintenance features of other fire protection systems.

7-6.7.7 Where the system serves more than one building, each building shall be considered separately.

SECTION 7-7 Automatic Sprinklers and Other Extinguishing Equipment

Supplement 3 of this *Handbook* contains additional information on sprinklers and automatic sprinkler systems.

7-7.1   Automatic Sprinklers.

7-7.1.1*   Each automatic sprinkler system required by another section of this *Code* shall be installed in accordance with NFPA 13, *Standard for the Installation of Sprinkler Systems*. Where partial sprinkler protection is permitted by another section of this *Code*, 4-1.2 of NFPA 13 shall apply.

Exception No. 1: NFPA 13R, Standard for the Installation of Sprinkler Systems in Residential Occupancies up to Four Stories in Height, shall be permitted for use as specifically referenced in Chapters 16 through 23 of this Code.

Exception No. 2: NFPA 13D, Standard for the Installation of Sprinkler Systems in One- and Two-Family Dwellings and Mobile Homes, shall be permitted for use as provided in Chapters 20 through 23 of this Code.

A-7-7.1.1   For a discussion of the effectiveness of automatic sprinklers as well as a general discussion on automatic sprinklers, see Section 18, Chapter 1, of the Seventeenth Edition of the NFPA *Fire Protection Handbook*. (*See Appendix B.*)

The requirements in the *Code* for automatic sprinklers have been carefully based on the sprinkler experience record, which shows that a sprinkler system is the most effective device, where installed properly, for protecting and safeguarding against loss of life and property. Occupants of a building who are aware of the presence of sprinkler protection can feel secure that any fire will be detected and fought at its origin and that an alarm will be given; therefore, it is probable that they will have time to evacuate a burning building before fire can cut off their escape.

Claims have been made by the uninformed that water in a sprinkler system can be heated to scalding temperatures and literally sprayed out onto occupants, thus causing injury and panic. Another fallacy is the belief that the mere spraying of large quantities of water will itself cause panic. As stated before, NFPA records of over a hundred thousand cases of sprinklers operating in building fires show no instances of this happening. In a fire, the small quantity of water in the system piping directly above the fire that might be heated before the sprinkler operates will quickly be dissipated, and cool water will begin to flow. Other misconceptions about sprinkler systems — for example, that occupants of a room might be drowned,

electrocuted, or scalded by steam — are unfounded and should be discounted.

NFPA 13, *Standard for the Installation of Sprinkler Systems*,[9] covers installation details for standard automatic sprinkler systems. In the interest of both life safety from fire and the protection of property, it will generally be beneficial to provide a complete standard automatic sprinkler installation to protect the entire property, even in situations where the *Code* requires sprinklers only for isolation and protection of hazardous areas.

NFPA 13 is the so-called "bible" for sprinkler systems with respect to design, installation, and character and adequacy of water supply. Even though there are usually some areas in a building where fires are more likely to start than in others, it is impossible to predict where a fire might start and hence protect those areas only. Thus, it is recommended that, where sprinklers are installed, they be installed throughout a building. The basic requirements of NFPA 13 for spacing, location, and position of sprinklers are based on principles that include sprinkler installation throughout the building, including combustible concealed spaces. The *Life Safety Code*, however, in an effort to promote the use of sprinkler systems by reducing the costs, allows sprinklers to be omitted from small closets and bathrooms in hotels and dormitories, apartment dwelling units, and lodging and rooming houses, and still considers those occupancies fully sprinklered.

NFPA 13 provides for the installation of systems of various types appropriate for the individual building protected, subject to the approval of the authority having jurisdiction.

NFPA 13R, *Standard for the Installation of Sprinkler Systems in Residential Occupancies up to and Including Four Stories in Height*,[14] is a new standard that was first published in 1989. It addresses residential sprinklers, which incorporate the quick response sprinkler technology described below in the commentary on NFPA 13D, *Standard for the Installation of Sprinkler Systems in One- and Two-Family Dwellings and Mobile Homes*.[15] NFPA 13R thus extends the technological and economic benefits of an NFPA 13D-type system to larger residential buildings while requiring extra provisions commensurate with increased building size that will help to ensure improved protection against injury and life loss to building residents, including those within the room of fire origin, and decreased property damage.

NFPA 13D was developed after extensive research, including full-scale fire tests. It introduced the concept of a quick response residential sprinkler that, unlike its industrial standard spray sprinkler counterpart which is inherently slow to fuse its relatively massive eutectic solder element, operates very quickly once its rated temperature is felt to begin controlling a fire early in its growth. In addition to being quick to respond, residential sprinklers, as mandated by NFPA 13D, have a specifically designed spray pattern that delivers water to nearly the full height of the walls of typical small rooms characteristic of residential occupancies.

NFPA 13A, *Recommended Practice for the Inspection, Testing, and Maintenance of Sprinkler Systems,*[16] provides information on recommended maintenance procedures. A proposed new NFPA document, tentatively titled the *Standard for the Inspection, Testing, and Maintenance of Water-Based Extinguishing Systems*, is under development with publication expected in 1992. The new standard will replace NFPA 13A and greatly expand coverage on the combined subjects of inspection, testing, and maintenance of sprinkler systems. Although this edition of the *Code* cannot reference a nonexisting document, the provisions of Section 1-6, "Equivalency Concepts," allow the authority having jurisdiction great latitude in accepting newer technologies as they become available. It is these Section 1-6 provisions that allowed many authorities having jurisdiction to recognize NFPA 13R residential sprinkler systems while enforcing the 1988 Edition of the *Life Safety Code* when the new NFPA 13R was released in 1989.

7-7.1.2 Sprinkler piping serving not more than six sprinklers for any isolated hazardous area shall be permitted to be connected directly to a domestic water supply system having a capacity sufficient to provide 0.15 gpm/sq ft (6.1 L/min/sq m) of floor area throughout the entire enclosed area. An indicating shut-off valve shall be installed in an accessible location between the sprinklers and the connection to the domestic water supply.

The general provisions of Section 6-4, "Special Hazard Protection," in combination with the specific requirements of each occupancy chapter -3.2 subsection, "Pro-

tection from Hazards," make extensive use of sprinklering hazardous area rooms in otherwise unsprinklered buildings. Paragraph 7-7.1.2 allows for such sprinklers to be supplied by the domestic water supply and its associated distribution piping. The domestic water supply must provide sufficient quantities of water at the appropriate pressures to deliver 0.15 gal/min/sq ft (6.1 L/min/sq m) of floor area within the hazardous area room. For a 100-sq ft (9.3-sq m) room, the water supply would have to provide at least 15 gal/min (57 L/min) at the pressure appropriate to such a discharge from a specific size and model of sprinkler. Additionally, the provisions of 7-7.1.2 can be used in lieu of a devoted sprinkler system piping network and water supply only if any given room requires six or fewer sprinklers for adequate protection based on the spacing and location rules of the proper installation standards referenced in 7-7.1.1. Another hazardous area room on the same floor or in some other part of the building can obtain its protection by repeating a similar maximum six sprinkler installation in accordance with 7-7.1.2.

7-7.1.3* In areas protected by automatic sprinklers, automatic heat detection devices required by other sections of this *Code* may be deleted.

A-7-7.1.3 Properly designed automatic sprinkler systems provide the dual function of both automatic alarms and automatic extinguishment.

The preceding is not true in those cases where early detection of incipient fire and early notification of occupants are needed to initiate actions in behalf of life safety earlier than can be expected from heat-sensitive fire detectors.

Properly designed automatic sprinkler systems provide the dual function of both automatic alarms and automatic extinguishment. Because the operation of an automatic sprinkler system is initiated by a heat sensing device and works on the same principle as an automatic heat detection and alarm system, the sprinkler system is judged to be capable of serving the same purpose. Even though some sprinkler systems may not sound an alarm on activation, most properly designed systems do. Furthermore, while a particular sprinkler system may not sound an alarm, it does begin immediate extinguishment, a feature that is equally, if not more, valuable than a system that sounds an alarm only

Detection of smoke, on the other hand, can be accomplished at the incipient stages of a fire and give rise to an earlier warning than that provided by heat detection, so it is considered in a somewhat different light. There are two schools of thought on the matter: some feel that a system that starts suppression of a fire immediately upon detection is better than one that simply detects the fire and sounds an alarm, even though the latter is quicker in initiation of signal indication. Others believe, however, that an early alarm system is more advantageous. The first group is concerned with immediate arrest or containment of fire — it may take a considerable amount of time for fire fighters to arrive; the second group stresses immediate notification of occupants.

7-7.1.4 Automatic sprinkler systems installed in order to make use of an alternative allowed by this *Code* shall be considered "required" systems and shall meet the provisions of this *Code* applicable to required systems.

The provisions of 7-7.1.4 were added to this edition of the *Code* to remind the user that an automatic sprinkler system voluntarily installed as a Code alternative then becomes a required system subject to the same requirements, including maintenance, applicable to a sprinkler system specifically mandated by the *Code*. For example, if an occupancy that does not require a sprinkler system does allow the use of the delayed release door lock addressed by 5-2.1.5, "Special Locking Arrangements," and the designer/building operator meets one of the unlocking provisions of 5-2.1.6 via the installation of an approved supervised automatic sprinkler system, the sprinkler system becomes a required system. Therefore, it must meet all the requirements applicable to a similar system installed to comply with the *Code* in addition to those of one installed to make use of an alternative provision, such as delayed release door locking.

7-7.2 **Supervision.**

Supervision is not required by this subsection. Where a supervised automatic sprinkler system is specified by this *Code* or where required by the authority having jurisdiction for approval, the requirements of 7-7.2 apply.

7-7.2.1* Where supervised automatic sprinkler systems are required by another section of this *Code*, a distinct supervisory signal shall be provided to indicate a condition that would impair the satisfactory operation of the sprinkler system. This shall include, but not be limited to, monitoring of control valves, fire pump power supplies and running conditions, water tank levels and temperatures, pressure of tanks, and air pressure on dry-pipe valves. Supervisory signals shall sound and be displayed either at a location within the protected building that is constantly attended by qualified personnel or at an approved remotely located receiving facility

A-7-7.2.1 NFPA 71, *Standard for the Installation, Maintenance, and Use of Signaling Systems for Central Station Service* (see Appendix B), gives details of standard practice in sprinkler supervision.

Subject to the approval of the authority having jurisdiction, sprinkler supervision may also be provided by direct connection to municipal fire departments or, in the case of very large establishments, to a private headquarters providing similar functions.

NFPA 72, *Standard for the Installation, Maintenance, and Use of Protective Signaling Systems* (see Appendix B), covers such matters. Where municipal fire alarm systems are involved, reference should also be made to NFPA 1221, *Standard for the Installation, Maintenance, and Use of Public Fire Communication Systems.* (See Appendix B.)

One reason why the automatic sprinkler system has attained a high level of satisfactory performance and response to fire conditions is that, through supervision, it can be kept in operative condition. Of course, keeping the system operative is dependent upon routine maintenance and the owner's willingness to repair the system when there are indications of some impairment. Features of the system can be automatically monitored, such as the opening and closing of water control valves, the power supplies for needed pumps, and water tank levels. If an undesirable situation develops, a signal is annunciated in the protected building or relayed to a central station.

A supervisory system will also indicate or activate a water flow alarm that, in addition to being transmitted to proprietary or control stations, can be transmitted directly to the fire department. The signals for mechanical problems need not burden the fire department unnecessarily, whereas those indicating a fire can be received directly.

For additional information on supervisory signal transmission, see the commentary following 7-6.7.6.

7-7.2.2 Alarm Signal Transmission. Where supervision of automatic sprinkler systems is provided in accordance with another provision of this *Code*, waterflow alarms shall be transmitted to an approved proprietary alarm receiving facility, a remote station, a central station, or the fire department. Such connection shall be installed in accordance with 7-6.1.4.

7-7.3* Other Automatic Extinguishing Equipment. In any occupancy where the character of the potential fuel for fire is such that extinguishment or control of fire may be more effectively accomplished by a type of automatic extinguishing system other than an automatic sprinkler system such as carbon dioxide, dry chemical, foam, Halon 1301, or water spray, a standard extinguishing system of other type may be installed in lieu of an automatic sprinkler system. Such systems shall be installed in accordance with appropriate NFPA standards.

A-7-7.3 Automatic extinguishing systems other than automatic sprinklers are covered by the following NFPA standards:

NFPA 11, *Standard for Low Expansion Foam and Combined Agent Systems.* (*See Appendix B.*)

NFPA 12, *Standard on Carbon Dioxide Extinguishing Systems.* (*See Appendix B.*)

NFPA 12A, *Standard on Halon 1301 Fire Extinguishing Systems.* (*See Appendix B.*)

NFPA 12B, *Standard on Halon 1211 Fire Extinguishing Systems.* (*See Appendix B.*)

NFPA 15, *Standard for Water Spray Fixed Systems for Fire Protection.* (*See Appendix B.*)

NFPA 17, *Standard for Dry Chemical Extinguishing Systems.* (*See Appendix B.*)

Use of special types of extinguishing systems is a matter of engineering judgment on the part of the designer, working in collaboration with the owner and the authorities concerned. Various NFPA standards are available to provide guidance in installation and maintenance procedures.

7-7.4 Manual Extinguishing Equipment.

7-7.4.1* Where required by the provisions of another section of this *Code*, portable fire extinguishers shall be installed in accordance with NFPA 10, *Standard for Portable Fire Extinguishers.*

A-7-7.4.1 For description of standard types of extinguishers and their installation, maintenance, and use, see NFPA 10, *Standard for Portable Fire Extinguishers* (*see Appendix B*). The labels of recognized testing laboratories on extinguishers provide evidence of tests indicating reliability and suitability of the extinguisher for its intended use. Many unlabeled extinguishers are offered for sale that are substandard by reason of insufficient extinguishing capacity, questionable reliability, ineffective extinguishing agents for fires in ordinary combustible materials, or because they pose a personal hazard to the user.

7-7.4.2 Where required by the provisions of another section of this *Code*, standpipe and hose systems shall be provided in accordance with NFPA 14, *Standard for the Installation of Standpipe and Hose Systems.*

Exception*: For buildings less than 150 ft (45 m) in height with supervised sprinkler systems installed throughout, combined system water demand need not exceed the larger of the following:

(a) Five hundred gpm (1,900 L/min) for light hazard or 1,000 gpm (3,800 L/min) for ordinary hazard sprinkler system classification, or

(b) The sprinkler system demand including hose stream requirements.

A-7-7.4.2 Exception It is not intended that the 500 gpm (1890 L/min) or 1000 gpm (3785 L/min) be available at 65 psig (450 kPa) automatically because fire department pumper capabilities are intended to provide the pressure requirement. It is intended that the volume capability be provided. The minimum automatic pressure requirement is the pressure required at the sprinkler system water demand.

The *Code* has requirements for standpipes or extinguishers only in some of the individual occupancy chapters. For example, standpipes are required on stages of assembly occupancies and in detention and correctional occupancies. Standpipe provisions also appear as part of the Section 30-8 menu of provisions applicable to high rise buildings. The occupancy chapters that address new assembly occupancies, new educational occupancies, new health care occupancies, new detention and correctional occupancies, new hotels and dormitories, and new apartment buildings mandatorily reference all of Section 30-8 and thus have standpipe requirements for high rise buildings.

Although 7-7.4.2 references the requirements of NFPA 14, *Standard for the Installation of Standpipe and Hose Systems,*[17] the Exception to 7-7.4.2 decreases the combined water demand for buildings up through 150 ft (45 m) in height with standpipe and sprinkler systems from that which would be required by NFPA 14. The reduction is based on the belief that fire department pumper capabilities will be used to supplement the standpipe capacity given that the minimum standpipe sizes per NFPA 14 will be required. For buildings more than 150 ft (45 m) in height, the more stringent water demands for combined systems per NFPA 14 are required.

Portable extinguishers are required throughout health care, detention and correctional, mercantile, and business occupancies but only in the hazardous areas of hotel, apartment, and large board and care occupancies. Where the *Code* requires portable extinguishers, the number, types, and locations required are beyond the scope of the *Code*; guidance can be found in NFPA 10, *Standard for Portable Fire Extinguishers.*[18]

References Cited in Commentary

[1]NFPA 70, *National Electrical Code,* National Fire Protection Association, Quincy, MA, 1990.

[2]NFPA 90A, *Standard for the Installation of Air Conditioning and Ventilating Systems,* National Fire Protection Association, Quincy, MA, 1989.

[3]NFPA 90B, *Standard for the Installation of Warm Air Heating and Air Conditioning Systems,* National Fire Protection Association, Quincy, MA, 1989.

[4]NFPA 96, *Standard for the Installation of Equipment for the Removal of Smoke and Grease-Laden Vapors from Commercial Cooking Equipment,* National Fire Protection Association, Quincy, MA, 1991.

[5]NFPA 92A, *Recommended Practice for Smoke Control Systems,* National Fire Protection Association, Quincy, MA, 1988.

[6]NFPA 92B, *Guide for Smoke Management Systems in Malls, Atria, and Large Areas,* National Fire Protection Association, Quincy, MA, 1991.

[7]ASME/ANSI A17.1, *Safety Code for Elevators and Escalators,* American Society of Mechanical Engineers, 345 East 47th Street, New York, NY 10017, 1987.

[8]ASME/ANSI A17.3, *Safety Code for Existing Elevators and Escalators,* American Society of Mechanical Engineers, 345 East 47th Street, New York, NY 10017, 1986.

[9]NFPA 13, *Standard for the Installation of Sprinkler Systems,* National Fire Protection Association, Quincy, MA, 1991.

[10]*ASME Handbook A17.1,* American Society of Mechanical Engineers, 345 East 47th Street, New York, NY 10017, 1990.

[11]NFPA 82, *Standard on Incinerators, Waste, and Linen Handling Systems and Equipment,* National Fire Protection Association, Quincy, MA, 1990.

[12]NFPA 72E, *Standard on Automatic Fire Detectors,* National Fire Protection Association, Quincy, MA, 1990.

[13]NFPA 72, *Standard for the Installation, Maintenance, and Use of Protective Signaling Systems,* National Fire Protection Association, Quincy, MA, 1990.

[14]NFPA 13R, *Standard for the Installation of Sprinkler Systems in Residential Occupancies up to and Including Four Stories in Height,* National Fire Protection Association, Quincy, MA, 1991.

[15]NFPA 13D, *Standard for the Installation of Sprinkler Systems in One- and Two-Family Dwellings and Mobile Homes,* National Fire Protection Association, Quincy, MA, 1991.

[16]NFPA 13A, *Recommended Practice for the Inspection, Testing and Maintenance of Sprinkler Systems,* National Fire Protection Association, Quincy, MA, 1987.

[17]NFPA 14, *Standard for the Installation of Standpipe and Hose Systems,* National Fire Protection Association, Quincy, MA, 1990.

[18]NFPA 10, *Standard for Portable Fire Extinguishers,* National Fire Protection Association, Quincy, MA, 1990.

8

New Assembly Occupancies

(See also Chapter 31.)

Assembly occupancies include, but are not limited to, all buildings or portions of buildings used for gatherings of 50 or more people for such purposes as deliberation, worship, entertainment, eating, drinking, amusement, or awaiting transportation. Assembly occupancies include, but are not limited to:

Armories	Gymnasiums
Assembly halls	Libraries
Auditoriums	Mortuary chapels
Bowling establishments	Motion picture theaters
Churches	Museums
Club rooms	Nightclubs
Conference rooms	Pool rooms
Courtrooms	Recreation piers
Dance halls	Restaurants
Discotheques	Skating rinks
Drinking establishments	Theaters
Exposition halls	

Passenger stations and terminals of air, surface, underground, and marine public transportation facilities. (If the jurisdiction enforcing the *Code* has adopted NFPA 130, *Standard for Fixed Guideway Transit Systems,*[1] there are some situations where transit stations would come under NFPA 130 rather than this *Code*. See NFPA 130 for additional details.)

Also note that 10-1.1.3 requires university and college classrooms having a capacity of 50 or more persons to comply with the requirements of the assembly occupancy chapters.

Assembly occupancies with an occupant load of less than 50 are considered incidental to the predominate occupancy in which they are located. For example, a small conference room in an office area is considered part of the overall business occupancy. If it is a freestanding occupancy or building, such as a small diner, a mercantile occupancy classification is normally assigned. In either case, the occupant load factors of 8-1.6 are used, since it is still an assembly use.

Assembly properties averaged 25,200 structure fires a year as reported to U.S. fire departments from 1984 to 1988. These fires caused an average of 25 civilian deaths and 376 civilian injuries per year. The majority of these fire deaths and injuries occurred in eating and drinking establishments (16,300 fires, 17 deaths, and 271 injuries a year), followed by churches and funeral parlors (2,700 fires, 2 deaths, and 28 injuries a year).

Large, multiple-death fires have been less common in assembly properties in recent years, with only three from 1985 to 1989. Two of these three involved New York social clubs, as did the 1990 Happy Land Social Club fire, which killed 87 people in the deadliest U.S. fire since the 1977 Beverly Hills Supper Club fire, which was also an assembly property. The potential for a major incident always exists by virtue of the nature of the occupancy, but there is also a steady incidence of fires that kill one or two people. In addition, from 1980 to 1988 two-thirds of those killed in assembly fires were not occupying the room in which the fire began. Fire protection would have provided several opportunities to prevent harm to occupants.[2,3,4,5]

The 1990 Happy Land Social Club fire in New York City, which killed 87 people, was a reminder of the enormous potential for loss of life in assembly properties. Following is a list of the deadliest U.S. assembly property fires of the 1980s:

Date	Place	Civilians Killed
December 4, 1980	Stouffer's Inn hotel conference center facility[6] Harrison, NY	26
May 11, 1984	Six Flags Amusement Park [7] Jackson Township, NJ	8
May 6, 1983	Hwa Yuan Restaurant (and apartments above) New York, NY	7
August 21, 1988	El Hoyo Social Club New York, NY	6
December 6, 1985	River Resturant Derby, CT	6
February 20, 1985	El Exclusivo Social Club New York, NY	5
January 15, 1984	Eagles Club (and apartments above) Webster, MA	5
June 28, 1981	Odyssey Lounge discotheque Houma, LA	5
February 22, 1980	Holy Trinity House of Prayer Chicago, IL	4

Chapter 31 specifies the life safety requirements for the operation of assembly occupancies.

SECTION 8-1   General Requirements

8-1.1 **Application.** The requirements of this chapter apply to new assembly occupancies. (*See 8-1.3 for definition.*)

The provisions for existing assembly occupancies are found in Chapter 9.

It should be noted that, if an existing building of some other occupancy were to have its classification changed to that of an assembly occupancy, that portion of the building housing the assembly occupancy must comply with this chapter for new assembly occupancies, even though it is part of an existing building (*see 1-7.4*). Also, should an existing assembly occupancy change occupancy subclassification, such as from Class C to Class B, it must meet the requirements for a new Class B assembly occupancy. (*See 1-7.4 and 9-1.1.*)

8-1.2 **Mixed Occupancies.** (*See also 1-5.7.*)

8-1.2.1* Any assembly occupancy and its access to exits in buildings of other occupancy, such as ballrooms in hotels, restaurants in stores, rooftop assembly occupancies, or assembly rooms in schools, shall be so located, separated, or protected as to avoid any undue danger to the occupants of the assembly occupancy from a fire originating in the other occupancy or smoke therefrom.

A-8-1.2.1 Depending upon the character of construction and the hazard of the occupancy, this will require some physical separation by walls of appropriate fire resistance, protection of the other occupancy by automatic sprinklers, or other appropriate measures. Where the building is of fire-resistive construction and the hazard of the other occupancy is low or ordinary, as in a school or hotel, no separation may be necessary.

The intent of this provision is to protect the occupants of the assembly occupancy from the effects of a fire originating in the other occupancy. While this can be achieved by several methods, there are two considerations to be taken into account, whichever method is chosen. First, consideration must be given to the protection of the means of egress of the assembly occupancy; second, the level of protection from the other occupancy that can be provided to the assembly occupancy itself must be considered. Methods that can be used to protect the assembly occupancy and its means of egress include construction of fire-rated partitions, use of independent exits, installation of automatic sprinklers, and careful analysis of the requirements of each occupancy when applying the provisions of 1-5.7 pertaining to mixed occupancies. (Also see the discussion on 8-3.5.)

8-1.2.2 Occupancy of any room or space for assembly purposes by fewer than 50 persons in a building of other occupancy and incidental to such other occupancy shall be classed as part of the other occupancy and subject to the provisions applicable thereto.

Fifty has traditionally been considered the minimum number of people assembled in one space for which the Code requires special provisions, such as requiring a door to swing in the direction of exit travel (See 5-2.1.4.1.). Therefore, in Chapter 8, 50 people constitute a level of risk to life safety high enough to require classifying an occupancy as an assembly occupancy and, consequently, to subject the occupancy to the special design requirements found within this chapter. Since the space still contains an assembly use, the occupant load factors of 8-1.6 are still used, even if the space is being regulated under another occupancy.

8-1.2.3 Assembly occupancies in buildings of other occupancy shall be permitted to use exits common to the assembly occupancy and the other occupancy provided that the assembly area and the other occupancy considered separately each have exits sufficient to meet the requirements of this *Code*.

Where the requirements of this section apply, consideration must also be given to the provisions of 1-5.7 pertaining to mixed occupancies. Those provisions require that, in mixed occupancies, the more restrictive requirements of either occupancy be used for both occupancies.

8-1.2.4 Exits shall be sufficient for simultaneous occupancy of both the assembly occupancy and other parts of the building.

Exception: Where the authority having jurisdiction determines that the conditions are such that simultaneous occupancy will not occur.

A-8-1.2.4 Exception. Example: An assembly room for the inmates of a detention occupancy will not normally be subjected to simultaneous occupancy.

In 8-1.2.3 through 8-1.2.4, the Code requires that each occupancy, considered separately, have sufficient exits and that, where it is possible for simultaneous occupancy to occur, the exits be sufficient for the combined occupant load.

The Exception to 8-1.2.4 should be used judiciously. Consideration should be given to all possible uses before a decision is reached. A school gymnasium may normally be used only by the school occupants; however, several times a year, the gymnasium may be used by an outside group during school hours. A common example of this is the use of school gymnasiums as polling places on election day. Consideration should be given to all possible uses to provide the owner/occupant maximum flexibility in the use of the space.

8-1.2.5 Combined Assembly and Residential Occupancies.

The concept that had previously been applied to mixed mercantile/residential is now also applied to mixed assembly/residential.

8-1.2.5.1 No dwelling unit of a residential occupancy shall have its sole means of egress pass through any assembly occupancy in the same building.

8-1.2.5.2 No multiple-dwelling unit of a residential occupancy shall be located above an assembly occupancy.

Exception No. 1: Where the dwelling unit of the residential occupancy and exits therefrom are separated from the assembly occupancy by construction having a fire resistance rating of at least 1 hr.

Exception No. 2: Where the assembly occupancy is protected throughout by an approved supervised automatic sprinkler system in accordance with Section 7-7.

The result of 8-1.2.5.2 and its exceptions is that, if an assembly occupancy has a multiple-dwelling occupancy located above it, either the assembly occupancy must be totally separated from the residential occupancy by 1-hour fire resistance rated construction or the assembly occupancy must be fully sprinklered.

8-1.3 Special Definitions.

Aisle Accessway.* That initial portion of an exit access that leads to an aisle.

A-8-1.3 Special Definitions.

Aisle Accessway. Aisle accessway is the name given to the previously unnamed means of egress component leading to an aisle or other means of egress. For example, circulation space between parallel rows of seats having a width of 1 to 2 ft (30.5 to 61 cm) and a maximum length of 100 ft (30 m), is an aisle accessway. Some of the circulation space between tables or seats in restaurants might be considered aisle accessway.

Depending on the width of aisle accessway, which is influenced by its length and expected utilization, the movement of a person through the aisle accessway might require other people to change their individual speed of movement, alter their posture, move their chairs out of the way, or proceed ahead of the person.

This definition has been added to clarify that part of the means of egress located between where you are sitting and an aisle. (*See 8-2.5.6 and 8-2.5.7.*)

Assembly Occupancies. Occupancies that include, but are not limited to, all buildings or portions of buildings used for gatherings of 50 or more persons for such purposes as deliberation, worship, entertainment, dining, amusement, or awaiting transportation.

Cyclorama. The name generally used for a neutral background that, with suitable lighting, can suggest the infinite space of the sky. It may be curved and may be painted to depict any required background.

The term "cyclorama" is used in the definition of "stage scenery." These definitions are included to better clarify the terms used by the movie and theater industry.

Drop. A large piece of scenic canvas that hangs vertically, usually across the stage area.

The definition of "drop" is intended to better clarify the *Code* with regard to stage productions.

Exhibitor. An individual or entity engaged in the display of the products or services offered.

Exhibits. A space or portable structure used for the display of products or services.

Exposition. An event held in which the display of products or services is organized to bring together the provider and user of the products or services.

Exposition Facility. A convention center, hotel, or other building at which exposition events are held.

The definitions of "exhibitor," "exhibits," "exposition," and "exposition facility" have been added to improve understanding of the provisions in 8-4.4. The terms are consistent with terms used by the exposition industry.

Flow Time. The time during which there is crowd flow past a point in the means of egress system, and it is a component of total evacuation time.

The term "flow time" has been used in the technical literature on egress, and it is worth understanding in relation to the *Code's* requirements for the capacity of means of egress. Flow time is the time taken by a crowd to pass, for example, through a doorway during a mass egress situation. This egress time component, along with other egress time components for responding to an alarm (before beginning egress movement) and for traveling along the length of an egress route, contributes to the total time needed to evacuate an area after an emergency situation is detected and an alarm is sounded. In the case of large assembly buildings, the flow time is often the largest component of total evacuation time. Therefore, explicit information about flow time is included in Chapters 8 and 9 of the *Code* to help improve understanding of the nominal performance expected where particular egress capacity requirements are satisfied.

Fly. The space over the stage of a theater where scenery and equipment can be hung out of view. Also called lofts and rigging lofts.

Fly Gallery. A narrow raised platform at the side of a legitimate stage from which the lines for flying scenery are manipulated.

Gridiron. The arrangement of beams over a legitimate stage that supports machinery for flying scenery and hanging battens from which lighting is hung.

Leg Drop. A long, narrow strip of fabric used for masking. Where used on either or both sides of the acting area, to provide entry to the stage for the actors, but also to mask. They may also be called "wings."

See commentary on the term "drop."

Life Safety Evaluation.* A written review dealing with the adequacy of life safety features relative to fire, storm, collapse, crowd behavior, and other related safety considerations.

A-8-1.3 Special Definitions.

Life Safety Evaluation. A life safety evaluation is a written review dealing with the adequacy of life safety features relative to fire, storm, collapse, crowd behavior, and other related safety considerations.

Topics to be considered may include, but are not limited to, the following:

(a) Human behavior.
(b) Exit system.
(c) Construction and structure.
(d) Contents and finishes.
(e) Detection.
(f) Emergency notification procedures and systems.
(g) Smoke management.
(h) Fire suppression systems.

Local conditions may dictate other considerations. (*Also see A-8-2.3.2.*)

This definition is for use in conjunction with 8-2.3.2. See the appendix note and commentary on 8-2.3.2. It is important to note that a life safety evaluation deals with more than firesafety. The evaluation must consider all life safety hazards that could endanger occupants and require rapid egress or other measures to maintain safety. In some large assembly facilities, for example, fire may not be the most likely hazard; there may be more injuries and deaths due to incidents arising from the large number and high density of people occupying a limited space. This can occur during normal occupancy conditions, such as where occupants become especially enthusiastic during a spectator event or where there is the possibility that occupants may have a strong desire to escape an area, e.g., when there is a sudden change of weather in the case of open facilities or where there is a collapse of part of the structure. Such possibilities must be taken into account when doing a life safety evaluation and, in some cases, special expertise will be required to properly assess and design or manage for social and behavioral factors in addition to factors of fire and structural safety. Generally, the evaluation must be based on a good understanding of the occupants — especially if densely crowded conditions exist — and the reason for the assembly of people.

Multipurpose Assembly Occupancy. An assembly room designed to accommodate temporarily any of several possible assembly uses.

This definition is needed to explain 8-3.5.1 Exception No. 2. The designer, user, and code enforcer need to evaluate the exit requirements and occupant loads for all potential uses of the multipurpose area. This evaluation should take into consideration simultaneous multiple use as well as any single purpose use.

Multipurpose assembly occupancies are often part of a school, office building, fellowship hall, or other occupancy. In these instances, the exiting and means of egress requirements must be considered, as they may affect or be affected by the use of the other occupancy.

Pinrail. A beam at one side of a legitimate stage through which wooden or metal pins are driven, and to which lines from the flies are fastened.

Platform.* That raised area within a building used for the presentation of music, plays, or other entertainment; the head tables for special guests; the raised area for lecturers and speakers; boxing and wrestling rings; theater-in-the-round; and for similar purposes wherein there are no overhead drops, pieces of scenery, or stage effects other than lighting and a screening valance.

A-8-1.3 Special Definitions.

Platform. It is not intended to prohibit the use of a curtain as a valance to screen or hide the electric conduit, lighting track, or similar fixtures.

This is not intended to prohibit the use of: curtains such as are used to obscure the back wall of the stage; a curtain between the auditorium and the stage (grand or house curtain), a maximum of four leg drops; a valance to screen light panels, plumbing, and similar equipment from view.

The definition, along with the appendix note, is intended to bring the nontheatrical "stages" of many schools under the definition of platform. Also see the definition of stage, as many school "stages" are regular stages, since they use scenery. Hanging curtains commonly used on platforms are normally used to conceal lighting or to provide a more aesthetic appearance.

Platform, Permanent. A platform erected within an area for more than 30 days.

Platform, Temporary. A platform erected within an area for not more than 30 days.

Proscenium Wall. The wall that separates the stage from the auditorium or house.

Smoke-Protected Assembly Seating.* Seating served by means of egress that is not subject to blockage by smoke accumulation within or under a structure.

A-8-1.3 Special Definitions.

Smoke-Protected Assembly Seating. An assembly area wherein the roof is not less than 15 ft (4.5 m) above the highest cross aisle or seat row, and having smoke-actuated venting facilities within that part of the roof sufficient to maintain the level of smoke at least 6 ft (183 cm) above the highest

seating or walking level, is considered to be smoke-protected assembly seating.

Special Amusement Building. Any building that is temporary, permanent or mobile that contains a device or system that conveys passengers or provides a walkway along, around, or over a course in any direction as a form of amusement so arranged that the egress path is not readily apparent due to visual or audio distractions or an intentionally confounded egress path, or is not readily available due to the mode of conveyance through the building or structure. Included are such amusements as a "haunted house," a "roller coaster" type ride within a building, a "merry-go-round" within a building, a "submarine" ride, and similar amusements where the occupants are not in the open air.

This definition is needed for the subsection 8-4.6, "Special Provisions for Special Amusement Buildings." It is the intent of the Committee that this definition address the structure and the use of the structure. The structure may be a permanent building or may be a semitrailer truck or other similar enclosure that is semipermanent or mobile. Special amusement buildings are designed to provide a full enclosure for patrons. Structures that are not fully enclosed, e.g., a merry-go-round with a roof and no sides, are not included in this definition. This definition also includes special amusement buildings within a larger structure, such as an amusement building within a shopping mall. Theaters, movie houses, or similar public assembly occupancies used for amusement or entertainment are not defined as special amusement buildings.

Stage. An area within a building used for the purpose of entertainment and utilizing drops or scenery or other stage effects, which shall be classified as one of the following:

(a) *Stage, Legitimate.* A stage wherein scenery is retractable mechanically, either horizontally or vertically or suspended overhead.

(b) *Stage, Regular.* A stage wherein scenery is not retractable. A valance, light trough, the main curtain, and a single backdrop may be retractable without the stage being considered a legitimate stage.

(c) *Stage, Thrust.* A platform extending beyond the proscenium arch and into the audience.

The intent is to better differentiate between stages and platforms (*see the definition of "platform"*).

This definition of stage should be examined in conjunction with the definition of platform. The intent is to include nontheatrical "stages," such as those in many lower grade level schools, under the definition of platform.

This definition of stage encompasses various types of stages, including arena stages (stages open to the audience on at least three sides).

The critical point in the definition of a stage is the hanging of curtains, leg drops, and scenery. If none of these is present, then the arrangement is most likely a platform. A potential problem is the arrangement commonly known as theater-in-the-round. For *Code* purposes, if the theater-in-the-round has scenery, leg drops, or curtains suspended on or above it, then it is a stage; if it has only lighting with a valance to hide the electrical fixtures, it is a platform.

A typical example of a thrust stage is illustrated in Figure 8-1. The so-called "runway" at Atlantic City that is used annually for the Miss America Pageant is probably the most famous thrust stage.

Stage Properties. Furniture, carpet, and similar materials generally having an overall height of less than 5 ft (152 cm) and used to provide an appearance simulating a room or area.

The Committee felt this definition would better clarify the difference between the props used on a stage and the scenery used to dress the stage. The definitions of "stage properties" and "stage scenery" are particularly important with regard to the flame-retardant requirements in 8-3.2.1.11.

Stage Scenery. Decorative materials such as flats, cycloramas, painted or photographic backings, and similar materials to "dress" the stage.

See commentary on stage properties.

A-8-1.3 Special Definitions.

The following definitions may be useful to the enforcer of the *Code* although the terms are not used within the *Code*.

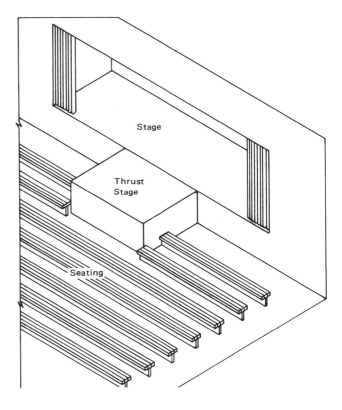

Figure 8-1. Thrust Stage.

Accessory Rooms. The accessory rooms are dressing rooms, property master's work and storage rooms, the carpenter's room, and similar rooms necessary for legitimate stage operations.

Batten. In general, a flown metal pipe or shape on which lights or scenery are fastened. While existing theater stages may still have wooden bars, they should not be used in new construction.

Scrim. Finely woven fabric that can be translucent or opaque depending upon how it is used.

Theater-in-the-Round. An acting area in the middle of a room with audience seating that surrounds it.

8-1.4 Classification of Occupancy. (*See 4-1.2.*)

8-1.4.1 Subclassification of Assembly Occupancies. Each assembly occupancy shall be subclassified according to its occupant load as follows: Class A, occupant load greater than

1000 persons; Class B, occupant load greater than 300 but not greater than 1000 persons; Class C, occupant load of 50 or more but not greater than 300 persons.

Formal Interpretation 85-10
Reference 8-1.4.1, 9-1.4.1

Question: Is it the intent of the Committee that subclassification of an assembly occupancy (i.e., Class A, Class B, or Class C) be determined on a room-by-room basis, or on overall building basis?

Answer: It is the intent of the Committee that assembly occupancy subclassification be based on a room-by-room basis as well as a floor-by-floor basis as well as a total building basis. Therefore, each room would be based on the occupant load of that room and each floor would be based on the occupant load of that floor, but the classification of the assembly building overall would be based on the total occupant load. Therefore, it is quite feasible to have several Class C assembly occupancies grouped together in a single building and that building would be a Class A assembly occupancy.

Issue Edition: 1985
Reference: 8-1.4.1, 9-1.4.1
Date: May 1985 ■

As each increment of "occupant load" is reached, the level of risk to life safety from exposure to fire increases. Therefore, the stringency of the requirements found in this chapter increases to counter each higher risk level.

8-1.5 **Classification of Hazard of Contents.** Contents of assembly occupancies shall be classified in accordance with the provisions of Section 4-2.

8-1.6 **Minimum Construction Requirements.** (*See 6-2.1.*) The location of an assembly occupancy shall be limited as follows:

It should be noted that the chart is arranged based on levels above the level of exit discharge (LED). Thus, in

Type of Construction	Below LED	Number of Levels Above LED				
		LED	1	2	3	4 and Above
I (443) I (332) II (222)	A†B†C† Any number of Levels	ABC	ABC	ABC	ABC	A†B†C
II (111)	A†B†C† One Level Below LED	ABC	ABC	A†BC	B†C†	N.P.
III (211) IV (2HH) V (111)	A†B†C† One Level Below LED	ABC	ABC	A†B†C	B†C†	N.P.
II (000)	B†C† One Level Below LED	A†BC	C†	N.P.	N.P.	N.P.
III (200) V (000)	B†C† One Level Below LED	BC	C†	N.P.	N.P.	N.P.

† Permitted if all the following are protected throughout by an approved supervised automatic sprinkler system in accordance with Section 7-7:
    (a) The level of the assembly occupancy, and
    (b) Any level below the level of the assembly occupancy, and
    (c) In the case of an assembly occupancy located below the level of exit discharge, any level intervening between that level and the level of exit discharge, including the level of exit discharge.
    N.P.: Not Permitted
    LED: Level of Exit Discharge
    NOTE: For the purpose of this table, a mezzanine is not counted as a level.

a normal building with the level of exit discharge at grade, column "1" in the table refers to the second story of the building.

Since the Cocoanut Grove Night Club fire in Boston (1942), the Subcommittee on Assembly and Educational Occupancies has placed a great deal of emphasis upon limiting the number of occupants in those assembly occupancies that provide only a minimum level of life safety because of the nature of the construction. The Cocoanut Grove fire illustrated the effect that a combustible structure (as well as combustible interior finish) and a multilevel configuration for an assembly occupancy can have on the severity of a fire and its high death count. More recently, the Beverly Hills Supper Club fire[3,4] (1977) also illustrated these consequences.

Paragraph 8-1.6 restricts the location of assembly occupancies. Type I and Type II (222) (fire-resistive) construction, with their "built-in-place" structural survivability (under fire attack), are acceptable for any assembly occupancy (hence, for any number of occupants) at the level of exit discharge and up to the fourth story. As the fire resistivity of the structure diminishes from Type II (111) (protected noncombustible) to Type V (000) (wood-frame) construction, the location of assembly occupancies (and the permitted number of occupants) is restricted. In addition, as the height of the building increases, so does the risk to the occupants; thus, the location of assembly occupancies is also restricted by height.

Formal Interpretation 81-25
Reference:
1-5.7, 8-1.6, 24-4.3.1

Given that per 8-1.6, a 3-story shopping mall with a food park (restaurant) on the third level is required to be of fire-resistive construction under the criteria for a Class A place of assembly above grade level.

Question 1: Is it possible to construct an anchor store of a different construction type from the mall building by separating it from the mall building by a 3-hour fire wall?

Question 2: Are 3-hour fire doors required for openings in this 3-hour wall between the mall and the anchor store?

Question 3: If the answer to Question 2 is no, is any type of opening protection required for openings between the mall and anchor store?

Answer: With only a few exceptions, the *Life Safety Code* sets no specific occupancy separation requirements. The authority having jurisdiction determines what separation is needed, if any, based on 1-5.7 and the 1.2 subsection of each occupancy chapter. The local building code or the model building codes may be consulted by the authority having jurisdiction in making this determination, keeping life safety rather than property protection in mind.

Issue Edition: 1981
Reference: 1-4.5, 8-1.6, 24-4.3.1
Date: October 1982 ■

Formal Interpretation 81-27
Reference: 8-1.6

Question: Taking guidance from 1-3.6 that states "the *Code* does not attempt to address those general fire prevention or building construction features that are normally a function of fire prevention and building codes," is it the intent of 8-1.6 to require fireproofing of the steel roof structure in Class A assembly areas, such as convention and exhibition centers, with ceiling heights greater than the 20-ft exemption point for fireproofing common to the model building codes?

Answer: The *Life Safety Code* establishes certain minimum construction types in some occupancies, such as assembly, but relies on NFPA 220, *Standard on Types of Building Construction,*[8] to define the construction types. NFPA 220 does not provide an exception for roof protection similar to the exceptions found in some of the model building codes. It should be noted that Section 1-6 allows the authority having jurisdiction to determine equivalencies. If the authority having jurisdiction determines that, due to roof height, building use, sprinkler protection, or other features, roof protection is not needed, it is the authority's prerogative to do so.

Issue Edition: 1981
Reference: 8-1.6
Date: March 1983 ■

The chart presents a major provision of the *Code* for assembly occupancies and recognizes the value of automatic sprinklers as a life safety device. Note that the table deals with the location of the assembly occupancy in relation to the level of exit discharge. Thus, for example, if the building in question were a seven-story, Type I (fire-resistive) building with the level of exit discharge at the first floor, a Class A assembly occupancy could be located at the fourth floor without sprinkler protection. However, 8-3.5.1 may still require sprinkler protection. If the Class A assembly occupancy were located at the fifth floor, automatic sprinkler protection would be required for the fifth floor and all floors below the fifth floor, including any basement levels (*see notes to chart*).

Any assembly occupancies located below the level of exit discharge require automatic sprinkler protection, as do all levels below the assembly occupancy and all levels intervening between the assembly level and the level of exit discharge (i.e., parts (a), (b), and (c) of the footnote apply).

The construction types shown in the chart following 8-1.6 are based on NFPA 220, *Standard on Types of Building Construction.*[8] (*See 6-2.1 and related appendix note.*)

8-1.7 Occupant Load.

8-1.7.1* The occupant load permitted in any assembly building, structure, or portion thereof shall be determined on the basis of the following occupant load factors:

For ease of using this *Handbook*, A-8-1.7.1 appears following all discussion on 8-1.7.1.

(a)* An assembly area of concentrated use without fixed seats such as an auditorium, place of worship, dance floor, discotheque, or lodge hall: one person per 7 net sq ft (0.65 net sq m).

In the 1988 *Code*, the terminology "7 sq ft (0.65 net sq m) per person" was changed to read "one person per 7 net sq ft (0.65 net sq m)." The intent of the Committee was to clarify the meaning of the *Code*. The intent is that one person is assumed for each 7 sq ft (0.65 sq m) that is available to be used by occupants after deducting space occupied by permanently fixed counters, furnishings, etc.

The 7-sq ft (0.65-sq m) occupant load factor is based on open floor space with people standing in comfortable surroundings. This factor also can be used to estimate occupant load in a multipurpose room where portable chairs are placed in rows for meetings, film viewing, or lectures.

A-8-1.7.1(a) This includes so-called "festival seating."

Festival seating is illustrated in Figure 8-2. This comfortable, low-density arrangement of people, which pro-

vides them with the ability to sit directly on the ground or floor and to move relatively easily through and out of the area, likely evolved from festivals held in open areas. This concept has been abused where applied to indoor or outdoor events where the assembled spectators are not controllable in terms of their numbers, location, or behavior. Rock music concerts are examples of events where the "festival seating" concept might become decidedly unfestive due to unmanageable crowds of standing (not seated) people in front of the stage area and a complete loss of any maintained circulation routes through the assembled crowd. Injuries due to bodies crushing against bodies or portions of structure are likely when this occurs. A description of a typical crush situation is found in a report titled, "Observations of Crowd Conditions at Rock Concert in Exhibition Stadium, Toronto, 16 July 1980," by J. L. Pauls. Because the number and arrangement of people in this instance was not maintained throughout the event, there were eventually some thirty to forty thousand people distributed unevenly in an area of about 125,000 sq ft (10,600 sq m), resulting in an average density of about 1 person per 3.5 sq ft (.33 sq m). However, due to localized crowding at the stage area, several thousand people were at crushing densities of about 1 person per 2 sq ft (.19 sq m). Both normal access and emergency access into this congested area were all but impossible, and management efforts to instruct people to move back toward less densely occupied areas proved futile. Incidents such as this one have led to the area limitations shown in 8-1.7.2, which provides for increases of occupant load in some situations.

(b) An assembly area of less concentrated use, such as a conference room, dining room, drinking establishment, exhibit room, gymnasium, or lounge: one person per 15 net sq ft (1.4 net sq m).

In the 1988 *Code*, the terminology "15 sq ft (1.4 sq m) per person" was changed to read "one person per 15 net sq ft (1.4 net sq m)." The intent of the Committee was to clarify the meaning of the *Code*. The intent is that one person is assumed for each 15 sq ft (1.4 sq m) that is available for use by occupants.

The 15-sq ft (1.4-sq m) occupant load factor is based on a use where a certain amount of space is occupied by

Photograph Courtesy of J. L. Pauls.

Figure 8-2. *Festival Seating at a Rock Music Concert Held in a Stadium.*

furniture or a use requiring a large amount of space per person to accomplish the use. Examples of these typical uses are spaces involving the use of tables and chairs, as in restaurants or conference rooms. Gymnasiums are an example of a use that requires space for the occupants to perform their function (i.e., exercising or sport games).

(c) Bleachers, pews, and similar bench-type seating: one person per 18 linear in. (45.7 linear cm).

(d) *Fixed Seating.* The occupant load of an area having fixed seats shall be determined by the number of fixed seats installed. Required aisle space serving the fixed seats shall not be used to increase the occupant load.

(e) *Kitchens.* One person per 100 gross sq ft (9.3 gross sq m).

This paragraph clarifies the method of calculating the total occupant load in restaurants and cafeterias where a portion of the building is used as a kitchen, whether it is a separate room or divided from the dining area by a serving counter. Note that this occupant load is calculated by using "gross sq ft (sq m)." This takes into consideration that there will be stoves, sinks, cutting boards, counters, and other culinary machinery necessary to operate a kitchen.

(f) *Libraries.* In stack areas: one person per 100 gross sq ft (9.3 gross sq m); in reading rooms: one person per 50 net sq ft (4.6 net sq m).

This takes into consideration the existence of bookshelves and permanent aisles. Reading rooms typically have large magazine racks, chairs, couches, and other furnishings that are arranged to make the area comfortable for the user.

A-8-1.7.1 Suggested occupant load factors for components of large airport terminal buildings are given. However, the authority having jurisdiction may elect to use different occupant load factors provided exit requirements are satisfied.

Airport Terminal	Sq Ft (Gross)	Sq M (Gross)
Concourse	100	[9.3]
Waiting Areas	15	[1.4]
Baggage Claim	20	[1.9]
Baggage Handling	300	[27.9]
Other	*(See table following A–5–3.1.2)*	

To assist in preventing serious overcrowding incidents in sports arenas, stadiums, and similar occupancies, spectator standing room should not be permitted between the seating areas and the playing areas, except in horse race and dog track facilities.

Where a capacity or near capacity audience is anticipated, all seating should be assigned with tickets showing the section, row, and seat number.

Where standing room is permitted, the capacity of the standing area should:

(a) Be determined on the basis of 5 sq ft (.46 sq m) per person,

(b) Have its capacity added to the seating capacity in determining egress requirements,

(c) Be located to the rear of the seating area, and

(d) Be given "standing room only" tickets according to the area designated for the purpose.

The number of tickets sold or otherwise distributed should not exceed the aggregate number of seats plus approved standing room numbers. (*See also A-8-2.3.2.*)

The occupant load factors of 8-1.7.1 reflect the data developed from surveys of typical occupancies.

Consideration should be given to the actual use of a room or space. A multiuse room may have several occupant loads depending upon its function on a given day. This is especially true of multipurpose rooms in schools and hotels.

Figure 8-3a illustrates a 2500-sq ft (230-sq m) room with two 46-in. (117-cm) clear width doors. If the room were to be used as a banquet room with tables and chairs, its occupant load would be based on the 15-sq ft (1.4-sq m) factor, resulting in an occupant load of 167 occupants. However, if the room were to be used for a stand-up cocktail party with essentially no furniture, then the occupant load would be based on the 7-sq ft (0.65-sq m) factor, resulting in an occupant load of 357 occupants. Thus, the room may have two occupant loads.

The exit capacity for the room is based on two 46-in. (117-cm) doors. Using only the criterion of exit capacity, the room can accommodate 460 occupants. Since either of the occupant loads calculated is less than the exit capacity, the situation is satisfactory.

As noted above, both criteria (exit capacity and occupant load) must be considered in establishing the permissible occupant load for a room or area. For example, the exit capacity of the room shown in Figure 8-3b is sufficient for an occupant load of 360 people. An occupant load calculated on the basis of the room size [3,600 sq ft (330 sq m) ÷ 7] would permit 514 people. Therefore, the exit capacity must be increased to 514 in accordance with Section 5-3, since exit capacity must be provided for the occupant load determined by application of the occupant load factor.

Many times there is controversy over where to use a 7-sq ft (0.65-sq m) versus a 15-sq ft (1.4-sq m) occupant load factor. It should be noted that these factors are based on "concentrated" versus "less concentrated" use, and choices are made strictly on the basis of judgment. Since the occupant load factor is used to establish exit capacity and subclassification (which determines construction, alarm, and sprinkler requirements), it is usually safer to allow a larger occupant load (with related increased safety requirements) than to try, usually with great difficulty, to enforce a small occupant load limit. (*Also see 8-1.7.2.*)

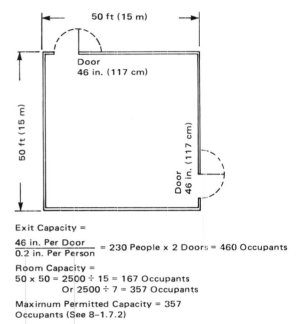

Exit Capacity =

$\dfrac{46 \text{ in. Per Door}}{0.2 \text{ in. Per Person}}$ = 230 People x 2 Doors = 460 Occupants

Room Capacity =
50 x 50 = 2500 ÷ 15 = 167 Occupants
        Or 2500 ÷ 7 = 357 Occupants
Maximum Permitted Capacity = 357 Occupants (See 8–1.7.2)

Figure 8-3a. Determination of Maximum Permitted Occupant Load for an Assembly Occupancy by Room Capacity.

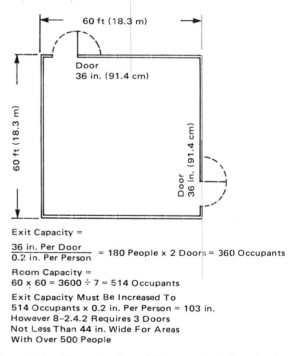

Exit Capacity =

$\dfrac{36 \text{ in. Per Door}}{0.2 \text{ in. Per Person}}$ = 180 People x 2 Doors = 360 Occupants

Room Capacity =
60 x 60 = 3600 ÷ 7 = 514 Occupants
Exit Capacity Must Be Increased To
514 Occupants x 0.2 in. Per Person = 103 in.
However 8-2.4.2 Requires 3 Doors
Not Less Than 44 in. Wide For Areas
With Over 500 People

Figure 8-3b. Determination of Minimum Exit Capacity for an Assembly Occupancy.

Formal Interpretation 85-5
Reference: 8-1.7.1 and 9-1.7.1

Question 1: Provided that sufficient exiting capacity is provided, is it the intent of 8-1.7.1 and 9-1.7.1 to allow the occupant load of an assembly occupancy, such as a cocktail lounge for example, to be calculated as the sum of the various net use areas (i.e., net area of dance floor at 7 square feet per person occupant load factor pus net area of seating and table area at 15 square feet per person occupant load factor, plus fixed seating area per the number of seats, etc.), rather than calculating the occupant load on the singular occupant load of 15 square feet per person based on the occupancy being a "drinking establishment?"

Answer: The method to determine the occupant load is adequately defined in Section 5-3 of the *Code*, particularly 5-3.1.2.

Question 2: Is the use of the provisions of 8-1.7.1 and 9-1.7.1 related to an increase in occupant load, allowable as a matter of right, as opposed to a discretionary allowance by the authority having jurisdiction, if necessary aisle and diagrams are provided?

Answer: The increase in occupant load is a matter of right if the provisions of 8-1.7.1 and 9-1.7.1 are followed. The owner or operator has the right to submit plans and receive an increase in occupant load if the plans comply with the *Code*. The authority having jurisdiction has a right to reject the plan for increase in occupant load if the plan is unrealistic, inaccurate, or otherwise does not properly reflect compliance with other code requirements. It is not the intent of the provisions of 8-1.7.1 and 9-1.7.1 to prohibit an increase in occupant load solely on the basis of exceeding the limits of 8-1.7.1 and 9-1.7.1.

Issue Edition: 1985
Reference: 8-1.7.1 and 9-1.7.1
Date: May 1985 ■

8-1.7.2 The occupant load permitted in a building or portion thereof may be increased above that specified in 8-1.7.1 if the necessary aisles and exits are provided. To increase the occupant load, a diagram indicating placement of equipment, aisles, exits, and seating shall be provided to and approved by the authority having jurisdiction prior to any increase in occupant load. In areas not greater than 10,000 sq ft (930 sq m), the occupant load shall not exceed one person in 5 sq ft (.46 sq m); in areas greater than 10,000 sq ft (930 sq m), the occupant load shall not exceed one person in 7 sq ft (.65 sq m).

The accessibility of room exits is as important as the exit capacity. Therefore, where an increase is permitted over the occupant load established by 8-1.7.1, it must be demonstrated that adequate aisle accessways and aisles leading to the room exits are provided. Spacing of tables must provide for occupied chairs plus an aisle. Consideration should be given to the likelihood that, when occupants leave during an emergency, they may not take time to move chairs out of the aisles. (*See 8-2.5.7.*)

Dining and drinking areas most frequently take advantage of the provision of 8-1.7.2. There have been large banquet layouts where the occupant load was successfully increased to reflect an occupant load factor of 11 sq ft (1 sq m) instead of the 15 sq ft (1.4 sq m) specified by 8-1.7.1(b). In all cases where an increase in the occupant load is permitted, the authority having jurisdiction should insist on complete fixture and furniture layouts and should strictly enforce adherence to approved layouts. As noted above, the same room may have several approved occupant loads depending on the various fixture and furniture layouts.

A major change made to this paragraph in the 1988 Edition of the *Code* was a revision to the limit on the increased occupant load. This limit, which is based on an occupant load factor of 5 sq ft (0.46 sq m), was instituted due to the Committee's concern for overcrowding, which affects the movement characteristics of the occupants. Due to problems with festival seating (*see 8-1.3*), the limit was modified in the 1988 Edition so as to be restricted to facilities not larger than 10,000 sq ft (930 sq m).

It has been shown in research by the National Research Council in Canada and by the London Transport Board that, if people are crowded into a space so that each person occupies less than 7 sq ft (0.65 sq m), movement approaches a "shuffle"; when each person occupies less than 3 sq ft (0.28 sq m), "jam point" is approached, and all movement by occupants comes to a virtual stop. Thus, the maximum occupant load factor of 5 sq ft (0.46 sq m) for areas less than or equal to 10,000 sq ft (930 sq m) was chosen by the Committee to prevent overcrowding and the attendant change in the movement characteristics of occupants. (*See Figures 8-4a and 8-4b for two examples of increasing occupant load.*)

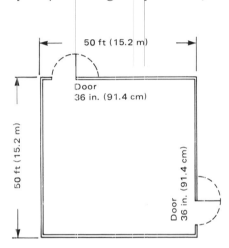

Exit Capacity =

$\dfrac{\text{36 in. Per Door}}{\text{0.2 in. Per Person}}$ = 180 People x 2 Doors = 360 Occupants

Room Capacity =
50 x 50 = 2500 ÷ 15 = 167 Occupants

A Diagram Has Been Submitted To And Approved By The Authority Having Jurisdiction As Required By 8-1.7.2. It Shows An Occupant Load Of 250 People [Approximately 10sq ft (.9 sq m) Per Person] Therefore, The Maximum Permitted Occupant Load is 250 People.

Figure 8-4a.   Determination of Maximum Permitted Occupant Load for an Assembly Occupancy. Note that a practical upper limit for the room's population that will still ensure rapid and orderly movement to an exit may be 500 people (2,500 ÷ 5) based on 8-1.7.2. Since the exit capacity provides for 360 people, the authority having jurisdiction could conceivably allow a maximum permitted occupant load of 360.

8-1.7.3 **Waiting Spaces.** In theaters and other assembly occupancies where persons are admitted to the building at times when seats are not available to them, or when the per-

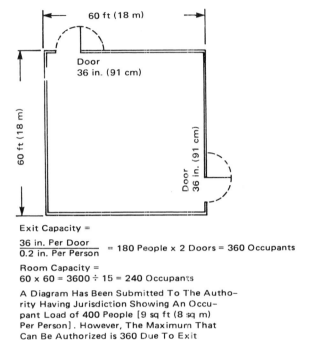

Exit Capacity =

$\dfrac{\text{36 in. Per Door}}{\text{0.2 in. Per Person}}$ = 180 People x 2 Doors = 360 Occupants

Room Capacity =
60 x 60 = 3600 ÷ 15 = 240 Occupants

A Diagram Has Been Submitted To The Authority Having Jurisdiction Showing An Occupant Load of 400 People [9 sq ft (8 sq m) Per Person]. However, The Maximum That Can Be Authorized is 360 Due To Exit Capacity.

Maximum Permitted Capacity = 360 Occupants

Figure 8-4b.   Determination of Maximum Permitted Occupant Load for an Assembly Occupancy by Exit Capacity. Note that a practical upper limit for the room's population that will still ensure rapid and orderly movement to an exit may be 720 people (3,600 ÷ 5) based on 8-1.7.2. However, the exit capacity of 360 must determine the maximum permitted occupant load.

mitted occupant load has been reached based on 8-1.7.1 or 8-1.7.2 and persons are allowed to wait in a lobby or similar space until seats or space are available, such use of lobby or similar space shall not encroach upon the required clear width of exits. Such waiting shall be restricted to areas other than the required means of egress. Exits shall be provided for such waiting spaces on the basis of one person for each 3 sq ft (0.28 sq m) of waiting space area. Such exits shall be in addition to the exits specified for the main auditorium area and shall conform in construction and arrangement to the general rules for exits given in this chapter.

This is most often used for night clubs, lounges, and in some restaurants. This space cannot be located in or interfere with the egress routes from the rest of the assembly occupancy.

SECTION 8-2 Means of Egress Requirements

8-2.1 General. All means of egress shall be in accordance with Chapter 5 and this chapter.

8-2.2 Means of Egress Components.

8-2.2.1 Components of means of egress shall be limited to the types described in 8-2.2.2 through 8-2.2.7.

Slide escapes and elevators are not suited for rapid evacuation of the large numbers of people found in these occupancies. Furthermore, elevators introduce other risk factors if used during a fire (*see Section 7-4*). Chapter 5 no longer allows escalators to be located in the means of egress in new construction. It should be noted that these devices can be installed, but they cannot obstruct or interfere with the required means of egress.

8-2.2.2 Doors.

8-2.2.2.1 Doors shall comply with 5-2.1.

8-2.2.2.2 Class C assembly occupancies in covered malls (*see 24-4.4.1 Exception*) shall be permitted to have horizontal or vertical security grilles or doors complying with 5-2.1.4.1 Exception No. 3 on the main entrance/exits.

This provision allows small restaurants in malls to use the security grilles or doors as provided in 5-2.1.4.1 Exception No. 3.

8-2.2.2.3 Panic Hardware or Fire Exit Hardware. Any door in a required means of egress from an area having an occupant load of 100 or more persons may be provided with a latch or lock only if it is panic hardware or fire exit hardware complying with 5-2.1.7.

Exception No. 1: In assembly occupancies having an occupant load not greater than 500, where the main exit consists of a single door or single pair of doors, locking devices complying with 5-2.1.5.1 Exception No. 2 shall be permitted on the main exit. Any latching device on this door(s) shall be released by panic hardware.

Exception No. 1 to 8-2.2.2.3 recognizes the provisions for locking doors contained in Chapter 5, "Means of Egress." These provisions recognize the need to lock doors for security purposes and provide limits on how this can be done. These provisions also acknowledge that, in order for the business to function, the main door must remain unlocked. If a latching device is used in addition to the lock, panic hardware is required to release the latch.

Exception No. 2: Special locking arrangements as permitted in 8-2.2.2.4.

8-2.2.2.4 Special locking arrangements complying with 5-2.1.6 are permitted on doors other than main entrance/exit doors.

Paragraph 8-2.2.2.4 allows delayed release hardware meeting the requirements of 5-2.1.6 to be used on all but the main exit. In addition to other requirements, 5-2.1.6 requires that the building be protected throughout by either an approved automatic sprinkler system or an approved supervised automatic fire detection system.

8-2.2.2.5 Revolving doors complying with 5-2.1.10 are permitted.

8-2.2.2.6 Turnstiles. No turnstiles or other devices to restrict the movement of persons shall be installed in any assembly occupancy in such a manner as to interfere in any way with required means of egress facilities.

8-2.2.3 Stairs. Stairs shall comply with 5-2.2.

8-2.2.4 Smokeproof Enclosures. Smokeproof enclosures shall comply with 5-2.3.

8-2.2.5 Horizontal Exits. Horizontal exits shall comply with 5-2.4.

8-2.2.6 Ramps.

8-2.2.6.1 Ramps shall comply with 5-2.5.

8-2.2.6.2 Ramps in Class A assembly occupancies shall be Class A ramps.

Exception: Ramps serving only stages or nonpublic areas and ramped aisles shall be permitted to have a slope not steeper than 1 in 8.

8-2.2.7 Exit Passageways. Exit passageways shall comply with 5-2.6.

8-2.3 Capacity of Means of Egress.

8-2.3.1 The capacity of means of egress shall be in accordance with Section 5-3 or, in the case of means of egress serving theater-type seating or similar seating arranged in rows, in accordance with 8-2.3.2.

8-2.3.2* Minimum clear widths of aisles and other means of egress shall be in accordance with Table 8-2.3.2(a) or, for buildings providing smoke-protected assembly seating and for which an approved life safety evaluation is conducted, in accordance with Table 8-2.3.2(b). For Table 8-2.3.2(b), the number of seats specified must be within a single assembly space, and interpolation shall be permitted between the specific values shown. For both tables, the minimum clear widths shown shall be modified in accordance with all of the following:

(a) If risers exceed 7 in. (17.8 cm) in height, multiply the stair width in the tables by factor A, where

$$A = 1 + \frac{(\text{riser height} - 7.0 \text{ in.})}{5}$$

(b) Stairs not having a handrail within a 30-in. (76-cm) horizontal distance shall be 25 percent wider than otherwise calculated, i.e., multiply by B = 1.25.

(c) Ramps steeper than 1 in 10 slope where used in ascent shall have their width increased by 10 percent, i.e., multiply by factor C = 1.10.

A-8-2.3.2 A life safety evaluation is a written review dealing with the adequacy of life safety features relative to fire, storm, collapse, crowd behavior, and other related safety considerations. This review should be done by a person acceptable to the authority having jurisdiction. Such an evaluation includes, for example, a documented case that shows products of com-

Table 8-2.3.2(a)   For Use Without Smoke-Protected Assembly Seating

No. of Seats	Nominal Flow Time (sec)	Inch of Clear Width Per Seat Served	
		Stairs	Passageways, Ramps, and Doorways
Unlimited	200	0.300 AB	0.220 C

(1 in. = 2.54 cm)

Table 8-2.3.2(b)   For Use With Smoke-Protected Assembly Seating

No. of Seats	Nominal Flow Time (sec)	Inch of Clear Width Per Seat Served	
		Stairs	Passageways, Ramps, and Doorways
2,000	200	0.300 AB	0.220 C
5,000	260	0.200 AB	0.150 C
10,000	360	0.130 AB	0.100 C
15,000	460	0.096 AB	0.070 C
20,000	560	0.076 AB	0.056 C
25,000 or more	660	0.060 AB	0.044 C

(1 in. = 2.54 cm)

bustion in all conceivable fire scenarios will not significantly endanger occupants using means of egress in the facility (for example, because of fire detection, automatic suppression, smoke control, large-volume space, or management procedures). Moreover, means of egress facilities plus facility management capabilities should be adequate to cope with scenarios where certain egress routes are blocked for some reason.

In addition to making realistic assumptions about the capabilities of persons in the facility (e.g., an assembled crowd including many disabled persons or persons unfamiliar with the facility), the life safety evaluation should include a factor of safety of at least 2.0 in all calculations relating hazard development time and required egress time (the combination of flow time and other time needed to detect and assess an emergency condition, initiate egress, and move along the egress routes). This takes into account the possibility that half of the egress routes may not be used (or usable) in certain situations.

Regarding crowd behavior, the potential hazards created by larger masses of people and greater crowd densities (which can be problematic during ingress, occupancy, and egress) demand that technology, going beyond fire protection engineering, be utilized by designers, managers, and authorities responsible for buildings based on the relaxed egress capacity provisions of Table 8-2.3.2(b). In very large buildings for assembly use, the hazard of crowd crushes can exceed that of fire or structural failure. Therefore, the building designers, managers, event planners, security personnel, police authorities, and fire authorities, as well as the building construction authorities, should understand the potential problems and solutions, including coordination of their activities. For crowd behavior, this understanding must include factors of space, energy, time, and information as well as specific crowd management techniques such as metering. Published guidance on these factors and techniques is found in the SFPE Handbook of Fire Protection Engineering, Section 1, Chapter 15, and in publications referenced therein. (*See Appendix B.*)

Tables 8-2.3.2(a) and 8-2.3.2.(b) are based on a linear relationship between number of seats and nominal flow time, with a minimum of 200 seconds (3.3 minutes) for 2,000 seats plus 1 second for every additional 50 seats up to 25,000. Beyond 25,000 total seats, the nominal flow time is limited to 660 seconds (11 minutes). Nominal flow time refers to the flow time for the most able group of patrons; some groups less familiar with the premises or less able groups may take longer to pass a point in the egress system. (Although three or more digits are noted in the tables, the resulting calculations should be assumed to provide only two significant figures of precision.)

An example calculation may help describe the use of Table 8-2.3.2(b).

Example: An arena providing smoke-protected assembly seating and having a total of 12,500 seats.

For capacity purposes only, what should be the clear width of an aisle stair with 8-in. (20.3-cm) risers and with a center handrail providing means of egress for 340 people? Interpolating between the widths (0.13 and 0.096 respectively) for 10,000-seat and 15,000-seat facilities, the required stair width in inches, per seat served, is 0.113 AB where A is 1.2 and B is 1.0. The aisle stair width, for capacity purposes, is the product of 340 (0.113) (1.2) (1.0) or 46.1 in. (117 cm). In this case, a minimum width criterion of 48 in. (122 cm) (*see 8-2.5.8.2*) will govern its width. Most previous editions of the

Code credited this aisle stair with a capacity of only 150 persons.

This paragraph applies only to egress serving theater-type seating or similar seating arranged in rows (*see 8-2.3.1*).

Generally, 8-2.3.2 takes into account the common practice of many intermediate-size facilities, such as arenas and stadiums, of providing means of egress that are designed to meet provisions that fall between the egress capacity requirements of previous editions of the *Code* and the less demanding egress capacity requirements that have been applied to large outdoor assembly facilities, such as those addressed by NFPA 102, *Standard for Assembly Seating, Tents, and Membrane Structures.*[9] Rather than merely giving a stamp of approval to this interpolation, the *Code* requires that extra caution be taken where a facility is considered for reduced egress capacities. In order to use the reduced egress capacities set out in Table 8-2.3.2(b), a case must first be made and accepted by the authority having jurisdiction demonstrating that all life safety hazards have been considered and control measures provided to ensure that occupants evacuating the building will not be endangered by conditions developing faster than it takes for the means of egress to be cleared. This is described as a "life safety evaluation," a process that should not be undertaken lightly or without special competence in a wide range of life safety issues including, but not limited to, firesafety.

The nominal flow time figures shown in Tables 8-2.3.2(a) and 8-2.3.2(b) are for reference and may be helpful to designers, consultants, managers, and others concerned with the expected performance of an egress system. They are not used for any further purposes (*see 8-1.3 for a definition of "flow time"*). Of course, if the facilities are to be used by groups of occupants who are unfamiliar with the facility or who are less able to move quickly and in dense groups than are younger individuals commonly found at athletic events, this will have to be taken into account, for example, when conducting the life safety evaluation and in operating the facility. Alternatively, the capacity of means of egress should be increased so that a more rapid egress is possible without endangering or otherwise taxing the less able occupants.

The need to consider the capabilities of occupants in relation to circulation facility geometry has led to the use of several correction factors in the columns for clear width in Tables 8-2.3.2(a) and 8-2.3.2(b). In new facilities, there will be much emphasis on keeping the geometries as good as possible and, therefore, the correction factors will be 1.0 or very close to 1.0. With existing facilities, this might not be possible; however, it should be noted that handrails can be retrofitted on aisles and other means of egress to significantly improve occupant safety and comfort — an important factor in situations where efficient movement is needed. These factors are taken into account here and in other *Code* requirements for means of egress.

It should be noted that 8-2.3 addresses means of egress generally. The increased flexibility provided by Table 8-2.3.2(b) must be used with caution for proper balance between the relative capacities (and flow times) of each part of a means of egress system encountered by occupants as they leave the facility. Otherwise, with an unbalanced system, there will be queuing or waiting at some points other than the point of origin.

Attention should be given to the occupants' acceptance of the queue or the wait in their seats before proceeding out of the building; however, if a "downstream" component of the means of egress system is relatively underdesigned, even greater attention should be given to the actual and perceived conditions faced by occupants.

Figure 8-5 shows egress from a large stadium that provides egress performance that is perceived to be acceptable in terms of time and other factors. Occupants' acceptance of the longer egress flow times, permitted by the *Code* for larger assembly facilities, should be taken into account when doing a life safety evaluation for the building. The photograph also shows a collection of people who can be expected to take somewhat longer to clear the building than is the case with football spectators [a reference group for the nominal flow time figures noted in Tables 8-2.3.2(a) and 8-2.3.2(b).]

8-2.3.3 **Main Entrance/Exit.** Every assembly occupancy shall be provided with a main entrance/exit. The main entrance/exit shall be of sufficient width to accommodate one-half of the total occupant load but shall be not less than the total required width of all aisles, exit passageways, and stairways leading thereto and shall be at the level of exit discharge or shall connect to

Photograph Courtesy of J. L. Pauls

Figure 8-5. *Crowd Egress from a Large Assembly Facility that Might be Eligible for Egress Capacity Provisions of Table 8-2.3.2(b).*

a stairway or ramp leading to a street. Each level of an assembly occupancy shall have access to the main entrance/exit, and such access shall have sufficient capacity to accommodate 50 percent of the occupant load of such levels.

Exception No. 1: A bowling establishment shall have a main entrance/exit of sufficient capacity to accommodate 50 percent of the total occupant load without regard to the number of aisles that it serves.

Exception No. 2*: In assembly occupancies where there is no well defined main entrance/exit, exits shall be permitted to be distributed around the perimeter of the building provided the total exit width furnishes a minimum of 100 percent of the width needed to accommodate the permitted occupant load.

A-8-2.3.3 **Exception No. 2.** The original *Code* wording permitted certain exceptions such as sports arenas and railway stations. If an assembly occupancy is not similar to one of these, it is frequently rejected. A listing of exceptions also raises the question as to why other occupancies are not included and necessitates more additions to the list. For example, an exhibit hall of very large size may have several main entrances/exits. A theater extending the width of a block cannot really have a main entrance/exit in one confined location. A restaurant may have a main entrance serving the parking lot and another main entrance for those entering from the street. The authority having jurisdiction must make a determination as to where this is acceptable.

The term "main exit" was replaced with the term "main entrance/exit" in the 1988 *Code*. The intent of the *Code* is to require that 50 percent of the occupants will be able to exit through the same door(s) they used to enter the building. It was brought to the Committee's attention that some building owners/managers did not want the "main entrance" to also be designated as the "main exit." Therefore, this terminology clarifies the intent of the *Code* and will require that the main entrance to a public assembly occupancy also be designated as the main exit.

The usual entrance to an assembly occupancy also generally serves as its main exit. As a rule, people desire to leave a building by way of their entrance to the structure. Therefore, the main exit needs to be sized to accommodate at least 50 percent of the occupants; however, it must not be less in width than the sum of the required widths of the aisles that it serves.

Bowling establishments usually have relatively few rows of seats for spectators but are necessarily wide to accommodate the alleys. Due to the limitation of the number of seats in a row, many more aisles are required than in other types of assembly occupancies. Exception No. 1 to 8-2.3.3 modifies what would be the excessive main exit width required to accommodate the sum of the required aisle widths served by the exit.

Exception No. 2 clarifies the intent of the *Code* to provide the same capacity for buildings having no main entrance as for those with a main entrance. The intent is to distribute the width as equally as possible among all exits. (*Also see 8-2.3.4.*)

8-2.3.4 **Other Exits.** Each level of an assembly occupancy shall have access to the main entrance/exit and shall be provided with additional exits of sufficient width to accommodate a minimum of one-half of the total occupant load served by that level. Such exits shall discharge in accordance with 8-2.7. Such exits shall be located as far apart as practicable and as far from the main entrance/exit as practicable. Such exits shall be accessible from a cross aisle or a side aisle. (*See 8-2.3.3.*)

Exception: In assembly occupancies where there is no well defined main entrance/exit, exits shall be permitted to be distributed around the perimeter of the building provided the total exit width furnishes a minimum of 100 percent of the width needed to accommodate the permitted occupant load.

A major change to the 1991 *Code* is the deletion of the requirement that the "other" exits must accommodate two-thirds of the occupant load, resulting in a 16⅔ percent overdesign. The Committee felt that, with current *Code* provisions, the overdesign was no longer needed.

As an example of the requirements of 8-2.3.4, if an assembly occupancy had an occupant load of 900, the main exit would have to accommodate 450 people (50 percent). If there were two additional exits, together they would have to accommodate 450 people. Also, 8-2.4.2 requires that, in a Class B assembly occupancy with a capacity of more than 500 people, at least three exits must be provided, and no exit may be less than 44 in. (112 cm) wide.

8-2.4 **Number of Exits.** (*See also Section 5-4.*)

As the concentration or number of people increases in an assembly occupancy, the chance of simultaneous exiting by a sizable group of occupants increases. Therefore, to reduce jamming at doorways (which leads to panic and disorder), more exits at a variety of locations are needed. Paragraphs 8-2.4.1 through 8-2.4.3 provide for this design requirement.

Since 8-1.2.2 specifies that assembly areas with individual occupant loads of fewer than 50 people in buildings other than those of assembly occupancy shall be classed as part of the other occupancy, no criteria are given by 8-2.4 for the number and location of exits in such an occupancy. (*Also see Formal Interpretation 85-10 for 8-1.4.1*).

8-2.4.1 Every Class A assembly occupancy shall have at least four separate means of egress as remotely located from each other as practicable.

8-2.4.2 Every Class B assembly occupancy shall have at least two separate means of egress as remotely located from each other as practicable and, if of an occupant load of over 500, at least three separate means of egress, each not less than 44 in. (112 cm) wide.

8-2.4.3 Every Class C assembly occupancy shall have at least two means of egress consisting of separate exits or doors leading to a corridor or other spaces that provide access to two separate and independent exits located in different directions.

Formal Interpretation 81-28
Reference: 8-2.4

Question: Is it the intent of 8-2.4 and its subsections to require four exits from each level of a Class A assembly occupancy building where, individually, the floors have populations that fall in the range assigned to a Class B assembly occupancy?

Answer: No.

Issue Edition: 1981
Reference: 8-2.4
Date: January 1983 ■

8-2.4.4 Balconies or mezzanines having an occupant load not greater than 50 shall be permitted to be served by a single means of egress and such means of egress shall be permitted to lead to the floor below.

The intent of the Committee was to provide relief for small balconies and mezzanines, such as choir lofts that accommodate not more than 50 people. [*Also see 8-2.5.1, which limits the common path of travel on single means of egress balconies to 75 ft (23 m)*].

8-2.4.5 Balconies or mezzanines having an occupant load greater than 50 but not greater than 100 shall have at least two remote means of egress, but both such means of egress shall be permitted to lead to the floor below.

These balconies might typically be found in restaurants or small theaters. The Committee felt it was necessary to have two remote means of egress, but since the total number of people would not be greater than 100, it would be reasonable to let occupants egress onto the floor below.

8-2.4.6 Balconies or mezzanines having an occupant load greater than 100 shall have means of egress provided as for a floor.

The Committee felt that any balcony or mezzanine that could accommodate more than 100 people should be treated as a separate floor with regard to number of means of egress in order to avoid overloading the means of egress from the floor below and to protect people during egress from the mezzanine.

8-2.5 Arrangement of Means of Egress. (*See also Section 5-5.*)

8-2.5.1 Exits shall be remote from each other and shall be arranged to minimize the possibility that they may be blocked by any emergency.

Exception No. 1: A common path of travel shall be permitted for the first 20 ft (6.1 m) from any point.

Exception No. 2: A common path of travel shall be permitted for the first 75 ft (23 m) for balconies or mezzanines in accordance with 8-2.4.4.

Exception No. 3: As provided in 8-2.5.6.4.

Separation of exits as far as practicable cannot be overemphasized. Two or more exits that are located too close to each other can become unusable quickly during the same incident. The fundamental principles of this *Code*, as expressed in Chapter 2, require remoteness of exits to the point that a single fire event will not simultaneously block both exits. This same concept applies to exit access doors. The remoteness requirements of Section 5-5 must be met.

Revolving rooftop places of assembly require special consideration; as the structure revolves, exit signs are often lost from view. To provide an unobstructed panoramic view, the exterior element revolves around a small stationary interior core in which the exits are often located. In many cases, the two exits are too close to each other to avoid both exits becoming involved in case of fire. Usually at least one stairway must be transferred from its position in the stationary core to the normal location of the building stairways. This transfer, since it is a continuation of the stairway, must be made in an exit passageway possessing a fire resistance equal to that required for the stair enclosure.

8-2.5.2 Areas accessible to people with severe mobility impairment shall have a minimum of two accessible means of egress.

Exception No. 1: Assembly occupancies protected throughout by approved supervised automatic sprinkler systems in accordance with Section 7-7.

Exception No. 2: If the accessible means of egress provide(s) the most direct routes (route) from the accessible areas, and if the fire protection system, the physical arrangement of the space, and the facility operation are all approved by the authority having jurisdiction, the authority having jurisdiction shall permit a reduction in the required number of accessible means of egress.

The definition of "accessible means of egress" in Chapters 3 and 5 is "...a path of travel that is usable by a person with a severe mobility impairment and that leads to a public way or an area of refuge." Therefore, unless the facility has an accessible path to a pubic way, an area of refuge in accordance with 5-2.12 will be required. (*See the commentary in 5-2.12 for additional information.*)

8-2.5.3 Means of egress shall not be permitted through kitchens, storerooms, restrooms, closets, or hazardous areas as described in 8-3.2.

The purpose of this requirement is to make clear that exit access travel is not permitted to pass through areas subject to locking or areas possessing a hazard level higher than that normal for the occupancy.

8-2.5.4 Where the floor area of auditoriums and arenas is used for areas described by 8-1.7.1, at least 50 percent of the occupant load shall have means of egress provided without passing through adjacent fixed seating areas.

8-2.5.5 **General Requirements for Aisles and Aisle Accessways Serving Seating.**

8-2.5.5.1* The width of aisle accessways and aisles shall provide sufficient egress capacity for the number of persons accommodated by the catchment area served by the aisle accessway or aisle in accordance with 8-2.3.1. Where aisle accessways or aisles converge to form a single path of egress travel, the required egress capacity of that path shall not be less than the combined required capacity of the converging aisle accessways and aisles.

This refers to the capacity-related width requirements of 8-2.3.1. The capacity-related requirements must be considered along with other width requirements set out in 8-2.5.8.2. The final minimum width required by the *Code* is the larger of the widths established by the two sets of requirements.

A-8-2.5.5.1 The catchment area served by an aisle accessway or aisle is the portion of the total space that is naturally served by the aisle accessway or aisle. Hence, the requirement for combining the required capacity where paths converge is in effect a restatement of the idea of a catchment area. The establishment of catchment areas should be based on a balanced use of all means of egress, with the number of persons in proportion to egress capacity.

Figure 8-6 illustrates how catchment areas would be allotted in the case of a theater with four egress doorways having approximately similar egress capacity. Note that catchment areas for normal, nonemergency uses of only some of the available means of egress — especially those provided by the main entrance/exit — may be quite different from the catchment areas based on a balanced distribution of people in proportion to egress capacity of individual means of egress. Facility management procedures must take into account the difficulties of informing people of and directing them to all the available means of egress, especially when normally used, familiar routes become blocked in an emergency.

Note that the term "required capacity" is used here to make clear that the combined required width of the egress routes might be smaller than their combined actual widths, especially where the individual widths are made wider than required by the *Code* for egress capacity purposes. Such wider widths, beyond *Code* minimums, might be justified by considerations such as normal operating convenience.

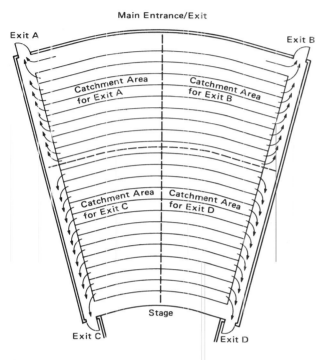

Main Entrance/Exit

Exit A

Catchment Area for Exit A

Catchment Area for Exit B

Exit B

Catchment Area for Exit C

Catchment Area for Exit D

Stage

Exit C

Exit D

Figure 8-6. Plan of a Theater Showing how Catchment Areas for Means of Egress Are Based on a Balanced Use of all Means of Egress, in Proportion to Egress Capacity.

8-2.5.5.2 Those portions of aisle accessways and aisles where egress is possible in either of two directions shall be uniform in required width.

Exception: Those portions of aisle accessways where the required width, not including the seat space described by 8-2.5.5.3. does not exceed 12 in. (30.5 cm).

This requirement prohibits making some aisles wider at their ends (in an hourglass shape) simply because there are more people using them at their ends. A tapered aisle is acceptable and effective where there is only one direction of egress travel possible and the number of people served by the aisle increases in the direction of egress travel. In the more general case, where there are two directions of egress travel possible in the aisle, the width must be kept uniform to accommodate efficient egress travel that might have to reverse direction because of blockage at one end.

8-2.5.5.3* Where nonfixed seating is located between a table and an aisle accessway or aisle, the measurement of required

clear width of the aisle accessway or aisle shall be made to a line 19 in. (48.3 cm) away from edge of the table. The 19-in. (48.3-cm) distance shall be measured perpendicularly to the edge of the table.

A-8-2.5.5.3 Figure A-8-2.5.5.3 shows typical measurements involving seating and tables abutting an aisle. Note that, for purposes of the means of egress requirements of this *Code*, seating at counters or other furnishings is considered to be the same as seating at tables.

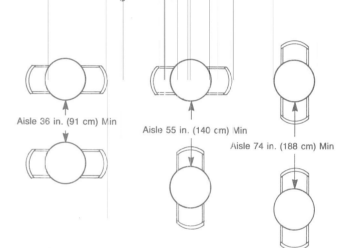

Aisle 36 in. (91 cm) Min

Aisle 55 in. (140 cm) Min

Aisle 74 in. (188 cm) Min

Figure A-8-2.5.5.3

Figure A-8-2.5.5.3 illustrates the provisions of 8-2.5.5.3. This provides guidance on how aisles with movable chairs are to be measured, an issue that has often been questioned by enforcement officials.

8-2.5.5.4 In the case of side boundaries, other than nonfixed seating at tables, for aisle accessways or aisles, the clear width shall be measured to boundary elements such as walls, guardrails, handrails, edges of seating, tables, and side edges of treads, with the measurement made horizontally to the vertical projection of the elements resulting in the smallest width measured perpendicularly to the line of travel.

8-2.5.6* Aisle Accessways Serving Seating Not at Tables.

A-8-2.5.6 For purposes of the means of egress requirements of this *Code*, tablet-arm chair seating is not considered seating at tables. Dinner theater style configurations must comply with the aisle accessway requirements applying to seating at tables and the aisle requirements of 8-2.5.8 if the aisles contain steps or are ramped. Generally, if aisles contain steps or are ramped, all of this *Code's* requirements for aisles, stairs, and ramps must be met, and attention is also drawn to 5-1.6 and A-5-1.6.

8-2.5.6.1* To determine the required clear width of aisle accessways between rows of seating, horizontal measurements shall be made (between vertical planes) from the back of one seat to the front of the most forward projection of the seat immediately behind it. Where the entire row consists of automatic or self-rising seats that comply with ASTM F851, *Test Method for Self-Rising Seat Mechanisms*, the measurement may be made with the seats in the up position.

A-8-2.5.6.1 Seats having reclining backs are assumed to be in their most upright position when unoccupied.

The requirement for the spacing between rows of chairs is illustrated in Figure 8-7.

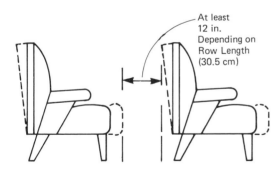

Figure 8-7. Correct Measurement of Minimum Spacing Between Rows of Chairs Without Self-Rising Seats.

8-2.5.6.2 The aisle accessway between rows of seating shall have a clear width of not less than 12 in. (30.5 cm), and this minimum shall be increased as a function of row length in accordance with 8-2.5.6.3 and 8-2.5.6.4.

Exception: If used by not more than four persons, there is no minimum clear width requirement for the portion of the aisle accessway having a length not exceeding 6 ft (1.8 m) measured from the center of the seat farthest from the aisle.

8-2.5.6.3* Rows of seating served by aisles or doorways at both ends shall have no more than 100 seats per row. The 12 in. (30.5 cm) minimum clear width of aisle accessway between such rows shall be increased by 0.3 in. (0.8 cm) for every seat over a total of 14, but need not exceed 22 in. (55.9 cm).

A-8-2.5.6.3 The system known as "continental seating" has one pair of egress doors provided for every five rows that is located close to the ends of the rows. In previous editions of the *Code*, such egress doors were required to provide a minimum clear width of 66 in. (168 cm) discharging into a foyer, lobby, or to the exterior of the building. This continental seating arrangement can result in egress flow times that are approximately one-half as long as those resulting where side aisles lead to more remote doors (i.e., with nominal flow times of approximately 100 seconds rather than 200 seconds). Such superior egress flow time performance may be desirable in some situations; however, special attention should be given either to a comparably good egress capacity for other parts of the egress system or to sufficient space to accommodate queuing outside the seating space.

This was a major change in the 1988 Edition of the *Code*. The appendix note relates the expected egress flow time performance of "continental seating," (see Figure 8-8a) as provided for by the *Code* prior to 1988, to the egress flow time performance of the more flexible newer requirements for egress width related to capacity (*see 8-2.3*). Additional design flexibility, built upon the continental seating principle of variable minimum seat row spacing and row length, was also introduced in the 1988 Edition of the *Code*. As reference points for each end of the range, the newer requirement uses the previously employed requirements of 12 in. (30.5 cm) of clearance for rows up to 14 seats in length and 22 in. (55.9 cm) for rows over 45 seats in length. For example, under the newer requirement, rows with 47 seats require a clearance of 21.9 in. (55.6 cm). This is calculated by subtracting 14 from 47 and multiplying the result, 33, by 0.3 in. to obtain 9.9 in., which is added to 12 in. to obtain the total required width clearance of 21.9 in. Rows with 48 to 100 seats require 22 in. (55.9 cm) of clear width.

The newer flexibility, applying to all fixed seating arranged in rows, is based on the assumption that the egress time required for a seating arrangement will be influenced more by the capacity of routes downstream from the rows of seating than by the rows' clear widths. Paragraph 8-2.3 provides a standardized method for calculating the widths of those routes serving the space containing the seating. The combination of 8-2.3 and 8-2.5.6 offers designers of theaters, especially, a great deal of flexibility in laying out blocks of seating while still requiring a standard of egress flow time performance that is based on traditionally accepted egress performance (nominally about 200 seconds of flow time) resulting from very specific requirements on aisle and cross aisle design. For example, rows longer than 14 seats are permitted, and egress door locations can be more flexibly determined than permitted under continental seating rules contained in previous *Code* editions.

Figure 8-8b illustrates the possibilities for a theater with 630 seats in one unbroken area with 21 rows ranging uniformly from 20 to 40 seats in length. The required minimum clear width between the front row (with 20 seats) and the one behind (with 21 seats) is 14.1 in. (35.8 cm). The required minimum clear width between the back row (with 40 seats) and the one in front of it (with 39 seats) is 19.8 in. (50.3 cm). The designer has the option of making all the clear widths uniform and at least 19.8 in. (50.3 cm), or progressively increasing them from front to back, from at least 14.1 in. to at least 19.8 in., as the row lengths increase.

The theater is a Class B assembly occupancy with over 500 seats; therefore, in accordance with 8-2.4.2, it requires at least three separate means of egress, each not less than 44 in. (112 cm) in width. A main set of doors located at the back of the seating and close to the main entrance/exit has to provide at least one-half the egress capacity. In this case, it must serve at least 315 persons. According to 8-2.3.2, the minimum total clear width of these

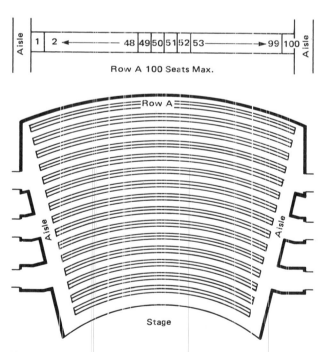

Figure 8-8a. *Arrangement of Seats and Aisles with Continental Seating. In prior editions of the Code, where there were more than 14 seats in a row, this arrangement was required. One hundred seats is the maximum number for one row.*

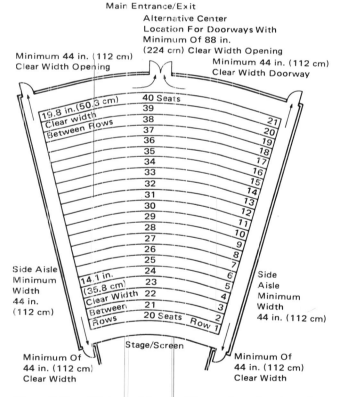

Figure 8-8b. *Minimum Means of Egress for a 630-Seat Theater Utilizing the Row Spacing and Aisle Length Provisions of 8-2.5.6.3.*

main doorways must be 70 in. (178 cm), and thus two doorways providing 35 in. (89 cm) clear width each would suffice for *Code* capacity purposes. However, 8-2.3.3 requires that the main entrance be as wide as all aisles leading to it, so the two 44-in. (112-cm) aisles require a 88-in. (224-cm) main entrance/exit. Two additional means of egress, providing total capacity for at least 315 seats in accordance with to 8-2.3.4, each need to have a minimum clear width of 35 in. (119 cm) (158 times 0.22 in.) in accordance with to 8-2.3.2 and not less than 44 in. (112 cm) in accordance with to 8-2.4.2. Minimum side aisle width connecting the front and back egress doorways would also have to be 44 in. (112 cm). Greater widths of aisle and doorways, especially those leading to the main entrance/exit, should be considered to help improve convenience and other features that go beyond the minimum *Code* requirements for means of egress.

In the example presented in Figure 8-8b, there is of course the option of doing a traditional layout with seats having no more than 6 intervening seats separating them from an aisle. This would require that more space be devoted to aisles and cross aisles, but this space loss could be offset by closer seat row spacings.

8-2.5.6.4 Rows of seating served by an aisle or doorway at one end only shall have a path of travel not exceeding 30 ft (9.1 m) in length from any seat to a point where a person has a choice of two paths of travel to separate exits. The 12 in. (30.5 cm) minimum clear width of aisle accessway between such rows shall be increased by 0.6 in. (1.6 cm) for every seat over a total of 7.

The incremental increase of 0.6 in. (1.5 cm) of required minimum clear width between rows for each additional seat to be passed to reach an aisle is the same here as in the case of the row served by aisles at each end. (*See 8-2.5.6.3.*)

The 30-ft (9.1-m) limit effectively means that only about 18 chairs can be put into a row served by an aisle at one end only, assuming that, when one reaches the aisle, it is possible to move in either of two directions to two exits. This requirement also influences the permitted maximum length of aisles providing a common path of travel to reach the two exits. (*Also see 8-2.5.8.1.*)

8-2.5.6.5 Chairs without dividing arms shall have their capacity determined by allowing 18 in. (45.7 cm) per person.

The fact that the *Code* uses the traditional 18-in. (45.7-cm) figure for seat width per person for determining maximum occupant load (and egress capacity) should not necessarily be taken as an endorsement for using the 18-in. (45.7-cm) figure as a basis for ticket sales. This is especially true where events are sold out and a specific seat is assigned on each ticket. Winter events, where spectators wear bulkier clothing, are examples of those for which a more generous seat spacing should be considered in the ticket sales policy. Generally, the 18-in. (45.7-cm) figure — applied to ticket sales — makes most sense with children and younger adults, under temperate weather conditions, and with a general admission policy when a full house is not expected. Otherwise, the space to be kept clear in aisles and other means of egress might be compromised.

8-2.5.6.6 Where bleacher or grandstand seating without backs is used indoors, rows of seats shall be spaced not less than 22 in. (55.9 cm) back to back.

Exception: Folding or telescopic seating shall comply with NFPA 102, Standard for Assembly Seating, Tents, and Membrane Structures, with a limit of dead ends in vertical aisles of 16 rows.

The elimination of backs allows the entire bleacher to be a path of exit access. Assuming they are fit and agile, people can simultaneously evacuate a bleacher upward or downward without using aisles. This compensates somewhat for the openness of bleacher-type structures, which can expose the entire population to a single fire either under or adjacent to the structure. The provisions of the *Code* concerning bleacher or grandstand seating and folding or telescopic seating have been modified to coordinate requirements with NFPA 102, *Standard for Assembly Seating, Tents, and Membrane Structures.*[9] It should be noted that, unless certain criteria are met (as required by NFPA 102), aisles are required for bleachers, and such aisles must meet requirements comparable to those in the *Code*.

8-2.5.6.7 Rows of seating including tablet-arm chairs shall only be permitted if the clear width of aisle accessways complies with the requirements of 8-2.5.6 when the tablet is in the usable position.

Exception: Tablet arms shall be permitted to be measured in the stored position where the tablet arm automatically returns to the stored position when raised manually to a vertical position in one motion and falls to the stored position by force of gravity.

The Committee carefully examined the subject of tablet-arm chairs with storing provisions and determined that these chairs present little threat to life safety. Where the tablet arm is fixed in the use position, tablet-arm chairs must be arranged to meet the row spacing requirements found in 8-2.5.6. Figure 8-9 illustrates this provision. Note the Exception to 8-2.5.6.7.

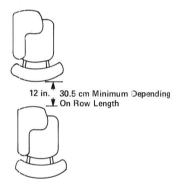

12 in.   30.5 cm Minimum Depending
On Row Length

Figure 8-9.   Minimum Spacing Between Rows of Seats with Fixed Tablet Arms. Measure with the tablet arm in the up (in-use) position. The clear space between the back of a seat and the leading edge of a tablet arm in normal seating is set by 8-2.5.6.7, depending on row length, but not less than 12 in. (30.5 cm).

8-2.5.7*   Aisle Accessways Serving Seating at Tables.

A-8-2.5.7   For purposes of the means of egress requirements of this *Code,* seating at counters or other furnishings is considered to be the same as seating at tables.

These provisions are new to the 1991 Edition of the *Code.* For the first time aisle accessways at tables are addressed (*see the new definition of aisle accessway in 8-1.3*). The appendix notes help explain the intent of the *Code.*

8-2.5.7.1*   The minimum required clear width of aisle accessway shall be 12 in. (30.5 cm) measured in accordance with 8-2.5.5 3 and increased as a function of length in accordance with 8-2.5.7.2.

Exception: If used by not more than four persons, there is no minimum clear width requirement for the portion of aisle accessway having a length not exceeding 6 ft (1.8 m) and located farthest from an aisle.

A-8-2.5.7.1   Effectively, where the aisle accessway is bounded by movable seating, the 12-in. (30.5-cm) minimum width might be increased by about 15 to 30 in. (38 to 76 cm) as seating is pushed in toward tables. Moreover, it is such movement of chairs during normal and emergency egress situations that makes the zero-clearance exception workable. The exception also applies to booth seating where people sitting closest to the aisle normally move out ahead of anyone farthest from the aisle.

8-2.5.7.2*   The minimum required clear width of aisle accessway measured in accordance with 8-2.5.5.3 and 8-2.5.5.4 shall be increased beyond the 12-in. (30.5-cm) requirement by 0.5 in. (1.3 cm) for each additional 12 in. (30.5 cm) or fraction thereof beyond 12 ft (3.7 m) of aisle accessway length measured from the center of the seat farthest from an aisle.

A-8-2.5.7.2   Minimum width requirement as a function of accessway length:

0 in. (0 cm) for the first 6 ft (1.8 m) of length toward the exit;

12 in. (30.5 cm) for the next 6 ft (1.8 m), i.e., up to 12 ft (3.7 m) of length;

12 in. to 24 in. (30.5 cm to 61 cm) for lengths from 12 ft to 36 ft (3.7 m to 10.9 m), the maximum length to the closest aisle or egress doorway permitted by 8-2.5.7.3.

Add to these widths any additional width needed for seating as described in 8-2.5.5.3.

8-2.5.7.3   The path of travel shall not exceed 30 ft (9.1 m) from any seat to the point where a person has a choice of two or more paths of travel to separate exits. The path of travel along the aisle accessway shall not exceed 36 ft (10.9 m) from any seat to the closest aisle or egress doorway.

8-2.5.8 Aisles Serving Seating Not at Tables.

8-2.5.8.1 Dead-end aisles shall not exceed 20 ft (6.1 m) in length.

Exception: A longer dead-end aisle is permitted where seats served by the dead-end aisle are not more than 24 seats from another aisle measured along a row of seats having a minimum clear width of 12 in. (30.5 cm) plus 0.6 in. (1.5 cm) for each additional seat over a total of 7 in the row.

The exception gives formal recognition to the inherent redundancy that exists where rows of seating are served by two or more aisles so that the blockage of any one aisle simply means that there is greater movement along rows to reach a somewhat more distant aisle. The exception recognizes that movement along rows, even with their constricted widths, provides many routes that permit faster movement to alternative aisles than would be possible with a dedicated cross aisle. As with the concept of wider clear spacings between rows where rows are longer (8-2.5.6.3), this exception gives additional credit for increased space to move along the rows to reach alternative aisles. At the row length limit of 24 seats, the required clear width spacing for use of this exception is 22.2 in. (56.4 cm). The exception may prove helpful in situations such as arenas and theaters where it is not easy to provide a cross aisle, doorway, etc., giving access to an exit, but where two or more aisles are relatively easy to reach when moving along rows. (*Also see 8-2.5.6.4.*)

8-2.5.8.2 The minimum clear width of aisles shall be sufficient to provide egress capacity in accordance with 8-2.3.2 but shall be not less than:

(a) 48 in. (122 cm) for stairs having seating on each side.

(b) 36 in. (91 cm) for stairs having seating on only one side.

(c) 23 in. (58 cm) between a handrail and seating or a guardrail where the aisle is subdivided by a handrail.

(d) 42 in. (107 cm) for level or ramped aisles having seating on both sides.

(e) 36 in. (91 cm) for level or ramped aisles having seating on only one side.

(f) 23 in. (58 cm) between a handrail or guardrail and seating where the aisle does not serve more than five rows on one side.

These requirements will often govern the final minimum widths of aisles, especially where a relatively limited amount of egress capacity is required by 8-2.3.1. The requirements of 8-2.5.8.2 take into account the width needed by individuals moving alone or with others, overtaking others, and moving in counterflow past others on aisles. Account is taken of the differing movement behavior and needs for handrails, for example, on various types of circulation facilities. Figures 8-10 and 8-11 illustrate how intensively a 48-in. (122-cm) aisle stair subdivided by a center handrail can be used. Figure 8-12 shows, in overhead plan view, a large male walking down one side of a similar aisle stair, 48 in. (122 cm) wide, subdivided by a handrail. Chair seating is shown adjoining the aisle in these photographs.

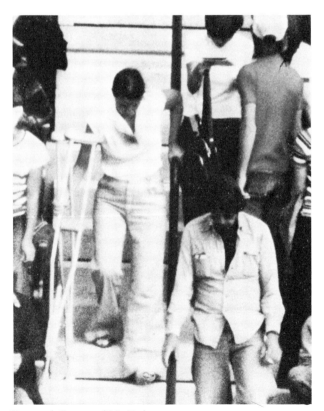

Photograph Courtesy of J. L. Pauls.
Figure 8-10. *Intensive Use of Aisle Stair, 48 in. (122 cm) Wide with Central Handrail, in a Stadium.*

Photograph Courtesy of J. L. Pauls.

Figure 8-11. *Intensive Use of Handrail at Center of 48-in. (122-cm) Aisle Stair in a Stadium. The handrail height is approximately 34 in. (86.3 cm).*

Paragraph 8-2.5.8.2(f) is based on the requirement for handrails in aisle stairs. It specifically addresses the allowance for extending such handrails down the center of aisles for as much as five rows, leaving only about 23 in. (58 cm) of nominal width clear to the side of the handrail. This width is readily used by individuals moving in single or staggered file and can be used with tolerable inconvenience where people must pass by each other on the same side of the handrail. This provision of the *Code* might be helpful in cases where a short stub aisle is needed to serve rows of seating immediately beside a vomitory.

Generally, it might be noted that the effective width of aisles is often somewhat wider than is the case for egress facilities that are bounded on both sides by construction. One important exception to this generalization

Photograph Courtesy of J. L. Pauls.

Figure 8-12. *Overhead Plan View of 48-in. (122-cm) Aisle Stair, with Center Handrail, Used by a Large Male.*

occurs where many people are attempting to sit on undivided benches or bleachers served by an aisle. The 18-in. (45.7-cm) spacing usually provided for each person is often too small, and there is a natural tendency for people to have their legs (sometimes several inches of hips and shoulders) occupying a significant part of the aisle width. Therefore, it is prudent when designing for crowded, nonchair seating to increase either the width of seat per person or the minimum aisle widths shown here by several inches on each side to facilitate normal circulation in the aisles.

8-2.5.8.3* **Aisle Stairs and Ramps.** Aisles having a gradient steeper than 1 in 20 but not steeper than 1 in 8 shall consist of a ramp. Aisles having a gradient steeper than 1 in 8 shall consist of an aisle stair.

A-8-2.5.8.3 Technical information about the convenience and safety of ramps and stairs having gradients in the region of 1 in 8 clearly suggests that the goal should be slopes for ramps that are less steep and better combinations of stair risers and treads than, for example, 4-in. (10.2-cm) risers and 32-in. (81-cm) treads. This should be kept in mind by designers in establishing the gradient of seating areas to be served by aisles.

Major changes relating to aisles were introduced in the 1985 Edition of the *Code*. The 1988 *Code* contained some minor changes that further emphasize the importance of design details for aisles. The 1991 *Code* has made some further modifications along with editorial renumbering. The changes in the previous and current editions address the need to design aisle stairs, for example, with all the attention and care required for stairs generally, plus additional care due to the unique design and use conditions encountered with aisles serving seating arranged in rows, especially where there are large elevation differences between the rows of seating. Paragraph 8-2.5.8.3 begins with a general requirement that divides aisles into two categories based on slope. Ideally, it would be preferable to avoid designing aisles having about a 1 in 8 slope; however, sightlines might dictate such slopes in some situations. Ramps of this slope are relatively steep and problematic for people with walking difficulties. Stairs with a very small rise and long treads also present problems, notably trips and missteps, because the presence of the low risers might not be evident, especially in a crowd situation. Generally, aisles also present unusual distractions for people because of their unusual length, the presence of other people in the aisles, and the presence of those entering the aisles from adjoining seating rows. Therefore, aisles of all slopes must be designed with considerable care and attention to human factors, for the sake of both the movement of individuals and that of crowds.

8-2.5.8.4 **Aisle Stair Treads.**

(a) There shall be no variation exceeding ⁹/₁₆ in. (0.5 cm) in the depth of adjacent treads.

Allowing unequal-sized treads within aisle stairs, a traditional practice once believed to be useful in facilitating access to seat rows, is not permitted by the *Code*. Even with the increased minimum tread size requirement of older editions of the *Code*, the end result (larger treads at the seat row entry level and smaller intermediate treads between seat row levels) was not as beneficial in terms of stair safety as consistently sized treads. This is true even for uniformly sized treads as large as about 20 in. (50.8 cm) in depth (assuming a relatively low riser height). Handrails, required by 8-2.5.8.6, help to compensate for the stretched but consistent stride length that may be needed in such long-tread aisle stairs. It is preferable to keep treads uniform so that the risk of misstepping, particularly the risk of overstepping of relatively smaller treads, is reduced.

It cannot be overemphasized that special attention must be given to careful design detailing and construction practice in relation to the placement of treads in aisle stairs. Careful site supervision is recommended to avoid serious problems both in cast-in-place concrete construction and in precast concrete construction of aisle stairs. Field research studies of situations where aisle step dimensions are not consistent indicate that the incidence of missteps rises significantly where tolerances of tread uniformity are not respected.

(b)* Treads shall be a minimum of 11 in. (27.9 cm).

A-8-2.5.8.4(b) Tread depth is more important to stair safety than is riser height. Therefore, in cases where seating area gradient is less than 5 in 11, it is recommended that the tread dimension be increased beyond 11 in. (27.9 cm) rather than reducing the riser height. Where seating area gradient exceeds 8 in 11, it is recommended that the riser height be increased while maintaining a tread depth of at least 11 in. (27.9 cm).

Figure 8-13 shows a side view of an aisle stair with 11-in. (28-cm) treads used by a person with footwear measuring 12 in. (30.5 cm) in length — a condition found in the case of 5 percent of adults generally and a condition that might be somewhat more common in those assembly situations attracting a higher proportion of male adults.

It should also be noted, in relation to 8-2.5.8.4(a), that there is apparently no difficulty when entering or leaving the aisles or when entering or leaving the seat row where the provision of the three equal-sized, 11-in. (17.9-cm) treads at each seat row are used, as shown in the photograph.

Photograph Courtesy of J. L. Pauls.

Figure 8-13. *Side View of Aisle Stair with 11-in. (17.9-cm) Treads in a Stadium.*

8-2.5.8.5 Aisle Stair Risers.

(a) Riser heights shall be a minimum of 4 in. (10.2 cm).

At the minimum slope limit set by the *Code* for aisle stairs (for slopes exceeding 1 in 8), there is a riser height of 4 in. (10.2 cm) where the seat platform is 32 in. (81.3 cm) deep. At such low riser heights, which present a tripping hazard if the risers are not detected by people, there is special significance in the tread nosing marking requirement in 8-2.5.8.7.

(b) Riser heights shall not exceed 8 in. (20.3 cm).

Exception No. 1 to (b): Where the gradient of an aisle is steeper than 8 in. (20.3 cm) in rise in 11 in. (27.9 cm) of run (to maintain necessary sight lines in the adjoining seating area), the riser height may exceed 8 in. (20.3 cm) but shall not exceed 9 in. (22.9 cm).

Exception No. 2 to (b): Folding and telescopic seating in accordance with NFPA 102, Standard for Assembly Seating, Tents, and Membrane Structures.

The 1988 Edition of the *Code* reduced the maximum riser height permitted for new aisle stairs from 11 in. (27.9 cm) to 9 in. (22.9 cm). In addition to reducing movement safety, the unusually high risers of some aisle stairs reduce the speed and efficiency of movement, especially in the descending direction. This is taken into account in 8-2.3.2 where, for each additional inch of riser height above 7 in. (17.9 cm), an additional 20 percent must be added to the required capacity-related width of the aisle to satisfy *Code* requirements and achieve an acceptable egress flow time performance.

(c) Riser heights shall be designed to be uniform in each aisle, and the construction-caused nonuniformities shall not exceed ³/₁₆ in. (0.5 cm) between adjacent risers.

Exception to (c): Riser height shall be permitted to be non-uniform only for the purpose of accommodating necessary changes in gradient to maintain sight lines within a seating area and shall be permitted to exceed ³/₈ in. (1 cm) in any flight. Where nonuniformities exceed ³/₁₆ in. (0.5 cm) between adjacent risers, the exact location of such nonuniformities shall be indicated by a distinctive marking stripe on each tread at the nosing or leading edge adjacent to the nonuniform risers.

A special case is made here for especially nonuniform riser heights, beyond the usual ³/₁₆-in. (0.5-cm) tolerance, only for situations where there is a break in the slope of a seating deck to maintain adequate sightlines. The seating deck slope may change incrementally at each row or, more commonly, there may be a large change at one or more locations. At such locations, there is often a change on the row-to-row elevation that greatly exceeds the usual ³/₁₆-in. (0.5-cm) tolerance. Aisle step riser heights will, as a consequence, change radically at this point. It is the special duty of the designer and owner to warn people using the aisle of this unusual change in the riser dimensions. This warning might go well beyond the usual marking of all step nosings required by 8-2.5.8.7. A distinctive color or other standard hazard marking is needed on the step nosings. Additional warning techniques may have to be employed in some cases to help reduce the risk of stumbles and falls.

8-2.5.8.6* **Aisle Handrails.** Ramped aisles having a gradient exceeding 1 in 12 and aisle stairs shall be provided with handrails at one side or along the centerline.

Where there is seating on both sides of the aisle, the handrails shall be discontinuous with gaps or breaks at intervals not exceeding five rows to facilitate access to seating and to permit crossing from one side of the aisle to the other. These gaps or breaks shall have a clear width of a least 22 in. (55.9 cm) and not greater than 36 in. (91 cm) measured horizontally, and the handrail shall have rounded terminations or bends. Where handrails are provided in the middle of aisle stairs, there shall be an additional intermediate rail located approximately 12 in. (30 cm) below the main handrail.

Exception No. 1: Handrails are not required for ramped aisles having a gradient not steeper than 1 in 8 and having seating on both sides.

Exception No. 2: The requirement for a handrail is satisfied by the use of a guard providing a rail that complies with the graspability requirements for handrails and is located at a consistent height between 34 in. (86 cm) and 42 in. (107 cm) measured vertically from the top of the rail to the leading edge (nosing) of stair treads or to the adjacent walking surface in the case of a ramp.

A-8-2.5.8.6 Failure to provide a handrail within a 30-in. (76-cm) horizontal distance of all required portions of the aisle stair width will mean that the egress capacity calculation must be modified as required by 8-2.3.2(b). This might lead to an increase in the aisle width. Although this will compensate for reduced egress efficiency, it does not help individuals walking on such portions of stairs to recover from missteps (other than possibly reducing marginally the crowding that might exacerbate the problem of falls). (*See also 5-2.2.4.*)

It should be noted that there is no longer an exception permitting aisle stairs without handrails in new construction where riser heights are less than 7 in. (17.9 cm). This is a result of increased experience with the provision and use of aisle handrails, as well as a general realization that aisles pose unique challenges to users that might go beyond those encountered on other ramps and stairs. Fig-

ures 8-10 and 8-11 illustrate the variety of use conditions in aisles and the extensive use of handrails. In field research studies, aisle stair handrail use has been shown to be used about twice as often as handrails provided to meet *Code* requirements for non-aisle stairs. When one considers the unusual lengths of aisles, the unusual step geometries, and the very complex use conditions (with people entering and leaving the aisle at many rows), this high level of use is not surprising. Aside from their value in increasing the safety and comfort of people using the aisles, the handrails also help to improve egress efficiency — a benefit taken into account in calculation of egress capacity. (*See 8-2.3.2.*)

The required gaps between sections of center-aisle handrails are illustrated in Figure 8-12. Spacing such gaps as frequently as every three rows is recommended where there is extensive use of aisles during events. A greater spacing of up to five rows between gaps might be acceptable where there is little use of the aisles during events and little counterflow at any time. Gap size should be kept at the lower end of the permitted range of 22 to 36 in. (55.9 cm to 91 cm) where the aisles are unusually steep and handrail use is especially valuable in reducing the risk of falls.

Exception No. 2 takes into account the proven utility of handrails that are higher than those permitted, even with the increased handrail height range introduced with the 1988 Edition of the *Code*. A guardrail that is 42 in. (107 cm) high, such as at the side of an aisle where there is a vomitory, can be considered a usable handrail if it offers graspability as required for handrails. (*See 5-2.2.4.5.*)

8-2.5.8.7* **Aisle Marking.** A contrasting marking stripe shall be provided on each tread at the nosing or leading edge such that the location of such tread is readily apparent, particularly when viewed in descent. Such stripes shall be at least 1 in. (2.5 cm) wide and shall not exceed 2 in. (5 cm) in width.

Exception: The marking stripe is not required where tread surfaces and environmental conditions under all conditions of use are such that the location of each tread is readily apparent, particularly when viewed in descent.

A-8-2.5.8.7 Certain tread covering materials such as plush carpets, which are often used in theaters, produce an inherently well-marked tread nosing under most lighting conditions. On the other hand, concrete treads (with nosings having a sharp edge), especially under outdoor lighting conditions, are difficult to discriminate and therefore require an applied marking stripe. Slip resistance of such marking stripes should be similar to the rest of the treads, and no tripping hazard should be created.

Figure 8-14 suggests some of the step visibility difficulties that are commonly encountered in outdoor facilities with concrete treads. Without the helpful shadows from the handrail posts, there would be little indication of the exact location of each tread nosing. This situation requires the applied nosing markings referred to in 8-2.5.8.7. The distractions of the playing field and the unusually long aisle add further justification for making the steps as obvious as possible. It should be stressed that each situation needs to be carefully evaluated (with mockups at the design stage and inspection of actual conditions during use) to determine whether any improvements are warranted in marking and lighting such aisles.

8-2.5.9 Aisles Serving Seating at Tables.

Photograph Courtesy of J. L. Pauls.
Figure 8-14. *View Down Aisle Stair, Provided with Center Handrail, in a Stadium.*

8-2.5.9.1* Aisles that contain steps or that are ramped, such as the aisles serving dinner theatre style configurations, shall comply with the requirements of 8-2.5.8.

A-8-2.5.9.1 See 5-1.6 and A-5-1.6 for special circulation safety precautions applicable where small elevation differences occur.

8-2.5.9.2* The minimum width of aisles serving seating at tables shall be 44 in. (112 cm) where serving an occupant load greater than 50 and 36 in. (91 cm) where serving an occupant load of 50 or less.

A-8-2.5.9.2 Attention is drawn to the need to make facilities accessible to people using wheelchairs, and reference is made to ANSI A117.1, *Standard for Buildings and Facilities — Providing Accessibility and Usability for Physically Handicapped People*, which provides guidance on appropriate aisle widths. (*See Appendix B.*)

Also see 8-2.5.5, which applies to all aisles.

8-2.5.10 Approval of Layouts.

8-2.5.10.1 Where required by the authority having jurisdiction, plans drawn to scale showing the arrangement of furnishings or equipment shall be submitted to the authority by the building owner, manager, or authorized agent to substantiate conformance with the provisions of this section and shall constitute the only acceptable arrangement until revised or additional plans are submitted and approved.

Exception: Temporary deviations from the specifications of the approved plans shall be permitted provided the occupant load is not increased and the intent of this section is maintained.

8-2.6 Travel Distance to Exits. Exits shall be so arranged that the total length of travel from any point to reach an exit will not exceed 150 ft (45 m) in any assembly occupancy. (*See also Section 5-6.*)

Exception: The travel distance shall not exceed 200 ft (60 m) in assembly occupancies protected throughout by an approved automatic sprinkler system.

Travel distance to exits from balconies or galleries that are served by unenclosed stairways must be measured to include the distance on the slope of the stair in the plane of the nosings and the distance from the bottom of the stair to the exit. Travel distance is measured as illustrated in Figure 8-15.

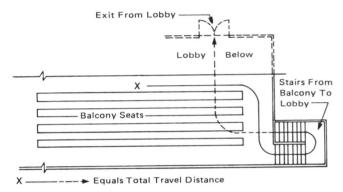

Figure 8-15. Measurement of Travel Distance to Exit Where Balconies Are Served by Unenclosed Stairs.

8-2.7 Discharge from Exits.

8-2.7.1 Exit discharge shall comply with Section 5-7.

8-2.7.2 The level of exit discharge shall be measured at the point of principal entrance to the building.

8-2.7.3 Where the principal entrance to an assembly occupancy is via a terrace, either raised or depressed, such terrace may be considered to be the level of exit discharge for the purposes of 8-1.6 if:

(a) The terrace is at least as long (measured parallel to the building) as the total width of the exit(s) it serves, but not less than 5 ft (152 cm) long, and

(b) The terrace is at least as wide (measured perpendicularly to the building) as the exit(s) it serves, but not less than 10 ft (3 m) wide, and

(c) Required stairs leading from the terrace to grade are protected in accordance with 5-2.2.6.3 or are a minimum of 10 ft (3 m) from the building.

The Committee determined that 10 ft (3 m) was the minimum distance necessary to allow people to exit the building in a depressed or raised area without causing a jamming effect at the exit. The same result was intended in requiring stairs to be at least 10 ft (3 m) from the face of the building unless they are protected as provided in Chapter 5.

The requirements of 8-2.7.3 are illustrated in Figure 8-16.

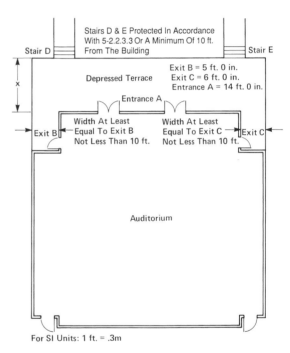

For SI Units: 1 ft. = .3m

Figure 8-16. Assembly Occupancy with Depressed Terrace as Principal Entrance. Assuming that Stair D serves Exit B plus one-half of Entrance A and that Stair E serves Exit C plus one-half of Entrance A, then X must be equal to or greater than the largest of the following: 10 ft (3 m) per 8-2.7.3(b); 5 ft (1.5 m) + ½ of 14 ft (4.2 m) = 12 ft (3.6 m); or 6 ft (1.8 m) + ½ of 14 ft (4.2 m) = 13 ft (3.9 m). Therefore, X ≥ 13 ft (3.9 m).

8-2.8 Illumination of Means of Egress. Means of egress shall be illuminated in accordance with Section 5-8.

8-2.9 Emergency Lighting. Emergency lighting shall be provided in accordance with Section 5-9.

See Formal Interpretation 76-72 on the next page.

8-2.10 Marking of Means of Egress. Means of egress shall have signs in accordance with Section 5-10.

Formal Interpretation 76-72
Reference: 8-2.9, 9-2.9

Question: Where the *Code* states that all assembly occupancies and the means of egress shall be provided with emergency lighting, does this include Class C Assembly Occupancies, such as restaurants and drive-ins that have glass almost all around the dining area?

Answer: Yes. However, the authority having jurisdiction may modify the requirements if the authority feels adequate lighting is maintained from external sources.

Issue Edition: 1976
Reference: 8-2.10
Date: September 1978 ∎

8-2.11 Special Features.

8-2.11.1 Railings.

(a) The fasciae of boxes, balconies, and galleries shall not rise less than 26 in. (66 cm) high above the adjacent floor or shall have substantial railings not less than 26 in. (66 cm) high above the adjacent floor.

(b) The height of the rail above footrests on the adjacent floor immediately in front of a row of seats shall be no less than 26 in. (66 cm). Railings at the ends of aisles shall be not less than 36 in. (91 cm) high for the full width of the aisle and shall be not less than 42 in. (107 cm) high for the width of the aisle where steps occur.

(c) Cross aisles shall be provided with railings not less than 26 in. (66 cm) high above the adjacent floor.

Exception: Where the backs of seats located at the front of the aisle project 24 in. (61 cm) or more above the adjacent floor of the aisle.

Figure 8-17a illustrates the requirements of 8-2.11.1(a) and (b). Rail height at the fascia end of a sloping aisle must not be less than 36 in. (91 cm). However, where the aisle is not ramped but has steps, the rail height must be at least 42 in. (107 cm). There is greater danger of people tripping on steps than on a sloping surface with a maximum gradient of 1 ft (0.3 m) of rise to 8 ft (2.44 m) of run.

The *Code* requires a barrier along the downhill side of a cross aisle. [*See 8-2.11.1(c).*] The barrier may be a rail or the backs of the seats that abut the downhill side of the aisle where the backs project 24 in. (60 cm) or more above the cross aisle. The difference between the 24-in. (60-cm) back height and the required 26-in. (66-cm) railing is not sufficient to require the railing. It is not the intent to reduce the height of guards where sight lines are not a problem, such as with cross aisles at the rear or top of seating areas or where cross aisles are sufficiently below seating that a proper height guard will not interfere with sight lines. (*See Figure 8-17b.*)

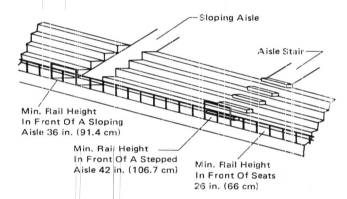

Min. Rail Height
In Front Of A Sloping
Aisle 36 in. (91.4 cm)

Min. Rail Height
In Front Of A Stepped
Aisle 42 in. (106.7 cm)

Min. Rail Height
In Front Of Seats
26 in. (66 cm)

Figure 8-17a. Railings Installed in Accordance with 8-2.11.1(a) and (b).

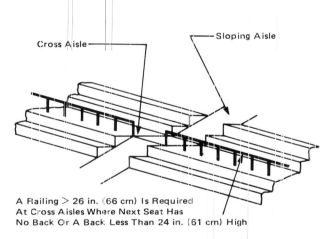

A Railing > 26 in. (66 cm) Is Required
At Cross Aisles Where Next Seat Has
No Back Or A Back Less Than 24 in. (61 cm) High

Figure 8-17b. Barrier for Cross Aisles in Accordance with 8-2.11.1(c). A railing [greater than 26 in. (66 cm)] is required unless the backs of seats in the row in front of the cross aisle are greater than 24 in. (60 cm) high above the cross aisle.

SECTION 8-3   Protection

8-3.1 **Protection of Vertical Openings.** Vertical openings shall be enclosed or protected in accordance with Section 6-2.

Exception No. 1: Unprotected vertical openings connecting not more than three floors in accordance with 6-2.4.5 shall be permitted.

Exception No. 2: Atriums in accordance with 6-2.4.6 shall be permitted.

Exception No. 3: Stairs or ramps shall be permitted to be unenclosed between balconies or mezzanines and main assembly areas located below provided the balcony or mezzanine is open to the main assembly area.*

A-8-3.1 **Exception No. 3.** The exception presumes the balcony or mezzanine complies with the other provisions of the *Code* such as travel distance to exits in accordance with 8-2.6 and numbers of exits in accordance with 8-2.4. For the purposes of this exception, a balcony with glazing that provides a visual awareness of the main assembly area is considered open.

Exceptions No. 1 and 2 permit the use of 6-2.4.5 and 6-2.4.6; see 6-2.4.5 and 6-2.4.6 for details. For egress requirements from balconies, see 8-2.4.4, 8-2.4.5, and 8-2.4.6.

8-3.2 **Protection from Hazards.**

8-3.2.1 **Stages and Platforms.** (*See 8-1.3.*)

Modern stages pose problems that didn't exist in the past. Scenery may be shifted horizontally, vertically, or both ways. The use of thrust stages and arena stages creates other problems.

The classic stage of the past rose high above the proscenium opening to accommodate the rigid asbestos curtain. The high void was a natural place to house combustible scenery for a performance, along with the rigging necessary for handling scene changes. This vertical storage area represented both a high fuel load and a space difficult to reach in case of fire. Many new theaters use

a flexible noncombustible curtain that does not require much height to accommodate it. Scenery on these stages is moved horizontally, thus reducing the distance necessary for storage between the top of the proscenium opening and the stage ceiling. Most combustible scenery is now stored in areas adjacent to the stage. All rigging and lighting is condensed in less vertical space.

8-3.2.1.1 **Materials and Design.** Materials used in the construction of platforms and stages shall conform to the applicable requirements of the local building code.

8-3.2.1.2 **Platform Construction.** Temporary platforms shall be permitted to be constructed of any materials. The space between the floor and the platform above shall not be used for any purpose other than electrical wiring to platform equipment.

Permanent platforms shall be constructed of materials as required for the type of construction of the building in which the permanent platform is located. Where the space beneath the platform is used for storage or any purpose other than equipment wiring or plumbing, the floor construction shall be not less than 1-hour fire-resistive. Where the space beneath the platform is not used for any purpose other than equipment wiring or plumbing, the underside of the permanent platform need not be protected.

8-3.2.1.3 **Stage Construction.** Regular stages and thrust stages shall be constructed of materials as required for the type of construction of the building in which they are located. In all cases the finish floor shall be permitted to be of wood.

Legitimate stages shall be constructed of materials required for Type I buildings except that the area extending from the proscenium opening to the back wall of the stage, and for a distance of 6 ft (183 cm) beyond the proscenium opening on each side, shall be permitted to be constructed of steel or heavy timber covered with a wood floor not less than 1½ in. (3.8 cm) in actual thickness.

Openings through stage floors (traps) shall be equipped with tight-fitting trap doors of wood having an actual thickness of not less than 1½ in. (3.8 cm) with approved safety locks.

8-3.2.1.4 **Accessory Rooms.** Dressing rooms, workshops, and storerooms accessory to stages shall be separated from each other and from the stage by not less than 1-hour fire-resistive construction, and openings within such separations shall be protected as required for corridors (20-minute fire door assemblies).

Exception: A separation is not required for platforms or regular stages having a floor area not exceeding 1000 sq ft (93 sq m).

8-3.2.1.5   Vents. Legitimate stages shall be provided with one or more vents constructed of noncombustible material. Ventilators shall be located near the center and above the highest part of the stage. They shall be raised above the stage roof and shall have a total ventilation area equal to at least 5 percent of the floor area of the stage.

Regular stages exceeding 1,000 sq ft (93 sq m) in area shall be provided with vents as required for legitimate stages or shall be provided with a mechanical vent installed in an exterior wall of the stage itself. Such vent shall be automatic upon operation of the sprinkler system and shall also be capable of manual operation. The capacity of the exhaust vent shall be approximately equivalent to that which would be provided for a legitimate stage.

Vents shall open by spring action or force of gravity sufficient to overcome the effects of neglect, rust, dirt, frost, snow, or expansion by heat or warping of the framework. Glass, if used in vents, shall be protected to guard against falling onto the stage. A wire screen, if used under the glass, shall be so placed that, if clogged, it cannot reduce the required vent area or interfere with the operating mechanism or obstruct the distribution of water from an automatic sprinkler. Vents shall be arranged to open automatically by the use of fusible links. The fusible links and operating cable shall hold each door closed against the minimum 30 lb (133 N) counterforce, which may be exerted by springs or counterweights. This minimum counterforce shall be exerted on each door through its entire arc of travel and for a minimum of 115 degrees. A manual control shall also be provided.

Springs, where employed to actuate doors, shall be capable of maintaining full required tension. Springs shall not be stressed more than 50 percent of their rated capacity and shall not be located directly in the air stream nor exposed to the outside.

A fusible link shall be placed in the cable control system on the underside of the vents at or above the roofline or as approved by the authority having jurisdiction and shall be so located as not to be affected by the operation of a fire sprinkler system. Remote, manual, or electrical controls shall provide for both opening and closing of the vent doors for periodic testing and shall be located at a point on the stage designated by the authority having jurisdiction. Where remote control vents are electrical, power failure shall not affect their instant operation in the event of fire. Hand winches shall be permitted to be employed to facilitate operation of manually controlled vents.

Small schools typically have multipurpose classrooms and classrooms separated by folding partitions. These schools commonly have "stages" that are greater than 500 sq ft (46.5 sq m) but less than 1000 sq ft (93 sq m). The Committee felt the venting requirements were too restrictive for facilities with small stages. (*Also note the definitions for* "*stage*" *and* "*platform*" *in 8-1.3.*)

8-3.2.1.6   Proscenium Walls. Legitimate stages shall be completely separated from the seating area by a proscenium wall of not less than 2-hour fire-resistive noncombustible construction. The proscenium wall shall extend at least 4 ft (122 cm) above the roof of the auditorium.

Proscenium walls shall be permitted to have, in addition to the main proscenium opening, one opening at the orchestra pit level and not more than two openings into the auditorium at the legitimate stage floor level. Each such opening shall not be more than 25 sq ft (2.3 sq m) in area.

All openings in the proscenium wall of a legitimate stage shall be protected by a fire assembly having a 1½-hour fire protection rating, except that the main proscenium opening used for viewing performances shall be provided with an automatic-closing fire-resistive curtain as described in 8-3.2.1.7.

8-3.2.1.7   Proscenium Curtain. The proscenium opening of every legitimate stage shall be provided with a curtain made of approved materials constructed and mounted so as to intercept hot gases, flames, and smoke and to prevent a glow from a severe fire on the stage from showing on the auditorium side for a period of 30 minutes. The closing of the curtain from the full open position shall be effected in less than 30 seconds, but the last 8 ft (244 cm) of travel shall require not less than 5 seconds.

The proscenium curtain shall be constructed as follows:

(a) *Asbestos Fabrics.* Where not prohibited by applicable federal, state, or local law, a curtain may be made of one or more thicknesses of a minimum 2³/₄-lb/sq yd (1.5-kg/m²) AAA grade wire-inserted asbestos fabric or of another wire-inserted asbestos fabric of greater fire resistance than 2³/₄-lb/sq yd (1.5-kg/m²) AAA grade wire-inserted fabric. Nonasbestos portions of these fabrics, if any, shall be flame resistant treated so as not to support combustion.

(b) *Other Fabrics.* Curtains not meeting the above criteria shall be made of one or more thicknesses of a noncombustible fabric or a fabric with a noncombustible base material, which shall be permitted to be given a coating provided the modified fabric meets the criteria detailed in this section. Curtain fabrics shall have a minimum weight of 2³/₈ lb/sq yd (1.3 kg/m²).

(c) *Tensile Strength Requirements.* Curtain fabric shall have minimum tensile strength requirements of 400 lbf/in. (540 N/m) in both the warp and fill directions.

(d) *Wire-Insertion Reinforcement Requirements.* The fabric shall be reinforced with noncorrosive wire intertwined with the base fiber at a minimum rate of 1 wire per yarn. Wire is not required and fabric weight shall be permitted to be less than 2³/₈ lb/sq yd (1.3 kg/m²) if it can be substantiated by approved tests that it is equivalent in strength and durability.

(e) *Fire Test.* A sample curtain with a minimum of two vertical seams shall be subjected to the standard fire test specified in NFPA 251, *Standard Methods of Fire Tests of Building Construction and Materials*, as applicable to nonbearing walls and partitions for a period of 30 minutes. The curtain shall overlap the furnace edges by an amount that is appropriate to seal the top and sides. It shall have a bottom pocket containing a minimum 4 lb/linear ft (5 kg/m) of batten. The unexposed surface of the curtain shall not glow, and neither flame nor smoke shall penetrate the curtain during the test period. Unexposed surface temperature and hose stream test requirements are not applicable to this proscenium firesafety curtain test.

(f) *Smoke Test.* Curtain fabrics shall have a smoke density of no greater than 25 when tested in accordance with NFPA 255, *Standard Method of Test of Surface Burning Characteristics of Building Materials*. The curtain fabric shall be tested in the condition in which it is to be used.

The complete installation of every proscenium curtain shall be subjected to operating tests, and any theatre in which a proscenium curtain is placed shall not be open to public performance until after the proscenium curtain has been accepted and approved by the authority having jurisdiction. The curtain is to be kept in the normally closed position when each day's performances are completed.

The curtain shall be automatic-closing without the use of applied power. The curtain shall also be capable of manual operation.

Substitutes for asbestos have been a concern of environmentalists, school officials, and others. It was the intent of the Committee to provide guidelines for the use of materials other than asbestos.

The Committee has provided a complete rewrite on the requirements for proscenium curtains for new assembly occupancies. The requirements are intended to provide fire resistance and strength. New proscenium curtains in existing buildings will also need to meet these requirements, but Chapter 9 has not changed the requirements for existing buildings.

An important change for the 1991 *Code* is the requirement that the curtain be tested and approved before being used for public performance. It now also mandates that it be kept in the closed position after the performance is over. This is routinely done in Europe and helps ensure the proper operation of the curtain in an emergency. Another benefit is that it will help prevent property damage if a fire occurs after hours. (*Also see 31-2.10.*)

8-3.2.1.8 **Gridirons, Fly Galleries, and Pinrails.** Gridirons, fly galleries, and pinrails shall be constructed of noncombustible materials.

8-3.2.1.9 **Fire Protection.** Every stage shall have a system of automatic sprinklers at the ceiling, in usable spaces under the stage, in auxiliary spaces, and in dressing rooms, storerooms, and workshops. Where there is a stage gridiron, sidewall sprinklers rated at 135°F (57°C) with heat-baffle plates shall be installed around the perimeter of the stage, except above the proscenium opening, at points not more than 30 in. (76 cm) below the gridiron, and with sprinklers positioned 4 to 6 in. (10.2 to 15.2 cm) below the baffle plate.

Exception: Regular and thrust stages less than 1000 sq ft (93 sq m) in area.

Note the definitions for "stage" and "platform" in 8-1.3.

8-3.2.1.10 **Special Exiting.** Each side of a legitimate stage shall be provided with at least one well-marked exit providing not less than 32 in. (81 cm) clear width. Such exit shall open directly to a street, exit court, or exit passageway leading to a street.

Fly galleries shall be provided with a means of egress stair not less than 30 in. (76 cm) in width. Each tier of dressing rooms shall be provided with two means of egress meeting the requirements of the *Code*.

Stairways required by this subsection are not required to be enclosed.

8-3.2.1.11 **Flame-Retardant Requirements.** Combustible scenery of cloth, film, vegetation (dry), and similar effects shall meet the requirements of NFPA 701, *Standard Methods of Fire Tests for Flame-Resistant Textiles and Films.* Foamed plastics (*see Section 3-2*) may be used only by specific approval of the authority having jurisdiction. Scenery and stage properties on thrust stages shall be either noncombustible or limited-combustible materials.

In theaters, motion picture theaters, and television stage settings with or without horizontal projections, and simulated caves and caverns of foamed plastic, any single fuel package shall have a maximum heat release rate of 100 kW when tested in accordance with UL 1975, *Standard for Fire Tests for Foamed Plastic Used for Decorative Purposes.*

It is the Committee's intent to reduce the amount of combustible material on stages. Experience demonstrates that foamed plastics, as described in Chapter 6 (*see Section 3-2*), have contributed to rapid fire spread.

8-3.2.1.12 **Standpipes.** Regular stages over 1000 sq ft (93 sq m) in area and all legitimate stages shall be equipped with a Class III standpipe located on the stage at each side installed in accordance with 7-7.4.2.

There must be a standpipe located on each side of a stage to provide stage hands and the responding fire department with a manual fire fighting capability at the area of a theater where a fire is most likely to occur. The installation of the standpipes must comply with NFPA 14, *Standard for the Installation of Standpipe and Hose Systems.*[10] NFPA 13E, *Recommendations for Fire Department Operations in Properties Protected by Sprinkler and Standpipe Systems,*[11] should also be consulted for a discussion of the necessity of a properly installed standpipe system. Standpipes are required regardless of whether the stage has automatic sprinkler protection.

8-3.2.2 **Projection Booths.**

8-3.2.2.1 Every assembly occupancy where an electric arc, xenon, or other light source that generates hazardous gases, dust, or radiation is used shall have a projection room that complies with 8-3.2.2.2 from which projections shall be made. Where cellulose nitrate film is used, the projection room shall comply with NFPA 40, *Standard for the Storage and Handling of Cellulose Nitrate Motion Picture Film.* (*See also Chapter 31.*)

The requirements for projection booths were developed jointly with those of NFPA 40, *Standard for the Storage and Handling of Cellulose Nitrate Motion Picture Film,*[12] and the motion picture industry at the height of movie popularity, when cellulose nitrate film was still being used. Although only safety film is now used (except at film festivals or revivals) and the risk level has been reduced, the primary function of these requirements is to build a shelter around the projection booth, eliminating it as an exposure threat to the theater audience.

The intent of 8-3.2.2.1 is to protect the audience from the dangers associated with light sources, such as electric arc or Xenon. Where incandescent light is used, projection booths are not required in assembly occupancies. Note that the booth is required based on the light source, not on the projection of film.

Paragraph 31-2.8 requires that, unless the construction of a projection booth complies with NFPA 40, *Standard for the Storage and Handling of Cellulose Nitrate Motion Picture Film*, a conspicuous sign must be posted on the door of the projection booth and also inside the booth.

The sign must state: "Safety Film Only Permitted in This Room." The intent is to ensure that cellulose nitrate film is projected only with adequate safeguards.

8-3.2.2.2 **Projection Rooms for Safety Film.** Projection rooms for safety film shall comply with 8-3.2.2.3 through 8-3.2.2.8.

It should be emphasized that 8-3.2.2.3 through 8-3.2.2.8 apply only to booths for the projection of cellulose acetate or other safety film. Although openings in the booth do not need to be protected, they must be provided with glass or other approved material that will completely close the opening and prevent gas, dust, or radiation from contaminating the audience or seating area.

8-3.2.2.3 Every projection room shall be of permanent construction consistent with the construction requirements for the type of building in which the projection room is located. Openings are not required to be protected. The room shall have a floor area of not less than 80 sq ft (7.4 sq m) for a single machine and at least 40 sq ft (3.7 sq m) for each additional machine. Each motion picture projector, floodlight, spotlight, or similar piece of equipment shall have a clear working space of not less than 30 in. (76 cm) on each side and at its rear, but only one such space shall be required between adjacent projectors.

The projection room and the rooms appurtenant thereto shall have a ceiling height of not less than 7 ft 6 in. (229 cm).

8-3.2.2.4 Each projection room shall have at least one outswinging, self-closing door not less than 30 in. (76 cm) wide and 6 ft 8 in. (203 cm) high.

8-3.2.2.5 The aggregate of ports and openings for projection equipment shall not exceed 25 percent of the area of the wall between the projection room and the auditorium.

All openings shall be provided with glass or other approved material so as to completely close the opening.

8-3.2.2.6 Projection room ventilation shall be not less than the following:

(a) *Supply Air.* Each projection room shall be provided with adequate air supply inlets so arranged to provide well distrib-

uted air throughout the room. Air inlet ducts shall provide an amount of air equivalent to the amount of air being exhausted by projection equipment. Air shall be permitted to be taken from the outside; from adjacent spaces within the building, provided the volume and infiltration rate is sufficient; or from the building air conditioning system, provided it is so arranged as to supply sufficient air whether or not other systems are in operation.

(b) *Exhaust Air.* Projection booths shall be permitted to be exhausted through the lamp exhaust system. The lamp exhaust system shall be positively interconnected with the lamp so that the lamp will not operate unless there is sufficient airflow required for the lamp. Exhaust air ducts shall terminate at the exterior of the building in such a location that the exhaust air cannot be readily recirculated into any air supply system. The projection room ventilation system shall be permitted to also serve appurtenant rooms, such as the generator room and the rewind room.

New projection equipment in new theaters have a console that draws air in at the floor and up through the projection machine, thus eliminating the need to provide ducts 12 in. (30.5 cm) off the floor.

The requirements for the ventilation of a projection booth are designed to effectively "isolate" the booth from the theater so that any products of combustion created by a fire in a projection booth are not circulated into the theater. This is achieved by providing an independent exhaust system for the booth, making certain that the exhaust outlet on the exterior of the building is located at a point where the air intake for the theater cannot recirculate the exhausted air.

If fresh air for the projection booth's ventilation system is supplied from the general system of the building, it is essential that the combined system be arranged to ensure the required air changes in the booth even when no air is supplied to the general system of the building.

8-3.2.2.7 Each projection machine shall be provided with an exhaust duct that will draw air from each lamp and exhaust it directly to the outside of the building. The lamp exhaust shall be permitted to serve to exhaust air from the projection room to provide room air circulation. Such ducts shall be of rigid materials, except for a flexible connector approved for the purpose. The projection lamp and projection room exhaust systems shall be permitted to be combined but shall not be interconnected with any other exhaust or return air system within the buildings.

(a) *Electric Arc Projection Equipment.* The exhaust capacity shall be 200 cfm (.09 cu m/s) for each lamp connected to the lamp exhaust system, or as recommended by the equipment manufacturer. Auxiliary air shall be permitted to be introduced into the system through a screened opening to stabilize the arc.

(b) *Xenon Projection Equipment.* The lamp exhaust system shall exhaust not less than 300 cfm (.14 cu m's) per lamp, or not less than that exhaust volume required or recommended by the equipment manufacturer, whichever is the greater.

The *Code* sets forth the minimum capacity for the exhaust system of a projection machine; however, a greater capacity must be provided where recommended by the manufacturer of the projection equipment. This system must be independent of any other ventilation system in the building housing the theater; however, it can be combined with projection room ventilation.

8-3.2.2.8 Miscellaneous Equipment and Storage.

(a) Each projection room shall be provided with rewind and film storage facilities.

(b) A maximum of four containers for flammable liquids of not greater than 16 oz (.5 L) capacity and of a nonbreakable type shall be permitted in each projection booth.

(c) Appurtenant electrical equipment, such as rheostats, transformers, and generators, may be located within the booth or in a separate room of equivalent construction.

The intent of the requirement for the storage and rewinding of film is to prevent these operations from occurring outside the projection booth at some less protected location where, if a fire occurred, the exposure to the theater would be significantly greater. All operations that relate to projection activities must be kept within the protected enclosure afforded by the projection booth.

8-3.2.3 Service Equipment, Hazardous Operations or Processes, and Storage Facilities.

8-3.2.3.1* Rooms containing high-pressure boilers, refrigerating machinery of other than domestic refrigerator type, large transformers, or other service equipment subject to possible explosion, shall not be located directly under or abutting required exits. All such rooms shall be separated from other parts of the building by fire barriers in accordance with 6-2.3 having a fire resistance rating of not less than 1 hour or protected by an automatic extinguishing system in accordance with Section 6-4.

A-8-3.2.3.1 See A-8-3.2.3.3(a) Exception.

The preservation of the integrity of exits in any building is one of the principal concerns of the *Code.* Therefore, hazardous areas, even if enclosed with the required fire resistant construction, must never be located where they might directly expose a required exit to fire.

8-3.2.3.2 Adequate vents to the outside air shall be provided in accordance with Section 6-4.

8-3.2.3.3 Rooms or spaces for the storage, processing, or use of material specified in this section shall be protected in accordance with the following:

(a)* Boiler and furnace rooms, rooms or spaces used for the storage of combustible supplies in quantities deemed hazardous by the authority having jurisdiction; hazardous materials in quantities deemed hazardous by recognized standards, or fuel shall be separated from the remainder of the building by fire barriers in accordance with 6-2.3 having a fire resistance rating of not less than 1 hour, or such rooms or spaces shall be protected by an automatic extinguishing system as required in Section 6-4.

A-8-3.2.3.3(a) It is not the intent of this provision to require a smoke barrier that meets the requirements of Section 6-3.

Exception to (a)*: Rooms enclosing air-handling equipment.

A-8-3.2.3.3(a) **Exception.** Rooms used solely for air-handling fans are excepted from the requirements of paragraph

8-3.2.3.3(a). However, if the air-handling room is used for storage, furnaces, boilers, or other uses outlined in 8-3.2.3.3(a) in addition to housing the air-handling equipment, the requirements of 8-3.2.3.3(a) should be applied.

(b) Laundries, maintenance shops, including woodworking and painting areas, rooms or spaces used for processing or use of combustible supplies in quantities considered hazardous by the authority having jurisdiction, hazardous materials, or flammable or combustible liquids in quantities deemed hazardous by recognized standards shall be separated from the remainder of the building by fire barriers in accordance with 6-2.3 having a fire resistance rating of not less than 1 hour and shall also be protected by an automatic extinguishing system as required in Section 6-4.

(c) Where automatic extinguishing is used to meet the requirements of this section, protection shall be permitted to be in accordance with 7-7.1.2.

Paragraph 8-3.2.3.3 has been revised in several ways. First, there is more reliance upon Section 6-4, which should be reviewed in conjunction with this paragraph since it has been rewritten. Second, some of the "typical" hazardous areas have been recategorized, with spaces that were previously mandated to be separated with 1-hour fire resistance rated construction now given the option of either 1-hour construction or sprinkler protection or, in some cases, mandated to have both. If sprinkler protection without fire rated separation is provided, then the intent of the Committee, through the reference to Section 6-4, is to restrict the passage of smoke by use of glass or other non-fire-rated material. This would not permit the use of "chicken-wire" or louvers but would not require all the components of a standard smoke barrier.

The Committee felt that the requirements identified in Chapter 7 for the use of six or fewer heads connected to the domestic system are adequate for these types of situations.

The intent of 8-3.2.3.3 is to specify the degree of protection necessary for certain hazardous areas. It has been divided into two sections based on the degree of hazard. The hazards noted in item (a) are required to be enclosed in 1-hour construction or protected by sprinklers. If the sprinkler option is chosen, an enclosure is still required;

however, the enclosure need not be rated, but only form a membrane against the passage of smoke.

The hazards noted in item (b) must be enclosed in 1-hour construction and be protected by automatic sprinklers.

The Exception to item (a) pertains to rooms housing air-handling equipment only. If the room is used for other purposes, then the provisions of item (a) or (b) apply.

Figures 8-18 a through c illustrate the methods of protection specified by 8-3.2.3.3.

The three different types of protection of hazardous areas are illustrated in these figures. Figures 8-18a and b illustrate the two options for complying with 8-3.2.3.3(a). Figure 8-18c illustrates the requirement of 8-3.2.3.3(b) that both fire-resistive separation and automatic protection be provided.

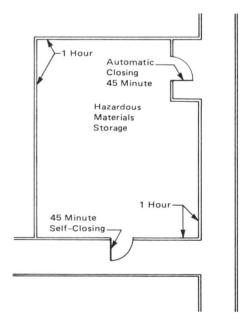

Figure 8-18a. Protection of Hazardous Areas. Figure 8-18a illustrates one method of complying with 8-3.2.3.3(a). [See Figure 8-18b for the alternate method.]

8-3.2.4 Special Provisions for Food Service Establishments.

8-3.2.4.1 All devices in connection with the preparation of food shall be so installed and operated as to avoid hazard to the safety of occupants.

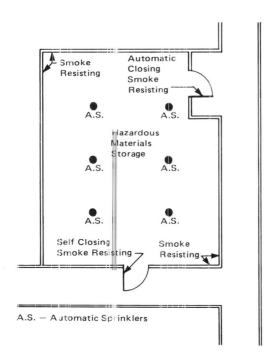

Figure 8-18b. *Protection of Hazardous Areas. Figure 8-18b illustrates an alternate method of complying with 8-3.2.3.3(a). Figure 8-18a illustrates another method of compliance.*

8-3.2.4.2 All devices in connection with the preparation of food shall be of an approved type and shall be installed in an approved manner.

An "approved type" of device means that, with regard to potential fire hazards, the unit is acceptable to the authority having jurisdiction. An "approved manner" of installation means installation in accordance with the requirements of the authority having jurisdiction.

8-3.2.4.3 Food preparation facilities shall be protected in accordance with 7-2.3 and are not required to have openings protected between food preparation areas and dining areas.

The *Code* depends on the automatic extinguishing system mandated by 7-2.3 to control any fire on the cooking surfaces and, thus, does not require enclosure by rated construction.

8-3.3 Interior Finish.

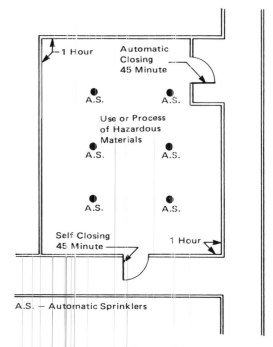

Figure 8-18c. *Protection of Hazardous Areas. Figure 8-18c illustrates the requirements for complying with 8-3.2.3.3(b). Both 1-hour separation and automatic sprinkler protection are required in this case.*

8-3.3.1 The interior finish requirements of this section shall be in accordance with Section 6-5.

8-3.3.2 Interior finish in all corridors and lobbies shall be Class A or B and, in enclosed stairways, Class A.

8-3.3.3 Interior finish in general assembly areas of Class A and B assembly occupancies shall be Class A or B. In Class C assembly occupancies, it shall be Class A, B, or C.

Exception: In any assembly occupancy, exposed portions of structural members complying with the requirements for Type IV (2HH) construction shall be permitted.

8-3.3.4 Screens on which pictures are projected shall comply with requirements of Class A or Class B interior finish.

8-3.4 Detection, Alarm, and Communication Systems.

8-3.4.1 General. Class A and Class B assembly occupancies and all theaters with more than one audience-viewing room shall be provided with an approved fire alarm system in accordance with 7-6.1 and this section.

Exception No. 1: Assembly occupancies that are a part of a mixed occupancy (see 1-5.7) shall be permitted to be served by a common fire alarm system provided the individual requirements of each occupancy are met.

Exception No. 2: Voice communication or public address systems complying with 8-3.4.3.3 are not required to comply with 7-6.1.

In Exception No. 1, the Committee wanted to clarify that the intent of the alarm requirements was to meet the requirements of each occupancy in a mixed occupancy situation. This would allow an assembly occupancy in a school, hotel, hospital, mall, or other building to be served by the same fire alarm as the predominate occupancy, provided it also met the requirements of the assembly occupancy. Although the intent of the Committee has not changed, the new Exception No. 2 makes it clear that, when a voice communication facility or public address system is installed to comply with 8-3.4.3.3, it is not intended to comply with 7-6.1. It is believed that the daily use of this system provides adequate self-supervision.

8-3.4.2 Initiation.

Also see 8-3.4.3.3 and 8-3.4.3.4.

8-3.4.2.1 Initiation of the required fire alarm system shall be by manual means in accordance with 7-6.2.1(a), which shall be provided with an emergency power source. The initiating device shall be capable of transmitting an alarm to a receiving station, located within the building, that is constantly attended when the assembly occupancy is occupied.

Exception No. 1: Initiation by means of an approved automatic fire detection system in accordance with 7-6.2.1(b) that provides fire detection throughout the building.

Exception No. 2: Initiation by means of an approved automatic sprinkler system in accordance with 7-6.2.1(c) that provides fire detection and protection throughout the building.

8-3.4.2.2* In all Class A and in all Class B assembly occupancies, automatic detection shall be provided in all hazardous areas that are not normally occupied.

Exception: Areas that are protected throughout by an approved automatic sprinkler system in accordance with 7-7.1.

A-8-3.4.2.2 The intent is to require detectors only in nonsprinklered hazardous areas that are unoccupied. When the building is occupied, the detectors in the unoccupied, unsprinklered hazardous areas will initiate occupant notification. If the building is unoccupied, the fire in the nonsprinklered hazardous area is not a life safety issue, and the detectors, upon activation, need not notify anyone. The signal from that detector may be sent to a control panel in an area that is occupied when the building is occupied but that is unoccupied when the building is unoccupied without the need for central station monitoring or equivalent.

This is a new provision for the 1991 *Code*. Non-sprinklered hazardous areas that are not occupied when the assembly area is in use could result in a fire developing that goes undiscovered. Although separated by 1-hour fire resistant barriers, such areas can present a significant hazard to occupants. Because a fire alarm system is already required, the additional requirement for either heat or smoke detection, as appropriate, is not a significant burden.

8-3.4.3 Notification.

8-3.4.3.1 The required fire alarm system shall sound an audible alarm in a constantly attended receiving station within the building when occupied for purposes of initiating emergency action.

8-3.4.3.2 Occupant notification shall be by means of voice announcements, either live or prerecorded, initiated by the person in the constantly attended location.

8-3.4.3.3 The announcement shall be made via an approved voice communication or public address system, provided with an emergency power source, that is audible above the ambient noise level of the assembly occupancy.

8-3.4.3.4 Where the authority having jurisdiction determines that it is impractical to have a constantly attended location, a fire alarm system in accordance with Section 7-6 that is initiated by manual stations in accordance with 7-6.2.1(a) or other approved means of initiation and that automatically provides prerecorded evacuation instructions in accordance with 7-6.3.8 shall be used.

The intent of the provisions of 8-3.4 is to provide an alarm system that will not elicit a panic reaction from occupants. Editions of the *Code* prior to 1981 required no alarm system. The intent of this section is to provide a system that will permit activation of the system by pull stations as required by 7-6.2.1, but that will not sound an audible alarm in the seating or audience areas of the assembly occupancy. In lieu of the audible alarm throughout the assembly occupancy, the system must sound an alarm in a constantly attended location. (Constantly attended, in this case, means that, during the time the assembly occupancy is in use, the alarm panel must be attended.) From that constantly attended location, voice messages that instruct the occupants can be issued via a public address system. This method allows for the orderly evacuation of the occupants and permits the issuance of proper evacuation instructions rather than simply sounding an evacuation alarm, which may produce panic. The *Code* permits the use of prerecorded evacuation instructions that will automatically be played upon initiation of the system. With the approval of the authority having jurisdiction, this arrangement may be used in lieu of the attended station.

8-3.5 Extinguishment Requirements. (*Also see 8-1.6, 8-2.6, 8-3.2, and 8-3.6.*)

8-3.5.1 Buildings containing Class A or Class B assembly occupancies shall be protected by an approved supervised automatic sprinkler system installed in accordance with Section 7-7 as follows:

(a) Throughout the story containing the assembly occupancy, and

(b) Throughout all stories below the story containing the assembly occupancy, and

(c) In the case of an assembly occupancy located below the level of exit discharge, throughout all stories intervening between that story and the level of exit discharge including the level of exit discharge.

Exception No. 1: Assembly occupancies used primarily for worship with fixed seating and not part of a mixed occupancy. (See 1-5.7.)

Exception No. 2: *Assembly occupancies consisting of a single multipurpose room of less than 12,000 sq ft (1,100 sq m) and not used for exhibition or display.*

A-8-3.5.1 **Exception No. 2.** It is the intent of the Committee to permit a "single multipurpose room of less than 12,000 sq ft (1,100 sq m)" to have certain small rooms as part of the single room. These rooms could be such as a kitchen, office, equipment room, and the like. It is also the intent that an addition could be made to an existing building without requiring that existing building be sprinklered where both the new and existing buildings have independent means of egress and a fire rated separation is provided to isolate one building from the other.

A school gymnasium with egress independent of and separated from the school would be included in this exception as would a function hall attached to a church with a similar egress arrangement.

Exception No. 3: Gymnasiums, skating rinks, and swimming pools used exclusively for participant sports with no audience facilities for more than 300.

This requirement was prompted by the occurrence of fires involving assembly occupancies, most notably the Beverly Hills Supper Club fire (1977)[3,4] and the MGM Grand Hotel fire (1980). The exceptions to the general requirement are important in that they limit the areas or buildings requiring the protection.

The concepts used in 8-1.6 are also used here with regard to which areas must be sprinklered. If a five-story building has an assembly occupancy on the first floor, only the first floor and any basements need to be sprinklered; if on the fifth floor, then the entire building would be required to be sprinklered.

The exceptions for auditoriums with fixed seating, passenger terminals at or above grade, and Class B assembly occupancies used exclusively for restaurants were eliminated in the 1988 *Code*. The Committee felt that these occupancies presented a sufficient life hazard to warrant automatic sprinkler protection where they had an occupant load greater than 300.

One clarification was added to the 1991 *Code* with regard to Exception No 1. If a mixed occupancy is involved, the exception cannot be used. This same concept is true for Exception No 2.

Exception No. 1 exempts places of worship with fixed seating. The life safety record is reasonably good in these occupancies.

Exception No. 2 exempts multipurpose assembly occupancies that are contained in one room and have an area of less than 12,000 sq ft (1100 sq m). If the multipurpose room is used as an exhibition hall or for a display room, the exception does not apply. Exhibit and display halls have been shown to be fire and life safety problems because of the high fuel load and potential for rapid fire spread.

An appendix has been added for the 1991 Edition to clarify that the Committee was not intending to prohibit normal ancillary spaces where applying Exception No 2. However, a number of assembly rooms or a mixed occupancy would not be permitted under this exception.

Exception No. 3 exempts gymnasiums, skating rinks (including ice and roller rinks), and swimming pools where there is an audience or spectator gallery having an occupant load of 300 or less. If the skating rink or swimming pool can be floored over and used for other purposes, then the multipurpose room requirements contained in Exception No. 2 apply. If the spectator gallery has an occupant load greater than 300, then an automatic system is required.

It should also be noted that automatic suppression systems may be required by 8-1.6 based on the location of the assembly occupancy, even though 8-3.5.1 may not normally require this protection.

Two major questions that arise with regard to 8-3.5.1 deal with (1) mixed occupancies, especially assembly/educational, and (2) multiple assembly occupancies, especially religious halls with multipurpose rooms.

With regard to mixed occupancies, Chapter 1 (*see 1-5.7*) clearly states that, if they are mixed, the more stringent requirements of the two must be met. Therefore, schools with assembly occupancies need to be fully sprinklered unless the assembly occupancy can be treated as a separate occupancy, which would normally require independent egress systems and fire separation. In this case, only the assembly occupancy would need to be sprinklered. Also, many school multipurpose rooms could potentially utilize Exception No. 2. This exception emphasizes that the assembly occupancy is essentially a single room and thus could not be part of a mixed occupancy.

Exception No. 2 was originally intended for a typical fellowship hall, such as VFW, American Legion, or Grange Hall. The Committee recognizes that there will be some ancillary rooms, such as kitchens, restrooms, storage rooms, or minor offices, and it is not the intent of the Committee that these ancillary spaces disqualify a facility from using this exception, but it is the intent that the facility consist essentially of only one "major" room. Often a church or similar facility would like to apply Exception No. 1 and Exception No. 2. This could be done only if each facility could be treated separately. In other words, the egress systems of each facility would have to be independent of each other and appropriate fire separation provided.

8-3.6 Corridors.

8-3.6.1 Interior corridors and lobbies shall be constructed in accordance with 5-1.3.4 and 6-2.3.

Exception No. 1: Corridor and lobby protection shall not be required where assembly rooms served by the corridor or lobby have at least 50 percent of their exit capacity discharging directly to the outside, independent of corridors and lobbies.

Exception No. 2: Corridor and lobby protection is not required in buildings protected throughout by an approved supervised automatic sprinkler system installed in accordance with Section 7-7.

Exception No. 3: Lobbies serving only one assembly area that meet the requirements for intervening rooms (see 5-5.1.7) need not have a fire resistance rating.

Subsection 8-3.6 was new to the 1988 *Code*. Prior to that edition, the corridor provisions of Chapter 5 ruled in assembly occupancies. The Committee felt that it was important to specify the corridor protection needed in assembly occupancies. Exception No. 1 allows for corridor protection to be eliminated but requires 50 percent of the exit capacity of each assembly room to be direct to the outside, independent of corridors or lobbies. This allows theaters, for example, to eliminate panic hardware on doors leading into the lobby where they meet the other requirements of this section.

Exception No. 2 recognizes the excellent record of automatic sprinkler systems. However, this exception requires the entire building to be sprinklered, not just the assembly area.

Exception No. 3 recognizes the situation where the lobby serves only one assembly space and can, from a fire perspective, be considered part of that assembly area.

SECTION 8-4   Special Provisions

8-4.1   Windowless or Underground Buildings.

8-4.1.1   Windowless or underground buildings shall comply with this chapter and Section 30-7.

8-4.1.2   Underground buildings or portions of buildings having a floor level more than 30 ft (9.1 m) below the level of exit discharge shall comply with the requirements contained in 8-4.1.3 through 8-4.1.5.

Exception No. 1: Areas within buildings used only for service to the building such as boiler/heater rooms, cable vaults, dead storage and the like.

Exception No. 2: Auditoriums without intervening occupiable levels complying with the requirements of Chapter 8.

In recognition of the potential hazard that underground buildings pose, the *Code* requires compliance with Section 30-7 and, in addition, requires compliance with the provisions of 8-4.1.3 through 8-4.1.5 if the underground building has an assembly occupancy more than 30 ft

(9.1 m) below the level of exit discharge, or if an assembly building has a floor level more than 30 ft (9.1 m) below the level of exit discharge.

Two exceptions to the requirements are provided for areas used only for service functions, such as boiler rooms, heater rooms, etc., and for assembly occupancies where there is no occupiable intervening level between the assembly occupancy and the level of exit discharge.

8-4.1.3   Each level more than 30 ft (9.1 m) below the level of exit discharge shall be divided into not less than two smoke compartments by a smoke barrier complying with Section 6-3 and having a 1-hour fire resistance rating.

(a) Each smoke compartment shall have access to at least one exit without passing through the other required compartment. Any doors connecting required compartments shall be tight-fitting, minimum 1-hour rated fire doors designed and installed to minimize smoke leakage and to close and latch automatically upon detection of smoke.

(b) Each smoke compartment shall be provided with a mechanical means of moving people vertically, such as an elevator or escalator.

(c) Each smoke compartment shall have an independent air supply and exhaust system capable of smoke control or smoke exhaust functions and provide a minimum smoke exhaust rate of six air changes per hour.

(d) Each smoke compartment shall be provided with an automatic smoke detection system throughout. The system shall be designed such that the activation of any two detectors shall cause the smoke control system to operate and the building voice alarm to sound.

8-4.1.4   Any required smoke control or exhaust system shall be provided with a standby power system complying with Article 701 of NFPA 70, *National Electrical Code.*®

8-4.1.5   The building shall be provided with an approved supervised voice alarm system in accordance with Section 7-6. The voice alarm system shall comply with 7-6.3.8. A prerecorded evacuation message shall be provided.

The provisions for underground buildings or portions of assembly buildings with an occupiable floor more than 30 ft (9.1 m) below the level of exit discharge are designed to provide areas of refuge on the subterranean level. This, coupled with a smoke control or smoke exhaust system, will provide sufficient time to exit the building. Note that elevators or escalators are required in each compartment to help rapidly evacuate the area. It is believed that these will not, themselves, create a life safety threat because of the other requirements of this section, including separate smoke compartments and smoke control or exhaust systems. It should also be recognized that the elevator or escalator is not being considered the required means of egress; normal exits are still required.

In order to provide redundancy in the life safety provisions, standby power as defined in Article 701 of NFPA 70, *National Electrical Code*,[13] is required for the smoke control or exhaust system.

In order to permit orderly evacuation and to reduce the possibility of panic, this section requires the use of a supervised voice alarm system that will sound a prerecorded evacuation message.

8-4.2 High Rise Buildings.
High rise assembly occupancy buildings and high rise mixed occupancy buildings that house assembly occupancies in the high rise portions of the building shall comply with Section 30-8.

A high rise public assembly occupancy has the same inherent life safety dangers that are found in other high rise buildings. Therefore, the Committee felt that protection provided for high rise buildings in general was appropriate and applicable to public assembly high rise occupancies and portions of high rise buildings that are used for public assembly.

8-4.3 Outdoor Assembly.

8-4.3.1
All assembly seating considered "smoke-protected assembly seating" as defined by NFPA 102, *Standard for Assembly Seating, Tents, and Membrane Structures*, outdoor assembly occupancies, tents, membrane structures, bleachers, grandstands, and stadiums shall comply with the requirements of NFPA 102, *Standard for Assembly Seating, Tents, and Membrane Structures*.

Exception: Smoke-protected assembly seating complying with 8-2.3.2 need not comply with 5-3.3 or NFPA 102, Standard for Assembly Seating, Tents, and Membrane Structures.

Where an outdoor assembly occupancy is created in an enclosed court so that exits can only be provided through a surrounding building, the requirements for exits, seating, and aisles must be the same as for an indoor assembly area.

8-4.4 Special Provisons for Exposition Facilities.

Exposition facilities have problems that differ from those of theaters, restaurants, or other assembly occupancies. They are large, multi-use facilities and have high ceilings appropriate to their size. Combustible materials are frequently displayed, and the containers in which the exhibits are shipped contribute to the fuel load. Due to the size of exhibition halls, most are required by 8-3.5 to be protected by automatic sprinklers.

This section had been expanded in the 1988 *Code* and is further revised for the 1991 *Code* to provide more comprehensive guidance to the many people who are responsible for the different aspects of a trade show or exposition. The authority having jurisdiction at the local level is often working with organizations that exhibit on a national basis and that are unaware of the local firesafety regulations. It is the Committee's intent that this *Code* provide more consistent and universal understanding of the firesafety regulations required in these occupancies and at the same time encourage more uniform enforcement practices.

The Committee learned that the trade show and exposition hall regulations used by many jurisdictions were very similar; however, there was no nationally recognized model code that could be referenced. It was also recognized by the Committee that this lack of a model code presents a hardship as well as confusion between the local authority having jurisdiction and persons responsible for the various functions of the trade show or exposition.

8-4.4.1
No display or exhibit shall be so installed or operated as to interfere in any way with access to any required exit or

with visibility of any required exit or any required exit sign; nor shall any display block access to fire fighting equipment.

It is advisable to have prepared plans or diagrams to show the arrangement of displays or exhibits, including any that are to be suspended from the ceiling or an overhead structure. Displays or exhibits must never interfere in any way with access to any required exit, and they must not conceal exit signs (*see Figure 8-19*). A display should not block access to fire fighting equipment nor interfere with the normal operation of automatic extinguishing equipment or devices for smoke evacuation.

Rows of booths become exit accesses; therefore, booths and other temporary construction should be of minimal combustible construction or protected to avoid undue hazard of fire that might endanger occupants before they can reach available exits.

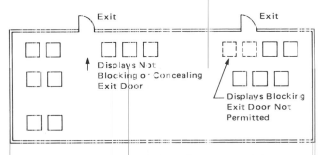

Figure 8-19. Arrangement of Displays in an Exhibition Hall.

8-4.4.2 A storage room having an enclosure consisting of a smoke barrier having a fire resistance rating of 1 hour and protected by an automatic extinguishing system shall be provided for combustible materials not on display, including combustible packing crates used to ship exhibitors' supplies and products.

Displays or exhibits of combustible material must be limited in quantity in order to reduce the fuel load to an acceptable level. Excess combustible display material and all other combustible materials that are not in use should be kept in a separate storage room until needed. A separation with a fire resistance rating of 1 hour is required between such a storage room and all other parts of the building, and the room must be protected by an automatic sprinkler system.

8-4.4.3   Exhibits.

8-4.4.3.1   Exhibits shall comply with 8-4.4.3.2 through 8-4.4.3.11.

8-4.4.3.2   The travel distance within the exhibit booth or exhibit enclosure to an exit access aisle shall not be greater than 50 ft (15 m).

This requirement applies to standard exhibit booth arrangements, whether constructed of pipe and drape, or a large exhibit enclosure designed and built from other materials, which could include small booths, open displays, large board displays, or other arrangements. Also included in this requirement are exhibit enclosures that are created by the arrangement of products such as machinery or vehicles. The intent is to have a travel distance not greater than 50 ft (15 m) for occupants that are inside the enclosure, whether they are employees or patrons. Note that this is not travel distance to an exit, but only to an aisle.

8-4.4.3.3   The upper deck of multilevel exhibits greater than 300 sq ft (27.9 sq m) in area shall have at least two remote means of egress.

This is a new requirement for the 1991 *Code*. It assures that larger exhibits with a second level provide at least two means of egress to prevent people from potentially becoming trapped on the second level.

8-4.4.3.4   Exhibit booths shall be constructed of:

(a) Noncombustible or limited-combustible materials.

(b) Wood greater than ¼ in. (.6 cm) nominal thickness or wood not greater than ¼ in. (.6 cm) nominal thickness that is pressure treated fire retardant wood meeting the requirements of NFPA 703, *Standard for Fire Retardant Impregnated Wood and Fire Retardant Coatings for Building Materials.*

(c)* Flame-retardant materials complying with NFPA 701, *Standard Methods of Fire Tests for Flame-Resistant Textiles and Films*, both small and large scale tests.

A-8-4.4.3.4(c)   The authority having jurisdiction may use the field flame test contained in NFPA 701 *Standard Methods of*

Fire Tests for Flame-Resistant Textiles and Films (see Appendix B), as one method of determining flame retardancy.

(d) Textile wall covering such as carpeting having napped, tufted, looped, or similar surface used as wall or ceiling finish complying with 6-5.2.3.

(e) Plastic that is limited to a Class A or Class B interior wall and ceiling finish.

(f) Foamed plastics and materials containing foamed plastics having a maximum heat release rate for any single fuel package of 100 kW when tested in accordance with UL 1975, *Standard for Fire Tests for Foamed Plastic Used for Decorative Purposes*.

Plastics are limited to Class A and Class B for wall and ceiling finishes. It is the Committee's intent to prohibit the use of foamed plastics because of their inherent burning characteristics unless they have been tested for heat release rate in accordance with UL 1975, *Standard for Fire Tests for Foamed Plastic Used for Decorative Purposes*,[14] and comply with part (f) of 8-4.4.3.4. Foamed plastics are found to be used in sign construction and display boards, and in some cases, the entire booth is constructed of foamed plastics.

(g) Cardboard, honeycombed paper, and other combustible materials having a maximum heat release rate for any single fuel package of 150 kW when tested in accordance with UL 1975, *Standard for Fire Tests for Foamed Plastic Used for Decorative Purposes*.

This section is intended to provide direction to manufacturers of exhibit booths as well as decorators, exhibitors, and the authority having jurisdiction. The focus of this section is on the construction components of the ceilings, walls, and floors of an exhibit booth or display area in addition to the finish treatment. It is the intent of the Committee to also include large signs and display boards; small signs [approximately 2 ft × 3 ft (61 cm × 91 cm) or smaller] would not normally be considered part of the wall covering. This section does not apply to the goods or products that are being displayed.

8-4.4.3.5 Curtains, drapes, and decorations shall comply with 31-1.4.

8-4.4.3.6 Acoustical and decorative material including, but not limited to, cotton, hay, paper, straw, moss, split bamboo, and wood chips shall be flame-retardant treated to the satisfaction of the authority having jurisdiction. Materials that cannot be treated for flame retardancy shall not be used. Foamed plastics and materials containing foamed plastics used as decorative objects such as, but not limited to, mannequins, murals, and signs shall have a maximum heat release rate for any single fuel package of 150 kW when tested in accordance with UL 1975, *Standard for Fire Tests for Foamed Plastic Used for Decorative Purposes*.

Exception: Where the aggregate area of such materials is less than 10 percent of the individual floor or wall area, such materials may be used subject to the approval of the authority having jurisdiction.

8-4.4.3.7 The following shall be protected by automatic extinguishing systems:

(a) Single level exhibit booths greater than 300 sq ft (27.9 sq m) and covered with a ceiling.

(b) The first level of multilevel exhibit booths.

(c) The second level of multilevel exhibit booths where the second level is covered with a ceiling.

(d) A single exhibit or group of exhibits with ceilings that do not require sprinklers shall be separated by a minimum of 10 ft (3 m) where the aggregate ceiling exceeds 300 sq ft (27.9 sq m).

The water supply and piping for the sprinkler system may be of approved temporary means taken from an existing domestic water supply, an existing standpipe system, or an existing sprinkler system.

Exception No. 1: Ceilings that are constructed of open grate design or listed dropout ceilings in accordance with NFPA 13, Standard for the Installation of Sprinkler Systems, shall not be considered ceilings within the context of this section.

Exception No. 2: Vehicles, boats, and similar exhibited products having over 100 sq ft (9.3 sq m) of roofed area shall be provided with smoke detectors acceptable to the authority having jurisdiction.

Exception No. 3: Where fire protection of multilevel exhibit booths is consistent with the criteria developed through a life safety evaluation of the exhibition hall, subject to approval of the authority having jurisdiction. (See A-8-2.3.2.)

Large booths and multistory booths pose special problems in exhibit halls. A fire in these booths could grow to large enough proportions to have a significant negative impact on the performance of the building's sprinkler system. It is the intent of the Committee to provide sprinkler protection in these booths by means of a temporary tap into the existing system. The Committee felt sprinklers would provide the protection necessary to extinguish a fire in its incipient stage, thus reducing the life hazard to occupants.

This paragraph has been significantly revised for the 1991 *Code*. It has been reorganized for clarification, the requirements have been modified, the need for temporary water supply has been recognized, and two new exceptions have been added.

New Exception No. 1 is not really an exception, since this is already recognized by the reference document, NFPA 13, *Standard for the Installation of Sprinkler Systems*.[15] It was added to emphasize that it is not the intent of the Committee to prohibit this provision of the standard.

Exception No. 2 exempts large vehicles, i.e., boats, mobile homes, and recreational vehicles, from the sprinkler requirement but requires a smoke detector if the vehicle is greater than 100 sq ft (9.3 sq m) in area. The intent of the Committee was to provide early warning in the immediate area to allow for orderly evacuation. This provision could most probably be met by single station, battery operated smoke detectors.

Exception No. 3 is also new in the 1991 *Code* and allows the exposition hall operators to work with the authority having jurisdiction to devise alternate methods of compliance.

8-4.4.3.8 Open flame devices within exhibit booths shall comply with 31-2.3.

Open flame devices should be prohibited except for religious ceremonies and, where allowed, should be restricted to minimize the danger of igniting combustibles. Any use of open flames should be allowed only after approval by the authority having jurisdiction.

8-4.4.3.9 Cooking and food warming devices in exhibit booths shall comply with 31-2.4 and the following:

(a) Gas fired devices.

(1) Natural gas fired devices shall be installed in accordance with 7-1.1.

Exception to (a) (1): Compressed natural gas may be used where permitted by the authority having jurisdiction.

(2) The use of LP-Gas cylinders is prohibited.

Exception to (a) (2): Nonrefillable cylinders may be used where permitted by the authority having jurisdiction.

Part (a) was revised for the 1991 *Code*. It does allow limited use of gas cylinders under specific permission of the authority having jurisdiction.

(b) Devices shall be isolated from the public by at least 4 ft (122 cm) or by a barrier between the devices and the public.

This requires distance or a barrier between the public and the device. The purpose is to guard against the possibility of accidental spills of hot greases or foods and to minimize the potential for ignition of combustibles, especially clothing worn by patrons.

(c) Multi-well cooking equipment using combustible oils or solids shall comply with 7-2.3.

(d) Single-well cooking equipment using combustible oils or solids shall:

(1) Have lids available for immediate use.

(2) Be limited to 288 sq in. (.19 sq m) of cooking surface.

(3) Be placed on noncombustible surface materials.

(4) Be separated from each other by a minimum horizontal distance of 2 ft (61 cm).

Exception to (d) (4): Multiple single-well cooking equipment where the aggregate cooking surface area does not exceed 288 sq in. (.19 sq m).

(5) Be kept a minimum horizontal distance of 2 ft (61 cm) from any combustible material.

Parts (c) and (d) were revised in the 1991 *Code* to clarify the intent of the Committee and provide some flexibility. The surface area was determined to be large enough to accommodate the average-sized deep-fat fryer. It was felt by the Committee that this would allow for exhibits that display deep-fat frying and at the same time provide reasonable safeguards.

Part (c) requires that multivat cooking equipment must comply with NFPA 96, Standard for the Installation of Equipment for the Removal of Smoke and Grease-Laden Vapors from Commercial Cooking Equipment.[16]

The object of the lid in part(d)(1) is to provide to the operator a ready method of smothering the fire.

Part(d)(3) is required due to the fact that the bottom surface of many devices could be subject to heating to temperatures that could ignite combustible surfaces.

The minimum separation distances in part(d)(4) are necessary to minimize the danger of a fire in one device extending into another device.

The same principle that applies to part(d)(4) applies to part(d)(5), except the exposure is combustible decorations or other products as opposed to another cooking device.

(e) A 20 B:C fire extinguisher shall be provided within the booth for each device, or an approved automatic extinguishing system shall be provided.

This requires a 20-B:C extinguisher for each cooking device. The intent is to provide an extinguisher near each cooking device so the operator is able to access the extinguisher readily if a lid does not extinguish the fire or cannot be applied. It is not the intent of the Committee to have all the extinguishers in one location.

The provisions of this section recognize the inherent dangers in cooking and warming devices that will be used for display purposes and are subject to large, transient crowds in assembly occupancies. As a result, several items in this section have been revised or clarified for the 1991 Edition.

8-4.4.3.10 Combustible materials within exhibit booths shall be limited to a one-day supply. Storage of combustible materials behind the booth is prohibited. (See 8-4.4.2 and 31-2.6.2.)

The intent of this section is to limit the amount of literature, brochures, boxes, give-aways, and other products that are kept in the booth. The amount necessary to constitute a one-day supply is obviously going to vary; however, the authority having jurisdiction should be able to make a judgment after reviewing the activity anticipated by the exhibitor. Additional supplies and combustible crates (used for shipping) should be kept in a separate storage area having a fire resistance rating of 1 hour and protected by an automatic sprinkler system.

8-4.4.3.11 Plans for the exposition, in an acceptable form, shall be submitted to the authority having jurisdiction for approval prior to the move-in of any exhibit. The plan shall show all details of the proposed exposition. No exposition shall occupy any exposition facility without approved plans.

The intent is to provide the authority having jurisdiction with a set of plans that shows aisle widths, travel distances, exits, booth locations, display area configurations, types of displays (e.g., cooking, machinery, drapery, arts and crafts, etc.), location of fire protection equipment (extinguishers, alarm pull stations, hose cabinets, etc.), and lobby and registration area usage. This is not a complete list, but it should provide some guidance in determining the plans that should be provided. The plan should also be drawn to scale. The scale used is not usually critical as long as it is indicated on the plan.

8-4.4.4 **Vehicles.** Vehicles on display within an exposition facility shall comply with the following:

(a) All fuel tank openings shall be locked and sealed in an approved manner to prevent the escape of vapors. Fuel tanks shall not be more than one-half full or contain more than 10 gal (37.9 L) of fuel, whichever is less.

It is important that fuel tank openings are locked to prevent tampering and accessibility to fuel. It is also important that the tank openings be taped to prevent the escape of flammable vapors. When the Committee reviewed the issue of amount of allowable fuel, it was found that some jurisdictions preferred empty tanks to eliminate fuel while others preferred full tanks to prevent vapors. It was determined that most exhibitors were unaware of the regulation until they arrived at the exhibit hall. After learning the specific rule (empty or full), they proceeded to make their adjustment in the adjacent parking area or some other unsuitable area. It is also difficult for the authority having jurisdiction to determine whether a tank is absolutely full or empty. The Committee felt that this fueling and defueling by exhibitors outside the hall presented a greater danger than the level of fuel in the tanks, given that they are locked, sealed, and ignition sources are eliminated from the vehicle. However, to avoid excessive quantities of fuel in the hall, the Code does limit the amount of fuel in tanks.

(b) At least one battery cable shall be removed from the batteries used to start the vehicle engine. The disconnected battery cable shall then be taped.

It is important that at least one of the battery cables is removed from each battery. Many vehicles have more than one battery. The intent is to eliminate the possibility of a spark from the battery that might ignite fuel or surrounding combustibles. It is usually suggested that battery cable connectors be thoroughly taped after they have been removed.

(c) Batteries used to power auxiliary equipment shall be permitted to be kept in service.

This new provision allows batteries that cannot be used to start the vehicle to remain in service. These present no more ignition hazard than does providing house current to the item on display.

(d) Fueling or defueling of vehicles shall be prohibited.

Fueling and defueling in and around the exhibit hall is extremely dangerous. [See comments on 8-4.4.4(a).]

(e) Vehicles shall not be moved during show hours.

The movement of vehicles inside the exhibit hall compromises exiting and access to means of egress. Vehicles should be positioned prior to the hall being made accessible to the public to avoid compromising these exits. There is also a serious concern regarding the effects of carbon monoxide inside an exhibit hall that is occupied.

This section on vehicles is intended to minimize the danger from both fuel and ignition sources.

8-4.4.5 Compressed flammable gases, flammable or combustible liquids, hazardous chemicals or materials, Class II or greater lasers, blasting agents, and explosives shall be prohibited within exhibit halls.

Exception: The authority having jurisdiction may permit the limited use of any of the above items under special circumstances.

Compressed gases are subject to damage that could cause an explosion or create a serious threat to life safety under fire conditions. Flammable and combustible liquids compromise life safety by their inherent capability to contribute to rapid fire spread. Hazardous materials present a variety of hazards to life safety, from flammability to toxicity. Class II or greater lasers can cause tissue damage to humans, and blasting agents and explosives can cause a large loss of life or injury if handled improperly. Many exhibitors wish to display explosives or pesticides or a type of compressed gas container, among other items.

These products can be effectively displayed without bringing the actual product into the hall by using empty containers.

The exception gives the authority having jurisdiction the discretion to permit small amounts of otherwise prohibited materials under special circumstances. For example, an exhibit or trade show for collectors of small arms ammunition or a highly supervised and closed (to the public) vocational trade show can be allowed where special controls and professional supervision are provided.

8-4.4.6 Alternatives. (*See Section 1-6, "Equivalency Concepts."*)

8-4.5* Special Provisions for the Handicapped. Where assembly occupancies are required to be made accessible to the handicapped, the assembly area shall have accommodations for not less than two such persons. (*Also see 8-2.5.2.*)

A-8-4.5 Unless accommodations are specifically provided for the handicapped, the placement of handicapped persons may endanger the proper use of exits by others by blocking aisles and exits. Reference is made to ANSI A117.1, *Standard for Buildings and Facilities — Providing Accessibility and Usability for Physically Handicapped People.* (*See Appendix B.*)

8-4.6* Special Provisions for Special Amusement Buildings.

A-8-4.6 Where a special amusement building is installed inside another building, such as within an exhibit hall, the special amusement building requirements apply only to the special amusement building. For example, the smoke detectors required by 8-4.6.3 need not be connected to the building's system. Where installed in an exhibit hall, it must also meet the requirements of an exhibit.

8-4.6.1 Special amusement buildings shall meet the requirements for assembly occupancies in addition to the requirements of this subsection. Special amusement buildings with an occupant load not greater than 300 persons shall be considered Class C assembly occupancies.

It is important to note that any special amusement building is considered an assembly occupancy, even if the occupant load is not greater than 50. However, special amusement buildings do not include theaters, movie houses, and other similar types of public assembly occupancies.

8-4.6.2* Every special amusement building shall be protected throughout by an approved automatic sprinkler system installed and maintained in accordance with Section 7-7. Where the special amusement building is movable or portable, sprinkler water supply may be by an approved temporary means.

A-8-4.6.2 It is the intent of the Committee to provide a suppression system that will act quickly to provide for life safety of the occupants.

It is felt that the residential or commercial quick-response heads would be appropriate in most cases. However, the design should be reviewed by competent automatic sprinkler designers and the authority having jurisdiction.

8-4.6.3 Where the nature of the special amusement building is such that it operates in reduced lighting levels, the building shall be protected throughout by an approved automatic smoke detection system in accordance with Section 7-6. Actuation of any smoke detection system device shall sound an alarm at a constantly attended location on the premises. Actu-

ation of the automatic sprinkler system or actuation of a smoke detection system having an approved verification or cross zoning operation capability shall:

(a) Cause illumination in the means of egress to increase to that required by Section 5-8, and

(b) Stop any conflicting or confusing sounds and visuals.

It is the intent of the Committee to have the exits and means of egress well lighted upon the activation of a smoke detector or suppression system. It is also important that any conflicting or confusing sounds or visuals be stopped and that, where a person's relative position to an exit is changed, additional exit signs be provided.

8-4.6.4 Exit Marking.

8-4.6.4.1 Exit marking shall be in accordance with Section 5-10.

8-4.6.4.2 Exit marking in mobile special amusement buildings shall be of the luminescent, self-luminous, or electroluminescent type.

8-4.6.4.3 Low level exit signs shall be provided in accordance with 5-10.1.4.

The Committee recognizes that in special amusement buildings knowledge of exits and location of exit signs is a critical problem. Low level exit signs should provide patrons an additional advantage in finding their way out under emergency conditions. (Also see commentary on 8-4.6.3.)

8-4.6.4.4* In special amusement buildings where mazes, mirrors, or other designs are used to confound the egress path, approved directional exit marking that will become apparent in an emergency shall be provided.

A-8-4.6.4.4 Consideration should be given to the provision of directional exit marking on or adjacent to the floor.

8-4.6.5 Interior Finish. Interior finish shall be Class A throughout in accordance with Section 6-5.

8-4.7 Operating Features. (*See Chapter 31.*)

SECTION 8-5 Building Services

8-5.1 **Utilities.** Utilities shall comply with the provisions of Section 7-1.

8-5.2 **Heating, Ventilating, and Air Conditioning Equipment.** Heating, ventilating, and air conditioning equipment shall comply with the provisions of Section 7-2.

8-5.3 **Elevators, Escalators, and Conveyors.** Elevators, escalators, and conveyors shall comply with the provisions of Section 7-4.

8-5.4 **Rubbish Chutes, Incinerators, and Laundry Chutes.** Rubbish chutes, incinerators, and laundry chutes shall comply with the provisions of Section 7-5.

References Cited in Commentary

[1] NFPA 130, Standard for Fixed Guideway Transit Systems, National Fire Protection Association, Quincy, MA, 1990.

[2] NFPA: Alert Bulletin, Social Club Fire, Bronx, New York, March 25, 1990.

[3] Richard L. Best, "Tragedy in Kentucky," Fire Journal, Vol. 72, No. 1, January 1978.

[4] Richard L. Best, "Reconstruction of a Tragedy," NFPA LS-72, 1978.

[5] Joseph A. Swartz, "Human Behavior in the Beverly Hills Fire," Fire Journal, Vol. 73, No. 3, May 1979.

[6] James R. Bell, "Investigation Report of the Fire at Stouffer's Inn of Westchester," Fire Journal, Vol. 76, No. 3, May 1982.

[7] John Bouchard, NFPA Investigation Report: "Fire in Haunted Castle Kills Eight," Fire Journal, Vol. 79, No. 5, September 1985.

[8] NFPA 220, Standard on Types of Building Construction, National Fire Protection Association, Quincy, MA, 1985.

[9] NFPA 102, Standard for Assembly Seating, Tents, and Membrane Structures, National Fire Protection Association, Quincy, MA, 1986.

[10] NFPA 14, Standard for the Installation of Standpipe and Hose Systems, National Fire Protection Association, Quincy, MA, 1990.

[11] NFPA 13E, Recommendations for Fire Department Operations in Properties Protected by Sprinkler and Standpipe Systems, National Fire Protection Association, Quincy, MA, 1989.

[12] NFPA 40, Standard for the Storage and Handling of Cellulose Nitrate Motion Picture Film, National Fire Protection Association, Quincy, MA, 1988.

[13] NFPA 70, National Electrical Code, National Fire Protection Association, Quincy, MA, 1990.

[14] UL 1975, Standard for Fire Tests for Foamed Plastic Used for Decorative Purposes, Underwriters Laboratories, Northbrook, IL.

[15] NFPA 13, Standard for the Installation of Sprinkler Systems, National Fire Protection Association, Quincy, MA, 1991.

[16] NFPA 96, Standard for the Installation of Equipment for the Removal of Smoke and Grease-Laden Vapors from Commercial Cooking Equipment, National Fire Protection Association, Quincy, MA, 1991.

9

Existing Assembly Occupancies

(See also Chapter 31.)

Assembly occupancies include, but are not limited to, all buildings or portions of buildings used for gatherings of 50 or more people for such purposes as deliberation, worship, entertainment, eating, drinking, amusement, or awaiting transportation. Assembly occupancies include, but are not limited to:

Armories	Gymnasiums
Assembly halls	Libraries
Auditoriums	Mortuary chapels
Bowling establishments	Motion picture theaters
Churches	Museums
Club rooms	Nightclubs
Conference rooms	Pool rooms
Courtrooms	Recreation piers
Dance halls	Restaurants
Discotheques	Skating rinks
Drinking establishments	Theaters
Exposition halls	

Passenger stations and terminals of air, surface, underground, and marine public transportation facilities. (If the jurisdiction enforcing the *Code* has adopted NFPA 130, *Standard for Fixed Guideway Transit Systems,*[1] there are some situations where transit stations would come under NFPA 130 rather than this *Code*. See NFPA 130 for additional details.)

Also note that 11-1.1.3 requires university and college classrooms having a capacity of 50 or more persons to comply with the requirements of the assembly occupancy chapters.

Assembly occupancies with an occupant load of less than 50 are considered incidental to the predominate occupancy in which they are located. For example, a small conference room in an office area is considered part of the overall business occupancy. If it is a freestanding occupancy or building, such as a small diner, a mercantile occupancy classification is normally assigned. In either case, the occupant load factors of 9-1.6 are used, since it is still an assembly use.

Assembly properties averaged 25,200 structure fires a year as reported to U.S. fire departments from 1984 to 1988. These fires caused an average of 25 civilian deaths and 376 civilian injuries per year. The majority of these fire deaths and injuries occurred in eating and drinking establishments (16,300 fires, 17 deaths, and 271 injuries a year), followed by churches and funeral parlors (2,700 fires, 2 deaths, and 28 injuries a year).

Large, multiple-death fires have been less common in assembly properties in recent years, with only three from 1985 to 1989. Two of these three involved New York social clubs, as did the 1990 Happy Land Social Club fire, which killed 87 people in the deadliest U.S. fire since the 1977 Beverly Hills Supper Club fire, which was also an assembly property. The potential for a major incident always exists by virtue of the nature of the occupancy, but there is also a steady incidence of fires that kill one or two people. In addition, from 1980 to 1988 two-thirds of those killed in assembly fires were not occupying the room in which the fire began. Fire protection would have provided several opportunities to prevent harm to occupants.[2,3,4,5]

The 1990 Happy Land Social Club fire in New York City, which killed 87 people, was a reminder of the enormous potential for loss of life in assembly properties. Following is a list of the deadliest U.S. assembly property fires of the 1980s:

Date	Place	Civilians Killed
December 4, 1980	Stouffer's Inn hotel conference center facility[6] Harrison, NY	26
May 11, 1984	Six Flags Amusement Park[7] Jackson Township, NJ	8
May 6, 1983	Hwa Yuan Restaurant (and apartments above) New York, NY	7
August 21, 1988	El Hoyo Social Club New York, NY	6
December 6, 1985	River Restaurant Derby, CT	6
February 20, 1985	El Exclusivo Social Club New York, NY	5
January 15, 1984	Eagles Club (and apartments above) Webster, MA	5
June 28, 1981	Odyssey Lounge discotheque Houma, LA	5
February 22, 1980	Holy Trinity House of Prayer Chicago, IL	4

Chapter 31 specifies the life safety requirements for the operation of assembly occupancies.

SECTION 9-1   General Requirements

9-1.1 Application.

9-1.1.1 The requirements of this chapter apply to existing assembly occupancies. (See 9-1.3 for definition.)

Exception: An existing building housing an assembly occupancy established prior to the effective date of this Code may be approved for continued use if it conforms to or is made to conform to the provisions of this Code to the extent that, in the opinion of the authority having jurisdiction, reasonable life safety against the hazards of fire, explosion, and panic is provided and maintained.

The provisions for new assembly occupancies are found in Chapter 8.

It should be noted that, if an existing building of some other occupancy were to have its classification changed to that of an assembly occupancy, that portion of the building housing the assembly occupancy must comply with Chapter 8 for new assembly occupancies, even though it is part of an existing building (see 1-7.4). Also, should an existing assembly occupancy change occupancy subclassification, such as from Class C to Class B, it must meet the requirements for a new Class B assembly occupancy. (See 1-7.4, 9-1.1.1, and 9-1.1.3.)

9-1.1.2 Additions to existing buildings shall conform to the requirements for new construction. Existing portions of the structure need not be modified provided that the new construction has not diminished the fire safety features of the facility.

Exception: Existing portions shall be upgraded if the addition results in a change of assembly classification. (See 9-1.4.1.)

The provisions of 9-1.1.2 make clear that the intent of the Code is to mandate that additions to existing assembly occupancies meet the requirements for new construction (see 1-5.5). If construction of the addition causes the classification of the assembly occupancy to change to a higher level (Class C to Class B, for example), then the existing portion of the building must be modified to meet the requirements for new construction.

9-1.1.3 An assembly occupancy that has an occupant load increase that results in a change of assembly classification (*see 9-1.4.1*) shall meet the requirements for new assembly occupancies.

The provisions of 9-1.1.3 are similar to those of 9-1.1.2 in that, if for some reason the occupant load of an assembly occupancy changes, resulting in a higher classification (Class C to Class B, for example), the existing building must be modified to comply with the requirements for new assembly occupancies. This may occur because of renovation of an existing building or because a higher occupant load is granted by the authority having jurisdiction under the provisions of 9-1.7.2.

9-1.2 Mixed Occupancies. (*See also 1-5.7.*)

9-1.2.1* Any assembly occupancy and its access to exits in buildings of other occupancy, such as ballrooms in hotels, restaurants in stores, rooftop assembly occupancies, or assembly rooms in schools, shall be so located, separated, or protected as to avoid any undue danger to the occupants of the assembly occupancy from a fire originating in the other occupancy or smoke therefrom.

A-9-1.2.1 Depending upon the character of construction and the hazard of the occupancy, this will require some physical separation by walls of appropriate fire resistance, protection of the other occupancy by automatic sprinklers, or other appropriate measures. Where the building is of fire-resistive construction and the hazard of the other occupancy is low or ordinary, as in a school or hotel, no separation may be necessary.

The intent of this provision is to protect the occupants of the assembly occupancy from the effects of a fire originating in the other occupancy. While this can be achieved by several methods, there are two considerations to be taken into account, whichever method is chosen. First, consideration must be given to the protection of the means of egress of the assembly occupancy; second, the level of protection from the other occupancy that can be provided

to the assembly occupancy itself must be considered. Methods that can be used to protect the assembly occupancy and its means of egress include construction of fire-rated partitions, use of independent exits, installation of automatic sprinklers, and careful analysis of the requirements of each occupancy where applying the provisions of 1-5.7 pertaining to mixed occupancies.

9-1.2.2 Occupancy of any room or space for assembly purposes by fewer than 50 persons in a building of other occupancy and incidental to such other occupancy shall be classed as part of the other occupancy and subject to the provisions applicable thereto.

Fifty has traditionally been considered the minimum number of people assembled in one space for which the *Code* requires special provisions, such as requiring a door to swing in the direction of exit travel (*see 5-2.1.4.1*). Therefore, in Chapter 9, 50 people constitute a level of risk to life safety high enough to require classifying an occupancy as an assembly occupancy and, consequently, to subject the occupancy to the special design requirements found within this chapter. Since the space still contains an assembly use, the occupant load factors of 9-1.6 are still used, even if the space is being regulated under another occupancy.

9-1.2.3 Assembly occupancies in buildings of other occupancy shall be permitted to use exits common to the assembly occupancy and the other occupancy provided that the assembly area and the other occupancy considered separately each have exits sufficient to meet the requirements of this *Code*.

Where the requirements of this section apply, consideration must also be given to the provisions of 1-5.7 pertaining to mixed occupancies. Those provisions require that, in mixed occupancies, the more restrictive requirements of either occupancy be used for both occupancies.

9-1.2.4 Exits shall be sufficient for simultaneous occupancy of both the assembly occupancy and other parts of the building.

Exception*: Where the authority having jurisdiction determines that the conditions are such that simultaneous occupancy will not occur.

A-9-1.2.4   Exception. Example: An assembly room for the inmates of a detention occupancy will not normally be subjected to simultaneous occupancy.

In 9-1.2.3 through 9-1.2.4, the *Code* requires that each occupancy, considered separately, have sufficient exits and that, where it is possible for simultaneous occupancy to occur, the exits be sufficient for the combined occupant load.

The Exception to 9-1.2.4 should be used judiciously. Consideration should be given to all possible uses before a decision is reached. A school gymnasium may normally be used only by the school occupants; however, several times a year, the gymnasium may be used by an outside group during school hours. A common example of this is the use of school gymnasiums as polling places on election day. Consideration should be given to all possible uses to provide the owner/occupant maximum flexibility in the use of the space.

9-1.2.5   Combined Assembly and Residential Occupancies.

The concept that had previously been applied to mixed mercantile/residential is now also applied to mixed assembly/residential.

9-1.2.5.1   No dwelling unit of a residential occupancy shall have its sole means of egress pass through any assembly occupancy in the same building.

9-1.2.5.2   No multiple-dwelling unit of a residential occupancy shall be located above an assembly occupancy.

Exception No 1: Where the dwelling unit of the residential occupancy and exits therefrom are separated from the assembly occupancy by construction having a fire resistance rating of at least 1 hour.

Exception No. 2: Where the assembly occupancy is protected throughout by an approved automatic sprinkler system in accordance with Section 7-7.

Exception No. 3: As permitted in 9-1.2.5.3.

The result of 9-1.2.5.2 and its exceptions is that, if an assembly occupancy has a multiple-dwelling occupancy located above it, either the assembly occupancy must be totally separated from the residential occupancy by 1-hour fire resistance rated construction or the assembly occupancy must be fully sprinklered.

9-1.2.5.3   A building with not more than two dwelling units of residential occupancy above an assembly occupancy shall be permitted provided that the assembly occupancy is protected by an automatic fire detection system in accordance with Section 7-6.

9-1.3   Special Definitions.

Aisle Accessway.* That initial portion of an exit access that leads to an aisle.

A-9-1.3   Special Definitions.

Aisle Accessway.   Aisle accessway is the name given to the previously unnamed means of egress component leading to an aisle or other means of egress. For example, circulation space between parallel rows of seats having a width of 1 to 2 ft (30.5 to 61 cm) and a maximum length of 100 ft (30 m) is an aisle accessway. Some of the circulation space between tables or seats in restaurants might be considered aisle accessway.

Depending on the width of aisle accessway, which is influenced by its length and expected utilization, the movement of a person through the aisle accessway might require other people to change their individual speed of movement, alter their postures, move their chairs out of the way, or proceed ahead of the person.

This definition has been added to clarify that part of the means of egress located between where you are sitting and an aisle. (*See 9-2.5.6 and 9-2.5.7.*)

Assembly Occupancies.   Occupancies that include, but are not limited to, all buildings or portions of buildings used for gatherings of 50 or more persons for such purpose as deliberation, worship, entertainment, dining, amusement, or awaiting transportation.

Cyclorama.   The name generally used for a neutral background that, with suitable lighting, can suggest the infinite space of the sky. It may be curved and may be painted to depict any required background.

The term "cyclorama" is used in the definition of "stage scenery." These definitions are included to better clarify the terms used by the movie and theater industry.

Drop. A large piece of scenic canvas that hangs vertically, usually across the stage area.

The definition of "drop" is intended to better clarify the *Code* with regard to stage productions.

Exhibitor. An individual or entity engaged in the display of the products or services offered.

Exhibits. A space or portable structure used for the display of products or services.

Exposition. An event held in which the display of products or services is organized to bring together the provider and user of the products or services.

Exposition Facility. A convention center, hotel, or other building at which exposition events are held.

The definitions of "exhibitor," "exhibits," "exposition," and "exposition facility" have been added to improve understanding of the provisions in 8-4.4. The terms are consistent with terms used by the exposition industry.

Flow Time. The time during which there is crowd flow past a point in the means of egress system, and it is a component of total evacuation time.

The term "flow time" has been used in the technical literature on egress, and it is worth understanding in relation to the *Code's* requirements for the capacity of means of egress. Flow time is the time taken by a crowd to pass, for example, through a doorway during a mass egress situation. This egress time component, along with other egress time components for responding to an alarm (before beginning egress movement) and for traveling along the length of an egress route, contributes to the total time needed to evacuate an area after an emergency situation is detected and an alarm is sounded. In the case of large assembly buildings, the flow time is often the larg-

est component of total evacuation time. Therefore, explicit information about flow time is included in Chapters 8 and 9 of the *Code* to help improve understanding of the nominal performance expected where particular egress capacity requirements are satisfied.

Fly. The space over the stage of a theater where scenery and equipment can be hung out of view. Also called lofts and rigging lofts.

Fly Gallery. A narrow raised platform at the side of a legitimate stage from which the lines for flying scenery are manipulated.

Gridiron. The arrangement of beams over a legitimate stage that supports machinery for flying scenery and hanging battens from which lighting is hung.

Leg Drop. A long narrow strip of fabric used for masking. Where used on either or both sides of the acting area, to provide entry to the stage for the actors, but also to mask. They may also be called "wings."

See commentary on the term "drop."

Life Safety Evaluation.* A written review dealing with the adequacy of life safety features relative to fire, storm, collapse, crowd behavior, and other related safety considerations.

A-9-1.3 Definitions.

Life Safety Evaluation. A life safety evaluation is a written review dealing with the adequacy of life safety features relative to fire, storm, collapse, crowd behavior, and other related safety considerations.

Topics to be considered may include, but are not limited to, the following:

(a) Human behavior.
(b) Exit system.
(c) Construction and structure.
(d) Contents and finishes.
(e) Detection.
(f) Emergency notification procedures and systems.
(g) Smoke management.
(h) Fire suppression systems.

Local conditions may dictate other considerations. (*Also see* *9-2.3.2.*)

This definition is for use in conjunction with 9-2.3.2. See the appendix note and commentary on 9-2.3.2. It is important to note that a life safety evaluation deals with more than firesafety. The evaluation must consider all life safety hazards that could endanger occupants and require rapid egress or other measures to maintain safety. In some large assembly facilities, for example, fire may not be the most likely hazard; there may be more injuries and deaths due to incidents arising from the large number and high density of people occupying a limited space. This can occur during normal occupancy conditions, such as where occupants become especially enthusiastic during a spectator event or where there is the possibility that occupants may have a strong desire to escape an area, e.g., when there is a sudden change of weather in the case of open facilities or where there is a collapse of part of the structure. Such possibilities must be taken into account when doing a life safety evaluation and, in some cases, special expertise will be required to properly assess and design or manage for social and behavioral factors in addition to factors of fire and structural safety. Generally, the evaluation must be based on a good understanding of the occupants — especially if densely crowded conditions exist — and the reason for the assembly of people.

Pinrail.   A beam at one side of a legitimate stage through which wooden or metal pins are driven and to which lines from the flies are fastened.

Platform.*   That raised area within a building used for the presentation of music, plays, or other entertainment; the head tables for special guests; the raised area for lecturers and speakers; boxing and wrestling rings; theater-in-the-round; and for similar purposes wherein there are no overhead drops, pieces of scenery, or stage effects other than lighting and a screening valance.

A-9-1.3 Definitions.

Platform.   It is not intended to prohibit the use of a curtain as a valance to screen or hide the electric conduit, lighting track or similar fixtures.

This is not intended to prohibit the use of: curtains such as are used to obscure the back wall of the stage; a curtain between the auditorium and the stage (grand or house curtain), a maximum of four leg drops; a valance to screen light panels, plumbing, and similar equipment from view.

The definition, along with the appendix note, is intended to bring the nontheatrical "stages" of many schools under the definition of platform. Also see the definition of stage, as many school "stages" are regular stages, since they use scenery. Hanging curtains commonly used on platforms are normally used to conceal lighting or to provide a more aesthetic appearance.

Platform, Permanent.   A platform erected within an area for more than 30 days.

Platform, Temporary.   A platform erected within an area for not more than 30 days.

Proscenium Wall.   The wall that separates the stage from the auditorium or house.

Smoke-Protected Assembly Seating.*   Seating served by means of egress that is not subject to blockage by smoke accumulation within or under a structure.

A-9-1.3 Definitions.

Smoke-Protected Assembly Seating.   An assembly area wherein the roof is not less than 15 ft (4.5 m) above the highest cross aisle or seat row, and having smoke-actuated venting facilities within that part of the roof sufficient to maintain the level of smoke at least 6 ft (183 cm) above the highest seating or walking level, is considered to be smoke-protected assembly seating.

Special Amusement Building.   Any building that is temporary, permanent, or mobile that contains a device or system that conveys passengers or provides a walkway along, around, or over a course in any direction as a form of amusement so arranged that the egress path is not readily apparent due to visual or audio distractions or an intentionally confounded egress path, or is not readily available due to the mode of conveyance through the building or structure. Included are such amusements as a "haunted house," a "roller coaster" type ride within a building, a "merry-go-round" within a building, a "submarine" ride, and similar amusements where the occupants are not in the open air.

This definition is needed for the new subsection 9-4.6, "Special Provisions for Special Amusement Buildings." It is the intent of the Committee that this definition address the structure and the use of the structure. The structure may be a permanent building or may be a semitrailer truck or other similar enclosure that is semipermanent or mobile. Special amusement buildings are designed to provide a full enclosure for patrons. Structures that are not fully enclosed, e.g., a merry-go-round with a roof and no sides, are not included in this definition. This definition also includes special amusement buildings within a larger structure, such as an amusement building within a shopping mall. Theaters, movie houses, or similar public assembly occupancies used for amusement or entertainment are not defined as special amusement buildings.

Stage. An area within a building used for the purpose of entertainment and utilizing drops or scenery or other stage effects, which shall be classified as one of the following:

(a) *Stage, Legitimate.* A stage wherein scenery is retractable mechanically either horizontally or vertically, or suspended overhead.

(b) *Stage, Regular.* A stage wherein scenery is not retractable. A valance or light trough, the main curtain, and a single backdrop may be retractable without the stage being considered a legitimate stage.

(c) *Stage, Thrust.* A platform extending beyond the proscenium arch and into the audience.

The intent is to better differentiate between stages and platforms (*see the definition of "platform"*). This definition of stage should be examined in conjunction with the definition of platform. The intent is to include nontheatrical stages, such as those in many lower grade level schools, under the definition of platform.

This definition of stage encompasses various types of stages, including arena stages (stages open to the audience on at least three sides).

The critical point in the definition of a stage is the hanging of curtains, leg drops, and scenery. If none of these is present, then the arrangement is most likely a platform. A potential problem is the arrangement commonly known as theater-in-the-round. For *Code* purposes, if the theater-in-the-round has scenery, leg drops, or curtains suspended on or above it, then it is a stage; if it has only lighting with a valance to hide the electrical fixtures, it is a platform.

A typical example of a thrust stage is illustrated in Figure 9-1. The so-called "runway" at Atlantic City that is used annually for the Miss America Pageant is probably the most famous thrust stage.

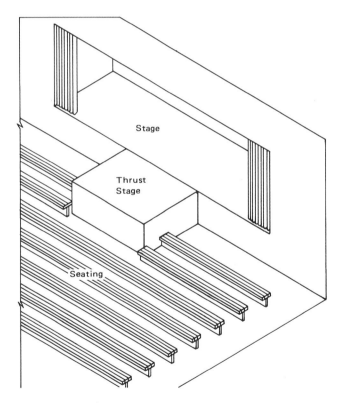

Figure 9-1. Thrust Stage.

Stage Properties. Furniture, carpet, and similar materials generally having an overall height of less than 5 ft (152 cm) and used to provide an appearance simulating a room or area.

The Committee felt this definition would better clarify the difference between the props used on a stage and the scenery used to dress the stage. The definitions of "stage properties" and "stage scenery" are particularly important with regard to the flame-retardant requirements in 9-3.2.1.11.

Stage Scenery.   Decorative materials such as flats, cyclo-ramas, painted or photographic backings, and similar materials to "dress" the stage.

See commentary on stage properties.

A-9.1.3   The following definitions may be useful to the enforcer of the *Code* although the terms are not used within the *Code*.

Accessory Rooms.   The accessory rooms are dressing rooms, property master's work and storage rooms, the carpenter's room and similar rooms necessary for legitimate stage operations.

Batten.   In general, a flown metal pipe or shape on which lights or scenery are fastened. While existing theater stages may still have wooden bars, they should not be used in new construction.

Scrim.   Finely woven fabric that can be translucent or opaque depending upon how it is used.

Theater-in-the-Round.   An acting area in the middle of a room with audience seating that surrounds it.

9-1.4   Classification of Occupancy. (*See 4-1.2.*)

9-1.4.1   Subclassification of Assembly Occupancies. Each assembly occupancy shall be subclassified according to its occupant load, as follows: Class A, occupant load greater than 1000 persons; Class B, occupant load greater than 300 but not greater than 1000 persons; Class C, occupant load of 50 or more but not greater than 300 persons.

As each increment of "occupant load" is reached, the level of risk to life safety from exposure to fire increases. Therefore, the stringency of the requirements found in this chapter increases to counter each higher risk level.

9-1.5   Classification of Hazard of Contents. Contents of assembly occupancies shall be classified in accordance with the provisions of Section 4-2.

Formal Interpretation 85-10
Reference 8-1.4.1, 9-1.4.1

Question: Is it the intent of the Committee that subclassification of an assembly occupancy (i.e., Class A, Class B, or Class C) be determined on a room-by-room basis, or on overall building basis?

Answer: It is the intent of the Committee that assembly occupancy subclassification be based on a room-by-room basis as well as a floor-by-floor basis as well as a total building basis. Therefore, each room would be based on the occupant load of that room and each floor would be based on the occupant load of that floor, but the classification of the assembly building overall would be based on the total occupant load. Therefore, it is quite feasible to have several Class C assembly occupancies grouped together in a single building and that building would be a Class A assembly occupancy.

Issue Edition: 1985
Reference: 8-1.4.1, 9-1.4.1
Date: May 1985 ∎

9-1.6   Minimum Construction Requirements. (*See 6-2.1.*) The location of an assembly occupancy shall be limited as follows:

It should be noted that the chart is arranged based on levels above the level of exit discharge (LED). Thus, in a normal building with the level of exit discharge at grade, column "1" in the table refers to the second story of the building.

Since the Cocoanut Grove Night Club fire in Boston (1942), the Subcommittee on Assembly and Educational Occupancies has placed a great deal of emphasis upon limiting the number of occupants in those assembly occupancies that provide only a minimum level of life safety because of the nature of the construction. The Cocoanut Grove fire illustrated the effect that a combustible structure (as well as combustible interior finish) and a multi-level configuration for an assembly occupancy can have

Type of Construction	Below LED	Number of Levels Above LED				
		LED	1	2	3	4 and Above
I (443) } I (332) } II (222)	A†B†C† Any number of Levels	ABC	ABC	ABC	ABC	A†BC
II (111)	A†B†C† One Level Below LED	ABC	ABC	A†BC	B†C†	N.P.
III (211) } IV (2HH) } V (111)	A†B†C† One Level Below LED	ABC	ABC	A†B†C	B†C†	N.P.
II (000)	B†C† One Level Below LED	A†BC	C†	N.P.	N.P.	N.P.
III (200) } V (000)	B†C† One Level Below LED	A†BC	C†	N.P.	N.P.	N.P.

†Permitted if the level of the assembly occupancy and any story intervening between that level and the level of exit discharge are protected throughout by an approved automatic sprinkler system. If there are any openings between the level of exit discharge and the exits serving the place of assembly, the level of exit discharge shall also be protected throughout by an approved automatic sprinkler system. (*See Section 7–7.*)
N.P.: Not Permitted
LED: Level of Exit Discharge
NOTE: For the purpose of this table, a mezzanine is not counted as a level.

on the severity of a fire and its high death count. More recently, the Beverly Hills Supper Club fire [3,4] (1977) also illustrated these consequences.

Paragraph 9-1.6 restricts the location of assembly occupancies. Type I and II (222) (fire-resistive) construction, with their "built-in-place" structural survivability (under fire attack), are acceptable for any assembly occupancy (hence, for any number of occupants) at the level of exit discharge and up to the fourth story. As the fire resistivity of the structure diminishes from Type II (111) (protected noncombustible) to Type V (000) (wood-frame) construction, the location of assembly occupancies (and the permitted number of occupants) is restricted. In addition, as the height of the building increases, so does the risk to the occupants; thus, the location of assembly occupancies is also restricted by height.

The chart presents a major provision of the *Code* for assembly occupancies and recognizes the value of auto-

matic sprinklers as a life safety device. Note that the chart deals with the location of the assembly occupancy in relation to the level of exit discharge. Thus, for example, if the building in question were a seven-story, Type I (fire-resistive) building with the level of exit discharge at the first floor, a Class A assembly occupancy could be located at the fourth floor without sprinkler protection. If the Class A assembly occupancy were located at the fifth floor, automatic sprinkler protection would be required for the fifth floor, as well as for the first through fourth floors (*see notes to table*). If the first floor of the building were so arranged that the exit stairs servicing the assembly floor were enclosed to the outside with no door openings into the first story or level of exit discharge, then sprinklers would not be required at that level.

Any assembly occupancies located below the level of exit discharge require automatic sprinkler protection, as do all levels intervening between the assembly level and the level of exit discharge. The same rule applies to openings into the stair at the level of exit discharge.

The construction types shown in the chart following are based on NFPA 220, *Standard on Types of Building Construction.*[8] *(See 6-2.1 and related appendix note.)*

9-1.7   Occupant Load.

9-1.7.1*   The occupant load permitted in any assembly building, structure, or portion thereof shall be determined on the basis of the following occupant load factors:

For ease of using this *Handbook*, A-9-1.7.1 appears following all discussion on 9-1.7.1.

(a)*   An assembly area of concentrated use without fixed seats, such as an auditorium, place of worship, dance floor, discotheque, or lodge hall: one person per 7 net sq ft (0.65 net sq m).

In the 1988 *Code*, the terminology "7 sq ft (0.65 sq m) per person" was changed to read "one person per 7 net sq ft (0.65 net sq m)." The intent of the Committee was to clarify the meaning of the *Code*. The intent is that one person is assumed for each 7 net sq ft (0.65 sq m) that is available to be used by occupants after deducting space occupied by permanently fixed counters, furnishings, etc.

The 7-sq ft (0.65-sq m) occupant load factor is based on open floor space with people standing in comfortable surroundings. This factor also can be used to estimate occupant load in a multipurpose room where portable chairs are placed in rows for meetings, film viewing, or lectures.

A-9-1.7.1(a)   This includes so-called "festival seating."

Festival seating is illustrated in Figure 9-2. This comfortable, low-density arrangement of people, which provides them with the ability to sit directly on the ground or floor and to move relatively easily through and out of the area, likely evolved from festivals held in open areas. This concept has been abused where applied to indoor or outdoor events where the assembled spectators are not controllable in terms of their numbers, location, or behavior. Rock music concerts are examples of events where the "festival seating" concept might become decidedly unfestive due to unmanageable crowds of standing (not seated) people in front of the stage area and a complete loss of any maintained circulation routes through the assembled crowd. Injuries due to bodies crushing against bodies or portions of structure are likely when this occurs. A description of a typical crush situation is found in a report titled, "Observations of Crowd Conditions at Rock Concert in Exhibition Stadium, Toronto, 16 July 1980," by J.L. Pauls. Because the number and arrangement of people in this instance was not maintained throughout the event, there were eventually some thirty to forty thousand people distributed unevenly in an area of about 125,000 sq ft (10,600 sq m), resulting in an average density of about 1 person per 3.5 sq ft (.33 sq m). However, due to localized crowding at the stage area, several thousand people were at crushing densities of about 1 person per 2 square ft (.19 sq m). Both normal access and emergency access into this congested area were all but impossible, and management efforts instructing people to move back toward less densely occupied areas proved futile. Incidents such as this one have led to the area limitations shown in 9-1.7.2, which provides for increases of occupant load in some situations.

Photograph Courtesy of J. L. Pauls.

Figure 9-2. *Festival Seating at a Rock Music Concert Held in a Stadium.*

(b) An assembly area of less concentrated use, such as a conference room, dining room, drinking establishment, exhibit room, gymnasium, or lounge: one person per 15 net sq ft (1.4 net sq m).

In the 1988 *Code*, the terminology "15 sq ft (1.4 sq m) per person" was changed to read "one person per 15 net sq ft (1.4 net sq m)." The intent of the Committee was to clarify the meaning of the *Code*. The intent is that one person is assumed for each 15 sq ft (1.4 sq m) that is available for use by occupants.

The 15-sq ft (1.4-sq m) occupant load factor is based on a use where a certain amount of space is occupied by furniture or a use requiring a large amount of space per person to accomplish the use. Examples of these typical uses are spaces involving the use of tables and chairs, as in restaurants or conference rooms. Gymnasiums are an example of a use that requires space for the occupants to perform their function (i.e., exercising or sport games).

(c) Bleachers, pews, and similar bench-type seating: one person per 18 linear in. (45.7 linear cm).

(d) *Fixed Seating.* The occupant load of an area having fixed seats shall be determined by the number of fixed seats installed. Required aisle space serving the fixed seats shall not be used to increase the occupant load.

(e) *Kitchens.* One person per 100 gross sq ft (9.3 gross sq m).

This paragraph clarifies the method of calculating the total occupant load in restaurants and cafeterias where a portion of the building is used as a kitchen, whether it is a separate room or divided from the dining area by a serving counter. Note this occupant load is calculated by using "gross sq ft (sq m)." This takes into consideration that there will be stoves, sinks, cutting boards, counters, and other culinary machinery necessary to operate a kitchen.

(f) *Libraries.* In stack areas: one person per 100 gross sq ft (9.3 gross sq m); in reading rooms: one person per 50 net sq ft (4.6 net sq m).

This takes into consideration the existence of bookshelves and permanent aisles. Reading rooms typically have large magazine racks, chairs, couches, and other furnishings that are arranged to make the area comfortable for the user.

Exception: The authority having jurisdiction may permit occupancy by a number of persons not to exceed that for which the existing means of egress are adequate, provided that measures are established to prevent occupancy by any number of persons greater than permitted by room area or by fixed seating.

A-9-1.7.1 Suggested occupant load factors for components of large airport terminal buildings are given. However, the authority having jurisdiction may elect to use different occupant load factors provided exit requirements are satisfied.

Airport Terminal	Sq Ft (Gross)	Sq M (Gross)
Concourse	100	[9.3]
Waiting Areas	15	[1.4]
Baggage Claim	20	[1.9]
Baggage Handling	300	[27.9]
Other	(See table following A–5–3.1.2)	

To assist in preventing serious overcrowding incidents in sports arenas, stadiums, and similar occupancies, spectator standing room should not be permitted between the seating areas and the playing areas, except in horse race and dog track facilities.

Formal Interpretation 85-5
Reference: 8-1.7.1 and 9-1.7.1

Question 1: Provided that sufficient exiting capacity is provided, is it the intent of 8-1.7.1 and 9-1.7.1 to allow the occupant load of an assembly occupancy, such as a cocktail lounge for example, to be calculated as the sum of the various net use areas (i.e., net area of dance floor at 7 square feet per person occupant load factor pus net area of seating and table area at 15 square feet per person occupant load factor, plus fixed seating area per the number of seats, etc.), rather than calculating the occupant load on the singular occupant load of 15 square feet per person based on the occupancy being a "drinking establishment"?

Answer: The method to determine the occupant load is adequately defined in Section 5-3 of the *Code*, particularly 5-3.1.2.

Question 2: Is the use of the provisions of 8-1.7.1 and 9-1.7.1 related to an increase in occupant load, allowable as a matter of right, as opposed to a discretionary allowance by the authority having jurisdiction, if necessary aisle and diagrams are provided?

Answer: The increase in occupant load is a matter of right if the provisions of 8-1.7.1 and 9-1.7.1 are followed. The owner or operator has the right to submit plans and receive an increase in occupant load if the plans comply with the *Code*. The authority having jurisdiction has a right to reject the plan for increase in occupant load if the plan is unrealistic, inaccurate, or otherwise does not properly reflect compliance with other code requirements. It is not the intent of the provisions of 8-1.7.1 and 9-1.7.1 to prohibit an increase in occupant load solely on the basis of exceeding the limits of 8-1.7.1 and 9-1.7.1.

Issue Edition: 1985
Reference: 8-1.7.1 and 9-1.7.1
Date: May 1985 ■

Where a capacity or near capacity audience is anticipated, all seating should be assigned with tickets showing the section, row, and seat number.

Where standing room is permitted, the capacity of the standing area should:

(a) Be determined on the basis of 5 sq ft (.46 sq m) per person,

(b) Have its capacity added to the seating capacity in determining egress requirements,

(c) Be located to the rear of the seating area, and

(d) Be given "standing room only" tickets according to the area designated for the purpose.

The number of tickets sold or otherwise distributed should not exceed the aggregate number of seats plus approved standing room numbers. (*See also A-9-2.3.2.*)

The occupant load factors of 9-1.7.1 reflect the data developed from surveys of typical occupancies.

Consideration should be given to the actual use of a room or space. A multiuse room may have several occupant loads depending upon its function on a given day. This is especially true of multipurpose rooms in schools and hotels.

Figure 9-3a illustrates a 2500-sq ft (230-sq m) room with two 46-in. (117-cm) clear width doors. If the room were to be used as a banquet room with tables and chairs, its occupant load would be based on the 15-sq ft (1.4-sq m) factor, resulting in an occupant load of 167 occupants. However, if the room were to be used for a stand-up cocktail party with essentially no furniture, then the occupant load would be based on the 7-sq ft (0.65-sq m) factor, resulting in an occupant load of 357 occupants. Thus, the room may have two occupant loads.

The exit capacity for the room is based on two 46-in. (117-cm) doors. Using only the criterion of exit capacity, the room can accommodate 460 occupants. Since either of the occupant loads calculated is less than the exit capacity, the situation is satisfactory.

As noted above, both criteria (exit capacity and occupant load) must be considered in establishing the permis-

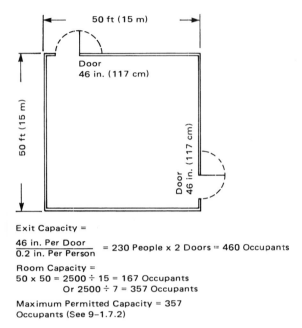

Exit Capacity =

$\dfrac{46 \text{ in. Per Door}}{0.2 \text{ in. Per Person}}$ = 230 People x 2 Doors = 460 Occupants

Room Capacity =
50 x 50 = 2500 ÷ 15 = 167 Occupants
Or 2500 ÷ 7 = 357 Occupants

Maximum Permitted Capacity = 357 Occupants (See 9–1.7.2)

Figure 9-3a.   Determination of Maximum Permitted Occupant Load for an Existing Assembly Occupancy by Room Capacity.

sible occupant load for a room or area. For example, the exit capacity of the room in Figure 9-3b is sufficient for an occupant load of 360 people. An occupant load calculated on the basis of the room size [3,600 sq ft (330 sq m) ÷ 7] would permit 514 people. The exit capacity of 360 must govern. This is allowed because of the special exception for existing buildings; in new construction, the exit capacity would be required to increase to 514 people in accordance with Section 5-3, since exit capacity must be provided for the occupant load determined by application of the occupant load factor.

Many times there is controversy over where to use a 7-sq ft (0.65-sq m) versus a 15-sq ft (1.4-sq m) occupant load factor. It should be noted that these factors are based on "concentrated" versus "less concentrated" use, and choices are made strictly on the basis of judgment. Since the occupant load factor is used to establish exit capacity and subclassification (which determines construction, alarm, and sprinkler requirements), it is usually safer to allow a larger occupant load (with related increased safety requirements) than to try, usually with great difficulty, to enforce a small occupant load limit. (*Also see 9-1.7.2.*)

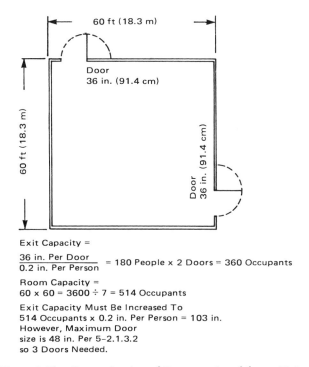

Exit Capacity =

$\dfrac{36 \text{ in. Per Door}}{0.2 \text{ in. Per Person}}$ = 180 People x 2 Doors = 360 Occupants

Room Capacity =
60 x 60 = 3600 ÷ 7 = 514 Occupants

Exit Capacity Must Be Increased To
514 Occupants x 0.2 in. Per Person = 103 in.
However, Maximum Door
size is 48 in. Per 5–2.1.3.2
so 3 Doors Needed.

Figure 9-3b. Determination of Occupant Load for an Existing Assembly Occupancy by Exit Capacity. Note: the Exception to 9-1.7.1 would allow the room to be restricted to an occupant load of 300.

9-1.7.2* The occupant load permitted in a building or portion thereof may be increased above that specified in 9-1.7.1 if the necessary aisles and exits are provided. To increase the occupant load, a diagram indicating placement of equipment, aisles, exits, and seating shall be provided to and approved by the authority having jurisdiction prior to any increase in occupant load. In areas not greater than 10,000 sq ft (930 sq m), the occupant load shall not exceed one person in 5 sq ft (.46 sq m); in areas greater than 10,000 sq ft (930 sq m), the occupant load shall not exceed one person in 7 sq ft (.65 sq m).

A-9-1.7.2 Existing auditorium and arena structures might not be designed for the added occupant load beyond the fixed seating. The authority having jurisdiction should consider exit access and aisles before granting additional occupant load such as festival seating, movable seating, etc. on the auditorium or arena floor area.

The accessibility of room exits is as important as the exit capacity. Therefore, where an increase is permitted over the occupant load established by 9-1.7.1, it must be demonstrated that adequate aisle accessways and aisles leading to the room exits are provided. Spacing of tables must provide for occupied chairs plus an aisle. Consideration should be given to the likelihood that, when occupants leave during an emergency, they may not take time to move chairs out of the aisles. (*See 9-2.5.7.*)

Dining and drinking areas most frequently take advantage of the provision of 9-1.7.2. There have been large banquet layouts where the occupant load was successfully increased to reflect an occupant load factor of 11 sq ft (1 sq m) instead of the 15 sq ft (1.4 sq m) specified by 9-1.7.1(b). In all cases where an increase in the occupant load is permitted, the authority having jurisdiction should insist on complete fixture and furniture layouts and should strictly enforce adherence to approved layouts. As noted above, the same room may have several approved occupant loads depending on the various fixture and furniture layouts.

A major change made to this paragraph in the 1988 Edition of the *Code* was a revision to the limit on the increased occupant load. This limit, which is based on an occupant load factor of 5 sq ft (0.46 sq m), was instituted due to the Committee's concern for overcrowding, which affects the movement characteristics of the occupants. Due to problems with festival seating (*see 9-1.3*), the limit was modified in the 1988 Edition so as to be restricted to facilities less than or equal to 10,000 sq ft (930 sq m).

It has been shown in research by the National Research Council in Canada and by the London Transport Board that, if people are crowded into a space so that each person occupies less than 7 sq ft (0.65 sq m), movement approaches a "shuffle"; when each person occupies less than 3 sq ft (0.28 sq m), "jam point" is approached, and all movement by occupants comes to a virtual stop. Thus, the maximum occupant load factor of 5 sq ft (0.46 sq m) for areas less than or equal to 10,000 sq ft (930 sq m) was chosen by the Committee to prevent overcrowding and the attendant change in the movement characteristics of occupants. (*See Figures 9-4a and 9-4b for two examples of increasing occupant load.*)

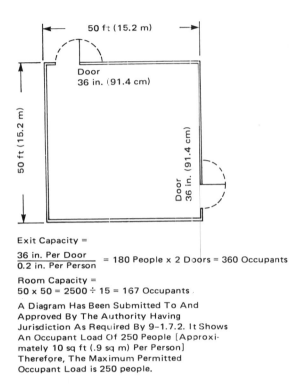

Exit Capacity =

$\dfrac{36 \text{ in. Per Door}}{0.2 \text{ in. Per Person}}$ = 180 People x 2 Doors = 360 Occupants

Room Capacity =
50 x 50 = 2500 ÷ 15 = 167 Occupants.

A Diagram Has Been Submitted To And Approved By The Authority Having Jurisdiction As Required By 9-1.7.2. It Shows An Occupant Load Of 250 People [Approximately 10 sq ft (.9 sq m) Per Person] Therefore, The Maximum Permitted Occupant Load is 250 people.

Figure 9-4a. Determination of Maximum Permitted Occupant Load for an Existing Assembly Occupancy by Room Capacity. Note that a practical upper limit for the room's population that will still ensure rapid and orderly movement to an exit may be 500 people (2,500 ÷ 5), based on 9-1.7.2. Since the exit capacity provides for 360 people, the authority having jurisdiction could conceivably allow a maximum permitted occupant load of 360.

9-1.7.3 **Waiting Spaces.** In theaters and other assembly occupancies where persons are admitted to the building at times when seats are not available to them, or when the permitted occupant load has been reached based on 9-1.7.1 or 9-1.7.2 and persons are allowed to wait in a lobby or similar space until seats or space are available, such use of a lobby or similar space shall not encroach upon the required clear width of exits. Such waiting shall be restricted to areas other than the required means of egress. Exits shall be provided for such waiting spaces on the basis of one person for each 3 sq ft (0.28 sq m) of waiting space area. Such exits shall be in addition to the exits specified for the main auditorium area and shall conform in construction and arrangement to the general rules for exits given in this chapter.

This is most often used for night clubs, lounges, and in some restaurants. This space cannot be located in or

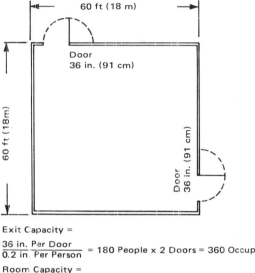

Exit Capacity =

$\dfrac{36 \text{ in. Per Door}}{0.2 \text{ in. Per Person}}$ = 180 People x 2 Doors = 360 Occupants

Room Capacity =
60 x 60 = 3600 ÷ 15 = 240 Occupants

A Diagram Has Been Submitted To The Authority Having Jurisdiction Showing An Occupant Load of 400 People [9 sq ft (8 sq m) Per Person]. However, The Maximum That Can Be Authorized is 360 Due To Exit Capacity.

Maximum Permitted Capacity = 360 Occupants

Figure 9-4b. Determination of Maximum Permitted Occupant Load for an Existing Assembly Occupancy by Exit Capacity. Note that a practical upper limit for the room's population that will still ensure rapid and orderly movement to an exit may be 3,600 ÷ 5 = 720 people, based on 9-1.7.2. However, the exit capacity of 360 must determine the maximum permitted occupant load.

interfere with the egress routes from the rest of the assembly occupancy.

SECTION 9-2   Means of Egress Requirements

9-2.1 **General.** All means of egress shall be in accordance with Chapter 5 and this chapter.

9-2.2 **Means of Egress Components.**

9-2.2.1 Components of means of egress shall be limited to the types described in 9-2.2.2 through 9-2.2.9.

Elevators and slide escapes (and revolving doors not meeting the requirements of 5-2.1.10) are not recognized as constituting required egress facilities in existing assembly occupancies. Slide escapes and elevators are not suited for rapid evacuation of the large numbers of people found in these occupancies. Furthermore, elevators introduce other risk factors if used during a fire (*see Section 7-4*). It should be noted that these devices can be installed, but cannot obstruct or interfere with the required means of egress.

9-2.2.2 Doors.

This provision allows small restaurants in malls to use the security grilles or doors as provided in 5-2.1.4.1 Exception No. 3.

9-2.2.2.1 Doors shall comply with 5-2.1.

9-2.2.2.2 Class C assembly occupancies in covered malls (*see 25-4.4.1 Exception*) shall be permitted to have horizontal or vertical security grilles or doors complying with 5-2.1.4.1 Exception No. 3 on the main entrance/exits.

9-2.2.2.3 **Panic Hardware or Fire Exit Hardware.** Any door in a required means of egress from an area having an occupant load of 100 or more persons may be provided with a latch or lock only if it is panic hardware or fire exit hardware complying with 5-2.1.7.

Exception No. 1: In assembly occupancies having an occupant load not greater than 600, where the main exit consists of a single door or single pair of doors, locking devices complying with 5-2.1.5.1 Exception No. 2 shall be permitted to be used on the main exit. Any latching device on this door(s) shall be released by panic hardware.

Exception No. 1 to 9-2.2.2.3 recognizes the provisions for locking doors contained in Chapter 5, "Means of Egress." These provisions recognize the need to lock doors for security purposes and provide limits on how this can be done. These provisions also acknowledge that, in order for the business to function, the main door must remain unlocked. If a latching device is used in addition to the lock, panic hardware is required to release the latch.

Exception No. 2: Special locking arrangements as permitted in 9-2.2.2.4.

9-2.2.2.4 Special locking arrangements complying with 5-2.1.6 are permitted on doors other than main entrance/exit doors.

Paragraph 9-2.2.2.4 allows delayed release hardware meeting the requirements of 5-2.1.6 to be used on all but the main exit. In addition to other requirements, 5-2.1.6 requires that the building be protected throughout by either an approved automatic sprinkler system or an approved supervised automatic fire detection system.

9-2.2.2.5 Revolving doors complying with the requirements of 5-2.1.10 for new construction are permitted.

9-2.2.2.6 **Turnstiles.** No turnstiles or other devices to restrict the movement of persons shall be installed in any assembly occupancy in such a manner as to interfere in any way with required means of egress facilities.

9-2.2.3 **Stairs.** Stairs shall comply with 5-2.2.

9-2.2.4 **Smokeproof Enclosures.** Smokeproof enclosures shall comply with 5-2.3.

9-2.2.5 **Horizontal Exits.** Horizontal exits shall comply with 5-2.4.

9-2.2.6 **Ramps.** Ramps shall comply with 5-2.5.

9-2.2.7 **Exit Passageways.** Exit passageways shall comply with 5-2.6.

9-2.2.8 **Escalators and Moving Walks.** Escalators and moving walks complying with 5-2.7 shall be permitted.

9-2.2.9 **Fire Escape Stairs.** Fire escape stairs complying with 5-2.8 shall be permitted.

9-2.3 Capacity of Means of Egress.

9-2.3.1 The capacity of means of egress shall be in accordance with Section 5-3 or, in the case of means of egress serving theater-type seating or similar seating arranged in rows, in accordance with 9-2.3.2.

9-2.3.2*   Minimum clear widths of aisles and other means of egress shall be in accordance with Table 9-2.3.2(a) or, for buildings providing smoke-protected assembly seating and for which an approved life safety evaluation is conducted, in accordance with Table 9-2.3.2(b). For Table 9-2.3.2(b), the number of seats specified must be within a single assembly space and interpolation shall be permitted between the specific values shown. For both tables, the minimum clear widths shown shall be modified in accordance with all of the following:

(a) If risers exceed 7 in. (17.8 cm) in height, multiply the stair width in the tables by factor A, where

$$A = 1 + \frac{(\text{riser height} - 7.0 \text{ in.})}{5}$$

(b) Stairs not having a handrail within a 30-in. (76-cm) horizontal distance shall be 25 percent wider than otherwise calculated; i.e., multiply by B = 1.25.

(c) Ramps steeper than 1 in 10 slope where used in ascent shall have their width increased by 10 percent; i.e., multiply by factor C = 1.10.

Table 9-2.3.2(a)   For Use Without Smoke-Protected Assembly Seating

No. of Seats	Nominal Flow Time (sec)	Inch of Clear Width Per Seat Served	
		Stairs	Passageways, Ramps, and Doorways
Unlimited	200	0.300 AB	0.220 C

(1 in. = 2.54 cm)

Table 9-2.3.2(b)   For Use With Smoke-Protected Assembly Seating

No. of Seats	Nominal Flow Time (sec)	Inch of Clear Width Per Seat Served	
		Stairs	Passageways, Ramps, and Doorways
2,000	200	0.300 AB	0.220 C
5,000	260	0.200 AB	0.150 C
10,000	360	0.130 AB	0.100 C
15,000	460	0.096 AB	0.070 C
20,000	560	0.076 AB	0.056 C
25,000 or more	660	0.060 AB	0.044 C

(1 in. = 2.54 cm)

A-9-2.3.2   A life safety evaluation is a written review dealing with the adequacy of life safety features relative to fire, storm, collapse, crowd behavior, and other related safety considerations. This review should be done by a person acceptable to the authority having jurisdiction. Such an evaluation includes, for example, a documented case that shows products of combustion in all conceivable fire scenarios will not significantly endanger occupants using means of egress in the facility (for example, because of fire detection, automatic suppression, smoke control, large-volume space, or management procedures). Moreover, means of egress facilities plus facility management capabilities should be adequate to cope with scenarios where certain egress routes are blocked for some reason.

In addition to making realistic assumptions about the capabilities of persons in the facility (e.g., an assembled crowd including many disabled persons or persons unfamiliar with the facility), the life safety evaluation should include a factor of safety of at least 2.0 in all calculations relating hazard development time and required egress time (the combination of flow time and other time needed to detect and assess an emergency condition, initiate egress, and move along the egress routes). This takes into account the possibility that half of the egress routes may not be used (or usable) in certain situations.

Regarding crowd behavior, the potential hazards created by larger masses of people and greater crowd densities (which can be problematic during ingress, occupancy, and egress) demand that technology, going beyond fire protection engineering, be utilized by designers, managers, and authorities responsible for buildings based on the relaxed egress capacity provisions of Table 9-2.3.2(b). In very large buildings for assembly use, the hazard of crowd crushes can exceed that of fire or structural failure. Therefore, the building designers, managers, event planners, security personnel, police authorities, and fire authorities, as well as the building construction authorities, should understand the potential problems and solutions, including coordination of their activities. For crowd behavior, this understanding must include factors of space, energy, time, and information as well as specific crowd management techniques such as metering. Published guidance on these factors and techniques is found in the SFPE Handbook of Fire Protection Engineering, Section 1, Chapter 15, and in publications referenced therein. (*See Appendix B.*)

Tables 9-2.3.2(a) and 9-2.3.2(b) are based on a linear relationship between number of seats and nominal flow time, with a minimum of 200 seconds (3.3 minutes) for 2,000 seats plus 1 second for every additional 50 seats up to 25,000. Beyond 25,000 total seats, the nominal flow time is limited to 660 seconds (11 minutes). Nominal flow time refers to the flow time for the most able group of patrons; some groups less familiar with the premises or less able groups may take longer to pass a point in the egress system. (Although three or more digits are noted in the tables, the resulting calculations should be assumed to provide only two significant figures of precision.)

An example calculation may help describe the use of Table 9-2.3.2(b).

Example: An arena providing smoke-protected assembly seating and having a total of 12,500 seats.

For capacity purposes only, what should be the clear width of an aisle stair with 8-in. (20.3-cm) risers and with a center handrail providing means of egress for 340 people? Interpolating between the widths (0.13 and 0.096 respectively) for 10,000-seat and 15,000-seat facilities, the required stair width in inches, per seat served, is 0.113 AB where A is 1.2 and B is 1.0. The aisle stair width, for capacity purposes, is the product of 340 (0.113) (1.2) (1.0) or 46.1 in. (117 cm). In this case, a minimum width criterion of 48 in. (122 cm) (*see 9-2.5.8.2*) will govern its width. Most previous editions of the *Code* credited this aisle stair with a capacity of only 150 persons.

This paragraph applies only to theater-type seating or similar seating arranged in rows (*see 9-2.3.1*).

Generally, 9-2.3.2 takes into account the common practice of many intermediate-size facilities, such as arenas and stadiums, of providing means of egress that are designed to meet provisions that fall between the egress capacity requirements of previous editions of the *Code* and the less-demanding egress capacity requirements that have been applied to large outdoor assembly facilities, such as those addressed by NFPA 102, *Standard for Assembly Seating, Tents, and Membrane Structures.*[9] Rather than merely giving a stamp of approval to this interpolation, the *Code* requires that extra caution be taken where a facility is considered for reduced egress capacities. In order to use the reduced egress capacities set out in Table 9-2.3.2(b), a case must first be made and accepted by the authority having jurisdiction demonstrating that all life safety hazards have been considered and

that control measures provided to ensure that occupants evacuating the building will not be endangered by conditions developing faster than it takes for the means of egress to be cleared. This is described as a "life safety evaluation," a process that should not be undertaken lightly or without special competence in a wide range of life safety issues including, but not limited to, firesafety.

The nominal flow time figures shown in Tables 9-2.3.2(a) and 9-2.3.2(b) are for reference and may be helpful to designers, consultants, managers, and others concerned with the expected performance of an egress system. They are not used for any other purpose (*see 9-1.3 for a definition of "flow time"*). Of course, if the facilities are to be used by groups of occupants who are unfamiliar with the facility or who are less able to move quickly and in dense groups than are younger individuals commonly found at athletic events, this will have to be taken into account, for example, when conducting the life safety evaluation and in operating the facility. Alternatively, the capacity of means of egress should be increased so that a more rapid egress is possible without endangering or otherwise taxing the less able occupants. The need to consider the capabilities of occupants in relation to circulation facility geometry has led to the use of several correction factors in the columns for clear width in Tables 9-2.3.2(a) and 9-2.3.2(b). In new facilities, there will be much emphasis on keeping the geometries as good as possible and, therefore, the correction factors will be 1.0 or very close to 1.0. With existing facilities, this might not be possible; however, it should be noted that handrails can be retrofitted on aisles and other means of egress to significantly improve occupant safety and comfort— an important factor in situations where efficient movement is needed. These factors are taken into account here and in other *Code* requirements for means of egress.

It should be noted that 9-2.3 addresses means of egress generally. The increased flexibility provided by Table 9-2.3.2(b) must be used with caution for proper balance between the relative capacities (and flow times) of each part of a means of egress system encountered by occupants as they leave the facility. Otherwise, with an unbalanced system, there will be queuing or waiting at some points other than the point of origin.

Attention should be given to the occupants' acceptance of the queue or the wait in their seats before proceeding out of the building; however, if a "downstream" component of the means of egress system is relatively underdesigned, even greater attention should be given to the actual and perceived conditions faced by occupants.

Figure 9-5 shows egress from a large stadium that provides egress performance that is perceived to be acceptable in terms of time and other factors. Occupants' acceptance of the longer egress flow times, permitted by the *Code* for larger assembly facilities, should be taken into account when doing a life safety evaluation for the building. The photograph also shows a collection of people who can be expected to take somewhat longer to clear the building than is the case with football spectators [a reference group for the nominal flow time figures noted in Tables 9-2.3.2(a) and 9-2.3.2(b)].

Photograph Courtesy of J. L. Pauls.

Figure 9-5. *Crowd Egress from a Large Assembly Facility that Might be Eligible for Egress Capacity Provisions of Table 9-2.3.2(b).*

9-2.3.3 **Main Entrance/Exit.** Every assembly occupancy shall be provided with a main entrance/exit. The main entrance/exit shall be of sufficient width to accommodate one-half of the total occupant load but shall be not less than the total required width of all aisles, exit passageways, and stairways leading thereto and shall be at the level of exit discharge or shall connect to a stairway or ramp leading to a street.

Exception No. 1: A bowling establishment shall have a main entrance/exit of sufficient capacity to accommodate 50 percent of the total occupant load without regard to the number of aisles that it serves.

Exception No. 2[*]: In assembly occupancies where there is no well defined main entrance/exit, exits shall be permitted to be distributed around the perimeter of the building provided the total exit width furnishes a minimum of 100 percent of the width needed to accommodate the permitted occupant load.

The term "main exit" was replaced with the term "main entrance/exit" in the 1988 *Code.* The intent of the *Code* is to require that 50 percent of the occupants will be able to exit through the same door(s) they used to enter the building. It was brought to the Committee's attention that some building owners/managers did not want the "main entrance" to also be designated as the "main exit." Therefore, this terminology clarifies the intent of the *Code* and will require that the main entrance to a public assembly occupancy also be designated as the main exit.

The usual entrance to an assembly occupancy also generally serves as its main exit. As a rule, people desire to leave a building by way of their entrance to the structure. Therefore, the main exit needs to be sized to accommodate at least 50 percent of the occupants; however, it must not be less in width than the sum of the required widths of the aisles that it serves.

Bowling establishments usually have relatively few rows of seats for spectators but are necessarily wide to accommodate the alleys. Due to the limitation of the number of seats in a row, many more aisles are required than in other types of assembly occupancies. Exception No. 1 to 9-2.3.3 modifies what would be the excessive main exit width required to accommodate the sum of the required aisle widths served by the exit.

Exception No. 2 clarifies the intent of the *Code* to provide the same for buildings having no main entrance as for those with a main entrance. The intent is to distribute the extra width as equally as possible among all exits. (*Also see 9-2.3.4.*)

A-9-2.3.3 **Exception No. 2.** The original *Code* wording permitted certain exceptions such as sports arenas and railway stations. If an assembly occupancy is not similar to one of these, it is frequently rejected. A listing of exceptions also raises the question as to why other occupancies are not included and necessitates more additions to the list. For example, an exhibit hall of very large size may have several main entrances/exits. A theater extending the width of a block cannot really have a main entrance/exit in one confined location. A restaurant may have a main entrance serving the parking lot and another main entrance for those entering from the street. The authority having jurisdiction must make a determination as to where this is acceptable.

9-2.3.4 **Other Exits.** Each level of an assembly occupancy shall have access to the main entrance/exit and shall be provided with additional exits of sufficient width to accommodate a minimum of one-half of the total occupant load served by that level. Such exits shall discharge in accordance with 9-2.7. Such exits shall be located as far apart as practicable and as far from the main entrance/exit as practicable. Such exits shall be accessible from a cross aisle or a side aisle. (*See 9-2.3.3.*)

Exception: In assembly occupancies where there is no well defined main entrance/exit, exits shall be permitted to be distributed around the perimeter of the building provided the total exit width furnishes a minimum of 100 percent of the width needed to accommodate the permitted occupant load.

A major change to the 1991 *Code* is the deletion of the requirement that the "other" exits must accommodate two-thirds of the occupant load, resulting in a $16\frac{2}{3}$ percent overdesign. The Committee felt that, with current *Code* provisions, the overdesign was no longer needed.

As an example of the requirements of 9-2.3.4, if an assembly occupancy had an occupant load of 900, the main exit would have to accommodate 450 people (50 percent). If there were two additional exits, together they would have to accommodate 450 people. Also, 9-2.4.2 requires that, in a Class B assembly occupancy with a capacity of more than 600 people, at least three exits must be provided, and no exit may be less than 44 in. (112 cm) wide.

9-2.4 **Number of Exits.** (*See also Section 5-4.*)

9-2.4.1 Every Class A assembly occupancy shall have at least four separate means of egress as remotely located from each other as practicable.

9-2.4.2 Every Class B assembly occupancy shall have at least two separate means of egress as remotely located from each other as practicable and, if of an occupant load of over 600, at least three separate means of egress, each not less than 44 in. (112 cm) wide.

9-2.4.3 Every Class C assembly occupancy shall have at least two means of egress consisting of separate exits or doors leading to a corridor or other spaces that provide access to two separate and independent exits located in different directions.

As the concentration or number of people increases in an assembly occupancy, the chance of simultaneous exiting by a sizable group of occupants increases. Therefore, to reduce jamming at doorways (which leads to panic and disorder), more exits at a variety of locations are needed. Paragraphs 9-2.4.1 through 9-2.4.3 provide for this design requirement.

Since 9-1.2.2 specifies that assembly areas with individual occupant loads of fewer than 50 people in buildings other than those of assembly occupancy shall be classed as part of the other occupancy, no criteria are given by 9-2.4 for the number and location of exits in such an occupancy. (*Also see Formal Interpretation 85-10 for 8-1.4.1.*)

9-2.4.4 Balconies or mezzanines having an occupant load not greater than 50 shall be permitted to be served by a single means of egress and such means of egress shall be permitted to lead to the floor below.

The intent of the Committee was to provide relief for small balconies and mezzanines, such as choir lofts that accommodate not greater than 50 people. [*Also see 9-2.5.1, which limits the common path of travel on single means of egress balconies to 75 ft (23 m).*]

9-2.4.5 Balconies or mezzanines having an occupant load greater than 50 but not greater than 100 shall have at least two remote means of egress, but both such means of egress shall be permitted to lead to the floor below.

These balconies might typically be found in restaurants or small theaters. The committee felt it was necessary to have two remote means of egress, but since the total number of people would not be greater than 100, it would be reasonable to let occupants egress onto the floor below.

9-2.4.6 Balconies or mezzanines having an occupant load greater than 100 shall have means of egress provided as for a floor.

The Committee felt than any balcony or mezzanine that could accommodate more than 100 people should be treated as a separate floor with regard to number of means of egress in order to avoid overloading the means of egress from the floor below and to protect people during egress from the mezzanine.

9-2.5 **Arrangement of Means of Egress.** (*See also Section 5-5.*)

9-2.5.1 Exits shall be remotely located from each other and shall be arranged to minimize the possibility that they may be blocked by any emergency.

Exception No. 1: A common path of travel shall be permitted for the first 20 ft (6.1 m) from any point.

Exception No. 2: A common path of travel shall be permitted for the first 75 ft (23 m) for balconies or mezzanines in accordance with 9-2.4.4.

Exception No. 3: As provided in 9-2.5.6.4.

Separation of exits as far as practicable cannot be over-emphasized. Two or more exits that are located too close to each other can become unusable quickly during the same incident. The fundamental principles of this *Code*, as expressed in Chapter 2, require remoteness of exits to the point that a single fire event will not simultaneously block both exits. This same concept applies to exit access doors. The remoteness requirements of Section 5-5 must be met.

Revolving rooftop assembly occupancies require special consideration; as the structure revolves, exit signs are often lost from view. To provide an unobstructed panoramic view, the exterior element revolves around a small stationary interior core in which the exits are often located. In many cases, the two exits are too close to each other to avoid both exits becoming involved in case of fire. Usually at least one stairway must be transferred from

its position in the stationary core to the normal location of the building stairways. This transfer, since it is a continuation of the stairway, must be made in an exit passageway possessing a fire resistance equal to that required for the stair enclosure.

9-2.5.2 Reserved.

9-2.5.3 Means of egress shall not be permitted through kitchens, storerooms, restrooms, closets, or hazardous areas as described in 9-3.2.

The purpose of this requirement is to make clear that exit access travel is not permitted to pass through areas subject to locking or areas possessing a hazard level higher than that normal for the occupancy.

9-2.5.4 Reserved.

9-2.5.5 **General Requirements for Aisles and Aisle Accessways Serving Seating.**

9-2.5.5.1* The width of aisle accessways and aisles shall provide sufficient egress capacity for the number of persons accommodated by the catchment area served by the aisle accessway or aisle in accordance with 9-2.3.1. Where aisle accessways or aisles converge to form a single path of egress travel, the required egress capacity of that path shall not be less than the combined required capacity of the converging aisle accessways and aisles.

This refers to the capacity-related width requirements of 9-2.3.1. The capacity-related requirements must be considered along with other width requirements set out in 9-2.5.8.2 and 9-2.5.9.2. The final minimum width required by the *Code* is the larger of the widths established by the two sets of requirements.

A-9-2.5.5.1 The catchment area served by an aisle accessway or aisle is the portion of the total space that is naturally served by the aisle accessway or aisle. Hence, the requirement for combining the required capacity where paths converge is in effect a restatement of the idea of a catchment area. The establishment of catchment areas should be based on a balanced use of all means of egress, with the number of persons in proportion to egress capacity.

Figure 9-6 illustrates how catchment areas would be allotted in the case of a theater with four egress doorways having approximately similar egress capacity. Note that catchment areas for normal, nonemergency uses of only some of the available means of egress — especially those provided by the main entrance/exit — may be quite different from the catchment areas based on a balanced distribution of people in proportion to egress capacity of individual means of egress. Facility management procedures must take into account the difficulties of informing people of and directing them to all the available means of egress, especially when normally used, familiar routes become blocked in an emergency.

Note that the term "required capacity" is used here to make clear that the combined required width of the egress routes might be smaller than their combined actual widths, especially where the individual widths are made wider than required by the *Code* for egress capacity purposes. Such wider widths, beyond *Code* minimums, might be justified by considerations such as normal operating convenience.

9-2.5.5.2 Those portions of aisle accessways and aisles where egress is possible in either of two directions shall be uniform in required width.

Exception: Those portions of aisle accessways where the required width, not including the seat space described by 9-2.5.4.4, does not exceed 12 in. (30.5 cm).

This requirement prohibits making some aisles wider at their ends (in an hourglass shape) simply because there are more people using them at their ends. A tapered aisle is acceptable and effective where there is only one direction of egress travel possible and the number of people served by the aisle increases in the direction of egress travel. In the more general case, where there are two directions of egress travel possible in the aisle, the width must be kept uniform to accommodate efficient egress travel that might have to reverse direction because of blockage at one end.

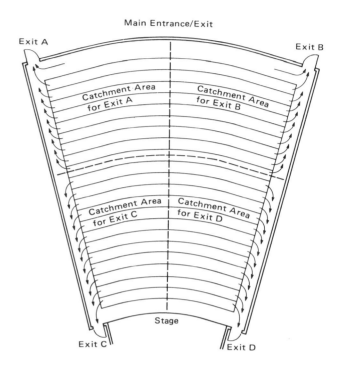

Figure 9-6. Plan of a Theater Showing how Catchment Areas for Means of Egress Are Based on a Balanced Use of All Means of Egress, in Proportion to Egress Capacity.

9-2.5.5.3* Where nonfixed seating is located between a table and an aisle accessway or aisle, the measurement of required clear width of the aisle accessway or aisle shall be made to a line 19 in. (48.3 cm) away from edge of the table. The 19-in. (48.3-cm) distance shall be measured perpendicularly to the edge of the table.

A-9-2.5.5.3 Figure A-9-2.5.5.3 shows typical measurements involving seating and tables abutting an aisle. Note that, for purposes of the means of egress requirements of this *Code*, seating at counters or other furnishings is considered to be the same as seating at tables.

Figure A-9-2.5.5.3 illustrates the provisions of 9-2.5.5.3. This provides guidance on how aisles with movable chairs are to be measured, an issue that has often been questioned by enforcement officials.

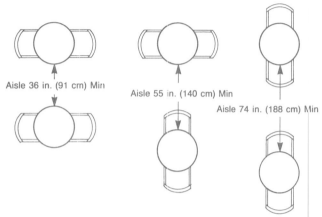

Figure A-9-2.5.5.3

9-2.5.5.4 In the case of side boundaries other than nonfixed seating at tables, for aisle accessways or aisles, the clear width shall be measured to boundary elements such as walls, guardrails, handrails, edges of seating, tables, and side edges of treads, with the measurement made horizontally to the vertical projection of the elements resulting in the smallest width measured perpendicularly to the line of travel.

9-2.5.6* Aisle Accessways Serving Seating Not at Tables.

A-9-2.5.6 For purposes of the means of egress requirements of this *Code*, tablet-arm chair seating is not considered seating at tables. Dinner theater style configurations must comply with the aisle accessway requirements applying to seating at tables and the aisle requirements of 9-2.5.8 if the aisles contain steps or are ramped. Generally, if aisles contain steps or are ramped, all of this *Code's* requirements for aisles, stairs, and ramps must be met, and attention is also drawn to 5-1.6 and A-5-1.6.

9-2.5.6.1* To determine the required clear width of aisle accessways between rows of seating, horizontal measurements shall be made (between vertical planes) from the back of one seat to the front of the most forward projection of the seat immediately behind it. Where the entire row consists of automatic or self-rising seats that comply with ASTM F851, *Test Method for Self-Rising Seat Mechanisms*, the measurement may be made with the seats in the up position.

A-9-2.5.6.1 Seats having reclining backs are assumed to be in their most upright position when unoccupied.

The requirement for the spacing between rows of chairs is illustrated in Figure 9-7.

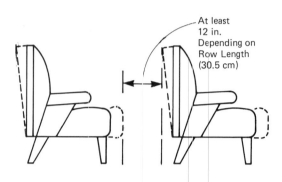

Figure 9-7. Correct Measurement of Minimum Spacing Between Rows of Chairs Without Self-Rising Seats.

9-2.5.6.2 The aisle accessway between rows of seating shall have a clear width of not less than 12 in. (30.5 cm), and this minimum shall be increased as a function of row length in accordance with 9-2.5.6.3 and 9-2.5.6.4.

Exception: If used by not more than four persons, there is no minimum clear width requirement for the portion of the aisle accessway having a length not exceeding 6 ft (1.8 m) measured from the center of the seat farthest from the aisle.

9-2.5.6.3* Rows of seating served by aisles or doorways at both ends shall have no more than 100 seats per row. The 12 in. (30.5 cm) minimum clear width of aisle accessway between such rows shall be increased by 0.3 in. (0.8 cm) for every seat over a total of 14, but need not exceed 22 in. (55.9 cm).

A-9-2.5.6.3 The system known as "continental seating" has one pair of egress doors provided for every five rows that is located close to the ends of the rows. In previous editions of the *Code*, such egress doors were required to provide a minimum clear width of 66 in. (168 cm) discharging into a foyer, lobby, or to the exterior of the building. This continental seating arrangement can result in egress flow times that are approximately one-half as long as those resulting where side aisles lead to more remote doors (i.e., with nominal flow times of approximately 100 seconds rather than 200 seconds). Such superior egress flow time performance may be desirable in some situations; however, special attention should be given either to a comparably good egress capacity for other parts of the egress system or to sufficient space to accommodate queuing outside the seating space.

This was a major change in the 1988 Edition of the *Code*. The appendix note relates the expected egress flow time performance of "continental seating," (*see Figure 9-8a*) as provided for by the *Code* prior to 1988, to the egress flow time performance of the more flexible new requirements for egress width related to capacity (*see 9-2.3*). Additional design flexibility, built upon the continental seating principle of variable minimum seat row spacing and row length, was also introduced with the 1988 Edition of the *Code*. As reference points for each end of the range, the newer requirement uses the previously employed requirements of 12 in. (30.5 cm) of clearance for rows up to 14 seats in length and 22 in. (55.9 cm) for rows over 45 seats in length. For example, under the newer requirement, rows with 47 seats require a clearance of 21.9 in. (55.6 cm). This is calculated by subtracting 14 from 47 and multiplying the result, 33, by 0.3 in. to obtain 9.9 in., which is added to 12 in. to obtain the total required width clearance of 21.9 in. Rows with 48 to 100 seats require 22 in. (55.9 cm) of clear width.

The newer flexibility, applying to all fixed seating arranged in rows, is based on the assumption that the egress time required for a seating arrangement will be influenced more by the capacity of routes downstream from the rows of seating than by the rows' clear widths. Paragraph 9-2.3 provides a standardized method for calculating the widths of those routes serving the space containing the seating. The combination of 9-2.3 and 9-2.5.6 offers designers of theaters, especially, a great deal of flexibility in laying out blocks of seating while still requiring a standard of egress flow time performance that is based on traditionally accepted egress performance (nominally about 200 seconds of flow time) resulting from very specific requirements on aisle and cross-aisle design. For example, rows longer than 14 seats are permitted, and egress door locations can be more flexibly determined than permitted under continental seating rules contained in previous *Code* editions.

Figure 9-8b illustrates the possibilities for a theater with 630 seats in one unbroken area with 21 rows ranging uni-

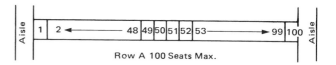

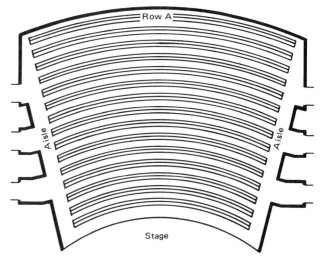

Figure 9-8a. Arrangement of Seats and Aisles with Continental Seating. In prior editions of the Code when more than 14 seats were in a row, this arrangement was required. One hundred seats is the maximum number for one row.

formly from 20 to 40 seats in length. The required minimum clear width between the front row (with 20 seats) and the one behind (with 21 seats) is 14.1 in. (35.8 cm). The required minimum clear width between the back row (with 40 seats) and the one in front of it (with 39 seats) is 19.8 in. (50.3 cm). The designer has the option of making all the clear widths uniform and at least 19.8 in. (50.3 cm), or progressively increasing them from front to back, from at least 14.1 in. to at least 19.8 in., as the row lengths increase.

The theater is a Class B assembly occupancy with over 500 seats; therefore, in accordance with 9-2.4.2, it requires at least three separate means of egress, each not less than 44 in. (112 cm) in width. A main set of doors located at the back of the seating and close to the main entrance/exit has to provide at least one-half the egress capacity. In this case, it must serve at least 315 persons. According to 9-2.3.2, the minimum total clear width of these main doorways must be 70 in. (178 cm), and thus two doorways providing 35 in. (89 cm) clear width each would suffice for *Code* capacity purposes. However,

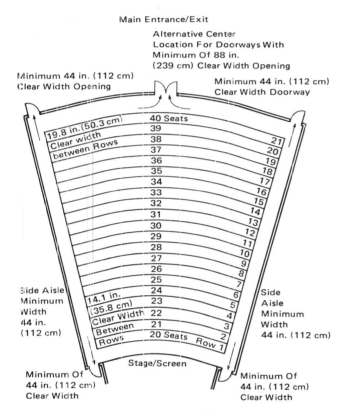

Figure 9-8b. *Minimum Means of Egress for a 630-Seat The-ater Utilizing the Row Spacing and Aisle Length Provisions of 9-2.5.6.3.*

9-2.3.3 requires that the main entrance be as wide as all aisles leading to it, so the two 44-in. (119-cm) aisles require an 88-in. (224-cm) main entrance/exit. Two additional means of egress, providing total capacity for at least 315 seats in accordance with 9-2.3.4, each need to have a minimum clear width of 35 in. (119 cm) (158 times 0.22 in.) in accordance with 9-2.3.2 and not less than 44 in. (112 cm) in accordance with 9-2.4.2. Minimum side aisle width connecting the front and back egress doorways would also have to be 44 in. (129 cm). Greater widths of aisle and doorways, especially those leading to the main entrance/exit, should be considered to help improve convenience and other features that go beyond the minimum *Code* requirements for means of egress.

In the example presented in Figure 9-8b there is of course the option of doing a traditional layout with seats having no more than 6 intervening seats separating them

from an aisle. This would require that more space be devoted to aisles and cross aisles, but this space loss could be offset by closer seat row spacings.

9-2.5.6.4 Rows of seating served by an aisle or doorway at one end only shall have a path of travel not exceeding 30 ft (9.1 m) in length from any seat to a point where a person has a choice of two paths of travel to separate exits. The 12 in. (30.5 cm) minimum clear width of aisle accessway between such rows shall be increased by 0.6 in. (1.6 cm) for every seat over a total of 7.

The incremental increase of 0.6 in. (1.5 cm) of required minimum clear width between rows for each additional seat to be passed to reach an aisle is the same here as in the case of the row served by aisles at each end. (*See 9-2.5.6.3.*)

The 30-ft (9.1-m) limit effectively means that only about 18 chairs can be put into a row served by an aisle at one end only, assuming that, when one reaches the aisle, it is possible to move in either of two directions to two exits. This requirement also influences the permitted maximum length of aisles providing a common path of travel to reach the two exits. (*Also see 9-2.5.8.1.*)

9-2.5.6.5 Chairs without dividing arms shall have their capacity determined by allowing 18 in. (45.7 cm) per person.

The fact that the *Code* uses the traditional 18-in. (45.7-cm) figure for seat width per person for determining maximum occupant load (and egress capacity) should not necessarily be taken as an endorsement for using the 18-in. (45.7-cm) figure as a basis for ticket sales. This is especially true where events are sold out and a specific seat is assigned on each ticket. Winter events, where spectators wear bulkier clothing, are examples of those for which a more generous seat spacing should be considered in the ticket sales policy. Generally, the 18-in. (45.7-cm) figure — applied to ticket sales — makes most sense with children and younger adults, under temperate weather conditions, and with a general admission policy when a full house is not expected. Otherwise, the space to be kept clear in aisles and other means of egress might be compromised.

9-2.5.6.6 Where bleacher or grandstand seating without backs is used indoors, rows of seats shall be spaced not less than 22 in. (55.9 cm) back to back.

Exception: Folding or telescopic seating shall comply with NFPA 102, Standard for Assembly Seating, Tents, and Membrane Structures, with a limit of dead ends in vertical aisles of 16 rows.

The elimination of backs allows the entire bleacher to be a path of exit access. Assuming that they are fit and agile, plus prepared to risk a serious misstep and fall, people can simultaneously evacuate a bleacher upward or downward without using aisles. This compensates somewhat for the openness of bleacher-type structures, which can expose the entire population to a single fire either under or adjacent to the structure. The provisions of the *Code* concerning bleachers or graduated seating and folding or telescopic seating have been modified to coordinate requirements with NFPA 102, *Standard for Assembly Seating, Tents, and Membrane Structures.*[9] It should be noted that, unless certain criteria are met (as required by NFPA 102), aisles are required for new bleachers, and such aisles must meet requirements comparable to those in the *Code*.

9-2.5.6.7 Rows of seating including tablet-arm chairs shall only be permitted if the clear width of aisle accessways complies with the requirements of 9-2.5.6 when the tablet is in the usable position.

Exception: Tablet arms shall be permitted to be measured in the stored position where the tablet arm automatically returns to the stored position when raised manually to a vertical position in one motion and falls to the stored position by force of gravity.

The Committee carefully examined the subject of tablet-arm chairs with storing provisions and determined that these chairs present little threat to life safety. Where the tablet arm is fixed in the use position, tablet-arm chairs must be arranged to meet the aisle spacing requirements found in 9-2.5.6. This applies to both normal seating and continental seating. Figure 9-9 illustrates this provision. Note the Exception to 9-2.5.6.7.

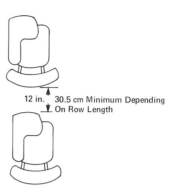

Figure 9-9. Minimum Spacing Between Rows of Seats with Fixed Tablet Arms. The clear space between the back of a seat and the leading edge of a tablet arm in normal seating and required row spacing is set by 9-2.5.6.7, depending on row length, but not less than 12 in. (30.5 cm).

9-2.5.7* Aisle Accessways Serving Seating at Tables.

A-9-2.5.7 For purposes of the means of egress requirements of this *Code*, seating at counters or other furnishings is considered to be the same as seating at tables.

These provisions are new to the 1991 Edition of the *Code*. For the first time aisle accessways at tables are addressed (*see the new definition of aisle accessway in 8-1.3*). The appendix notes help explain the intent of the *Code*.

9-2.5.7.1* The minimum required clear width of aisle accessway shall be 12 in. (30.5 cm) measured in accordance with 9-2.5.5.3 and increased as a function of length in accordance with 9-2.5.7.2.

Exception: If used by not more than four persons, there is no minimum clear width requirement for the portion of aisle accessway having a length not exceeding 6 ft (1.8 m) and located farthest from an aisle.

A-9-2.5.7.1 Effectively, where the aisle accessway is bounded by movable seating, the 12-in. (30.5-cm) minimum width might be increased by about 15 to 30 in. (38 to 76 cm) as seating is pushed in toward tables. Moreover, it is such movement of chairs during normal and emergency egress situations that makes the zero-clearance exception workable. The exception also applies to booth seating where people sitting closest to the aisle normally move out ahead of anyone farthest from the aisle.

9-2.5.7.2* The minimum required clear width of aisle accessway measured in accordance with 9-2.5.5.3 and 9-2.5.5.4 shall be increased beyond the 12-in. (30.5-cm) requirement by 0.5 in. (1.3 cm) for each additional 12 in. (30.5 cm) or fraction thereof beyond 12 ft (3.7 m) of aisle accessway length measured from the center of the seat farthest from an aisle.

A-9-2.5.7.2 Minimum width requirement as a function of accessway length:

0 in. (0 cm) for the first 6 ft (1.8 m) of length toward the exit;

12 in. (30.5 cm) for the next 6 ft (1.8 m), i.e., up to 12 ft (3.7 m) of length;

12 in. to 24 in. (30.5 cm to 61 cm) for lengths from 12 ft to 36 ft (3.7 m to 10.9 m), the maximum length permitted by 9-2.5.7.3 to the closest aisle or egress doorway.

Add to these widths any additional width needed for seating as described in 9-2.5.5.3.

9-2.5.7.3 The path of travel shall not exceed 30 ft (9.1 m) from any seat to the point where a person has a choice of two or more paths of travel to separate exits. The path of travel along the aisle accessway shall not exceed 36 ft (10.9 m) from any seat to the closest aisle or egress doorway.

9-2.5.8 Aisles Serving Seating Not at Tables.

9-2.5.8.1 Dead-end aisles shall not exceed 20 ft (6.1 m) in length.

Exception: A longer dead-end aisle is permitted where seats served by the dead-end aisle are not more than 24 seats from another aisle measured along a row of seats having a minimum clear width of 12 in. (30.5 cm) plus 0.6 in. (1.5 cm) for each additional seat over a total of 7 in the row.

The exception gives formal recognition to the inherent redundancy that exists where rows of seating are served by two or more aisles so that the blockage of any one aisle simply means that there is greater movement along rows to reach a somewhat more distant aisle. The

exception recognizes that movement along rows, even with their constricted widths, provides many routes that permit faster movement to alternative aisles than would be possible with a dedicated cross aisle. As with the concept of wider clear spacings between rows where rows are longer (9-2.5.6.3), this exception gives additional credit for increased space to move along the rows to reach alternative aisles. At the row length limit of 24 seats, the required clear width spacing for use of this exception is 22.2 in. (56.4 cm). The exception may prove helpful in situations such as arenas and theaters where it is not easy to provide a cross aisle, doorway, etc., giving access to an exit, but where two or more aisles are relatively easy to reach when moving along rows. (*Also see* 9-2.5.6.4.)

9-2.5.8.2 The minimum clear width of aisles shall be sufficient to provide egress capacity in accordance with 9-2.3.2 but not less than:

(a) 42 in. (107 cm) for stairs having seating on each side.

Exception to (a): 30 in. (76 cm) for catchment areas having no more than 60 seats.

(b) 36 in. (91 cm) for stairs having seating on only one side.

Exception to (b): 30 in. (76 cm) for catchment areas having no more than 60 seats.

(c) 20 in. (51 cm) between a handrail and seating or a guardrail where the aisle is subdivided by a handrail.

(d) 42 in. (107 cm) for level or ramped aisles having seating on both sides.

Exception to (d): 30 in. (76 cm) for catchment areas having no more than 60 seats.

(e) 36 in. (91 cm) for level or ramped aisles having seating on only one side.

Exception to (e): 30 in. (76 cm) for catchment areas having no more than 60 seats.

(f) 23 in. (58 cm) between a handrail or guardrail and seating where aisle does not serve more than five rows on one side.

These requirements will often govern the final minimum widths of aisles especially where a relatively limited amount of egress capacity is required by 9-2.3.1.

While the requirements for existing aisle widths are somewhat different from those for new facilities (as described in 8-2.5.8.2), it is useful to consider the benefits of widths similar to those required in new facilities. Figures 9-10 and 9-11 illustrate how intensively a 48-in. (122-cm) aisle stair subdivided by a center handrail can be used. Figure 9-12 shows, in overhead plan view, a large male walking down one side of a similar aisle stair, 48 in. (122 cm) wide, subdivided by a handrail. Chair seating is shown adjoining the aisle in these photographs.

Photograph Courtesy of J. L. Pauls.
Figure 9-11. *Intensive Use of Handrail at Center of 48-in. (122-cm) Aisle Stair in a Stadium. The handrail height is approximately 34 in. (86.3 cm).*

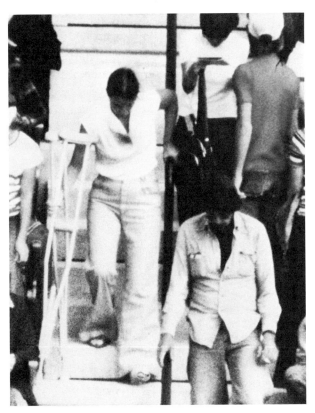

Photograph Courtesy of J. L. Pauls.
Figure 9-10. *Intensive Use of Aisle Stair, 48 in. (122 cm) Wide with Central Handrail, in a Stadium.*

Paragraph 9-2.5.8.2(f) is based on the requirement for handrails in aisle stairs. It specifically addresses the allowance for extending such handrails down the center of aisles for as much as five rows, leaving only about 23 in. (58 cm) of nominal width clear to the side of the handrail. This width is readily used by individuals moving in single or staggered file and can be used with tolerable inconvenience where people must pass by each other on the same side of the handrail. This provision of the *Code* might be helpful in cases where a short stub aisle is needed to serve rows of seating immediately beside a vomitory.

Generally, it might be noted that the effective width of aisles is often somewhat wider than is the case for egress facilities that are bounded on both sides by construction. One important exception to this generalization occurs where many people are attempting to sit on undivided benches or bleachers served by an aisle. The 18-in. (45.7-cm) spacing usually provided for each person is often too small, and there is a natural tendency for people to have their legs (sometimes several inches of hips and shoulders) occupying a significant part of the aisle width. Therefore, it is prudent when designing for crowded, nonchair seating to increase the width of seat per person to facilitate normal circulation in the aisles.

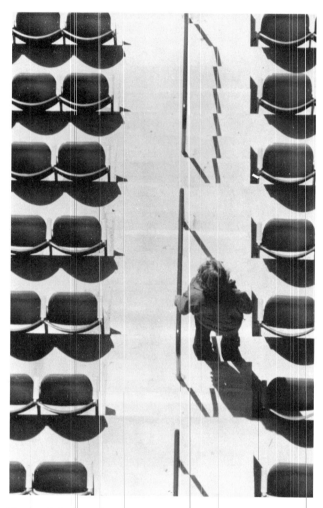

Photograph Courtesy of J. L. Pauls.
***Figure 9-12.** Overhead, Plan View of 48-inch (122-cm) Aisle Stair, with Center Handrail, Used by a Large Male.*

9-2.5.8.3* Aisle Stairs and Ramps. Aisles having a gradient steeper than 1 in 20 but not steeper than 1 in 8 shall consist of a ramp. Aisles having a gradient steeper than 1 in 8 shall consist of an aisle stair.

A-9-2.5.8.3 Technical information about the convenience and safety of ramps and stairs having gradients in the region of 1 in 8 clearly suggests that the goal should be slopes for ramps that are less steep and better combinations of stair risers and treads than, for example, 4-in. (10.2-cm) risers and 32-in. (81-cm) treads. This should be kept in mind by designers in establishing the gradient of seating areas to be served by aisles.

Major changes relating to aisles were introduced in the 1985 Edition of the *Code*. The 1988 *Code* contained some minor changes that further emphasize the importance of design details for aisles. The 1991 *Code* has made some further modifications along with editorial renumbering. The changes in the previous and current editions address the need to design aisle stairs, for example, with all the attention and care required for stairs generally, plus additional care due to the unique design and use conditions encountered with aisles serving seating arranged in rows, especially where there are large elevation differences between the rows of seating. Paragraph 9-2.5.8.3 begins with a general requirement that divides aisles into two categories based on slope. Ideally, it would be preferable to avoid designing aisles having about a 1 in 8 slope; however, sightlines might dictate such slopes in some situations. Ramps of this slope are relatively steep and problematic for people with walking difficulties. Stairs with a very small rise and long treads also present problems, notably trips and missteps, because the presence of the low risers might not be evident, especially in a crowd situation. Generally, aisles also present unusual distractions for people because of their unusual length, the presence of other people in the aisles, and the presence of those entering the aisles from adjoining seating rows. Therefore, aisles of all slopes must be treated with considerable care and attention to human factors, for the sake of both the movement of individuals and that of crowds.

9-2.5.8.4 Aisle Stair Treads.

(a)* There shall be no variation exceeding ³/₁₆ in. (0.5 cm) in the depth of adjacent treads.

A-9-2.5.8.4(a) Completely uniform tread dimensions are preferred over aisle stair designs where tread depths alternate between relatively small intermediate treads between seating platforms and relatively larger treads at seating platforms. A larger tread, level with the seating platform, is not needed to facilitate easy access to and egress from a row of seating. If this arrangement is used, it is important to provide a better than minimum tread depth for the intermediate tread; hence, 13 in. (33.0 cm) is specified. Where nonuniformities occur due to construction tolerance, they should not exceed ³/₁₆ in. (0.5 cm) between adjacent treads.

Field research studies of situations where aisle step dimensions are not consistent indicate that the incidence of missteps rises significantly where tolerances of tread uniformity are not respected.

Exception to (a): In aisle stairs where a single intermediate tread is provided halfway between seating platforms, such intermediate treads may have a relatively smaller but uniform depth, but not less than 13 in. (33 cm).

Allowing unequal-sized treads within aisle stairs, a traditional practice once believed to be useful in facilitating access to seat rows, is no longer permitted by the *Code* for new facilities; however, an exception is included for existing facilities. Even with the increased minimum tread size requirement [13 in. (33 cm)], the end result (larger treads at the seat row entry level and smaller intermediate treads between seat row levels) is not as beneficial in terms of stair safety as consistently sized treads. This is true even for uniformly sized treads as large as about 20 in. (50.8 cm) in depth (assuming a relatively low riser height). Handrails, required in many cases by 9-2.5.8.6, help to compensate for the stretched stride length that may be needed in aisle stairs. It is preferable to keep treads uniform so that the risk of misstepping, particularly the risk of overstepping of relatively smaller treads, is reduced.

(b)* Treads shall be a minimum of 11 in. (27.9 cm).

A-9-2.5.8.4(b) Tread depth is more important to stair safety than is riser height. Therefore, in cases where seating area gradient is less than 5 in 11, it is recommended that the tread dimension be increased beyond 11 in. (27.9 cm) rather than reducing the riser height. Where seating area gradient exceeds 8 in 11, it is recommended that the riser height be increased while maintaining a tread depth of at least 11 in. (27.9 cm).

Figure 9-13 shows a side view of an aisle stair with 11-in. (28-cm) treads used by a person with footwear measuring 12 in. (30.5 cm) in length — a condition found in the case of about 5 percent of adults generally, and a condition that might be somewhat more common in those assembly situations attracting a higher proportion of male adults.

It should also be noted, in relation to 9-2.5.8.4(a), that there is apparently no difficulty when entering or leaving the aisle or when entering or leaving the seat row where the provision of the three equal-sized, 11-in. (17.9-cm) treads at each seat row are used, as shown in the photograph.

Photograph Courtesy of J. L. Pauls.

Figure 9-13. *Side View of Aisle Stair with 11-in. (17.9-cm) Treads in a Stadium.*

9-2.5.8.5 Aisle Stair Risers.

(a) Riser heights shall be a minimum of 4 in. (10.2 cm).

At the minimum slope limit set by the *Code* for aisle stairs (for slopes exceeding 1 in 8), there is a riser height of 4 in. (10.2 cm) where the seat platform is 32 in. (81.3 cm) deep. At such low riser heights, which present a tripping hazard if the risers are not detected by people, there is special significance in the tread nosing marking requirement in 9-2.5.8.7.

(b) Riser heights shall not exceed 8 in. (20.3 cm).

Exception No. 1 to (b): Where the gradient of an aisle is steeper than 8 in. (20.3 cm) in rise in 11 in. (27.9 cm) of run (to maintain necessary sight lines in the adjoining seating area), the riser height may exceed 8 in. (20.3 cm) but shall not exceed 11 in. (27.9 cm).

Exception No. 2 to (b): Folding and telescopic seating in accordance with NFPA 102, Standard for Assembly Seating, Tents, and Membrane Structures.

The 1988 Edition of the *Code* reduced the maximum riser height permitted for new aisle stairs from 11 in. (27.9 cm) to 9 in. (22.9 cm). In addition to reducing movement safety, the unusually high risers of some aisle stairs reduce the speed and efficiency of movement, especially in the descending direction. However, to cover the situation of some existing aisles, the *Code* permits risers up to 11 in. (27.9 cm) high in existing situations. This is taken into account in 9-2.3.2 where, for each additional inch of riser height above 7 in. (17.9 cm), an additional 20 percent must be added to the required capacity-related width of the aisle to satisfy *Code* requirements and achieve an acceptable egress flow time performance.

(c) Riser heights shall be designed to be uniform in each aisle, and the construction-caused nonuniformities shall not exceed ³⁄₁₆ in. (0.5 cm) between adjacent risers.

A special case is made here for especially nonuniform riser heights, beyond the usual ³⁄₁₆-in. (0.5-cm) tolerance, only for situations where there is a break in the slope of a seating deck to maintain adequate sightlines. The seating deck slope may change incrementally at each row or, more commonly, there may be a large change at one or more locations. At such locations, there is often a change on the row-to-row elevation that greatly exceeds the usual ³⁄₁₆-in. (0.5-cm) tolerance. Aisle step riser heights will, as a consequence, change radically at this point. It is the special duty of the designer and owner to warn people using the aisle of this unusual change in the riser dimensions. This warning might go well beyond the usual marking of all step nosings required by 9-2.5.8.7. A distinctive color or other standard hazard marking is needed on the step nosings. Additional warning techniques may have to be employed in some cases to help reduce the risk of stumbles and falls.

Exception to (c): Riser height shall be permitted to be nonuniform only for the purpose of accommodating necessary changes in gradient to maintain necessary sight lines within a seating area and shall be permitted to exceed ³⁄₈ in. (1.0 cm) in any flight. Where nonuniformities exceed ³⁄₁₆ in. (0.5 cm)

between adjacent risers, the exact location of such nonuniformities shall be indicated by a distinctive marking stripe on each tread at the nosing or leading edge adjacent to the nonuniform risers.

9-2.5.8.6* Aisle Handrails. Ramped aisles having a gradient exceeding 1 in 12 and aisle stairs shall be provided with handrails at one side or along the centerline.

Where there is seating on both sides of the aisle, the handrails shall be discontinuous with gaps or breaks at intervals not exceeding five rows to facilitate access to seating and to permit crossing from one side of the aisle to the other. These gaps or breaks shall have a clear width of at least 22 in. (55.9 cm) and not greater than 36 in. (91 cm) measured horizontally, and the handrail shall have rounded terminations or bends. Where handrails are provided in the middle of aisle stairs, there shall be an additional intermediate rail located approximately 12 in. (30 cm) below the main handrail.

Exception No. 1: Handrails are not required for ramped aisles having a gradient not steeper than 1 in 8 and having seating on both sides.

Exception No. 2: The requirement for a handrail is satisfied by the use of a guard providing a rail that complies with the graspability requirements for handrails and is located at a consistent height between 34 in. (86 cm) and 42 in. (107 cm) measured vertically from the top of the rail to the leading edge (nosing) of stair treads or to the adjacent walking surface in the case of a ramp.

Exception No. 3: Handrails are not required where risers do not exceed 7 in. (17.8 cm) in height.

A-9-2.5.8.6 Failure to provide a handrail within a 30-in. (76-cm) horizontal distance of all required portions of the aisle stair width will mean that the egress capacity calculation must be modified as required by 9-2.3.2(b). This might lead to an increase in the aisle width. Although this will compensate for reduced egress efficiency, it does not help individuals walking on such portions of stairs to recover from missteps (other than possibly reducing marginally the crowding that might exacerbate the problem of falls). (*See also 5-2.2.4.*)

It should be noted that in 8-2.5.8.6 there is no longer an exception permitting new aisle stairs without handrails where riser heights are less than 7 in. (17.9 cm). This is a result of increased experience with the provision and use of aisle handrails, as well as a general realization that aisles pose unique challenges to users that may go beyond those encountered on other ramps and stairs. Figures 9-10 and 9-11 illustrate the variety of use conditions in aisles and the extensive use of handrails. In field research studies, aisle stair handrail use has been shown to be used about twice as often as handrails provided to meet *Code* requirements for non-aisle stairs. When one considers the unusual lengths of aisles, the unusual step geometries, and the very complex use conditions (with people entering and leaving the aisle at many rows), this high level of use is not surprising. Aside from their value in increasing the safety and comfort of people using the aisles, the handrails also help to improve egress efficiency — a benefit taken into account in calculation of egress capacity. (*See 9-2.3.2.*)

The required gaps between sections of center-aisle handrails are illustrated in Figure 9-12. Spacing such gaps as frequently as every three rows is recommended where there is extensive use of aisles during events. A greater spacing of up to five rows between gaps might be acceptable where there is little use of the aisles during events and little counterflow at any time. Gap size should be kept at the lower end of the permitted range of 22 to 36 in. (55.9 cm to 91 cm) where the aisles are unusually steep and handrail use is especially valuable in reducing the risk of falls.

Exception No. 2 takes into account the proven utility of handrails that are higher than those permitted even with the increased handrail height range introduced with the 1988 Edition of the *Code*. A guardrail that is 42 in. (107 cm) high, such as at the side of an aisle where there is a vomitory, can be considered a usable handrail if it offers graspability as required for handrails. (*See 5-2.2.4.5.*)

9-2.5.8.7* **Aisle Marking.** A contrasting marking stripe shall be provided on each tread at the nosing or leading edge such that the location of such tread is readily apparent, particularly when viewed in descent. Such stripes shall be at least 1 in. (2.5 cm) wide and shall not exceed 2 in. (5 cm) in width.

Exception: The marking stripe is not required where tread surfaces and environmental conditions under all conditions of use are such that the location of each tread is readily apparent, particularly when viewed in descent.

Figure 9-14 suggests some of the step visibility difficulties that are commonly encountered in outdoor facilities with concrete treads. Without the helpful shadows from the handrail posts, there would be little indication of the exact location of each tread nosing. This situation requires the applied nosing markings referred to in 9-2.5.8.7. The distractions of the playing field and the unusually long aisle add further justification for making the steps as obvious as possible. It should be stressed that each situation needs to be carefully evaluated (with mock-ups at the design stage and inspection of actual conditions during use) to determine whether any improvements are warranted in marking and lighting such aisles.

Photograph Courtesy of J. L. Pauls.
Figure 9-14. *View Down Aisle Stair, Provided with Center Handrail, in a Stadium.*

A-9-2.5.8.7 Certain tread covering materials such as plush carpets, which are often used in theaters, produce an inherently well-marked tread nosing under most lighting conditions. On the other hand, concrete treads (with nosings having a sharp edge), especially under outdoor lighting conditions, are difficult to discriminate and therefore require an applied marking stripe. Slip resistance of such marking stripes should be similar to the rest of the treads, and no tripping hazard should be created.

9-2.5.9 Aisles Serving Seating at Tables.

9-2.5.9.1* Aisles that contain steps or are ramped, such as the aisles serving dinner theatre style configurations, shall comply with the requirements of 9-2.5.8.

A-9-2.5.9.1 See 5-1.6 and A-5-1.6 for special circulation safety precautions applicable where small elevation differences occur.

9-2.5.9.2* The minimum width of aisles serving seating at tables shall be 44 in. (112 cm) where serving an occupant load greater than 50 and 36 in. (91 cm) where serving an occupant load of 50 or less.

A-9-2.5.9.2 Attention is drawn to the need to make facilities accessible to people using wheelchairs, and reference is made to ANSI A117.1, *Standard for Buildings and Facilities — Providing Accessibility and Usability for Physically Handicapped People*, which provides guidance on appropriate aisle widths. (*See Appendix B.*)

Also see 9-2.5.5, which applies to all aisles.

9-2.5.10 Approval of Layouts.

9-2.5.10.1 Where required by the authority having jurisdiction, plans drawn to scale showing the arrangement of furnishings or equipment shall be submitted to the authority by the building owner, manager, or authorized agent to substantiate conformance with the provisions of this section and shall constitute the only acceptable arrangement until revised or additional plans are submitted and approved.

Exception: Temporary deviations from the specifications of the approved plans shall be permitted provided the occupant load is not increased and the intent of this section is maintained.

9-2.6 **Travel Distance to Exits.** Exits shall be so arranged that the total length of travel from any point to reach an exit will not exceed 150 ft (45 m) in any assembly occupancy. (*See also Section 5-6.*)

Exception: The travel distance shall not exceed 200 ft (60 m) in assembly occupancies protected throughout by an approved automatic sprinkler system.

Travel distance to exits from balconies or galleries that are served by unenclosed stairways must be measured to include the distance on the slope of the stair in the plane of the nosings and the distance from the bottom of the stairs to the exit. Travel distance is measured as illustrated in Figure 9-15.

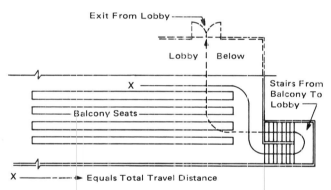

Figure 9-15. *Measurement of Travel Distance to Exit Where Balconies Are Served by Unenclosed Stairs.*

9-2.7 **Discharge from Exits.**

9-2.7.1 Exit discharge shall comply with Section 5-7.

9-2.7.2 The level of exit discharge shall be measured at the point of principal entrance to the building.

9-2.7.3 Where the principal entrance to an assembly occupancy is via a terrace, either raised or depressed, such terrace may be considered to be the level of exit discharge for the purposes of 9-1.6 if:

(a) The terrace is at least as long (measured parallel to the building) as the total width of the exit(s) it serves, but not less than 5 ft (152 cm) long, and

(b) The terrace is at least as wide (measured perpendicularly to the building) as the exit(s) it serves, but not less than 5 ft (152 cm) wide, and

(c) Required stairs leading from the terrace to grade are protected in accordance with 5-2.2.6.3 or are a minimum of 10 ft (3 m) from the building.

For existing assembly occupancies, the minimum width remains at 5 ft (152 cm). However, while the 1985 *Code* was silent on stairs, the 1988 and 1991 *Codes* require stairs to be at least 10 ft (3 m) from the face of the building, unless they are protected as provided in Chapter 5.

The requirements of 9-2.7.3 are illustrated in Figure 9-16.

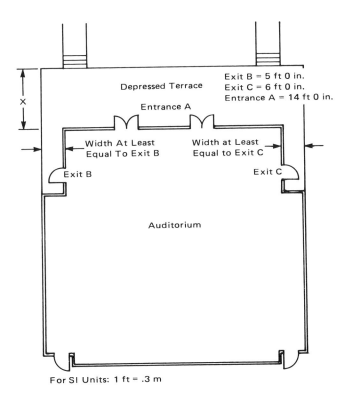

For SI Units: 1 ft = .3 m

Figure 9-16. Assembly Occupancy with Depressed Terrace as Principal Entrance. Assuming that each stair serves one-half of Entrance A and one of the two other exits, then X must be equal to or greater than the largest of the following: 5 ft (1.5 m) per 9-2.7.3(b); 5 ft (1.5 m) + ½ of 14 ft (4.2 m) = 12 ft (3.6 m); or 6 ft (1.8 m) + ½ of 14 ft (4.2 m) = 13 ft (3.9 m). Therefore, X ≥ 13ft (3.9 m).

9-2.8 **Illumination of Means of Egress.** Means of egress shall be illuminated in accordance with Section 5-8.

9-2.9 **Emergency Lighting.** Emergency lighting shall be provided in accordance with Section 5-9.

Exception: Class C assembly occupancies used exclusively for a place of worship shall not be required to have emergency lighting.

See Formal Interpretation 76-72, which follows.

Formal Interpretation 76-72
Reference: 8-2.9, 9-2.9

Question: Where the *Code* states that all assembly occupancies and the means of egress shall be provided with emergency lighting, does this include Class C Assembly Occupancies, such as restaurants and drive-ins, that have glass almost all around the dining area?

Answer: Yes. However, the authority having jurisdiction may modify the requirements if the authority feels adequate lighting is maintained from external sources.

Issue Edition: 1976
Reference: 8-2.10
Date: September 1978 ∎

The exception to the requirement for emergency lighting is intended to apply only to Class C assembly occupancies (50 to 300 people) that are not likely to be used for any purpose except religious worship because they contain permanently fixed furnishings such as pews, pulpits, or altars.

9-2.10 **Marking of Means of Egress.** Means of egress shall have signs in accordance with Section 5-10.

9-2.11 **Special Features.**

9-2.11.1 **Railings.**

(a) The fasciae of boxes, balconies, and galleries shall not rise less than 26 in. (66 cm) high above the adjacent floor or shall have substantial railings not less than 26 in. (66 cm) high above the adjacent floor.

(b) The height of the rail above footrests on the adjacent floor immediately in front of a row of seats shall be not less than 26 in. (66 cm). Railings at the ends of aisles shall be not less than 36 in. (91 cm) high for the full width of the aisle and shall be not less than 42 in. (107 cm) high for the width of the aisle where steps occur.

(c) Cross aisles shall be provided with railings not less than 26 in. (66 cm) high above the adjacent floor.

Exception No. 1: Where the backs of seats located at the front of the aisle project 24 in. (61 cm) or more above the adjacent floor of the aisle.

Exception No. 2: Existing railings 36 in. (91 cm) high at the ends of aisles where steps occur shall be permitted to continue to be used.

Figure 9-17a illustrates the requirements of 9-2.11.1(a) and (b). Rail height at the fascia end of a sloping aisle must not be less than 36 in. (91 cm). However, where the aisle is not ramped but has steps, the rail height must be at least 42 in. (107 cm). There is greater danger of people tripping on steps than on a sloping surface with a maximum gradient of 1 ft (0.3 m) of rise to 8 ft (2.44 m) of run. Exception No. 2 permits continued use of existing 36-in. (91-cm) high railings. This avoids the hardship that would be placed on existing facilities if the railing had to be raised 6 in. (15.2 cm).

The *Code* requires a barrier along the downhill side of a cross aisle. [*See 9-2.11.1(c).*] The barrier may be a rail or the backs of the seats that abut the downhill side of the aisle where the backs project 24 in. (60 cm) or more above the cross aisle. The difference between the 24-in. (60-cm) back height and the required 26-in. (66-cm) railing is not sufficient to require the railing. It is not the intent to reduce the height of guards where sight lines are not a problem, such as with cross aisles at the rear or top of seating areas or where cross aisles are sufficiently below seating that a proper height guard will not interfere with sight lines. (*See Figure 9-17b.*)

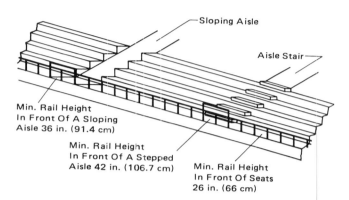

Figure 9-17a. *Railings Installed in Accordance with 9-2.11.1(a) and (b).*

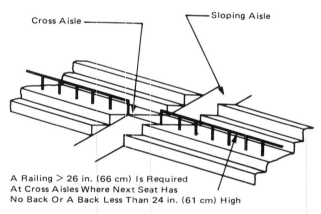

A Railing > 26 in. (66 cm) Is Required At Cross Aisles Where Next Seat Has No Back Or A Back Less Than 24 in. (61 cm) High

Figure 9-17b. *Barrier for Cross Aisles in Accordance with 9-2.11.1(c). A railing [greater than 26 in. (66 cm)] is required unless the backs of seats in the row in front of the cross aisle are greater than 24 in. (60 cm) above the cross aisle.*

SECTION 9-3   Protection

9-3.1 Protection of Vertical Openings. Vertical openings shall be enclosed or protected in accordance with Section 6-2.

Exception No. 1: Unprotected vertical openings connecting not more than three floors in accordance with 6-2.4.5 shall be permitted.

Exception No. 2: Atriums in accordance with 6-2.4.6 shall be permitted.

Exception No. 3*: Stairs or ramps shall be permitted to be unenclosed between balconies or mezzanines and main assembly areas located below provided the balcony or mezzanine is open to the main assembly area.

A-9-3.1 **Exception No. 3.** The exception presumes the balcony or mezzanine complies with the other provisions of the *Code* such as travel distance to exits in accordance with 9-2.6 and numbers of exits in accordance with 9-2.4. For the purposes of this exception, a balcony with glazing that provides a visual awareness of the main assembly area is considered open.

Exception No. 4: Existing wood lath and plaster, existing ¹/₂-in. (1.3-cm) gypsum wallboard, existing installations of ¹/₄-in. (.6-cm) thick wired glass that are, or are rendered, inoperative and fixed in the closed position, or other existing materials having similar fire resistance capabilities shall be acceptable. All such assemblies shall be in good repair and free of any condition that would diminish their original fire resistance characteristics.

Exceptions No. 1 and No. 2 permit the use of 6-2.4.5 and 6-2.4.6; see 6-2.4.5 and 6-2.4.6 for details. For egress requirements from balconies, see 9-2.4.4, 9-2.4.5, and 9-2.4.6.

9-3.2 **Protection from Hazards.**

9-3.2.1 **Stages and Platforms.** *(See 9-1.3.)*

Note the definitions for stages and platforms in 9-1.3. Modern stages pose problems that didn't exist in the past. Scenery may be shifted horizontally, vertically, or both ways. The use of thrust stages and arena stages creates other problems.

The classic stage of the past rose high above the proscenium opening to accommodate the rigid asbestos curtain. The high void was a natural place to house combustible scenery for a performance, along with the rigging necessary for handling scene changes. This vertical storage area represented both a high fuel load and a space difficult to reach in case of fire. Many new theaters use a flexible noncombustible curtain that does not require much height to accommodate it. Scenery on these stages

is moved horizontally, thus reducing the distance necessary for storage between the top of the proscenium opening and the stage ceiling. Most combustible scenery is now stored in areas adjacent to the stage. All rigging and lighting is condensed in less vertical space.

9-3.2.1.1 **Materials and Design.** (Reserved.)

9-3.2.1.2 **Platform Construction.** (Reserved.)

9-3.2.1.3 **Stage Construction.** (Reserved.)

9-3.2.1.4 **Accessory Rooms.** (Reserved.)

9-3.2.1.5 **Vents.** Legitimate stages shall be provided with one or more vents constructed of noncombustible material. Ventilators shall be located near the center and above the highest part of the stage. They shall be raised above the stage roof and shall have a total ventilation area equal to at least 5 percent of the floor area of the stage.

Regular stages exceeding 1,000 sq ft (93 sq m) in area shall be provided with vents as required for legitimate stages or shall be provided with a mechanical vent installed in an exterior wall of the stage itself. Such vent shall be automatic upon operation of the sprinkler system and shall also be capable of manual operation. The capacity of the exhaust vent shall be approximately equivalent to that which would be provided for a legitimate stage.

Vents shall open by spring action or force of gravity sufficient to overcome the effects of neglect, rust, dirt, frost, snow, or expansion by heat or warping of the framework. Glass, if used in vents, shall be protected to guard against falling onto the stage. A wire screen, if used under the glass, shall be so placed that, if clogged, it cannot reduce the required vent area or interfere with the operating mechanism or obstruct the distribution of water from an automatic sprinkler. Vents shall be arranged to open automatically by the use of fusible links. The fusible links and operating cable shall hold each door closed against the minimum 30 lb (133 N) counterforce, which may be exerted by springs or counterweights. This minimum counterforce shall be exerted on each door through its entire arc of travel and for a minimum of 115 degrees. A manual control shall also be provided.

Springs, where employed to actuate doors, shall be capable of maintaining full required tension. Springs shall not be stressed more than 50 percent of their rated capacity and shall not be located directly in the air stream nor exposed to the outside.

A fusible link shall be placed in the cable control system on the underside of the vents at or above the roofline or as approved by the authority having jurisdiction and shall be so located as not to be affected by the operation of a fire sprinkler system. Remote, manual, or electrical controls shall provide for both opening and closing of the vent doors for periodic testing and shall be located at a point on the stage designated by the authority having jurisdiction. Where remote control vents are electrical, power failure shall not affect its instant operation in the event of fire. Hand winches shall be permitted to be employed to facilitate operation of manually controlled vents.

Small schools typically have multipurpose classrooms and classrooms separated by folding partitions. These schools commonly have " stages" that are greater than 500 sq ft (46.5 sq m) but less than 1000 sq ft (93 sq m). The Committee felt the venting requirements were too restrictive for facilities with small stages. (*Also note the definitions of "stage" and "platform" in 9-1.3.*)

9-3.2.1.6 Proscenium Walls. Where automatic sprinkler protection is not provided, the proscenium wall of every theater using movable scenery or decorations shall not have more than two openings entering the stage, exclusive of the proscenium opening. Such openings shall not exceed 21 sq ft (2 sq m) each and shall be fitted with self-closing fire doors.

9-3.2.1.7 Proscenium Curtain. The proscenium opening of every legitimate stage shall be provided with a curtain constructed and mounted so as to intercept hot gases, flames, and smoke and to prevent flame from a fire on the stage from becoming visible from the auditorium side for a 5-minute period where the curtain is of asbestos. Other materials shall be permitted if they have passed a 30-minute fire test in a small scale 3 ft × 3 ft (91 cm × 91 cm) furnace with the sample mounted in the horizontal plane at the top of the furnace and subjected to the standard time-temperature curve.

The curtain shall be automatic-closing without the use of applied power.

Exception No. 1: In lieu of the protection required herein, all the following shall be provided:

(a) A noncombustible opaque fabric curtain so arranged that it will close automatically, and

(b) An automatic fixed waterspray deluge system shall be located on the auditorium side of the proscenium opening and be so arranged that the entire face of the curtain will be wetted. The system shall be activated by combination of rate-of-rise and fixed-temperature detectors located on the ceiling of the stage. Detectors shall be spaced in accordance with their listing. The water supply shall be controlled by a deluge valve and shall be sufficient to keep the curtain completely wet for 30 minutes or until the valve is closed by fire department personnel, and

(c) The curtain shall be automatically operated in case of fire by a combination of rate-of-rise and fixed-temperature detectors that also activates the deluge spray system. Stage sprinklers and vents shall be automatically operated by fusible elements in case of fire, and

(d) Operation of the stage sprinkler system or spray deluge valve shall automatically activate the emergency ventilating system and close the curtain, and

(e) The curtain, vents, and spray deluge system valve shall also be capable of manual operation.

Exception No. 2: Proscenium curtains complying with 8-3.2.1.7.

Substitutes for asbestos have been a concern of environmentalists, school officials, and others. It was the intent of the Committee to provide guidelines for the use of materials other than asbestos. A small-scale furnace test was considered appropriate by the Committee for this purpose. This has been further refined for new curtains. (*See Chapter 8.*)

If, instead of the fire resistant curtain specified in 9-3.2.1.7, a flexible proscenium curtain is used, the *Code* requires an automatic water spray system with nozzles on the auditorium side of the curtain. This system must be capable of completely wetting the curtain and of maintaining wetness for at least 30 minutes or until the deluge valve is closed by the fire department. Specifications for the installation of sprinkler systems in general are found in NFPA 13, *Standard for the Installation of Sprinkler Systems.*[10] Of course, for any sprinkler system to effectively minimize the hazards from fire to life safety or property, regular inspection and maintenance of the system is essential. NFPA 13A, *Recommended Practice for the Care and Maintenance of Sprinkler Systems*,[11] provides recommendations for ensuring that an extinguishing system will not fail in an emergency.

The spray nozzle system for the curtain is required to operate automatically by a combination of rate-of-rise and fixed temperature heat detectors. NFPA 72E, *Standard on Automatic Fire Detectors*,[12] and its appendix contain specifications and recommendations on the installation of heat detectors.

To complete the protection system, operation of the stage sprinklers or water spray system must also automatically close the proscenium curtain and activate the emergency ventilating system.

Exception No. 2 recognizes the new curtains mandated in Chapter 8 without repeating all the specifications.

9-3.2.1.8 Gridirons, Fly Galleries, and Penrails. (Reserved.)

9-3.2.1.9 Fire Protection. Every stage (legitimate, regular, or thrust) larger than 1000 sq ft (93 sq m) in area shall have a system of automatic sprinklers at the ceiling, in usable spaces under the stage, in auxiliary spaces and dressing rooms, storerooms, and workshops. Where there is a stage gridiron, sidewall sprinklers rated at 135°F (57°C) with heat-baffle plates shall be installed around the perimeter of the stage, except above the proscenium opening, at points not more than 30 in. (76 cm) below the gridiron, and with sprinklers positioned 4 to 6 in. (10.2 to 15.2 cm) below the baffle plate.

Note the definitions of "stage" and "platform" in 9-1.3.

9-3.2.1.10 Auxiliary Stage Spaces. Auxiliary stage spaces, such as understage areas, dressing rooms, workshops, and similar spaces associated with the functioning of a stage, shall comply with the following:

(a) No point within any auxiliary space shall be more than 50 ft (15 m) from a door providing access to an exit.

(b) There shall be at least two exits available from every auxiliary stage space, one of which shall be available within

a travel distance of 75 ft (23 m). A common path of travel of 20 ft (6.1 m) shall be permitted.

(c) Auxiliary stage spaces shall be equipped with automatic sprinklers where required by 9-3.2.1.9.

(d) No workshop involving the use of combustible or flammable paints, liquids, or gases or their storage shall open directly upon a stage.

Auxiliary stage spaces are sources of serious hazards. It is therefore necessary to provide automatic fire protection and adequate exits within a short travel distance from such spaces.

9-3.2.1.11 Flame-Retardant Requirements. Combustible scenery of cloth, film, vegetation (dry), and similar effects shall meet the requirements of NFPA 701, *Standard Methods of Fire Tests for Flame-Resistant Textiles and Films*. Foamed plastics (*see Section 3-2*) may be used only by specific approval of the authority having jurisdiction. Scenery and stage properties on thrust stages shall be either noncombustible or limited-combustible materials.

It is the Committee's intent to reduce the amount of combustible material on stages. Experience demonstrates that foamed plastics as described in Chapter 6 (*see Section 3-2*) have contributed to rapid fire spread.

9-3.2.1.12 Standpipes. Each legitimate or regular stage over 1,000 sq ft (93 sq m) shall be equipped with a Class III standpipe located on each side of the stage, installed in accordance with 7-7.4.2.

There must be a standpipe located on each side of a stage to provide stage hands and the responding fire department with a manual fire fighting capability at the area of a theater where a fire is most likely to occur. The installation of the standpipes must comply with NFPA 14, *Standard for the Installation of Standpipe and Hose Systems*.[13] NFPA 13E, *Recommendations for Fire Department Operations in Properties Protected by Sprinkler and Standpipe Systems*,[14] should also be consulted for a discussion of the necessity of a properly installed standpipe system. Standpipes are required regardless of whether the stage has automatic sprinkler protection.

9-3.2.2 Projection Booths.

9-3.2.2.1 Every place of assembly where an electric arc, xenon, or other light source that generates hazardous gases, dust, or radiation is used shall have a projection room that complies with 9-3.2.2.2 from which projections shall be made. Where cellulose nitrate film is used, the projection room shall comply with NFPA 40, *Standard for the Storage and Handling of Cellulose Nitrate Motion Picture Film.* (*See also Chapter 31.*)

The requirements for projection booths were developed jointly with those of NFPA 40, *Standard for the Storage and Handling of Cellulose Nitrate Motion Picture Film*,[15] and the motion picture industry at the height of movie popularity, when cellulose nitrate film was still being used. Presently, only safety film is used (except at film festivals or revivals) and the risk level has been reduced. The primary function of these requirements is to build a shelter around the projection booth, eliminating it as an exposure threat to the theater audience.

The intent of 9-3.2.2.1 is to protect the audience from the dangers associated with light sources, such as electric arc or Xenon. Where incandescent light is used, projection booths are not required in assembly occupancies. Note that the booth is required based on the light source, not on the projection of film.

Paragraph 31-2.8 requires that unless the construction of a projection booth complies with NFPA 40, *Standard for the Storage and Handling of Cellulose Nitrate Motion Picture Film*, a conspicuous sign must be posted on the door of the projection booth and also inside the booth. The sign must state: "Safety Film Only Permitted in This Room." The intent is to ensure that cellulose nitrate film is projected only with adequate safeguards.

9-3.2.2.2 **Projection Rooms for Safety Film.** Projection rooms for safety film shall meet the requirements of 9-3.2.2.3 through 9-3.2.2.8.

It should be emphasized that 9-3.2.2.3 through 9-3.2.2.8 apply only to booths for the projection of cellulose acetate or other safety film. Although openings in the booth do not need to be protected, they must be provided with glass or other approved material that will completely close the opening and prevent gas, dust, or radiation from contaminating the audience or seating area.

9-3.2.2.3 Every projection room shall be of permanent construction consistent with the construction requirements for the type of building in which the projection room is located. Openings are not required to be protected. The room shall have a floor area of not less than 80 sq ft (7.4 sq m) for a single machine and at least 40 sq ft (3.7 sq m) for each additional machine. Each motion picture projector, floodlight, spotlight, or similar piece of equipment shall have a clear working space not less than 30 in. (76 cm) on each side and at the rear thereof, but only one such space shall be required between adjacent projectors.

The projection room and the rooms appurtenant thereto shall have a ceiling height of not less than 7 ft 6 in. (229 cm).

9-3.2.2.4 Each projection room shall have at least one out-swinging, self-closing door not less than 30 in. (76 cm) wide and 6 ft 8 in. (203 cm) high.

9-3.2.2.5 The aggregate of ports and openings for projection equipment shall not exceed 25 percent of the area of the wall between the projection room and the auditorium.

All openings shall be provided with glass or other approved material, so as to completely close the opening.

9-3.2.2.6 Projection room ventilation shall be not less than the following:

(a) *Supply Air.* Each projection room shall be provided with adequate air supply inlets so arranged to provide well distributed air throughout the room. Air inlet ducts shall provide an amount of air equivalent to the amount of air being exhausted by projection equipment. Air shall be permitted to be taken from the outside; from adjacent spaces within the building, provided the volume and infiltration rate is sufficient; or from the building air conditioning system, provided it is so arranged as to supply sufficient air whether or not other systems are in operation.

(b) *Exhaust Air.* Projection booths shall be permitted to be exhausted through the lamp exhaust system. The lamp exhaust system shall be positively interconnected with the lamp so that the lamp will not operate unless there is sufficient airflow required for the lamp. Exhaust air ducts shall terminate at the exterior of the building in such a location that the exhaust air cannot be readily recirculated into any air supply system. The projection room ventilation system shall be permitted to also serve appurtenant rooms, such as the generator room and the rewind room.

New projection equipment in new theaters have a console that draws air in at the floor and up through the projection machine, thus eliminating the need to provide ducts 12 in. (30.5 cm) off the floor.

The requirements for the ventilation of a projection booth are designed to effectively "isolate" the booth from the theater so that any products of combustion created by a fire in a projection booth are not circulated into the theater. This is achieved by providing an independent exhaust system for the booth, making certain that the exhaust outlet on the exterior of the building is located at a point where the air intake for the theater cannot recirculate the exhausted air.

If fresh air for the projection booth's ventilation system is supplied from the general system of the building, it is essential that the combined system be arranged to ensure the required air changes in the booth even when no air is supplied to the general system of the building.

9-3.2.2.7 Each projection machine shall be provided with an exhaust duct that will draw air from each lamp and exhaust it directly to the outside of the building. The lamp exhaust shall be permitted to serve to exhaust air from the projection room to provide room air circulation. Such ducts shall be of rigid materials, except for a flexible connector approved for the purpose. The projection lamp and projection room exhaust systems shall be permitted to be combined but shall not be interconnected with any other exhaust or return air system within the buildings.

(a) *Electric Arc Projection Equipment.* The exhaust capacity shall be 200 cfm (.09 cu m/s) for each lamp connected to the lamp exhaust system, or as recommended by the equipment manufacturer. Auxiliary air shall be permitted to be introduced into the system through a screened opening to stabilize the arc.

(b) *Xenon Projection Equipment.* The lamp exhaust system shall exhaust not less than 300 cfm (.14 cu m/s) per lamp, or not less than that exhaust volume required or recommended by the equipment manufacturer, whichever is the greater.

The *Code* sets forth the minimum capacity for the exhaust system of a projection machine; however, a greater capacity must be provided where recommended by the manufacturer of the projection equipment. This system must be independent of any other ventilation system in the building housing the theater; however, it can be combined with projection room ventilation.

9-3.2.2.8 Miscellaneous Equipment and Storage.

(a) Each projection room shall be provided with rewind and film storage facilities.

(b) A maximum of four containers for flammable liquids not greater than 16 oz (.5 L) capacity and of a nonbreakable type shall be permitted in each projection booth.

(c) Appurtenant electrical equipment, such as rheostats, transformers, and generators, shall be permitted to be located within the booth or in a separate room of equivalent construction.

The intent of the requirement for the storage and rewinding of film is to prevent these operations from occurring outside the projection booth at some less protected location where, if a fire occurred, the exposure to the theater would be significantly greater. All operations that relate to projection activities must be kept within the protected enclosure afforded by the projection booth.

9-3.2.3 Service Equipment, Hazardous Operations or Processes, and Storage Facilities.

9-3.2.3.1 Rooms containing high pressure boilers, refrigerating machinery of other than domestic refrigerator type, large transformers, or other service equipment subject to possible explosion shall not be located directly under or abutting required exits. All such rooms shall be separated from other parts of the building by fire barriers in accordance with 6-2.3 having a fire resistance rating of not less than 1 hour or shall be protected by automatic extinguishing systems in accordance with Section 6-4.

The preservation of the integrity of exits in any building is one of the principal concerns of the *Code*. Therefore, hazardous areas, even if enclosed with the required fire resistant construction, must never be located where they might directly expose a required exit to fire.

9-3.2.3.2 Adequate vents to the outer air shall be provided in accordance with Section 6-4.

9-3.2.3.3 Rooms or spaces for the storage, processing, or use of the materials specified in this section shall be protected in accordance with the following:

(a) Boiler and furnace rooms, laundries, maintenance shops including woodworking and painting areas, rooms or spaces used for the storage of combustible supplies in quantities deemed hazardous by the authority having jurisdiction, hazardous materials in quantities deemed hazardous by recognized standards, or fuel shall be separated from the remainder of the building by fire barriers in accordance with 6-2.3 having a fire resistance rating of not less than 1 hour, or such rooms or spaces shall be protected by an automatic extinguishing system as required in Section 6-4.

Exception to (a)*: Rooms enclosing air-handling equipment.

A-9-3.2.3.3(a) **Exception.** Rooms used solely for air-handling fans are excepted from the requirements of paragraph 9-3.2.3.3(a). However, if the air-handling room is used for storage, furnaces, boilers, or other uses outlined in 9-3.2.3.3(a) in addition to housing the air-handling equipment, the requirements of 9-3.2.3.3(a) should be applied.

(b) Rooms or spaces used for processing or use of combustible supplies in quantities deemed hazardous by the authority having jurisdiction, hazardous materials, or for flammable or combustible liquid in quantities deemed hazardous by recognized standards shall be separated from the remainder of the building by fire barriers in accordance with 6-2.3 having a fire resistance rating of not less than 1 hour and shall also be protected by an automatic extinguishing system as required in Section 6-4.

(c) Where automatic extinguishing is used to meet the requirements of this section, protection shall be permitted to be in accordance with 7-7.1.2.

Paragraph 9-3.2.3.3 has been revised in several ways. First, there is more reliance upon Section 6-4, which should be reviewed in conjunction with this paragraph, since it has been rewritten. Second, some of the "typical" hazardous areas have been recatagorized, with spaces that were previously mandated to be separated with 1-hour fire resistance rated construction now given the option of either 1-hour construction or sprinkler protection or, in some cases, mandated to have both. If sprinkler protection without fire rated separation is provided, then the intent of the Committee is to restrict the passage of smoke by use of glass or other non-fire-rated material. This would not permit the use of "chicken-wire" or louvers but would not require all the components of a standard smoke barrier.

The Committee felt that the requirements identified in Chapter 7 for the use of six or fewer heads connected to the domestic system are adequate for these types of situations.

The intent of 9-3.2.3.3 is to specify the degree of protection necessary for certain hazardous areas. It has been divided into two sections based on the degree of hazard. The hazards noted in item (a) are required to be enclosed in 1-hour construction or protected by sprinklers. If the sprinkler option is chosen, an enclosure is still required; however, the enclosure need not be rated, but only form a membrane against the passage of smoke.

The hazards noted in item (b) must be enclosed in 1-hour construction and be protected by automatic sprinklers.

The Exception to item (a) pertains to rooms housing air-handling equipment only. If the room is used for other purposes, then the provisions of item (a) or (b) apply.

Figures 9-18a through c illustrate the methods of protection specified by 9-3.2.3.3.

The three different types of protection of hazardous areas are illustrated in these figures. Figures 9-18a and b illustrate the two options for complying with 9-3.2.3.3(a). Figure 9-18c illustrates the requirement of 9-3.2.3.3(b) that both fire-resistive separation and automatic protection be provided.

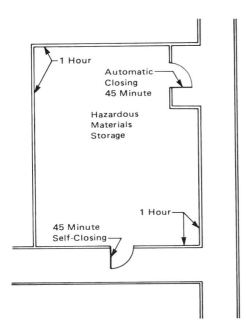

Figure 9-18a. *Protection of Hazardous Areas. Figure 9-18a illustrates one method of complying with 9-3.2.3.3(a). (See Figure 9-18b for the alternate method.)*

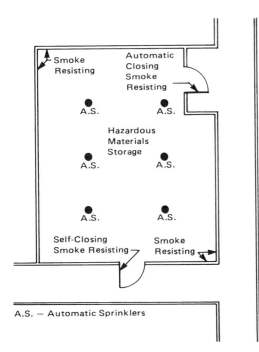

Figure 9-18b. *Protection of Hazardous Areas. Figure 9-18b illustrates an alternate method of complying with 9-3.2.3.3(a). Figure 9-18a illustrates another method of compliance.*

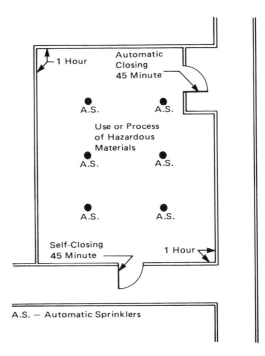

Figure 9-18c. *Protection of Hazardous Areas. Figure 9-18c illustrates the requirements for complying with 9-3.2.3.3(b). Both 1-hour separation and automatic sprinkler protection are required in this case.*

9-3.2.4 Special Provisions for Food Service Establishments.

9-3.2.4.1 All devices in connection with the preparation of food shall be so installed and operated as to avoid hazard to the safety of occupants.

9-3.2.4.2 All devices in connection with the preparation of food shall be of an approved type and shall be installed in an approved manner.

An "approved type" of device means that, with regard to potential fire hazards, the unit is acceptable to the authority having jurisdiction. An "approved manner" of installation means installation in accordance with the requirements of the authority having jurisdiction.

9-3.2.4.3 Food preparation facilities shall be protected in accordance with 7-2.3 and are not required to have openings protected between food preparation areas and dining areas.

The *Code* depends on the automatic extinguishing system mandated by 7-2.3 to control any fire on the cooking surfaces and, thus, does not require enclosure by rated construction.

9-3.3 Interior Finish.

9-3.3.1 The interior finish requirements of this section shall be in accordance with Section 6-5.

9-3.3.2 Interior finish in all corridors and lobbies shall be Class A or B and, in enclosed stairways, Class A.

9-3.3.3 Interior finish in general assembly areas of Class A or Class B assembly occupancies shall be Class A or Class B. In Class C assembly occupancies, it shall be Class A, B, or C.

Exception: In any assembly occupancy, exposed portions of structural members complying with the requirements for Type IV (2HH) construction shall be permitted.

9-3.3.4 Screens on which pictures are projected shall comply with requirements of Class A or Class B interior finish.

Interior finish requirements for new assembly occupancies are unequivocal and are subject to rigid interpretation. Evaluation of interior finish in existing facilities is sometimes difficult. Where flame spread characteristics cannot be readily determined using the test procedure in NFPA 255, *Method of Test of Surface Burning Characteristics of Building Materials,*[16] the questionable material should be removed or treated with approved flame retardants. Where treatment cannot reduce flame spread to required limits, automatic sprinklers may be provided to compensate for the remaining deficiency.

9-3.4 Detection, Alarm, and Communication Systems.

9-3.4.1 General. Class A and Class B assembly occupancies and all theaters with more than one audience-viewing room shall be provided with an approved fire alarm system in accordance with this section.

Exception No. 1: Assembly occupancies that are a part of a mixed occupancy (see 1-5.7) shall be permitted to be served by a common fire alarm system provided the individual requirements of each occupancy are met.

Exception No. 2: Assembly occupancies where, in the judgement of the authority having jurisdiction, adequate alternative provisions exist or are provided for the discovery of a fire condition and for alerting the occupants promptly.

The *Code* requires an approved alarm system in all Class A and Class B assembly occupancies. In Exception No.1, the Committee wanted to clarify that the intent of the alarm requirements was to meet the requirements of each occupancy in a mixed occupancy situation. This would allow an assembly occupancy in a school, hotel, hospital, mall, or other building to be served by the same fire alarm as in the predominate occupancy, provided it also met the requirements of the assembly occupancy.

Exception No. 2 to 9-3.4.1 specifically allows the authority having jurisdiction to permit continued use of fire alarm systems previously installed, provided the authority is satisfied with system arrangement.

9-3.4.2 Initiation.

9-3.4.2.1 Initiation of the required fire alarm system shall be by manual means in accordance with 7-6.2.1(a), which shall be provided with an emergency power source. The initiating device shall be capable of transmitting an alarm to a receiving station, located within the building, that is constantly attended when the assembly occupancy is occupied.

Exception No. 1: Initiation by means of an approved automatic fire detection system in accordance with 7-6.2.1(b) that provides fire detection throughout the building.

Exception No. 2: Initiation by means of an approved automatic sprinkler system in accordance with 7-6.2.1(c) that provides fire detection and protection throughout the building.

9-3.4.2.2* In all Class A and in all Class B assembly occupancies, automatic detection shall be provided in all hazardous areas that are not normally occupied.

Exception: Areas that are protected throughout by an approved automatic sprinkler system in accordance with 7-7.1.

A-9-3.4.2.2 The intent is to require detectors only in non-sprinklered hazardous areas that are unoccupied. When the building is occupied, the detectors in the unoccupied, unsprinklered hazardous areas will initiate occupant notification. If the building is unoccupied, the fire in the nonsprinklered hazardous area is not a life safety issue, and the detectors, upon activation, need not notify anyone. The signal from that detector may be sent to a control panel in an area that is occupied when the building is occupied but that is unoccupied when the building is unoccupied without the need for central station monitoring or equivalent.

This is a new provision for the 1991 *Code*. Nonsprinklered hazardous areas that are not occupied when the assembly area is in use could result in a fire developing that goes undiscovered. Although separated by 1-hour fire resistant barriers, such areas can present a significant hazard to occupants. Because a fire alarm system is already required, the additional requirement for either heat or smoke detection, as appropriate, is not a significant burden.

9-3.4.3 **Notification.**

9-3.4.3.1 The required fire alarm system shall sound an audible alarm in a constantly attended receiving station within the building when occupied for purposes of initiating emergency action.

9-3.4.3.2 Occupant notification shall be by means of voice announcements, either live or prerecorded, initiated by the person in the constantly attended location.

9-3.4.3.3 The announcement shall be made via an approved voice communication or public address system that is audible above the ambient noise level of the assembly occupancy.

9-3.4.3.4 Where the authority having jurisdiction determines that it is impractical to have a constantly attended location, a fire alarm system in accordance with Section 7-6 that is initiated by manual stations in accordance with 7-6.2.1(a) or other

approved means of initiation and that automatically provides prerecorded evacuation instructions in accordance with 7-6.3.8 shall be used.

The intent of the provisions of 9-3.4 is to provide an alarm system that will not elicit a panic reaction from occupants. Editions of the *Code* prior to 1981 required no alarm system. The intent of this section is to provide a system which will permit activation of the system by pull stations as required by 7-6.2.1, but that will not sound an audible alarm in the seating or audience areas of the assembly occupancy. In lieu of the audible alarm throughout the assembly occupancy, the system must sound an alarm in a constantly attended location. (Constantly attended, in this case, means that, during the time the assembly occupancy is in use, the alarm panel must be attended.) From that constantly attended location, voice messages that instruct the occupants can be issued via a public address system. This method allows for the orderly evacuation of the occupants and permits the issuance of proper evacuation instructions rather than simply sounding an evacuation alarm, which may produce panic. A change introduced in the 1985 Edition of the *Code* permits the use of prerecorded evacuation instructions that will automatically be played upon initiation of the system. With the approval of the authority having jurisdiction, this arrangement may be used in lieu of the attended station.

9-3.5 **Extinguishment Requirements.** (*Also see 9-1.6, 9-2.6, and 9-3.2.*)

9-3.5.1 **Fire Suppression Systems.** Any assembly occupancy used or capable of being used for exhibition or display purposes shall be protected throughout by an approved automatic sprinkler system in accordance with Section 7-7 where the exhibition or display area exceeds 15,000 sq ft (1,400 sq m).

This requirement applies to assembly occupancies used or capable of being used for exhibition or display purposes. This would apply to many facilities over 15,000 sq ft (1,400 sq m) unless fixed seating or similar obstruction to this use is provided.

9-3.6 Corridors. (Reserved.)

9-3.6.1 Interior Corridor and Lobby Construction. (Reserved.)

SECTION 9-4 Special Provisions

9-4.1 Windowless or Underground Buildings. Windowless or underground buildings shall comply with this chapter and Section 30-7.

Many buildings that house assembly occupancies are windowless by design. In theaters, opera halls, concert halls, etc., windows are detrimental to operations. In recent years, large exhibition halls have also been constructed without windows.

Windowless buildings with an occupant load of 100 or more must be provided with a complete automatic extinguishing system, usually sprinklers. All windowless assembly occupancies must be provided with emergency lighting in accordance with Section 5-9 of the *Code*.

Subterranean assembly occupancies require special consideration. Although they are similar to windowless buildings, additional problems of access for fire fighting and rescue are created where they are located in basements or subbasements of buildings. Exits, and where possible the exit accesses, must be adequately cut off from the assembly area by construction of partitions, walls, and doors of sufficient fire resistance. Positive means must be provided to prevent smoke from contaminating the exits. Like any windowless building, a subterranean assembly occupancy requires automatic sprinkler protection, emergency lighting, and a smoke evacuation system.

9-4.2 High Rise Buildings. (*See 9-1.6.*)

9-4.3 Outdoor Assembly.

9-4.3.1 All grandstands, tents, and other places of outdoor assembly shall comply with the requirements of NFPA 102, *Standard for Assembly Seating, Tents, and Membrane Structures.*

Where an outdoor assembly occupancy is created in an enclosed court so that exits can only be provided through a surrounding building, the requirements for exits, seating, and aisles must be the same as for an indoor assembly area.

9-4.4 Special Provisons for Exposition Facilities.

Exposition facilities have problems that differ from those of theaters, restaurants, or other assembly occupancies. They are large, multi-use facilities and have high ceilings appropriate to their size. Combustible materials are frequently displayed, and the containers in which the exhibits are shipped contribute to the fuel load. Paragraph 9-3.5.1 requires most exhibition halls to be protected by automatic sprinklers.

This section had been expanded in the 1988 *Code* and is further revised for the 1991 *Code* to provide more comprehensive guidance to the many people who are responsible for the different aspects of a trade show or exposition. The authority having jurisdiction at the local level is often working with organizations that exhibit on a national basis and that are unaware of the local firesafety regulations. It is the Committee's intent that this *Code* provide more consistent and universal understanding of the firesafety regulations required in these occupancies and at the same time encourage more uniform enforcement practices.

The Committee learned that the trade show and exposition hall regulations used by many jurisdictions were very similar; however, there was no nationally recognized model code that could be referenced. It was also recognized by the Committee that this lack of a model code presents a hardship as well as confusion between the local authority having jurisdiction and persons responsible for the various functions of the trade show or exposition.

9-4.4.1 No display or exhibit shall be so installed or operated as to interfere in any way with access to any required exit or with visibility of any required exit or any required exit sign; nor shall any display block access to fire fighting equipment.

It is advisable to have prepared plans or diagrams to show the arrangement of displays or exhibits, including any that are to be suspended from the ceiling or an overhead structure. Displays or exhibits must never interfere in any way with access to any required exit, and they must not conceal exit signs (*see Figure 9-19*). A display should not block access to fire fighting equipment nor interfere with the normal operation of automatic extinguishing equipment or devices for smoke evacuation.

Rows of booths become exit accesses; therefore, booths and other temporary construction should be of minimal combustible construction or protected to avoid undue hazard of fire that might endanger occupants before they can reach available exits.

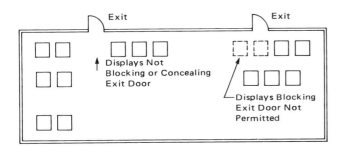

Figure 9-19. Arrangement of Displays in an Exhibition Hall.

9-4.4.2 A storage room having an enclosure consisting of a smoke barrier having a fire resistance rating of 1 hour and protected by an automatic extinguishing system shall be provided for combustible materials not on display, including combustible packing crates used to ship exhibitors' supplies and products.

Displays or exhibits of combustible material must be limited in quantity in order to reduce the fuel load to an acceptable level. Excess combustible display material and all other combustible materials that are not in use should be kept in a separate storage room until needed. A separation with a fire resistance rating of 1 hour is required between such a storage room and all other parts of the building, and the room must be protected by an automatic sprinkler system.

9-4.4.3 Exhibits.

9-4.4.3.1 Exhibits shall comply with 9-4.4.3.2 through 9-4.4.3.11.

9-4.4.3.2 The travel distance within the exhibit booth or exhibit enclosure to an exit access aisle shall not be greater than 50 ft (15 m).

This requirement applies to standard exhibit booth arrangements, whether constructed of pipe and drape, or a large exhibit enclosure designed and built from other materials, which could include small booths, open displays, large board displays, or other arrangements. Also included in this requirement are exhibit enclosures that are created by the arrangement of products such as machinery or vehicles. The intent is to have a travel distance not greater than 50 ft (15 m) for occupants that are inside the enclosure, whether they are employees or patrons. Note that this is not travel distance to an exit, but only to an aisle.

9-4.4.3.3 The upper deck of multilevel exhibits greater than 300 sq ft (27.9 sq m) in area shall have at least two remote means of egress.

This is a new requirement for the 1991 *Code*. It assures that larger exhibits with a second level provide at least two means of egress to prevent people from potentially becoming trapped on the second level.

9-4.4.3.4 Exhibit booths shall be constructed of:

(a) Noncombustible or limited-combustible materials.

(b) Wood greater than 1/4 in. (.6 cm) nominal thickness or wood not greater than 1/4 in. (.6 cm) nominal thickness that is pressure treated fire retardant wood meeting the requirements of NFPA 703, *Standard for Fire Retardant Impregnated Wood and Fire Retardant Coatings for Building Materials*.

(c)* Flame-retardant materials complying with NFPA 701, *Standard Methods of Fire Tests for Flame-Resistant Textiles and Films*; both small and large scale tests.

A-9-4.4.3.4(c) The authority having jurisdiction may use the field flame test contained in NFPA 701, *Standard Methods of*

Fire Tests for Flame-Resistant Textiles and Films (see Appendix B), as one method of determining flame retardancy.

(d) Textile wall covering such as carpeting having napped, tufted, looped, or similar surface used as wall or ceiling finish complying with 6-5.2.3.

(e) Plastic that is limited to a Class A or Class B interior wall and ceiling finish.

(f) Foamed plastics and materials containing foamed plastics having a maximum heat release rate for any single fuel package of 100 kW when tested in accordance with UL 1975, *Standard for Fire Tests for Foamed Plastic Used for Decorative Purposes.*

Plastics are limited to Class A and Class B for wall and ceiling finishes. It is the Committee's intent to prohibit the use of foamed plastics because of their inherent burning characteristics unless they have been tested for heat release in accordance with UL 1975, *Standard for Fire Tests for Foamed Plastic Used for Decorative Purposes,*[17] and comply with part (f) of 9-4.4.3.4. Foamed plastics are found to be used in sign construction and display boards, and in some cases, the entire booth is constructed of foamed plastics.

(g) Cardboard, honeycombed paper, and other combustible materials having a maximum heat release rate for any single fuel package of 150 kW when tested in accordance with UL 1975, *Standard for Fire Tests for Foamed Plastic Used for Decorative Purposes.*

This section is intended to provide direction to manufacturers of exhibit booths as well as decorators, exhibitors, and the authority having jurisdiction. The focus of this section is on the construction components of the ceilings, walls, and floors of an exhibit booth or display area in addition to the finish treatment. It is the intent of the Committee to also include large signs and display boards. Small signs [approximately 2 ft × 3 ft (61 cm × 91 cm) or smaller] would not normally be considered part of the wall covering. However, this section does not apply to the goods or products that are being displayed.

9-4.4.3.5 Curtains, drapes, and decorations shall comply with 31-1.4.

9-4.4.3.6 Acoustical and decorative material including, but not limited to, cotton, hay, paper, straw, moss, split bamboo, and wood chips shall be flame-retardant treated to the satisfaction of the authority having jurisdiction. Materials that cannot be treated for flame retardancy shall not be used. Foamed plastics and materials containing foamed plastics used as decorative objects such as, but not limited to, mannequins, murals, and signs shall have a maximum heat release rate for any single fuel package of 150 kW when tested in accordance with UL 1975, *Standard for Fire Tests for Foamed Plastic Used for Decorative Purposes.*

Exception: Where the aggregate area of such materials is less than 10 percent of the individual floor or wall area, such materials may be used subject to the approval of the authority having jurisdiction.

9-4.4.3.7 The following shall be protected by automatic extinguishing systems:

(a) Single level exhibit booths greater than 300 sq ft (27.9 sq m) and covered with a ceiling.

(b) The first level of multilevel exhibit booths.

(c) The second level of multilevel exhibit booths where the second level is covered with a ceiling.

(d) A single exhibit or group of exhibits with ceilings that do not require sprinklers shall be separated by a minimum of 10 ft (3 m) where the aggregate ceiling exceeds 300 sq ft (27.9 sq m).

The water supply and piping for the sprinkler system may be of approved temporary means taken from an existing domestic water supply, an existing standpipe system, or an existing sprinkler system.

Exception No. 1: Ceilings that are constructed of open grate design or listed dropout ceilings in accordance with NFPA 13, Standard for the Installation of Sprinkler Systems, shall not be considered ceilings within the context of this section.

Exception No. 2: Vehicles, boats, and similar exhibited products having over 100 sq ft (9.3 sq m) of roofed area shall be provided with smoke detectors acceptable to the authority having jurisdiction.

Exception No. 3: Where fire protection of multilevel exhibit booths is consistent with the criteria developed through a life safety evaluation of the exhibition hall, subject to approval of the authority having jurisdiction. (See A-9-2.3.2.)

Large booths and multistory booths pose special problems in exhibit halls. A fire in these booths could grow to large enough proportions to have a significant negative impact on the performance of the building's sprinkler system. It is the intent of the Committee to provide sprinkler protection in these booths by means of a temporary tap into the existing system. The Committee felt sprinklers would provide the protection necessary to extinguish a fire in its incipient stage, thus reducing the life hazard to occupants.

This paragraph has been significantly revised for the 1991 *Code*. It has been reorganized for clarification, the requirements have been modified, the need for temporary water supply has been recognized, and two new exceptions have been added.

New Exception No. 1 is not really an exception since this is already recognized by the reference document, NFPA 13, *Standard for the Installation of Sprinkler Systems*.[10] It was added to emphasize that it is not the intent of the Committee to prohibit this provision of the standard.

Exception No. 2 would exempt large vehicles, i.e., boats, mobile homes, and recreational vehicles, from the sprinkler requirement but requires a smoke detector if the vehicle is greater than 100 sq ft (9.3 sq m) in area. The intent of the Committee was to provide early warning in the immediate area to allow for orderly evacuation. This provision could most probably be met by single station, battery operated smoke detectors.

Exception No. 3 is also new in the 1991 *Code* and allows the exposition hall operators to work with the authority having jurisdiction to devise alternate methods of compliance.

9-4.4.3.8 Open flame devices within exhibit booths shall comply with 31-2.3.

Open flame devices should be prohibited except for religious ceremonies and, where allowed, should be restricted to minimize the danger of igniting combustibles. Any use of open flames should be allowed only after approval by the authority having jurisdiction.

9-4.4.3.9 Cooking and food warming devices in exhibit booths shall comply with 31-2.4 and the following:

(a) Gas fired devices.

(1) Natural gas fired devices shall be installed in accordance with 7-1.1.

Exception to (a) (1): Compressed natural gas may be used where permitted by the authority having jurisdiction.

(2) The use of LP-Gas cylinders is prohibited.

Exception to (a) (2): Nonrefillable cylinders may be used where permitted by the authority having jurisdiction.

Part (a) was revised for the 1991 *Code*. It does allow limited use of gas cylinders under specific permission of the authority having jurisdiction.

(b) Devices shall be isolated from the public by at least 4 ft (122 cm) or by a barrier between the devices and the public.

This requires distance or a barrier between the public and the device. The purpose is to guard against the possibility of accidental spills of hot greases or foods and to minimize the potential for ignition of combustibles, especially clothing worn by patrons.

(c) Multi-well cooking equipment using combustible oils or solids shall comply with 7-2.3.

(d) Single-well cooking equipment using combustible oils or solids shall:

(1) Have lids available for immediate use.

(2) Be limited to 288 sq in. (.19 sq m) of cooking surface.

(3) Be placed in noncombustible surface materials.

(4) Be separated from each other by a minimum horizontal distance of 2 ft (61 cm).

Exception to (d) (4): Multiple single-well cooking equipment where the aggregate cooking surface area does not exceed 288 sq in. (.19 sq m).

(5) Be kept a minimum horizontal distance of 2 ft (61 cm) from any combustible material.

Parts (c) and (d) were revised in the 1991 *Code* to clarify the intent of the Committee and provide some flexibility. The surface area was determined to be large enough to accommodate the average-sized deep-fat fryer. It was felt by the Committee that this would allow for exhibits that display deep-fat frying and at the same time provide reasonable safeguards.

The object of the lid in part (d)(1) is to provide to the operator a ready method of smothering the fire.

Part (c) requires that multivat cooking equipment must comply with NFPA 96, *Standard for the Installation of Equipment for the Removal of Smoke and Grease-Laden Vapors from Commercial Cooking Equipment.*[18]

Part (d)(3) is required due to the fact that the bottom surface of many devices could be subject to heating to temperatures that could ignite combustible surfaces. The minimum separation distances in part (d)(4) are necessary to minimize the danger of a fire in one device extending into another device.

The same principle that applies to part (d)(4) applies to part (d)(5), except the exposure is combustible decorations or other products as opposed to another cooking device.

(e) A 20 B:C fire extinguisher shall be provided within the booth for each device, or an approved automatic extinguishing system shall be provided.

This requires a 20-B:C extinguisher for each cooking device. The intent is to provide an extinguisher near each cooking device so the operator is able to access the extinguisher readily if a lid does not extinguish the fire or cannot be applied. It is not the intent of the Committee to have all the extinguishers in one location.

The provisions of this section recognize the inherent dangers in cooking and warming devices that will be used for display purposes and are subject to large, transient crowds in assembly occupancies. As a result, several items in this section have been revised or clarified for the 1991 Edition.

9-4.4.3.10 Combustible materials within exhibit booths shall be limited to a one-day supply. Storage of combustible materials behind the booth is prohibited. (*See 9-4.4.2 and 31-2.6.2.*)

The intent of this section is to limit the amount of literature, brochures, boxes, give-aways and other products that are kept in the booth. The amount necessary to con-

stitute a one-day supply is obviously going to vary; however, the authority having jurisdiction should be able to make a judgment after reviewing the activity anticipated by the exhibitor. Additional supplies and combustible crates (used for shipping) should be kept in a separate storage area having a fire resistance rating of 1-hour and protected by an automatic sprinkler system.

9-4.4.3.11 Plans for the exposition, in an acceptable form, shall be submitted to the authority having jurisdiction for approval prior to the move-in of any exhibit. The plan shall show all details of the proposed exposition. No exposition shall occupy any exposition facility without approved plans.

The intent is to provide the authority having jurisdiction with a set of plans that shows aisle widths, travel distances, exits, booth locations, display area configurations, types of displays (e.g., cooking, machinery, drapery, arts and crafts, etc.), location of fire protection equipment (extinguishers, alarm pull stations, hose cabinets, etc.), and lobby and registration area usage. This is not a complete list, but it should provide some guidance in determining the plans that should be provided. The plan should also be drawn to scale. The scale used is not usually critical as long as it is indicated on the plan.

9-4.4.4 **Vehicles.** Vehicles on display within an exposition facility shall comply with the following:

(a) All fuel tank openings shall be locked and sealed in an approved manner to prevent the escape of vapors. Fuel tanks shall not be more than one-half full or contain more than 10 gal (37.9 L) of fuel, whichever is less.

It is important that the fuel tank openings are locked to prevent tampering and accessibility to fuel. It is also important that the tank openings be taped to prevent the escape of flammable vapors. When the Committee reviewed the issue of amount of allowable fuel, it was found that some jurisdictions preferred empty tanks to eliminate fuel while others preferred full tanks to prevent vapors. It was determined that most exhibitors were unaware of the regulation until they arrived at the exhibit hall. After learning the specific rule (empty or full) they proceeded to make their adjustment in the adjacent parking area or some other unsuitable area. It is also difficult for the authority having jurisdiction to determine whether a tank is absolutely full or empty. The committee felt that this fueling and defueling by exhibitors outside the hall presented a greater danger than the level of fuel in the tanks, given that they are locked, sealed, and ignition sources are eliminated from the vehicle. However, to avoid excessive quantities of fuel in the hall, the *Code* does limit the amount of fuel in tanks.

(b) At least one battery cable shall be removed from the batteries used to start the vehicle engine. The disconnected battery cable shall then be taped.

It is important that at least one of the battery cables is removed from each battery. Many vehicles have more than one battery. The intent is to eliminate the possibility of a spark from the battery that might ignite fuel or surrounding combustibles. It is usually suggested that battery cable connectors be thoroughly taped after they have been removed.

(c) Batteries used to power auxiliary equipment shall be permitted to be kept in service.

This new provision allows batteries that cannot be used to start the vehicle to remain in service. These present no more ignition hazard than does providing house current to the item on display.

(d) Fueling or defueling of vehicles shall be prohibited.

Fueling and defueling in and around the exhibit hall is extremely dangerous. [*See comments on 9-4.4.4(a).*]

(e) Vehicles shall not be moved during show hours.

The movement of vehicles inside the exhibit hall compromises exiting and access to means of egress. Vehicles should be positioned prior to the hall being accessible to the public to avoid compromising these exits. There is also a serious concern regarding the effects of carbon monoxide inside an exhibit hall that is occupied.

This section on vehicles is intended to minimize the danger from both fuel and ignition sources.

9-4.4.5 Compressed flammable gases, flammable or combustible liquids, hazardous chemicals or materials, Class II or greater lasers, blasting agents, and explosives shall be prohibited within exhibit halls.

Exception: The authority having jurisdiction may permit the limited use of any of the above items under special circumstances.

Compressed gases are subject to damage that could cause an explosion or create a serious threat to life safety under fire conditions. Flammable and combustible liquids compromise life safety by their inherent capability to contribute to rapid fire spread. Hazardous materials present a variety of hazards to life safety, from flammability to toxicity. Class II or greater lasers can cause tissue damage to humans, and blasting agents and explosives can cause a large loss of life or injury if handled improperly. Many exhibitors wish to display explosives or pesticides or a type of compressed gas container, among other items.

These products can be effectively displayed without bringing the actual product into the hall by using empty containers.

The exception gives the authority having jurisdiction the discretion to permit small amounts of otherwise prohibited materials under special circumstances. For example, an exhibit or trade show for collectors of small arms ammunition or a highly supervised and closed (to the public) vocational trade show can be allowed where special controls and professional supervision are provided.

9-4.4.6 Alternatives. (*See Section 1-6, "Equivalency Concepts."*)

9-4.5 Special Provisions for the Handicapped. (Reserved.)

9-4.6* Special Provisions for Amusement Buildings.

A-9-4.6 Where a special amusement building is installed inside another building, such as within an exhibit hall, the special amusement building requirements apply only to the special amusement building. For example, the smoke detectors required by 9-4.6.3 need not be connected to the building's system. Where installed in an exhibit hall, it must also meet the requirements of an exhibit.

9-4.6.1 Special amusement buildings shall meet the requirements for assembly occupancies in addition to the requirements of this subsection. Special amusement buildings with an occupant load not greater than 300 persons shall be considered Class C assembly occupancies.

It is important to note that any special amusement building is considered an assembly occupancy, even if the occupant load is not greater than 50. However, special amusement buildings do not include theaters, movie houses, and other similar types of public assembly occupancies.

9-4.6.2* Every special amusement building shall be protected throughout by an approved automatic sprinkler system installed and maintained in accordance with Section 7-7. Where the special amusement building is movable or portable, sprinkler water supply may be by an approved temporary means.

A-9-4.6.2 It is the intent of the Committee to provide a suppression system that will act quickly to provide for life safety of the occupants.

It is felt that the residential or commercial quick-response heads would be appropriate in most cases. However, the design should be reviewed by competent automatic sprinkler designers and the authority having jurisdiction.

9-4.6.3 Where the nature of the special amusement building is such that it operates in reduced lighting levels, the building shall be protected throughout by an approved automatic smoke detection system in accordance with Section 7-6. Actuation of any smoke detection system device shall sound an alarm at a constantly attended location on the premises. Actuation of the automatic sprinkler system or actuation of a smoke detection system having an approved verification or cross zoning operation capability shall:

(a) Cause illumination in the means of egress to increase to that required by Section 5-8, and

(b) Stop any conflicting or confusing sounds and visuals.

It is the intent of the Committee to have the exits and means of egress well lighted upon the activation of a

smoke detector or suppression system. It is also important that any conflicting or confusing sounds or visuals be stopped and that, where a person's relative position to an exit is changed, additional exit signs be provided.

9-4.6.4 **Exit Marking**.

9-4.6.4.1 Exit marking shall be in accordance with Section 5-10.

9-4.6.4.2 Exit marking in mobile special amusement buildings shall be of the luminescent, self-luminous, or electroluminescent type.

9-4.6.4.3 Low level exit signs shall be provided in accordance with 5-10.1.4.

The Committee recognizes that in special amusement buildings knowledge of exits and location of exit signs is a critical problem. Low level exit signs should provide patrons an additional advantage in finding their way out under emergency conditions. (*Also see commentary on 9-4.6.3.*)

9-4.6.4.4* In special amusement buildings where mazes, mirrors, or other designs are used to confound the egress path, approved directional exit marking that will become apparent in an emergency shall be provided.

A-9-4.6.4.4 Consideration should be given to the provision of directional exit marking on or adjacent to the floor.

9-4.6.5 **Interior Finish**. Interior finish shall be Class A throughout in accordance with Section 6-5.

9-4.7 **Operating Features**. (*See Chapter 31.*)

SECTION 9-5   Building Services

9-5.1 **Utilities**. Utilities shall comply with the provisions of Section 7-1.

9-5.2 **Heating, Ventilating, and Air Conditioning Equipment.** Heating, ventilating, and air conditioning equipment shall comply with the provisions of Section 7-2.

9-5.3 **Elevators, Escalators, and Conveyors.** Elevators, escalators, and conveyors shall comply with the provisions of Section 7-4.

9-5.4 **Rubbish Chutes, Incinerators, and Laundry Chutes.** Rubbish chutes, incinerators, and laundry chutes shall comply with the provisions of Section 7-5.

References Cited in Commentary

[1]NFPA 130, *Standard for Fixed Guideway Transit Systems,* National Fire Protection Association, Quincy, MA, 1990.

[2]NFPA: Alert Bulletin, Social Club Fire, Bronx, New York, March 25, 1990.

[3]Richard L. Best, "Tragedy in Kentucky," *Fire Journal,* Vol. 72, No. 1, January 1978.

[4]Richard L. Best, "Reconstruction of a Tragedy," *NFPA LS-2, 1978.*

[5]Joseph A. Swartz, "Human Behavior in the Beverly Hills Fire," *Fire Journal,* Vol. 73, No. 3, May 1979.

[6]James R. Bell, "Investigation Report of the Fire at Stouffer's Inn of Westchester," *Fire Journal,* Vol. 76, No. 3, May 1982.

[7]John Bouchard, NFPA Investigation Report: "Fire in Haunted Castle Kills Eight," *Fire Journal,* Vol. 79, No. 5, September, 1985.

[8]NFPA 220, *Standard on Types of Building Construction,* National Fire Protection Association, Quincy, MA, 1985.

[9]NFPA 102, *Standard for Assembly Seating, Tents, and Membrane Structures,* National Fire Protection Association, Quincy, MA, 1986.

[10]NFPA 13, *Standard for the Installation of Sprinkler Systems,* National Fire Protection Association, Quincy, MA, 1987.

[11]NFPA 13A, *Recommended Practice for the Care and Maintenance of Sprinkler Systems,* National Fire Protection Association, Quincy, MA, 1987.

[12]NFPA 72E, *Standard on Automatic Fire Detectors,* National Fire Protection Association, Quincy, MA, 1990.

[13]NFPA 14, *Standard for the Installation of Standpipe and Hose Systems,* National Fire Protection Association, Quincy, MA, 1990.

[14]NFPA 13E, *Recommendations for Fire Department Operations in Properties Protected by Sprinkler and Standpipe Systems,* National Fire Protection Association, Quincy, MA, 1989.

[15]NFPA 40, *Standard for the Storage and Handling of Cellulose Nitrate Motion Picture Film,* National Fire Protection Association, Quincy, MA, 1988.

[16]NFPA 255, *Standard Method of Test of Surface Burning Characteristics of Building Materials,* National Fire Protection Association, Quincy, MA, 1990.

[17]UL 1975, *Standard for Fire Tests for Foamed Plastic Used for Decorative Purposes,* Underwriters Laboratories, Northbrook, IL.

[18]NFPA 96, *Standard for the Installation of Equipment for the Removal of Smoke and Grease-Laden Vapors from Commercial Cooking Equipment,* National Fire Protection Association, Quincy, MA, 1991.

10

New Educational Occupancies

(See also Chapter 31.)

SECTION 10-1   General Requirements

Educational occupancies include all buildings used for gatherings of six or more people for purposes of instruction through the twelfth grade for four or more hours per day or more than twelve hours per week. Educational occupancies include:

Academies   Nursery schools
Kindergartens   Schools

Educational occupancies averaged 9500 structure fires per year as reported to U.S. fire departments from 1984 to 1988. These fires caused an average of three civilian deaths and 181 civilian injuries each year.

Fatal fires have been extremely rare in educational occupancies for many years. Those few that do occur tend to involve either employees in accidental fires (e.g., fires caused by floor cleaning with flammable liquids) or, more often, firesetters trapped by their own fires. Children killed in school fires in recent years have been largely limited to juvenile firesetters, acting as individuals or groups, who are on school grounds after hours without permission. At the same time, about one-third of those killed in educational occupancy fires from 1980 to 1988 were not occupying the same room as the fire when it began.

The worst recent fatal fire where deaths of school children occurred on the premises during normal school hours was a 1982 Oklahoma fire involving a Boiling Liquid Expanding Vapor Explosion (BLEVE) by an 85-gallon hot water heater. Also notable was a single fatality in a 1973 fire in a Virginia school in which a haunted house maze was set up for Halloween. Much attention has been focused on life safety in the educational setting since the Our Lady of Angels elementary school fire claimed the lives of 95 people in 1958.

Day-care facilities for both children and adults are provided for separately in Sections 10-7, 10-8, and 10-9.

Other occupancies associated with educational occupancies must be in accordance with the appropriate parts of this *Code*.

Operational features for educational occupancies are specified in Chapter 31, "Operating Features."

10-1.1 Application.

10-1.1.1 The requirements of this chapter apply to new buildings.

In accordance with Chapter 1, additions must comply with the requirements for new construction, and alterations, modernizations, and renovations must meet the requirements for new construction to the extent practical.

Existing educational occupancies are addressed in Chapter 11.

10-1.1.2* Educational occupancies shall make provisions for the physically handicapped.

A-10-1.1.2 Reference is made to ANSI A117.1, *Standard for Buildings and Facilities—Providing Accessibility and Usability for Physically Handicapped People. (See Appendix B.)*

Enacted by Congress (1990), the Americans with Disabilities Act (ADA), which eliminates discrimination against physically handicapped individuals, requires that buildings providing public accommodations be made accessible to and usable by mobility impaired individuals as well as individuals with other physical handicaps. Included are educational facilities, which must provide equal access to education for the physically handicapped. In addition, the ADA and many states prohibit the concept of segregating handicapped students from other pupils, making it impossible to locate all physically handicapped pupils at the level of exit discharge.

To minimize the level of risk created by permitting occupancy by the handicapped at all levels and locations within an educational building, horizontal exits permitting horizontal movement away from the area of a fire can easily be designed for new construction. This parallels the design concept in Chapter 12, "New Health Care Occupancies," for the evacuation of litter-borne, bedridden, or handicapped patients from health care occupancies. Standards for the construction of elevators are discussed in Chapter 7 and in ASME/ANSI A17.1, *Safety Code for Elevators and Escalators.*[1] Standards for making buildings accessible to the handicapped are presented in ANSI A117.1, *Standard for Buildings and Facilities — Providing Accessibility and Usability for Physically*

Handicapped People.[2] The 1991 Edition of the *Life Safety Code* has attempted to address the issue by introducing the concept of accessible means of egress, which ensures a usable egress path for those with severe mobility impairments. Chapter 10 adopts this concept. (*See 10-2.11.2 regarding accessible means of egress.*)

10-1.1.3 Educational facilities that do not meet the definition of an educational occupancy need not comply with this chapter but shall comply with the following requirements:

(a) Instructional Building — Business Occupancy.
(b) Classrooms under 50 persons — Business Occupancy.
(c) Classrooms 50 persons and over — Assembly Occupancy.
(d) Laboratories, Instructional — Business Occupancy.
(e) Laboratories, Noninstructional — Industrial.

As defined in Chapter 4 and repeated in 10-1.4.1, Chapter 10 is intended to regulate those buildings or portions of buildings educating students through and including the twelfth grade. The provisions of 10-1.1.3 recognize that colleges, universities, and similar educational facilities that do not meet the definition of educational occupancies do not pose the same problem as elementary and high schools. Because of the maturity of their occupants, college buildings more properly resemble office occupancies. Thus, this paragraph identifies those uses and refers to other appropriate provisions of the *Code*. (*Also see 10-1.4.1.*)

10-1.2 Mixed Occupancies. (*See also 10-1.4.*)

10-1.2.1 Where other types of occupancy occur in the same building as an educational occupancy, the requirements of 1-5.7 of this *Code* shall be applicable.

Exception: As otherwise specified in this chapter.

Paragraph 1-5.7 of the *Code* specifies that, where separate safeguards for each occupancy cannot be maintained, the more stringent requirement of either occupancy will apply to both occupancies. Another way of stating this is that the requirement providing the highest level of life safety would apply to both occupancies.

10-1.2.2 **Assembly and Educational.** Spaces subject to assembly occupancy shall comply with Chapter 8, including 8-1.2, which provides that where auditorium and gymnasium exits lead through corridors or stairways also serving as exits for other parts of the building, the exit capacity shall be sufficient to permit simultaneous exit from auditorium and classroom sections.

Exception: In the case of an assembly occupancy of a type suitable only for use by the school occupant load (and therefore not subject to simultaneous occupancy), the same exit capacity shall be permitted to serve both sections.

In focusing on the most typical mixed educational occupancy, the reasoning of the *Code* is that, if classrooms and an assembly occupancy are likely to be occupied simultaneously, the exit capacity of the building must be designed and arranged for the combined use. For example, classrooms are often used during the evening for adult or remedial education while a school's gymnasium or auditorium is being used by another group. In such cases, the exception would not apply, even though during the day the place of assembly is used only by the school's population.

Chapter 8 contains several requirements that could have a significant impact on the school if the building is not designed so occupancies can be treated separately. If treated as a mixed occupancy, the building will most likely have to be sprinklered throughout. (*See 8-3.5.*)

10-1.2.3 **Dormitory and Classrooms.** Any building used for both classroom and dormitory purposes shall comply with the applicable provisions of Chapter 16 in addition to complying with Chapter 10. Where classroom and dormitory sections are not subject to simultaneous occupancy, the same exit capacity shall be permitted to serve both sections.

10-1.3 **Special Definitions.**

Common Atmosphere. A common atmosphere is the atmosphere that exists between rooms, spaces, or areas within a building, that are not separated by an approved smoke barrier.

Flexible Plan and Open Plan Educational Buildings. These include every building or portion of a building designed for multiple teaching stations.

(a) Flexible plan buildings have movable corridor walls and movable partitions of full-height construction with doors leading from rooms to corridors.

(b) Open plan buildings have rooms and corridors delineated by use of tables, chairs, desks, bookcases, counters, low-height [maximum 5-ft (152-cm)] partitions, or similar furnishings.

Although becoming less common, flexible and open plan schools still exist. However, in this edition of the *Code*, most of the requirements for flexible and open plan schools are built into the basic educational requirements, with 10-4.3 providing some additional requirements for flexible and open plan facilities.

Separate Atmosphere. A separate atmosphere is the atmosphere that exists between rooms, spaces, or areas that are separated by an approved smoke barrier.

Separate Means of Egress. A means of egress separated in such a manner from other required means of egress as to provide an atmospheric separation that precludes contamination of both means of egress by the same fire. (*See Section 6-3.*)

10-1.4 **Classification of Occupancy.** (*See 4-1.3.*)

10-1.4.1 Educational occupancies shall include all buildings used for educational purposes through the twelfth grade by six or more persons for four or more hours per day or more than twelve hours per week.

This paragraph exempts three types of schools: those with small numbers of students (fewer than six), such as facilities providing private tutoring or individual lessons; those with limited operating hours, such as some sports schools or Sunday schools; and those educating people above the high school level, as in the case of universities or military training.

The exemption of the first two categories is rarely questioned, but the exemption for upper level education is often questioned. The Committee believes that beyond high school the level of protection does not need to be greater simply because education is continued, while business or industry receives a different level of protection. Paragraph 10-1.1.3 provides guidance in determining how some facilities that fail to meet the definition of educational occupancy would be classified.

For purposes of determining occupant load, a classroom area is still an educational "use," although it may not be categorized as an educational occupancy, and the occupant load factors provided by 10-1.7 are still appropriate.

Where instruction is incidental to other occupancies, the requirements for the occupancy in which the instruction takes place are applicable. Church schools used for instruction for a few hours during one or two days of the week are generally classed as assembly occupancies.

10-1.4.2 Educational occupancies include part-day preschools, kindergartens, and other schools whose purpose is primarily educational even though the children are of preschool age.

The *Code* classifies part-time day-care facilities as educational occupancies if they primarily provide education in addition to care services. This classification parallels federal guidelines for subsidizing day-care/educational activities at both the federal and state levels. By requiring educational criteria and related activities, it was believed that a higher quality of staff would be provided for these facilities. This does not describe the "typical" day-care facility. Sections 10-7, 10-8, and 10-9 contain special requirements for "typical" noneducational day-care facilities.

10-1.4.3 In cases where instruction is incidental to some other occupancy, the section of this *Code* governing such other occupancy shall apply.

This paragraph is not as significant as it was before 10-1.4.1 removed places of higher education from Chapter 10. The following examples describe uses that would nevertheless be exempted from Chapter 10 by 10-1.4.1.

In an office building or factory, a few rooms may be used for orientation or instruction in the work requirements; these rooms are subject to the *Code* requirements for offices or factories. Barber colleges and beauty schools

are frequently located in commercial buildings and should be governed by the requirements of the buildings in which they occur.

10-1.4.4 Day-care facilities, whether for adults or children, shall meet the requirements of Section 10-7, 10-8, or 10-9 as appropriate.

Exception: Day-care facilities whose purpose is primarily educational as indicated in 10-1.4.2.

This paragraph is important in that it specifically conveys the *Code's* intent that day-care centers (adult and child) be regulated by Sections 10-7 through 10-9, depending on the number of clients, and that reference to Sections 10-2 through 10-6 is not required.

10-1.4.5 Adult day-care shall include any building or portion thereof used for nonsleeping purposes for less than 24 hours per day to house four or more adults requiring care, maintenance, and supervision by other than their relative(s). Clients shall be ambulatory or semiambulatory and shall not be bedridden. They shall not exhibit behavior that is harmful to themselves or others.

The definition of an adult day-care occupancy in this chapter is recognition of the fact that more and more senior citizens are being cared for in day-care centers similar to child day-care centers. The definition of the occupancy itself includes a definition of the type of adult who may be cared for in this occupancy. Essentially, the stated definition of an adult is to clarify that these occupancies are not nursing homes or old age homes but are occupancies used by persons who are capable of self-preservation, yet who require limited attendance, supervision, or observation.

Previous editions of the *Code* included several cues for the identification of those adults meeting the definition. However, to eliminate the appearance of requiring a medical background to be qualified to assess such adults, these cues were removed from the *Code*. It may be appropriate, however, to use some of the following previously published guidelines to determine acceptability of a client for adult day-care:

(a) Client does not require medical injections from staff but may require the administration of oral medication by staff personnel when and as prescribed by a licensed medical examiner, and

(b) Client may require limited supervision, attendance, or observation, and

(c) Client exhibits acceptable behavior (not harmful to self or others).

Adult day-care occupancies are covered with child day-care occupancies in Sections 10-7, 10-8, and 10-9.

10-1.4.6 Other occupancies associated with educational institutions shall be in accordance with the appropriate parts of this *Code. (See Chapters 12, 16, 18, 20, 28, 29, and 30 and 1-5.7.)*

10-1.5 Classification of Hazard of Contents. Contents of educational occupancies shall be classified in accordance with the provisions of Section 4-2.

In general, educational occupancies contain ordinary hazard contents. Some laboratories and storage areas may contain high hazard contents. (*See Section 5-11 for additional egress requirements for areas with high hazard.*)

10-1.6 Minumum Construction Requirements. No requirements.

10-1.7 Occupant Load.

10-1.7.1 The occupant load of educational buildings or any individual story or section thereof for the purpose of determining exits shall be as determined by the authority having jurisdiction but not less than one person for each 20 sq ft (1.9 sq m) of net classroom area or 50 sq ft (4.6 sq m) of net area of shops, laboratories, and similar vocational rooms. In day-care centers, the occupant load shall be not less than one person for each 35 sq ft (3.3 sq m) of net area.

It is not the intent of this paragraph to establish a minimum number of sq ft (sq m) per child but to ensure adequate exit capacity is provided for those present. Efficient use of classroom space may result in a greater number of occupants than these occupant load factors would yield.

Paragraph 10-1.7.3 clearly allows this, provided all requirements based on this higher number are met.

10-1.7.2 The occupant load of an area having fixed seats shall be determined by the number of fixed seats installed. Required aisle space serving the fixed seats shall not be used to increase the occupant load.

10-1.7.3 The capacity of an educational occupancy or a portion thereof may be modified from that specified above if the necessary aisles and exits are provided. An approved aisle or seating diagram shall be required by the authority having jurisdiction to substantiate such a modification.

See commentary on 10-1.7.1

10-1.7.4 The occupant load for determining exit requirements of individual lecture rooms, gymnasiums, or cafeterias used for assembly purposes of more than 50 persons shall be determined in accordance with 8-1.7 of this *Code.*

The intent of this paragraph is to indicate that rooms that may be used as assembly occupancies should have their occupant loads calculated using the occupant load factors found in Chapter 8 of the *Code.* As noted for assembly occupancies, this may result in a room with more than one occupant load, depending on its use. School cafeterias are generally capable of other uses and should likely be considered as multipurpose rooms.

SECTION 10-2 Means of Egress Requirements

10-2.1 General.

10-2.1.1 Means of egress shall be in accordance with Chapter 5 and this section.

10-2.1.2 Rooms normally occupied by preschool, kindergarten, or first-grade pupils shall not be located above or below the level of exit discharge. Rooms normally occupied by second-grade pupils shall not be located more than one story above the level of exit discharge.

The restrictions on the location of rooms used by preschool, kindergarten, or first- or second-grade pupils were developed to avoid the danger of older (and larger) children overrunning the very young on stairs or ramps during a fire or other incident requiring rapid evacuation of a building. Paragraph 10-2.1.2 also recognizes that young children, based on their size and limited motor skills, may need assistance traversing stairs or may have to be rescued.

10-2.2 Means of Egress Components.

Note that slide escapes, escalators, fire escape stairs, alternating tread devices and revolving doors are not permitted to be credited as required egress components. Escalators and revolving doors may be installed, but cannot be considered as part of the required egress and must not obstruct or otherwise confuse required egress path.

10-2.2.1 Components of means of egress shall be limited to the types described in 10-2.2.2 through 10-2.2.7.

10-2.2.2 Doors.

10-2.2.2.1 Doors shall comply with 5-2.1.

10-2.2.2.2 Panic Hardware or Fire Exit Hardware. Any door in a required means of egress from an area having an occupant load of 100 or more persons may be provided with a latch or lock only if it is panic hardware or fire exit hardware complying with 5-2.1.7.

This paragraph is based on the total occupant load of the area served and not the required capacity of the door. For example, if an area has an occupant load of 120 persons and is served by 3 doors, each door need only have capacity for 40 persons, but since all these doors serve an area with "100 or more persons," then any latches on these doors must be released by panic hardware or fire exit hardware.

10-2.2.2.3 Special locking arrangements complying with 5-2.1.6 shall be permitted.

The provisions of 5-2.1.6 apply to special delayed release devices. Note that one of the requirements of 5-2.1.6 is that the building must be either fully sprinklered or fully protected by an automatic fire detection system.

It is interesting to note that the concept portrayed in 5-2.1.6, which is now employed in many occupancies, was developed to address security concerns in the educational environment.

10-2.2.2.4 Door Closure. Any exit door that is designed to normally be kept closed shall conform with 5-2.1.8.

10-2.2.2.5 Only one locking or latching device shall be permitted on a door or a leaf of a pair of doors.

10-2.2.2.6 Horizontal sliding doors shall be permitted in a means of egress serving an occupant load of less than 50 in accordance with 5-2.1.14.1. The doors shall be operable by force not to exceed 15 lbf (67 N) applied to the operating device in the direction of egress.

10-2.2.2.7 Horizontal sliding doors shall be permitted in smoke barriers in accordance with 5-2.1.14.1. In addition, the doors shall be operable by a force not to exceed 15 lbf (67 N) applied to the operating device in the direction of egress.

Both 10-2.2.2.6 and 10-2.2.2.7 permit horizontal sliding doors in accordance with 5-2.1.14. Although the force qualifier may appear to modify the requirements of 5-2.1.14, in fact they are now also part of 5-2.1.14.

10-2.2.3* Stairs. Stairs shall comply with 5-2.2.

A-10-2.2.3 See Appendix A-5-2.2.4.5(a) Exception No. 3 regarding additional handrails on stairs that are used extensively by children 5 years or less in age.

10-2.2.4 Smokeproof Enclosures. Smokeproof enclosures shall comply with 5-2.3.

10-2.2.5 Horizontal Exits. Horizontal exits shall comply with 5-2.4.

10-2.2.6   Ramps. Ramps shall comply with 5-2.5.

10-2.2.7   Exit Passageways. Exit passageways shall comply with 5-2.7.

10-2.3   Capacity of Means of Egress.

10-2.3.1 Capacity of means of egress shall be in accordance with Section 5-3.

10-2.3.2   Minimum Corridor Width.

10-2.3.2.1 Exit access corridors shall be not less than 6 ft (183 cm) clear width.

Note that this requirement applies regardless of the required capacity of the corridor. Larger widths may be necessary for corridors handling large numbers of students. (*See 10-2.3.1.*)

This paragraph applies to exit access corridors and not to nonrequired service corridors that are provided for convenience only.

"Clear width" means a 6-ft (183-cm) wide clear space with no obstructions. Paragraph 5-3.2 details how to measure the width of a portion of the means of egress.

The intent of a 6-ft (183-cm) corridor is to permit two files of children with sufficient room for teachers or monitors to supervise. Extremely short corridors serving only one room may warrant consideration for some reduction in width.

10-2.3.2.2 Drinking fountains or other equipment, fixed or movable, shall not be so placed as to obstruct the required minimum 6-ft (183-cm) corridor width.

10-2.4   Number of Exits. There shall be at least two exits available from every floor area. (*See Section 5-4.*)

10-2.5   Arrangement of Means of Egress. (*See also Section 5-5.*)

This section had been rewritten for the 1988 Edition and has been further edited for the 1991 Edition in order to simplify the *Code*. Section 5-5 provides the detail required to establish proper exiting.

10-2.5.1 Means of egress shall be arranged in accordance with Section 5-5. No common path of travel shall exceed 75 ft (23 m); no dead end shall exceed 20 ft (6.1 m).

Paragraph 5-5.1.6 makes individual chapters responsible for establishing dead-end limits. Twenty feet (6.1 m) has been the standard dead-end requirement for educational occupancies in the past, and the Committee felt it was still reasonable. A common path limitation of 75 ft (23 m) has been added to the 1991 Edition.

A school plan with outside doors or stairways at both ends of a central corridor meets the dead-end requirement. Small pockets may be created where stairways are not located at the end of corridors but are located at intermediate points. (*See Figure 10-1.*)

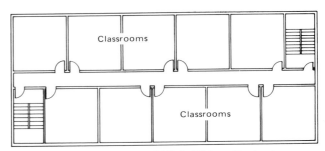

Preferred Arrangement Of Exits Without Deadends

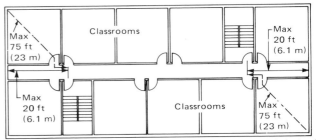

Acceptable Arrangement Of Exits With Deadends, Up To 20 ft (6.1 m) And, Common Paths Limited To 75 ft (23 m).

◄————► Dead End
– – –► Common Path

Figure 10-1.   Arrangement of Means of Egress in Accordance with 10-2.5.1.

10-2.5.2 Every room that is normally occupied shall have an exit access door leading directly to an exit access corridor or exit.

Exception No. 1: If there is an exit door opening directly to the outside or to an exterior balcony or corridor as described in 10-2.5.6.

Exception No. 2: One room may intervene between a normally occupied student room and an exit access corridor provided:

(1) The total travel from a room served by an intervening room and the corridor door or exit shall not exceed 75 ft (23 m), and

(2) Clothing, personal effects, or other materials deemed hazardous by the authority having jurisdiction shall be stored in metal lockers provided they do not obstruct the exit access, or the intervening room shall be sprinklered in accordance with Section 7-7, and either

(3) The intervening room shall have approved fire detection installed that will activate the building alarm, or

(4) The building shall be protected by an approved automatic sprinkler system installed in accordance with Section 7-7.

To ensure the integrity of the exit access portion within the means of egress, Chapter 10 requires most normally occupied rooms to have a door open directly into an exit access corridor. This is intended to avoid the need for occupants to pass through intervening rooms, which may not be arranged or maintained in a fashion to permit the orderly evacuation of an occupied space.

Exempted from the base requirement are normally occupied rooms that have doors opening directly to the outside at grade or to an exterior exit access balcony. Also exempted are normally occupied rooms having only one intervening room in which:

1. Travel distance through the intervening room to the corridor door is limited to 75 ft (23 m), and
2. Personal effects such as coats and other belongings or other contents deemed hazardous by the authority having jurisdiction are kept in metal lockers or the intervening room is sprinklered, and
3. Either the intervening room is supplied with fire detectors connected to the building alarm system, or the entire building is protected throughout by an approved automatic sprinkler system.

It is the *Code's* intent that, when one chooses to place personal belongings in metal lockers along with choosing the intervening room fire detection option, smoke detectors would be the form of detection selected to provide for rapid occupant notification. However, one has the option of selecting heat detectors if nuisance alarms are anticipated (i.e., automotive or wood shops with attached classrooms).

Figures 10-2 and 10-3 represent several possible intervening room configurations that comply with the *Code.*

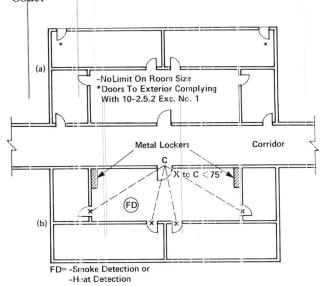

Figure 10-2. Room Arrangements Complying with 10-2.5.2, Including Exception No. 1. Configuration (a) has no limit on size other than satisfying the arrangement and travel distance provisions of 10-2.5. Each "normally occupied" room has a door opening either directly to the corridor or to the exterior (opening at grade or to an exterior exit access balcony) as permitted by Exception No. 1 to 10-2.5.2. Configuration (b) is permitted as long as travel distance from the normally occupied rooms to the corridor (x to c) is limited to 75 ft (23 m) and clothing and other personal effects in the intervening room are stored in metal lockers along with a fire detection system designed to provide occupant notification (preferably smoke detection for earliest possible notification).

10-2.5.3 Every room or space with a capacity of more than 50 persons or more than 1,000 sq ft (93 sq m) in area shall have at least two doorways as remotely located from each other as practicable. Such doorways shall provide access to separate exits, but where egress is through corridors, they shall be permitted to open upon a common corridor leading to separate exits located in opposite directions.

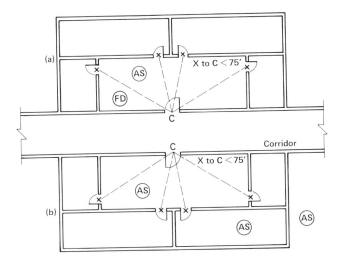

Figure 10-3. Room Arrangements Complying with 10-2.5.2 Exception No. 2. Configurations (a) and (b) represent acceptable intervening room arrangements. Configuration (a) illustrates limited travel distance from x to c along with the intervening room sprinkler system permitted by Exception No. 2 (2) to 10-2.5.2 and the intervening room fire detection system as selected by Exception No. 2 (3). Configuration (b) represents a building protected throughout by an approved automatic sprinkler system satisfying both parts (2) and (4) of Exception No. 2. In effect, even the installation of an approved automatic sprinkler system within the intervening room, connected to the building fire alarm system, would satisfy the language contained in Exception No. 2 to 10-2.5.2, as automatic sprinklers are considered heat detectors. Hence, this approach would satisfy both parts (2) and (3) to Exception No. 2 to 10-2.5.2.

Prior to the 1991 Edition, Chapter 10 did not establish a maximum common path of travel but set a maximum room size with one door and limited dead-end corridors. Currently, however, the *Code* does limit common path in addition to setting a maximum room size served by one door. This approach better reflects the *Code's* intent.

(See 5-2.1.4.1 and 5-2.1.4.2 for information on direction of door swing.)

10-2.5.4 Doors that swing into an exit access corridor shall be recessed to prevent interference with corridor traffic; any doors not so recessed shall open 180 degrees to stop against the wall. Doors in any position shall not reduce the required corridor width by more than one-half.

See 5-2.1.4.3 for more information on doors swinging into corridors.

10-2.5.5 **Aisles.** Where there are more than 60 seats, every aisle shall be not less than 3 ft (91 cm) wide where serving seats on one side only and not less than 3 ft 6 in. (107 cm) wide where serving seats on both sides. Where serving 60 seats or less, aisles shall not be less than 30 in. (76 cm) wide. The space between parallel rows of seats does not constitute an aisle. No more than six seats shall intervene between any seat and an aisle.

10-2.5.6* **Exterior Corridors or Balconies.**

A-10-2.5.6 A corridor roofed over and enclosed on its long side and open to the atmosphere at the end may be considered an exterior corridor if either:

(a) Clear story openings for the corridor are provided on both sides of the corridor and above adjacent roofs or buildings, and such clear openings are not less than one-half the height of the corridor walls, or

(b) The corridor roof has unobstructed openings to the sky not less than 50 percent of the area of the roof.

The openings are to be equally distributed, and if louvers are installed, they are to be fixed open with a clear area based on the actual openings between louver vanes.

See Figures 10-4a and 10-4b on the following page.

10-2.5.6.1 Exterior exit access shall comply with 5-5.3.

10-2.5.6.2* Where exterior corridors or balconies are provided as means of egress, they shall open to the outside air except for railings or balustrades with stairs or level exits to grade not over the allowable travel distance apart and so located that an exit will be available in either direction from the door to any individual room or space, with dead ends not to exceed 20 ft (6.1 m). If balconies are enclosed by glass or in any other manner, they shall be treated as interior corridors.

A-10-2.5.6.2 School design providing classroom exits directly to the outside or to exterior balconies open to the outside air with exterior stairways available to either direction to grade is

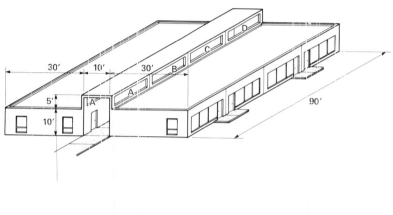

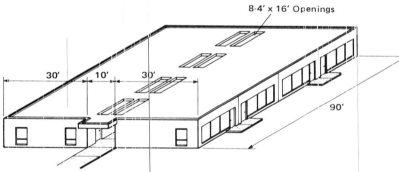

Figure 10-4a (top). Exterior Corridor Using Clear Story Openings. A, B, C, and D are clear story openings. The building height is 10 ft (3 m). In order for a corridor to be considered an outside corridor, the minimum height allowable for the corridor roof must be 5 ft (1.5 m). In this figure, the minimum clear story height requirements have been met.

Figure 10-4b (below). Exterior Corridor Using Roof Openings. The alternative to the clear story openings is that the roof have unobstructed openings to the sky that equal not less than 50 percent of the corridor roof. The example shown has eight openings. Each opening is 4 ft × 16 ft (1.2 m × 4.9 m), or 64 sq ft (5.9 sq m) each. The total square footage of the roof area equals 900 sq ft (84 sq m). The total unobstructed opening equals 512 sq ft (48 sq m) (greater than 50 percent of the total roof area). This would be an acceptable design.

considered preferable, from the firesafety standpoint, to the more conventional design using interior corridors, which can become untenable from the accumulation of smoke and heat.

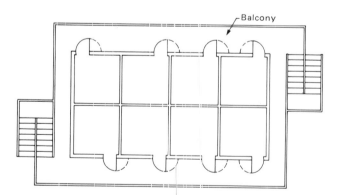

Figure 10-5. Stair Placement, Exterior Balcony. Distance between stairs must not be greater than the allowable travel distance would permit.

10-2.5.6.3 The floors of balconies (exterior corridors) and stairs shall be solid, without openings, and shall comply with requirements for outside stairs with respect to balustrades or railings, width and pitch of stairs, and other details. However, they are not required to be shielded from fire within the building by blank walls, wired glass windows, or the like where the stairs are located on the side of the balcony or corridor away from the building and are separated from the building by the full required width of the balcony or corridor. Regardless of other provisions, exterior balconies and stairs shall be permitted to be of the same type of construction as the building that they serve.

Stairs from exterior balconies must not pass or come close to windows or other openings in stories below. Preferable stair placements complying with 10-2.5.6.1, 10-2.5.6.2, 10-2.5.6.3, and 5-5.3 are illustrated in Figures 10-6 and 10-7.

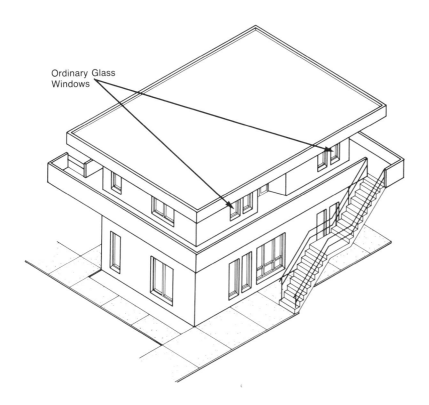

Ordinary Glass
Windows

Figure 10-6.   Stair Placement, Exterior Balcony. Since stairs are separated from the building by the full width of the balcony, blank walls or wired glass windows are not required near the stairs.

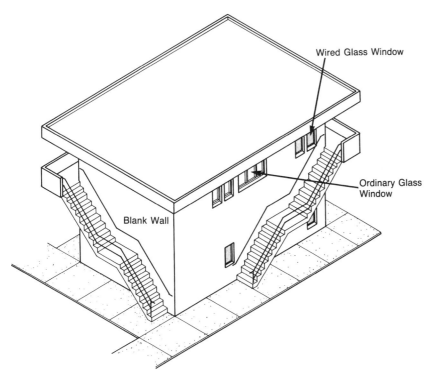

Wired Glass Window

Ordinary Glass
Window

Blank Wall

Figure 10-7.   Stair Placement, Exterior Balcony. The stair placed directly against the building must not pass near unprotected openings. (See 5-2.2 for protection requirements on outside stairs.)

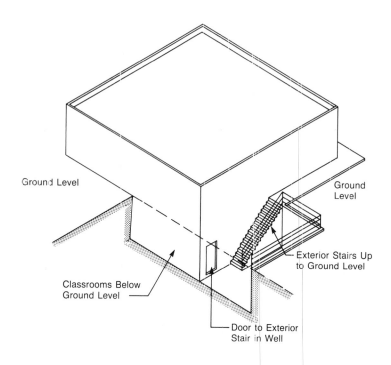

Figure 10-8. *Exit from Classroom Below Floor of Exit Discharge.*

Ground Level

Ground Level

Exterior Stairs Up to Ground Level

Classrooms Below Ground Level

Door to Exterior Stair in Well

10-2.6 **Travel Distance to Exits.** Travel distance to an exit shall not exceed 150 ft (45 m) from any point in a building. (*See also Section 5-6.*)

Exception: Travel distance shall not exceed 200 ft (60 m) in educational occupancies protected throughout by an approved automatic sprinkler system installed in accordance with Section 7-7.

10-2.7 **Discharge from Exits.** Discharge from exits shall be arranged in accordance with Section 5-7.

Exception: Every classroom or room used for educational purposes or student occupancy below the floor of exit discharge shall have access to at least one exit that leads directly to the exterior at level of discharge without entering the floor above.

The exception is a slight relaxation of the requirement in Section 5-7 in that the exception requires at least one exit to discharge directly to the outside, while 5-7.2 requires 50 percent of the exits to discharge directly outside. Figures 10-8 and 10-9 illustrate two types of exits that will satisfy the requirements of the Exception to 10-2.7. The enclosed stair in Figure 10-9 may serve other floors if it meets all the requirements of Chapter 5.

10-2.8 **Illumination of Means of Egress.** Means of egress shall be illuminated in accordance with Section 5-8.

10-2.9 **Emergency Lighting.** Emergency Lighting shall be provided in accordance with Section 5-9 in the following areas:

(a) In all interior stairs and corridors.
(b) In all normally occupied spaces.

Exception to (b):
1. *Administrative areas.*
2.* *General classrooms.*
3. *Mechanical rooms and storage areas.*

A-10-2.9(b) **Exception to (b)2.** This does not exempt shops and laboratories.

(c) In flexible and open plan buildings.
(d) In all interior or windowless portions of buildings.

The Exceptions to 10-2.9(b) indicate that normal classrooms, offices, and storage or mechanical spaces do not require emergency lighting. Shops, laboratories, and assembly rooms would require emergency lighting as would portions of the building that are interior or windowless. (*See Figure 10-10.*)

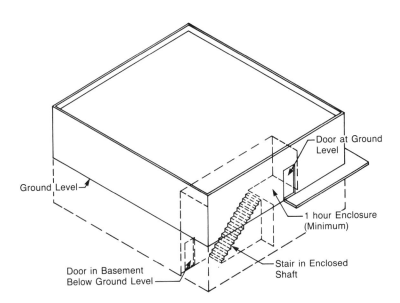

Figure 10-9. Exit from Classroom Below Floor of Exit Discharge. The enclosed stair could be located on the outside of the building.

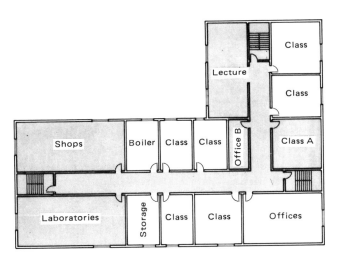

Figure 10-10. Areas that Require and Do Not Require Emergency Lighting. Shaded areas indicate where emergency lighting is required. Classroom A and Office B are windowless; therefore, 10-2.9(d) overrides the Exception to 10-2.9(b). Laboratories, shops, and lecture halls do not qualify as general classrooms.

10-2.10 Marking of Means of Egress. Means of egress shall have signs in accordance with Section 5-10.

Exception: Signs are not required in situations where locations of exits are otherwise obvious and familiar to all occupants, such as in small elementary school buildings.

10-2.11 Special Features.

10-2.11.1* Windows for Rescue and Ventilation. Every room or space greater than 250 sq ft (23.2 sq m) used for classroom or other educational purposes or normally subject to student occupancy shall have at least one outside window for emergency rescue or ventilation. Such window shall be openable from the inside without the use of tools and shall provide a clear opening of not less than 20 in. (50.8 cm) in width, 24 in. (61 cm) in height, and 5.7 sq ft (.53 sq m) in area. The bottom of the opening shall be not more than 44 in. (112 cm) above the floor, and any latching device shall be capable of being operated from not more than 54 in. (137 cm) above the finished floor. Such windows shall be accessible by the fire department and shall open into an area having access to a public way.

Exception No. 1: In buildings protected throughout by an approved automatic sprinkler system in accordance with Section 7-7.

Exception No. 2: Where the room or space has a door leading directly to the outside of the building.

Exception No. 3: In rooms located higher than three stories above grade, the openable clear height, width, and area of the window may be modified to the dimensions necessary for ventilation.

A-10-2.11.1 It is highly desirable to have all windows of a type that can be readily opened from inside and to have them large enough and low enough for use by students, teachers, and fire fighters. Windows may serve as a supplementary means of emergency escape, particularly where ladders can be raised by fire fighters or others. Even where the location is such as to preclude the use of windows for escape purposes, they may provide air for breathing in a smoke-filled room while trapped occupants are awaiting rescue.

The 1991 Edition has been amended to exclude smaller rooms [those less than 250 sq ft (23.2 sq m)] such as those used for music instruction and student counseling, as they are subject to occupancy by very few children.

The dimensions specified for windows used for emergency rescue or for ventilation are based on simulations of emergency rescue conducted by the San Diego Fire Department. Windows providing clear openings of identical dimensions are also required for rescue or ventilation in one- and two-family dwellings. Figure 10-11 illustrates two configurations that achieve the required area of 5.7 sq ft (.53 sq m).

Although the *Code* intends the fire department or others to assist students, particularly over ladders, if these windows must be used as a supplementary means of escape, the windows must permit small children in the lower grades to escape unaided. Therefore, storm sashes, screens, or devices in front of the windows must be easy to open or remove, and the sills must be low enough for children to reach.

The *Code* has also been modified to ensure that the windows will be accessible to the fire department and that children, once they escape from the window, will have access to a public way.

Windows may be omitted if a classroom has a door leading directly to the outside or if the building is totally sprinklered.

Note that Exception No. 1 requires that the building be protected throughout by an automatic sprinkler system. One question often asked is: If there are only a couple of windowless classrooms, can sprinklering be limited to those rooms only? The answer is no! It should be noted that the purpose of the window is to provide ventilation

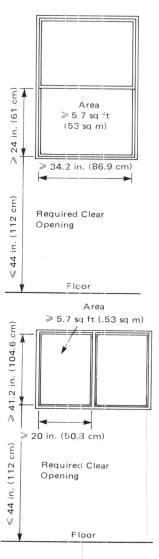

Figure 10-11. Windows for Rescue or Ventilation, Minimum Required Dimensions.

or means of escape when the interior corridor is blocked by smoke from a fire in another part of the building. Installing sprinklers in the windowless rooms only would do nothing to provide protection from smoke emanating from other areas.

The Committee did not believe it was practical to expect a window above the third story to be used as an escape window. However, it is reasonable to expect the window to be used for ventilation during a fire.

10-2.11.2 Areas accessible to people with severe mobility impairment shall have a minimum of two accessible means of egress.

Exception No. 1: Educational occupancies protected throughout by approved supervised automatic sprinkler systems in accordance with Section 7-7.

Exception No. 2: If the accessible means of egress provide(s) the most direct routes (route) from the accessible areas and if the fire protection system, the physical arrangement of the space, and the facility operation are all approved by the authority having jurisdiction, the authority having jurisdiction shall permit a reduction in the required number of accessible means of egress.

Chapter 10 has adopted the concept of accessible means of egress introduced to the 1991 Edition of the *Code*. As defined in Chapters 3 and 5, an accessible means of egress is a path of travel usable by a person with a severe mobility impairment ("severe" mobility impairment means possessing the ability to move to stairs without the ability to use them, e.g., a wheelchair-bound individual) that leads to a public way or an area of refuge. Hence, all areas accessible to those with severe mobility impairments (which are likely to be all areas of educational use facilities in light of the recently enacted Americans with Disabilities Act) shall be provided with two accessible means of egress. (*See 5-1.2.2 and 5-2.12.*)

SECTION 10-3   Protection

10-3.1   Protection of Vertical Openings.

10-3.1.1 Any vertical opening shall be enclosed and protected in accordance with Section 6-2.

Exception No. 1: In buildings protected throughout by an approved supervised automatic sprinkler system installed in accordance with Section 7-7, unprotected vertical openings connecting not more than three floors shall be permitted in accordance with 6-2.4.5.

Exception No. 2: Atriums in accordance with 6-2.4.6 shall be permitted.

Exception No. 3: Stairway enclosures shall not be required for a stairway that serves only one adjacent floor except a basement and that is not connected with stairways serving other floors and that is not connected to corridors.

Chapter 10 requires all vertical openings with the exception of the 6-2.4.5 open and unobstructed "mini-atrium" opening connecting three floors or less, the 6-2.4.6 atrium, or what is commonly referred to as a "convenience stair" to be enclosed in accordance with Section 6-2. This "convenience stair" may be useful, especially for libraries or offices within schools. Basements are excluded because basements usually contain hazardous areas with high fuel loads, such as storage rooms, boiler rooms, or workshops. While not specified in 6-2.4.5, Exception No. 1 to 10-3.1.1 requires a building to be fully sprinklered in order to use the "mini-atrium" exception. (*See Figures 10-12 and 10-13.*)

10-3.2   Protection from Hazards.

10-3.2.1 Rooms or spaces for the storage, processing, or use of the materials specified in this section shall be protected in accordance with the following:

(a) Rooms or spaces used for the storage of combustible supplies in quantities deemed hazardous by the authority having jurisdiction, hazardous materials in quantities deemed hazardous by recognized standards, or fuel shall be separated from the remainder of the building by construction having not less than a 1-hour fire resistance rating with all openings protected by self-closing or smoke-actuated fire doors, or such rooms or spaces shall be protected by an automatic extinguishing system as required in Section 6-4.

(b) Rooms or spaces used for processing or use of combustible supplies in quantities considered hazardous by the authority having jurisdiction, hazardous materials, or for flammable or combustible liquids in quantities deemed hazardous by recognized standards shall be separated from the remainder of the building by construction having not less than a 1-hour fire resistance rating with all openings protected by self-closing or smoke-actuated fire doors and shall also be protected by an automatic extinguishing system as required in Section 6-4.

(c) Boiler and furnace rooms, laundries, and maintenance shops, including woodworking and painting areas, shall be sep-

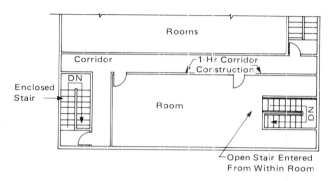

Figure 10-12. *Open Stair Complying with 10-3.1.1 Exception No. 3.*

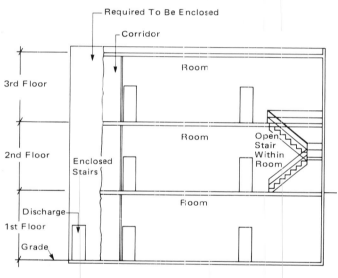

Figure 10-13. *Open Stair Complying with 10-3.1.1 Exception No. 3. Stair serves only one floor and is not connected to a corridor.*

arated from the remainder of the building by construction having not less than a 1-hour fire resistance rating with all openings protected by self-closing or smoke-actuated fire doors.

Exception to (c): Rooms enclosing air-handling equipment.

(d)* Where automatic extinguishing systems are used to meet the requirements of this section, the rooms or spaces shall be separated from the remainder of the building by construction that resists the passage of smoke.

A-10-3.2.1(d)   It is not the intent of this provision to require a smoke barrier that meets the requirements of Section 6-3.

(e) Where automatic extinguishing is used to meet the requirements of this section, the protection shall be permitted to be in accordance with 7-7.1.2.

Figure 10-14 illustrates the various protection requirements of 10-3.2.1.

The intent of 10-3.2.1 is to specify the degree of protection necessary for certain hazardous areas. It has been divided into three sections based on the degree of hazard. The hazards noted in part (a) are required to be enclosed in 1-hour construction or protected by sprinklers. If the sprinkler option is chosen, an enclosure is still required by part (d); however, the enclosure need not be rated but needs only to form a membrane against the passage of smoke.

The Committee reasoned that, although sprinklers are provided and fire-rated barriers may not be needed [*see (a)*], some barrier to control smoke migration is needed. Solid construction materials, such as glass or other non-fire-rated materials, are acceptable if they are installed in a manner that will resist smoke passing from one compartment to another. The appendix note emphasizes that it is not the intent to require smoke barriers as provided in Section 6-3. This eliminates the more costly construction of a smoke barrier, which would require dampers and other required equipment.

Art rooms and some shops need special attention. Potentially dangerous operations involving flammable materials, specialized ovens, and ignition sources in these areas are becoming more prevalent and create increased hazards to the entire facility. It may be advisable at the high school level to include these rooms as hazardous spaces.

The hazards noted in part (b) must be enclosed in 1-hour construction and be protected by automatic sprinklers.

The hazards noted in part (c) are required to be enclosed in 1-hour construction with no option for a sprinkler equivalency for the enclosure. The Exception to part (c) pertains to rooms housing air-handling equipment only. If the room is used for other purposes, then the provisions of part (a) or (b) apply.

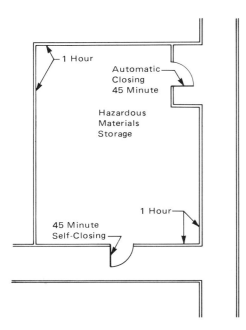

Figure 10-14a. *Protection of Hazardous Areas. Figure 10-14a illustrates one method of complying with 10-3.2.1(a). (See Figure 10-14b for the alternate method.)*

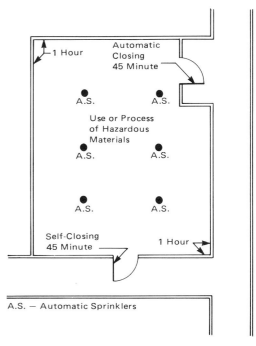

Figure 10-14c. *Protection of Hazardous Areas Complying with 10-3.2.1(b). Both 1-hour separation and automatic sprinkler protection are required in this case.*

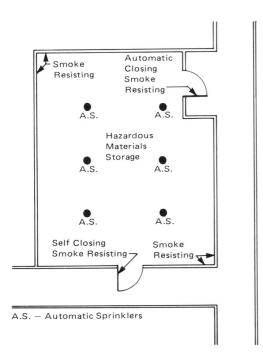

Figure 10-14b. *Protection of Hazardous Areas. Figure 10-14b illustrates an alternate method of complying with 10-3.2.1(a). Figure 10-14a illustrates another method of compliance.*

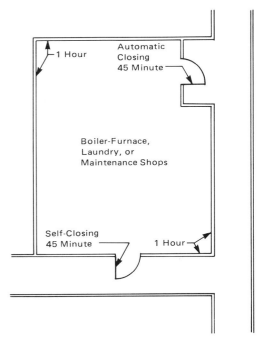

Figure 10-14d. *Protection of Hazardous Areas Complying with 10-3.2.1(c). Note that the automatic sprinkler option does not exist for these hazardous areas.*

Part (e) is intended to highlight the fact that Chapter 7 makes these requirements available to the user of the *Code*. Paragraph 7-7.1.2 provides an economical way of providing sprinkler protection in small rooms. (*See 10-3.2.3.*)

10-3.2.2 Food preparation facilities shall be protected in accordance with 7-2.3 and are not required to have openings protected between food preparation areas and dining areas.

Openings in the wall between kitchens and dining areas are not restricted and do not need to be protected. The *Code* relies upon the provision of the automatic extinguishing system to control any fire on the cooking surfaces and, thus, does not require openings between the kitchen and dining areas to be protected.

10-3.2.3 Janitor closets shall be protected by an automatic sprinkler system, which shall be permitted to be in accordance with 7-7.1.2. Doors to janitor closets shall be permitted to have ventilating louvers.

Where janitor closets are located off of corridors, a louvered door is usually provided for ventilation. It is necessary to provide these spaces with automatic sprinkler protection, since the louvered door offers little fire resistance and permits a fire in the closet to directly affect the corridor. Paragraph 7-7.1.2 contains an economical method of providing sprinkler protection for such closets. To achieve this protection at reasonable cost, these sprinklers (not more than six in number) may be supplied from the domestic water supply if the supply is capable of providing the required quantity of water. It is advisable to provide a water-flow switch (*see Chapter 6*) to initiate an alarm when a sprinkler is opened.

The minimum flow of 0.15 gpm/sq ft (6.1 L/min/sq m) is based on the requirements of NFPA 13, *Standard for the Installation of Sprinkler Systems*,[3] for protecting buildings containing ordinary hazards. It is important to ensure that the domestic water supply can provide the required flow and pressure at the location.

10-3.2.4 Laboratories that use chemicals shall comply with NFPA 45, *Standard on Fire Protection for Laboratories Using Chemicals*.

10-3.2.5 Stages shall be protected in accordance with Chapter 8.

10-3.3 Interior Finish.

10-3.3.1 Interior finish, in accordance with Section 6-5, shall be as follows:

(a) Exits — Class A.
(b) Other than exits — Class A or B.

Exception to (b): Fixtures and low-height partitions not over 5 ft (152 cm) in height shall be Class A, B, or C.

Exception*: The exposed portions of structural members complying with the requirements for Type IV (2HH) construction shall be permitted.

A-10-3.3.1 **Exception.** NFPA 220, *Standard on Types of Building Construction (see Appendix B)*, defines Type IV (2HH) construction. (*Also see A-6-2.1.*)

Section 6-5 permits the use of fire retardant or intumescent paints and surface coatings to reduce the surface flame spread of an interior finish. These coatings will not render a finish noncombustible; they will simply delay the eventual ignition of a finish exposed to fire.

Some coatings have a short life and require frequent reapplication. Over the life of a building, all coatings may eventually have to be renewed. Also, some coatings will severely mar or alter the appearance of the finish. Due to these liabilities, the option of using coatings and paints may not provide the best fire protection at a reasonable cost in all cases.

Sections 31-1 and 31-3 establish limitations on decorations and student artwork on walls.

10-3.3.2 **Interior Floor Finish.** No requirements.

10-3.4 Detection, Alarm, and Communication Systems.

10-3.4.1 General.
Educational occupancies shall be provided with a fire alarm system in accordance with Section 7-6.

10-3.4.2 Initiation.

10-3.4.2.1 Initiation of the required fire alarm system shall be by manual means in accordance with 7-6.2.1(a).

Exception: In buildings where all normally occupied spaces are provided with a two-way communication system between such spaces and a constantly attended receiving station from where a general evacuation alarm can be sounded, the manual pull stations are not required except in locations specifically designated by the authority having jurisdiction.

The Exception to 10-3.4.2.1 is intended to give local authorities the ability to deal with the false alarm and vandalism problems present in today's schools. Where there is a two-way communication system between classrooms and a continuously attended location where a general alarm can be sounded, the need for pull stations is obviated. To qualify to use this exception, the authority having jurisdiction must agree on which pull stations can be omitted. For the purposes of this provision, the "continuously attended" location means a location attended while the school building is in use as a school. This may involve providing personnel at this location during night school, when the regular school office staff is not present.

10-3.4.2.2 In buildings provided with automatic sprinkler protection, the operation of the sprinkler system shall automatically activate the fire alarm system in addition to the initiation means required above.

10-3.4.3 Notification.

10-3.4.3.1 Occupant notification shall be by means of an audible alarm in accordance with 7-6.3.

10-3.4.3.2 Where acceptable to the authority having jurisdiction, the fire alarm system may be used to designate class

change provided that the fire alarm is distinctive in signal and overrides all other use.

10-3.5 Extinguishment Requirements.

10-3.5.1 Every portion of educational buildings below the level of exit discharge shall be protected throughout by an approved automatic sprinkler system in accordance with Section 7-7.

This provision will normally require basements of schools to be sprinklered. But since the level of exit discharge could sometimes be located between two stories (e.g., one walks up from the first floor and walks down from the second floor to the level of exit discharge), the lower story would need to be sprinklered (*see Figure 10-15*). This protection is required regardless of the story's use. Where they contain assembly occupancies, schools are often required to be sprinklered. (*See Chapter 8.*)

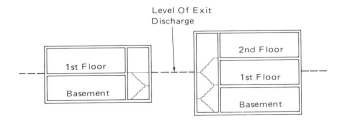

Figure 10-15. Automatic Sprinkler Protection for Levels Below the Level of Exit Discharge. The arrangement on the left illustrates a simple example where only the basement is required to be protected by sprinklers. The diagram on the right illustrates a case where the level of exit discharge is between floors and requires that the first floor and basement be sprinklered.

10-3.6 Interior Corridors.

10-3.6.1 Every interior corridor shall be constructed of fire barriers having not less than a 1-hour fire resistance rating in accordance with 6-2.3. Corridors shall comply with 6-2.2.2.

Exception No. 1: Such corridor protection shall not be required where all spaces normally subject to student occupancy have at least one door opening directly to the outside or to an exterior exit access balcony or corridor in accordance with 10-2.5.6.

Exception No. 2: In buildings protected throughout by an approved supervised automatic sprinkler system installed in accordance with Section 7-7, corridor walls are not required to be rated provided such walls, in conjunction with openings therein and ceilings at which they terminate, resist the passage of smoke.

Exception No. 2 allows the wall to terminate at the ceiling as long as the ceiling resists the passage of smoke, given the protection of an approved supervised sprinkler system throughout the building. Although doors in fire-rated partitions are required to be self-closing or automatic-closing, which causes significant operation and maintenance problems in schools, this exception would allow the omission of door closures on doors other than those required to be self-closing for other reasons, such as stair doors. This recognizes the teacher's/administrator's ability to close doors upon evacuation, thus maintaining the assembly's smoke resisting capability.

It is important that this wall (non-rated) and the ceiling together resist the passage of smoke, but it is not intended that they meet all the requirements of Section 6-3 for smoke barriers.

Exception No. 3: Where the corridor ceiling is constructed with materials that would have a 1-hour fire resistance rating when tested as a wall, the corridor may terminate at the corridor ceiling.

Exception No. 3 to 10-3.6.1 was new to the 1985 Edition of the *Code*. Its intent is to legitimize the common practice of designing a "corridor" protection system by building a tunnel, the walls and ceilings of which are constructed to meet the requirements for a 1-hour rated wall assembly.

Exception No. 4: Lavatories need not be separated from corridors provided they are separated from all other spaces by fire barriers having not less than a 1-hour fire resistance rating in accordance with 6-2.3.

Recognizing the typically low fuel loads associated with lavatories in addition to the need to provide door louvers for ventilation, Exception No. 4 exempts the wall separating the lavatory from the corridor from the 1-hour

rating requirement as long as the continuity of the rated corridor wall is maintained around the lavatory.

10-3.6.2 Clothing and personal effects shall not be stored in corridors and lobbies.

Racks of clothing and personal effects create two specific problems. The first problem relates to the large amount of combustibles in the means of egress. Fires in clothing racks in corridors will seriously hamper safe evacuation from the area served by the corridor. This problem should not be underestimated. Two recent fires, one in New York (Stouffers Hotel) and one in Massachusetts (Lexington), dramatically demonstrated the tremendous fire load posed by clothing on open coatracks. The second problem is created where the minimum acceptable width of the corridor is reduced.

Exception: Metal lockers shall be permitted in corridors for storage of clothing and personal effects provided the corridor width is maintained.

The first problem stated above can be corrected by providing metal lockers for storage of clothing and personal effects. This reduces accessibility of the combustibles to arsonists and also compartmentalizes the combustibles. Most fires in school lockers do not extend beyond the locker of origin. Those that do extend do not usually extend beyond the locker(s) adjacent to the locker of origin. However, the corridor must be of such width that it will allow at least the minimum required corridor width to be maintained after the lockers are installed.

10-3.7 Subdivision of Building Spaces.

10-3.7.1 School buildings shall be subdivided into compartments by smoke barriers having a 1-hour fire resistance rating and complying with Section 6-3 where:

(a) The maximum area of a compartment, including the aggregate area of all floors having a common atmosphere, exceeds 30,000 sq ft (2,800 sq m); or

(b) The length or width of the building exceeds 300 ft (91 m).

Exception No. 1: Where all spaces normally subject to student occupancy have at least one door opening directly to the outside or to an exterior or exit access balcony or corridor in accordance with 10-2.5.6.

Exception No. 2: Buildings that consist of only one story and are protected throughout by an approved supervised automatic sprinkler system installed in accordance with Section 7-7.

The 300-ft (91-m) limit bears a direct relationship to the travel distance criteria in Chapter 10 and reflects the Committee's concern regarding the maximum area within an educational facility that would be immediately contaminated by products of combustion from a fire.

The Committee felt it was reasonable and prudent to require smoke barriers at maximum intervals of 300 ft (91 m) so that the products of combustion would affect a limited number of exits at one time.

The provisions of this section were changed in the 1985 Edition of the *Code* to make the provision easier to understand and enforce. Previous editions spaced smoke barriers by corridor length. By spacing barriers according to compartment size, the intent of the provision is clarified and confusion in enforcement is reduced.

A primary concern of the Committee is a situation where a corridor becomes clogged with smoke resulting in the elimination of exit access. Spaces normally subject to student occupancy with exterior exit access provide the occupants a ready alternate means of escape in the event that a corridor fills with smoke.

The Committee believed that the record of automatic fire sprinklers was a good reason to reduce the compartmentation requirements. However, in multistory arrangements, the Committee believed compartmentation was important to provide refuge for occupants on upper floors. This requirement is especially important for the handicapped or others who are temporarily impaired physically. (*Also see 10-2.11.2.*)

10-3.7.2 The maximum area of a smoke compartment shall not exceed 30,000 sq ft (2,800 sq m) with no dimension exceeding 300 ft (91 m).

This provision applies only if 10-3.7.1 applies. If an exception to 10-3.7.1 applies, then 10-3.7.2 does not apply.

SECTION 10-4 Special Provisions

10-4.1 Windowless or Underground Buildings.

The provisions of this chapter pertaining to underground buildings were totally revised in the 1985 Edition of the *Code*. In recognition of the potential hazard that underground buildings pose, the *Code* requires compliance with Section 30-7 and, in addition, requires compliance with the provisions of 10-4.1.3 through 10-4.1.6 if the underground building has an educational occupancy more than 30 ft (9.1 m) below the level of exit discharge, or if an educational building has a floor level more than 30 ft (9.1 m) below the level of exit discharge.

Two exceptions to the requirements are provided for areas used only for service functions, such as boiler rooms and heater rooms, and for assembly uses where there is no occupiable intervening level between the assembly occupancy and the level of exit discharge.

10-4.1.1 Windowless or underground buildings shall comply with this chapter and Section 30-7.

10-4.1.2 Underground buildings or portions of buildings having a floor level more than 30 ft (9.1 m) below the level of exit discharge shall comply with the requirements contained in 10-4.1.3 through 10-4.1.6.

Exception No. 1: Areas within buildings used only for service to the building such as boiler/heater rooms, cable vaults, dead storage, and the like.

Exception No. 2: Auditoriums without intervening occupiable levels complying with the requirements of Chapter 8.

10-4.1.3 Each level more than 30 ft (9.1 m) below the level of exit discharge shall be divided into not less than two smoke compartments by a smoke barrier complying with Section 6-3 and having a 1-hour fire resistance rating.

(a) Each smoke compartment shall have access to at least one exit without passing through the other required compartment. Any doors connecting required compartments shall be tight-fitting, 1-hour fire doors designed and installed to minimize passage of smoke and to close and latch automatically upon detection of smoke.

(b) Each smoke compartment shall be provided with a mechanical means of moving people vertically, such as an elevator or escalator.

(c) Each smoke compartment shall have an independent air supply and exhaust system that is capable of smoke control or smoke exhaust functions and that provides a minimum smoke exhaust rate of six air changes per hour.

(d) Each smoke compartment shall be provided with an automatic smoke detection system throughout. The system shall be designed such that the activation of any two detectors shall cause the smoke control system to operate and the building voice alarm to sound.

10-4.1.4 The building shall be provided with emergency lighting in accordance with Section 5-9.

10-4.1.5 Any required smoke control or exhaust system shall be provided with a standby power system complying with Article 701 of NFPA 70, *National Electrical Code*.

10-4.1.6 The building shall be provided with an approved supervised voice alarm system in accordance with Section 7-6. The voice alarm system shall comply with 7-6.3.8. A prerecorded evacuation message shall be permitted.

10-4.2 **High Rise Buildings.** High rise buildings shall comply with Section 30-8.

The Committee believes that an educational high rise building poses many of the same problems for the occupants and fire fighting forces as are posed by other occupancy classes in high rise buildings.

10-4.3 Flexible Plan and Open Plan Buildings.

The 1985 Edition of the *Code* contained a major revision of the provisions pertaining to flexible and open plan schools. The intent of the revision was to make the *Code*

easier to use while improving life safety in these special arrangements. This section requires that flexible and open plan schools comply with Sections 10-1 through 10-5, except as modified by this section.

10-4.3.1 Flexible and open plan buildings shall comply with the requirements of this chapter and 10-4.3.2 through 10-4.3.4.

10-4.3.2 Each room occupied by more than 300 persons shall have two or more means of egress entering into separate atmospheres. Where three or more means of egress are required, not more than two of them shall enter into the same atmosphere.

Rooms occupied by more than 300 persons require special treatment in flexible and open plan schools. To ensure the safety of this great a number of persons contained in one room, means of egress must be arranged so that each of the separate egress paths traverse atmospheres separate from each other. If more than two separate means of egress paths are required, no more than two shall pass through the same atmosphere. By this arrangement, one fire cannot contaminate or block all exits in an open plan or flexible plan building.

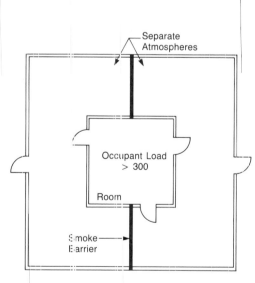

Figure 10-16. Example of Room in Open Plan Building Requiring Two or More Means of Egress into Separate Atmospheres.

10-4.3.3 Flexible plan schools may have walls and partitions rearranged periodically only if revised plans or diagrams have been approved by the authority having jurisdiction.

Approval of revised plans or diagrams is necessary to avoid the possibility of circuitous exit paths or other arrangements that do not comply with the intent of the *Code*. Also note that flexible plan buildings are required to meet the requirements for corridor protection as well as subdivision of building spaces.

10-4.3.4 Flexible plan buildings shall be evaluated while all folding walls are extended and in use as well as when they are in the retracted position.

10-4.4 Operating Features. (*See Chapter 31.*)

SECTION 10-5 Building Services

10-5.1 Utilities. Utilities shall comply with the provisions of Section 7-1.

10-5.2 Heating, Ventilating, and Air Conditioning Equipment.

10-5.2.1 Heating, ventilating, and air conditioning equipment shall comply with the provisions of Section 7-2.

10-5.2.2 Unvented fuel-fired heating equipment shall be prohibited.

The Committee did not believe that it was in the interest of reasonable life safety to have unvented fuel-fired equipment in a school building occupied by children. It was believed that the typical use of unvented equipment would jeopardize the life safety of the students, because proper venting may not be provided and potential misuse by students or injury to students, especially younger children, may occur.

10-5.3 Elevators, Escalators, and Conveyors. Elevators, escalators, and conveyors shall comply with the provisions of Section 7-4.

10-5.4 Rubbish Chutes, Incinerators, and Laundry Chutes. Rubbish chutes, incinerators, and laundry chutes shall comply with the provisions of Section 7-5.

SECTION 10-6 (Reserved)

SECTION 10-7 Day-Care Centers

The day-care provisions are arranged to stand on their own, independent of the rest of the chapter. The provisions of Sections 10-2 through 10-5 do not apply unless specifically referenced. The provisions include adult day-care. Throughout the sections, the term "child" has been changed to "client" so that the provisions cover the entire age spectrum. Of course, in certain instances, provisions apply only to children; in those cases, the text has retained the term "child."

Day-care properties averaged 500 structure fires a year reported to U.S. fire departments in 1984-88, with an associated 5 civilian injuries a year and no deaths. These figures apply to day child-care centers and probably miss the many sites where day care is provided at someone's home. These sites are indistinguishable from other homes in the fire incident data.

In homes in general, pre-school children constistute a high-risk group, averaging more than twice as many fire deaths relative to population as all other age groups combined. The leading cause of these fire deaths is fireplay by children, although the victims are often not the same children who start the fires. Pre-school children are also at elevated risk from most other causes.

10-7.1 General Requirements.

Table 10-1 summarizes the *Code's* requirements for the three types of day-care centers.

Table 10-1.	Minimum Requirements for Day-Care Centers		
	Center	Group Home	Family Home
Number of Clients	>12	7 to 12	≤6
Number of Clients under Two Years	Any	3	2
Recommended Staff-to-Client Ratio	Age (yrs)　Ratio <2　　　1:3 2–3　　　1:5 3–5　　　1:10 5–7　　　1:12 >7　　　1:15	2:12	1:6
Building Construction (permissible height vs. age of clients)	See 10-7.1.6.1	Rec. meet applicable building codes	Rec. meet applicable building codes
Occupant Load Factor	1 person/35 sq ft*	NR	NR
Area of Refuge	See 10-7.2.2.5 and 10-7.2.11.2	NR	NR
Number of Exits	2 remote (see 10-7.2.4)	2 remote (see 10-8.2.4)	2 remote (see 10-9.2.4)
Travel Distance to Exit† (ft)*	100 (from room door) 150 (from any point in a room)	100 (from room door) 150 (from any point in a room)	100 (from room door) 150 (from any point in a room)
Exit Discharge	To outside	At least one directly to outside	At least one directly to outside
Illumination of Means of Egress	Per Section 5-8	Per Section 5-8	Per Section 5-8
Emergency Lighting	Per 10-2.9	NR (See 31-3.5)	NR (See 31-3.5)
Door Latches (closet)	Child opens from inside	Child opens from inside	Child opens from inside
Door Locks (bathroom)	Staff unlocks	Staff unlocks	Staff unlocks
Protection of Vertical Openings	See Section 6-2	See 10-8.3.1	NR
Hazard Protection	1-hr enclosure or automatic sprinklers (see 10-7.3.2)	NR	NR
Class of Interior Finish	A (stairways, corridors, lobbies) B (other areas)	B (corridors, stairways, lobbies, and exits) C (all other spaces)	B (exits) C (all other spaces)
Class of Interior Floor Finish	I or II (corridors and exits)	NR	NR
Alarm System	Manual (direct connection to fire department if >100 clients	NR	NR
Smoke Detectors	See 10-7.3.4.5	See 10-8.3.4	See 10-9.3.4
Extinguishers	Standpipes if building ≥6 stories		
Corridor Protection	Per 10-3.6.1	NR	NR
Electric Equipment	See NFPA 70 (receptacle covers required, Chapter 7)	See NFPA 70 (receptacle covers required, Chapter 7)	See NFPA 70 (receptacle covers required, Chapter 7)
HVAC	See Chapter 7	See 10-8.5.2	See 10-9.5.2

*Conversion: 1 ft = .3048 m   NR = No requirement.   † 50-ft increase if sprinklered.

attention on code

Formal Interpretation 76-108
Reference: 10-7 (11-7), 10-8 (11-8), 10-9 (11-9)

Question 1: Do the requirements of Sections 10-7 (11-7), 10-8 (11-8), or 10-9 (11-9) apply to church programs that provide day-care services to church members only, on a nonprofit basis?

Answer: Yes.

Question 2: Are churches also required to meet the provisions of Sections 10-7 (11-7), 10-8 (11-8), or 10-9 (11-9) in order to operate a church nursery while church services are being held?

Answer: Yes.

Question 3: Does Section 1-6 permit the city to grant an exception in these cases?

Answer: The authority having jurisdiction is given the power to grant exceptions where it is clearly evident that reasonable safety is thereby secured.

Issue Edition: 1976
Reference: 9-5.3, 9-5.4, 9-5.5
Date: March 1979 ■

10-7.1.1 Application.

10-7.1.1.1* The requirements detailed in Section 10-7, "Day-Care Centers" (more than 12 clients), are based on the minimum staff-to-client ratios that follow:

Staff Ratio	Age
1:3	0 to 2
1:5	2 to 3
1:10	3 to 5
1:12	5 to 7
1:15	7 and over

The staff-to-client ratios may be modified by the authority having jurisdiction where safeguards in addition to those specified by this section are provided.

A-10-7.1.1.1 It should be noted that this paragraph does not require the staff ratios indicated but only states that the requirements of this section are based on these staff ratios. If these staff ratios are not maintained, it would be the responsibility of the authority having jurisdiction to determine what additional safeguards above and beyond the requirements of this section would be necessary. Typical additional provisions may include restricting the day-care center to the level of exit discharge, requiring additional smoke detection, requiring automatic sprinkler protection, requiring better or additional means of egress, and similar types of items depending upon the situation.

10-7.1.1.2* This section establishes life safety requirements for day-care centers in which more than 12 clients receive care, maintenance, and supervision by other than their relative(s) or legal guardian(s) for less than 24 hours per day. The provisions of Sections 10-2 through 10-6 shall not apply to this section unless a specific requirement is referenced by this section.

A-10-7.1.1.2 Day-care centers do not provide for the full-time maintenance of a client. Occupancies that provide primary place of residence are dealt with in other occupancies. (*See Chapters 16 through 22, "Residential Occupancies."*)

The intent of 10-7.1.1.2 is to differentiate between institutions where clients are in residence 24 hours a day (such as orphanages) and day-care facilities where clients who normally reside at another location are provided care. A facility supplying "total care" for each client would provide laundries, dormitories, cafeterias, and other ancillary services not found in a day-care center. The life safety requirements of such a facility would be governed by other occupancy provisions of the *Code*.

10-7.1.1.3 Centers housing children 6 years of age and older shall conform to the requirements for educational occupancies, except as noted herein.

Centers that provide care only for children of school age are required to conform to the requirements for educational occupancies and to the special requirements for such facilities where they are located in buildings of other occupancies.

10-7.1.1.4 Where a facility houses more than one age group, the requirements for the younger group shall apply unless the area housing the younger group is maintained as a separate fire area.

Exception: Staff-to-client ratios listed in 10-7.1.1.1 shall be based on the number of clients in each age category.*

A-10-7.1.1.4 Exception. An example of this exception is illustrated as follows: A center has 43 children;

3 children under age 2 (1:3)	1 staff
10 children ages 2 to 3 (1:5)	2 staff
30 children ages 3 to 5 (1:10)	3 staff
Total	6 staff

Therefore, the required staff for this center is 6, not 15, which would be required for 43 children on a 1 to 3 staff ratio.

A separate fire area is usually constructed with walls that have a fire resistance rating of 2 hours. Most facilities governed by this chapter will be maintained as separate atmospheres through smoke barriers having a 1-hour fire resistance rating.

It was brought to the Committee's attention that this section has been interpreted by some as applying to staff ratios. The Committee felt that to use the youngest age group to establish staff-to-client ratios for the entire group was too restrictive and did not meet the intent of the *Code* and, therefore, the exception and appendix note were added.

10-7.1.2 Mixed Occupancies.

(a) *General.* Where centers are located in a building containing mixed occupancies, the occupancies shall be separated by 1-hour fire barriers constructed in accordance with 6-2.3.

Exception to (a): In assembly occupancies used primarily for worship.

(b) *Centers in Apartment Buildings.*
  (1) If the two exit accesses from the center enter the same corridor as the apartment occupancy, the exit accesses shall be separated in the corridor by a smoke barrier having not less than a 1-hour fire resistance rating constructed in accordance with Section 6-3. The smoke barrier shall be so located that it has an exit located on each side.
  (2) The door in the smoke barrier shall be not less than 36 in. (91 cm) wide.

Where a center is located in a building housing another occupancy, the operators of the center usually have no control of the safety procedures and precautions practiced outside the center. Paragraph 10-7.1.2 requires additional protection to minimize the clients' exposure to potential hazards outside the center.

The corridor subdivision by smoke barriers in accordance with Section 6-3 when day-care centers are in an apartment building is the same concept as that used in Chapters 12 and 13 for health care facilities. This minimum construction will provide sufficient protection against flame and a good seal against smoke spread. The 20-minute door, coupled with the 1-hour wall, provides a barrier that will either contain a fire within a space for a limited time after it has been evacuated or will prevent a fire from entering an occupied space for a period of time.

10-7.1.3 Special Definitions. (None.)

10-7.1.4 Classification of Occupancy. For the purposes of this section, clients are classified in age groups as follows: clients under 6 years of age and clients 6 years of age and older.

10-7.1.5 Classification of Hazard of Contents. The contents shall be classified as ordinary hazard in accordance with Section 4-2.

10-7.1.6 Minimum Construction Requirements.

10-7.1.6.1 Centers shall not be located above the heights indicated for the types of construction given in Table 10-7.1.6.1. (*See 6-2.1.*)

Also see 10-7.4.2 for additional requirements when a day-care center is in the high rise portion of a building.

10-7.1.6.2 Location. The story below the level of exit discharge shall be permitted to be used in buildings of any construction type other than Type II (000), Type III (200), and Type V (000). (*See 10-7.2.4.2.*)

Table 10-7.1.6.1 Height and Construction Limits

Type of Construction	Age Group	Number of Stories (Stories are counted starting at floor of exit discharge)			
		1	2	3	4 and Over
I (443) I (332) II (222)	0 through 5	X	X	X	X
	6 and older	X	X	X	X
II (111) III (211) V (111)	0 through 5	X	X†	N.P.	N.P.
	6 and older	X	X	X†	N.P.
IV (2HH)	0 through 5	X	X†	N.P.	N.P.
	6 and older	X	X†	N.P.	N.P.
II (000)	0 through 5	X	X†	N.P.	N.P.
	6 and older	X	X†	N.P.	N.P.
III (200) V (000)	0 through 5	X†	X†	N.P.	N.P.
	6 and older	X	X†	N.P.	N.P.

X: Permitted construction type
N.P.: Not Permitted
X†: Permitted if entire building is protected throughout by an approved automatic sprinkler system.

10-7.1.7 Occupant Load. The occupant load for which means of egress shall be provided for any floor shall be the maximum number of persons intended to occupy that floor but not less than one person for each 35 sq ft (3.3 sq m) of net floor area used by the clients.

Many states require that day-care facilities provide 35 sq ft (3.3 sq m) of net area per child. It is not the intent of this *Code* to affect such a requirement, which is provided for the welfare of the child for purposes other than life safety. Where a center occupies a portion of a floor on which another occupancy exists, the occupant load for that floor is the sum of the occupant loads of the two occupancies. For example:

Net Floor Area (ft²)		Occupant Load Factor (ft²/person)		Occupant Load
Day-Care Center 1,750	÷	35	=	50
Assembly Occupancy 3,000	÷	7	=	429

Using addition, the total occupant load for which means of egress must be provided would be 479. (*Also see commentary on 10-1.7.*)

10-7.2 Means of Egress Requirements.

10-7.2.1 General. Means of egress shall be in accordance with Chapter 5 and this section.

10-7.2.2 Means of Egress Components.

10-7.2.2.1 Components of means of egress shall be limited to the types described in 10-7.2.2.2 through 10-7.2.2.7.

10-7.2.2.2 Doors.

(a) *General.* Doors shall comply with 5-2.1.

(b) *Panic Hardware or Fire Exit Hardware.* Any door in a required means of egress from an area having an occupant load of 100 or more persons may be provided with a latch or lock only if it is panic hardware or fire exit hardware.

This paragraph is based on the total occupant load of the area served and not the required capacity of the door. For example, if an area has an occupant load of 120 persons and is served by 3 doors, each door need only have capacity for 40 persons. However, since all these doors serve an area with "100 or more persons," any latches on these doors must be released by panic hardware or fire exit hardware.

(c) *Door Closure.* Any exit door designed to normally be kept closed shall comply with 5-2.1.8.

(d) *Locks and Latches.* Only one locking or latching device shall be permitted on a door or a leaf of a pair of doors.

(e) *Special Locking Arrangements.* Special locking arrangements complying with 5-2.1.6 shall be permitted.

(f)* *Closet Doors.* Every closet door latch shall be such that children can open the door from inside the closet.

A-10-7.2.2.2(f) The purpose of this requirement is to prevent arrangements where a child can be trapped in a closet.

It is intended that this provision be broadly interpreted by the authority having jurisdiction to include equipment such as refrigerators or freezers.

(g) *Bathroom Doors.* Every bathroom door lock shall be designed to permit opening of the locked door from the outside in an emergency. The opening device shall be readily accessible to the staff.

10-7.2.2.3* Stairs shall comply with 5-2.2.

A-10-7.2.2.3 See A-5-2.2.4.5(a) Exception No. 3 regarding additional handrails on stairs that are used extensively by children 5 years or less in age.

10-7.2.2.4 **Smokeproof Enclosures.** Smokeproof enclosures shall comply with 5-2.3.

10-7.2.2.5 **Horizontal Exits.**

(a) Horizontal exits shall comply with 5-2.4.

(b) Areas of refuge shall be provided by horizontal exits for occupants of day-care centers located above the fifth story.

In all cases, where day-care centers are found on upper floors of tall buildings, areas of refuge must be designed so that the clients will survive a fire. Five stories or approximately 75 ft (23 m) is the maximum height at which the fire department can be expected to rescue the occupants of a building from outside. However, many fire departments do not have the equipment to reach this height, and in such locations, areas of refuge are necessary at lower levels.

In any event, dependence on rescue by the fire department is not prudent. The time, number of personnel, and effort involved in rescuing one person by using an extension ladder is so great that it is not possible to rescue a large number of occupants by this method.

Also see 10-7.4.2 for additional requirements when day-care centers are located in high rise portions of a building. (*Also see 10-7.2.11.2.*)

10-7.2.2.6 **Ramps.** Ramps shall comply with 5-2.5.

10-7.2.2.7 **Exit Passageways.** Exit passageways shall comply with 5-2.7.

10-7.2.3 **Capacity of Means of Egress.**

10-7.2.3.1 Capacity of means of egress shall be in accordance with Section 5-3.

10-7.2.4 **Number of Exits.**

10-7.2.4.1 Each floor occupied by clients shall have not less than two remotely located exits in accordance with Chapter 5.

10-7.2.4.2 Where the story below the level of exit discharge is occupied as a day-care center, the following shall apply:

(a) One means of egress shall be an outside or interior stair in accordance with 5-2.2. An interior stair, if used, shall only serve the story below the level of exit discharge. The interior stair shall be permitted to communicate with the level of exit discharge; however, the exit route from the level of exit discharge shall not pass through the stair enclosure.

(b) The second means of egress shall be permitted to be via an unenclosed stairway separated from the level of exit discharge in accordance with 6-2.4.4. The path of egress travel on the level of exit discharge shall be protected in accordance with 5-1.3.4.

Figure 10-17 illustrates the intent of 10-7.2.4.2.

10-7.2.5 **Arrangement of Means of Egress.** (*Where the story below the level of exit discharge is used, see also 10-7.2.4.2.*)

10-7.2.5.1 Means of egress shall be arranged in accordance with Section 5-5. Dead ends shall not exceed 20 ft (6.1 m).

Chapter 5 does not allow dead-end corridors except in accordance with the occupancy chapters. The Committee recognized that 20 ft (6.1 m) has been the accepted standard in educational occupancies and believed that to retain it would be reasonable.

10-7.2.5.2 Every room or space with a capacity of more than 50 persons or more than 1,000 sq ft (93 sq m) in area shall have at least two doorways as remotely located from each other as practicable. Such doorways shall provide access to

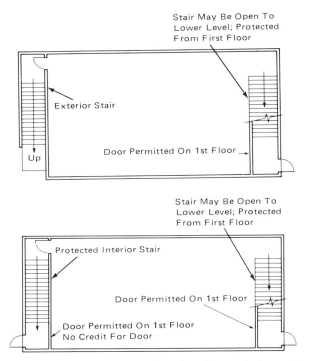

Figure 10-17. Egress for Levels Below the Level of Exit Discharge. Two methods of complying with 10-7.2.4.2 are illustrated. One stair, either an interior or outside stair, must be a properly protected exit discharging outside. The other stair may be open to the lower level but must be separated from the first floor. This second way out either discharges directly outside or discharges through a corridor protected in accordance with 5-1.3.4.

separate exits, but where egress is through corridors, they shall be permitted to open upon a common corridor leading to separate exits located in opposite directions.

Although Section 10-7 does not establish common path limitations, it does set a maximum room size permitted to be served by a single door, in addition to limiting dead-end space.

10-7.2.6 **Travel Distance to Exits.**

10-7.2.6.1 Travel distance shall be measured in accordance with Section 5-6.

10-7.2.6.2 Travel distance:

(a) Between any room door intended as exit access and an exit shall not exceed 100 ft (30 m);

(b) Between any point in a room and an exit shall not exceed 150 ft (45 m);

(c) Between any point in a sleeping room and an exit access door of that room shall not exceed 50 ft (15 m).

Exception: The travel distance in (a) and (b) above shall be permitted to be increased by 50 ft (15 m) in buildings protected throughout by an approved supervised automatic sprinkler system in accordance with Section 7-7.

Paragraph 10-7.2.6.2 is structured to state the same requirement in several different ways. As shown in Figure 10-18, the maximum travel distance from a room door (exit access to the corridor) to an exit door is 100 ft (30 m). The total travel distance from any point (such as in a room) to an exit is 150 ft (45 m). The maximum travel distance from a point in a sleeping room to an exit access door is 50 ft (15 m). This in-room travel distance limit may not be increased even if the building is sprinklered.

Note that the *Code* requires the sprinkler system to be supervised in order to take advantage of the allowance for additional travel distance.

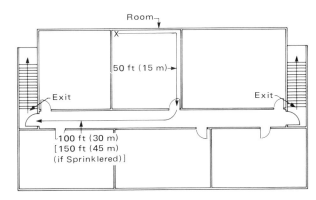

Figure 10-18. Maximum Travel Distance to Exit, Day-Care Center.

10-7.2.7 **Discharge from Exits.** Discharge from exits shall be arranged in accordance with Section 5-7.

Exception: As provided in 10-7.2.4.2.

10-7.2.8 **Illumination of Means of Egress.** Illumination of the means of egress shall be provided in accordance with Section 5-8.

10-7.2.9 **Emergency Lighting.** Emergency lighting shall be provided in accordance with 10-2.9.

10-7.2.10 **Marking of Means of Egress.** Means of egress shall have signs in accordance with Section 5-10.

10-7.2.11 **Special Features.**

10-7.2.11.1 **Windows for Rescue and Ventilation.** Every room or space normally subject to client occupancy, other than bathrooms, shall have at least one outside window for emergency rescue or ventilation. Such window shall be openable from the inside without the use of tools and shall provide a clear opening of not less than 20 in. (50.8 cm) in width, 24 in. (61 cm) in height, and 5.7 sq ft (.53 sq m) in area. The bottom of the opening shall be not more than 44 in. (112 cm) above the floor.

In rooms located higher than three stories above grade, the openable clear height, width, and area of the window may be modified to the dimensions necessary for ventilation.

Exception No. 1: In buildings protected throughout by an approved automatic sprinkler system in accordance with Section 7-7.

Exception No. 2: Where the room or space has a door leading directly to the outside of the building.

The dimensions specified for windows used for emergency rescue or for ventilation are based on simulations of emergency rescue conducted by the San Diego Fire Department. Windows providing clear openings of identical dimensions are also required for rescue or ventilation in one- and two-family dwellings. Figure 10-11 on page 350 illustrates two configurations that achieve the required area of 5.7 sq ft (.53 sq m).

Although the *Code* intends the fire department or others to assist students, particularly over ladders, if these windows must be used as a supplementary means of escape, the windows should permit younger children to escape unaided. Therefore, storm sashes, screens, or devices in front of the windows must be easy to open or

remove, and the sills must be low enough for children to reach.

Where the location of windows precludes their use for rescue or escape, they may still provide trapped children with air for breathing in smoke-filled rooms.

The Committee did not believe it was practical to expect a window above the third story to be used as an escape window. However, it is reasonable to expect the window to be used for ventilation during a fire.

Windows may be omitted if a room has a door leading directly to the outside or if the building is totally sprinklered.

Note that Exception No. 1 requires that the building be protected throughout by an automatic sprinkler system. One question often asked is: If there are only a couple of windowless rooms, can sprinklering be limited to those rooms only? The answer is no! It should be noted that the purpose of the window is to provide ventilation or means of escape when the interior corridor is blocked by smoke from a fire in another part of the building. Installing sprinklers in the windowless rooms only would do nothing to provide protection from smoke emanating from other areas.

10-7.2.11.2 Areas accessible to people with severe mobility impairment shall have a minimum of two accessible means of egress.

Exception No. 1: Day-care occupancies provided throughout by an approved supervised automatic sprinkler system in accordance with Section 7-7.

Exception No. 2: If the accessible means of egress provide(s) the most direct routes (route) from the accessible areas and if the fire protection system, the physical arrangement of the space, and the facility operation are all approved by the authority having jurisdiction, the authority having jurisdiction shall permit a reduction in the required number of accessible means of egress.

Section 10-7 has adopted the concept of accessible means of egress introduced to the 1991 Edition of the *Code*. As defined in Chapters 3 and 5, an accessible means of egress is a path of travel usable by a person with a severe mobility impairment ("severe" mobility impairment means possessing the ability to move to stairs without the ability to use them) that leads to a public way or an area of refuge. Hence, all areas accessible to those with severe mobility impairments shall be provided with two accessible means of egress.

In addition to exempting day-care centers housed in fully sprinklered buildings based on the system's ability to limit fire growth and spread, the *Code* grants the authority having jurisidiction the ability to review and approve configurations that would provide the desired level of safety. If the center is arranged such that a direct, noncircuitous path of travel is available, combined with a combination of building arrangement features and fire protection features to support the one direct route from each area, then the authority having jurisdiction may reduce the number of accessible means of egress.

10-7.3 Protection.

10-7.3.1 Protection of Vertical Openings. Any vertical opening shall be enclosed and protected in accordance with Section 6-2.

10-7.3.2 Protection from Hazards.

10-7.3.2.1 Rooms or spaces for the storage, processing, or use of the materials specified in this section shall be protected in accordance with the following:

(a) Rooms or spaces used for the storage of combustible supplies in quantities deemed hazardous by the authority having jurisdiction, hazardous materials in quantities deemed hazardous by recognized standards, or fuel shall be separated from the remainder of the building by construction having not less than a 1-hour fire resistance rating with all openings protected by self-closing or smoke-actuated fire doors, or such rooms or spaces shall be protected by an automatic extinguishing system as required in Section 6-4.

(b) Rooms or spaces used for processing or use of combustible supplies in quantities considered hazardous by the authority having jurisdiction, hazardous materials, or for flammable or combustible liquids in quantities deemed hazardous by recognized standards shall be separated from the remainder of the building by construction having not less than a 1-hour fire resistance rating with all openings protected by self-closing

or smoke-actuated fire doors and shall also be protected by an automatic extinguishing system as required in Section 6-4.

(c) Boiler and furnace rooms, laundries, and maintenance shops, including woodworking and painting areas, shall be separated from the remainder of the building by construction having not less than a 1-hour fire resistance rating with all openings protected by self-closing or smoke-actuated fire doors.

Exception to (c): Rooms enclosing air-handling equipment.

(d)* Where automatic extinguishing systems are used to meet the requirements of this section, the rooms or spaces shall be separated from the remainder of the building by construction that resists the passage of smoke.

A-10-7.3.2.1(d) It is not the intent of this provision to require a smoke barrier that meets the requirements of Section 6-3.

(e) Where automatic extinguishing is used to meet the requirements of this section, protection in accordance with 7-7.1.2 shall be permitted.

Exception: Food preparation facilities protected in accordance with 7-2.3 are not required to have openings protected between food preparation areas and dining areas. Where domestic cooking equipment is used for food warming or limited cooking, protection or segregation of food preparation facilities is not required if approved by the authority having jurisdiction.

The intent of 10-7.3.2.1 is to specify the degree of protection necessary for certain hazardous areas. It has been divided into three sections based on the degree of hazard. The hazards noted in part (a) are required to be enclosed in 1-hour construction or protected by sprinklers. If the sprinkler option is chosen, an enclosure is still required by part (d); however, the enclosure need not be rated but needs only to form a membrane against the passage of smoke.

The Committee reasoned that, although sprinklers are provided and fire-rated barriers may not be needed, some barrier to control smoke migration is needed. Solid construction materials, such as glass or other non-fire-rated materials, are acceptable if they are installed in a manner that will resist smoke passing from one compartment to another. The appendix note emphasizes that it is not the intent to require smoke barriers as provided in Section 6-3. This eliminates the more costly construction of

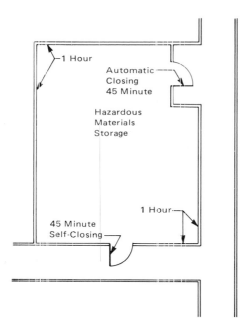

Figure 10-19a. Protection of Hazardous Areas. Figure 10-19a Illustrates one method of complying with 10-7.3.2.1(a). [See Figure 10-19b for the alternate method.]

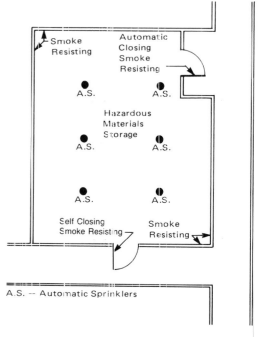

Figure 10-19b. Protection of Hazardous Areas. Figure 10-19b illustrates an alternate method of complying with 10-7.3.2.1(a). Figure 10-19a illustrates another method of compliance.

a smoke barrier, which would require dampers and other required equipment.

The hazards noted in part (b) must be enclosed in 1-hour construction and be protected by automatic sprinklers.

The hazards noted in part (c) are required to be enclosed in 1-hour construction with no option for a sprinkler equivalency for the enclosure. The Exception to part (c) pertains to rooms housing air-handling equipment only. If the room is used for other purposes, then the provisions of part (a) or (b) apply.

Part (e) has been provided to highlight the fact that Chapter 7 makes these requirements available to the user of the Code. Paragraph 7-7.1.2 provides an economical way of providing sprinkler protection in small rooms.

The intent of the exception is to provide some barrier between cooking areas and dining areas. Openings in this barrier are not restricted and do not need to be protected. The Code relies upon the provision of the automatic extinguishing system to control any fire on the cooking surfaces and, thus, does not require enclosure by rated construction. The second sentence of the exception is sig-

nificant, since this limited use of cooking equipment is often found in day-care centers.

Figure 10-19 illustrates the different protection requirements of 10-7.3.2.1.

10-7.3.2.2   Janitor closets shall be protected by an automatic sprinkler system, which shall be permitted to be in accordance with 7-7.1.2. Doors to janitor closets shall be permitted to have ventilating louvers.

Where janitor closets are located off of corridors, a louvered door is usually provided for ventilation. It is necessary to provide these spaces with automatic sprinkler protection, since the louvered door offers little fire resistance and permits a fire in the closet to directly affect the corridor. Paragraph 7-7.1.2 contains an economical method of providing sprinkler protection for such closets. To achieve this protection at reasonable cost, these sprinklers (not more than six in number) may be supplied from the domestic water supply if the supply is capable

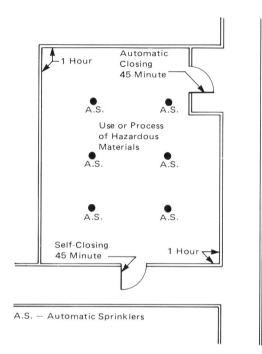

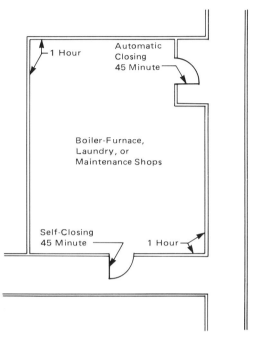

Figure 10-19c. Protection of Hazardous Areas. Figure 10-19c illustrates the requirements for complying with 10-7.3.2.1(b). Both 1-hour separation and automatic sprinkler protection are required in this case.

Figure 10-19d. Protection of Hazardous Areas. Figure 10-19d illustrates the requirements for complying with 10-7.3.2.1(c). Note that the automatic sprinkler option does not exist for these hazardous areas.

of providing the required quantity of water. It is advisable to provide a water-flow switch (*see Chapter 7*) to initiate an alarm when a sprinkler is opened.

The minimum flow of 0.15 gpm/sq ft (6.1 L/min/sq m) is based on the requirements of NFPA 13, *Standard for the Installation of Sprinkler Systems,*[3] for protecting buildings containing ordinary hazards. It is important to ensure that the domestic water supply can provide the required flow and pressure at the location.

10-7.3.3 Interior Finish.

10-7.3.3.1 Interior finish for all walls and ceilings shall be Class A or Class B in accordance with Section 6-5. Interior finish in stairways, corridors, and lobbies shall be Class A.

10-7.3.3.2 Floor coverings within corridors and exits shall be Class I or Class II in accordance with Section 6-5.

10-7.3.4 Detection, Alarm, and Communication Systems.

10-7.3.4.1 **General.** Day-care centers shall be provided with a fire alarm system in accordance with Section 7-6.

Exception No. 1: Day-care centers housed in one room.

Exception No. 2: Day-care centers with a required staff of fewer than four persons based on 10-7.1.1.1.

10-7.3.4.2 **Initiation.** Initiation of the required fire alarm system shall be by manual means and by operation of any required smoke detectors. (See 10-7.3.4.5.)

Exception: Single station smoke detectors.

Single station smoke detectors by definition are not connected to an alarm system and are normally installed to provide a local alarm that will alert people in the immediate vicinity that they should exit the area.

10-7.3.4.3 **Occupant Notification.** Occupant notification shall be by means of an audible alarm in accordance with 7-6.3.

10-7.3.4.4 Emergency Forces Notification. Fire department notification shall be accomplished in accordance with 7-6.4.

Exception: Day-care centers with not more than 100 clients.

In all day-care centers, manually operated fire alarm systems should be directly connected to the fire department. The Committee felt compelled to emphasize that this arrangement is essential in centers that serve more than 100 clients. There are fire departments that will not accept direct alarms. In such cases, positive provisions must be made for rapid notification of the fire department by remote or central station systems.

10-7.3.4.5 Detection. A smoke detection system shall be installed in accordance with Section 7-6 with placement of detectors in each story in front of doors to the stairways and in the corridors of all floors occupied by the center. Detectors shall also be installed in lounges, recreation areas, and sleeping rooms in the center.

Exception: Centers housed in only one room.

The purpose of this requirement is obvious, yet worth noting. In centers housing children younger than six, nap and sleep time are provided. The *Code* also recognizes that parents who work the "third shift" may place their children in the center for the purpose of sleeping through the night. Also, regardless of sleeping, the detectors will provide critical extra time to evacuate clients from danger. An exception is provided for centers housed in a single room where a fire will be obvious simultaneously to all occupants.

10-7.3.5 Extinguishment Requirements. (*See 10-7.4.2.*)

10-7.3.6 Corridors. Exit access corridors within day-care centers shall comply with 10-3.6.1. (*See 10-7.1.2.*)

The purpose of 10-7.3.6 is to provide a minimum level of compartmentation by use of corridor separation. (*See commentary on 10-3.6.1.*)

10-7.4 Special Provisions.

10-7.4.1 Windowless or Underground Buildings. Windowless or underground buildings shall comply with Section 30-7.

10-7.4.2 High Rise Buildings. High rise buildings that house day-care centers on floors more than 75 ft (23 m) above the lowest level of fire department vehicle access shall comply with Section 30-8.

As written, this brings Section 30-8, "High Rise Buildings," into effect (i.e., automatic sprinkler, alarm, detection, communication, standby power, and central control station requirements) where a center is located on a floor above the 75-ft (23-m) level.

Also see 10-7.2.2.5(b) with regard to horizontal exits where the day-care is located above the fifth story.

This requirement will force careful review when considering the placement of a new day-care center above the 75-ft (23-m) level in an existing high rise building. The building will already comply with the requirements of Section 30-8, or the entire building will need to be brought into compliance with Section 30-8 provisions in order to comply with the alteration/modification provision of 1-5.6.

10-7.4.3 Operating Features. (*See Chapter 31.*)

10-7.5 Building Services.

10-7.5.1 Utilities.

10-7.5.1.1 Utilities shall comply with the provisions of Section 7-1.

10-7.5.1.2 Special protective covers for all electrical receptacles shall be installed in all areas occupied by children under 6 years of age.

Children are subject to serious injury if they insert foreign objects into electrical receptacles. Protective covers must be provided and maintained in order to avoid such accidents.

10-7.5.2 Heating, Ventilating, and Air Conditioning Equipment.

10-7.5.2.1 Heating, ventilating, and air conditioning equipment shall be installed in accordance with Section 7-2.

10-7.5.2.2 Unvented fuel-fired room heaters shall not be permitted.

The Committee does not believe that the interest of reasonable life safety is served by allowing the use of unvented fuel-fired equipment in buildings occupied by children. (*Also see commentary on 10-5.2.2.*)

10-7.5.2.3 Any heating equipment in spaces occupied by children shall be provided with partitions, screens, or other means to protect children under 6 years of age from hot surfaces and open flames. If solid partitions are used to provide such protection, provisions shall be made to assure adequate air for combustion and ventilation for the heating equipment.

The Committee believes it important that safeguards be provided to protect younger children from the hot surfaces of heating equipment. Young children do not always understand the dangers of hot surfaces. The burn injury record clearly indicates that protection be provided. The Committee also wanted to make certain that adequate air is provided for combustion by the heating equipment. Incomplete or inadequate combustion could cause serious injury or death to occupants.

10-7.5.3 Elevators, Escalators, and Conveyors. Elevators, escalators, and conveyors shall comply with the provisions of Section 7-4.

10-7.5.4 Rubbish Chutes, Incinerators, and Laundry Chutes. Rubbish chutes, incinerators, and laundry chutes shall comply with the provisions of Section 7-5.

SECTION 10-8   Group Day-Care Homes

10-8.1 General Requirements.

10-8.1.1 Application.

10-8.1.1.1* This section establishes life safety requirements for group day-care homes in which at least 7 but not more than 12 clients receive care, maintenance, and supervision by other than their relatives or legal guardian(s) for less than 24 hours

---

Formal Interpretation 76-108
Reference: 10-7 (11-7), 10-8 (11-8), 10-9 (11-9)

Question 1: Do the requirements of Sections 10-7 (11-7), 10-8 (11-8), or 10-9 (11-9) apply to church programs that provide day-care services to church members only, on a nonprofit basis?

Answer: Yes.

Question 2: Are churches also required to meet the provisions of Sections 10-7 (11-7), 10-8 (11-8), or 10-9 (11-9) in order to operate a church nursery while church services are being held?

Answer: Yes.

Question 3: Does Section 1-6 permit the city to grant an exception in these cases?

Answer: The authority having jurisdiction is given the power to grant exceptions where it is clearly evident that reasonable safety is thereby secured.

Issue Edition: 1976
Reference: 9-5.3, 9-5.4, 9-5.5
Date: March 1979 ■

---

per day (generally within a dwelling unit). The provisions of Sections 10-2 through 10-6 shall not apply to this section unless a specific requirement is referenced by this section.

A-10-8.1.1.1 Group day-care homes do not provide for the full-time maintenance of a client. Occupancies that provide a primary place of residence are addressed in other occupancies. (*See Chapters 16 through 22, "Residential Occupancies."*)

These provisions take into account that the typical group day-care home is usually located in a residential setting.

10-8.1.1.2 The requirements detailed in Section 10-8 are based on a minimum staff-to-client ratio of two staff for up to twelve clients, with no more than three clients under age 2. This staff-to-client ratio may be modified by the authority having jurisdiction where safeguards in addition to those specified by this section are provided.

If these staff ratios are not maintained, it would be the responsibility of the authority having jurisdiction to determine what additional safeguards above and beyond the requirements of this section would be necessary. Typical additional provisions may include restricting the group day-care home to the level of exit discharge, requiring additional smoke detection, requiring automatic sprinkler protection, requiring better or additional means of egress, or similar types of features, depending upon the situation.

10-8.1.2 Mixed Occupancies.

(a) *General.* Where a group day-care home is located in a building containing mixed occupancies, the occupancies shall be separated by 1-hour fire barriers constructed in accordance with Section 6-2.3.

Exception to (a): In assembly occupancies used primarily for worship.

(b) *Homes in Apartment Buildings.*

(1) If the two exit accesses from the home enter the same corridor as the apartment occupancy, the exit accesses shall be separated in the corridor by a smoke barrier having not less than a 1-hour fire resistance rating constructed in accordance with Section 6-3. The smoke barrier shall be so located that it has an exit located on each side.

(2) The door in the smoke barrier shall be not less than 36 in. (91 cm) wide.

Group day-care homes are often found in buildings housing occupancies such as apartments, stores, offices or assembly occupancies. Where a center is located in a building housing another occupancy, the operators of the center usually have no control of the safety procedures and precautions practiced outside the center. Paragraph 10-8.1.2 requires additional protection to minimize the clients' exposure to potential hazards outside the center.

The corridor subdivision by smoke barriers in accordance with Section 6-3 when day-care centers are in an apartment building is the same concept as that used in Chapters 12 and 13 for health care facilities. This minimum construction will provide sufficient protection against flame and a good seal against smoke spread. The 20-minute door, coupled with the 1-hour wall, provides a barrier that will either contain a fire within a space

for a limited time after it has been evacuated or will prevent a fire from entering an occupied space for a period of time.

10-8.1.3 Special Definitions. (None.)

10-8.1.4 Classification of Occupancy. No requirements.

10-8.1.5 Classification of Hazard of Contents. The contents shall be classified as ordinary hazard in accordance with Section 4-2.

10-8.1.6 Minimum Construction Requirements. (None.)

10-8.1.7 Occupant Load. No special requirements.

10-8.2 Means of Egress Requirements.

10-8.2.1 General. (None.)

10-8.2.2 Types of Exits. (*See 10-8.2.4.*)

10-8.2.3 Capacity of Means of Egress. Capacity of means of egress shall be in accordance with Section 5-3.

10-8.2.4 Number of Exits.

10-8.2.4.1 Each story occupied by clients shall have not less than two remotely located means of escape.

This is similar to the requirements of Chapter 21 for one- and two-family dwellings; however, 10-8.2.4.3 and 10-8.2.4.5 provide for an increase over that which would normally be required for a private dwelling where clients occupy the second story or basement.

10-8.2.4.2 Every room used for sleeping, living, or dining purposes shall have at least two means of escape, at least one of which shall be a door or stairway providing a means of unobstructed travel to the outside of the building at street or ground level. The second means of escape shall be permitted to be a window in accordance with 10-2.11.1. No room or space shall be occupied for living or sleeping purposes that is accessible only by a ladder or folding stairs or through a trap door.

These are the same requirements as those for a one- or two-family dwelling.

10-8.2.4.3 Where spaces on the story above the story of exit discharge are used by clients, at least one means of egress shall be an exit discharging directly to the outside. The second means of escape shall be permitted to be a window in accordance with 10-2.11.1.

The second floor of a typical single family dwelling is served by an open stair. This would require that the second floor be served by an enclosed exit or an outside exit stair (not a fire escape) if clients are upstairs. (*Also see 10-8.3.1.*)

10-8.2.4.4 Where clients are occupying a story (basement) below the level of exit discharge, at least one means of egress shall be an exit discharging directly to the outside, and the vertical travel to ground level shall not exceed 8 ft (244 cm). The second means of escape shall be permitted to be a window in accordance with 10-2.11.1. No facility shall be located more than one story below the ground. Any stairway to the story above shall be cut off by a fire barrier containing a door having at least a 20-minute fire protection rating and equipped with a self-closing device.

This requirement is similar to that of 10-8.2.4.3 for a second floor and mandates that, where clients are below the level of exit discharge, at least one true exit shall be provided. In addition, any stairway to the first floor would require at least 20-minute protection.

As illustrated in Figure 10-20, where a group day-care center is located in a basement, there must be an exit that opens directly to the outside, with vertical travel to ground level not exceeding 8 ft (244 cm). If a stairway to the story above were provided, it would have to be cut off from the basement by a fire barrier containing a door with a fire protection rating of at least 20 minutes. This separation need be provided only at the top or bottom of the stair, not at both. (*Also see 10-8.3.1.*)

10-8.2.5 Arrangement of Means of Egress. (*Where a story above or below the exit discharge is used, see 10-8.2.4.*)

10-8.2.5.1 Means of egress shall be arranged in accordance with Section 5-5. Dead ends shall not exceed 20 ft (6.1 m).

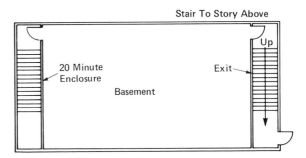

Figure 10-20. *Exit Requirements for Group Day-Care Center in Basement.*

Chapter 5 does not allow for dead ends unless provided for by the occupancy chapters. The Committee felt that 20 ft (6.1 m) continues to be a reasonable distance for these types of occupancies.

10-8.2.6 Travel distance:

(a) Between any room door intended as exit access and an exit shall not exceed 100 ft (30 m);

(b) Between any point in a room and an exit shall not exceed 150 ft (45 m);

(c) Between any point in a sleeping room and an exit access to that room shall not exceed 50 ft (15 m).

Exception: The travel distance in (a) and (b) above shall be permitted to be increased by 50 ft (15 m) in buildings protected throughout by an approved supervised automatic sprinkler system in accordance with Section 7-7.

10-8.2.7 Discharge from Exits. (*Where the story above or below the exit discharge is used, see 10-8.2.4.*)

10-8.2.8 Illumination of Means of Egress. Illumination of the means of egress shall be provided in accordance with Section 5-8.

10-8.2.9 Emergency Lighting. No requirements.

10-8.2.10 Marking of Means of Egress. No requirements.

10-8.2.11 Special Requirements.

10-8.2.11.1* Every closet door latch shall be such that children can open the door from the inside of the closet.

A-10-8.2.11.1 The purpose of this requirement is to prevent arrangements where a child can be trapped in a closet. It is intended that this provision be broadly interpreted by the authority having jurisdiction to include equipment like refrigerators or freezers.

10-8.2.11.2 Every bathroom door lock shall be designed to permit opening of the locked door from outside in an emergency. The opening device shall be readily accessible to the staff.

10-8.3 Protection.

10-8.3.1 Protection of Vertical Openings. The doorway between the level of exit discharge and any story below shall be equipped with a door assembly having a 20-minute fire protection rating. Where the story above the story of exit discharge is used for sleeping purposes, there shall be a door assembly having a 20-minute fire protection rating at the top or bottom of each stairway.

Also see 10-8.2.4.3 and 10-8.2.4.4.

10-8.3.2 Protection from Hazards. No requirements.

10-8.3.3 Interior Finish.

10-8.3.3.1 The interior finish in corridors, stairways, lobbies, and exits shall be Class A or B in accordance with Section 6-5.

10-8.3.3.2 Interior finish in occupied spaces in the home shall be Class A, B, or C in accordance with Section 6-5.

10-8.3.4 Detection, Alarm, and Communication Systems.

10-8.3.4.1 Within the group day-care home, smoke detectors shall be installed in accordance with 7-6.2.9.

Exception: Homes that house clients 6 years of age or older if no sleeping facilities are provided.

10-8.3.4.2 Where the group day-care home is located within a building of another occupancy, such as in an apartment or office building, any corridors serving the group day-care home shall be provided with a smoke detection system in accordance with Section 7-6.

10-8.3.4.3 Single station smoke detectors in accordance with 7-6.2.9 powered by the building electrical system or system detectors with integral sounding devices in accordance with 7-6.1.4 shall be provided in all rooms used for sleeping.

The provisions of 10-8.3.4 are three-fold: first, to provide smoke detection within the group day-care home in accordance with NFPA 74, *Standard for the Installation, Maintenance, and Use of Household Fire Warning Equipment;*[4] and second, to provide a smoke detection system in the corridor serving the group day-care home where in a building of mixed occupancy. Third, 10-8.3.4.3 requires that either single station smoke detectors or system smoke detectors designed with integral sounding devices be installed in each sleeping room, which is not required by NFPA 74.

10-8.4 Special Provisions.

10-8.4.1 Windowless or Underground Buildings. Windowless or underground buildings shall comply with Section 30-7.

10-8.4.2 High Rise Buildings. (Reserved.)

10-8.4.3 Operating Features. (*See Chapter 31.*)

10-8.5 Building Services.

10-8.5.1 Electrical Services.

10-8.5.1.1 Electrical wiring shall be installed in accordance with Section 7-1.

10-8.5.1.2 Special protective covers for electrical receptacles shall be installed in all areas occupied by children under 6 years of age.

Children are subject to serious injury if they insert foreign objects into electrical receptacles. Protective covers must be provided and maintained in order to avoid such accidents.

10-8.5.2 Heating, Ventilating, and Air Conditioning Equipment.

10-8.5.2.1 Heating, ventilating, and air conditioning equipment shall be installed in accordance with Section 7-2.

10-8.5.2.2 Unvented fuel-fired room heaters shall not be permitted.

The Committee does not believe that the interest of reasonable life safety is served by allowing the use of unvented fuel-fired equipment in buildings occupied by children. (*Also see commentary on 10-5.2.2.*)

10-8.5.2.3 Any heating equipment in spaces occupied by children shall be provided with partitions, screens, or other means to protect children under 6 years of age from hot surfaces and open flames. If solid partitions are used to provide such protection, provisions shall be made to assure adequate air for combustion and ventilation for the heating equipment.

The Committee believes it important that safeguards be provided to protect younger children from the hot surfaces of heating equipment. Young children do not always understand the dangers of hot surfaces. The burn injury record clearly indicates that protection be provided. The Committee also wanted to make certain that adequate air is provided for combustion by the heating equipment. Incomplete or inadequate combustion could cause serious injury or death to occupants.

Screens that separate heating equipment from spaces occupied by children must be of closely spaced wire or expanded metal, of heavy gage, and must be securely attached to elements of the building. The purpose is to prevent children from bending the screens or inserting their fingers through the mesh.

SECTION 10-9   Family Day-Care Homes

10-9.1 General Requirements.

10-9.1.1 Application.

10-9.1.1.1* This section establishes life safety requirements for family day-care homes in which more than 3 but fewer than

---

Formal Interpretation 76-108
Reference: 10-7 (11-7), 10-8 (11-8), 10-9 (11-9)

Question 1: Do the requirements of Sections 10-7 (11-7), 10-8 (11-8), or 10-9 (11-9) apply to church programs that provide day-care services to church members only, on a nonprofit basis?

Answer: Yes.

Question 2: Are churches also required to meet the provisions of Sections 10-7 (11-7), 10-8 (11-8), or 10-9 (11-9) in order to operate a church nursery while church services are being held?

Answer: Yes.

Question 3: Does Section 1-6 permit the city to grant an exception in these cases?

Answer: The authority having jurisdiction is given the power to grant exceptions where it is clearly evident that reasonable safety is thereby secured.

Issue Edition: 1976
Reference: 9-5.3, 9-5.4, 9-5.5
Date: March 1979 ∎

---

7 clients receive care, maintenance, and supervision by other than their relatives or legal guardian(s) for less than 24 hours per day (generally within a dwelling unit). The provisions of Sections 10-2 through 10-6 shall not apply to this section unless a specific requirement is referenced by this section.

A-10-9.1.1.1 Family day-care homes do not provide for the full-time maintenance of a client. Occupancies that provide a primary place of residence are addressed in other occupancies. (*See Chapters 16 through 22, "Residential Occupancies."*)

Prior to the 1988 *Code*, this section dealt with "licensed" facilities.

The Committee recognizes that licensing practices vary among jurisdictions. It was also a concern that the term "licensed family day-care home" would mean that, according to the *Code*, if a facility were not licensed, it did not have to meet the requirements of the *Code*. It is the intent of the Committee to include all family day-care centers as defined in 10-9.1.1.1, regardless of licensing.

Family day-care homes are usually situated in single-family dwellings or in apartment houses. If they are located in apartment houses, they must also comply with the applicable requirements of 10-9.1.2. The 1991 Edition has been revised to reflect the provision that family day-care homes provide accommodations for more than three but fewer than seven clients. This recognizes that up to three outsiders are permitted in one- and two-family dwellings. (*See Chapter 21.*)

10-9.1.1.2 The requirements detailed in Section 10-9 are based on a minimum staff-to-client ratio of one staff for up to six clients, including the caretaker's own children under age 6, with no more than two children under age 2.

Many family day-care homes are located in single-family residences. The Committee recognizes that, in these types of situations, the caretaker's children should also be a consideration in determining staff-to-client ratios. This paragraph clarifies that distinction. The limit of two children under age 2 recognizes the stricter staff-to-client ratio requirements for this age group. (*For example, see staff-to-client ratio requirements for ages 0 to 2 in 10-7.1.1.1.*)

10-9.1.2 Mixed Occupancies. Where family day-care homes are located in a building containing mixed occupancies, the occupancies shall be separated by 1-hour fire barriers.

Exception: In assembly occupancies used primarily for worship.

10-9.1.3 Special Definitions. (None.)

10-9.1.4 Classification of Occupancies. No requirements.

10-9.1.5 Classification of Hazard of Contents. The contents shall be classified as ordinary hazard in accordance with Section 4-2.

10-9.1.6 Minimum Construction Requirements. (None.)

10-9.1.7 Occupant Load. No special requirements.

10-9.2 Means of Egress Requirements.

10-9.2.1 General. (None.)

10-9.2.2 Types of Exits. (*See 10-9.2.4.*)

10-9.2.3 Capacity of Means of Egress. Capacity of means of egress shall be in accordance with Section 5-3.

10-9.2.4 Number of Exits.

10-9.2.4.1 Every room used for sleeping, living, or dining purposes shall have at least two means of escape, at least one of which shall be a door or stairway providing a means of unobstructed travel to the outside of the building at street or ground level. The second means of escape shall be permitted to be a window in accordance with 10-2.11.1. No room or space shall be occupied for living or sleeping purposes that is accessible only by a ladder or folding stairs or through a trap door.

This paragraph has the same requirements as those for one- and two-family dwellings. The change from means of egress to means of escape also recognizes a window of proper size as one method of escaping a fire.

10-9.2.4.2 Where clients are located on a story (basement) below the level of exit discharge, at least one means of egress shall be an exit discharging directly to the outside, and the vertical travel to ground level shall not exceed 8 ft (244 cm). The second means of escape shall be permitted to be a window in accordance with 10-2.11.1. No facility shall be located more than one story below the ground.

This requires either a door directly outside with an outside stair leading up to grade or an enclosed interior exit stair discharging directly outside. This provides clients in the basement with a way out should a fire occur on the first floor.

10-9.2.5 Arrangement of Means of Egress. (*See 10-9.2.4.*)

10-9.2.6 Travel distance:

(a) Between any room door intended as exit access and an exit shall not exceed 100 ft (30 m);

(b) Between any point in a room and an exit shall not exceed 150 ft (45 m);

(c) Between any point in a sleeping room and an exit access to that room shall not exceed 50 ft (15 m).

Exception: The travel distance in (a) and (b) above shall be permitted to be increased by 50 ft (15 m) in buildings protected throughout by an approved supervised automatic sprinkler system in accordance with Section 7-7.

10-9.2.7 **Discharge from Exits.** (*See 10-9.2.4.*)

10-9.2.8 **Illumination of Means of Egress.** Illumination of the means of egress shall be in accordance with Section 5-8.

10-9.2.9 **Emergency Lighting.** No requirements.

10-9.2.10 **Marking of Means of Egress.** No requirements.

10-9.2.11 **Special Features.**

10-9.2.11.1 Each door in a means of egress shall not be less than 28 in. (71 cm) wide.

Exception: Bathroom doors shall be not less than 24 in. (64 cm) wide.

10-9.2.11.2* Every closet door latch shall be such that children can open the door from inside the closet.

A-10-9.2.11.2 The purpose of this requirement is to prevent arrangements where a child can be trapped in a closet. It is intended that this provision be broadly interpreted by the authority having jurisdiction to include equipment like refrigerators or freezers.

10-9.2.11.3 Every bathroom door lock shall be designed to permit the opening of the locked door from the outside in an emergency. The opening device shall be readily accessible to the staff.

10-9.3 **Protection.**

10-9.3.1 **Protection of Vertical Openings.** (No special provisions.)

10-9.3.2 **Protection from Hazards.** No requirements.

10-9.3.3 **Interior Finish.**

10-9.3.3.1 The interior finish in exits shall be Class A or B in accordance with Section 6-5.

10-9.3.3.2 Interior finish in occupied spaces in the home shall be Class A, B, or C in accordance with Section 6-5.

10-9.3.4 **Detection, Alarm, and Communication Systems.**

10-9.3.4.1 Within the family day-care home, smoke detectors shall be installed in accordance with 7-6.2.9.

Exception: Homes that house clients 6 years of age or older if no sleeping facilities are provided.

10-9.3.4.2 Where the family day-care home is located within a building of another occupancy such as in an apartment or office building, any corridors serving the family day-care home shall be provided with a smoke detection system in accordance with Section 7-6.

10-9.3.4.3 Single station smoke detectors in accordance with 7-6.2.9 powered by the building electrical system or system detectors with integral sounding devices in accordance with 7-6.1.4 shall be provided in all rooms used for sleeping.

The provisions of 10-9.3.4 are three-fold: first, to provide single station smoke detectors within the family day-care home in accordance with NFPA 74, *Standard for the Installation, Maintenance, and Use of Household Fire Warning Equipment;*[4] and second, to provide a smoke detection system in the corridor serving the family day-care home where in a building of mixed occupancy. Third, 10-9.3.4.3 requires that either single station smoke detectors or system smoke detectors designed with integral sounding devices be installed in each sleeping room, which is not required by NFPA 74.

10-9.4 **Special Provisions.**

10-9.4.1 **Windowless or Underground Buildings.** Windowless or underground buildings shall comply with Section 30-7.

10-9.4.2 High Rise Buildings. (Reserved.)

10-9.4.3 Operating Features. (*See Chapter 31.*)

10-9.5 Building Services.

10-9.5.1 Electrical Services.

10-9.5.1.1 Electrical wiring shall be installed in accordance with Section 7-1.

10-9.5.1.2 Special protective covers for all electrical receptacles shall be installed in all areas occupied by children in homes for children under 6 years of age.

Children are subject to serious injury if they insert foreign objects into electrical receptacles. Protective covers must be provided and maintained in order to avoid such accidents.

10-9.5.2 Heating, Ventilating, and Air Conditioning Equipment.

10-9.5.2.1 Heating, ventilating, and air conditioning equipment shall be installed in accordance with Section 7-2.

10-9.5.2.2 Unvented fuel-fired room heaters shall not be permitted.

The Committee does not believe that the interest of reasonable life safety is served by allowing the use of unvented fuel-fired equipment in buildings occupied by children. (*Also see commentary on 10-5.2.2.*)

10-9.5.2.3 Any heating equipment in spaces occupied by children shall be provided with partitions, screens, or other means to protect children under 6 years of age from hot surfaces and open flames. If solid partitions are used to provide such protection, provisions shall be made to ensure adequate air for combustion and ventilation for the heating equipment.

The Committee believes it important that safeguards be provided to protect younger children from the hot surfaces of heating equipment. Young children do not always understand the dangers of hot surfaces. The burn injury record clearly indicates that protection be provided. The Committee also wanted to make certain that adequate air is provided for combustion for the heating equipment. Incomplete or inadequate combustion could cause serious injury or death to occupants.

Screens that separate heating equipment from spaces occupied by children must be of closely spaced wire or expanded metal, of heavy gage, and must be securely attached to elements of the building. The purpose is to prevent children from bending the screens or inserting their fingers through the mesh.

References Cited in Commentary

[1]ASME/ANSI A17.1, *Safety Code for Elevators and Escalators*, American Society of Mechanical Engineers, 345 East 47th Street, New York, NY 10017, 1984.

[2]ANSI A117.1, *Standard for Buildings and Facilities — Providing Accessibility and Usability for Physically Handicapped People*, American National Standards Institute, 1430 Broadway, New York, NY 10018, 1961 (reaff. 1971).

[3]NFPA 13, *Standard for the Installation of Sprinkler Systems*, National Fire Protection Association, Quincy, MA, 1991.

[4]NFPA 74, *Standard for the Installation, Maintenance, and Use of Household Fire Warning Equipment*, National Fire Protection Association, Quincy, MA, 1989.

11

Existing Educational Occupancies

(See also Chapter 31.)

SECTION 11-1   General Requirements

Educational occupancies include all buildings used for gatherings of six or more people for purposes of instruction through the twelfth grade for four or more hours per day or more than twelve hours per week. Educational occupancies include:

Academies	Nursery schools
Kindergartens	Schools

Educational occupancies averaged 9500 structure fires per year as reported to U.S. fire departments from 1984 to 1988. These fires caused an average of three civilian deaths and 181 civilian injuries each year.

Fatal fires have been extremely rare in educational occupancies for many years. Those few that do occur tend to involve either employees in accidental fires (e.g., fires caused by floor cleaning with flammable liquids) or, more often, firesetters trapped by their own fires. Children killed in school fires in recent years have been largely limited to juvenile firesetters, acting as individuals or groups, who are on school grounds after hours without permission. At the same time, about one-third of those killed in educational occupancy fires from 1980 to 1988 were not occupying the same room as the fire when it began.

The worst recent fatal fire where deaths of school children occurred on the premises during normal school hours was a 1982 Oklahoma fire involving a Boiling Liquid Expanding Vapor Explosion (BLEVE) by an 85-gallon hot water heater. Also notable was a single fatality in a 1973 fire in a Virginia school in which a haunted house maze was set up for Halloween. Much attention has been focused on life safety in the educational setting since the Our Lady of Angels elementary school fire claimed the lives of 95 people in 1958.

Day-care facilities for both children and adults are provided for separately in Sections 11-7, 11-8, and 11-9.

Other occupancies associated with educational occupancies must be in accordance with the appropriate parts of this *Code*.

Operational features for educational occupancies are specified in Chapter 31, "Operating Features."

11-1.1 Application.

11-1.1.1 The requirements of this chapter apply to existing buildings.

Alterations, renovations, and modernizations to existing buildings are to be done, to the extent practical, in compliance with Chapter 10. (*See 1-5.6.*)

11-1.1.2 Reserved.

11-1.1.3 Educational facilities that do not meet the definition of an educational occupancy need not comply with this chapter but shall comply with the following requirements:

(a) Instructional Building — Business Occupancy.

(b) Classrooms under 50 persons — Business Occupancy.

(c) Classrooms 50 persons and over — Assembly Occupancy.

(d) Laboratories, Instructional — Business Occupancy.

(e) Laboratories, Noninstructional — Industrial.

As defined in Chapter 4 and repeated in 11-1.4.1, Chapter 11 is intended to regulate those buildings or portions of buildings educating students through and including the twelfth grade. The provisions of 11-1.1.3 recognize that colleges, universities, and similar educational facilities that do not meet the definition of educational occupancies do not pose the same problems as elementary and high schools. Because of the maturity of their occupants, college buildings more properly resemble business (office) occupancies. Thus, this paragraph identifies those uses and refers to other appropriate provisions of the *Code*. (*Also see 11-1.4.1.*)

11-1.2 Mixed Occupancies. (*See also 11-1.4.*)

11-1.2.1 Where other types of occupancy occur in the same building as an educational occupancy, the requirements of 1-5.7 of this *Code* shall be applicable.

Exception: As otherwise specified in this chapter.

Paragraph 1-5.7 of the *Code* specifies that, where separate safeguards for each occupancy cannot be maintained, the more stringent requirement of either occupancy will apply to both occupancies. Another way of stating this is that the requirement providing the highest level of life safety would apply to both occupancies.

11-1.2.2 Assembly and Educational. Spaces subject to assembly occupancy shall comply with Chapter 9, including 9-1.2, which provides that where auditorium and gymnasium exits lead through corridors or stairways also serving as exits for other parts of the building, the exit capacity shall be sufficient to permit simultaneous exit from auditorium and classroom sections.

Exception: In the case of an assembly occupancy of a type suitable only for use by the school occupant load (and therefore not subject to simultaneous occupancy), the same exit capacity shall be permitted to serve both sections.

In focusing on the most typical educational mixed occupancy, the reasoning of the *Code* is that, if classrooms and an assembly occupancy are likely to be occupied simultaneously, the exit capacity of the building must be designed and arranged for the combined use. For example, classrooms are often used during the evening for adult or remedial education while a school's gymnasium or auditorium is being used by another group. In such cases, the exception would not apply, even though during the day the place of assembly is used only by the school's population.

11-1.2.3 Dormitory and Classrooms. Any building used for both classroom and dormitory purposes shall comply with the applicable provisions of Chapter 17 in addition to complying with Chapter 11. Where classroom and dormitory sections are not subject to simultaneous occupancy, the same exit capacity shall be permitted to serve both sections.

11-1.3 Special Definitions.

Common Atmosphere. A common atmosphere is the atmosphere that exists between rooms, spaces, or areas within a building that are not separated by an approved smoke barrier.

Flexible Plan and Open Plan Educational Buildings. These include every building or portion of a building designed for multiple teaching stations.

(a) Flexible plan buildings have movable corridor walls and movable partitions of full-height construction with doors leading from rooms to corridors.

(b) Open plan buildings have rooms and corridors delineated by use of tables, chairs, desks, bookcases, counters, low-height [maximum 5-ft (152-cm)] partitions, or similar furnishings.

Although becoming less common, flexible and open plan schools still exist. However, in this edition of the *Code*, most of the requirements for flexible and open plan schools are built into the basic educational requirements, with 10-4.3 providing some additional requirements for flexible and open plan facilities

Separate Atmosphere. A separate atmosphere is the atmosphere that exists between rooms, spaces, or areas that are separated by an approved smoke barrier.

Separate Means of Egress. A means of egress separated in such a manner from other required means of egress to provide an atmospheric separation that precludes contamination of both means of egress by the same fire. (*See Section 6-3.*)

Story of Exit Discharge. The story of exit discharge is that story or stories from which the exits are primarily doors discharging directly outside essentially at grade (level of exit discharge). Where no such story exists, the story of exit discharge shall be that story with the smallest elevation change needed to reach the level of exit discharge.

The Committee recognizes the confusion that exists in trying to determine which story in an existing building should be considered the level of exit discharge where no single story is built exactly at grade level. The Committee felt this definition would help clarify the intent by designating the floor that has the shortest distance required to reach grade level as the story of exit discharge.

11-1.4 Classification of Occupancy. (*See 4-1.3.*)

11-1.4.1 Educational occupancies shall include all buildings used for educational purposes through the twelfth grade by 6 or more persons for four or more hours per day or more than twelve hours per week.

This paragraph exempts three types of schools: those with small numbers of students (fewer than 6), such as facilities providing private tutoring or individual lessons; those with limited operating hours, such as some sports schools or Sunday schools; and those educating people over the high school level, as in the case of universities or military training.

The exemption of the first two categories is rarely questioned but the exemption on upper level education is often questioned. The Committee believes that beyond high school the level of protection does not need to be greater simply because education is continued, while business or industry receives a different level of protection. Paragraph 11-1.1.3 provides guidance in determining how some facilities that fail to meet the definition of educational occupancy would be classified.

For purposes of determining occupant load, a classroom area is still an educational "use," although it may not be categorized as an educational occupancy, and the occupant load factors provided by 11-1.7 are still appropriate.

Where instruction is incidental to other occupancies, the requirements for the occupancy in which the instruction takes place are applicable. Church schools used for instruction for a few hours during one or two days of the week are generally classed as assembly occupancies.

11-1.4.2 Educational occupancies include part-day preschools, kindergartens, and other schools whose purpose is primarily educational even though the children are of preschool age.

The *Code* classifies part-time day-care facilities as educational occupancies if they primarily provide education in addition to care services. This parallels federal guidelines for subsidizing day-care/educational activities at both the federal and state levels. By requiring educational criteria and related activities, it was believed that a higher quality of staff would be provided for these facilities by these standards. This is not the "typical" day-care facility. Sections 11-7, 11-8, and 11-9 contain special requirements for "typical" noneducational day-care facilities.

11-1.4.3 In cases where instruction is incidental to some other occupancy, the section of this *Code* governing such occupancy shall apply.

This paragraph is not as significant as it was before 11-1.4.1 removed places of higher education from Chapter 11. The following examples describe uses that would nevertheless be exempted from Chapter 11 by 11-1.4.1.

In an office building or factory, a few rooms may be used for orientation or instruction in the work requirements; these rooms are subject to the *Code* requirements for offices or factories. Barber colleges and beauty schools are frequently located in commercial buildings and should be governed by the requirements of the buildings in which they occur.

11-1.4.4 Day-care facilities, whether for adults or children, shall meet the requirements of Section 11-7, 11-8, or 11-9 as appropriate.

Exception: Day-care facilities whose purpose is primarily educational as indicated in 11-1.4.2.

This paragraph is important in that it specifically conveys the *Code's* intent that day-care centers (adult and child) be regulated by Sections 11-7 through 11-9, depending on the number of clients, and that reference to Sections 11-2 through 11-6 is not required.

11-1.4.5 Adult day-care shall include any building or portion thereof used for nonsleeping purposes for less than 24 hours per day to house four or more adults requiring care, maintenance, and supervision by other than their relative(s). Clients shall be ambulatory or semiambulatory and shall not be bedridden. They shall not exhibit behavior that is harmful to themselves or others.

The definition of an adult day-care occupancy in this chapter is recognition of the fact that more and more senior citizens are being cared for in day-care centers similar to child day-care centers. The definition of the occupancy itself includes a definition of the type of adult who may be cared for in this occupancy. Essentially, the stated definition of an adult is to clarify that these occupancies are not nursing homes or old age homes but are occupancies used by persons who are capable of self-preservation, yet who require limited attendance, supervision, or observation.

Previous editions of the *Code* included cues for the identification of those adults meeting the definition. How-

ever, to eliminate the appearance of requiring a medical background to be qualified to assess such adults, these cues were removed from the *Code*. It may be appropriate, however, to use some of the following previously published guidelines to determine acceptability of a client for adult day-care:

(a) Client does not require medical injections from staff, but may require the administration of oral medication by staff personnel when and as prescribed by a licensed medical examiner, and

(b) Client may require limited supervision, attendance or observation, and

(c) Client exhibits acceptable behavior (not harmful to self or others).

Adult day-care occupancies are covered with child day-care occupancies in Sections 11-7, 11-8, and 11-9.

11-1.4.6 Other occupancies associated with educational institutions shall be in accordance with the appropriate parts of this *Code*. (*See Chapters 13, 17, 19, 20, 28, 29, and 30 and 1-5.7.*)

11-1.5 **Classification of Hazard of Contents.** Contents of educational occupancies shall be classified in accordance with the provisions of Section 4-2.

In general, educational occupancies contain ordinary hazard contents. Some laboratories and storage areas may contain high hazard contents. (*See Section 5-11 for additional egress requirements for areas with high hazard.*)

11-1.6 **Minimum Construction Requirements.** No requirements.

11-1.7 **Occupant Load.**

11-1.7.1 The occupant load of educational buildings or any individual story or section thereof for the purpose of determining exits shall be as determined by the authority having jurisdiction but not less than one person for each 20 sq ft (1.9 sq m) of net classroom area or 50 sq ft (4.6 sq m) of net area of shops, laboratories, and similar vocational rooms. In day-care centers, the occupant load shall be not less than one person for each 35 sq ft (3.3 sq m) of net area.

It is not the intent of this paragraph to establish a minimum number of sq ft (sq m) per child but to ensure adequate exit capacity is provided for those present. Efficient use of classroom space may result in a greater number of occupants than these occupant load factors would yield. Paragraph 11-1.7.3 clearly allows this, provided all requirements based on this higher number are met.

11-1.7.2 The occupant load of an area having fixed seats shall be determined by the number of fixed seats installed. Required aisle space serving the fixed seats shall not be used to increase the occupant load.

11-1.7.3 The capacity of an educational occupancy or a portion thereof may be modified from that specified above if the necessary aisles and exits are provided. An approved aisle or seating diagram shall be required by the authority having jurisdiction to substantiate such a modification.

See commentary on 11-1.7.1

11-1.7.4 The occupant load for determining exit requirements of individual lecture rooms, gymnasiums, or cafeterias used for assembly purposes of more than 50 persons shall be determined in accordance with 9-1.7 of this *Code*.

The intent of this paragraph is to indicate that rooms that may be used as assembly occupancies should have their occupant loads calculated using the occupant load factors found in Chapter 9 of the *Code*. As noted for assembly occupancies, this may result in a room with more than one occupant load, depending on its use. School cafeterias are generally capable of other uses and should likely be considered as multipurpose rooms.

SECTION 11-2 Means of Egress Requirements

11-2.1 General.

11-2.1.1 Means of egress shall be in accordance with Chapter 5 and this section.

11-2.1.2 Rooms normally occupied by preschool, kindergarten, or first-grade pupils shall not be located above or below the story of exit discharge. Rooms normally occupied by second-grade pupils shall not be located more than one story above the story of exit discharge.

The restrictions on the location of rooms used by preschool, kindergarten, first-grade or second-grade pupils were developed to avoid the danger of older (and larger) children overrunning the very young on stairs or ramps during a fire or other incident requiring rapid evacuation of a building. Paragraph 11-2.1.2 also recognizes that young children, based on their size and limited motor skills, may need assistance traversing stairs or may have to be rescued.

This provision is significantly different than in Chapter 10. It is a little more flexible by using the definition of story of exit discharge (*see 11-1.3*). What may have been a floor above or below the level of exit discharge may qualify as the story of exit discharge. See Figure 11-1.

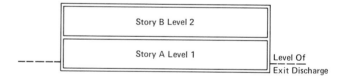

Figure 11-1. Level 1 Is Below the Level of Exit Discharge under Prior Editions. Under the definition of "Story of Exit Discharge" it qualifies.

11-2.2 Means of Egress Components.

Note that slide escapes, escalators, fire escape stairs, alternating tread devices and revolving doors are not permitted to be credited as required egress components. Escalators and revolving doors may be installed, but cannot be considered as part of required egress and must not obstruct or otherwise confuse required egress paths.

11-2.2.1 Components of means of egress shall be limited to the types described in 11-2.2.2 through 11-2.2.7.

11-2.2.2 Doors.

11-2.2.2.1 Doors shall comply with 5-2.1.

11-2.2.2.2 Panic Hardware or Fire Exit Hardware. Any required exit door subject to use by 100 or more persons may be provided with a latch or lock only if it is panic hardware or fire exit hardware complying with 5-2.1.7.

The requirement for panic hardware in existing educational occupancies is slightly less restrictive than for new occupancies. Here panic hardware or fire exit hardware is required only on exit doors rather than egress doors; therefore, the scope of the paragraph is reduced so that it does not address exit access doors, such as corridor doors and smoke barrier doors. In addition, Chapter 10 addresses the number of people in the area served while here it addresses the required capacity of the door. Chapter 10 was made more stringent for the 1985 *Code*, but the Committee did not consider this to be of significant enough importance to require existing buildings to be retrofitted. If panic hardware or fire exit hardware is already installed in accordance with Chapter 10, it must be maintained, as removal would be an alteration, and 1-5.6 requires alterations to comply with Chapter 10.

11-2.2.2.3 Special locking arrangements complying with 5-2.1.6 shall be permitted.

The provisions of 5-2.1.6 apply to special delayed release devices. Note that one of the requirements of 5-2.1.6 is that the building must be either fully sprinklered or fully protected by an automatic fire detection system.

It is interesting to note that the concept portrayed in 5-2.1.6, which is now employed in many occupancies, was developed to address security concerns in the educational environment.

11-2.2.2.4 Door Closure. Any exit door that is designed to normally be kept closed shall conform with 5-2.1.8.

11-2.2.2.5 Only one locking or latching device shall be permitted on a door or a leaf of a pair of doors.

11-2.2.2.6 Horizontal sliding doors shall be permitted in a means of egress serving an occupant load of less than 50 in accordance with 5-2.1.14.1. The doors shall be operable by force not to exceed 15 lbf (67 N) applied to the operating device in the direction of egress.

11-2.2.2.7 Horizontal sliding doors shall be permitted in smoke barriers in accordance with 5-2.1.14.1. In addition, the doors shall be operable by a force not to exceed 15 lbf (67 N) applied to the operating device in the direction of egress.

Both 11-2.2.2.6 and 11-2.2.2.7 permit horizontal sliding doors in accordance with 5-2.1.14. Although the force qualifier may appear to modify the requirements of 5-2.1.14, in fact they are now also part of 5-2.1.14. It should be noted that the requirements of 5-2.1.14 are quite stringent and are not "typical" sliding doors.

11-2.2.3* Stairs.

A-11-2.2.3 See A-5-2.2.4.5(a) Exception No. 3 regarding additional handrails on stairs that are used extensively by children 5 years or less in age.

11-2.2.3.1 Stairs shall comply with 5-2.2.

11-2.2.3.2 Stairs shall be Class A.

Exception: Class B stairs shall be permitted where not used for student access.

11-2.2.4 Smokeproof Enclosures. Smokeproof enclosures shall comply with 5-2.3.

11-2.2.5 Horizontal Exits. Horizontal exits shall comply with 5-2.4.

11-2.2.6 Ramps. Ramps shall comply with 5-2.5.

11-2.2.7 Exit Passageways. Exit passageways shall comply with 5-2.6.

11-2.3 Capacity of Means of Egress.

11-2.3.1 Capacity of means of egress shall be in accordance with Section 5-3.

11-2.3.2 Minimum Corridor Width.

11-2.3.2.1 Exit access corridors shall be not less than 6 ft (183 cm) clear width.

Note that this requirement applies regardless of the required capacity of the corridor. Larger widths may be necessary for corridors handling large numbers of students (*see 11-2.3.1*).

This paragraph applies to exit access corridors and not to nonrequired service corridors that are provided for convenience only.

"Clear width" means a 6-ft (183-cm) wide clear space with no obstructions. Paragraph 5-3.2 details how to measure the width of a portion of the means of egress.

The intent of a 6-ft (183-cm) corridor is to permit two files of children with sufficient room for teachers or monitors to supervise. Extremely short corridors serving only one room may warrant consideration for some reduction in width.

11-2.3.2.2 Drinking fountains or other equipment, fixed or movable, shall not be so placed as to obstruct the required minimum 6-ft (183-cm) corridor width.

11-2.4 Number of Exits. There shall be at least two exits available from every floor area. (*See Section 5-4.*)

11-2.5 Arrangement of Means of Egress. (*See also Section 5-5.*)

This section had been rewritten for the 1988 Edition and has been further edited for the 1991 Edition. Section 5-5 provides the detail required to establish proper exiting.

11-2.5.1 Means of egress shall be arranged in accordance with Section 5-5. No common path of travel shall exceed 75 ft (23 m); no dead end shall exceed 20 ft (6.1 m).

Paragraph 5-5.1.6 makes individual chapters responsible for establishing dead-end limits. Twenty feet (6.1 m) has been the standard dead-end requirement for educational occupancies in the past, and the Committee felt it was still reasonable. A common path limitation of 75 ft (23 m) has been added to the 1991 Edition.

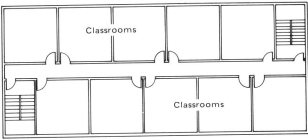

Preferred Arrangement Of Exits Without Deadends

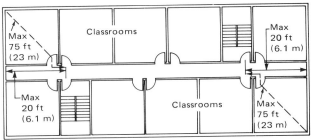

Acceptable Arrangement Of Exits With Deadends, Up To 20 ft (6.1 m) And, Common Paths Limited To 75 ft (23 m).

←——→ Dead End
— — → Common Path

Figure 11-2. Arrangement of Means of Egress in Accordance with 11-2.5.1.

Prior to the 1991 Edition, Chapter 11 did not establish a maximum common path of travel but set a maximum room size with one door and limited dead-end corridors. Currently, however, the *Code* does limit common path in addition to setting a maximum room size served by one door. This approach better reflects the *Code's* intent.

A school plan with outside doors or stairways at both ends of a central corridor meets the dead-end requirement. Small pockets may be created where stairways are not located at the end of corridors but are located at intermediate points. (*See Figure 11-2.*)

(*See 5-2.1.4.1 and 5-2.1.4.2 for information on direction of door swing.*)

11-2.5.2 Every room that is normally occupied shall have an exit access door leading directly to an exit access corridor or exit.

Exception No. 1: If there is an exit door opening directly to the outside or to an exterior balcony or corridor as described in 11-2.5.6.

Exception No. 2: One room may intervene between a normally occupied student room and an exit access corridor provided:

(1) The total travel from a room served by an intervening room and the corridor door or exit shall not exceed 75 ft (23 m), and

(2) Clothing, personal effects, or other materials deemed hazardous by the authority having jurisdiction shall be stored in metal lockers provided they do not obstruct the exit access, or the intervening room shall be sprinklered in accordance with Section 7-7, and either

(3) The intervening room shall have approved fire detection installed that will activate the building alarm, or

(4) The building shall be protected by an approved automatic sprinkler system installed in accordance with Section 7-7.

Exception No. 3: Previously approved arrangements may continue to be used with the approval of the authority having jurisdiction.

To ensure the integrity of the exit access portion within the means of egress, Chapter 11 requires most normally occupied rooms to have a door open directly into an exit access corridor. This is intended to avoid the need for occupants to pass through intervening rooms, which may not be arranged or maintained in a fashion to permit the orderly evacuation of an occupied space.

Exempted from the base requirement are normally occupied rooms that have doors opening directly to the outside at grade or to an exterior exit access balcony. Also exempted are normally occupied rooms having only one intervening room in which:

1. Travel distance through the intervening room to the corridor door is limited to 75 ft (23 m), and
2. Personal effects such as coats and other belongings or other contents deemed hazardous by the authority having jurisdiction are kept in metal lockers or the intervening room is sprinklered, and
3. Either the intervening room is supplied with fire detectors connected to the building alarm system, or the entire building is protected throughout by an approved automatic sprinkler system.

It is the *Code's* intent that, when one chooses to place personal belongings in metal lockers along with choosing the intervening room fire detection option, smoke

detectors would be the form of detection selected to provide for rapid occupant notification. However, one has the option of selecting heat detectors if nuisance alarms are anticipated (i.e., automotive or wood shops with attached classrooms).

Exception No. 3 would permit the existence of a previously approved configuration subject to approval by the authority having jurisdiction that the arrangement permits an adequate level of life safety.

Figures 11-3a and 11-3b represent several possible intervening room configurations that comply with the *Code.*

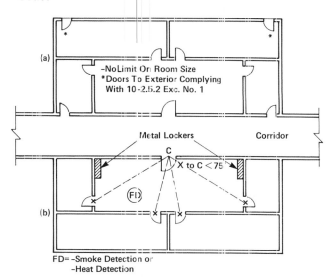

FD= –Smoke Detection or
–Heat Detection

Figure 11-3a. Room Arrangements Complying with 11-2.5.2, Including Exception No. 1. Configuration (a) has no limit on size other than satisfying the arrangement and travel distance provisions of 11-2.5. Each "normally occupied" room has a door opening either directly to the corridor or to the exterior (opening at grade or to an exterior exit access balcony) as permitted by Exception No. 1 to 11-2.5.2. Configuration (b) is permitted as long as travel distance from the normally occupied rooms to the corridor (x to c) is limited to 75 ft (23 m) and clothing and other personal effects in the intervening room are stored in metal lockers along with a fire detection system designed to provide occupant notification (preferably smoke detection for earliest possible notification).

11-2.5.3   Every room or space with a capacity of more than 50 persons or more than 1,000 sq ft (93 sq m) in area shall have at least two doorways as remotely located from each other as practicable. Such doorways shall provide access to separate exits, but where egress is through corridors, they shall

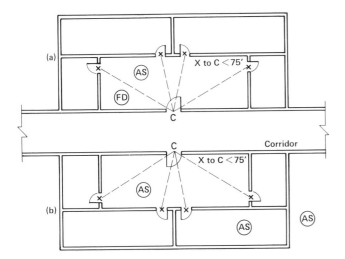

Figure 11-3b. Room Arrangements Complying with 11-2.5.2 Exception No. 2. Configurations (a) and (b) represent acceptable intervening room arrangements. Configuration (a) illustrates limited travel distance from x to c along with the intervening room sprinkler system permitted by Exception No. 2 (2) to 11-2.5.2 and the intervening room fire detection system as selected by Exception No. 2 (3). Configuration (b) represents a building protected throughout by an approved automatic sprinkler system satisfying both parts (2) and (4) of Exception No. 2. In effect, even the installation of an approved automatic sprinkler system within the intervening room, connected to the building fire alarm system, would satisfy the language contained in the Exception No. 2 to 11-2.5.2, as automatic sprinklers are considered heat detectors. Hence, this approach would satisfy both parts (2) and (3) to Exception No. 2 to 11-2.5.2.

be permitted to open upon a common corridor leading to separate exits located in opposite directions.

11-2.5.4 Doors that swing into an exit access corridor shall be recessed to prevent interference with corridor traffic; any doors not so recessed shall open 180 degrees to stop against the wall. Doors in any position shall not reduce the required corridor width by more than one-half.

See 5-2.1.4.3 for more information on doors swinging into corridors.

11-2.5.5 **Aisles.** Where there are more than 60 seats, every aisle shall be not less than 3 ft (91 cm) wide where serving seats on one side only and not less than 3 ft 6 in. (107 cm) where serving seats on both sides. Where serving 60 seats or less, aisles shall not be less than 30 in. (76 cm) wide. The space between parallel rows of seats does not constitute an aisle. No

more than six seats shall intervene between any seat and an aisle.

11-2.5.6* **Exterior Corridors or Balconies.**

A-11-2.5.6 A corridor roofed over and enclosed on its long side and open to the atmosphere at the end may be considered an exterior corridor if either:

(a) Clear story openings for the corridor are provided on both sides of the corridor and above adjacent roofs or buildings and such clear openings are not less than one-half the height of the corridor walls, or

(b) The corridor roof has unobstructed openings to the sky not less than 50 percent of the area of the roof.

The openings are to be equally distributed, and if louvers are installed, they are to be fixed open with a clear area based on the actual openings between louver vanes.

See Figures 11-4a and b for examples of A-11-2.5.6.

11-2.5.6.1 Exterior exit access shall comply with 5-5.3.

11-2.5.6.2* Where exterior corridors or balconies are provided as means of egress, they shall open to the outside air except for railings or balustrades with stairs or level exits to grade not over the allowable travel distance apart and so located that an exit will be available in either direction from the door to any individual room or space, with dead ends not to exceed 20 ft (6.1 m). If balconies are enclosed by glass or in any other manner, they shall be treated as interior corridors.

A-11-2.5.6.2 School design providing classroom exits directly to the outside or to exterior balconies open to the outside air with exterior stairways available to either direction to grade is considered preferable, from the firesafety standpoint, to the more conventional design using interior corridors, which can become untenable from the accumulation of smoke and heat.

See Figure 11-5.

11-2.5.6.3 The floors of balconies (exterior corridors) and stairs shall be solid, without openings, and shall comply with requirements for outside stairs with respect to balustrades or railings, width and pitch of stairs, and other details. However, they are not required to be shielded from fire within the building by blank walls, wired glass windows, or the like where the

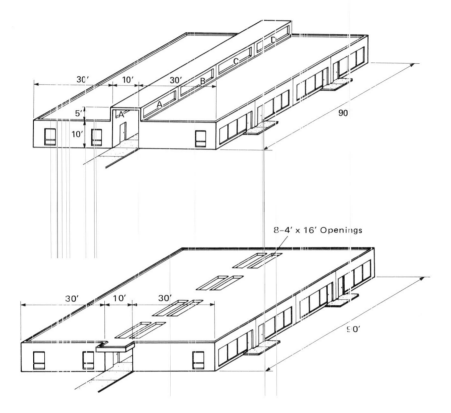

Figure 11-4a (top). Exterior Corridor Using Clear Story Openings. A, B, C, and D are clear story openings. The building height is 10 ft (3 m). The minimum height allowable for the corridor roof must be 5 ft (1.5 m). In this figure, the minimum clear story height requirements have been met.

Figure 11-4b (below). Exterior Corridor Using Roof Openings. The alternative is that the roof have unobstructed openings to the sky that equal not less than 50 percent of the corridor roof. The example has eight openings. Each opening is 4 ft × 16 ft (1.2 m × 4.9 m), or 64 sq ft (5.9 sq m) each. The total square footage of the roof area equals 900 sq ft (84 sq m). The total unobstructed opening equals 512 sq ft (48 sq m) (greater than 50 percent of the total roof area). This would be an acceptable design.

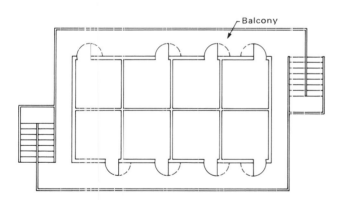

Figure 11-5. Stair Placement, Exterior Balcony. Distance between stairs must not be greater than the allowable travel distance would permit.

stairs are located on the side of the balcony or corridor away from the building and are separated from the building by the full required width of the balcony or corridor. Regardless of other provisions, exterior balconies and stairs shall be permitted to be of the same type of construction as the building that they serve.

Stairs from exterior balconies must not pass or come close to windows or other openings in stories below. Preferable stair placements complying with 11-2.5.6.1, 11-2.5.6.2, 11-2.5.6.3, and 5-5.3 are illustrated in Figures 11-6 and 11-7.

11-2.6 Travel Distance to Exits. Travel distance to an exit shall not exceed 150 ft (45 m) from any point in a building. (See also Section 5-6.)

Exception No. 1: Travel distance shall not exceed 200 ft (60 m) in educational occupancies protected throughout by an approved automatic sprinkler system installed in accordance with Section 7-7.

Exception No. 2: Previously approved travel distances.

The Committee recognizes that there are existing educational occupancies that may have travel distances that have been previously approved by the authority having jurisdiction.

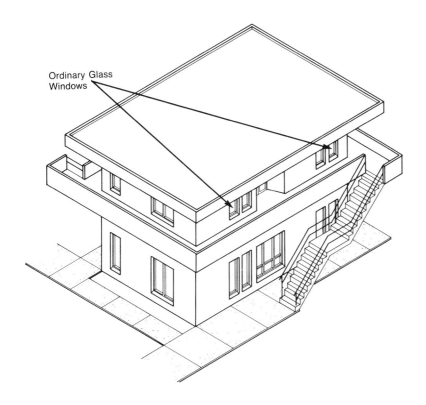

Ordinary Glass
Windows

Figure 11-6. *Stair Placement, Exterior Balcony. Since stairs are separated from the building by the full width of the balcony, blank walls or wired glass windows are not required near the stairs.*

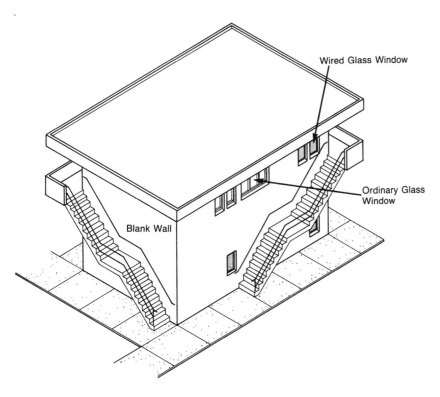

Wired Glass Window

Ordinary Glass
Window

Blank Wall

Figure 11-7. *Stair Placement, Exterior Balcony. The stair placed directly against the building must not pass near unprotected openings. (See 5-2.2 for protection requirements on outside stairs.)*

11-2.7 **Discharge from Exits.** Discharge from exits shall be arranged in accordance with Section 5-7.

Exception: Every classroom or room used for educational purposes or student occupancy below the floor of exit discharge shall have access to at least one exit that leads directly to the exterior at level of discharge without entering the floor above.

The exception is a slight relaxation of the requirement in Section 5-7 in that the exception requires at least one exit to discharge directly to the outside, while 5-7.2 requires 50 percent of the exits to discharge directly outside. Figures 11-8 and 11-9 illustrate two types of exits that will satisfy the requirements of the Exception to 11-2.7. The enclosed stair in Figure 11-9 may serve other floors if it meets all the requirements of Chapter 5.

11-2.8 **Illumination of Means of Egress.** Means of egress shall be illuminated in accordance with Section 5-8.

11-2.9 **Emergency Lighting.** Emergency lighting shall be provided in accordance with Section 5-9 in the following areas:

(a) In all interior stairs and corridors.
(b) In all normally occupied spaces.

Exception to (b):
1. *Administrative areas.*
2.* *General classrooms.*

A-11-2.9(b) **Exception to (b)2.** This does not exempt shops and laboratories.

3. *Mechanical rooms and storage areas.*

(c) In flexible and open plan buildings.
(d) In all interior or windowless portions of buildings.

The Exceptions to 11-2.9(b) indicate that normal classrooms, offices, and storage or mechanical spaces do not require emergency lighting. Shops, laboratories, and assembly rooms would require emergency lighting as would portions of the building that are interior or windowless. (*See Figure 11-10.*)

11-2.10 **Marking of Means of Egress.** Means of egress shall have signs in accordance with Section 5-10.

Exception: Signs are not required in situations where locations of exits are otherwise obvious and familiar to all occupants, such as in small elementary school buildings.

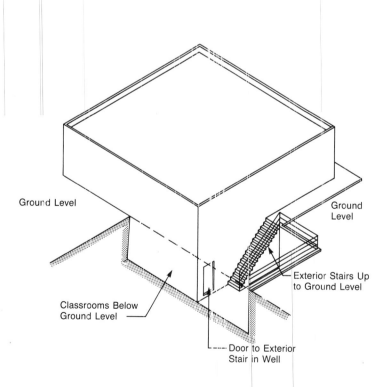

Figure 11-8. Exit from Classroom Below Floor of Exit Discharge.

Ground Level

Ground Level

Exterior Stairs Up to Ground Level

Classrooms Below Ground Level

Door to Exterior Stair in Well

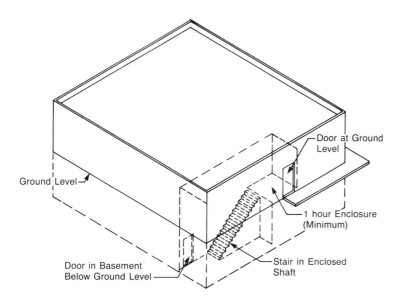

Figure 11-9. Exit from Class-room Below Floor of Exit Discharge. The enclosed stair could be located on the outside of the building.

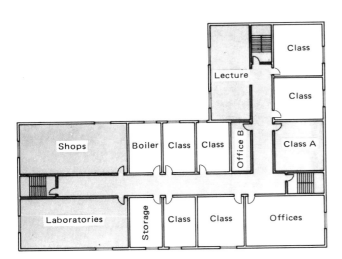

Figure 11-10. Areas that Require and Do Not Require Emergency Lighting. Shaded areas indicate where emergency lighting is required. Classroom A and Office B are windowless; therefore, 11-2.9(d) overrides the Exception to 11-2.9(b). Laboratories, shops, and lecture halls do not qualify as general classrooms.

11-2.11 Special Features.

11-2.11.1* Windows for Rescue and Ventilation.
Every room or space greater than 250 sq ft (23.2 sq m) used for classroom or other educational purposes or normally subject to student occupancy shall have at least one outside window for emergency rescue or ventilation. Such window shall be openable from the inside without the use of tools and shall provide a clear opening of not less than 20 in. (50.8 cm) in width, 24 in. (61 cm) in height, and 5.7 sq ft (.53 sq m) in area. The bottom of the opening shall be not more than 44 in. (112 cm) above the floor.

Exception No. 1: In buildings protected throughout by an approved automatic sprinkler system in accordance with Section 7-7.

Exception No. 2: Where the room or space has a door leading directly to the outside of the building.

Exception No. 3: In rooms located higher than three stories above grade, the openable clear height, width, and area of the window may be modified to the dimensions necessary for ventilation.

Exception No. 4: Awning or hopper type windows that are hinged or subdivided to provide a clear opening not less than 600 sq in. (0.39 sq m) in area nor any dimension less than 22 in. (55.9 cm) shall be permitted to be continued in use. Screen walls or devices in front of required windows shall not interfere with normal rescue requirements.

Exception No. 5: Where the room or space complies with the following:

(a) Doors exist that allow travel between adjacent classrooms and, when used to travel from classroom to classroom, provide direct access to exits in both directions or direct access to an exit in one direction and to a separate smoke compartment that provides access to another exit in the other direction, and

(b) The corridor is separated from the classrooms by a wall that resists the passage of smoke, and all doors between the classrooms and the corridor are self-closing or automatic-closing in accordance with 5-2.1.8, and

(c) The length of travel to exits along such paths shall not exceed 150 ft (45 m), and

(d) Each communicating door shall be marked in accordance with Section 5-10, and

(e) No locking device shall be allowed on the communicating doors.

A-11-2.11.1   It is highly desirable to have all windows of a type that can be readily opened from inside and to have them large enough and low enough for use by students, teachers, and fire fighters. Windows may serve as a supplementary means of emergency escape, particularly where ladders can be raised by fire fighters or others. Even where the location is such as to preclude the use of windows for escape purposes, they may provide air for breathing in a smoke-filled room while trapped occupants are awaiting rescue.

The 1991 Edition has been amended to exclude smaller rooms [those less than 250 sq ft (23 m)] such as those used for music instruction and student counseling, as they are subject to occupancy by very few children.

The dimensions specified for windows used for emergency rescue or for ventilation are based on simulations of emergency rescue conducted by the San Diego Fire Department. Windows providing clear openings of identical dimensions are also required for rescue or ventilation in one- and two-family dwellings. Figures 11-11a and b illustrate two configurations that achieve the required area of 5.7 sq ft (.53 sq m). Figure 11-11b illustrates Exception No. 3.

Although the *Code* intends the fire department or others to assist students, particularly over ladders, if these windows must be used as a supplementary means of escape, the windows should permit small children in the

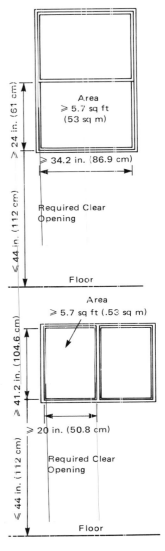

Figure 11-11a. *Windows for Rescue or Ventilation, Minimum Required Dimensions.*

lower grades to escape unaided. Therefore, storm sashes, screens, or devices in front of the windows must be easy to open or remove, and the sills must be low enough for children to reach.

The *Code* also ensures that the windows will be accessible to the fire department and that children, once they escape from the window, will have access to a public way.

Windows may be omitted if a classroom has a door leading directly to the outside or if the building is totally sprinklered.

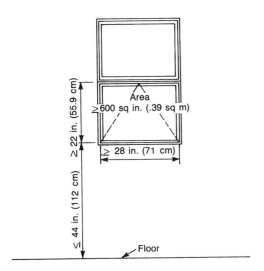

Figure 11-11b. Windows for Ventilation (Awning or Hopper-type), Minimum Dimensions.

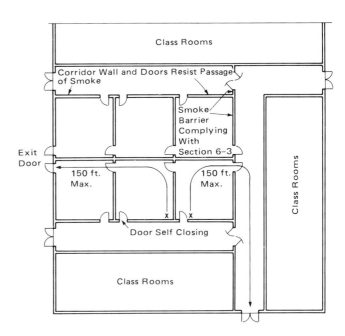

Figure 11-12. One Method of Compensating for a Windowless Classroom in an Existing Building.

Note that Exception No. 1 requires that the building be protected throughout by an automatic sprinkler system. One question often asked is: If there are only a couple of windowless classrooms, can sprinklering be limited to those rooms only? The answer is no! The purpose of the window is to provide ventilation or means of escape when the interior corridor is blocked by smoke from a fire in another part of the building. Installing sprinklers in the windowless rooms only would do nothing to provide protection from smoke emanating from other areas.

In Exception No. 3, the Committee did not believe it was practical to expect a window above the third story to be used as an escape window. However, it is reasonable to expect the window to be used for ventilation during a fire.

Exception No. 4 is provided in acknowledgment of a feature that was formerly recognized by the *Code*. Although the Committee felt that it should no longer be allowed in new construction, it can continue to be permitted in existing facilities.

Exception No. 5 was new to the 1988 Edition and is allowed only in existing buildings. It recognizes a concept that was alluded to in older editions of the *Code* for the purpose of solving egress problems but was never detailed specifically in the *Code*. Figure 11-12 illustrates how Exception No. 4 can be used.

SECTION 11-3 Protection

11-3.1 Protection of Vertical Openings.

11-3.1.1 Any vertical opening shall be enclosed and protected in accordance with Section 6-2.

Exception No. 1: In buildings protected throughout by an approved supervised automatic sprinkler system installed in accordance with Section 7-7, unprotected vertical openings connecting not more than three floors shall be permitted in accordance with 6-2.4.5.

Exception No. 2: Atriums in accordance with 6-2.4.6 shall be permitted.

Exception No. 3: Stairway enclosure shall not be required for a stairway serving only one adjacent floor except a basement. Such stairways shall not be connected with stairways serving other floors nor with corridors serving other than the two floors involved.

Chapter 11 requires all vertical openings with the exception of the 6-2.4.5 open and unobstructed "mini-atrium" opening connecting three floors or less, the 6-2.4.6 atrium, or what is commonly referred to as a "convenience stair" to be enclosed in accordance with Section 6-2. This "convenience stair" may be useful, especially for libraries or offices within schools. Basements are excluded because basements usually contain hazardous areas with high fuel loads, such as storage rooms, boiler rooms, or workshops. However, the "convenience stair" exception in Chapter 11 is different, since it allows a two-story school building to have open egress stairs between the first and second floor. This is not permitted by Chapter 10. While not specified in 6-2.4.5, Exception No. 1 to 11-3.1.1 requires a building to be fully sprinklered in order to use the "mini-atrium" exception.

11-3.2   **Protection from Hazards.**

11-3.2.1   Rooms or spaces used for the storage, processing, or use of the materials specified in this section shall be protected in accordance with the following:

(a) Rooms or spaces used for the storage of combustible supplies in quantities deemed hazardous by the authority having jurisdiction, hazardous materials in quantities deemed hazardous by recognized standards, or fuel shall be separated from the remainder of the building by construction having not less than a 1-hour fire resistance rating with all openings protected by self-closing or smoke-actuated fire doors, or such rooms or spaces shall be protected by an automatic extinguishing system as required in Section 6-4.

(b) Rooms or spaces used for processing or use of combustible supplies in quantities considered hazardous by the authority having jurisdiction, hazardous materials, or for flammable or combustible liquids in quantities deemed hazardous by recognized standards shall be separated from the remainder of the building by construction having not less than a 1-hour fire resistance rating with all openings protected by self-closing or smoke-actuated fire doors and shall also be protected by an automatic extinguishing system as required in Section 6-4.

(c) Boiler and furnace rooms, laundries, and maintenance shops, including woodworking and painting areas, shall be separated from the remainder of the building by construction hav-

ing not less than a 1-hour fire resistance rating with all openings protected by self-closing or smoke-actuated fire doors, or such areas shall be protected throughout by an approved automatic sprinkler system in accordance with Section 7-7.

Exception to (c): Rooms enclosing air-handling equipment.

(d)* Where automatic extinguishing systems are used to meet the requirements of this section, the rooms or spaces shall be separated from the remainder of the building by construction that resists the passage of smoke.

A-11-3.2.1(d)   It is not the intent of this provision to require a smoke barrier that meets the requirements of Section 6-3.

(e) Where automatic extinguishing is used to meet the requirements of this section, the protection shall be permitted to be in accordance with 7-7.1.2.

The intent of 11-3.2.1 is to specify the degree of protection necessary for certain hazardous areas. It has been divided into three sections based on the degree of hazard. The hazards noted in parts (a) and (c) are required to be enclosed in 1-hour construction or protected by sprinklers. If the sprinkler option is chosen, an enclosure is still required by part (d); however, the enclosure need not be rated but needs only to form a membrane against the passage of smoke.

The Committee reasoned that, although sprinklers are provided and fire-rated barriers may not be needed, some barrier to control smoke migration is needed. Solid construction materials, such as glass or other non-fire-rated materials, are acceptable if they are installed in a manner that will resist smoke passing from one compartment to another. The appendix note emphasizes that it is not the intent to require smoke barriers as provided in Section 6-3. This eliminates the more costly construction of a smoke barrier, which would require dampers and other required equipment.

Art rooms and some shops need special attention. Potentially dangerous operations involving flammable materials, specialized ovens, and ignition sources in these areas are becoming more prevalent and create increased hazards to the entire facility. It may be advisable at the high school level to include these rooms as hazardous spaces.

The hazards noted in part (b) must be enclosed in 1-hour construction and be protected by automatic sprinklers.

The Exception to part (c) pertains to rooms housing air-handling equipment only. If the room is used for other purposes, then the provisions of part (a) or (b) apply.

Part (e) is intended to highlight the fact that Chapter 7 makes these requirements available to the user of the *Code*. Paragraph 7-7.1.2 provides an economical way of providing sprinkler protection in small rooms. (*See 11-3.2.3.*)

Figure 11-13 illustrates the various protection requirements of 11-3.2.1.

11-3.2.2 Food preparation facilities shall be protected in accordance with 7-2.3 and are not required to have openings protected between food preparation areas and dining areas.

Openings in the wall between kitchens and dining areas are not restricted and do not need to be protected. The *Code* relies upon the provision of the automatic extinguishing system to control any fire on the cooking surfaces and, thus, does not require openings between the kitchen and dining areas to be protected.

11-3.2.3 Janitor closets shall be protected by an automatic sprinkler system, which shall be permitted to be in accordance with 7-7.1.2. Doors to janitor closets shall be permitted to have ventilating louvers.

Where janitor closets are located off of corridors, a louvered door is usually provided for ventilation. It is necessary to provide these spaces with automatic sprinkler protection, since the louvered door offers little fire resistance and permits a fire in the closet to directly affect the corridor. Paragraph 7-7.1.2 contains an economic method of providing sprinkler protection for such closets. To achieve this protection at reasonable cost, these sprinklers (not more than six in number) may be supplied from the domestic water supply if the supply is capable of providing the required quantity of water. It is advisable to provide a water-flow switch (*see Chapter 7*) to initiate an alarm when a sprinkler is opened.

The minimum flow of 0.15 gpm/sq ft (6.1 L/min/sq m) is based on the requirements of NFPA 13, *Standard for the Installation of Sprinkler Systems*,[1] for protecting buildings containing ordinary hazards. It is important to ensure that the domestic water supply can provide the required flow and pressure at the location.

11-3.2.4 Laboratories that use chemicals shall comply with NFPA 45, *Standard on Fire Protection for Laboratories Using Chemicals.*

11-3.2.5 Stages shall be protected in accordance with Chapter 9.

11-3.3 Interior Finish.

11-3.3.1 Interior finish, in accordance with Section 6-5, shall be as follows:

(a) Exits — Class A.
(b) Corridors and lobbies — Class A or B.

Exception to (b): Fixtures and low-height partitions not over 5 ft (152 cm) in height shall be Class A, B, or C.

(c) All other locations — Class A, B, or C.

Exception: *The exposed portions of structural members complying with the requirements for Type IV (2HH) construction shall be permitted.*

A-11-3.3.1 Exception. NFPA 220, *Standard on Types of Building Construction (see Appendix B)*, defines Type IV (2HH) construction. (*Also see A-6-2.1.*)

Section 6-5 permits the use of fire retardant or intumescent paints and surface coatings to reduce the surface flame spread of an interior finish. These coatings will not render a finish noncombustible; they will simply delay the eventual ignition of a finish exposed to fire.

Some coatings have a short life and require frequent reapplication. Over the life of a building, all coatings may eventually have to be renewed. Also, some coatings will

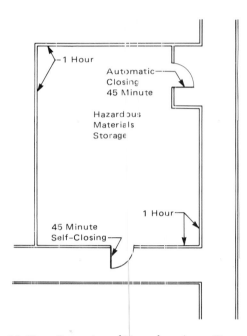

Figure 11-13a.   Protection of Hazardous Areas. Figure 11-13a illustrates one method of complying with 11-3.2.1(a). [See Figure 11-13b for the alternate method.]

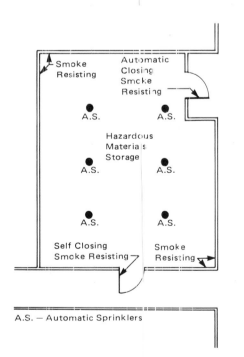

Figure 11-13b.   Protection of Hazardous Areas. Figure 11-13b illustrates an alternate method of complying with 11-3.2.1(a). Figure 11-13a illustrates another method of compliance.

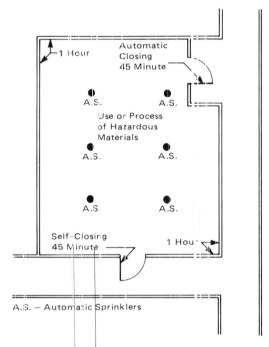

Figure 11-13c.   Protection of Hazardous Areas. Figure 11-13c illustrates the requirements for complying with 11-3.2.1(b). Both 1-hour separation and automatic sprinkler protection are required in this case.

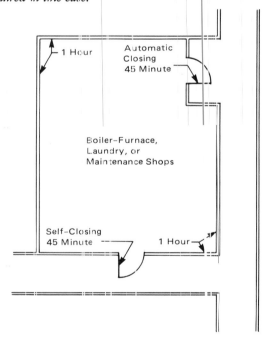

Figure 11-13d.   Protection of Hazardous Areas. Figure 11-13d illustrates the requirements to comply with 11-3.2.1(c). However, in existing buildings, boilers rooms, furnace rooms, and similar areas may use the sprinkler option as illustrated in Figure 11-13b.

severely mar or alter the appearance of the finish. Due to these liabilities, the option of using coatings and paints may not provide the best fire protection at a reasonable cost in all cases.

Sections 31-1 and 31-3 establish limitations on decorations and student artwork on walls.

11-3.3.2 Interior Floor Finish. No requirements.

11-3.4 Detection, Alarm, and Communication Systems.

11-3.4.1 General. Educational occupancies shall be provided with a fire alarm system in accordance with Section 7-6.

11-3.4.2 Initiation.

11-3.4.2.1 Initiation of the required fire alarm system shall be by manual means in accordance with 7-6.2.1(a).

Exception: In buildings where all normally occupied spaces are provided with a two-way communication system between such spaces and a constantly attended receiving station from where a general evacuation alarm can be sounded, the manual pull stations are not required except in locations specifically designated by the authority having jurisdiction.

The Exception to 11-3.4.2.1 is intended to give local authorities the ability to deal with the false alarm and vandalism problems present in today's schools. Where there is a two-way communication system between classrooms and a continuously attended location where a general alarm can be sounded, the need for pull stations is obviated. To qualify to use this exception, the authority having jurisdiction must agree on which pull stations can be omitted. For the purposes of this provision, the "continuously attended" location means a location attended while the school building is in use as a school. This may involve providing personnel at this location during night school, when the regular school office staff is not present.

11-3.4.2.2 In buildings provided with automatic sprinkler protection, the operation of the sprinkler system shall automatically activate the fire alarm system in addition to the initiation means required above.

11-3.4.3 Notification.

11-3.4.3.1 Occupant notification shall be by means of an audible alarm in accordance with 7-6.3.

11-3.4.3.2 Where acceptable to the authority having jurisdiction, the fire alarm system may be used to designate class change provided that the fire alarm is distinctive in signal and overrides all other use.

11-3.5 Extinguishment Requirements.

11-3.5.1 Wherever student occupancy occurs below the story of exit discharge, every portion of such floor shall be protected throughout by an approved automatic sprinkler system in accordance with Section 7-7. Where student occupancy does not occur on floors below the story of exit discharge, such floors shall be separated from the rest of the building by 1-hour fire resistance rated construction or shall be protected throughout by an approved automatic sprinkler system in accordance with Section 7-7.

Exception: Where student occupancy occurs below the story of exit discharge, automatic sprinkler protection is not required, subject to the approval of the authority having jurisdiction, if windows for rescue and ventilation are provided in accordance with 11-2.11.1.

Stories below the stories of exit discharge are not necessarily below grade (*see Figure 11-14*) This paragraph differs from that in Chapter 10 in that it allows an option for stories not occupied by students to be separated by 1-hour fire resistance rated construction or to be sprinklered.

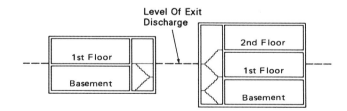

Figure 11-14. Protection for Stories Below the Stories of Exit Discharge. The arrangement on the left illustrates a simple example where only the basement is required to be sprinklered or separated. The diagram on the right illustrates a case where the level of exit discharge is between floors and requires that the story of exit discharge be determined using the definition in 11-1.3. If the 1st floor is, in fact, the story of exit discharge, only the basement is required to be sprinklered or separated.

If students occupy the floor, then it must be sprinklered. This option was first introduced in the 1985 *Code*.

11-3.6 Interior Corridors.

11-3.6.1 Every interior corridor shall be constructed of fire barriers having not less than a 20-minute fire resistance rating in accordance with 6-2.3. Corridors shall comply with 6-2.2.2.

Exception No. 1: Such corridor protection shall not be required where all spaces normally subject to student occupancy have at least one door opening directly to the outside or to an exterior exit access balcony or corridor in accordance with 11-2.5.6.

Exception No. 2: In buildings protected throughout by an approved automatic sprinkler system with valve supervision installed in accordance with Section 7-7, corridor walls are not required to be rated provided such walls in conjunction with openings therein and ceilings at which they terminate resist the passage of smoke.

Exception No. 3: Existing doors may be 1¾-in. (4.4-cm) thick solid bonded wood core doors or the equivalent.

Exception No. 4: Lavatories need not be separated from corridors provided they are separated from all other spaces by fire barriers having a 20-minute fire resistance rating in accordance with 6-2.3.

The intent of specifying 20-minute walls is to recognize that a lath and plaster wall maintained in good condition will provide approximately 20 minutes of fire resistance.

Exception No. 2 allows the wall to terminate at the ceiling as long as the ceiling resists the passage of smoke, given the protection of an approved supervised sprinkler system throughout the building. Although doors in fire-rated partitions are required to be self-closing or automatic-closing, which causes significant operation and maintenance problems in schools, this exception would allow the omission of door closures on doors other than those required to be self-closing for other reasons, such as stair doors. This recognizes the teacher's/administrator's ability to close doors upon evacuation, thus maintaining the assembly's smoke resisting capability.

It is important that this wall (non-rated) and the ceiling together resist the passage of smoke, but it is not intended that they meet all the requirements of Section 6-3 for smoke barriers.

Recognizing the typically low fuel loads associated with lavatories in addition to the need to provide door louvers for ventilation, Exception No. 4 exempts the wall separating the lavatory from the corridor from the 1-hour rating requirement as long as the continuity of the rated corridor wall is maintained around the lavatory.

11-3.6.2 Clothing and personal effects shall not be stored in corridors and lobbies.

Racks of clothing and personal effects create two specific problems. The first problem relates to the large amount of combustibles in the means of egress. Fires in clothing racks in corridors will seriously hamper safe evacuation from the area served by the corridor. This problem should not be underestimated. Two recent fires, one in New York (Stouffers Hotel) and one in Massachusetts (Lexington), dramatically demonstrated the tremendous fire load posed by clothing on open coatracks. The second problem is created where the minimum acceptable width of the corridor is reduced.

Exception: Metal lockers shall be permitted in corridors for storage of clothing and personal effects provided the corridor width is maintained.

The first problem stated above can be corrected by providing metal lockers for storage of clothing and personal effects. This reduces accessibility of the combustibles to arsonists and also compartmentalizes the combustibles. Most fires in school lockers do not extend beyond the locker of origin. Those that do extend do not usually extend beyond the locker(s) adjacent to the locker of origin. However, the corridor must be of such width that it will allow at least the minimum required corridor width to be maintained after the lockers are installed.

11-3.7 Subdivision of Building Spaces.

11-3.7.1 School buildings shall be subdivided into compartments by smoke barriers complying with Section 6-3 where:

(a) The maximum area of a compartment, including the aggregate area of all floors having a common atmosphere, exceeds 30,000 sq ft (2,800 sq m); or

(b) Where the length or width of the building exceeds 300 ft (91 m).

Exception No. 1: Where all classrooms have exterior exit access in accordance with 5-5.3.

Exception No. 2: Buildings protected throughout by an approved automatic sprinkler system in accordance with Section 7-7.

The 300-ft (91-m) limit bears a direct relationship to the travel distance criteria in Chapter 11 and reflects the Committee's concern regarding the maximum area within an educational facility that would be immediately contaminated by products of combustion from a fire.

The Committee felt it was reasonable and prudent to require smoke barriers at maximum intervals of 300 ft (91 m) so that the products of combustion would affect a limited number of exits at one time.

The provisions of this section were changed in the 1985 Edition of the *Code* to make the provisions easier to understand and enforce. Previous editions spaced smoke barriers by corridor length. By spacing barriers according to compartment size, the intent of the provision is clarified, and confusion in enforcement is reduced.

A primary concern of the Committee is a situation where a corridor becomes clogged with smoke resulting in the elimination of exit access. Spaces normally subject to student occupancy with exterior exit access provide the occupants a ready alternate means of escape in the event that a corridor fills with smoke.

The Committee believed that the record of automatic fire sprinklers was a good reason to reduce the compartmentation requirements.

11-3.7.2 The maximum area of a smoke compartment shall not exceed 30,000 sq ft (2,800 sq m) with no dimension exceeding 300 ft (91 m).

This provision applies only if 11-3.7.1 applies. If an exception to 11-3.7.1 applies, then 11-3.7.2 does not apply.

11-3.7.3 Doors in such barriers shall be self-latching.

SECTION 11-4 Special Provisions

11-4.1 **Windowless or Underground Buildings.** Windowless buildings and underground structures shall comply with Section 30-7.

The Committee believes that Section 30-7 provides adequate provisions for existing windowless or underground buildings.

11-4.2 **High Rise Buildings.** (Reserved.)

11-4.3 **Flexible Plan and Open Plan Buildings.**

The 1985 Edition of the *Code* contained a major revision of the provisions pertaining to flexible and open plan schools. The intent of the revision was to make the *Code* easier to use while improving life safety in the special arrangements. This section requires that flexible and open plan schools comply with Sections 11-1 through 11-5, except as modified by this section.

11-4.3.1 Flexible and open plan buildings shall comply with the requirements of this chapter and 11-4.3.2 through 11-4.3.4.

11-4.3.2 Each room occupied by more than 300 persons shall have two or more means of egress entering into separate atmospheres. Where three or more means of egress are required, not more than two of them shall enter into the same atmosphere.

Rooms occupied by more than 300 persons require special treatment in flexible and open plan schools. To ensure the safety of this great a number of persons contained in one room, means of egress must be arranged so that each of the separate egress paths traverse separate atmospheres from each other. If more than two separate means of egress paths are required, no more than two shall pass through the same atmosphere. By this arrangement, one fire cannot contaminate or block all exits in an open plan or flexible plan building. (*See Figure 11-15.*)

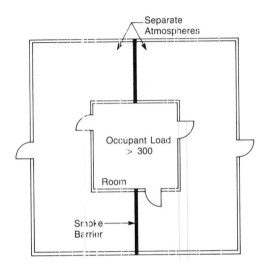

Figure 11-15. Example of Room in Open Plan Building Requiring Two or More Means of Egress into Separate Atmospheres.

11-4.3.3 Flexible plan schools may have walls and partitions rearranged periodically only if revised plans or diagrams have been approved by the authority having jurisdiction.

Approval of revised plans or diagrams is necessary to avoid the possibility of circuitous exit paths or other arrangements that do not comply with the intent of the *Code*. Also note that flexible plan buildings are required to meet the requirements for corridor protection as well as subdivision of building spaces.

11-4.3.4 Flexible plan buildings shall be evaluated while all folding walls are extended and in use as well as when they are in the retracted position.

11-4.4 Operating Features. (*See Chapter 31.*)

SECTION 11-5   Building Services

11-5.1 Utilities. Utilities shall comply with the provisions of Section 7-1.

11-5.2 Heating, Ventilating, and Air Conditioning Equipment.

11-5.2.1 Heating, ventilating, and air conditioning equipment shall comply with the provisions of Section 7-2.

11-5.2.2 Unvented fuel-fired heating equipment shall be prohibited.

The Committee did not believe it was in the interest of reasonable life safety to have unvented fuel-fired equipment in a school building occupied by children. It was believed that the typical use of unvented equipment would jeopardize the life safety of the students, because proper venting may not be provided and potential misuse by students or injury to students, especially younger children, may occur.

11-5.3 Elevators, Escalators, and Conveyors. Elevators, escalators, and conveyors shall comply with the provisions of Section 7-4.

11-5.4 Rubbish Chutes, Incinerators, and Laundry Chutes. Rubbish chutes, incinerators, and laundry chutes shall comply with the provisions of Section 7-5.

SECTION 11-6   (Reserved)

SECTION 11-7   Day-Care Centers

The day-care provisions are arranged to stand on their own, independent of the rest of the chapter. The provisions of Sections 11-2 through 11-5 do not apply unless specifically referenced. The provisions include adult day-care. Throughout the sections, the term "child" has been changed to "client" so that the provisions cover the entire age spectrum. Of course, in certain instances, provisions apply only to children; in those cases, the text has retained the term "child."

Day-care properties averaged 500 structure fires a year reported to U.S. fire departments in 1984-88, with an associated 5 civilian injuries a year and no deaths. These figures apply to day child-care centers and probably miss the many sites where day care is provided at someone's home. These sites are indistinguishable from other homes in the fire incident data.

In homes in general, preschool children constitute a high-risk group, averaging more than twice as many fire deaths relative to population as all other age groups combined. The leading cause of these fire deaths is fireplay by children, although the victims are often not the same children who start the fires. Preschool children are also at elevated risk from most other causes.

Formal Interpretation 76-108
Reference: 10-7 (11-7), 10-8 (11-8), 10-9 (11-9)

Question 1: Do the requirements of Sections 10-7 (11-7), 10-8 (11-8), or 10-9 (11-9) apply to church programs that provide day-care services to church members only, on a nonprofit basis?

Answer: Yes.

Question 2: Are churches also required to meet the provisions of Sections 10-7 (11-7), 10-8 (11-8), or 10-9 (11-9) in order to operate a church nursery while church services are being held?

Answer: Yes.

Question 3: Does Section 1-6 permit the city to grant an exception in these cases?

Answer: The authority having jurisdiction is given the power to grant exceptions where it is clearly evident that reasonable safety is thereby secured.

Issue Edition: 1976
Reference: 9-5.3, 9-5.4, 9-5.5
Date: March 1979 ■

Table 11-1 summarizes the *Code's* requirements for the three types of day-care centers.

11-7.1 General Requirements.

11-7.1.1 Application.

11-7.1.1.1* The requirements detailed in Section 11-7, "Day-Care Centers" (more than 12 clients), are based on the minimum staff-to-client ratios that follow:

Staff Ratio	Age
1:3	0 to 2
1:5	2 to 3
1:10	3 to 5
1:12	5 to 7
1:15	7 and over

The staff-to-client ratios may be modified by the authority having jurisdiction where safeguards in addition to those specified by this section are provided.

A-11-7.1.1.1 It should be noted that this paragraph does not require the staff ratios indicated but only states that the requirements of this section are based on these staff ratios. If these staff ratios are not maintained, it would be the responsibility of the authority having jurisdiction to determine what additional safeguards above and beyond the requirements of this section would be necessary. Typical additional provisions may include restricting the day-care center to the level of exit discharge, requiring additional smoke detection, requiring automatic sprinkler protection, requiring better or additional means of egress, and similar types of items depending upon the situation.

11-7.1.1.2* This section establishes life safety requirements for day-care centers in which more than 12 clients receive care, maintenance, and supervision by other than their relative(s) or legal guardian(s) for less than 24 hours per day. The provisions of Sections 11-2 through 11-6 shall not apply to this section unless a specific requirement is referenced by this section.

A-11-7.1.1.2 Day-care centers do not provide for the full-time maintenance of a client. Occupancies that provide a primary place of residence are dealt with in other occupancies. (*See Chapters 16 through 22, "Residential Occupancies."*)

The intent of 11-7.1.1.2 is to differentiate between institutions where clients are in residence 24 hours a day (such as orphanages) and day-care facilities where clients who normally reside at another location are provided care. A facility supplying "total care" for each client would pro-

Table 11-1. Minimum Requirements for Day-Care Centers

	Center		Group Home	Family Home
Number of Clients	> 12		7 to 12	≤6
Number of Clients under Two Years	Any		3	2
Recommended Staff-to-Client Ratio	Age (yrs) <2 2-3 3-5 5-7 >7	Ratio 1:3 1:5 1:10 1:12 1:15	2:12	1:6
Building Construction (permissible height vs. age of clients)	See 11-7.1.6.1		Rec. meet applicable building codes	Rec. meet applicable building codes
Occupant Load Factor	1 person/35 sq ft*		NR	NR
Area of Refuge	If center above fifth floor		NR	NR
Number of Exits	2 remote (see 11-7.2.4)		2 remote (see 11-8.2.4)	2 remote (see 11-9.2.4)
Travel Distance to Exit† (ft)*	100 (from room door) 150 (from any point in a room)		100 (from room door) 150 (from any point in a room)	100 (from room door) 150 (from any point in a room)
Exit Discharge	To outside		At least one directly to outside	At least one directly to outside
Illumination of Means of Egress	Per Section 5-8		Per Section 5-8	Per Section 5-8
Emergency Lighting	Per 11-2.9		NR (See 31-3.5)	NR (See 31-3.6)
Door Latches (closet)	Child opens from inside		Child opens from inside	Child opens from inside
Door Locks (bathroom)	Staff unlocks		Staff unlocks	Staff unlocks
Protection of Vertical Openings	See Section 6-2		See 11-8.2.4 and 11-8.3.1	See 11-9.2.4
Hazard Protection	1-hr enclosure or automatic sprinklers (see 11-7.3.2)		NR	NR
Class of Interior Finish	B (all areas)		B (exits) C (all other spaces)	B (exits) C (all other spaces)
Class of Interior Floor Finish	I or II (corridors and exits)		NR	NR
Alarm System	Manual (direct connection to fire department if >100 clients)		NR	NR
Smoke Detectors	See 11-7.3.4.5		See 11-8.3.4	See 11-9.3.4
Extinguishers	Standpipes if building ≥ 6 stories			
Corridor Protection	Per 11-3.6.1		NR	NR
Electric Equipment	See NFPA 70 (receptacle covers required, Chapter 7)		See NFPA 70 (recaptacle covers required, Chapter 7)	See NFPA 70 (receptacle covers required, Chapter 7)
HVAC	See Chapter 7		See 11-8.5.2	See 11-9.5.2

*Conversion: 1 ft = .3048 m.   NR = No requirement.   †50-ft increase if sprinklered.

vide laundries, dormitories, cafeterias, and other ancillary services not found in a day-care center. The life safety requirements of such a facility would be governed by other occupancy provisions of the *Code*.

11-7.1.1.3 Centers housing children 6 years of age and older shall conform to the requirements for educational occupancies, except as noted herein.

Centers that provide care only for children of school age are required to conform to the requirements for educational occupancies and to the special requirements for such facilities where they are located in buildings of other occupancies.

11-7.1.1.4 Where a facility houses more than one age group, the requirements for the younger group shall apply, unless the area housing the younger group is maintained as a separate fire area.

Exception*: Staff-to-client ratios listed in 11-7.1.1.1 shall be based on the number of clients in each age category.

A-11-7.1.1.4 Exception. An example of this exception is illustrated as follows: A center has 43 children;

3 children under age 2 (1:3)	1 staff
10 children ages 2 to 3 (1:5)	2 staff
30 children ages 3 to 5 (1:10)	3 staff
Total	6 staff

Therefore, the required staff for this center is 6, not 15, which would be required for 43 children on a 1 to 3 staff ratio.

A separate fire area is usually constructed with walls that have a fire resistance rating of 2 hours. Most facilities governed by this chapter will be maintained as separate atmospheres through smoke partitions having a 1-hour fire resistance rating.

It was brought to the Committee's attention that this section has been interpreted by some as applying to staff ratios. The Committee felt that to use the youngest age group to establish staff-to-client ratios for the entire group was too restrictive and did not meet the intent of the Code, and, therefore, the exception and appendix note were added.

11-7.1.2 Mixed Occupancies.

(a) *General.* Where centers are located in a building containing mixed occupancies, the occupancies shall be separated by 1-hour fire barriers constructed in accordance with 6-2.3.

Exception to (a): In assembly occupancies used primarily for worship.

(b) *Centers in Apartment Buildings.*

(1) If the two exit accesses from the center enter the same corridor as the apartment occupancy, the exit accesses shall be separated in the corridor by a smoke barrier having not less than a 1-hour fire resistance rating constructed in accordance with Section 6-3. The smoke barrier shall be so located that it has an exit located on each side.

(2) The door in the smoke barrier shall be not less than 36 in. (91 cm) wide.

Exception to (b)(2): Existing doors not less than 32 in. (81 cm) wide.

Where a center is located in a building housing another occupancy, the operators of the center usually have no control of the safety procedures and precautions practiced outside the center. Paragraph 11-7.1.2 requires additional protection to minimize the clients' exposure to potential hazards outside the center.

The corridor subdivision by smoke barriers in accordance with Section 6-3 when day-care centers are in an apartment building is the same concept as that used in Chapters 12 and 13 for health care facilities. This minimum construction will provide sufficient protection against flame and a good seal against smoke spread. The 20-minute door, coupled with the 1-hour wall, provides a barrier that will either contain a fire within a space for a limited time after it has been evacuated or will prevent a fire from entering an occupied space for a period of time.

11-7.1.3 Special Definitions. (None.)

11-7.1.4 Classification of Occupancy. For the purposes of this section, clients are classified in age groups as follows: clients under 6 years of age and clients 6 years of age and older.

11-7.1.5 Classification of Hazard of Contents. The contents shall be classified as ordinary hazard in accordance with Section 4-2.

11-7.1.6 Minimum Construction Requirements.

11-7.1.6.1 Centers shall not be located above the heights indicated for the types of construction given in Table 11-7.1.6.1. (*See 6-2.1.*)

Table 11-7.1.6.1   Height and Construction Limits

Type of Construction	Age Group	Number of Stories (Stories are counted starting at floor of exit discharge)			
		1	2	3	4 and Over
I (443) I (332) II (222)	0 through 5 6 and older	X X	X X	X X	X X
II (111) III (211) V (111)	0 through 5 6 and older	X X	X† X	N.P. X†	N.P. N.P.
IV (2HH)	0 through 5 6 and older	X X	X† X†	N.P. N.P.	N.P. N.P.
II (000)	0 through 5 6 and older	X X	X† X†	N.P. N.P.	N.P. N.P.
III (200) V (000)	0 through 5 6 and older	X† X	X† X†	N.P. N.P.	N.P. N.P.

X: Permitted construction type
N.P.: Not Permitted
X†: Permitted if entire building is protected throughout by an approved automatic sprinkler system.

11-7.1.6.2 Location. The story below the level of exit discharge shall be permitted to be used in buildings of any construction type other than Type II (000), Type III (200), and Type V (000). (*See 11-7.2.4.2.*)

11-7.1.7 Occupant Load. The occupant load for which means of egress shall be provided for any floor shall be the maximum number of persons intended to occupy that floor but not less than one person for each 35 sq ft (3.3 sq m) of net floor area used by the clients.

Many states require that day-care facilities provide 35 sq ft (3.3 sq m) of net area per child. It is not the intent of this *Code* to affect such a requirement, which is provided for the welfare of the child for purposes other than life safety. Where a center occupies a portion of a floor on which another occupancy exists, the occupant load for that floor is the sum of the occupant loads of the two occupancies. For example:

Net Floor Area (ft²)		Occupant Load Factor (ft²/person)		Occupant Load
Day-Care Center 1,750	÷	35	=	50
Assembly Occupancy 3,000	÷	7	=	429

Using addition, the total occupant load for which means of egress must be provided would be 479. (*Also see commentary on 11-1.7.*)

11-7.2 Means of Egress Requirements.

11-7.2.1 General. Means of egress shall be in accordance with Chapter 5 and this section.

11-7.2.2 Means of Egress Components.

11-7.2.2.1 Components of means of egress shall be limited to the types described in 11-7.2.2.2 through 11-7.2.2.7.

11-7.2.2.2 Doors.

(a) *General.* Doors shall comply with 5-2.1.

(b) *Panic Hardware or Fire Exit Hardware.* Any door in a required means of egress from an area having an occupant load of 100 or more persons may be provided with a latch or lock only if it is panic hardware or fire exit hardware.

This paragraph is based on the total occupant load of the area served and not the required capacity of the door. For example, if an area has an occupant load of 120 persons and is served by 3 doors, each door need only have capacity for 40 persons. However, since all these doors serve an area with "100 or more persons," any latches on these doors must be released by panic hardware or fire exit hardware.

(c) *Door Closure.* Any exit door designed to normally be kept closed shall comply with 5-2.1.8.

(d) *Locks and Latches.* Only one locking or latching device shall be permitted on a door or a leaf of a pair of doors.

(e) *Special Locking Arrangements.* Special locking arrangements complying with 5-2.1.6 shall be permitted.

(f)* *Closet Doors.* Every closet door latch shall be such that children can open the door from inside the closet.

A-11-7.2.2.2(f) The purpose of this requirement is to prevent arrangements where a child can be trapped in a closet. It is intended that this provision be broadly interpreted by the authority having jurisdiction to include equipment such as refrigerators or freezers.

(g) *Bathroom Doors.* Every bathroom door lock shall be designed to permit opening of the locked door from the outside in an emergency. The opening device shall be readily accessible to the staff.

11-7.2.2.3* **Stairs.**

(a) Stairs shall comply with 5-2.2.
(b) Stairs shall be Class A.

Exception: Class B stairs shall be permitted where not used by clients.

A-11-7.2.2.3 See A-5-2.2.4.5(a) Exception No. 3 regarding additional handrails on stairs that are used extensively by children 5 years or less in age.

11-7.2.2.4 **Smokeproof Enclosures.** Smokeproof enclosures shall comply with 5-2.3.

11-7.2.2.5 **Horizontal Exits.**

(a) Horizontal exits shall comply with 5-2.4.
(b) Areas of refuge shall be provided by horizontal exits for occupants of day-care centers located above the fifth story.

Exception to (b): Buildings provided with smokeproof enclosures.

In all cases where day-care centers are found on upper floors of tall buildings, areas of refuge (smokeproof enclosures or horizontal exits) must be designed so that the clients will survive a fire. Five stories or approximately 75 ft (23 m) is the maximum height at which the fire department can be expected to rescue the occupants of a building from outside. However, many fire departments do not have the equipment to reach this height, and in such locations, areas of refuge are necessary at lower levels.

In any event, dependence on rescue by the fire department is not prudent. The time, number of personnel, and effort involved in rescuing one person by using an extension ladder is so great that it is not possible to rescue a large number of occupants by this method.

11-7.2.2.6 **Ramps.** Ramps shall comply with 5-2.5.

11-7.2.2.7 **Exit Passageways.** Exit passageways shall comply with 5-2.7.

11-7.2.3 Capacity of Means of Egress.

11-7.2.3.1 Capacity of means of egress shall be in accordance with Section 5-3.

11-7.2.4 **Number of Exits.**

11-7.2.4.1 Each floor occupied by clients shall have not less than two remotely located exits in accordance with Chapter 5.

11-7.2.4.2 Where the story below the level of exit discharge is occupied as a day-care center, the following shall apply:

(a) One means of egress shall be an outside or interior stair in accordance with 5-2.2. An interior stair, if used, shall only serve the story below the level of exit discharge. The interior stair shall be permitted to communicate with the level of exit discharge; however, the exit route from the level of exit discharge shall not pass through the stair enclosure.

(b) The second means of egress shall be permitted to be via an unenclosed stairway separated from the level of exit discharge in accordance with 6-2.4.4. The path of egress travel on the level of exit discharge shall be protected in accordance with 5-1.3.4.

Exception to (b): The path of travel on the level of exit discharge may be unprotected if the level of exit discharge and the level below the level of exit discharge are protected throughout by a smoke detection system or an approved automatic sprinkler system.

Figure 11-16 illustrates the intent of 11-7.2.4.2.

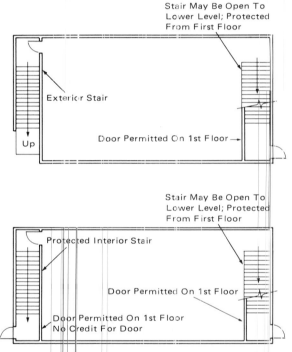

Figure 11-16. *Egress for Levels Below the Level of Exit Discharge. Two methods of complying with 11-7.2.4.2 are illustrated. One stair, either an interior or outside stair, must be a properly protected exit discharging outside. The other stair may be open to the lower level but must be separated from the first floor. This second way out either discharges directly outside or discharges through a corridor protected in accordance with 5-1.3.3. Note the exception for corridor protection if both levels are sprinklered.*

11-7.2.5 Arrangement of Means of Egress. (*Where the story below the level of exit discharge is used, see also 11-7.2.4.2.*)

11-7.2.5.1 Means of egress shall be arranged in accordance with Section 5-5. Dead ends shall not exceed 20 ft (6.1 m).

Chapter 5 does not allow dead-end corridors except in accordance with the occupancy chapters. The Committee recognized that 20 ft (6.1 m) has been the accepted standard in educational occupancies and believed that to retain it would be reasonable.

11-7.2.5.2 Every room or space with a capacity of more than 50 persons or more than 1,000 sq ft (93 sq m) in area shall have at least two doorways as remotely located from each other as practicable. Such doorways shall provide access to separate exits, but where egress is through corridors, they shall be permitted to open upon a common corridor leading to separate exits located in opposite directions.

Although Section 11-7 does not establish common path limitations, it does set a maximum room size permitted to be served by a single door, in addition to limiting dead-end space.

11-7.2.6 Travel Distance to Exits.

11-7.2.6.1 Travel distance shall be measured in accordance with Section 5-6.

11-7.2.6.2 Travel distance:

(a) Between any room door intended as exit access and an exit shall not exceed 100 ft (30 m);

(b) Between any point in a room and an exit shall not exceed 150 ft (45 m);

(c) Between any point in a sleeping room and an exit access door of that room shall not exceed 50 ft (15 m).

Exception: The travel distance in (a) and (b) above shall be permitted to be increased by 50 ft (15 m) in buildings protected throughout by an approved automatic sprinkler system in accordance with Section 7-7.

Paragraph 11-7.2.6.2 is structured to state the same requirement in several different ways. As shown in Figure 11-17, the maximum travel distance from a room door (exit access to the corridor) to an exit door is 100 ft (30 m). The total travel distance from any point (such as in a room) to an exit is 150 ft (45 m). The maximum travel distance from a point in a sleeping room to an exit access door is 50 ft (15 m). This in-room travel distance limit may not be increased even if the building is sprinklered.

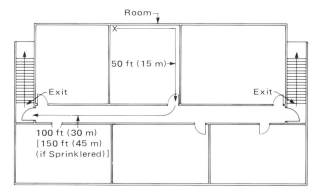

Figure 11-17. *Maximum Travel Distance to Exit, Day-Care Center.*

11-7.2.7 **Discharge from Exits.** Discharge from exits shall be arranged in accordance with Section 5-7.

Exception: As provided in 11-7.2.4.2.

11-7.2.8 **Illumination of Means of Egress.** Illumination of the means of egress shall be provided in accordance with Section 5-8.

11-7.2.9 **Emergency Lighting.** Emergency lighting shall be provided in accordance with 11-2.9.

11-7.2.10 **Marking of Means of Egress.** Means of egress shall have signs in accordance with Section 5-10.

11-7.2.11 **Special Features.**

11-7.2.11.1 **Windows for Rescue and Ventilation.** Every room or space normally subject to client occupancy, other than bathrooms, shall have at least one outside window for emergency rescue or ventilation. Such window shall be openable from the inside without the use of tools and shall provide a clear opening of not less than 20 in. (50.8 cm) in width, 24 in. (61 cm) in height, and 5.7 sq ft (.53 sq m) in area. The bottom of the opening shall be not more than 44 in. (112 cm) above the floor.

In rooms located higher than three stories above grade, the openable clear height, width, and area of the window may be modified to the dimensions necessary for ventilation.

Exception No. 1: In buildings protected throughout by an approved automatic sprinkler system in accordance with Section 7-7.

Exception No. 2: Where the room or space has a door leading directly to the outside of the building.

The dimensions specified for windows used for emergency rescue or for ventilation are based on simulations of emergency rescue conducted by the San Diego Fire Department. Windows providing clear openings of identical dimensions are also required for rescue or ventilation in one- and two-family dwellings. Figures 11-11a and 11-11b on pages 392 and 393 illustrate two configurations that achieve the required area of 5.7 sq ft (.53 sq m).

Although the *Code* intends the fire department or others to assist students, particularly over ladders, if these windows must be used as a supplementary means of escape, the windows should permit younger children to escape unaided. Therefore, storm sashes, screens, or devices in front of the windows must be easy to open or remove, and the sills must be low enough for children to reach.

Where the location of windows precludes their use for rescue or escape, they may still provide trapped children with air for breathing in smoke-filled rooms.

The Committee did not believe it was practical to expect a window above the third story to be used as an escape window. However, it is reasonable to expect the window to be used for ventilation during a fire.

Windows may be omitted if a classroom has a door leading directly to the outside or if the building is totally sprinklered.

Note that Exception No. 1 requires that the building be protected throughout by an automatic sprinkler system. One question often asked is: If there are only a couple of windowless rooms, can sprinklering be limited to those rooms only? The answer is no! It should be noted that the purpose of the window is to provide ventilation or means of escape when the interior corridor is blocked by smoke from a fire in another part of the building.

Installing sprinklers in the windowless rooms only would do nothing to provide protection from smoke emanating from other areas.

11-7.3 Protection.

11-7.3.1 Protection of Vertical Openings. Any vertical opening shall be enclosed and protected in accordance with Section 6-2.

11-7.3.2 Protection from Hazards.

11-7.3.2.1 Rooms or spaces for the storage, processing, or use of the materials specified in this section shall be protected in accordance with the following:

(a) Rooms or spaces used for the storage of combustible supplies in quantities deemed hazardous by the authority having jurisdiction, hazardous materials in quantities deemed hazardous by recognized standards, or fuel shall be separated from the remainder of the building by construction having not less than a 1-hour fire resistance rating with all openings protected by self-closing or smoke-actuated fire doors, or such rooms or spaces shall be protected by an automatic extinguishing system as required in Section 6-4.

(b) Rooms or spaces used for processing or use of combustible supplies in quantities considered hazardous by the authority having jurisdiction, hazardous materials, or for flammable or combustible liquids in quantities deemed hazardous by recognized standards shall be separated from the remainder of the building by construction having not less than a 1-hour fire resistance rating with all openings protected by self-closing or smoke-actuated fire doors and shall also be protected by an automatic extinguishing system as required in Section 6-4.

(c) Boiler and furnace rooms, laundries, and maintenance shops, including woodworking and painting areas, shall be separated from the remainder of the building by construction having not less than a 1-hour fire resistance rating with all openings protected by self-closing or smoke-actuated fire doors, or such areas shall be protected throughout by an approved automatic extinguishing system as set forth in Section 6-4.

Exception to (c): Rooms enclosing air-handling equipment.

(d)* Where automatic extinguishing systems are used to meet the requirements of this section, the rooms or spaces shall be separated from the remainder of the building by construction that resists the passage of smoke.

A-11-7.3.2.1(d) It is not the intent of this provision to require a smoke barrier that meets the requirements of Section 6-3.

(e) Where automatic extinguishing is used to meet the requirements of this section, protection in accordance with 7-7.1.2 shall be permitted.

Exception: Food preparation facilities protected in accordance with 7-2.3 are not required to have openings protected between food preparation areas and dining areas. Where domestic cooking equipment is used for food warming or limited cooking, protection or segregation of food preparation facilities is not required if approved by the authority having jurisdiction.

The intent of 11-7.3.2.1 is to specify the degree of protection necessary for certain hazardous areas. It has been divided into three sections based on the degree of hazard. The hazards noted in parts (a) and (c) are required to be enclosed in 1-hour construction or protected by sprinklers. If the sprinkler option is chosen, an enclosure is still required by part (d); however, the enclosure need not be rated but needs only to form a membrane against the passage of smoke.

The Committee reasoned that, although sprinklers are provided and fire-rated barriers may not be needed, some barrier to control smoke migration is needed. Solid construction materials, such as glass or other non-fire-rated materials, are acceptable if they are installed in a manner that will resist smoke passing from one compartment to another. The appendix note emphasizes that it is not the intent to require smoke barriers as provided in Section 6-3. This eliminates the more costly construction of a smoke barrier, which would require dampers and other required equipment.

The hazards noted in part (b) must be enclosed in 1-hour construction and be protected by automatic sprinklers.

The Exception to part (c) pertains to rooms housing air-handling equipment only. If the room is used for other purposes, then the provisions of part (a) or (b) apply.

Part (e) has been provided to highlight the fact that Chapter 7 makes these requirements available to the user of the *Code*. Paragraph 7-7.1.2 provides an economical way of providing sprinkler protection in small rooms.

The intent of the exception is to provide some barrier between cooking areas and dining areas. Openings in this barrier are not restricted and do not need to be protected. The *Code* relies upon the provision of the automatic extinguishing system to control any fire on the cooking surfaces and, thus, does not require enclosure by rated construction. The second sentence of the exception is significant, since this limited use of cooking equipment is often found in day-care centers.

Figure 11-18 illustrates the different protection requirements of 11-7.3.2.1.

11-7.3.2.2 Janitor closets shall be protected by an automatic sprinkler system, which shall be permitted to be in accordance with 7-7.1.2. Doors to janitor closets shall be permitted to have ventilating louvers.

Where janitor closets are located off of corridors, a louvered door is usually provided for ventilation. It is necessary to provide these spaces with automatic sprinkler protection, since the louvered door offers little fire resistance and permits a fire in the closet to directly affect the corridor. Paragraph 7-7.1.2 contains an economical method of providing sprinkler protection for such closets. To achieve this protection at reasonable cost, these sprinklers (not more than six in number) may be supplied from the domestic water supply if the supply is capable of providing the required quantity of water. It is advisable to provide a water-flow switch (*see Chapter 7*) to initiate an alarm when a sprinkler is opened.

The minimum flow of 0.15 gpm/sq ft (6.1 L/min/sq m) is based on the requirements of NFPA 13, *Standard for the Installation of Sprinkler Systems*,[1] for protecting buildings containing ordinary hazards. It is important to ensure that the domestic water supply can provide the required flow and pressure at the location.

11-7.3.3 Interior Finish.

11-7.3.3.1 Interior finish for all walls and ceilings shall be Class A or Class B in accordance with Section 6-5.

11-7.3.4 Detection, Alarm, and Communication Systems.

11-7.3.4.1 General. Day-care centers shall be provided with a fire alarm system in accordance with Section 7-6.

Exception No. 1: Day-care centers housed in one room.

Exception No. 2: Day-care centers with a required staff of fewer than four persons based on 11-7.1.1.1.

11-7.3.4.2 Initiation. Initiation of the required fire alarm system shall be by manual means and by operation of any required smoke detectors. (*See 11-7.3.4.5.*)

Exception: Single station smoke detectors.

Single station smoke detectors by definition are not connected to an alarm system and are normally installed to provide a local alarm that will alert people in the immediate vicinity that they should exit the area.

11-7.3.4.3 Occupant Notification. Occupant notification shall be by means of an audible alarm in accordance with 7-6.3.

11-7.3.4.4 Emergency Forces Notification. Fire department notification shall be accomplished in accordance with 7-6.4.

Exception: Day-care centers with not more than 100 clients.

In all day-care centers, manually operated fire alarm systems should be directly connected to the fire department. The Committee felt compelled to emphasize that this arrangement is essential in centers that serve more than 100 clients. There are fire departments that will not accept direct alarms. In such cases, positive provisions must be made for rapid notification of the fire department by remote or central station systems.

11-7.3.4.5 Detection. A smoke detection system shall be installed in accordance with Section 7-6 with placement of

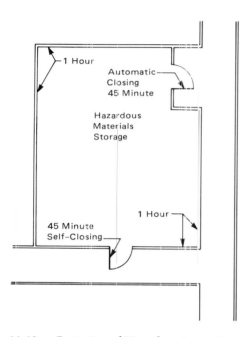

Figure 11-18a.   *Protection of Hazardous Areas. Figure 11-18a illustrates one method of complying with 11-7.3.2.1(a). [See Figure 11-18b for the alternate method.]*

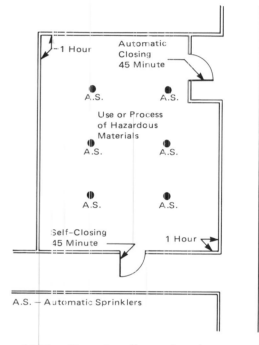

Figure 11-18c.   *Protection of Hazardous Areas. Figure 11-18c illustrates the requirements for complying with 11-7.3.2.1(b). Both 1-hour separation and automatic sprinkler protection are required in this case.*

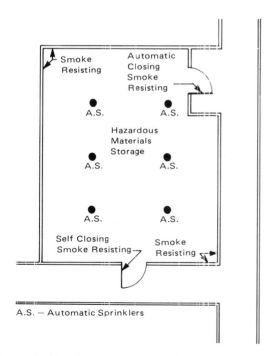

Figure 11-18b.   *Protection of Hazardous Areas. Figure 11-18b illustrates an alternate method of complying with 11-7.3.2.1(a). Figure 11-18a illustrates another method of compliance.*

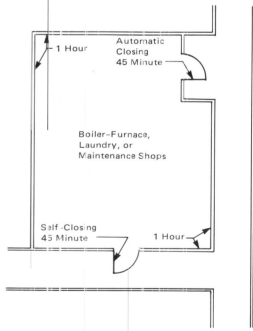

Figure 11-18d.   *Protection of Hazardous Areas. Figure 11-18d illustrates the requirements for complying with 11-7.3.2.1(c). However, in existing buildings, boilers rooms, furnace rooms, and similar areas may use the sprinkler option as illustrated in Figure 11-18b.*

detectors in each story in front of doors to the stairways and in the corridors of all floors occupied by the center. Detectors shall also be installed in lounges, recreation areas, and sleeping rooms in the center.

Exception No. 1: Centers housed in only one room.

Exception No. 2: Centers housing clients 6 years of age or older if no sleeping facilities are provided.

The purpose of this requirement is obvious yet worth noting. In centers housing children younger than six, nap and sleep time are provided. The *Code* also recognizes that parents who work the "third shift" may place their children in the center for the purpose of sleeping through the night. Also, regardless of sleeping, the detectors will provide critical extra time to evacuate clients from danger. Exceptions are provided for centers housing only older clients and centers housed in a single room where a fire will be obvious to all occupants.

11-7.3.5 **Extinguishment Requirements.**

11-7.3.6 **Corridors.** Exit access corridors within day-care centers shall comply with 11-3.6.1. (*See 11-7.1.2.*)

The purpose of 11-7.3.6 is to provide a minimum level of compartmentation by use of corridor separation. (*See commentary on 11-3.6.1.*)

11-7.4 **Special Provisions.**

11-7.4.1 **Windowless or Underground Buildings.** Windowless or underground buildings shall comply with Section 30-7.

11-7.4.2 **High Rise Buildings.** (Reserved.)

11-7.4.3 **Operating Features.** (*See Chapter 31.*)

11-7.5 **Building Services.**

11-7.5.1 **Utilities.**

11-7.5.1.1 Utilities shall comply with the provisions of Section 7-1.

11-7.5.1.2 Special protective covers for all electrical receptacles shall be installed in all areas occupied by children under 6 years of age.

Children are subject to serious injury if they insert foreign objects into electrical receptacles. Protective covers must be provided and maintained in order to avoid such accidents.

11-7.5.2 **Heating, Ventilating, and Air Conditioning Equipment.**

11-7.5.2.1 Heating, ventilating, and air conditioning equipment shall be installed in accordance with Section 7-2.

11-7.5.2.2 Unvented fuel-fired room heaters shall not be permitted.

The Committee does not believe that the interest of reasonable life safety is served by allowing the use of unvented fuel-fired equipment in buildings occupied by children. (*Also see commentary on 11-5.2.2.*)

11-7.5.2.3 Any heating equipment in spaces occupied by children shall be provided with partitions, screens, or other means to protect children under 6 years of age from hot surfaces and open flames. If solid partitions are used to provide such protection, provisions shall be made to assure adequate air for combustion and ventilation for the heating equipment.

The Committee believes it important that safeguards be provided to protect younger children from the hot surfaces of heating equipment. Young children do not always understand the dangers of hot surfaces. The burn injury record clearly indicates that protection be provided. The Committee also wanted to make certain that adequate air is provided for combustion by the heating equipment. Incomplete or inadequate combustion could cause serious injury or death to occupants.

11-7.5.3 **Elevators, Escalators, and Conveyors.** Elevators, escalators, and conveyors shall comply with the provisions of Section 7-4.

11-7.5.4 Rubbish Chutes, Incinerators, and Laundry Chutes. Rubbish chutes, incinerators, and laundry chutes shall comply with the provisions of Section 7-5.

SECTION 11-8 Group Day-Care Homes

11-8.1 General Requirements.

11-8.1.1 Application.

11-8.1.1.1* This section establishes life safety requirements for group day-care homes in which at least 7 but not more than 12 clients receive care, maintenance, and supervision by other than their relative(s) or legal guardian(s) for less than 24 hours per day (generally within a dwelling unit). The provisions of Sections 11-2 through 11-6 shall not apply to this section unless a specific requirement is referenced by this section.

Formal Interpretation 76-108
Reference: 10-7 (11-7), 10-8 (11-8), 10-9 (11-9)

Question 1: Do the requirements of Sections 10-7 (11-7), 10-8 (11-8), or 10-9 (11-9) apply to church programs that provide day-care services to church members only, on a nonprofit basis?

Answer: Yes.

Question 2: Are churches also required to meet the provisions of Sections 10-7 (11-7), 10-8 (11-8), or 10-9 (11-9) in order to operate a church nursery while church services are being held?

Answer: Yes.

Question 3: Does Section 1-6 permit the city to grant an exception in these cases?

Answer: The authority having jurisdiction is given the power to grant exceptions where it is clearly evident that reasonable safety is thereby secured.

Issue Edition: 1976
Reference: 9-5.3, 9-5.4, 9-5.5
Date: March 1979 ■

A-11-8.1.1.1 Group day-care homes do not provide for the full-time maintenance of a client. Occupancies that provide a primary place of residence are dealt with in other occupancies. (*See Chapters 16 through 22, "Residential Occupancies."*)

These provisions take into account that the typical group day-care home is usually located in a residential setting.

11-8.1.1.2 The requirements detailed in Section 11-8 are based on a minimum staff-to-client ratio of two staff for up to twelve clients, with no more than three clients under age 2. This staff-to-client ratio may be modified by the authority having jurisdiction where safeguards in addition to those specified by this section are provided.

If these staff ratios are not maintained, it would be the responsibility of the authority having jurisdiction to determine what additional safeguards above and beyond the requirements of this section would be necessary. Typical additional provisions may include restricting the group day-care home to the level of exit discharge, requiring additional smoke detection, requiring automatic sprinkler protection, requiring better or additional means of egress, or similar types of features, depending upon the situation.

11-8.1.2 Mixed Occupancies.

(a) *General.* Where a group day-care home is located in a building containing mixed occupancies, the occupancies shall be separated by 1-hour fire barriers constructed in accordance with Section 6-2.3.

Exception to (a): In assembly occupancies used primarily for worship.

(b) *Homes in Apartment Buildings.*

(1) If the two exit accesses from the home enter the same corridor as the apartment occupancy, the exit accesses shall be separated in the corridor by a smoke barrier having not less than a 1-hour fire resistance rating constructed in accordance with Section 6-3. The smoke barrier shall be so located that it has an exit located on each side.

(2) The door in the smoke barrier shall be not less than 36 in. (91 cm) wide.

Group day-care homes are often found in buildings housing occupancies such as apartments, stores, offices, or assembly occupancies. In such buildings, exit accesses usually open into a corridor.

Where a center is located in a building housing another occupancy, the operators of the center usually have no control of the safety procedures and precautions practiced outside the center. Paragraph 11-8.1.2 requires additional protection to minimize the clients' exposure to potential hazards outside the center.

The corridor subdivision by smoke barriers in accordance with Section 6-3 when day-care centers are in an apartment building is the same concept as that used in Chapters 12 and 13 for health care facilities. This minimum construction will provide sufficient protection against flame and a good seal against smoke spread. The 20-minute door, coupled with the 1-hour wall, provides a barrier that will either contain a fire within a space for a limited time after it has been evacuated or will prevent a fire from entering an occupied space for a period of time.

Exception to (b)(2): Existing doors not less than 32 in. (81 cm) wide.

11-8.1.3 Special Definitions. (None.)

11-8.1.4 Classification of Occupancy. No requirements.

11-8.1.5 Classification of Hazard of Contents. The contents shall be classified as ordinary hazard in accordance with Section 4-2.

11-8.1.6 Minimum Construction Requirements. (None.)

11-8.1.7 Occupant Load. No special requirements.

11-8.2 Means of Egress Requirements.

11-8.2.1 General. (None.)

11-8.2.2 Types of Exits. (*See 11-8.2.4.*)

11-8.2.3 Capacity of Means of Egress. Capacity of means of egress shall be in accordance with Section 5-3.

11-8.2.4 Number of Exits.

11-8.2.4.1 Each story occupied by clients shall have not less than two remotely located means of escape.

This is similar to the requirements of Chapter 21 for one- and two-family dwellings; however, 11-8.2.4.3 and 11-8.2.4.4 provide for an increase over that which would normally be required for a private dwelling where clients occupy the second story or basement.

11-8.2.4.2 Every room used for sleeping, living, or dining purposes shall have at least two means of escape, at least one of which shall be a door or stairway providing a means of unobstructed travel to the outside of the building at street or ground level. The second means of escape shall be permitted to be a window in accordance with 11-2.11.1. No room or space shall be occupied for living or sleeping purposes that is accessible only by a ladder or folding stairs or through a trap door.

These are the same requirements as those for a one- or two-family dwelling.

11-8.2.4.3 Where spaces on the story above the story of exit discharge are used by clients, at least one means of egress shall be an exit discharging directly to the outside. The second means of escape shall be permitted to be a window in accordance with 11-2.11.1.

The second floor of a typical single family dwelling is served by an open stair. This would require that the second floor be served by an enclosed exit or an outside exit stair (not a fire escape) if clients are upstairs.

11-8.2.4.4 Where clients are occupying a story (basement) below the level of exit discharge, at least one means of egress shall be an exit discharging directly to the outside and the vertical travel to ground level shall not exceed 8 ft (244 cm). The second means of escape shall be permitted to be a window in accordance with 11-2.11.1. No facility shall be located more than one story below the ground. Any stairway to the story above shall be cut off by a fire barrier containing a door having at least a 20-minute fire protection rating and equipped with a self-closing device.

This requirement is similar to that of 11-8.2.4.3 for a second floor and mandates that, where clients are below the level of exit discharge, at least one true exit shall be provided. In addition, any stairway to the first floor would require at least 20-minute protection.

As illustrated in Figure 11-19, where a group day-care center is located in a basement, there must be an exit that opens directly to the outside, with vertical travel to ground level not exceeding 8 ft (244 cm). If a stairway to the story above were provided, it would have to be cut off from the basement by a fire barrier containing a door with a fire protection rating of at least 20 minutes. This separation need be provided only at the top or bottom of the stair, not at both.

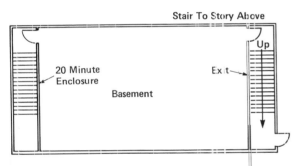

Figure 11-19. Exit Requirements for Group Day-Care Center in Basement.

11-8.2.5 Arrangement of Means of Egress. (*Where a story above or below the exit discharge is used, see 11-8.2.4.*)

11-8.2.5.1 Means of egress shall be arranged in accordance with Section 5-5. Dead ends shall not exceed 20 ft (6.1 m).

Chapter 5 does not allow for dead ends unless provided for by the occupancy chapters. The Committee felt that 20 ft (6.1 m) continues to be a reasonable distance for these types of occupancies.

11-8.2.6 Travel distance:

(a) Between any room door intended as exit access and an exit shall not exceed 100 ft (30 m);

(b) Between any point in a room and an exit shall not exceed 150 ft (45 m);

(c) Between any point in a sleeping room and an exit access to that room shall not exceed 50 ft (15 m).

Exception: The travel distance in (a) and (b) above shall be permitted to be increased by 50 ft (15 m) in buildings protected throughout by an approved supervised automatic sprinkler system in accordance with Section 7-7.

11-8.2.7 Discharge from Exits. (*Where the story above or below the exit discharge is used, see 11-8.2.4.*)

11-8.2.8 Illumination of Means of Egress. Illumination of the means of egress shall be provided in accordance with Section 5-8.

11-8.2.9 Emergency Lighting. No requirements.

11-8.2.10 Marking of Means of Egress. No requirements.

11-8.2.11 Special Requirements.

11-8.2.11.1* Every closet door latch shall be such that children can open the door from the inside of the closet.

A-11-8.2.11.1 The purpose of this requirement is to prevent arrangements where a child can be trapped in a closet. It is intended that this provision be broadly interpreted by the authority having jurisdiction to include equipment like refrigerators or freezers.

11-8.2.11.2 Every bathroom door lock shall be designed to permit opening of the locked door from outside in an emergency. The opening device shall be readily accessible to the staff.

11-8.3 Protection.

11-8.3.1 Protection of Vertical Openings. The doorway between the level of exit discharge and any story below shall be equipped with a door assembly having a 20-minute fire protection rating. Where the story above the story of exit discharge is used for sleeping purposes, there shall be a door assembly having a 20-minute fire protection rating at the top or bottom of each stairway.

Exception: Existing self-closing 1 ³/₄-in. (4.4-cm) thick solid bonded wood core doors without rated frames may be accepted by the authority having jurisdiction.

Also see 11-8.2.4.3 and 11-8.2.4.4.

11-8.3.2 **Protection from Hazards.** No requirements.

11-8.3.3 **Interior Finish.**

11-8.3.3.1 The interior finish in exits shall be Class A or B in accordance with Section 6-5.

11-8.3.3.2 Interior finish in occupied spaces in the home shall be Class A, B, or C in accordance with Section 6-5.

11-8.3.4 **Detection, Alarm, and Communication Systems.**

11-8.3.4.1 Within the group day-care home, smoke detectors shall be installed in accordance with 7-6.2.9.

Exception: Homes that house clients 6 years of age or older if no sleeping facilities are provided.

11-8.3.4.2 Where the group day-care home is located within a building of another occupancy, such as in an apartment or office building, any corridors serving the group day-care home shall be provided with a smoke detection system in accordance with Section 7-6.

11-8.3.4.3 Single station smoke detectors in accordance with 7-6.2.9 powered by the building electrical system or system detectors with integral sounding devices in accordance with 7-6.1.4 shall be provided in all rooms used for sleeping.

Exception: Existing battery-powered detectors rather than house electrical service-powered detectors shall be accepted where, in the opinion of the authority having jurisdiction, the facility has demonstrated testing, maintenance, and battery replacement programs that ensure reliability of power to the detectors.

The provisions of 11-8.3.4 are three-fold: first, to provide smoke detection within the group day-care home in accordance with NFPA 74, *Standard for the Installation, Maintenance, and Use of Household Fire Warning Equip-*

ment;[2] and second, to provide a smoke detection system in the corridor serving the group day-care home where in a building of mixed occupancy. Third, 11-8.3.4.3 requires that either single station smoke detectors or system smoke detectors designed with integral sounding devices be installed in each sleeping room, which is not required by NFPA 74.

11-8.4 **Special Provisions.**

11-8.4.1 **Windowless or Underground Buildings.** Windowless or underground buildings shall comply with Section 30-7.

11-8.4.2 **High Rise Buildings.** (Reserved.)

11-8.4.3 **Operating Features.** (*See Chapter 31.*)

11-8.5 **Building Services.**

11-8.5.1 **Electrical Services.**

11-8.5.1.1 Electrical wiring shall be installed in accordance with Section 7-1.

11-8.5.1.2 Special protective covers for electrical receptacles shall be installed in all areas occupied by children under 6 years of age.

Children are subject to serious injury if they insert foreign objects into electrical receptacles. Protective covers must be provided and maintained in order to avoid such accidents.

11-8.5.2 **Heating, Ventilating, and Air Conditioning Equipment.**

11-8.5.2.1 Heating, ventilating, and air conditioning equipment shall be installed in accordance with Section 7-2.

11-8.5.2.2 Unvented fuel-fired room heaters shall not be permitted.

The Committee does not believe that the interest of reasonable life safety is served by allowing the use of unvented fuel-fired equipment in buildings occupied by children. (*Also see commentary on 11-5.2.2.*)

11-8.5.2.3 Any heating equipment in spaces occupied by children shall be provided with partitions, screens, or other means to protect children under 6 years of age from hot surfaces and open flames. If solid partitions are used to provide such protection, provisions shall be made to assure adequate air for combustion and ventilation for the heating equipment.

The Committee believes it important that safeguards be provided to protect younger children from the hot surfaces of heating equipment. Young children do not always understand the dangers of hot surfaces. The burn injury record clearly indicates that protection be provided. The Committee also wanted to make certain that adequate air is provided for combustion by the heating equipment. Incomplete or inadequate combustion could cause serious injury or death to occupants.

Screens that separate heating equipment from spaces occupied by children must be of closely spaced wire or expanded metal, of heavy gage, and must be securely attached to elements of the building. The purpose is to prevent children from bending the screens or inserting their fingers through the mesh.

SECTION 11-9 Family Day-Care Homes

11-9.1 General Requirements.

11-9.1.1 Application.

11-9.1.1.1* This section establishes life safety requirements for family day-care homes in which more than 3 but fewer than 7 clients receive care, maintenance, and supervision by other than their relative(s) or legal guardian(s) for less than 24 hours per day (generally within a dwelling unit). The provisions of Sections 11-2 through 11-6 shall not apply to this section unless a specific requirement is referenced by this section.

A-11-9.1.1.1 Family day-care homes do not provide for the full-time maintenance of a client. Occupancies that provide a primary place of residence are dealt with in other occupancies. (See Chapters 16 through 22, "Residential Occupancies.")

Formal Interpretation 76-108
Reference: 10-7 (11-7), 10-8 (11-8), 10-9 (11-9)

Question 1: Do the requirements of Sections 10-7 (11-7), 10-8 (11-8), or 10-9 (11-9) apply to church programs that provide day-care services to church members only, on a nonprofit basis?

Answer: Yes.

Question 2: Are churches also required to meet the provisions of Sections 10-7 (11-7), 10-8 (11-8), or 10-9 (11-9) in order to operate a church nursery while church services are being held?

Answer: Yes.

Question 3: Does Section 1-6 permit the city to grant an exception in these cases?

Answer: The authority having jurisdiction is given the power to grant exceptions where it is clearly evident that reasonable safety is thereby secured.

Issue Edition: 1976
Reference: 9-5.3, 9-5.4, 9-5.5
Date: March 1979 ■

Prior to the 1988 *Code,* this section dealt with "licensed" facilities.

The Committee recognizes that licensing practices vary among jurisdictions. It was also a concern that the term "licensed family day-care home" would mean that, according to the *Code,* if a facility were not licensed, it did not have to meet the requirements of the *Code.* It is the intent of the Committee to include all family day-care centers as defined in 11-9.1.1.1, regardless of licensing.

Family day-care homes are usually situated in single-family dwellings or in apartment houses. If they are located in apartment houses, they must also comply with the applicable requirements of 11-9.1.2. The 1991 Edition has been revised to reflect the provision that family day-care homes provide accommodations for more than three but fewer than seven clients. This recognizes that up to three outsiders are permitted in one- and two-family dwellings. (See Chapter 21.)

11-9.1.1.2 The requirements detailed in Section 11-9 are based on a minimum staff-to-client ratio of one staff for up to six clients, including the caretaker's own children under age 6, with no more than two children under age 2.

Many family day-care homes are located in single-family residences. The Committee recognizes that, in these types of situations, the caretaker's children should also be a consideration in determining staff-to-client ratios. This paragraph clarifies that distinction. The limit of two children under age 2 recognizes the stricter staff-to-client ratio requirements for this age group. (*For example, see staff-to-client ratio requirements for ages 0 to 2 in 11-7.1.1.1.*)

11-9.1.2 **Mixed Occupancies.** Where family day-care homes are located in a building containing mixed occupancies, the occupancies shall be separated by 1-hour fire barriers.

Exception: In assembly occupancies used primarily for worship.

11-9.1.3 **Special Definitions.** (None.)

11-9.1.4 **Classification of Occupancies.** No requirements.

11-9.1.5 **Classification of Hazard of Contents.** The contents shall be classified as ordinary hazard in accordance with Section 4-2.

11-9.1.6 **Minimum Construction Requirements.** (None.)

11-9.1.7 **Occupant Load.** No special requirements.

11-9.2 **Means of Egress Requirements.**

11-9.2.1 **General.** (None.)

11-9.2.2 **Types of Exits.** (*See 11-9.2.4.*)

11-9.2.3 **Capacity of Means of Egress.** Capacity of means of egress shall be in accordance with Section 5-3.

11-9.2.4 **Number of Exits.**

11-9.2.4.1 Every room used for sleeping, living, or dining purposes shall have at least two means of escape, at least one of which shall be a door or stairway providing a means of unobstructed travel to the outside of the building at street or ground level. The second means of escape shall be permitted to be a window in accordance with 11-2.11.1. No room or space shall be occupied for living or sleeping purposes that is accessible only by a ladder or folding stairs or through a trap door.

This paragraph has the same requirements as those for one- and two-family dwellings. The change from means of egress to means of escape also recognizes a window of proper size as one method of escaping a fire.

11-9.2.4.2 Where clients are located on a story (basement) below the level of exit discharge, at least one means of egress shall be an exit discharging directly to the outside, and the vertical travel to ground level shall not exceed 8 ft (244 cm). The second means of escape shall be permitted to be a window in accordance with 11-2.11.1. No facility shall be located more than one story below the ground.

This requires either a door directly outside with an outside stair leading up to grade or an enclosed interior exit stair discharging directly outside. This provides clients in the basement with a way out should a fire occur on the first floor.

11-9.2.5 **Arrangement of Means of Egress.** (*See 11-9.2.4.*)

11-9.2.6 Travel distance:

(a) Between any room door intended as exit access and an exit shall not exceed 100 ft (30 m);

(b) Between any point in a room and an exit shall not exceed 150 ft (45 m);

(c) Between any point in a sleeping room and an exit access to that room shall not exceed 50 ft (15 m).

Exception: The travel distance in (a) and (b) above shall be permitted to be increased by 50 ft (15 m) in buildings protected throughout by an approved supervised automatic sprinkler system in accordance with Section 7-7.

11-9.2.7 Discharge from Exits. (*See 11-9.2.4.*)

11-9.2.8 Illumination of Means of Egress. Illumination of the means of egress shall be in accordance with Section 5-8.

11-9.2.9 Emergency Lighting. No requirements.

11-9.2.10 Marking of Means of Egress. No requirements.

11-9.2.11 Special Features.

11-9.2.11.1 Each door in a means of egress shall not be less than 28 in. (71 cm) wide.

Exception: Bathroom doors shall be not less than 24 in. (64 cm) wide.

11-9.2.11.2* Every closet door latch shall be such that children can open the door from inside the closet.

A-11-9.2.11.2 The purpose of this requirement is to prevent arrangements where a child can be trapped in a closet. It is intended that this provision be broadly interpreted by the authority having jurisdiction to include equipment like refrigerators or freezers.

11-9.2.11.3 Every bathroom door lock shall be designed to permit the opening of the locked door from the outside in an emergency. The opening device shall be readily accessible to the staff.

11-9.3 Protection.

11-9.3.1 Protection of Vertical Openings. No special provisions.

11-9.3.2 Protection from Hazards. No requirements.

11-9.3.3 Interior Finish.

11-9.3.3.1 The interior finish in exits shall be Class A or B in accordance with Section 6-5.

11-9.3.3.2 Interior finish in occupied spaces in the home shall be Class A, B, or C in accordance with Section 6-5.

11-9.3.4 Detection, Alarm, and Communication Systems.

11-9.3.4.1 Within the family day-care home, smoke detectors shall be installed in accordance with 7-6.2.9.

Exception: Homes that house clients 6 years of age or older if no sleeping facilities are provided.

11-9.3.4.2 Where the family day-care home is located within a building of another occupancy, such as in an apartment or office building, any corridors serving the family day-care home shall be provided with a smoke detection system in accordance with Section 7-6.

11-9.3.4.3 Single station smoke detectors in accordance with 7-6.2.9 powered by the building electrical system or system detectors with integral sounding devices in accordance with 7-6.1.4 shall be provided in all rooms used for sleeping.

Exception: Existing battery-powered detectors rather than house electric service-powered detectors shall be accepted where, in the opinion of the authority having jurisdiction, the facility has demonstrated testing, maintenance, and battery replacement programs that ensure reliability of power to the detectors.

The provisions of 11-9.3.4 are three-fold: first, to provide single station smoke detectors within the family day-care home in accordance with NFPA 74, *Standard for the Installation, Maintenance, and Use of Household Fire Warning Equipment;*[2] and second, to provide a smoke detection system in the corridor serving the family day-care home where in a building of mixed occupancy. Third, 11-9.3.4.3 requires that either single station smoke detectors or system smoke detectors designed with integral sounding devices be installed in each sleeping room, which is not required by NFPA 74.

11-9.4 Special Provisions.

11-9.4.1 Windowless or Underground Buildings. Windowless or underground buildings shall comply with Section 30-7.

11-9.4.2 High Rise Buildings. (Reserved.)

11-9.5 Building Services.

11-9.5.1 Electrical Services.

11-9.5.1.1 Electrical wiring shall be installed in accordance with Section 7-1.

11-9.5.1.2 Special protective covers for all electrical receptacles shall be installed in all areas occupied by children in homes for children under 6 years of age.

Children are subject to serious injury if they insert foreign objects into electrical receptacles. Protective covers must be provided and maintained in order to avoid such accidents.

11-9.5.2 Heating, Ventilating, and Air Conditioning Equipment.

11-9.5.2.1 Heating, ventilating, and air conditioning equipment shall be installed in accordance with Section 7-2.

11-9.5.2.2 Unvented fuel-fired room heaters shall not be permitted.

The Committee does not believe that the interest of reasonable life safety is served by allowing the use of unvented fuel-fired equipment in buildings occupied by children. (*Also see commentary on 11-5.2.2.*)

11-9.5.2.3 Any heating equipment in spaces occupied by children shall be provided with partitions, screens, or other means to protect children under 6 years of age from hot surfaces and open flames. If solid partitions are used to provide such protection, provisions shall be made to ensure adequate air for combustion and ventilation for the heating equipment.

The Committee believes it important that safeguards be provided to protect younger children from the hot surfaces of heating equipment. Young children do not always understand the dangers of hot surfaces. The burn injury record clearly indicates that protection be provided. The Committee also wanted to make certain that adequate air is provided for combustion of the heating equipment. Incomplete or inadequate combustion could cause serious injury or death to occupants.

Screens that separate heating equipment from spaces occupied by children must be of closely spaced wire or expanded metal, of heavy gage, and must be securely attached to elements of the building. The purpose is to prevent children from bending the screens or inserting their fingers through the mesh.

References Cited in Commentary

[1]NFPA 13, *Standard for the Installation of Sprinkler Systems*, National Fire Protection Association, Quincy, MA, 1991.

[2]NFPA 74, *Standard for the Installation, Maintenance, and Use of Household Fire Warning Equipment*, National Fire Protection Association, Quincy, MA, 1989.

12

New Health Care Occupancies

(See also Chapter 31.)

This chapter covers the requirements for new health care occupancies. In editions of the *Code* prior to 1976, these occupancies were known as "Institutional Occupancies."

Detention and correctional occupancies are discussed in Chapters 14 and 15.

Health care occupancies are those used for medical or other treatment or care of four or more persons suffering from physical or mental illness, disease or infirmity, and for the care of infants, convalescents, or infirm aged persons.

Health care occupancies addressed in this chapter include:

1. Hospitals
2. Nursing Homes
3. Limited Care Facilities
4. Ambulatory Health Care Centers.

Hospitals, nursing homes, and limited care facilities provide sleeping facilities for the occupants and are occupied by persons who are mostly incapable of self-preservation because of age, physical or mental disability, or because of security measures not under the occupants' control.

Ambulatory health care centers are significantly different from other health care occupancies, since they do not provide sleeping facilities and are, therefore, covered in Section 12-6.

Among health care facilities, those that care for the sick accounted for 5,500 structure fires per year as reported to U.S. fire departments from 1984 to 1988. These fires were responsible for 11 civilian deaths and 166 civilian injuries per year. Facilities that care for older people accounted for 3,900 structure fires per year from 1986 to 1988 and an associated 19 civilian deaths and 204 civilian injuries per year. The other major health care category is facilities that care for the mentally handicapped (e.g., mental institutions, institutions for the mentally retarded), which accounted for 2,500 structure fires per year from 1984 to 1988 and an associated 1 civilian death and 60 civilian injuries per year.

Health care facilities accounted for three multiple-death fires (i.e., fires where at least 3 people died) in the last half of the 1980s: a 1989 Virginia nursing home fire that killed 12, a 1988 Tennessee nursing home fire that killed 3, and a 1985 hospice fire that killed 8. Usage of detectors, sprinklers, and other features of fire protection tends to be more prevalent in health care facilities than in almost any other property class. Because of the effectiveness and widespread use of these systems, a relatively low 37 percent of the fire fatalities in facilities that care for the sick, older adults, or the mentally handicapped occurred outside the room of fire origin. In facilities that care for the sick, the figure is reduced to 18 percent. Victims of fire found outside the room of origin are more likely to be occupants of the other two classes of health care facilities.

SECTION 12-1   General Requirements

12-1.1   Application. (See also Section 1-5.)

12-1.1.1   General.

12-1.1.1.1 New health care facilities shall comply with the provisions of this chapter. (See Chapter 31 for operating features.)

Exception: Facilities where the authority having jurisdiction has determined equivalent safety has been provided in accordance with Section 1-6.

A-12-1.1.1.1 Exception. In determining equivalancy for conversions, modernizations, renovations, or unusual design concepts of hospitals or nursing homes, the authority having jurisdiction may accept evaluations based on Chapter 3 of NFPA 101M, *Alternative Approaches to Life Safety* (see Appendix B), utilizing the parameters for new construction.

The Exception to 12-1.1.1.1 emphasizes that Section 1-6 permits alternative designs to literal Code requirements that would still comply with the *Code*. However, the authority having jurisdiction ultimately determines whether or not equivalent safety has been provided.

Paragraph 12-1.1.1.1 and the accompanying exception are not intended to limit the methods an authority having jurisdiction might use to determine equivalency. However, as noted in A-12-1.1.1.1, Chapter 3 of NFPA 101M,

Alternative Approaches to Life Safety,[1] provides an "equivalency system" that uses numerical values to analyze the firesafety effectiveness of a building design. This system is known as the Firesafety Evaluation System (FSES). The system provides a method by which alternative designs can be evaluated as options to literal Code compliance. In providing the equivalency system, it is not the intent to limit equivalency evaluations solely to this system. The authority having jurisdiction retains the power to evaluate and approve alternative designs on the basis of appropriate supporting data. The FSES may be used to aid in this evaluation. This exception in no way mandates the use of the FSES, nor does it require the authority having jurisdiction to accept the results of an evaluation using the system.

Although the FSES was developed primarily to evaluate alternative designs in existing buildings, it is particularly useful in determining equivalency for conversions, modernizations, renovations, or unusual design concepts, all of which would be considered new construction. However, the FSES is a tool to help determine equivalency, and it should not be used to circumvent *Code* requirements. In new construction, *Code* requirements must be met, or equivalent safety must be provided by alternative means approved by the authority having jurisdiction.

It should be noted that the 1988 Edition of NFPA 101M was coordinated to be used with the 1988 Edition of NFPA 101. It cannot be used to evaluate the 1991 Edition of NFPA 101. At the time this *Handbook* went to press, the Committee on Safety to Life was preparing a revision of NFPA 101M to coordinate with the 1991 Edition of NFPA 101. It is anticipated that this will be the 1992 Edition of NFPA 101M.

12-1.1.1.2 This chapter establishes life safety requirements for the design of all new hospitals, nursing homes, and limited care facilities. Where requirements vary, the specific occupancy is named in the paragraph pertaining thereto. Section 12-6 establishes life safety requirements for the design of all new ambulatory health care centers.

Renovations, alterations, and modernizations must be performed in accordance with the requirements of this chapter to the maximum extent possible. (*See also 12-1.1.4.5 and accompanying commentary*.)

Chapter 13 provides the requirements for existing health care facilities and existing ambulatory health care centers.

12-1.1.1.3 Health care occupancies are those used for purposes such as medical or other treatment or care of persons suffering from physical or mental illness, disease or infirmity; for the care of infants, convalescents, or infirm aged persons.

A psychiatric hospital or other facility having locked doors but housing patients primarily for treatment of mental disorders or substance abuse, for example, would be classified as a health care occupancy.

12-1.1.1.4 Health care facilities provide sleeping accommodations for their occupants and are occupied by persons who are mostly incapable of self-preservation because of age, physical or mental disability, or because of security measures not under the occupants' control.

12-1.1.1.5 This chapter also covers ambulatory health care centers as defined in 12-1.3(a). (*See Section 12-6 for requirements.*)

Since ambulatory health care centers do not provide sleeping accommodations, they are treated separately in Section 12-6.

12-1.1.1.6 Buildings or sections of buildings that primarily house patients who, in the opinion of the governing body of the facility and the governmental agency having jurisdiction, are capable of judgment and appropriate physical action for self-preservation under emergency conditions may come under chapters of the *Code* other than Chapter 12.

12-1.1.1.7 It shall be recognized that, in buildings housing certain types of patients or having detention rooms or a security section, it may be necessary to lock doors and bar windows to confine and protect building inhabitants. In such instances, the authority having jurisdiction shall make appropriate modifications to those sections of this *Code* that would otherwise require exits to be kept unlocked.

12-1.1.1.8 Buildings or sections of buildings that house older persons and that provide activities that foster continued independence but do not include those services distinctive to health care facilities [as defined in 12-1.3(c)] may be subject to the requirements of other sections of this *Code*, such as Chapter 18 or 22.

12-1.1.1.9 Health care occupancies shall include all buildings or parts thereof with occupancy as described in this chapter under 12-1.3, "Special Definitions."

12-1.1.1.10 Except for ambulatory health care centers, facilities that do not provide housing on a 24-hour basis for their occupants are classified as other occupancies and are covered by other chapters of the *Code*.

Paragraphs 12-1.1.1.3 through 12-1.1.1.10 contain explanatory material that describes some general characteristics of the occupants of health care occupancies. A few fundamental safeguards are also provided. Formal definitions are established in 12-1.3.

As implied by the definitions of 12-1.3 and stated in 12-1.1.1.4, health care facilities, except ambulatory health care centers, are buildings that provide sleeping facilities (24-hour care) for occupants. Occupants in a health care facility may be restrained but are housed primarily for treatment of mental or physical infirmities. Where occupants are restrained for penal or correctional purposes, the building would be classified as a detention and correctional occupancy. Such occupancies are addressed in Chapters 14 and 15.

If a building is used for the treatment or housing of patients, including the mentally handicapped (*see 12-1.1.1.6*) or older persons (*see 12-1.1.1.8*), the building may be classed as an occupancy other than health care under the following conditions:

1. Occupants are not restrained by locked doors or other devices, and
2. The patients are ambulatory, and
3. The occupants are capable of perceiving threat and taking appropriate action for self-preservation.

Occupants of health care facilities are considered to be incapable of self-preservation (*see 12-1.1.1.4*) due to age, physical or mental disability, or security measures not under the occupants' control. A significant number of occupants in health care facilities are assumed to be nonambulatory or bedridden. Other occupants, while capable of self-movement, may have impaired judgment.

Although locking exit doors and barring windows is always undesirable in terms of life safety, the *Code* recognizes that, in some cases, it is necessary to restrain people. In these instances, provision should be made for the continuous supervision and prompt release of restrained persons (*see 12-1.1.1.7*). Release of occupants should be achieved by a system capable of automatically unlocking doors in the means of egress or by continuously available attendants equipped with keys. In either case, continuous supervision is considered essential. (*See 12-2.2.2.4 and 12-2.2.2.5.*)

12-1.1.1.11* The requirements of this chapter are based on the assumption that staff is available in all patient occupied areas to perform certain firesafety functions as required in other paragraphs of this chapter.

A-12-1.1.1.11 The *Code* recognizes that certain functions necessary for the life safety of building occupants, such as the closing of corridor doors, operation of manual fire alarm devices, and the removal of patients from the room of fire origin require the intervention of facility staff. It is not the intent of this paragraph to specify the levels or locations of staff necessary to meet this requirement.

The *Code* has always assumed that staff will be in continuous attendance in all health care facilities. In fact, staff is assigned certain critical functions during a fire emergency, such as rescuing patients from the room of origin, closing the door to the room, and activating the fire alarm system. The *Code* does not specify minimum staff/patient ratios, as such provisions are included in state licensing criteria, and compliance with licensing criteria will normally satisfy the *Code*. The 1991 *Life Safety Code* has been revised to mandate that staff be present. A staff person should be situated to supervise each smoke compartment housing patients. A nursing station located to allow visual supervision of two or more smoke compartments is considered adequate. If, because of some unusual arrangement, staff is not continuously available (24 hours a day) to provide supervision, alternate means should be provided to ensure an adequate level of firesafety that is in compliance with the *Code*.

12-1.1.2* Objective. The objective of this chapter is to provide a reasonable level of safety by reducing the probability of injury and loss of life from the effects of fire with due consideration for functional requirements. This is accomplished by limiting the development and spread of a fire emergency to the room of fire origin and reducing the need for occupant evacuation, except from the room of fire origin.

A-12-1.1.2 This objective is accomplished in the context of the physical facilities, the type of activities undertaken, the provisions for the capabilities of staff, and the needs of all occupants through requirements directed at the:

(a) Prevention of ignition.
(b) Detection of fire.
(c) Control of fire development.
(d) Confinement of the effects of fire.
(e) Extinguishment of fire.
(f) Provision of refuge and/or evacuation facilities.
(g) Staff reaction.

It should be recognized that the well-being of an individual located in the room of fire origin can be reasonably ensured only through control of that individual's environment. That is, only through complete control of the environment, including building members, building finishes, furnishings, decorations, clothing, linens, bedding, and the like, can the individual be protected against fire. However, no code can prevent injury resulting from a person's careless actions.

Although an effort should be made to protect the individual through fire prevention, the primary objective of the requirements of Chapter 12 is to limit fire size or to prevent fire from escaping the room of origin and thereby limit the threat to individuals outside the room of origin.

12-1.1.3 Total Concept. All health care facilities shall be so designed, constructed, maintained, and operated as to minimize the possibility of a fire emergency requiring the evacuation of occupants. Because the safety of health care occupants cannot be assured adequately by dependence on evacuation of the building, their protection from fire shall be provided by appropriate arrangement of facilities, adequate staffing, and careful development of operating and maintenance procedures composed of the following:

(a) Proper design, construction, and compartmentation; and

(b) Provision for detection, alarm, and extinguishment; and

(c) Fire prevention and the planning, training, and drilling in programs for the isolation of fire, transfer of occupants to areas of refuge, or evacuation of the building.

Vertical movement of patients within a health care facility is an inefficient, time consuming process. In one study, it was demonstrated through the simulated evacuation of patients from a second-story ward to ground level that more than 30 minutes may be required for evacuation during a fire.

The provisions of Chapter 12, therefore, are based upon a "defend in place" philosophy, which minimizes the probability of a fire necessitating vertical movement of occupants. Patients in critical care areas may be connected to life-support equipment, which makes movement difficult and, in some cases, impossible. Barriers are required to provide for the horizontal movement of patients to safe areas of refuge on a single floor level and to maintain a manageable limit on the number of occupants exposed to any single fire. Vertical means of egress (stairs or ramps) are specified by Chapter 12 as escape routes for visitors and staff and as a "last line of defense" for the movement of patients.

12-1.1.4 Additions, Conversions, Modernization, Renovation, and Construction Operations. (*See also 1-5.5 and 1-5.6.*)

12-1.1.4.1 Additions. Additions shall be separated from any existing structure not conforming to the provisions within Chapter 13 by a fire barrier having at least a 2-hour fire resistance rating and constructed of materials as required for the addition.

Paragraph 12-1.1.4.1 establishes separation criteria for additions to existing structures where existing structures do not conform to the provisions of Chapter 13. It should be emphasized that, where an existing building meets the provisions of Chapter 13, the building would be in compliance with the *Code*, and the addition would not require separation.

Where additions must be separated, barriers must be constructed of assemblies providing a minimum of 2-hour

fire resistance. Where the structural framing of the addition or the existing buildings are of assemblies of less than 2-hour fire resistance, special provision must be made to ensure the necessary separation will be maintained for the 2-hour period.

Materials used in the construction of the barrier should be "constructed to the standards of the addition." That is, if the addition is required to be constructed of noncombustible or limited-combustible materials (construction Types I or II), then the materials used in the barrier must be limited-combustible or noncombustible as defined in NFPA 220, *Standard on Types of Building Construction.*[2] Conversely, if the addition is permitted to be constructed of combustible materials, then combustible materials may be used as a portion of the barrier.

12-1.1.4.2 Communicating openings in dividing fire barriers required by 12-1.1.4.1 shall occur only in corridors and shall be protected by approved self-closing fire doors. (*See also Section 6-2.*)

12-1.1.4.3 Doors in barriers required by 12-1.1.4.1 shall normally be kept closed.

Exception: Doors shall be permitted to be held open if they meet the requirements of 12-2.2.2.6.

Openings in barriers separating additions from nonconforming existing structures are limited to those that are absolutely necessary, i.e., corridors (*see 12-1.1.4.2*). Openings are required to be protected by 1½-hour, "B"-labeled fire door assemblies. The fire doors are required to be self-closing and are to remain closed, or they may be held open by an automatic device in accordance with 12-2.2.2.6. (*See Figure 12-1.*)

12-1.1.4.4 Conversions. Conversions shall comply with 1-7.4. A conversion from a hospital to a nursing home or from a nursing home to a hospital is not a change in occupancy or suboccupancy classification.

Any building converted to a health care facility from some other type of occupancy (dormitory, for example) must be altered to comply with the provisions of Chapter 12 for new health care facilities. It is sometimes questioned whether the conversion of a hospital to a nursing

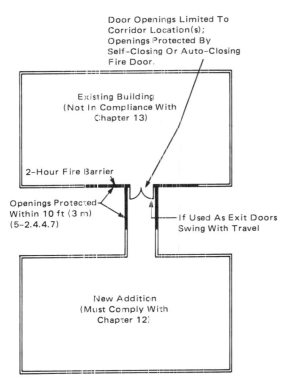

Figure 12-1.   Separation of New Addition from Existing Building Not in Compliance with Chapter 13. If the addition is of fire-resistive or noncombustible (Type I or II) construction, noncombustible or limited-combustible materials must be used in the 2-hour fire barrier. (See NFPA 220, Standard on Types of Building Construction).[2]

home represents a change in occupancy. Conversion of a hospital to a nursing home or vice versa does not constitute a change in occupancy. Therefore, prior to and after such a conversion, the facility must comply with the criteria of Chapter 13 for existing health care facilities.

12-1.1.4.5*   Renovations, Alterations, and Modernizations.
Renovations, alterations, and modernizations shall comply to the extent practical, with requirements for new construction in accordance with 1-5.6. Where renovations, alterations, or modernizations are done in a nonsprinklered facility, the automatic sprinkler requirements of Chapter 12 shall apply to the smoke compartment undergoing the renovation, alteration or modernization. However, in such case where the building is not protected throughout by an approved automatic sprinkler system, the requirements of 13-1.6 and 13-2.3.2 shall also apply. Exception No. 2 to 12-3.7.3 shall be permitted only

where adjacent smoke compartments are protected throughout by an approved supervised automatic sprinkler system in accordance with 12-3.5.2. Where minor renovations, alterations, modernizations, or repairs are done in a nonsprinklered facility, the requirements of 12-3.5.1 shall not apply, but in such cases the renovations, alterations, modernizations, or repairs shall not reduce life safety below that which existed before, nor below the requirements of Chapter 13 for nonsprinklered buildings.

A-12-1.1.4.5   The *Code* does not attempt to establish specific monetary limits or percentage values to determime "minor," as this requires judgment. It is not the intent of this paragraph to exempt significant renovations and modernization projects for which the *Code* does intend to apply the automatic sprinkler mandate.

For the purpose of this requirement, a floor that is not divided by a smoke barrier is considered one smoke compartment.

Alterations in health care facilities are regulated by 1-5.6 and 12-1.1.4.5. Alterations may not reduce the level of life safety below that which exists prior to the alterations; however, provisions in excess of the requirements for new construction are not required to be maintained. For example, an existing hospital has a 6-ft (1.8-m) wide corridor, and a portion of the hospital is to be renovated. While the hospital is an existing building, a minimum 6-ft (1.8-m) wide corridor must be maintained. Conversely, if a portion of an existing hospital that has a 10-ft (3.1-m) wide corridor is to be altered, the corridor may be reduced to 8 ft (2.4 m), which is the requirement for new construction. If alterations require replacement of a small portion of a hospital corridor wall in a nonsprinklered area, this portion of the wall should provide 1-hour fire separation in accordance with the nonsprinklered requirements for new construction contained in previous editions. However, it would not be required that the corridor width be increased to 8 ft (2.4 m) unless it was practical to do so. As a minimum, in all instances, whether or not renovations or alterations are planned, existing buildings must comply with the requirements contained in Chapter 13.

This paragraph has undergone major revision in the 1991 *Code*. Automatic sprinkler protection is now required for all new health care facilities. The requirements of Chapter 12 contemplate complete automatic sprinkler protection, and numerous exceptions are included to eliminate redundant features of protection. Existing health care facilities may be nonsprinklered. Renovations of nonsprinklered health care facilities must comply with the requirements for new construction to the extent practical. However, Chapter 12 no longer contains a nonsprinklered option. Therefore, whenever a nonsprinklered facility undergoes alteration, and the alterations are of such a minor nature that automatic sprinklers are not required, the *Code* specifies that the level of firesafety existing prior to the renovations must be maintained. As a minimum, the requirements of Chapter 13 for nonsprinklered buildings, including fire separation of corridors, must be met.

Only that portion of a facility that is being renovated is required to comply with Chapter 12. For example, assume a floor of a hospital is subdivided into three smoke compartments, and only one smoke compartment is undergoing renovation. Only the renovated smoke compartment would require compliance, to the extent practical, with Chapter 12. Accordingly, the smoke compartment undergoing alteration must be sprinklered in accordance with 12-3.5. However, where a building is only partially protected with sprinklers, the construction requirements of 13-1.6 for nonsprinklered buildings must be met, and exit capacity must be based on nonsprinklered criteria. Smoke dampers may only be omitted for ducted penetrations of smoke barriers where the smoke compartments on both sides of the smoke barrier are fully sprinklered in accordance with 12-3.5.

Although an effort should always be made to satisfy the criteria for new construction during a building alteration or the installation of new equipment, the *Code* recognizes that such modifications cannot always be achieved. Guidance for achieving equivalency to life safety is provided in Section 1-6. Regardless of circumstances, alterations or the installation of new building service equipment must be achieved in such a manner that the level of life safety that results is equivalent or superior to that prescribed for existing buildings.

12-1.1.4.6 **Construction Operations.** See 1-7.3 and Chapter 31 for life safety provisions during construction.

The introduction of "outside" workers and activities associated with the construction of an addition creates unusual risks of fire in health care occupancies. Special precautions should be taken to guard against the potential exposure created by the introduction of flammable substances or by other hazardous practices that could pose a threat to occupants. (*See 31-1.1.2.*)

Temporary fire resistant barriers should be erected to separate the new construction and associated activity from the functioning areas of the existing buildings. Care should be taken to prevent blockage of means of egress for the existing building by the construction of such barriers. Special care is also necessary to ensure that all existing equipment for fire protection and all portions of the required means of egress are maintained in full working order. (*See 1-7.3.*)

Adequate escape facilities should be provided and continuously maintained for the use of construction workers. (*See 31-1.1.1 and NFPA 241, Standard for Safeguarding Construction, Alteration, and Demolition Operations*).[3]

12-1.2 **Mixed Occupancies.** (*See also 1-5.7.*)

12-1.2.1* Sections of health care facilities shall be permitted to be classified as other occupancies if they meet all of the following conditions:

(a) They are not intended to serve health care occupants for purposes of:

(1) Housing, or

(2) Treatment, or

(3) Customary access by patients incapable of self-preservation.

(b) They are adequately separated from areas of health care occupancies by construction having a fire resistance rating of at least 2 hours.

A-12-1.2.1 Doctors' offices, treatment and diagnostic facilities intended solely for outpatient care and physically separated from facilities for the treatment or care of inpatients, but otherwise associated with the management of an institution, may be classified as business occupancy, rather than health care occupancy.

12-1.2.2 Ambulatory care centers, medical clinics, and similar facilities that are contiguous to health care occupancies but are primarily intended to provide outpatient services shall be permitted to be classified as a business occupancy or ambulatory health care occupancy provided the facilities are separated from the health care occupancy by not less than 2-hour fire resistance-rated construction and the facility is not intended to provide services simultaneously for four or more health care patients who are litter-borne.

Paragraphs 12-1.2.1 and 12-1.2.2 contain criteria for classifying spaces as "other" occupancies, although they are located in buildings used primarily for health care purposes. For example, 12-1.2.1 would allow offices to be classified as business occupancies, cafeterias to be classified as assembly occupancies, or dormitories to be classified as residential occupancies if both (a) and (b) of 12-1.2.1 are met. Paragraph 12-1.2.1(a) notes that customary access by patients incapable of self-preservation is not permitted within the other occupancy. This paragraph is intended to allow an occasional ambulatory inpatient to visit a doctor's office in an adjacent business occupancy, for example, without requiring classification of the business occupancy as a health care facility. However, if either (a) or (b) is not met, the area would be considered a mixed occupancy and require that the more restrictive life safety provisions of 1-5.7 apply. (*See 1-5.7.*)

Paragraph 12-1.2.2 addresses a subject similar to that of 12-1.2.1 but specifically covers ambulatory care centers, medical clinics, and similar areas that primarily provide outpatient services and are associated with or attached to a health care facility. If these facilities are separated by 2-hour fire-resistive construction, they may be classified as ambulatory health care centers or as business occupancies, whichever applies. If, however, four or more litter-borne inpatients are treated simultaneously, the facility must meet the requirements for health care occupancies. Conversely, three or fewer litter-borne inpatients may be present in the outpatient facility on a regular basis, and such a facility would be classified as other than health care. The provisions of business occupancies and ambulatory health care centers were written on the assumption that most people are treated on an outpatient basis.

Note that, subject to certain qualifications, 12-1.2.4 allows the means of egress from health care areas using a horizontal exit to traverse non-health care spaces.

12-1.2.3 Health care occupancies in buildings housing other occupancies shall be completely separated from them by construction having a fire resistance rating of at least 2 hours as provided for additions in 12-1.1.4.

Paragraph 12-1.2.3 requires that, if a health care occupancy is located in a building of another classification (such as business, storage, mercantile, or industrial), the health care occupancy must be separated from the other occupancy by construction having a fire resistance rating of 2 hours, as detailed in 12-1.1.4. (*Also see commentary following 12-1.1.4.1.*)

Note that 12-1.2.3 deals with occupancy classification and not with hazard of contents. Hazard of contents is treated in 12-1.2.6 and 12-1.2.7.

12-1.2.4 All means of egress from health care occupancies that traverse non-health care spaces shall conform to requirements of this *Code* for health care occupancies.

Exception: It is permissible to exit through a horizontal exit into other contiguous occupancies that do not conform with health care egress provisions but that do comply with requirements set forth in the appropriate occupancy chapter of this Code as long as the occupancy does not contain high hazard contents. The horizontal exit shall comply with the requirements of 12-2.2.5.

Paragraph 12-1.2.4 specifies that the means of egress from health care occupancies that traverse non-health care spaces must conform to the requirements for health care occupancies. However, an exception is allowed where a 2-hour barrier is provided and such barrier is used as a horizontal exit. Where a 2-hour barrier serves as a horizontal exit, it is acceptable to exit into a different occupancy, if the other occupancy complies with the provisions of the *Code* that would be applicable thereto and if it does not contain high hazard contents. For example, if a horizontal exit is provided between a health care facility and a business occupancy, inpatients may exit into the business occupancy through a horizontal exit. In this instance, corridor width, corridor partitions, stairway details, and similar features must conform to the provisions of either Chapters 26 or 27, which address business occupancies. However, the horizontal exit must comply with all the requirements of 12-2.2.5.

12-1.2.5 Auditoriums, chapels, staff residential areas, or other occupancies provided in connection with health care facilities shall have means of egress provided in accordance with other applicable sections of the *Code*.

Auditoriums, chapels, and other areas separated by 2-hour construction and meeting the criteria of 12-1.2.1 and 12-1.2.2 for other occupancies are required to be designed in accordance with the appropriate occupancy chapter governing their use.

Spaces used for non-health care purposes but located within a health care facility should have means of egress features designed in accordance with the use of the space. For example, if a space located in a health care facility is used as a chapel or auditorium, occupant loads should be calculated on the basis of an assembly occupancy. Assuming an occupant load is in excess of 50, egress features should be designed as would be appropriate for an assembly occupancy. In such circumstances, doors in the means of egress should be side-hinged swinging doors, arranged to swing in the direction of exit travel (*see 5-2.1.4.1*), and should not be equipped with a latch or lock unless such a latch or lock is operated by panic hardware. (*See 8-2.2.2.3.*)

Exit capacity, however, should be computed on the basis of occupant characteristics. If, for example, the space is used only by staff, visitors, and others who are mobile and otherwise capable of self-preservation, then exit capacity could be computed in accordance with Chapter 8. However, if the space is used by health care occupants, the exit capacity should be calculated in accordance with Chapter 12, despite the fact that the occupant load might be calculated in accordance with Chapter 8.

12-1.2.6 Any area with a hazard of contents classified higher than that of the health care occupancy and located in the same building shall be protected as required in 12-3.2.

Paragraph 12-1.2.6 regulates spaces in a health care facility that, although comprising only a portion of the facility, contain more hazardous materials (in quantity or type) than are usually found in most other spaces.

Spaces such as rooms used for the storage of combustible materials, trash collection rooms, gift shops, and paint shops must be protected in accordance with 12-3.2.

12-1.2.7 Non-health care related occupancies classified as containing high hazard contents shall not be permitted in buildings housing health care occupancies.

Paragraph 12-1.2.7 prohibits another occupancy (such as storage) that contains highly hazardous contents (such as flammable liquids) from being located in a building housing health care occupancies.

This paragraph limits use, based upon occupancy classification, with regard to hazard of contents. For example, the paragraph does not intend to exclude laboratory operations from being part of a health care facility. The intent is to prevent a portion of a hospital from being converted to or designed for use as an educational or research facility (which would be classed as an educational or possibly an industrial occupancy) where laboratories use and store sizable quantities of flammable liquids.

12-1.3 Special Definitions.

(a) *Ambulatory Health Care Centers.* A building or part thereof used to provide services or treatment to four or more patients at the same time that meets the criteria of either (1) or (2) below.

(1) Those facilities that provide, on an outpatient basis, treatment for patients that would render them incapable of taking action for self-preservation under emergency conditions without assistance from others.

(2) Those facilities that provide, on an outpatient basis, surgical treatment requiring general anesthesia.

(b) *Hospital.* A building or part thereof used on a 24-hour basis for the medical, psychiatric, obstetrical, or surgical care of four or more inpatients. The term hospital, wherever used in this *Code*, shall include general hospitals, psychiatric hospitals, and specialty hospitals.

(c) *Limited Care Facility.* A building or part thereof used on a 24-hour basis for the housing of four or more persons who are incapable of self-preservation because of age, physical limitation due to accident or illness, or mental limitations such as mental retardation/developmental disability, mental illness, or chemical dependency.

(d) *Nursing Home.* A building or part thereof used on a 24-hour basis, for the housing and nursing care of four or more persons who, because of mental or physical incapacity, may be unable to provide for their own needs and safety without the assistance of another person. The term nursing home, wherever used in this *Code*, shall include nursing and convalescent homes, skilled nursing facilities, intermediate care facilities, and infirmaries in homes for the aged.

Paragraph 12-1.3(a) through (d) defines the characteristics of the occupancies covered by Chapter 12. Except as discussed below for ambulatory health care, a building must house four or more people incapable of self-preservation on a 24-hour basis in order to be classed as a health care occupancy.

Occupants of hospitals or nursing homes are assumed to be nonambulatory and incapable of self-preservation. In making this judgment, due consideration should be given to the use of physical restraints and tranquilizing drugs, which can render occupants immobile. Variable staffing criteria and levels of care make differentiation between hospitals and nursing homes apparent. The difference between nursing homes and limited care facilities is less clear.

Although limited care facilities house four or more occupants incapable of self-preservation due to age or physical or mental limitations, occupants are generally considered to be ambulatory and to require only limited assistance during emergency evacuation. Buildings that house ambulatory occupants who are mentally handicapped or undergoing treatment for alcohol or drug abuse and who can be expected to evacuate a structure with limited assistance meet the criteria for limited care facilities. Day-care facilities that provide care for the aged, children, mentally handicapped, or others would be classified as other than health care if the care or treatment is not provided on a 24-hour basis. (*See Chapter 10.*)

Although age itself is not sufficient justification for developing a separate classification for a health care occupancy, it should be recognized that the elderly pose a unique problem in the achievement of firesafety. Experiences in buildings where the elderly are housed demonstrate that the response of the elderly to a fire may not be in the interest of self-preservation. Upon discovering a fire, elderly occupants may ignore it, become transfixed by it, or seek refuge from it in their rooms and fail to notify anyone of the fire. In some cases, the elderly have resisted efforts to remove them from the building and familiar surroundings.

Terms such as "residential," "lodging and boarding," and "custodial care," previously used in 12-1.3, have been deleted to avoid confusion with a residential occupancy classification included in Chapter 21 (Chapters 22 and 23 in the 1991 *Code*), which was added to the 1985 Edition of the *Code*. Board and care facilities, personal care homes, halfway houses, or similar facilities house occupants who may require medication and personal care but do not require the close supervision and services typical of the occupants in a health care facility. Therefore, these would be classified as residential occupancies. Occupant capability must be carefully evaluated to determine whether application of health care criteria (Chapter 12) or application of lesser safeguards associated with residential occupancies (Chapter 22) is more appropriate.

Prior to the 1981 Edition of the *Code*, occupancies that offered medical services on an outpatient basis would have been regulated within the chapter covering business occupancies. The threat to life in an outpatient facility where four or more patients may be subject to medical procedures requiring general anesthesia, treatments such as hemodialysis, or freestanding emergency service is significantly greater than that typical of a business occupancy. Conversely, application of the requirements for health care facilities that contemplate 24-hour care would be inappropriate and would be unnecessarily restrictive. In establishing the occupancy classification of an ambulatory health care center, the intent was to develop requirements that fall between the restrictions applicable to business occupancies and health care facilities in terms of level of life safety achieved.

12-1.4 Classification of Occupancy. (*See Special Definitions, 12-1.3.*)

12-1.5 Classification of Hazard of Contents. The classification of hazard of contents shall be as defined in Section 4-2.

12-1.6 Minimum Construction Requirements.

12-1.6.1 For the purpose of 12-1.6, the number of stories shall be counted starting with the primary level of exit discharge and ending with the highest occupiable level. For the purposes of this section, the primary level of exit discharge of a building shall be that floor that is level with or above finished grade of the exterior wall line for 50 percent or more of its perimeter. Building levels below the primary level shall not be counted as a story in determining the height of a building.

Allowable building construction types are determined according to the number of stories in a building. The first story is considered to be the primary level of exit discharge. Only occupiable levels are counted in determining story height. For example, an unoccupied attic would not constitute a story.

Difficulties have been experienced in determining story height where a building is located on a sloping grade. Paragraph 12-1.6.1 notes that a story on a sloping site that is partially below grade should be counted as a story if the floor is level with or above grade along 50 percent or more of the perimeter of the building at the exterior wall. (*See Figure 12-2.*)

12-1.6.2 Health care occupancies shall be limited to the following types of building construction (*see 6-2.1*):

Table 12–1.6.2

Construction Type	1 Story	2 Stories	3 Stories and <45 ft (13.7m)	4 or More Stories or >45 ft (13.7 m)
I (443) ⎫ I (332) ⎬ II (222) ⎭	X	X	X	X
II (111)	X	X	X	N.P.
II (000)	X	N.P.	N.P.	N.P.
III (211)	X	N.P.	N.P.	N.P.
III (200)	N.P.	N.P.	N.P.	N.P.
IV (2HH)	X	N.P.	N.P.	N.P.
V (111)	X	N.P.	N.P.	N.P.
V (000)	N.P.	N.P.	N.P.	N.P.

X: Permitted type of construction
N.P.: Not Permitted

Formal Interpretation 81-3
Reference: 12-1.6.1

Question: Where stories are counted from an established "primary level of exit discharge," is it the intent of 12-1.6.1 that any story below not be counted regardless of the degree to which it is exposed above finished grade of exterior wall line?

Answer: See answer below.

Question: If, due to grade differences, a building has two "primary levels of exit discharge," each with the required number of exits, is it the intent of 12-1.6.1 that stories can be counted starting at the upper of the two discharge levels?

Answer: See answer below.

Question: If, due to grade differences, a building has an upper "primary level of exit discharge" and a lower level with separate independent exits to outside grade [disregarding communicating stairway(s)], is it the intent of 12-1.6.1 that stories can be counted starting at the upper "primary level of exit discharge?"

Answer: For the purpose of determining construction type and related minimum building requirements, the level of exit discharge is determined as being the lowest story having at least 50 percent of the perimeter exposed above grade. Each building can have only one primary level of exit discharge.

Issue Edition: 1981
Reference: 12-1.6.1
Date: August 1981 ■

Exception: Any building of Type I or Type II (222 or 111) construction shall be permitted to include roofing systems involving combustible supports, decking, or roofing provided: (1) the roof covering meets Class A requirements in accordance with NFPA 256, Standard Methods of Fire Tests of Roof Coverings, and (2) the roof is separated from all occupied portions of the building by a noncombustible floor assembly having at least a 2-hour fire resistance rating that includes at least 2½ in. (6.4 cm) of concrete or gypsum fill.

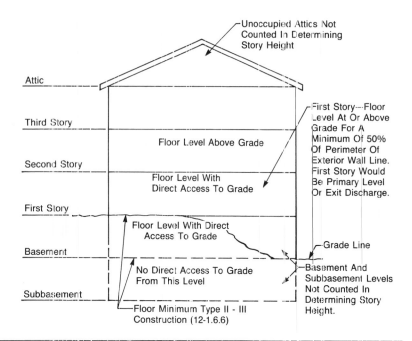

Figure 12-2. *Building Section View Illustrates Application of 12-1.6.1 and 12-1.6.6.*

Construction types permitted in new health care facilities are indicated as a function of height in 12-1.6.2. See NFPA 220, *Standard on Types of Building Construction,*[2] for definitions of construction types.

Multistory health care facilities are required to be constructed of noncombustible materials. A minimum 2-hour fire resistance rating is required for building members of structures exceeding three stories. It is recognized that it may not be possible to move patients, and occupants of a health care facility may be required to remain in the structure for the duration of the fire. In specifying 2-hour fire resistance, it is intended that building members be adequately protected against the effects of fire to ensure building stability for the projected fire duration.

In certain areas, it has been common practice to erect a building with a flat, concrete roof deck. A wood deck on a wood frame peaked roof is then added for weather protection. Paragraph 12-1.6.2 contains an exception that permits, under certain conditions, construction of such a combustible roof system on a multistory building without jeopardizing the building construction (Type I or II) classification. The provisions in previous editions that required automatic sprinklers in attic spaces formed by

a combustible roof system have been deleted, as all new facilities must now be sprinklered (*see 12-3.5*). Attic spaces of new health care facilities using combustible roof decks in accordance with the Exception to 12-1.6.2 must be protected by automatic sprinklers.

12-1.6.3 All interior walls and partitions in buildings of Type I or Type II construction shall be of noncombustible or limited-combustible materials.

NFPA 220, *Standard on Types of Building Construction,*[2] establishes restrictions on the use of combustible building materials within structures required to be constructed of noncombustible or limited-combustible materials. NFPA 220 should be consulted for specific limitations. The terms noncombustible and limited-combustible are defined within NFPA 220 and are repeated in Chapter 3 of the *Code* for easy reference.

12-1.6.4 Openings for the passage of pipes or conduit in walls or partitions that are required to have fire or smoke resisting capability shall be protected in accordance with 6-2.3.6.2 or 6-3.6.1.

Fire and smoke may spread across a fire-rated barrier or fire-rated wall via openings created by the passage of pipes, conduit, or other building services. Paragraph 12-1.6.4 specifies that, where such penetrations occur, suitable appliances such as metal plates, masonry fill, or other products approved for the purpose should be installed to maintain the fire and smoke resisting capability of the barrier. (For *fire and draft stopping in walls, ceilings, and attics, see 6-2.6.*)

12-1.6.5 For construction requirements of enclosures of vertical openings between floors, see 12-3.1.

12-1.6.6 All buildings with more than one level below the level of exit discharge shall have all such lower levels separated from the level of exit discharge by at least Type II (111) construction.

12-1.7 Occupant Load. The occupant load for which means of egress shall be provided for any floor shall be the maximum number of persons intended to occupy that floor but not less than one person for each 120 sq ft (11.1 sq m) gross floor area in health care sleeping departments, and not less than one person for each 240 sq ft (22.3 sq m) of gross floor area of inpatient health care treatment departments. Gross floor areas shall be measured within the exterior building walls with no deductions. (*See Chapter 3.*)

Paragraph 12-1.7 specifies criteria for projecting occupant loads. The minimum occupant load for which exits must be provided in all buildings cannot be less than that established by projections involving (1) a single person for each 120 sq ft (11.1 sq m) of gross floor area in health care sleeping areas, and (2) one person for each 240 sq ft (22.3 sq m) of gross floor area in inpatient health care treatment areas. However, if by actual count, the number of persons exceeds that number projected by area calculations, the actual number of persons present becomes the minimum occupant load for which exits must be provided.

The maximum number of people allowed to occupy a space is limited by available exit capacity and other functional considerations. It is not intended to limit populations based upon the area projections contained in this paragraph.

SECTION 12-2 Means of Egress Requirements

12-2.1* General. Every aisle, passageway, corridor, exit discharge, exit location, and access shall be in accordance with Chapter 5.

Exception: As modified in the following paragraphs.

A-12-2.1 The specifications in Chapter 12 for door widths are minimums based on actual door width (leaf width). The provisions in Chapter 5 for clear width, as indicated in 5-2.1.2, apply only for purposes of capacity calculations, not for minimum widths as indicated in this chapter.

Means of egress details are to conform to the fundamental provisions of Chapter 5, except as modified in Chapter 12. Exit door width and exit capacity calculations using 12-2.3.2 shall be determined using "clear width" in accordance with 5-2.1.2. Where minimum door widths are established within Chapter 12 (in 12-2.3.5, for example), door widths are to be determined using actual door leaf width. Where door widths are specified in Chapter 12, hinge stile and stops that project into the door opening are to be ignored, since these projections were taken into consideration when the door widths specified in Chapter 12 were developed.

12-2.2* Means of Egress Components.

A-12-2.2 In planning exits, arrangements should be made to transfer patients from one section of a floor to another section of the same floor separated by a fire barrier or smoke barrier in such a manner that patients confined to their beds may be transferred in their beds. Where the building design will permit, the section of the corridor containing an entrance or elevator lobby should be separated from corridors leading from it by fire or smoke barriers. Such arrangement, where the lobby is centrally located, will, in effect, produce a smoke lock, placing a double barrier between the area to which patients may be taken and the area from which they must be evacuated because of threatening smoke and fire.

12-2.2.1 Components of the means of egress shall be limited to the types described in 12-2.2.2 through 12-2.2.7.

12-2.2.2 Doors.

12-2.2.2.1 Doors shall comply with 5-2.1.

12-2.2.2.2 Locks shall not be permitted on patient sleeping room doors.

Exception No. 1: Key locking devices that restrict access to the room from the corridor and that are operable only by staff from the corridor side shall be permitted. Such devices shall not restrict egress from the room.

This exception allows rooms that are not being used to be secured by staff. However, in the event that the room is occupied, the *Code* requires that the lock cannot restrict egress from the room.

Exception No. 2: Door locking arrangements are permitted in health care occupancies or portions of health care occupancies where the clinical needs of the patients require specialized security measures for their safety, provided keys are carried by staff at all times.

Some health care facilities may be required to provide resident security, but the *Code* requires that staff must have immediate access to patient rooms. See also paragraph 12-2.2.2.5, which limits the number of locks per door and specifies that keys must be carried by staff at all times, or other provisions must be made for the immediate release of patients using remotely controlled locking devices.

12-2.2.2.3 Doors not in a required means of egress are permitted to be subject to locking.

12-2.2.2.4 Doors within a required means of egress shall not be equipped with a latch or lock that requires the use of a tool or key from the egress side.

Exception No. 1: Door locking arrangements are permitted in health care occupancies or portions of health care occupancies where the clinical needs of the patients require specialized security measures for their safety, provided keys are carried by staff at all times. (See 12-1.1.1.7 and 12-2.2.2.5.)

Note that 12-1.1.1.7 allows the authority having jurisdiction to make appropriate modifications to compensate

for locking of egress doors. (*See commentary on 12-2.2.2.2 Exception No. 2.*)

Exception No. 2: *Special locking arrangements complying with 5-2.1.6 shall be permitted provided not more than one such device is located in any egress path.*

A-12-2.2.2.4 **Exception No. 2.** The intent of the provision is that a person following the natural path of the means of egress not encounter more than one delay release device along that path of travel to an exit. Thus, each door from the multiple floors of a building that opens into an enclosed stair may have its own delay release device, but an additional delay release device could not be present at the level of exit discharge on the door that discharges people from the enclosed stair to the outside.

Paragraph 5-2.1.6 specifies minimum requirements for delayed release hardware, including the requirement that the building must be protected throughout by automatic sprinklers or automatic fire detection.

The exception permits the use of time-delay locks on any door. However, only one door in each means of egress for any given space may use such a feature.

12-2.2.2.5 Doors located in the means of egress that are permitted to be locked under other provisions of this chapter shall have adequate provisions made for the rapid removal of occupants by such reliable means as the remote-control of locks or by keying all locks to keys carried by staff at all times. Only one such locking device is permitted on each door.

Exception: Locks installed in accordance with 12-2.2.2.4 Exception No. 2.

In buildings where it is necessary to lock doors, continuous supervision by staff must be provided. Provisions must be made for the prompt release of persons who are restrained by equipping staff with keys or by providing remote unlocking capabilities for doors. Where staff relies on the use of keys, consideration should be given to a master key system, which would facilitate the quick release of occupants. (*See commentary following Exception No. 2 to 12-2.2.2.2.*)

12-2.2.2.6* Any door in an exit passageway, stairway enclosure, horizontal exit, smoke barrier, or hazardous area enclosure (except boiler rooms, heater rooms, and mechanical equipment rooms) shall be permitted to be held open only by an automatic release device that complies with 5-2.1.8. The automatic sprinkler system, the fire alarm system, and the systems required by 5-2.1.8(c) shall be arranged so as to initiate the closing action of all such doors by zone or throughout the entire facility.

A-12-2.2.2.6 It is desirable to keep doors in exit passageways, stair enclosures, horizontal exits, smoke barriers, and required enclosures around hazardous areas closed at all times to impede the travel of smoke and fire gases. Functionally, however, this involves decreased efficiency and limits patient observation by the staff of an institution. To accommodate these necessities, it is practical to presume that such doors will be kept open even to the extent of employing wood chocks and other makeshift devices. Doors in exit passageways, horizontal exits, and smoke barriers should, therefore, be equipped with automatic hold-open devices activated by the methods described, regardless of whether or not the original installation of the doors was predicated on a policy of keeping them closed.

12-2.2.2.7 Where doors in a stair enclosure are held open by an automatic device as permitted in 12-2.2.2.6, initiation of a door closing action on any level shall cause all doors at all levels in the stair enclosure to close.

Where fire doors are held open, an automatic device must close doors upon operation of the manual fire alarm system. In addition, the doors must be designed to close automatically by actuation of either (1) a complete smoke detection system covering the entire building, or (2) smoke detectors installed to detect smoke on either side of the door. Sprinkler activation must initiate automatic-closing of the doors [*see also 5-2.1.8(d) and NFPA 72E, Standard on Automatic Fire Detectors*].[4] As a further safeguard for stairways, any automatic action that closes a stairway door on one level must close all stairway doors on all levels. (*See 12-2.2.2.7 and 12-3.1.2.*)

12-2.2.2.8 High rise health care occupancies shall comply with the provisions of 5-2.1.5.2. Selected doors on stairways are permitted to be equipped with hardware that prevents reentry in accordance with 5-2.1.5.2 Exception No. 1.

Paragraph 12-2.2.2.8 regulates stairway reentry in buildings having occupied floor levels more than 75 ft (23 m) above the lowest level of fire department access. In doing so, the *Code* exempts low rise health care occupancies from the requirements of 5-2.1.5.2. Stair doors in new high rise health care facilities must allow for reentry in accordance with Chapter 5. All stair doors must be unlocked or must be interlocked with the building fire alarm in order to unlock automatically in the event of alarm actuation. Exception No. 1 to 5-2.1.5.2 allows doors to be locked, provided the following requirements are met: a minimum of two doors must be maintained unlocked; there must be a maximum of four intervening floors between operable doors; reentry must be possible at the top or next to top floor level; reentry on the top or next to top floor level must provide access to a different exit; and doors that are unlocked must be appropriately marked on the stairwell side.

12-2.2.2.9 Horizontal sliding doors shall be permitted in a means of egress serving an occupant load of less than 50 in accordance with 5-2.1.14.2. Sliding doors that are not automatic-closing shall be limited to a single leaf and shall have a latch or other mechanism that will ensure that doors will not rebound into a partially open position if forcefully closed in an emergency.

Paragraph 12-2.2.2.9 permits horizontal sliding doors complying with 5-2.1.14.2 to be used in a means of egress where occupant loads are limited. Where sliding doors are to be closed manually, the doors must consist of a single leaf (to avoid openings at the meeting edges of the two leafs), and provisions must be made, by use of a latch or other means, to prevent the door from impacting the frame and rebounding to a partially open position when closed forcefully.

The requirements of 5-2.1.14.2 should be closely reviewed. The sliding door described is highly specialized, and all requirements of 5-2.1.14.2 must be met.

12-2.2.3 Stairs. Stairs shall comply with 5-2.2.

12-2.2.4 Smokeproof Enclosures. Smokeproof enclosures shall comply with 5-2.3.

12-2.2.5 **Horizontal Exits.** Horizontal exits shall comply with 5-2.4, modified as follows:

(a) At least 30 net sq ft (2.8 net sq m) per patient in a hospital or nursing home or 15 net sq ft (1.4 net sq m) per resident in a limited care facility shall be provided within the aggregated area of corridors, patient rooms, treatment rooms, lounge or dining areas, and other low hazard areas on each side of the horizontal exit. On stories not housing bed or litter patients, at least 6 net sq ft (.56 net sq m) per occupant shall be provided on each side of the horizontal exit for the total number of occupants in adjoining compartments.

(b) A single door shall be permitted in a horizontal exit if the exit serves one direction only. Such door shall be a swinging door or a horizontal sliding door complying with 5-2.1.14. The door shall be a minimum of 44 in. (112 cm) in width.

(c) A horizontal exit involving a corridor 8 ft (244 cm) or more in width serving as a means of egress from both sides of the doorway shall have the opening protected by a pair of swinging doors arranged to swing in opposite directions from each other, with each door having a width of at least 44 in. (112 cm), or a horizontal sliding door complying with 5-2.1.14 and providing a clear opening of at least 88 in. (224 cm).

(d) A horizontal exit involving a corridor 6 ft (183 cm) or more in width serving as a means of egress from both sides of the doorway shall have the opening protected by a pair of swinging doors, arranged to swing in opposite directions from each other, with each door having a width of at least 34 in. (86 cm), or a horizontal sliding door complying with 5-2.1.14 and providing a clear opening of at least 68 in. (173 cm).

(e) An approved vision panel is required in each horizontal exit. Center mullions are prohibited.

(f) The total exit capacity of the other exits (stairs, ramps, doors leading outside the building) shall not be reduced below one-third that required for the entire area of the building.

The requirements for horizontal exits in 12-2.2.5(a) through (f) are illustrated in Figures 12-3 and 12-4.

Doors in horizontal exits are required to swing in the direction of exit travel. In the case of a fire barrier that serves as a horizontal exit for two adjoining fire areas, a pair of doors arranged with each leaf to swing in a direction opposite from the other, or some equivalent arrangement, must be used. If a fire barrier serves as a horizontal exit from only one fire area, the door opening may be protected by a single door [44 in. (112 cm) wide in hospitals and nursing homes or 34 in. (86 cm) wide in limited care facilities] arranged to swing in the direction of exit travel.

The *Code* recognizes the use of sliding doors complying with 5-2.1.14 for the protection of openings in horizontal exits. The use of power-operated sliding doors results in an obstruction-free opening for normal traffic while still providing adequate fire protection for openings.

The provisions of 5-2.14.2, which must be complied with, are highly specialized, and all requirements must be met.

Corridors in limited care facilities and psychiatric hospitals are required to be 6 ft (183 cm) wide; therefore, it would not be practical to install a pair of 44-in. (112-cm) wide doors to protect corridor openings in a horizontal exit. In recognition of this practical consideration, and because no obstructions such as mullions are permitted, doors protecting openings in horizontal exits of such facilities are required to be a minimum of 34 in. (86 cm) wide.

In prohibiting center mullions, the intent is to eliminate any obstructions in the corridor that would restrict the movement of patients in beds, wheelchairs, or on litters.

Because of practical difficulties involving vertical exit travel in health care facilities, special recognition is given to horizontal travel and the use of horizontal exits. Up to two-thirds of the total required exit capacity for a given fire area may be provided by horizontal exits [*see* 12-2.2.5(f)]. It should be noted, however, that every floor and every fire section must have at least one exit consisting of a door leading directly outside the building, an interior stair, an outside stair, a smokeproof enclosure, a ramp, or an exit passageway (*see* 12-2.4.2). No fire area can be served by horizontal exits only. In the event a horizontal exit also serves as a smoke barrier, see commentary following 12-2.4.3, and also see subsection 12-3.7.

12-2.2.6 **Ramps.**

12-2.2.6.1 Ramps shall be Class A and shall comply with 5-2.5.

Exception: A Class B ramp shall be permitted where the height of the ramp is 1 ft (30.5 cm) or less.

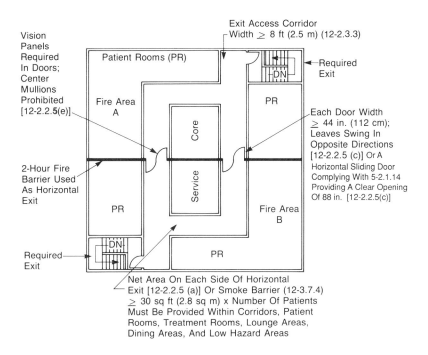

Vision Panels Required In Doors; Center Mullions Prohibited [12-2.2.5(e)]

Patient Rooms (PR)

Fire Area A

Core

Service

PR

PR

PR

Exit Access Corridor
Width ≥ 8 ft (2.5 m) (12-2.3.3)

DN

Required Exit

Each Door Width ≥ 44 in. (112 cm); Leaves Swing In Opposite Directions [12-2.2.5 (c)] Or A Horizontal Sliding Door Complying With 5-2.1.14 Providing A Clear Opening Of 88 in. [12-2.2.5(c)]

Fire Area B

2-Hour Fire Barrier Used As Horizontal Exit

DN

Required Exit

Net Area On Each Side Of Horizontal Exit [12-2.2.5 (a)] Or Smoke Barrier (12-3.7.4) ≥ 30 sq ft (2.8 sq m) x Number Of Patients Must Be Provided Within Corridors, Patient Rooms, Treatment Rooms, Lounge Areas, Dining Areas, And Low Hazard Areas

Figure 12-3. *Horizontal Exits in a New Hospital or Nursing Facility. At least one exit for each fire area must be an interior stair, smokeproof enclosure, outside stair, Class A ramp, exit passageway, or door to outside (see 12-2.4.2). Such an exit must provide at least one-third the required exit capacity of the fire area that it serves. [See 12-2.2.5(f).]*

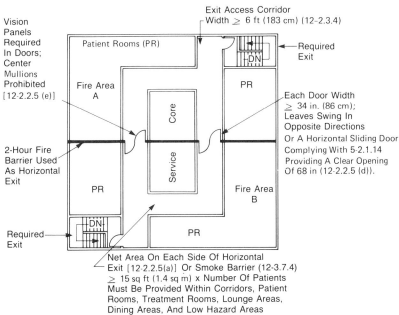

Vision Panels Required In Doors; Center Mullions Prohibited [12-2.2.5 (e)]

Patient Rooms (PR)

Fire Area A

Core

Service

PR

PR

PR

Exit Access Corridor
Width ≥ 6 ft (183 cm) (12-2.3.4)

DN

Required Exit

Each Door Width ≥ 34 in. (86 cm); Leaves Swing In Opposite Directions Or A Horizontal Sliding Door Complying With 5-2.1.14 Providing A Clear Opening Of 68 in (12-2.2.5 (d)).

Fire Area B

2-Hour Fire Barrier Used As Horizontal Exit

DN

Required Exit

Net Area On Each Side Of Horizontal Exit [12-2.2.5(a)] Or Smoke Barrier (12-3.7.4) ≥ 15 sq ft (1.4 sq m) x Number Of Patients Must Be Provided Within Corridors, Patient Rooms, Treatment Rooms, Lounge Areas, Dining Areas, And Low Hazard Areas

Figure 12-4. *Horizontal Exits in a New Limited Care Facility. At least one exit for each fire area must be an interior stair, smokeproof enclosure, outside stair, Class A ramp, exit passageway, or door to outside (see 12-2.4.2). Such an exit must provide at least one-third the required exit capacity of the fire area that it serves. [See 12-2.2.5(f).]*

12-2.2.6.2 Ramps enclosed as exits shall be of sufficient width to provide exit capacity in accordance with 12-2.3.2.

Ramps are undesirable in hospitals and nursing homes due to the potential for accidents in both normal and

emergency traffic, except in the case of ramps of extremely gradual slope, which require so much space as to be impracticable in most situations. They are, however, the only practicable method of moving patients in beds from one story to another, except by elevators, which may not be available during fire conditions. The best plan is to provide for horizontal egress to another section of the building, minimizing the need for complete evacuation.

Ramps may be the best means for providing egress from doors two or three steps above or below the grade level (*see 5-1.5*) and may also compensate for minor differences in floor levels between adjoining sections of buildings. Such ramps must be constructed in accordance with 12-2.2.6.1.

12-2.2.7   Exit Passageways. Exit passageways shall comply with 5-2.6.

12-2.3   Capacity of Means of Egress.

12-2.3.1   The capacity of any required means of egress shall be based on its width as defined in Section 5-3.

12-2.3.2   The capacity of means of egress providing travel by means of stairs shall be 0.3 in. (0.8 cm) per person, and the capacity of means of egress providing horizontal travel (without stairs) by means such as doors, ramps, or horizontal exits shall be 0.2 in. (0.5 cm) per person.

Exit capacity is calculated using a concept of "effective width" (*see Chapter 2 of NFPA 101M, Manual on Alternative Approaches to Life Safety.*)[1] This calculation method relates the usable width of an exit and the anticipated egress flow. This approach was developed using research that demonstrates that exit capacity varies with exit width and is based upon a linear relationship, rather than on the step function used in older editions of the *Code*.

Older editions of the *Code* calculated exit capacity based upon units of exit width [22 in. (55.9 cm)]. Increases in exit capacity were permitted only for minimum increases of 12 in. (30.5 cm) (½ unit of exit width). Therefore, exit capacity for a 44-in. (112-cm) stair (2 units) was computed at 44 people (22 people per unit × 2 units). No increase in capacity was allowed for stair width increases up to an additional 11 in. (27.9 cm) [e.g., a 55-in. (139.7-cm) stair]. A 56-in. (142.2-cm) stair [44-in. (112-cm) + 12 in. (30.5 cm) = 2.5 units] had a capacity of 55 persons (22 people per unit × 2.5 units).

The method currently prescribed acknowledges that increasing the width of egress systems results in increasing the flow. The new arrangement computes stair egress capacity in sprinklered buildings on the basis of 0.3 in. (6.8 cm) per person. Therefore, a 44-in. (112-cm) stair provides adequate egress for 146 persons [44 in. (112 cm) ÷ 0.3 in. (0.8 cm) per person]. Similarly, a 50-in. (127-cm) stair would have a capacity of 166 persons. The capacity of level passageways and doors in fully sprinklered buildings is computed on the basis of 0.2 in. (0.5 cm) per person. Exit capacity calculations must use clear width as defined in 5-2.1.2.1 and 5-2.2.2.1.

The origin of the design of exits using an exit unit concept evolved in the early part of the century. A philosophy developed that used exit stair enclosures in health care facilities as areas of refuge. The capacity of health care exits was set conservatively in recognition of the slow rate of travel for patients and the fact that space had to be provided for patients on litters and in wheelchairs.

Recent editions of the *Code* use a different concept for exit design. Life safety from fire in health care facilities relies upon a defend in place principle. Horizontal exits or smoke barriers are used to subdivide each story to provide an area of refuge on each story without requiring travel by means of stairs. Flow rates for exits (capacity) are established on the assumption that exit stairs will be used principally by able-bodied staff, visitors, and ambulatory patients for emergency evacuation. Nonambulatory patients will remain in the building, with those on the floor of fire origin being moved horizontally to an area of refuge. The defend in place principle is complemented by the requirement that all new health care facilities be fully protected by automatic sprinklers.

	Capacity (Inches per person)	
	Nonsprinklered†	Sprinklered
Stairs	0.6	0.3
Level Travel	0.5	0.2

†Existing buildings only, see 12-1.1.4.5.

12-2.3.3*   Aisles, corridors, and ramps required for exit access in a hospital or nursing home shall be at least 8 ft (244 cm) in clear and unobstructed width. Where ramps are used as exits, see 12-2.2.6.

Exception: Aisles, corridors, and ramps in adjunct areas not intended for the housing, treatment, or use of inpatients shall be a minimum of 44 in. (112 cm) in clear and unobstructed width.

A-12-2.3.3 Occupant characteristics are an important factor to be evaluated in setting exit criteria. Exit components in nonpatient use areas, such as administrative office spaces, should be evaluated based upon actual use. A minimum "clear" corridor width of 44 in. (112 cm) is specified, assuming occupants in nonpatient areas will be mobile and capable of evacuation without assistance.

Formal Interpretation 76-130
Reference: 12-2.3.3

Question: Is it the intent of 12-2.3.3, given a treatment suite subject to "inpatient use" that is subdivided by noncombustible partitions into individual treatment rooms without doors, that the access to these treatment rooms is required to be 8 ft (244 cm) wide?

Answer: No.

Issue Edition: 1976
Reference: 10-2.2.5.2
Date: January 1980 ∎

Exit access routes in hospitals and nursing homes are required to be 8 ft (244 cm) in clear width based on the assumption that, during a fire emergency, some patients may require movement on litters or in wheelchairs. Conversely, 44-in. (112-cm) wide access routes are considered acceptable within areas not subject to use by inpatients, such as administrative office spaces where occupants are assumed to be mobile and capable of evacuation without assistance. (*See Figure 12-5.*)

Ramps enclosed and otherwise arranged and used as exits must be of sufficient width to adequately accommodate the required exit capacity on the basis of 0.2 in. (0.5 cm) per person (*see 12-2.3.2*). For example, if a Class A ramp is to be used as an exit for 280 persons, the ramp must be a minimum of 56 in. (142 cm) wide.

12-2.3.4* Aisles, corridors, and ramps required for exit access in a limited care facility or hospital for psychiatric care shall be at least 6 ft (183 cm) in clear and unobstructed width. Where ramps are used as exits, see 12-2.2.6.

Exception: Aisles, corridors, and ramps in adjunct areas not intended for the housing, treatment, or use of inpatients shall be a minimum of 44 in. (112 cm) in clear and unobstructed width.

A-12-2.3.4 (*See A-12-2.3.3.*)

Occupants of limited care facilities are generally capable of movement with limited assistance. Since these patients will generally not require evacuation in beds or litters, the exit access widths are set at 6 ft (183 cm). (*See Figure 12-5. Also see commentary following 12-2.3.3.*)

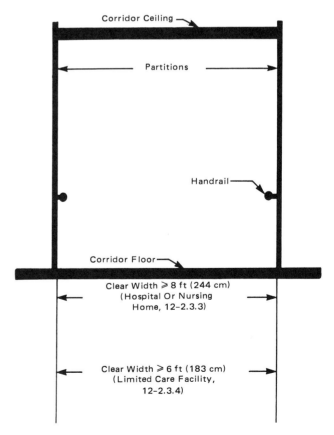

Figure 12-5. Corridor in Exit Access in New Health Care Facility.

12-2.3.5 The minimum width of doors in the means of egress from sleeping rooms; diagnostic and treatment areas, such as X-ray, surgery, or physical therapy; and nursery rooms shall be as follows:

(a) Hospitals and nursing homes: 44 in. (112 cm).

(b) Psychiatric hospitals and limited care facilities: 36 in. (91 cm).

Exception No. 1: Doors that are so located as not to be subject to use by any health care occupant shall be not less than 34 in. (86 cm) wide.

Exception No. 2: Doors in exit stair enclosures shall be not less than 36 in. (91 cm) wide.

Exception No. 3: Doors serving newborn nurseries shall be not less than 36 in. (91 cm) wide.

Exception No. 4: A 36-in. (91-cm) door leaf shall be permitted in conjunction with an inactive leaf of at least 8 in. (20.3 cm) with a rabbet, bevel, or astragal at the meeting edge.

The provisions of 12-2.3.5 are illustrated in Figures 12-6a through 12-6d.

Egress door width must be determined on the basis of required capacity and is measured using clear width in accordance with 5-2.1.2. Where minimum door widths are specified within Chapter 12 (in 12-2.3.5, for example), door widths are to be determined using actual door leaf width. Where minimum door widths are specified in Chapter 12, hinge stile and stops that project into the door opening are to be ignored, since these projections were taken into account when the door widths specified in Chapter 12 were developed.

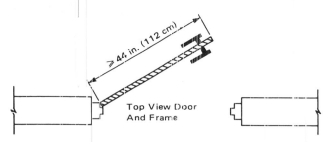

Figure 12-6a. *Minimum Width of Doors in Means of Egress that are from Sleeping Rooms, Diagnostic Areas, and Treatment Areas in New Hospitals and Nursing Homes. Maximum width is 48 in. (122 cm). (See 5-2.1.3.2.)*

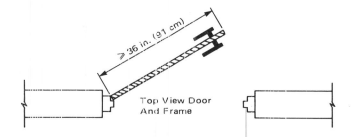

Figure 12-6b. *Minimum Width of Doors in the Means of Egress from Sleeping Rooms in New Limited Care Facilities, Hospitals for Psychiatric Care, and from Nursery Rooms in Health Care Occupancies. Maximum width is 48 in. (122 cm). (See 5-2.1.3.2.)*

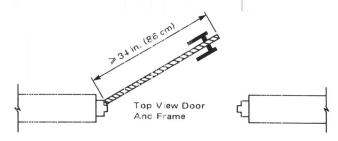

Figure 12-6c. *Minimum Width of Doors in Means of Egress That Are Not Subject to Use by Health Care Occupants in New Health Care Occupancies. Maximum width is 48 in. (122 cm). (See 5-2.1.3.2.)*

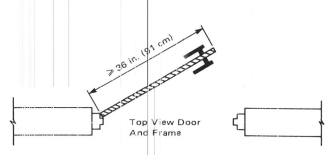

Figure 12-6d. *Minimum Width of Doors for Access to Exit Stair Enclosures in New Health Care Occupancies. Maximum width is 48 in. (122 cm) (see 5-2.1.3.2). Doors must swing in direction of exit travel. (See 5-2.1.4.1.)*

12-2.4 Number of Exits.

12-2.4.1 At least two exits of the types described in 12-2.2.2 through 12-2.2.7, remotely located from each other, shall be provided for each floor or fire section of the building.

12-2.4.2 At least one exit from each floor or fire section shall be one of the following:

(a) A door leading directly outside the building, or

(b) A stair, or

(c) A smokeproof enclosure, or

(d) A ramp, or

(e) An exit passageway.

Any fire section not meeting these requirements shall be considered as part of an adjoining zone. Egress shall not require return through the zone of fire origin.

12-2.4.3* At least two exits of the types described in 12-2.2.2 through 12-2.2.7 shall be accessible from each smoke compartment. Egress shall be permitted through adjacent compartment(s), but shall not require return through the compartment of fire origin.

A-12-2.4.3 An exit is not necessary for each individual smoke compartment if there is access to an exit through other smoke compartments without passing through the smoke compartment of fire origin.

Figure 12-7 can be used to illustrate the application of 12-2.4.2 and 12-2.4.3. If both Wall I and Wall II are horizontal exits, then three fire compartments or fire sections are formed. Paragraph 12-2.4.2 would then require that Area B must also be provided with one of the five types of exits listed. Specifically, Area B must be provided with an exit other than a horizontal exit, even though two horizontal exits are already provided from that area. Without this additional exit, Area B must be considered part of one of the adjoining areas: part of Area A, where the horizontal exit of Wall I is not recognized, or part of Area C, where the horizontal exit of Wall II is not recognized. Prior to the 1985 Edition of the *Code*, this also would have applied to smoke barriers. However, the *Code* now allows egress through adjoining smoke compartments. If both Wall I and Wall II are smoke barriers, the arrangement is acceptable. If Wall I is a smoke barrier and Wall II is a horizontal exit, the arrangement is also acceptable, since Areas A and B would be one fire area and Area C would be the other fire area. Consequently, all requirements of 12-2.4.2 and 12-2.4.3 would be met.

There are two reasons for using caution in determining the number of smoke compartments that can be safely traveled before reaching the final exit. First, excessive moving of patients should be avoided, and, second, each compartment must have sufficient area to handle all the patients it serves. In the previous example, where Wall I is a smoke barrier and Wall II is a horizontal exit, each area would have to be sufficient in size to comply with 12-2.2.5(a) for horizontal exits or 12-3.7.4 for smoke barriers, based on figures calculated for the entire floor, since all three areas are an integral part of the horizontal evacuation design for the floor. This is easily justified since, if a fire started near the exit for Area A, thus requiring evacuation into Area B, ultimate evacuation could be achieved only through Area C, since there is no exit from Area B. In such a case, Area C would have to have sufficient area to handle patients from Areas A and B as well as those patients originally in Area C.

In order to ensure that egress does not require return through the compartment of fire origin, each compartment formed must be analyzed to ensure that a path of travel to an exit other than a horizontal exit is available. (*See Figure 12-7.*)

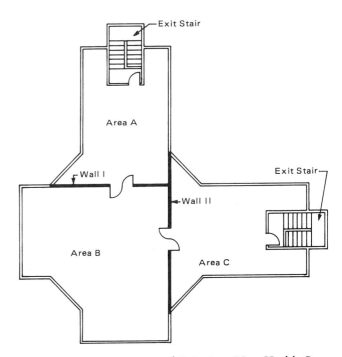

Figure 12-7. Arrangement of Exits in a New Health Care Occupancy Involving Smoke Barriers and Horizontal Exits. (See commentary following 12-2.4.3 for discussion of figure.)

12-2.5 Arrangement of Means of Egress.

12-2.5.1 Every habitable room shall have an exit access door leading directly to an exit access corridor.

Exception No. 1: If there is an exit door opening directly to the outside of the room at ground level.

Exception No. 2: Patient sleeping rooms shall be permitted to have one intervening room if the intervening room is not used to serve as an exit access for more than eight patient sleeping beds.

Exception No. 3: Special nursing suites are permitted to have one intervening room where the arrangment allows for direct and constant visual supervision by nursing personnel.

Exception No. 4: For rooms other than patients' sleeping rooms, one or more adjacent rooms shall be permitted to intervene in accordance with 12-2.5.7.

The term "habitable room" is used in 12-2.5.1 in lieu of "patient sleeping room" to clarify that all occupied rooms in a health care facility must have access to a corridor leading to an exit. (*See commentary following 12-2.4.3.*)

Figures 12-8a and b illustrate the intent of 12-2.5.1. Figure 12-9 illustrates Exception No. 2 to 12-2.5.1.

Nursing suites and various treatment areas are frequently arranged with an intervening workroom located between the exit access corridor and a treatment room. Exception No. 4 to 12-2.5.1, in combination with 12-2.5.7, will allow egress through spaces that are closely related in function to the treatment room and, therefore, are under the immediate control of staff who, along with patients, would be forced to travel across such rooms. Where such an arrangement is used, locking hardware on doors is not permitted to restrict egress from the nursing suite or intervening room. (*See 12-2.2.2.*)

Maximum travel distance limitations to reach the exit access door of nonsleeping suites are specified in 12-2.5.7 [*for sleeping suites, see 12-2.6.2(d)*]. Where applying Exception Nos. 2, 3, and 4 to 12-2.5.1, 12-2.5.4 prohibits intervening rooms from being hazardous areas.

12-2.5.2 Any patient sleeping room, or any suite that includes patient sleeping rooms, of more than 1,000 sq ft (93 sq m) shall have at least two exit access doors remotely located from each other.

Any room or any suite of rooms, other than patient sleeping rooms, of more than 2,500 sq ft (230 sq m) shall have at least two exit access doors remotely located from each other.

Patient sleeping rooms or suites with sleeping rooms that are greater than 1,000 sq ft (93 sq m) require two exit access doors. The doors may open onto a common corridor but are required to be as remotely located from each other as possible. Rooms or suites not used for patient sleeping purposes may be up to 2,500 sq ft (230 sq m) in area and require only one door, based on the premise that occupants are alert or ambulatory or are, in most instances, accompanied by staff who can assist in evacuating

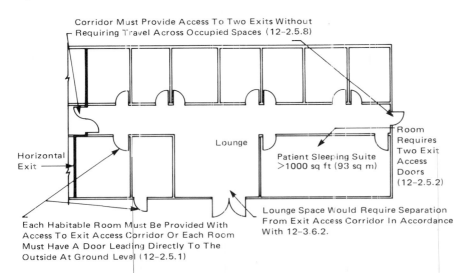

Corridor Must Provide Access To Two Exits Without Requiring Travel Across Occupied Spaces (12-2.5.8)

Horizontal Exit

Lounge

Patient Sleeping Suite >1000 sq ft (93 sq m)

Room Requires Two Exit Access Doors (12-2.5.2)

Each Habitable Room Must Be Provided With Access To Exit Access Corridor Or Each Room Must Have A Door Leading Directly To The Outside At Ground Level (12-2.5.1)

Lounge Space Would Require Separation From Exit Access Corridor In Accordance With 12-3.6.2.

Figure 12-8a. Arrangement of Exit Access in New Health Care Facility. Improper lounge arrangement, as lounge must be separated from exit access corridor (see Figure 12-8b for proper lounge arrangement). Paragraph 12-2.5.1 Exception No. 1, 12-2.5.2, and 12-2.5.8 are also illustrated.

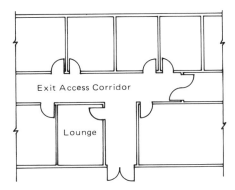

Figure 12-8b. *Proper Arrangement of Exit Access in New Health Care Facility (see Figure 12-8a). Lounge is separated from exit access corridor in accordance with 12-3.6.2 as required by 12-2.5.8. (See also 12-3.6.1 Exception Nos. 1 and 2, where a waiting space may be open to an exit access corridor.)*

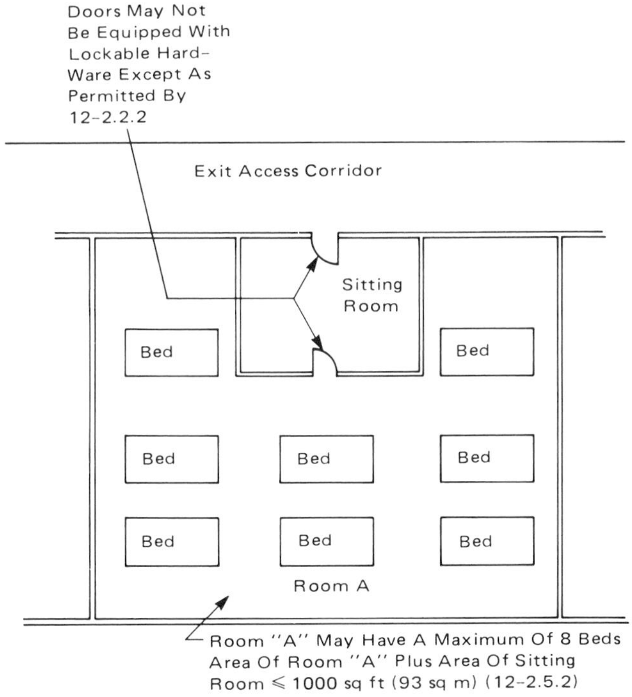

Figure 12-9. Exit Access from a Patient Sleeping Room Through an Adjacent Room in a New Health Care Occupancy. Illustration complies with 12-2.5.1 Exception No. 2 and 12-2.5.2.

the space during fire or other emergency. For sleeping suites, refer to 12-2.5.1, 12-2.5.3, 12-2.5.4, and 12-2.5.5 for additional requirements. For nonsleeping suites, refer

to 12-2.5.1, 12-2.5.3, 12-2.5.4, 12-2.5.6, and 12-2.5.7 for additional requirements. Figures 12-10a and 12-10b illustrate the requirements for sleeping suites. Figures 12-11a, 12-11b, and 12-11c illustrate the requirements for nonsleeping suites.

12-2.5.3 Any suite of rooms that complies with the requirements of this section shall be permitted to be subdivided with non-fire-rated, noncombustible, or limited-combustible partitions.

12-2.5.4 Intervening rooms shall not be hazardous areas as defined by 12-3.2.

12-2.5.5 Suites of sleeping rooms shall not exceed 5,000 sq ft (460 sq m).

Paragraph 12-2.5.5 contains provisions for nursing suites, such as Intensive Care Units (ICU) or Coronary Care Units (CCU). Interior suite arrangements are not required to comply with 12-2.3.3 or 12-3.6 relative to corridor access to exits. For example, interior corridors within special nursing units are not required to be 8 ft (244 cm) wide. Doors to individual cubicles may be sliding doors. (*See Figures 12-10a and b.*)

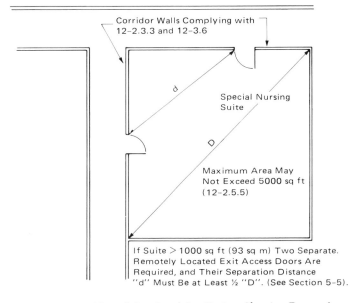

Figure 12-10a. Suites Involving Patient Sleeping Rooms in a New Health Care Occupancy. The requirements of 12-2.5.2 and 12-2.5.5 are illustrated here. (The suite must comply with Figures 12-10a and 12-10b.)

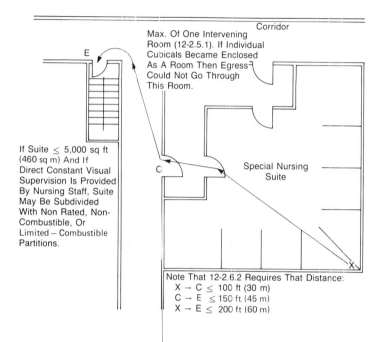

Corridor

Max. Of One Intervening Room (12-2.5.1). If Individual Cubicals Became Enclosed As A Room Then Egress Could Not Go Through This Room.

E

If Suite ≤ 5,000 sq ft (460 sq m) And If Direct Constant Visual Supervision Is Provided By Nursing Staff, Suite May Be Subdivided With Non Rated, Non-Combustible, Or Limited — Combustible Partitions.

C

Special Nursing Suite

X

Note That 12-2.6.2 Requires That Distance:
X → C ≤ 100 ft (30 m)
C → E ≤ 150 ft (45 m)
X → E ≤ 200 ft (60 m)

Figure 12-10b. *Suites Involving Patient Sleeping Rooms in a New Health Care Occupancy. The requirements of 12-2.5.1, 12-2.5.2, 12-2.5.5, and 12-2.6.2 for patient sleeping suites are illustrated. The suite must comply with Figures 12-10a and b.*

12-2.5.6 Suites of rooms, other than patient sleeping rooms, shall not exceed 10,000 sq ft (930 sq m).

12-2.5.7 Suites of rooms, other than patient sleeping rooms, shall be permitted to have one intervening room if the travel distance within the suite to the exit access door is not greater than 100 ft (30 m) and shall be permitted to have two intervening rooms where the travel distance within the suite to the exit access door is not greater than 50 ft (15 m).

The requirements of 12-2.5.2, 12-2.5.6, and 12-2.5.7 are illustrated in Figures 12-11a, 12-11b, and 12-11c.

12-2.5.8 Every corridor shall provide access to at least two approved exits in accordance with Section 5-4 and Section 5-5 without passing through any intervening rooms or spaces other than corridors or lobbies.

12-2.5.9 Every exit or exit access shall be so arranged that no corridor, aisle, or passageway has a pocket or dead end exceeding 30 ft (9.1 m).

See Figure 12-12.

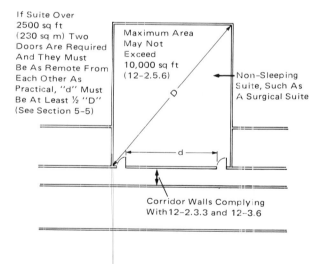

If Suite Over 2500 sq ft (230 sq m) Two Doors Are Required And They Must Be As Remote From Each Other As Practical, "d" Must Be At Least ½ "D" (See Section 5-5)

Maximum Area May Not Exceed 10,000 sq ft (12-2.5.6)

Non–Sleeping Suite, Such As A Surgical Suite

D

d

Corridor Walls Complying With 12-2.3.3 and 12-3.6

Figure 12-11a. *Suites Not Involving Patient Sleeping Rooms in a New Health Care Occupancy. This illustrates the provisions of 12-2.5.2 and 12-2.5.6. The suites must comply with Figures 12-11a and b or Figures 12-11a and c.*

12-2.6 Travel Distance to Exits.

12-2.6.1 Travel distance shall be measured in accordance with Section 5-6.

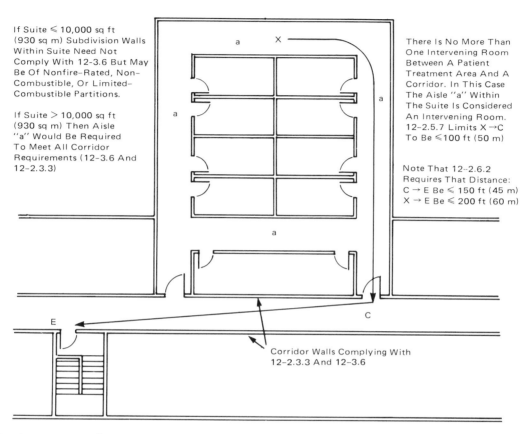

If Suite ≤ 10,000 sq ft (930 sq m) Subdivision Walls Within Suite Need Not Comply With 12-3.6 But May Be Of Nonfire–Rated, Non–Combustible, Or Limited–Combustible Partitions.

If Suite > 10,000 sq ft (930 sq m) Then Aisle "a" Would Be Required To Meet All Corridor Requirements (12-3.6 And 12-2.3.3)

There Is No More Than One Intervening Room Between A Patient Treatment Area And A Corridor. In This Case The Aisle "a" Within The Suite Is Considered An Intervening Room. 12-2.5.7 Limits X →C To Be ≤100 ft (50 m)

Note That 12-2.6.2 Requires That Distance: C → E Be ≤ 150 ft (45 m) X → E Be ≤ 200 ft (60 m)

Corridor Walls Complying With 12-2.3.3 And 12-3.6

Figure 12-11b. *Suites Not Involving Patient Sleeping Rooms in a New Health Care Occupancy. The requirements of 12-2.5.2 and 12-2.5.6 are illustrated in Figure 12-11a. Figures 12-11b and 12-11c illustrate the requirements of 12-2.5.7 and 12-2.6.2. The suites must comply with Figures 12-11a and b or 12-11a and c.*

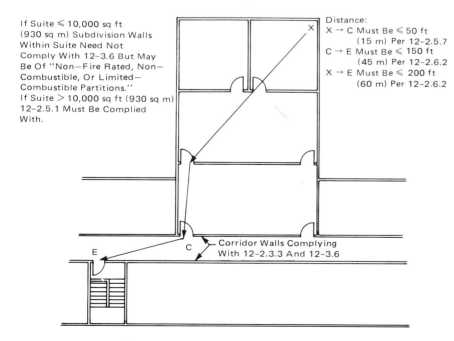

If Suite ≤ 10,000 sq ft (930 sq m) Subdivision Walls Within Suite Need Not Comply With 12-3.6 But May Be Of "Non–Fire Rated, Non–Combustible, Or Limited–Combustible Partitions." If Suite > 10,000 sq ft (930 sq m) 12-2.5.1 Must Be Complied With.

Distance: X → C Must Be ≤ 50 ft (15 m) Per 12-2.5.7 C → E Must Be ≤ 150 ft (45 m) Per 12-2.6.2 X → E Must Be ≤ 200 ft (60 m) Per 12-2.6.2

Corridor Walls Complying With 12-2.3.3 And 12-3.6

Figure 12-11c. *Suites Not Involving Patient Sleeping Rooms in a New Health Care Occupancy. The requirements of 12-2.5.7 and 12-2.6.2 for suites not involving patient sleeping rooms are illustrated. The suites must comply with Figures 12-11a and b or 12-11a and c.*

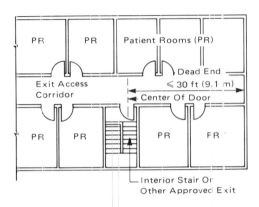

Figure 12-12. Exit Access Corridor with Dead End Allowed by 12-2.5.9 in a New Health Care Occupancy.

12-2.6.2 Travel distance:

(a) Between any room door required as exit access and an exit shall not exceed 150 ft (45 m);

(b) Between any point in a room and an exit shall not exceed 200 ft (60 m);

(c) Between any point in a health care sleeping room and an exit access door of that room shall not exceed 50 ft (15 m);

(d) Between any point in a suite of sleeping rooms as permitted by 12-2.5 and an exit access door of that suite shall not exceed 100 ft (30 m) and shall meet the requirements of (b) above.

The requirements of 12-2.6.1 and 12-2.6.2 are illustrated in Figure 12-13. Travel distance is measured only to the closest exit. It is not measured to the second exit required by 12-2.4.1. It should be noted that the 50-ft

(15-m) restriction within a room applies only to sleeping rooms. (*See also 12-2.5.7 and Figures 12-10 and 12-11.*)

12-2.7 Discharge from Exits.

12-2.7.1 Discharge from exits shall be arranged in accordance with Section 5-7.

All exit stairs or exit ramps are required to discharge to the outside either directly or through an enclosed exit passageway. Where an exit passageway is used, the fire-resistive separation of the enclosure must be the same as required for the enclosure of a stair or ramp (*see 5-2.5*). Openings into the passageway must be suitably protected and limited to doors leading to spaces that are normally occupied [*see 5-1.3.1(a) through (e)*]. Under certain conditions, a maximum of 50 percent of the required exits may discharge to the outside through the level of exit discharge in accordance with 5-7.2.

12-2.8 Illumination of Means of Egress.

12-2.8.1 Means of egress shall be illuminated in accordance with Section 5-8.

12-2.9 Emergency Lighting.

12-2.9.1 Emergency lighting shall be provided in accordance with Section 5-9.

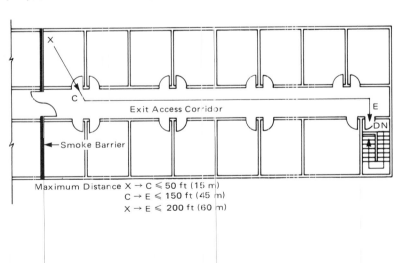

Figure 12-13. Travel Distance in New Health Care Occupancy.

12-2.9.2   Buildings equipped with or in which patients require the use of life support systems (*see 12-5.1.3*) shall have emergency lighting equipment supplied by the life safety branch of the electrical system as described in NFPA 99, *Standard for Health Care Facilities.*

12-2.10   **Marking of Means of Egress.**

12-2.10.1   Means of egress shall have signs in accordance with Section 5-10.

12-2.10.2   Buildings equipped with or in which patients require the use of life support systems (*see 12-5.1.3*) shall have illumination of the required exit and directional signs supplied by the life safety branch of the electrical system as described in NFPA 99, *Standard for Health Care Facilities.*

Exception: Self-luminous exit signs as permitted by 5-10.3.3 Exception No. 2.

Each health care facility equipped with or requiring the use of life-support systems is required to have the marking of the means of egress and emergency lighting supplied by the life safety branch of the electrical systems described in Chapter 3, "Electrical Systems," of NFPA 99, *Standard for Health Care Facilities.*[5]

A facility would not be required to have an emergency generator if the building is a freestanding unit in which, as a normal practice, (1) management maintains admitting and discharge policies that preclude the provision of care for any patient or resident who may need to be sustained by electrical life-support equipment, such as respirators or suction apparatus, and (2) no surgical treatment requiring general anesthesia is offered, and (3) battery-operated systems or equipment are provided to maintain power to exit lights and illumination of exit corridors, stairways, medical preparation areas, and the like, for a minimum of 1½ hours. Additionally, battery power would be required to be supplied to all alarm systems. For additional information, refer to NFPA 99, *Standard for Health Care Facilities.*[5]

NFPA 99 requires that emergency power supplies be arranged and protected so as to minimize the possibility of a single incident affecting both normal and emergency power supplies simultaneously. Circuits are to be run separately. Emergency and normal circuits are "joined" at the transfer switch. Damage to the transfer switch would interrupt normal and emergency power supplies simultaneously. The transfer switch is therefore a critical item and should be separated from any potential source of fire, including the emergency generator and attendant fuel supply.

NFPA 99, *Standard for Health Care Facilities,*[5] specifies that emergency generators must be inspected at least weekly and exercised for a minimum of 30 minutes a month under load. (*Also see 31-1.3.8.*)

12-2.11   **Special Features.** (Reserved.)

SECTION 12-3   Protection

12-3.1   **Protection of Vertical Openings.**

12-3.1.1   Any stairway, ramp, elevator hoistway, light or ventilation shaft, chute, or other vertical opening between stories shall be enclosed in accordance with 6-2.4 with construction having the following minimum fire resistance ratings:

   (a) 1-hour in buildings required to be of 1-hour construction.
   (b) 1-hour for enclosures connecting not more than three floors.
   (c) 2-hour for enclosures connecting more than three floors.

Exception No. 1: Vertical openings that are not concealed within the building construction that do not connect to a corridor, do not connect more than two levels, and do not serve as a means of egress need not comply with these regulations.

Exception No. 2: Duct penetrations of floor assemblies that are protected in accordance with NFPA 90A, Standard for the Installation of Air Conditioning and Ventilating Systems.

Exception No. 3: Floor and ceiling openings for pipes or conduits where the opening around the pipes or conduits is sealed in an approved manner. (See 6-2.3.6.2.)

Exception No. 4: An atrium shall be permitted in accordance with 6-2.4.6. Exception No. 1 to 6-2.4.6(g) shall not apply to patient sleeping and treatment rooms.

Paragraph 12-3.1.1 has been reorganized for clarity in the 1991 Edition. Exceptions contained in previous editions have been eliminated by the reorganization; however, the requirements remain essentially the same.

Paragraph 12-3.1 specifies protection levels required to maintain floor-to-floor separation in health care facilities. Two-hour enclosures are required around vertical openings connecting more than three stories in buildings (also see 12-1.6.2). One-hour enclosure of vertical openings is required in all other buildings.

Exception No. 1 to 12-3.1.1 is illustrated in Figure 12-14. In previous editions of the Code, Exception No. 1 was limited to stairs. This exception has been broadened in the 1991 Edition to apply to all vertical openings. However, an additional restriction is included to prohibit vertical openings connecting stories that are concealed in building construction. This exception would allow a light well to connect two stories or allow a stair to connect two levels of a medical library, file storage area, or an administrative office, for example. The exception would not allow omission of firestopping around pipe penetrations of a floor slab or omission of protection for duct penetrations.

Air-handling ducts that transfer air from floor to floor should be protected as specified in NFPA 90A, Standard for the Installation of Air Conditioning and Ventilating Systems.[6] Note that the Exception to 3-3.4.1 of NFPA 90A permits elimination of vertical shaft enclosures and allows provision of a fire damper at each point where a floor is pierced on the condition that air-handling ducts extend through one floor only. Exception No. 2 would allow this practice to be followed in health care facilities.

Exception No. 3 will allow piping and conduit to penetrate floors without requiring an enclosed shaft. Floor penetrations, however, must be adequately protected in an approved manner to maintain the required fire resistance of the floor system. The penetrations should be sealed in a fashion that will minimize the transfer of smoke.

Exception No. 4 permits atriums in health care facilities in accordance with 6-2.4.6. Patient sleeping and treatment rooms must be separated from the atrium by partitions complying with 12-3.6. Special requirements for

smoke barriers in atriums in health care facilities are illustrated in Figures 12-21a through 12-21d in 12-3.7.

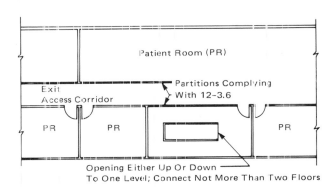

Figure 12-14. *Unprotected Vertical Opening in Accordance with 12-3.1.1 Exception No. 1 in New Health Care Occupancies.*

Formal Interpretation 76-15
Reference: 12-3.1.1

Question: Does 12-3.1.1 intend to permit combustible materials in vertical enclosure walls unless otherwise prohibited by 12-1.6.5?

Answer: Yes.

Issue Edition: 1976
Reference: 10-2.3.1.1
Date: August 1977 ∎

12-3.1.2 A door in a stair enclosure shall be self-closing and shall normally be kept in a closed position.

Exception: Doors in stair enclosures held open under the conditions specified by 12-2.2.2.6 and 12-2.2.2.7.

Paragraph 12-3.1.2 requires fire doors protecting openings in stairway enclosures to be self-closing and normally maintained in a closed position. However, the Exception to 12-3.1.2 permits stairway doors with certain qualifications to be held open by an automatic-closing device. Refer to the commentary following 12-2.2.2.6 and 12-2.2.2.7. Where stair doors are normally maintained in a closed position, they should be provided with a sign that states in large letters "Fire Exit — Keep Door Closed."

12-3.2 Protection from Hazards.

12-3.2.1* Hazardous Areas. Any hazardous area shall be protected in accordance with Section 6-4. The following areas listed shall be protected as indicated. Where sprinkler protection without fire rated separation is used, the areas shall be separated from other spaces by partitions complying with 6-3.2, with doors complying with 6-3.4.

Description	Separation/Protection
Boiler and fuel-fired heater rooms	1-hr
Employee locker rooms	See 12-3.6.3.3
Gift/retail shops	See 12-3.6.3.3
Handicraft shops	See 12-3.6.3.3
Laboratories that use hazardous materials that would cause classification as severe hazard in accordance with NFPA 99, *Standard for Health Care Facilities*	1-hr
Central/bulk laundries more than 100 sq ft (9.3 sq m) in area	1-hr
Paint shops employing hazardous substances and materials in quantities less than that which would cause classification as severe hazard	1-hr
Physical Plant Maintenance Shops	1-hr
Soiled linen rooms	1-hr
Storage rooms more than 50 sq ft (4.6 sq m) in area but not more than 100 sq ft (9.3 sq m) in area storing combustible material.	See 12-3.6.3.3
Storage rooms more than 100 sq ft (9.3 sq m) storing combustible material	1-hr
Trash collection rooms	1-hr

A-12-3.2.1 Provisions for the enclosure of rooms used for charging linen and waste chutes or for rooms into which these chutes empty are provided in Chapter 7.

Hazardous areas are spaces containing materials that, due to their basic nature (as in the case of flammable liquids) or because of the quantity of combustible materials involved, represent a significantly higher hazard than would otherwise be typical in the general areas of health care facilities.

A list of typical hazardous areas is included in 12-3.2.1. The list is meant to be representative, not all inclusive.

The general reference to Section 6-4 provides the authority having jurisdiction with the opportunity to regulate any space judged to represent a significantly higher hazard than most spaces. The 1991 Edition requires automatic sprinkler protection throughout all new health care facilities. Therefore, all hazardous spaces must be sprinklered. Where a hazardous area is judged to represent a severe exposure, such as in the case of boiler rooms, laundries, paint shops, and soiled linen rooms, 1-hour separation is also necessary. Hazardous areas that are not judged to be severe also require a separation, but the separation may use a non-fire-rated enclosure capable of retarding the transfer of smoke. Doors protecting openings in such partitions must be tight-fitting and equipped with a closing device (*see 12-3.6.3.3 and Section 6-3*). Door openings in 1-hour partitions must be protected with $^{3}/_{4}$-hour fire door assemblies.

(*See commentary on 12-3.2.2 for discussion of laboratories.*)

Formal Interpretation 76-71
Reference: 12-3.2.1

Question 1: Is it the intent of the Committee that this categorical definition of a soiled linen room as a severely hazardous area, which requires both separation and automatic extinguishment, pertains only to the central collection room of soiled linen in the facility?

Answer: No.

Question 2: Is it the intent of the Committee that this definition and is requirement also pertain to the smaller soiled linen rooms on various floors in various wings of a facility, from which the soiled linen is periodically removed to the central collection room of the facility?

Answer: Yes, however the authority having jurisdiction may modify this requirement in accordance with Section 1-5.

Issue Edition: 1976
Reference: 10-2.3.5.1
Date: May 1978 ■

Formal Interpretation 73-37
Reference: 12-3.2.1

Question: Are soiled linen and trash collection areas which serve only one patient room included as a hazardous area?

Answer: No.

Question: Are soiled linen and trash collection areas where linen and trash are held no more than 8 hours included as hazardous areas?

Answer: Yes.

Question: Are soiled linen and trash collection areas where linen and trash are held no more than 24 hours included as hazardous areas?

Answer: Yes.

Issue Edition: 1973
Reference: 10-1371
Date: June – July 1977 ■

12-3.2.2*   Laboratories. Laboratories employing quantities of flammable, combustible, or hazardous materials that are considered as severe hazard shall be protected in accordance with NFPA 99, *Standard for Health Care Facilities.*

A-12-3.2.2   The hazard level of a laboratory is considered severe if quantities of flammable, combustible or hazardous materials are present that are capable of sustaining a fire condition of sufficient magnitude to breach a 1-hour fire separation.

See NFPA *Fire Protection Handbook* (*see Appendix B*), Section 7, Chapter 9, for guidance.

Laboratories that contain "ordinary" combustibles and flammable liquids in sufficient quantity to threaten a 1-hour fire separation [e.g., wood-equivalent fuel loads in the range of 5 to 10 lb/sq ft (25 to 50 kg/sq m)] are considered a severe hazard]. Laboratories posing a severe hazard must be protected in accordance with Chapter 10, "Laboratories," of NFPA 99, *Standard for Health Care Facilities.*[5] Protection would include 1-hour fire resistance separation and automatic sprinkler protection.

Where fuel loads of lesser amounts are involved and quantities of flammable liquids are limited, laboratories would simply be considered hazardous areas and would require either 1-hour separation or automatic sprinkler protection, as indicated in 12-3.2.1 and Section 6-4.

12-3.2.3   Anesthetizing Locations. Anesthetizing locations shall be protected in accordance with NFPA 99, *Standard for Health Care Facilities.*

12-3.2.4   Medical Gas. Medical gas storage and administration areas shall be protected in accordance with NFPA 99, *Standard for Health Care Facilities.*

12-3.2.5   Gift Shops. Gift shops shall be protected as hazardous areas where used for the storage or display of combustibles in quantities considered hazardous. Gift shops not considered hazardous and having separately protected storage shall be permitted to be:

(a) Open to a lobby or corridor if the gift shop is not greater than 500 sq ft (46.5 sq m), or

(b) Separated from a lobby or corridor with non-fire-rated walls.

Many gift shops, particularly those containing combustible storage and having sizable retail areas, do pose a hazard well beyond that normal to patient-occupied spaces and, thus, merit special protection. However, it is recognized that many small retail areas [less than 500 sq ft (46.5 sq m), for example] constitute a relatively minor hazard that is adequately mitigated by automatic sprinkler protection. This paragraph provides the authority having jurisdiction with guidance in judging the degree of hazard and offers the facility some flexibility in the design and operation of gift shops.

It should be noted that to use either of the two options offered, the gift shop must be judged nonhazardous and must have separately protected storage areas.

12-3.2.6   Cooking Facilities. Cooking facilities shall be protected in accordance with 7-2.3.

Exception*: Where domestic cooking equipment is used for food warming or limited cooking, protection or segregation of food preparation facilities is not required.

A-12-3.2.6 **Exception.** This exception is intended to permit small appliances used for reheating, such as microwave ovens, hot plates, toasters, and nourishment centers to be exempt from requirements of commercial cooking equipment.

Commercial cooking equipment must be installed and protected in accordance with NFPA 96, *Standard for the Installation of Equipment for the Removal of Smoke and Grease-Laden Vapors from Commercial Cooking Equipment.*[7] A regularly serviced, fixed, automatic fire extinguishing system would be required for the protection of cooking surfaces and exhaust and duct systems where cooking operations involve the potential for grease-laden vapors. Cooking operations that do not involve the release of smoke or grease-laden vapors are not subject to compliance with NFPA 96 and would not normally be treated as hazardous operations.

The exception notes that 12-3.2.6 would not apply to a room used as a staff lounge equipped with a domestic-type range or microwave oven. Such a room would be considered similar to a treatment room and would require separation as indicated in 12-3.6.1.

12-3.3 **Interior Finish.**

12-3.3.1 Interior finish of walls and ceilings throughout shall be Class A or B in accordance with Section 6-5. The provisions of 6-5.7.1 shall not apply.

Exception No. 1: Walls and ceilings shall be Class A, B, or C interior finish in individual rooms having a capacity of not over four persons.

Exception No. 2: Corridor wall finish up to 4 ft (122 cm) in height that is restricted to the lower half of the wall shall be Class A, B, or C.

Interior finishes on walls and ceilings are limited to Class A or B materials, except in rooms of four or fewer persons, where Class C materials are allowed.

Exception No. 2 to 12-3.3.1 allows wall finish in corridors to be of Class C materials where located 4 ft (122 cm) or less in height above the floor. This provision recognizes fire research[8] that has shown the finish on the lower half of the wall to be far less significant in its influ-

ence on early fire growth than the finish on the upper portion of the wall. In the case of textile materials on walls or ceilings, 6-5.2.3 would take precedence and require automatic sprinkler protection in conjunction with Class A materials, or such wall and ceiling materials must be proven safe by room/corner testing.

The wall and ceiling limitations in 12-3.3.1 contemplate automatic sprinkler protection. Therefore, to prevent a "double credit" for automatic sprinklers, 12-3.3.1 notes that 6-5.7.1 does not apply.

12-3.3.2 **Interior Floor Finish.** No requirements.

It has been shown that floor coverings will not spread a fire until the fire becomes large, i.e., approaches flashover (*see commentary on 6-5.4*). Automatic sprinklers will activate well in advance of any significant involvement of a floor covering. Therefore, the limitations on interior floor finish for sprinklered facilities have been deleted in the 1991 Edition.

12-3.4 **Detection, Alarm, and Communication Systems.**

12-3.4.1 **General.**

12-3.4.1.1 Health care occupancies shall be provided with a fire alarm system in accordance with Section 7-6.

12-3.4.1.2 All required fire alarm systems and detection systems shall be provided with a secondary power supply in accordance with 7-6.1.4.

12-3.4.2 **Initiation.** Initiation of the required fire alarm systems shall be by manual means in accordance with 7-6.2 and by means of any sprinkler system water flow alarms, detection devices, or detection systems required.

Exception: Fire alarm pull stations in patient sleeping areas are not required at exits if located at all nurses' control stations or other continuously attended staff location, provided such pull stations are visible and continuously accessible and that travel distances required by 7-6.2.4 are not exceeded.

Formal Interpretation 76-18
Reference: 12-3.4.2

Question: Does 12-3.4.2 intend to require a local device designed to detect smoke on either side of an opening, as referenced in 12-2.2.2.6, to be connected to the fire alarm system?

Answer: Yes. The Committee intended that, in new construction, all required fire detection devices be connected to the fire alarm system.

Issue Edition: 1976
Reference: 10-2.3.3.7
Date: August 1977 ∎

12-3.4.3 Notification.

12-3.4.3.1 Occupant Notification. Occupant notification shall be accomplished automatically, without delay, upon operation of any fire alarm activating device by means of an internal audible alarm in accordance with 7-6.3. Presignal systems are prohibited.

12-3.4.3.2 Emergency Forces Notification. Fire department notification shall be accomplished in accordance with 7-6.4.

Exception: Smoke detection devices or smoke detection systems equipped with reconfirmation features need not automatically notify the fire department unless the alarm condition is reconfirmed after a maximum 120-second time period.

An independent study by the National Bureau of Standards indicates a high rate of false alarms for smoke detectors installed in health care facilities.[9] The study determined 4.4 false alarms occurred per 100 smoke detectors per year. Furthermore, approximately 14 false alarms occurred for every actual alarm. Because of the high incidence of false alarms, the *Code* permits delaying fire department notification for up to 120 seconds where smoke detectors or smoke detection systems are equipped with a reconfirmation feature.

12-3.4.4 Emergency Control. Operation of any activating device in the required fire alarm system shall be arranged to automatically accomplish, without delay, any control functions to be performed by that device. (*See 7-6.5.*)

12-3.4.5 Detection.

12-3.4.5.1 Corridors. An approved automatic smoke detection system shall be installed in all corridors of nursing homes and limited care facilities. Such system shall be installed in accordance with Section 7-6.

Exception No. 1: Where each patient sleeping room is protected by an approved smoke detection system, and a smoke detector is provided at smoke barriers and horizontal exits, such corridor systems will not be required on the patient sleeping room floors.

Exception No. 2: Corridor detection systems are not required within a smoke compartment where the compartment is fully protected by a supervised automatic sprinkler system equipped with quick response sprinklers.

12-3.4.5.2 Spaces Open to Corridors. (*See 12-3.6.1.*)

Paragraphs 12-3.4.1 through 12-3.4.5 deal with required fire alarm equipment. Reliability is of prime importance; therefore, electrical supervision of the system and system components is specified by reference to Section 7-6. In the event of circuit fault, component failure, or other "trouble," continuous "trouble indication" is required and should be provided at a constantly attended location.

A manual fire alarm system is required by 12-3.4.2. Manual pull stations are normally located along the natural routes of egress and are also located so as to adequately cover all portions of the building. The Exception to 12-3.4.2 allows pull stations, with certain qualifications, to be located at continuously attended staff positions in sleeping areas. This arrangement provides the opportunity for prompt notification of fire without requiring staff to leave their normal work station. In any case, manual pull stations should always be located so that those qualified to send an alarm may summon aid without having to leave their zone of ordinary activity or pass out of the sight and hearing of people immediately exposed to or in direct view of a fire. In new installations, it would normally be desirable to have manual pull stations at all attended staff locations and at entrances to exits, as the additional cost of the extra pull stations would be minimal. The operation of a manual fire alarm station should automatically summon attendants who can assist in removing physically helpless occupants and who can help control mentally disabled occupants.

The system required by 12-3.4.2 may be incorporated into an automatic system equipped to detect a fire and initiate an alarm.

Actuation of any required fire or smoke detector, activation of a required sprinkler system, or operation of a manual pull station must automatically, without delay, sound audible alarm devices within the building. Presignal systems are not permitted.

The alarm must automatically transmit to a point outside the facility. Where automatic transmission of alarms to the fire department legally committed to serve the facility is not permitted, arrangements are to be made for the prompt notification of the fire department or such other assistance as may be available in the case of fire or other emergency. Paragraph 7-6.4 lists various methods acceptable for automatically notifying the fire department. The fire department should still be called manually to verify and confirm the automatic transmission of the alarm. In larger facilities, this may be the responsibility of the facility telephone operator; in smaller facilities, it may be the responsibility of the nursing staff.

Paragraph 12-3.4.5.1 requires smoke detectors to be located in all corridors of new nursing homes and new limited care facilities. As an option to locating smoke detectors in corridors, smoke detectors may be installed in each patient's room and at smoke barriers and horizontal exits. Exception No. 2 allows omission of corridor detection systems in smoke compartments that are fully sprinklered by means of quick response sprinklers.

In recognition of varied staffing criteria, smoke detectors are not required in hospitals where staff is expected to be present to sound the alarm.

Actuation of the fire alarm must initiate the operation of audible alerting devices that will sound throughout the affected zone or building, as appropriate. Visible alerting devices may be used but may not serve as a substitute for audible devices.

12-3.5 Extinguishment Requirements.

12-3.5.1* Buildings containing health care facilities shall be protected throughout by an approved supervised automatic sprinkler system installed in accordance with Section 7-7.

Exception: In Types I and II construction, where approved by the authority having jurisdiction, alternative protection measures may be substituted for sprinkler protection in specified areas where the authority having jurisdiction has prohibited sprinklers, without causing a building to be classified as nonsprinklered.

A-12-3.5.1 In areas where the replenishment of water supplies is not immediately available from on-site sources, alternate provisions for the water-fill rate requirements of NFPA 13, *Standard for the Installation of Sprinkler Systems*, and NFPA 22, *Standard for Water Tanks for Private Fire Protection*, acceptable to the authority having jurisdiction should be provided. Appropriate means for the replenishment of these supplies from other sources, such as fire department tankers, public safety organizations, or other independent contractors should be incorporated into the overall firesafety plan of the facility.

With automatic sprinkler protection required throughout new health care facilities and quick response sprinklers required in smoke compartments containing patient sleeping rooms, the Committee is of the opinion that a fire and its life threatening byproducts could be reduced, thereby allowing the defend in place concept to continue. The Committee in its deliberations considered the difficulty in maintaining the proper integrity of life safety elements and is of the opinion that a probability of a sprinkler system operating as designed is equal to or greater than other life safety features.

12-3.5.2* Listed quick response or listed residential sprinklers shall be used throughout smoke compartments containing patient sleeping rooms.

Exception No. 1: Standard response sprinklers shall be permitted for use in areas where quick response and residential sprinklers are prohibited from being installed by their listing.

Exception No. 2: Standard response sprinklers shall be permitted for use in hazardous areas protected in accordance with Section 12-3.2.1.

A-12-3.5.2   The requirements for use of quick response sprinklers intends that quick response sprinklers be the predominant type of sprinkler installed in the smoke compartment. It is recognized, however, that quick response sprinklers may not be approved for installation in all areas such as those where NFPA 13, *Standard for the Installation of Sprinkler Systems*, requires sprinklers of the intermediate – or high-temperature classification. It is not the intent of the 12-3.5.1 requirements to prohibit the use of standard sprinklers in limited areas of a smoke compartment where intermediate – or high-temperature sprinklers are required.

Where the installation of quick response sprinklers is not practicable in patient sleeping room areas, appropriate equivalent protection features acceptable to the authority having jurisdiction should be provided. It is recognized that the use of quick response sprinklers may be limited in facilities housing certain types of patients, or due to the installation limitations of quick response sprinklers.

Paragraph 12-3.5.1 requires automatic sprinkler protection throughout all new health care facilities, and 12-3.5.2 requires the use of quick response or residential sprinklers throughout all compartments containing patient sleeping rooms. Exception Nos. 1 and 2 to 13-3.5.2 allow the use of standard sprinklers in those isolated instances where the use of quick response or residential sprinklers are disallowed or inappropriate. For example, residential sprinklers are only approved for use under flat, smooth, horizontal ceilings. Quick response heads may not be suitable for installation in areas subject to elevated temperatures, such as spaces under skylights or near ceiling unit heaters. These sprinklers have not been evaluated for use in hazardous spaces, and, therefore, Exception No. 2 permits the use of standard heads in such locations.

Where sprinkler protection is specified, complete building coverage in accordance with the provisions of NFPA 13, *Standard for the Installation of Sprinkler Systems*,[10] is required. The *Code* does not exempt any area of the building from protection (*see Section 7-7*). However, where automatic sprinkler protection is omitted from certain spaces at the mandate of the authority having jurisdiction and the authority having jurisdiction approves alternative protective measures, the building is still considered fully protected throughout. Sprinklers may only

be omitted from isolated areas in buildings of fire rated, noncombustible construction, where the building will have sufficient structural fire resistance to outlast most fires. Use of alternative protective measures to automatic sprinklers should be carefully evaluated to ensure equivalent protection. Where fixed automatic fire extinguishing systems (those using halon, for example) are used as an alternative to sprinklers for specific spaces, it is suggested that the spaces also be separated by fire resistant construction.

The term "supervised" in 12-3.5.1 means a distinct supervisory signal must be provided to a constantly attended location in the event of any malfunction or action that would impair sprinkler performance. Supervision must be provided, for example, for water supply and sprinkler control valves, fire pump power and running conditions, water tank levels and temperatures, pressure in pressure tanks, air pressure in dry-pipe systems, building temperature, and city water pressure. Supervision should include all sprinkler sectional control valves in addition to main control valves. (*See also Section 7-7.2.*)

12-3.5.3   Portable fire extinguishers shall be provided in all health care occupancies in accordance with 7-7.4.l.

12-3.6   Corridors.

Section 12-3.6 contains provisions for construction of corridor partitions. This section has undergone major revision in the 1991 Edition due to the requirement for automatic sprinklers in 12-3.5.1. Requirements for sprinklered buildings remain fundamentally unchanged. The requirements of 12-3.6.1 through 12-3.6.4 essentially stipulate that all areas that contain combustibles in sufficient quantities to produce a life-threatening fire must be separated from exit access corridors by partitions. Partitions must be able to retard the transfer of smoke but need not be fire rated.

Paragraph 12-3.6.1 establishes requirements for the existence and location of corridor partitions.

Paragraph 12-3.6.2 establishes construction requirements for corridor partitions.

Paragraph 12-3.6.3 establishes requirements for doors in corridor partitions.

Paragraph 12-3.6.4 addresses transfer grilles.

12-3.6.1 Corridors shall be separated from all other areas by partitions complying with 12-3.6.2 through 12-3.6.5. (*Also see 12-2.5.8.*)

Exception No. 1: Spaces shall be permitted to be unlimited in area and open to the corridor provided:

(a) The spaces are not used for patient sleeping rooms, treatment rooms, or hazardous areas, and

(b) The corridors onto which the spaces open in the same smoke compartment are protected by an electrically supervised automatic smoke detection system installed in accordance with 12-3.4, or the smoke compartment in which the space is located is protected throughout by quick response sprinklers, and

(c) The open space is protected by an electrically supervised automatic smoke detection system installed in accordance with 12-3.4, or the entire space is arranged and located to permit direct supervision by the facility staff from a nursing station or similar space, and

(d) The space does not obstruct access to required exits.

Exception No. 2: Waiting areas shall be permitted to be open to the corridor provided:

(a) The aggregate waiting area in each smoke compartment does not exceed 600 sq ft (55.7 sq m), and

(b) Each area is protected by an electrically supervised automatic smoke detection system installed in accordance with 12-3.4, or each area is arranged and located to permit direct supervision by the facility staff from a nursing station or similar space, and

(c) The area does not obstruct access to required exits.

Exception No. 3*: Space for nurses' stations.

A-12-3.6.1 **Exception No. 3.** A typical nurses' station would normally contain one or more of the following with associated furniture and furnishings.

(a) Charting area.
(b) Clerical area.
(c) Nourishment station.
(d) Storage of small amounts of medications, medical equipment and supplies, clerical supplies, and linens.
(e) Patient monitoring and communication equipment.

Exception No. 4: Gift shops open to the corridor where protected in accordance with 12-3.2.5.

Exception No. 5: In a limited care facility, group meeting or multipurpose therapeutic spaces shall be permitted to open to the corridor provided:

(a) The space is not a hazardous area, and

(b) The space is protected by an electrically supervised automatic smoke detection system installed in accordance with 12-3.4, or the space is arranged and located to permit direct supervision by the facility staff from the nurses' station or similar location, and

(c) The area does not obstruct any access to required exits.

See also commentary following Exception No. 8(e) to 13-3.6.1.

Paragraph 12-3.6.1 requires that all spaces be separated from corridors by partitions. Exceptions are provided to allow specific areas to be open to the corridor. The intent is to limit the risk of exposing the corridor to fire. Exceptions Nos. 1 through 5 to 12-3.6.1 specify those areas that are permitted to be open to corridors.

Exception No. 1 to 12-3.6.1 contains provisions for spaces such as recreation/lounge/waiting areas that may be open to the corridor but not subject to the area restrictions imposed by Exception No. 2. The open space must be visually supervised by staff from a permanent staff location, or the space must be protected with a smoke detection system. Interconnected corridors that are not separated from the space must be equipped with an electrically supervised smoke detection system, or the smoke compartment must be sprinklered throughout using quick response sprinklers. (*See Figure 12-15a.*)

Waiting areas, which may not total over 600 sq ft (55.7 sq m) in any one smoke compartment, may be open to the corridor in accordance with Exception No. 2. Each waiting area must be located to permit direct visual supervision by the staff or must be equipped with an electrically supervised automatic smoke detection system. In all cases, waiting spaces must be arranged so as not to obstruct access to exits. (*See Figure 12-15b.*)

Exception No. 1 to 12-3.6.1 will not permit treatment spaces to be open to corridors. Exception No. 5, however, will permit multipurpose treatment spaces to be open to corridors in limited care facilities. The space may not be used for hazardous operations such as woodworking involving occupational therapy.

Exception No. 5 and Exception Nos. 1 and 2 specify that the space must be supervised by staff or protected by a smoke detection system. The "supervision" required by Exception Nos. 1, 2, and 5 (and assumed in Exception No. 3) is important. It allows the staff to see, hear, or smell a developing fire or to prevent the ignition of a fire by virtue of their presence. The use of closed-circuit television or mirrors does not provide for all the above and should not be relied upon in new construction. Adequate supervision is not provided if the staff cannot readily supervise the space without extraordinary effort (e.g., looking around a corner).

Areas used for charting and communication by doctors and nurses may be open to the corridor.

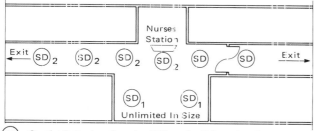

(SD)₁ : Smoke Detectors Required Where Staff Does Not Provide Supervision Of Space. Probably Not Required In This Example

(SD)₂ : Smoke Detector Required Unless Entire Smoke Compartment Protected By Quick Response Sprinklers

Figure 12-15a.   Area Open to Corridor. Unlimited size area open to corridor in accordance with Exception No. 1 to 12-3.6.1.

12-3.6.2   Construction of Corridor Walls.

12-3.6.2.1* Corridor walls shall form a barrier to limit the transfer of smoke. Such walls shall be permitted to terminate at the ceiling where the ceiling is constructed to limit the transfer of smoke. No fire resistance rating is required for corridor walls.

A-12-3.6.2.1 It is the *Code's* intent that there be no required fire resistance nor area limitations for vision panels in corridor walls and doors.

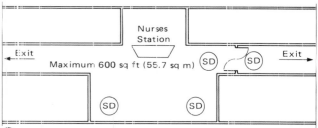

(SD) Smoke Detectors Required If Staff Does Not Provide Supervision Of Waiting Space. Probably Not Required In This Example.

Figure 12-15b.   Waiting Spaces. Waiting area complying with Exception No. 2 to 12-3.6.1.

Corridor partitions must be constructed of materials selected on the basis of the construction types allowed by 12-1.6.2. All construction materials in buildings of Type I or Type II construction must satisfy the criteria for noncombustible or limited-combustible materials. (*See 12-1.6.3.*)

Corridor partitions need not be fire rated but must nevertheless be constructed to resist the passage of smoke. Where suspended ceilings are provided, partitions may be terminated at the suspended ceiling without any additional special protection if the suspended ceiling will resist the passage of smoke. The ability to resist the passage of smoke must be carefully evaluated. There are no restrictions in terms of area or fire resistance for glazing used in corridor partitions. (*See Figure 12-16.*)

12-3.6.3*   Corridor Doors.

A-12-3.6.3 While it is recognized that closed doors serve to maintain tenable conditions in a corridor and adjacent patient rooms, such doors, which under normal or fire conditions are self-closing, may create a special hazard for the personal safety of a room occupant. These closed doors may present a problem of delay in discovery, confining fire products beyond tenable conditions.

Since it is critical for responding staff members to be able to immediately identify the specific room involved, it is suggested that consideration be given that rooms having doors equipped with closing devices be protected by approved automatic smoke detection that is interconnected with the building fire alarm. Such detection may be located at any approved point within the room. When activated, the detector must

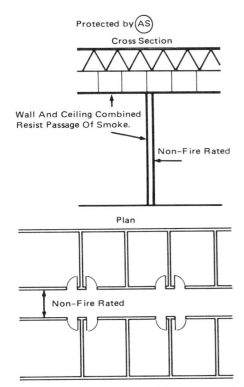

Protected by (AS)

Cross Section

Wall And Ceiling Combined
Resist Passage Of Smoke.

Non-Fire Rated

Plan

Non-Fire Rated

Figure 12-16. Corridor Walls. In buildings protected throughout by an approved automatic sprinkler system, walls may terminate at ceilings, provided the wall and ceiling resist the passage of smoke. (See 12-3.6.2.1.)

provide warning that indicates the specific room of involvement by activation of fire alarm annunciator, nurse call system, or any other device acceptable to the authority having jurisdiction.

12-3.6.3.1 Doors protecting corridor openings shall be constructed to resist the passage of smoke.

Exception: Doors to toilet rooms, bathrooms, shower rooms, sink closets, and similar auxiliary spaces that do not contain flammable or combustible materials.

12-3.6.3.2 Doors shall be provided with positive latching hardware. Roller latches are prohibited.

Exception: Doors to toilet rooms, bathrooms, shower rooms, sink closets, and similar auxiliary spaces that do not contain flammable or combustible materials.

The *Code* now clearly requires positive latching hardware on corridor walls. The purpose is to ensure that doors, once closed by staff, remain closed.

12-3.6.3.3 Door-closing devices are not required on doors in corridor wall openings other than those serving required enclosures of vertical openings, exits, or hazardous areas.

12-3.6.3.4 Dutch doors shall be permitted where they conform to 12-3.6.3, and in addition, both upper leaf and lower leaf shall be equipped with a latching device, and the meeting edges of the upper and lower leaves shall be equipped with an astragal, rabbet, or bevel.

Dutch doors protecting openings in enclosures around hazardous areas shall comply with NFPA 80, *Standard for Fire Doors and Windows.*

Doors protecting openings in corridor partitions must be able to resist the passage of smoke but are not required to have a fire protection rating. Doors must be equipped with a positive latch that cannot be held in the retracted position. Roller latches are not permitted. The latch should be capable of holding the door in a closed position. Door-closing devices are not required except on doors protecting openings in exit enclosures, vertical openings, or required enclosures of hazardous areas. There are no restrictions in terms of area or fire resistance for glazing used in corridor doors, as all facilities are now required to be sprinklered.

12-3.6.4 **Transfer Grilles.** Transfer grilles, whether or not protected by fusible link operated dampers, shall not be used in these walls or doors.

Exception: Doors to toilet rooms, bathrooms, shower rooms, sink closets, and similar auxiliary spaces that do not contain flammable or combustible materials.

The use of an exit access corridor as an exhaust, supply, or return air plenum for a building's air-handling system is not permitted. Corridor doors may not be undercut to facilitate transfer of air, nor are transfer grilles allowed in corridor partitions (*see 12-3.6.4*) or corridor doors (*see also 2-3.11.1 of NFPA 90A, Standard for the Installation of Air Conditioning and Ventilating Systems).*[6] However, sink closets, bathrooms, and toilets may have doors equipped with a fixed grille or louver to allow exhaust air to be "made up" from the corridor (*see Exception to 12-3.6.3.1*). Where a door to a sink closet, bathroom, or toilet is equipped with a grille or louver, such spaces may not be used for the storage of flammable or combustible supplies. Caution must be exercised where using this exception for sink closets, as they are often used for storage of combustibles.

12-3.6.5   In other than smoke compartments containing patient sleeping rooms, miscellaneous openings such as mail slots, pharmacy pass-through windows, laboratory pass-through windows, and cashier pass-through windows shall be permitted in vision panels or doors without special protection provided the aggregate area of openings per room does not exceed 20 sq in. (.013 sq m) and the openings are installed at or below half the distance from the floor to the room ceiling.

Paragraph 12-3-6.5 establishes restrictions for miscellaneous openings in corridor partitions. For practical reasons, there are many small openings required in corridor partitions for use as mail slots, cashier windows, and for passing items to laboratory or pharmacy spaces. Paragraph 12-3.6.5 was added in the 1991 Edition to regulate such openings. Openings are not allowed in compartments having sleeping rooms. In other compartments, the opening must be limited to a maximum of 20 sq in. (.013 sq m) and must be located in the lower half of the partition. Calculations indicate the smoke flow through a 20-sq in. (.013-sq m) opening located at midheight [4 ft (122 cm) above the floor] during a fire where sprinklers are operating will be limited to approximately 40-50 cfm (1.3 cu m/s) with a smoke temperature of 200-250°F (90-120°C) when the smoke layer has descended to floor level.

12-3.7*   Subdivision of Building Spaces.

A-12-3.7   See A-12-2.2.

12-3.7.1   Smoke barriers shall be provided as follows:

(a) To divide every story used by inpatients for sleeping or treatment into at least two smoke compartments, and

(b) To divide every story having an occupant load of 50 or more persons, regardless of use, into at least two smoke compartments, and

(c) To limit the size of each smoke compartment to an area not exceeding 22,500 sq ft (2,100 sq m), and

Exception to (c): The area of an atrium separated in accordance with 6-2.4.6 shall not be limited in size.

(d) To limit the travel distance from any point to reach a smoke barrier door to 200 ft (60 m).

Item (a) requires subdivision of any floor used by inpatients for sleeping or treatment, regardless of its size and the number of patients. Item (b) requires subdivision of any other floor that has an occupant load of 50 or more persons, regardless of size or use.

Items (c) and (d) specify dimensional criteria for smoke compartments to establish limits for maximum size. The maximum area of 22,500 sq ft (2,100 sq m) [150 ft (45 m) × 150 ft (45 m)] specified in previous editions has been retained. However, to provide the facility and designer with flexibility in the arrangement of smoke compartments, the arbitrary 150-ft (45-m) length and width limits have been deleted in favor of a 200-ft (60-m) travel distance [see 12-3.7.1(d)]. Smoke compartments must be designed so that a person is able to reach a smoke barrier door within a travel distance of 200 ft (60 m) or less from any point in a compartment, measured along the natural path of travel in accordance with 5-6.2.

Horizontal exits may be substituted for smoke barriers. In such cases, the horizontal exit would also have to be constructed to comply with smoke barrier requirements. (*See Section 6-3.*)

Areas open to atriums may not be used for patient sleeping or treatment areas (*see Exception No. 4 to 12-3.1.1*). A maximum of three levels may be open to the atrium in accordance with 6-2.4.6, with additional stories separated by 1-hour partitions or glass walls with special sprinkler protection. Atrium smoke compartments arranged in accordance with 6-2.4.6 are not limited in size.

12-3.7.2   Smoke barriers shall be provided on stories that are usable but unoccupied.

12-3.7.3 Any required smoke barrier shall be constructed in accordance with Section 6-3 and shall have a fire resistance rating of at least 1 hour.

Exception No. 1: Where an atrium is used, smoke barriers shall be permitted to terminate at an atrium wall constructed in accordance with Exception No. 2 to 6-2.4.6(g). A minimum of two separate smoke compartments shall be provided on each floor.

Exception No. 2: Dampers are not required in duct penetrations of smoke barriers in fully ducted HVAC systems.

12-3.7.4 At least 30 net sq ft (2.8 net sq m) per patient in a hospital or nursing home or 15 net sq ft (1.4 net sq m) per resident in a limited care facility shall be provided within the aggregate area of corridors, patient rooms, treatment rooms, lounge or dining areas, and other low hazard areas on each side of the smoke barrier. On stories not housing bed or litter patients, at least 6 net sq ft (.56 net sq m) per occupant shall be provided on each side of the smoke barrier for the total number of occupants in adjoining compartments.

12-3.7.5* Doors in smoke barriers shall be substantial doors, such as 1¾-in. (4.4-cm) thick, solid bonded wood core or construction that will resist fire for at least twenty minutes. Cross corridor openings in smoke barriers shall be protected by a pair of swinging doors or a horizontal sliding door complying with 5-2.1.14. Swinging doors shall be arranged so that each door will swing in a direction opposite from the other. The minimum door leaf width for swinging doors shall be as follows:

(a) Hospitals and nursing homes: 44 in. (112 cm).

(b) Hospitals for psychiatric care and limited care facilities: 34 in. (86 cm).

The minimum clear opening for horizontal sliding doors shall be as follows:

(a) Hospitals and nursing homes: 88 in. (224 cm).

(b) Hospitals for psychiatric care and limited care facilities: 68 in. (173 cm).

A-12-3.7.5 Smoke partition doors are intended to provide access to adjacent zones. The pair of cross corridor doors must be opposite swing. Access to both zones must be provided.

12-3.7.6* Doors in smoke barriers shall comply with 6-3.4 and shall be self-closing or automatic-closing in accordance with 12-2.2.2.6.

A-12-3.7.6 Smoke barriers may include walls having door openings other than cross-corridor doors. There is no restriction in the *Code* regarding which doors or how many doors form part of a smoke barrier. For example, doors from the corridor to individual rooms may form part of a smoke barrier.

12-3.7.7 Vision panels consisting of a fixed fire window assembly in accordance with 6-2.3.4 shall be provided in each cross corridor swinging door and at each cross corridor horizontal sliding door in a smoke barrier.

12-3.7.8 Rabbets, bevels, or astragals are required at the meeting edges, and stops are required at the head and sides of door frames in smoke barriers. Positive latching hardware is not required. Center mullions are prohibited.

The requirements of 12-3.7.1 through 12-3.7.8 for subdividing building spaces through the use smoke barriers are illustrated in Figures 12-17 through 12-21. Paragraph 12-2.2.5 discusses horizontal exits.

During a fire, the emergency evacuation of patients in a health care facility is an inefficient, time consuming process. Realistically, if patients must be moved, sizable numbers of occupants can be relocated only through horizontal travel. Smoke barriers and horizontal exits used to subdivide a building serve three purposes fundamental to the protection of inpatients:

1. They limit the spread of fire and smoke,
2. They limit the number of occupants exposed to a single fire, and
3. They provide for horizontal relocation of patients by creating an area of refuge on the same floor level.

The *Code* essentially requires each story to be subdivided by a barrier into a minimum of two compartments. Although not stated in the *Code*, it would be desirable to subdivide health care facilities in such a way as to have separate banks of elevators in different smoke zones. Should evacuation of the building become necessary, patients can first be moved horizontally to a temporary area of refuge and then be removed from the building via elevators.

Openings between the meeting edges of pairs of doors and between the doors and frames must be closed to retard the transfer of smoke. Since 12-3.7.5 requires these doors to swing in opposite directions from each other, the protection at the meeting edge does not create a coordination problem and, therefore, is simple to provide.

Dampers are no longer required in ducted penetrations of smoke barriers (see Exception No. 2 to 12-3.7.3.) This exception anticipates that fire size will be limited by automatic sprinklers, and duct systems will also inhibit the transfer of smoke. This does not prohibit the installation of smoke dampers, nor does it exempt the smoke damper if required for other reasons. For example, if the building has a smoke-control system that needs a smoke damper at the smoke barrier, then it must be installed. An automatic-closing damper, activated a by a smoke detector, would be required to protect a transfer grille.

12-3.8 Special Features.

12-3.8.1* Every patient sleeping room shall have an outside window or outside door arranged and located so that it can be opened from the inside to permit the venting of products of combustion and to permit any occupant to have direct access to fresh air in case of emergency. (See 12-1.1.1.7 for

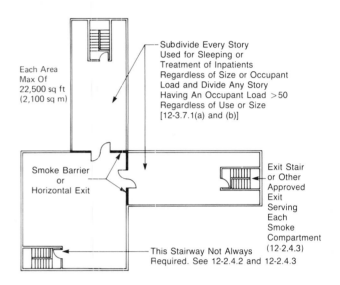

Each Area Max Of 22,500 sq ft (2,100 sq m)

Subdivide Every Story Used for Sleeping or Treatment of Inpatients Regardless of Size or Occupant Load and Divide Any Story Having An Occupant Load >50 Regardless of Use or Size [12-3.7.1(a) and (b)]

Smoke Barrier or Horizontal Exit

Exit Stair or Other Approved Exit Serving Each Smoke Compartment (12-2.4.3)

This Stairway Not Always Required. See 12-2.4.2 and 12-2.4.3

Figure 12-17.   Subdivision of Building Spaces in New Health Care Occupancies — Maximum Size (see also Figures 12-3, 12-4, and 12-7). Travel distance to reach a smoke barrier door is also restricted. (See Figure 12-19.)

detention screen requirements.) The maximum allowable sill height shall not exceed 36 in. (91 cm) above the floor. Where windows require the use of tools or keys for operation, the tools or keys shall be located on the floor involved at a prominent location accessible to staff.

Figure 12-18.   Subdivision of Building Spaces in New Health Care Occupancies — Details.

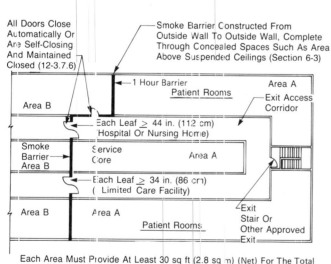

All Doors Close Automatically Or Are Self-Closing And Maintained Closed (12-3.7.6)

Smoke Barrier Constructed From Outside Wall To Outside Wall, Complete Through Concealed Spaces Such As Area Above Suspended Ceilings (Section 6-3)

1 Hour Barrier
Patient Rooms

Area A

Exit Access Corridor

Area B

Each Leaf ≥ 44 in. (112 cm) (Hospital Or Nursing Home)

Smoke Barrier Area B

Service Core

Area A

Each Leaf ≥ 34 in. (86 cm) (Limited Care Facility)

Area B

Area A

Patient Rooms

Exit Stair Or Other Approved Exit

Each Area Must Provide At Least 30 sq ft (2.8 sq m) (Net) For The Total Number Of Bed Patients (Hospitals & Nursing Homes), At Least 15 sq ft (1.4 sq m) (Net) For The Total Number Of Residents In a Limited Care Facility, And At Least 6 sq ft (.56 sq m) (Net) For The Total Number Other Occupants (12-3.7.4)

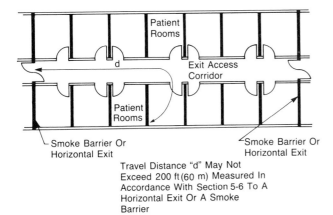

Figure 12-19. Subdivision of Building Spaces in New Health Care Occupancy — Maximum Travel Distance to a Smoke Barrier.

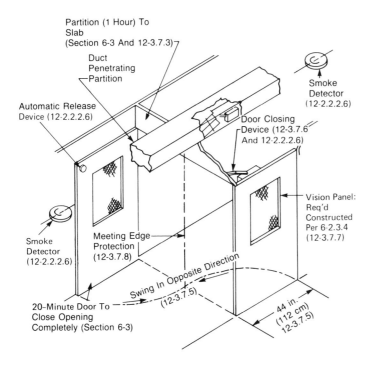

Figure 12-20. Subdivision of Building Spaces in New Health Care Occupancies.

Exception No. 1: The window sill in special nursing care areas such as those housing ICU, CCU, hemodialysis, and neonatal patients shall not exceed 60 in. (152 cm) above the floor.

Exception No. 2: Rooms intended for occupancy for less than 24 hours, such as those housing obstetrical labor beds, recovery beds, and observation beds in the emergency department, and newborn nurseries.

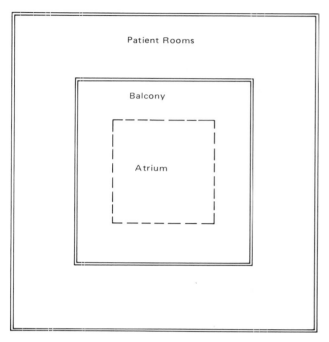

Figure 12-21a. *Illustration of a Noncomplying Atrium Arrangement in a New Health Care Occupancy. (See Figure 12-21b for complying arrangement. Also see Figures 12-21c and 12-21d.)*

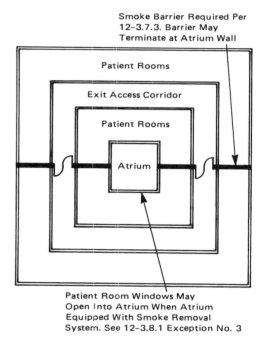

Figure 12-21c. *New Health Care Occupancy with Complying Atrium Arrangement.*

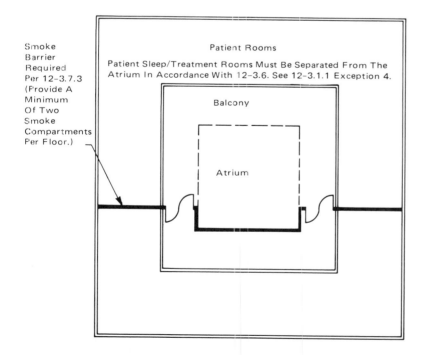

Figure 12-21b. *New Health Care Occupancy with Complying Atrium Arrangement.*

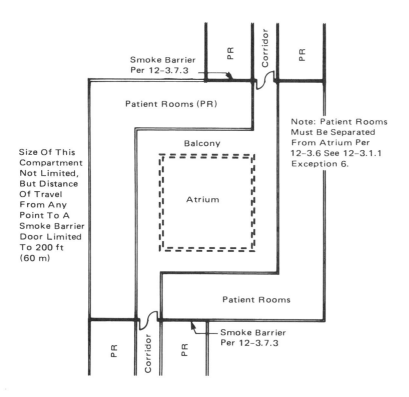

Figure 12-21d. *New Health Care Occupancy with Complying Atrium Arrangement.*

Exception No. 3: Windows opening into atriums where the atrium has a smoke removal system are, for the purposes of this requirement, considered outside windows; such windows shall normally be closed and operable only with the use of tool or key.

Exception No. 4: The window sill in limited care facilities shall not exceed 44 in. (112 cm) above the floor.

Exception No. 5: Buildings designed with approved engineered smoke control systems in accordance with Section 7-3 need not comply with the operable features of this requirement.

A-12-3.8.1 Individual sleeping cubicles within sleeping suites as permitted by 12-2.5.3 need not have an outside window or outside door in each cubicle provided at least one outside window or outside door is provided in the suite or the requirements of Exceptions No. 3 or 5 are met.

Paragraph 12-3.8.1 requires an outside door or outside window in each room where patients sleep. The win-

dow must be equipped with an operable section to be opened in an emergency to provide access to fresh air. The maximum allowable sill height is specified as 36 in. (91 cm), except in special nursing care areas (e.g., recovery rooms, intensive care units, coronary care units, and dialysis units) where the sill height may not be more than 60 in. (152 cm) above the floor. Limited care facilities are frequently designed similarly to residential type buildings. Sill height has been set at a maximum of 44 in. (112 cm) above the floor in such facilities, consistent with residential construction practices. Sill heights are limited to ensure access to window latches so that the operable section may be opened without special equipment.

To install windows with a latching arrangement that requires special knowledge to operate, or to place the latches at a level that requires the use of a chair or ladder for access, would not meet the intent of this section, even if the criteria for sill height were satisfied. Conversely, a window with a sill height exceeding that specified by this section, but equipped with a mechanical linkage that permits operation of the window from floor level without special tools, knowledge, or other special equipment, could satisfy the intent of this section.

It is desirable to have operable windows that have the capability of being opened without requiring a tool or a key. However, windows may be locked, provided keys are readily available. The *Code* recognizes that detention screens are sometimes necessary. Rooms so equipped should be limited in number to those where such precautions are deemed necessary. Continuous supervision should be provided for such areas. (*See 12-1.1.1.7.*)

Rooms that are occupied for less than 24 hours, such as those used for recovery, child delivery, or emergency care, or rooms used for newborn nurseries, need not be provided with a window. In excepting these rooms from the requirements for windows, the Committee felt that the high incidence of direct nursing supervision of all patients in these areas reduces the likelihood that patients will be trapped in a smoky fire. However, where it is not possible to provide windows, a conservative design should provide some added protection, such as individual sprinkler protection of enclosed areas (closets and pantries), early warning by smoke detectors, or high-volume exhaust ventilation.

For a discussion of Exception No. 3 and atrium windows, refer to the commentary on 12-3.1 and Figure 12-21c. To avoid interfering with smoke control systems, patient room windows that open into an atrium must be operated with a tool or key.

SECTION 12-4   Special Provisions

12-4.1   Windowless Buildings. Windowless buildings or windowless portions of buildings shall not be used for patient sleeping rooms. Windowless buildings or windowless portions of buildings shall comply with Section 30-7.

Windowless portions of health care facilities must comply with the requirements of Chapter 12 in addition to the criteria specified for such structures in Section 30-7. Paragraph 12-4.1 does not obviate the requirements for openable patient room windows contained within 12-3.8.1.

12-4.2   High Rise Buildings. High rise buildings shall comply with 30-8.2.

12-4.3   Operating Features. (*See Chapter 31.*)

SECTION 12-5   Building Services

12-5.1   Utilities.

12-5.1.1   Utilities shall comply with the provisions of Section 7-1.

12-5.1.2   Power for alarms, emergency communication systems, and the illumination of generator set locations shall be in accordance with the life safety branch requirements of NFPA 99, *Standard for Health Care Facilities.*

12-5.1.3   Any health care occupancy as indicated in 12-1.1.1.2 that normally utilizes life support devices shall have electrical systems designed and installed in accordance with NFPA 99, *Standard for Health Care Facilities.*

Exception: This requirement does not apply to a facility that has life support equipment for emergency purposes only.

It is not uncommon to lose all or some power supplies during a fire emergency. Therefore, it is important that life-support equipment be powered by properly designed and installed electrical systems so as not to create additional problems during the emergency.

12-5.2   Heating, Ventilating, and Air Conditioning.

12-5.2.1   Heating, ventilating, and air conditioning shall comply with Section 7-2 and shall be installed in accordance with the manufacturer's specifications.

Exception: As modified in 12-5.2.2.

12-5.2.2*   Any heating device other than a central heating plant shall be so designed and installed that combustible material will not be ignited by it or its appurtenances. If fuel-fired, such heating devices shall be chimney or vent connected, shall take air for combustion directly from outside, and shall be so designed and installed to provide for complete separation of the combustion system from the atmosphere of the occupied area. Any heating device shall have safety features to immediately stop the flow of fuel and shut down the equipment in case of either excessive temperatures or ignition failure.

Exception No. 1: Approved suspended unit heaters shall be permitted in locations other than means of egress and patient sleeping areas, provided such heaters are located high enough to be out of the reach of persons using the area and provided they are equipped with the safety features required above.

Exception No. 2: Fireplaces shall be permitted and used only in areas other than patient sleeping areas, provided that these areas are separated from patient sleeping spaces by construction having a 1-hour fire resistance rating and they comply with NFPA 211, Standard for Chimneys, Fireplaces, Vents, and Solid Fuel Burning Appliances. In addition thereto, the fireplace shall be equipped with a hearth that shall be raised at least 4 in. (10.2 cm) and a fireplace enclosure guaranteed against breakage up to a temperature of 650°F (343°C) and constructed of heat tempered glass or other approved material. If, in the opinion of the authority having jurisdiction, special hazards are present, a lock on the enclosure and other safety precautions may be required.

A-12-5.2.2 For both new and existing buildings, it is the intent of the Committee to permit the installation and use of fireplace stoves and room heaters utilizing solid fuel as defined in Chapter 8 of NFPA 211, *Standard for Chimneys, Fireplaces, Vents, and Solid Fuel Burning Appliances*, provided that all such devices are installed, maintained, and used in accordance with the appropriate provisions of that standard and all manufacturers' specifications. These requirements are not intended to permit freestanding solid fuel burning appliances such as freestanding wood-burning stoves.

Paragraphs 12-5.2.1 and 12-5.2.2 specify safeguards for air conditioning, ventilating, heating, and other service equipment in order to minimize the possibility of such devices serving as a source of ignition. Fuel-fired heating devices, except central heating systems, must be designed to provide complete separation of the combustion system from the occupied spaces. Air for combustion must be taken directly from the outside.

A major concern of the *Code* is the prevention of ignition of clothing, bedclothes, furniture, and other furnishings by a heating device. Therefore, 31-4.7 prohibits portable heating devices in areas used by patients.

12-5.3 **Elevators, Escalators, and Conveyors.** Elevators, escalators, and conveyors shall comply with the provisions of Section 7-4.

Although not counted as required exits, elevators may constitute a valuable supplemental facility for evacuating patients from health care buildings. In some cases, movement of critically ill patients or patients in restraining devices may be realistically accomplished only by an elevator.

Elevators, however, have many inherent weaknesses that tend to limit reliability. Elevator access doors are designed with operating tolerances that permit smoke transfer into the shaft. Power failure during a fire could result in trapping persons on elevators that stop between floors. Elevators may, during their descent from upper floors, stop automatically at the floor where the fire is burning, allow the doors to open, and expose the occupants to the fire.

Many of these weaknesses can be minimized by providing emergency power, separating the elevator lobby from other building spaces using rated construction, designing detection and alarm equipment to prevent elevators from stopping at a floor exposed to a fire, providing an emergency smoke-control system, and by pressurizing the elevator shaft and adjacent lobbies (*see Section 7-3*). This represents good fire protection judgment but is not the result of any requirements of this *Code*.

Through emergency planning and staff training, crowding of elevators (another potential problem) may be avoided. Emergency plans may make effective use of elevators by transferring patients through a horizontal exit, for example, to a separate fire area. Within the separate fire area, a staged evacuation program could be instituted, the elevators ultimately taking patients to the outside at ground level.

12-5.4 **Rubbish Chutes, Incinerators, and Laundry Chutes.**

12-5.4.1 Rubbish chutes, incinerators, and laundry chutes shall comply with the provisions of Section 7-5.

12-5.4.2 Any rubbish chute or linen chute, including pneumatic rubbish and linen systems, shall be provided with automatic extinguishing protection installed in accordance with Section 7-7. (*See Section 7-5.*)

12-5.4.3 Any trash chute shall discharge into a trash collecting room used for no other purpose and protected in accordance with Section 6-4.

12-5.4.4 An incinerator shall not be directly flue-fed nor shall any floor charging chute directly connect with the combustion chamber.

SECTION 12-6   New Ambulatory Health Care Centers

12-6.1   General Requirements.

12-6.1.1   Application.

12-6.1.1.1 Ambulatory health care centers shall comply with the provisions of Chapter 26 and (this) Section 12-6, whichever is more stringent. The provisions of Sections 12-2 through 12-5 shall not apply to this section unless a specific requirement is referenced by this section.

12-6.1.1.2 This section establishes life safety requirements, in addition to those required in Chapter 26, for the design of all ambulatory health care centers and outpatient surgical centers that meet the requirements of 12-1.3(a).

Ambulatory health care centers exhibit some of the occupancy characteristics of business occupancies and some of the characteristics of health care facilities. In developing Section 12-6, it was intended to prescribe a level of life safety from fire that would be greater than that typically specified for business occupancies but less than that typically found in health care facilities. (*See commentary for 12-1.3.*)

Ambulatory health care centers are required to comply with the provisions of Chapter 26 pertaining to business occupancies, except as more restrictive provisions are established within Section 12-6.

Ambulatory health care facilities are not identifiable as such in the national fire incident data bases. Their fires are probably recorded under those of clinics, doctors' offices, and unclassified or unknown-type facilities that care for the sick. Collectively, these properties accounted for 1,600 structure fires per year during 1984 to 1988, with 2 civilian deaths and 22 civilian injuries per year. Ambulatory health care facilities presumably account for some fraction of those totals.

12-6.1.2 Reserved.

12-6.1.3 Special Definitions. (*See 12-1.3.*)

12-6.1.4 Classification of Occupancy. (*See 12-1.3.*)

12-6.1.5 Reserved.

12-6.1.6 Minimum Construction Requirements.

12-6.1.6.1 For purposes of 12-6.1.6, the number of stories shall be counted starting with the primary level of exit discharge and ending with the highest occupiable level. For the purposes of this section, the primary level of exit discharge of a building shall be that floor that is level with or above finished grade of this exterior wall line for 50 percent or more of its perimeter.

Allowable building construction types are determined as a function of the number of stories in a building. In determining the number of stories, the first story is considered to be the primary level of exit discharge. Only occupiable levels are counted in determining story height. For example, an unoccupied attic would not constitute a story.

Problems have occurred in determining story height where a building is located on a sloping grade. Paragraph 12-6.1.6.1 notes that a story on a sloping site that is partially below grade should be counted as a story if the floor is level with or above grade along 50 percent or more of the perimeter of the building at the exterior wall. (*See Figure 12-22.*)

12-6.1.6.2 Buildings of one story in height housing ambulatory health care centers shall be of Type I, II, III, IV, or V construction. (*See 6-2.1.*)

12-6.1.6.3 Buildings of two or more stories in height housing ambulatory health care centers shall be of Type I (443) or (332), Type II (222) or (111), Type III (211), Type IV (2HH), or Type V (111) construction. (*See 6-2.1.*)

Exception: Buildings constructed of Type II (000), III (200), or V (000) if protected throughout by an approved supervised automatic sprinkler system in accordance with Section 7-7.

Construction types permitted in ambulatory health care centers are summarized in Table 12-1. (*See NFPA 220, Standard on Types of Building Construction.*)[2]

12-6.1.6.4 Any level below the level of exit discharge shall be separated from the level of exit discharge by at least Type II (111), Type III (211), or Type V (111) construction. (*See 6-2.1.*)

Exception: Separation is not required for such levels if they are under the control of the ambulatory health care center and any hazardous spaces are protected in accordance with Section 6-4.

See Figure 12-22.

12-6.1.6.5 Where new ambulatory health care centers are located in existing buildings, the authority having jurisdiction may accept construction systems of lesser fire resistance than required above if it can be demonstrated to the authority's sat-

Table 12-1   Construction Types Permitted in Ambulatory Health Care Occupancies

| | Stories | |
Construction Type	1	2 or more
I (443), I (332), II (222), II (111) (Fire Resistive and Protected Noncombustible)	X	X
II (000) (Unprotected Noncombustible)	X	X*
III (211) (Protected Ordinary)	X	X
III (200) (Unprotected Ordinary)	X	X*
IV (2HH) (Heavy Timber)	X	X
V (111) (Protected Wood Frame)	X	X
V (000) (Unprotected Wood Frame)	X	X*

X = Construction types allowed.
* = Automatic sprinkler protection required.

isfaction that prompt evacuation of the center can be achieved in case of fire or that the exposing occupancies and materials of construction present no threat of fire penetration from such occupancy to the ambulatory health care center or to the collapse of the structure.

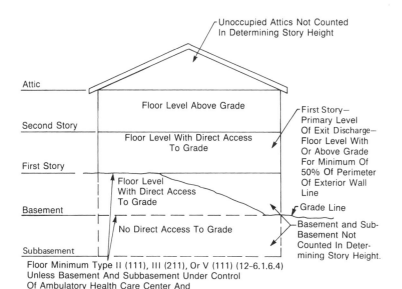

Figure 12-22. Illustration of the Application of 12-6.1.6.1 and 12-6.1.6.4.

Unoccupied Attics Not Counted In Determining Story Height

Attic

Floor Level Above Grade

Second Story

Floor Level With Direct Access To Grade

First Story—Primary Level Of Exit Discharge—Floor Level With Or Above Grade For Minimum Of 50% Of Perimeter Of Exterior Wall Line

First Story

Floor Level With Direct Access To Grade

Basement

Grade Line

No Direct Access To Grade

Basement and Sub-Basement Not Counted In Determining Story Height.

Subbasement

Floor Minimum Type II (111), III (211), Or V (111) (12-6.1.6.4) Unless Basement And Subbasement Under Control Of Ambulatory Health Care Center And Hazardous Spaces Protected Per Section 6-4

This paragraph is meant to liberalize the construction requirements applicable to a new ambulatory health care center that is to be placed in an existing building. Adequate supporting data must be supplied to the authority having jurisdiction to justify such a reduction.

12-6.1.7 Occupant Load. *(See 26-1.7.)*

12-6.2 Means of Egress Requirements.

12-6.2.1 General. Every aisle, passageway, corridor, exit discharge, exit location, and access shall be in accordance with Chapter 5.

Exception: As modified in the following paragraphs.

Means of egress details are to conform to the fundamental provisions expressed in Chapter 5, except as modified in Chapter 12. For example, egress capacity for doors must be calculated on the basis of clear width in accordance with 5-2.1.2, whereas minimum door widths specified by 12-6.2.3.3 are to be determined using actual door leaf width.

12-6.2.2 Means of Egress Components.

12-6.2.2.1 Components of means of egress shall be limited to the types described in 26-2.2.

12-6.2.2.2 Special locking arrangements complying with 5-2.1.6 are permitted on exterior doors.

Paragraph 5-2.1.6 establishes minimum requirements for delayed release hardware, including the requirement that the building must be protected throughout by an automatic sprinkler system or automatic fire detection system.

12-6.2.2.3 Any door in an exit passageway, horizontal exit, smoke barrier, stairway enclosure, or hazardous area enclosure shall be permitted to be held open only by an automatic release device that complies with 5-2.1.8. The required manual fire alarm system and the systems required by 5-2.1.8(c) shall be arranged so as to initiate the closing action of all such doors by zone or throughout the entire facility.

12-6.2.2.4 Where doors in a stair enclosure are held open by an automatic device as permitted in 12-6.2.2.3, initiation of a door closing action on any level shall cause all doors at all levels in the stair enclosure to close.

It is desirable to keep doors in exit enclosures, stair enclosures, horizontal exits, smoke barriers, and hazardous areas closed at all times to impede the spread of smoke and gases caused by a fire. However, some doors will be kept open for reasons of either operating efficiency or comfort. Where doors in required fire or smoke barriers are to be held open, such doors must be equipped with automatic devices that are designed to close the doors by the methods described within 12-6.2.2.3 and 5-2.1.8.

The automatic device must cause the doors to close upon operation of the manual fire alarm system. The doors must also be designed to close by actuation of a smoke detector located to detect smoke on either side of the door opening or by actuation of a complete automatic fire extinguishing or complete automatic fire detection system.

It is especially important in facilities providing health care to maintain floor-to-floor separation. Doors protecting openings in a stair enclosure may be held open by an automatic device only if arranged to close as specified above. Initiation of any action that causes a door to close at one level must cause all doors protecting openings within the stair enclosure to close and latch at all levels.

12-6.2.3 Capacity of Means of Egress.

12-6.2.3.1 The capacity of any required means of egress shall be determined in accordance with the provisions of 26-2.3 and shall be based on its width as defined in Section 5-3.

The capacity of the means of egress in ambulatory health care centers is determined on the basis of provisions in Chapter 26 that address business occupancies. Paragraph 26-2.3.1 refers to Section 5-3, which requires the capacity of level exit components to be computed on the basis of 0.2 in. (0.5 cm) per person, whereas stair capacity is computed using 0.3 in. (0.8 cm) per person. These capacities are considered reasonable based on the assumption that the majority of occupants will be ambulatory.

12-6.2.3.2 The minimum width of any corridor or passageway required for exit access shall be 44 in. (112 cm) clear.

Corridor widths greater than 44 in. (112 cm) may be required within ambulatory health care centers. However, the minimum width for public corridors used as common exit access corridors or passageways is 44 in. (112 cm). The 44-in. (112-cm) width is stipulated on the assumption that most occupants will be ambulatory.

12-6.2.3.3 Doors in the means of egress from diagnostic or treatment areas such as X-ray, surgical, or physical therapy shall be at least 34 in. (86 cm) wide.

In many instances, doors wider than 34 in. (86 cm) will be required. This paragraph intends to address doors used by the public or those doors that provide access to public hallways and corridors. The 34-in. (86-cm) minimum width is specified for doors on the assumption that most occupants will be ambulatory.

12-6.2.4 **Number of Exits.**

12-6.2.4.1 At least two exits of the types described in 26-2.2 that are remotely located from each other shall be provided for each floor or fire section of the building.

12-6.2.4.2 Any room and any suite of rooms of more than 1,000 sq ft (93 sq m) shall have at least two exit access doors remotely located from each other.

12-6.2.5 **Arrangement of Means of Egress.** (*See 26-2.5.*)

12-6.2.6 **Travel Distance to Exits.**

12-6.2.6.1 Travel distance shall be measured in accordance with Section 5-6.

12-6.2.6.2 Travel distance:

(a) Between any room door required as exit access and an exit shall not exceed 100 ft (30 m); and
(b) Between any point in a room and an exit shall not exceed 150 ft (45 m).

Exception: The maximum travel distance permitted in (a) or (b) above shall be increased by 50 ft (15 m) in buildings protected throughout by an approved automatic sprinkler system.

Travel distance is measured only to the closest exit, not to both exits required by 12-6.2.4.1. The requirements of 12-6.2.6.2 are illustrated in Figure 12-23.

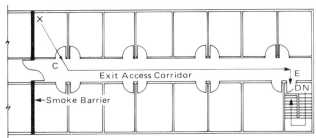

Maximum Distance C → E ≤ 100 ft (30 m) [150 ft (45 m) if Building is sprinklered]
X → E ≤ 150 ft (45 m) [200 ft (60 m) if Building is sprinklered] Also See 26-2.5

Figure 12-23. *Travel Distance in an Ambulatory Health Care Facility.*

12-6.2.7 **Discharge from Exits.** (*See 26-2.7.*)

12-6.2.8 **Illumination of Means of Egress.** Means of egress shall be illuminated in accordance with Section 5-8.

12-6.2.9 **Emergency Lighting and Essential Electrical Systems.**

12-6.2.9.1 Emergency lighting shall be provided in accordance with Section 5-9.

12-6.2.9.2 Where general anesthesia or life support equipment is used, each ambulatory health care center shall be provided with an essential electrical system in accordance with NFPA 99, *Standard for Health Care Facilities.*

Exception: Where battery operated equipment is provided and acceptable to the authority having jurisdiction.

All ambulatory health care centers are required to be equipped with emergency lighting. If medical procedures requiring general anesthesia are practiced, or if life-support equipment is required, ambulatory health care centers are required to be served by electrical systems meeting the criteria for essential electrical systems as detailed in Chapter 3, "Electrical Systems," of NFPA 99, *Standard for Health Care Facilities.*[5]

A facility would not be required to have an emergency generator if the building is a freestanding unit and if, as a normal practice, (1) management maintains admitting and discharge policies that preclude the provision of care for any patient or resident who may need to be sustained by electrical life-support equipment, such as respirators, or suction apparatus, and (2) no surgical treatment requiring general anesthesia is offered, and (3) battery-operated systems or equipment are provided that would maintain power to exit lights and illumination for exit corridors, stairways, medical preparation areas, and the like, for a minimum of 1½ hours. Additionally, battery power would be required to be supplied to all alarm systems.

12-6.2.10   Marking of Means of Egress. Means of egress shall have signs in accordance with Section 5-10.

12-6.2.11   Special Features. (Reserved.)

12-6.3   Protection.

12-6.3.1   Protection of Vertical Openings. (*See 26-3.1.*)

12-6.3.2   Protection from Hazards. (*See 26-3.2.*)

12-6.3.2.1 Laboratories employing quantities of flammable, combustible, or hazardous materials that are considered as severe hazard shall be protected in accordance with NFPA 99, *Standard for Health Care Facilities.*

Laboratories that contain "ordinary" combustibles and flammable liquids in sufficient quantity to threaten a 1-hour fire separation [e.g., wood-equivalent fuel loads in the range of 5 to 10 lb/sq ft (25 to 50 kg/sq m)] are considered a severe hazard. Laboratories representing a severe hazard must be protected in accordance with Chapter 10 of NFPA 99, *Standard for Health Care Facilities.*[5] Protection would include 1-hour fire resistance separation and automatic sprinkler protection.

Where fuel loads of lesser amounts are involved and quantities of flammable liquids are limited, laboratories

would simply be considered hazardous areas and would require either 1-hour separation or automatic sprinkler protection.

12-6.3.2.2 Anesthetizing locations shall be protected in accordance with NFPA 99, *Standard for Health Care Facilities.*

12-6.3.3   Interior Finish. (*See 26-3.3.*)

12-6.3.4   Detection, Alarm, and Communication Systems.

12-6.3.4.1   General. Centers shall be provided with a fire alarm system in accordance with Section 7-6, except as modified below.

12-6.3.4.2   Initiation. Initiation of the required fire alarm systems shall be by manual means in accordance with 7-6.2 and by means of any detection devices or detection systems required.

12-6.3.4.3   Occupant Notification. Occupant notification shall be accomplished automatically, without delay, upon operation of any fire alarm activating device by means of an internal audible alarm in accordance with 7-6.3.

Exception: The presignal system allowed by 7-6.3.2 Exception No. 1 shall not be permitted.

12-6.3.4.4   Emergency Forces Notification. Fire department notification shall be accomplished in accordance with 7-6.4.

12-6.3.4.5   Emergency Control. Operation of any activating device in the required fire alarm system shall be arranged to automatically accomplish, without delay, any control functions required to be performed by that device. (*See 7-6.5.*)

Paragraphs 12-6.3.4.1 through 12-6.3.4.5 address required fire alarm equipment. Reliability is of prime importance; therefore, electrical supervision of the system and system components is specified by the standards referenced in Section 7-6. In the event of circuit fault, component failure, or other "trouble," a continuous "trouble indication" signal is required and should be provided at a constantly attended location.

A manual fire alarm system is required by 12-6.3.4.2. Manual pull stations should be located along the natural routes of egress and located so as to adequately cover all portions of the building. Manual pull stations should always be located so that those qualified to send an alarm may summon aid without having to leave their zone of ordinary activities or pass beyond the view and hearing of people immediately exposed to, or in direct view of, a fire. The operation of a manual fire alarm station should automatically summon attendants who can assist in removing physically helpless occupants.

The system required by 12-6.3.4.2 may be incorporated into an automatic system equipped to detect a fire and initiate an alarm.

Actuation of any required fire or smoke detector, activation of a required sprinkler system, or operation of a manual pull station must automatically, without delay, sound audible alarm devices within the building. Presignal systems are not permitted.

The alarm must automatically transmit to a point outside the facility. Where automatic transmission of alarms to the fire department legally committed to serve the facility is not permitted, arrangements are to be made for the prompt notification of the fire department or such other assistance as may be available in the case of fire or other emergency. Paragraph 7-6.4 lists various methods acceptable for automatically notifying the fire department. The fire department should still be called manually to verify and confirm the automatic transmission of the alarm. In larger facilities, this may be the responsibility of the facility telephone operator; in smaller facilities, it may be the responsibility of the nursing staff.

Actuation of the fire alarm must cause audible alerting devices to sound throughout the affected zone or building as appropriate. Visible alerting devices may be used but may not serve as a substitute for audible devices.

12-6.3.5 Extinguishment Requirements. (See 26-3.5.)

12-6.3.5.1 Isolated hazardous areas shall be permitted to be protected in accordance with 7-7.1.2. Where more than two sprinklers are installed in a single area, water flow detection shall be provided to sound the building fire alarm or notify by a signal any constantly attended location, such as PBX, security, or emergency room, whereby necessary corrective action shall be directed.

12-6.3.5.2 Portable fire extinguishers shall be provided in ambulatory health care occupancies in accordance with 7-7.4.1.

12-6.3.6 Corridors. (See 26-3.6.)

12-6.3.6.1 In other than smoke compartments containing patient sleeping rooms, miscellaneous openings such as mail slots, pharmacy pass-through windows, laboratory pass-through windows, and cashier pass-through windows may be installed in vision panels or doors without special protection provided the aggregate area of openings per room does not exceed 20 sq in. (.013 sq m) and the openings are installed at or below half the distance from the floor to the room ceiling.

See commentary for 12-3.6.5.

12-6.3.7 Subdivision of Building Space.

12-6.3.7.1 Ambulatory health care occupancies shall be separated from other tenants and occupancies by walls having at least a 1-hour fire resistance rating. Such walls shall extend from the floor slab below to the floor or roof slab above. Doors shall be constructed of at least 1¾-in. (4.4-cm) thick solid bonded wood core or the equivalent and shall be equipped with positive latches. These doors shall be self-closing and kept in the closed position except when in use. Any vision panels shall be of fixed fire window assemblies in accordance with 6-2.3.4.

Ambulatory health care centers are frequently located within buildings used for a variety of purposes. Location within buildings containing hazardous occupancies should be avoided. Where ambulatory health care centers are located within buildings of mixed use, the ambulatory health care center must be separated from adjacent tenants and occupancies by minimum 1-hour fire-rated partitions. Doors protecting openings in such partitions must be of at least 1¾-in. (4.5-cm) thick solid bonded wood core or of equivalent construction that will resist fire for a minimum of 20 minutes. The doors must be equipped with positive latching hardware of a type that cannot be held in the retracted position. Roller latches cannot be used. These doors must be self-closing and normally maintained in the closed position, or, if the doors are to be held open, an automatic device must be used as specified in 12-6.2.2.3.

Glazing within doors and partitions will generally involve a maximum area of 1,296 sq in. (0.84 sq m) of wired glass, set in approved metal frames. Each wired glass panel should be limited to a maximum dimension of 54 in. (137 cm). The glass should be labeled, should be ¼-in. (0.6-cm) thick, and be well embedded in putty, with all exposed joints between the metal and the glass struck and pointed (*see NFPA 80, Standard for Fire Doors and Windows*).[11] A number of wired glass panels may be used in a single partition, provided that each 1,296-sq in. (.84-sq m) section is separated from adjacent panels by a metal mullion. The excessive use of wired glass panels should be avoided. It should be recognized that the use of wired glass panels in a partition reduces the effectiveness of the partition due to the fact that radiant energy transfer through the glass panel will readily occur. Other fire rated glazing is available and, where used, should be installed in accordance with the manufacturer's instructions and listing.

Partitions separating ambulatory health care centers from other occupancies must extend from the floor to the floor or roof deck above, extending completely through concealed spaces above suspended ceilings, for example. The partition must form a continuous barrier. Openings around penetrations involving building services should be adequately protected to maintain the 1-hour separation. Special attention should be paid to penetrations involving air-handling ducts. In general, steel ducts will not require a fire damper. Penetrations involving nonmetallic ducts or aluminum ducts should be carefully evaluated. Fire dampers should be provided to protect duct penetrations where the projected fire exposure is judged sufficient to jeopardize the required separation because of the duct penetration. The possible movement of air from space to space under conditions of system operation and conditions of system shutdown should be evaluated for both conditions. If there is a significant potential for the transfer of smoke from an adjacent space to the ambulatory health care center or from the ambulatory health care center to a corridor, fire dampers should be provided for duct penetrations, even though the *Code* does not specifically require such protection. (*See Figure 12-24.*)

12-6.3.7.2 The ambulatory health care facility shall be divided into at least two smoke compartments on patient treatment floors.

Exception: Facilities of less than 2,000 sq ft (185 sq m) and protected by an approved automatic smoke detection system.

12-6.3.7.3 Any required smoke barrier shall be constructed in accordance with Section 6-3 and shall have a fire resistance rating of at least 1 hour.

12-6.3.7.4 Vision panels in the smoke barrier shall be of fixed fire window assemblies in accordance with 6-2.3.4.

12-6.3.7.5 At least 15 net sq ft (1.4 net sq m) per ambulatory health care facility occupant shall be provided within the aggregate area of corridors, patient rooms, treatment rooms, lounges, and other low hazard areas on each side of the smoke compartment for the total number of occupants in adjoining compartments. The length and width of each smoke compartment shall be limited to no more than 150 ft (45 m).

Exception: One dimension may be extended provided that the total width plus length does not exceed 300 ft (91 m) and provided that travel distance from a room door to smoke barrier door or horizontal exit is not more than 150 ft (45 m).

12-6.3.7.6* Doors in smoke barriers shall be at least 1¾-in. (4.4-cm) thick solid bonded wood core or the equivalent and shall be self-closing. A vision panel is required.

A-12-6.3.7.6 Smoke barriers may include walls having door openings other than cross-corridor doors. There is no restriction in the *Code* regarding which doors or how many doors form part of a smoke barrier. For example, doors from the corridor to individual rooms may form part of a smoke barrier.

12-6.3.7.7 Doors in smoke barriers shall normally be kept closed, or if held open, they shall be equipped with automatic devices that will release the doors upon activation of:

(a) The fire alarm system, and either

(b) A local smoke detector, or

(c) A complete automatic fire extinguishing system or complete automatic fire detection system.

The requirements of 12-6.3.7.1 through 12-6.3.7.7 for subdividing building spaces through smoke barriers are illustrated in Figures 12-24 and 12-25. Paragraph 12-2.2.5 discusses horizontal exits.

During a fire, the emergency evacuation of patients in an ambulatory health care facility can be an inefficient, time consuming process. Realistically, if nonambulatory patients must be moved, any number of occupants can be relocated, but this can be done only through horizontal travel. Smoke barriers and horizontal exits used to subdivide a building serve three purposes fundamental to the protection of inpatients because they:

1. Limit the spread of fire and fire-produced contaminants,

2. Limit the number of occupants exposed to a single fire, and

3. Provide for horizontal relocation of patients by creating an area of refuge on the same floor level.

12-6.4 Special Provisions. (See Section 26-4.)

12-6.5 Building Services.

12-6.5.1 Utilities. Utilities shall comply with the provisions of Section 7-1.

12-6.5.2 Heating, Ventilating, and Air Conditioning.

12-6.5.2.1 Heating, ventilating, and air conditioning shall comply with the provisions of Section 7-2 and shall be installed in accordance with the manufacturer's specifications.

Exception: As modified in 12-6.5.2.2.

12-6.5.2.2 Any heating device other than a central heating plant shall be so designed and installed that combustible material will not be ignited by it or its appurtenances. If fuel-fired, such heating devices shall be chimney or vent connected, shall take air for combustion directly from the outside, and shall be so designed and installed to provide for complete separation of the combustion system from the atmosphere of the occupied area. Any heating device shall have safety features to immediately stop the flow of fuel and shut down the equipment in case of either excessive temperature or ignition failure.

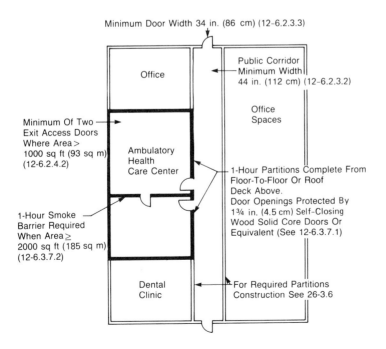

Minimum Door Width 34 in. (86 cm) (12-6.2.3.3)

Figure 12-24. Subdivision Requirements for an Ambulatory Health Center.

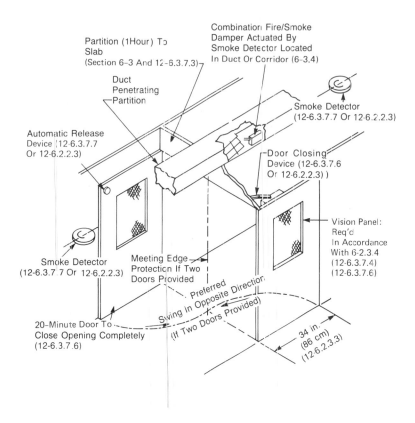

Partition (1Hour) To Slab (Section 6-3 And 12-6.3.7.3)

Duct Penetrating Partition

Combination Fire/Smoke Damper Actuated By Smoke Detector Located In Duct Or Corridor (6-3.4)

Smoke Detector (12-6.3.7.7 Or 12-6.2.2.3)

Automatic Release Device (12-6.3.7.7 Or 12-6.2.2.3)

Door Closing Device (12-6.3.7.6 Or 12-6.2.2.3))

Smoke Detector (12-6.3.7.7 Or 12-6.2.2.3)

Meeting Edge Protection If Two Doors Provided

Vision Panel: Req'd In Accordance With 6-2.3.4 (12-6.3.7.4) (12-6.3.7.6)

Preferred Swing In Opposite Direction (If Two Doors Provided)

20-Minute Door To Close Opening Completely (12-6.3.7.6)

34 in. (86 cm) (12-6.2.3.3)

Figure 12-25. Smoke Barrier for a New Ambulatory Care Facility.

Exception: Approved suspended unit heaters shall be permitted in locations other than means of egress and patient treatment areas, provided such heaters are located high enough to be out of the reach of persons using the area and provided they are equipped with the safety features called for above.

Paragraphs 12-6.5.2.1 and 12-6.5.2.2 specify safeguards for air conditioning, ventilating, heating, and other service equipment in order to minimize the possibility of such devices serving as a source of ignition. Fuel-fired heating devices, except central heating systems, must be designed to provide complete separation of the combustion system from the occupied spaces. Air for combustion must be taken directly from the outside.

A major concern of the *Code* is to prevent the ignition of clothing, bedclothes, furniture, and other furnishings by a heating device. Therefore, 31-4.7 prohibits portable heating devices in areas used by patients.

12-6.5.3 Elevators, Escalators, and Conveyors. Elevators, escalators, and conveyors shall comply with the provisions of Section 7-4.

12-6.5.4 Rubbish Chutes, Incinerators, and Laundry Chutes. Rubbish chutes, incinerators, and laundry chutes shall comply with the provisions of Section 7-5.

References Cited in Commentary

[1]NFPA 101M, *Manual on Alternative Approaches to Life Safety*, National Fire Protection Association, Quincy, MA.†

[2]NFPA 220, *Standard on Types of Building Construction*, National Fire Protection Association, Boston, MA, 1985.

[3]NFPA 241, *Standard for Safeguarding Construction, Alteration, and Demolition Operations*, National Fire Protection Association, Quincy, MA, 1989.

[4]NFPA 72E, *Standard on Automatic Fire Detectors*, National Fire Protection Association, Quincy, MA, 1990.

[5]NFPA 99, *Standard for Health Care Facilities*, National Fire Protection Association, Quincy, MA, 1990.

---

†The edition of NFPA 101M that corresponds with the 1991 *Life Safety Code* will be published in 1992.

[6]NFPA 90A, *Standard for the Installation of Air Conditioning and Ventilating Systems*, National Fire Protection Association, Quincy, MA, 1989.

[7]NFPA 96, *Standard for the Installation of Equipment for the Removal of Smoke and Grease-Laden Vapors from Commercial Cooking Equipment*, National Fire Protection Association, Quincy, MA, 1991.

[8]W.J. Christian and T.E. Waterman, "Flame Spread in Corridors: Effects of Location and Area of Wall Finish," *Fire Journal*, Vol. 65, No. 4, pp. 25-32, July 1971.

[9]R.W. Bukowski and S.M. Istvan, "A Survey of Field Experience with Smoke Detectors in Health Care Facilities," NBSIR 80-2130, Center for Fire Research, National Bureau of Standards, October 1980.

[10]NFPA 13, *Standard for the Installation of Sprinkler Systems*, National Fire Protection Association, Quincy, MA, 1991.

[11]NFPA 80, *Standard for Fire Doors and Windows*, National Fire Protection Association, Quincy, MA, 1990.

13

Existing Health Care Occupancies

(See also Chapter 31.)

This chapter covers the requirements for existing health care occupancies. In editions of the *Code* prior to 1976, these occupancies were known as "Institutional Occupancies."

Detention and correctional occupancies are covered in Chapters 14 and 15.

Health care occupancies are those used for medical or other treatment or care of four or more persons suffering from physical or mental illness, disease or infirmity, and for the care of infants, convalescents, or aged persons.

Health care occupancies addressed in this chapter include:

1. Hospitals
2. Nursing Homes
3. Limited Care Facilities
4. Ambulatory Health Care Centers

Hospitals, nursing homes, and limited care facilities provide sleeping facilities for the occupants and are occupied by persons who are mostly incapable of self-preservation because of age, physical or mental disability, or because of security measures not under the occupants' control.

Ambulatory health care centers are significantly different from other health care occupancies, since they do not provide sleeping facilities and are, therefore, covered separately in Section 13-6.

Among health care facilities, those that care for the sick accounted for 5,500 structure fires per year as reported to U.S. fire departments from 1984 to 1988. These fires were responsible for 11 civilian deaths and 166 civilian injuries per year. Facilities that care for older people accounted for 3,900 structure fires per year from 1986 to 1988 and an associated 19 civilian deaths and 204 civilian injuries per year. The other major category is facilities that care for the mentally handicapped (e.g., mental institutions, institutions for the mentally retarded), which accounted for 2,500 structure fires per year from 1984 to 1988 and an associated 1 civilian death and 60 civilian injuries per year.

Health care facilities accounted for three multiple-death fires (i.e., fires where at least 3 people died) in the last half of the 1980s: a 1989 Virginia nursing home fire that killed 12, a 1988 Tennessee nursing home fire that killed 3, and a 1985 hospice fire that killed 8. Usage of detectors, sprinklers, and other features of fire protection tends to be more prevalent in health care facilities than in almost any other property class. Because of the effectiveness and widespread use of these systems, a relatively low 37 percent of the fire fatalities in facilities that care for the sick, older adults, or the mentally handicapped occurred outside the room of fire origin. In facilities that care for the sick, the figure is reduced to 18 percent. Victims of fire found outside the room of origin are more likely to be occupants of the other two classes of health care facilities.

SECTION 13-1   General Requirements

13-1.1   Application. (See also Section 1-5.)

13-1.1.1   General.

13-1.1.1.1   Existing health care facilities shall comply with the provisions of this chapter. (See Chapter 31 for operating features.)

Exception*: Facilities where the authority having jurisdiction has determined equivalent safety has been provided in accordance with Section 1-6.

A-13-1.1.1.1   Exception. In determining equivalency for existing hospitals or nursing homes, the authority having jurisdiction may accept evaluations based on Chapter 3 of NFPA 101M, *Alternative Approaches to Life Safety*, utilizing the parameters for existing buildings.

Chapter 13 has been prepared for application solely to existing buildings. Prior to the 1973 Edition of the *Code*, the sections dealing with existing health care occupancies made reference to provisions contained within the section dealing with new construction. Since the 1973 Edition of the *Code*, those sections dealing with existing facilities have been complete and are intended to be applied without reference to the requirements for new construction.

This section is to be applied retroactively. Due consideration has been given to the practical difficulties of making alterations in existing, functioning facilities. The specified provisions, viewed as a whole, establish minimum acceptable criteria for life safety that reasonably minimize the likelihood of a life-threatening fire.

The requirements of Chapter 13 may be modified in instances of practical difficulty or where alternate, but equal, provisions are proposed. The modifications must provide a level of protection equivalent to that achieved by compliance with the corresponding *Code* provisions.

A Firesafety Evaluation System (FSES) has been developed and is located in Chapter 3 of NFPA 101M, *Alternative Approaches to Life Safety*.[1] The FSES uses numerical values to analyze the firesafety effectiveness of existing building arrangements or improvements proposed within existing structures. The system provides a method by which alternative improvement programs can be evaluated as options to literal *Code* compliance. In providing the equivalency system, it is not the intent to limit equivalency evaluations solely to this system. The authority having jurisdiction retains the power to evaluate and approve alternative improvement programs on the basis of appropriate supporting data. The FSES may be used to aid in this evaluation. This exception in no way mandates the use of the FSES, nor does it require the authority having jurisdiction to accept the results of an evaluation using the system. The exception to 13-1.1.1.1 emphasizes that Section 1-6 permits alternative designs to literal *Code* requirements that would still be considered in compliance with the *Code*. However, the authority having jurisdiction ultimately determines whether or not equivalent safety has been provided.

It should be noted that the 1988 Edition of NFPA 101M was coordinated to be used with the 1988 Edition of NFPA 101. It cannot be used to evaluate the 1991 Edition of NFPA 101. At the time this *Handbook* went to press, the Committee on Safety to Life was preparing a revision of NFPA 101M to coordinate with the 1991 Edition of NFPA 101. It is anticipated that this will be the 1992 Edition of NFPA 101M.

13-1.1.1.2   This chapter establishes life safety requirements for all existing hospitals, nursing homes, and limited care facilities. Where requirements vary, the specific occupancy is

named in the paragraph pertaining thereto. Section 13-6 establishes life safety requirements for all existing ambulatory health care centers.

Chapter 12 provides the requirements for new health care facilities and new ambulatory health care centers or for renovations to existing facilities. (*See 13-1.1.4.5.*)

13-1.1.1.3 Health care occupancies are those used for purposes such as medical or other treatment or care of persons suffering from physical or mental illness, disease or infirmity; for the care of infants, convalescents, or infirm aged persons.

13-1.1.1.4 Health care facilities provide sleeping accommodations for their occupants and are occupied by persons who are mostly incapable of self-preservation because of age, physical or mental disability, or because of security measures not under the occupants' control.

13-1.1.1.5 This chapter also covers ambulatory health care centers as defined in 13-1.3(a). (*See Section 13-6 for requirements.*)

Since ambulatory health care centers do not provide sleeping accommodations, they are treated separately in Section 13-6.

13-1.1.1.6 Buildings or sections of buildings that primarily house patients who, in the opinion of the governing body of the facility and the governmental agency having jurisdiction, are capable of judgment and appropriate physical action for self-preservation under emergency conditions may come under chapters of the *Code* other than Chapter 13.

13-1.1.1.7 It shall be recognized that, in buildings housing certain types of patients or having detention rooms or a security section, it may be necessary to lock doors and bar windows to confine and protect building inhabitants. In such instances, the authority having jurisdiction shall make appropriate modifications to those sections of this *Code* that would otherwise require exits to be kept unlocked.

13-1.1.1.8 Buildings or sections of buildings that house older persons and that provide activities that foster continued independence but do not include those services distinctive to health

care facilities [as defined in 13-1.3(c)] may be subject to the requirements of other sections of this *Code*, such as Chapter 19 or 23.

13-1.1.1.9 Health care occupancies shall include all buildings or parts thereof with occupancy as described in this chapter under 13-1.3, "Special Definitions."

13-1.1.1.10 Except for ambulatory health care centers, facilities that do not provide housing on a 24-hour basis for their occupants are classified as other occupancies and are covered by other chapters of the *Code*.

Paragraphs 13-1.1.1.3 through 13-1.1.1.10 contain explanatory material that describes some general characteristics of the occupants of health care occupancies. A few fundamental safeguards are also provided. Formal definitions are established in 13-1.3.

As implied by the definitions of 13-1.3 and stated in 13-1.1.1.4, health care facilities, except ambulatory health care centers, are buildings that provide sleeping facilities (24-hour care) for occupants. Occupants in a health care facility may be restrained but are housed primarily for treatment of mental or physical infirmities. Where occupants are restrained for penal or correctional purposes, the building would be classified as a detention and correctional occupancy. Such occupancies are addressed in Chapters 14 and 15.

If a building is used for the treatment or housing of patients, including the mentally handicapped (*see 13-1.1.1.6*) or older persons (*see 13-1.1.1.8*) the building may be classed as an occupancy other than health care under the following conditions:

1. Occupants are not restrained by locked doors or other devices, and
2. The patients are ambulatory, and
3. The occupants are capable of perceiving threat and taking appropriate action for self-preservation.

Occupants of health care facilities are considered to be incapable of self-preservation (*see 13-1.1.1.4*) due to age, physical or mental disability, or security measures not under the occupants' control. A significant number of occupants in health care facilities are assumed to be nonambulatory or bedridden. Other occupants, while capable of self-movement, may have impaired judgment.

Although locking exit doors and barring windows is always undesirable in terms of life safety, the *Code* recognizes that, in some cases, it is necessary to restrain people. In these instances, provision should be made for the continuous supervision and prompt release of restrained persons (*see 13-1.1.1.7*). Release of occupants should be achieved by a system capable of automatically unlocking doors in the means of egress or by continuously available attendants equipped with keys. In either case, continuous supervision is considered essential. (*See 13-2.2.2.4 and 13-2.2.2.5.*)

13-1.1.1.11*   The requirements of this chapter are based on the assumption that staff is available in all patient occupied areas to perform certain firesafety functions as required in other paragraphs of this chapter.

A-13-1.1.1.11   The *Code* recognizes that certain functions necessary for the life safety of building occupants, such as the closing of corridor doors, operation of manual fire alarm devices, and the removal of patients from the room of fire origin require the intervention of facility staff. It is not the intent of this paragraph to specify the levels or locations of staff necessary to meet this requirement.

The *Code* has always assumed that staff will be in continuous attendance in all health care facilities. In fact, staff is assigned certain critical functions during a fire emergency, such as rescuing patients from the room of origin, closing the door to the room, and activating the fire alarm system. The *Code* does not specify minimum staff/patient ratios, as such provisions are included in state licensing criteria, and compliance with licensing criteria will normally satisfy the *Code*. The 1991 *Life Safety Code* has been revised to mandate that staff be present. A staff person should be situated to supervise each smoke compartment housing patients. A nursing station located to allow visual supervision of two or more smoke compartments is considered adequate. If, because of some unusual arrangement, staff is not continuously available (24 hours a day) to provide supervision, alternative means should be provided to ensure an adequate level of firesafety that is in compliance with the *Code*.

13-1.1.2*   **Objective.** The objective of this chapter is to provide a reasonable level of safety by reducing the probability of injury and loss of life from the effects of fire with due consideration for functional requirements. This is accomplished by limiting the development and spread of a fire emergency to the room of fire origin and reducing the need for occupant evacuation, except from the room of fire origin.

A-13-1.1.2   This objective is accomplished in the context of: the physical facilities, the type of activities undertaken, the provisions for the capabilities of staff, and the needs of all occupants through requirements directed at the:

- (a) Prevention of ignition.
- (b) Detection of fire.
- (c) Control of fire development.
- (d) Confinement of the effects of fire.
- (e) Extinguishment of fire.
- (f) Provision of refuge and/or evacuation facilities.
- (g) Staff reaction.

It should be recognized that the well-being of an individual located in the room of fire origin can be reasonably ensured only through control of that individual's environment. That is, only through complete control of the environment, including building members, building finishes, furnishings, decorations, clothing, linens, bedding, and the like, can the individual be protected against fire. However, no code can prevent injury resulting from a person's careless actions.

Although an effort should be made to protect the individual through fire prevention, the primary objective of the requirements of Chapter 13 is to limit fire size or to prevent fire from escaping the room of origin and thereby limit the threat posed to individuals outside the room of origin.

13-1.1.3   **Total Concept.** All health care facilities shall be so designed, constructed, maintained, and operated as to minimize the possibility of a fire emergency requiring the evacuation of occupants. Because the safety of health care occupants cannot be assured adequately by dependence on evacuation of the building, their protection from fire shall be provided by appropriate arrangement of facilities, adequate staffing, and careful development of operating and maintenance procedures composed of the following:

(a) Proper design, construction, and compartmentation; and

(b) Provision for detection, alarm, and extinguishment; and

(c) Fire prevention and the planning, training, and drilling in programs for the isolation of fire, transfer of occupants to areas of refuge, or evacuation of the building.

Vertical movement of patients within a health care facility is an inefficient, time consuming process. In one study, it was demonstrated through the simulated evacuation of patients from a second-story ward to ground level that more than 30 minutes may be required for evacuation during a fire.

The provisions of Chapter 13, therefore, are based upon a "defend in place" philosophy, which minimizes the probability of a fire necessitating vertical movement of occupants. Patients in critical care areas may be connected to life-support equipment, which makes movement difficult and, in some cases, impossible. Barriers are required to provide for the horizontal movement of patients to safe areas of refuge on a single floor level and to maintain a manageable limit on the number of occupants exposed to any single fire. Vertical means of egress (stairs or ramps) are specified by Chapter 13 as escape routes for visitors and staff and as a "last line of defense" for the movement of patients.

13-1.1.4 Additions, Conversions, Modernization, Renovation, and Construction Operations. (*See also 1-5.5 and 1-5.6.*)

13-1.1.4.1 Additions. Additions shall be separated from any existing structure not conforming to the provisions within Chapter 13 by a fire barrier having at least a 2-hour fire resistance rating and constructed of materials as required for the addition.

Paragraph 13-1.1.4.1 establishes separation criteria for additions to existing structures where existing structures do not conform to the provisions of Chapter 13. It should be emphasized that, where an existing building meets the provisions of Chapter 13, the building would be in com-

pliance with the *Code*, and the addition would not require separation.

Where additions must be separated, barriers must be constructed of assemblies providing a minimum of 2-hour fire resistance. Where the structural framing of the addition or the existing buildings are of assemblies of less than 2-hour fire resistance, special provision must be made to ensure the necessary separation will be maintained for the 2-hour period.

Materials used in the construction of the barrier should be "constructed to the standards of the addition." That is, if the addition is required to be constructed of noncombustible or limited-combustible materials (construction Types I or II), then the materials used in the barrier must be limited-combustible or noncombustible as defined in NFPA 220, *Standard on Types of Building Construction.*[2] Conversely, if the addition is permitted to be constructed of combustible materials, then combustible materials may be used as a portion of the barrier. Any new additions must conform to the requirements of Chapter 12.

13-1.1.4.2 Communicating openings in dividing fire barriers required by 13-1.1.4.1 shall occur only in corridors and shall be protected by approved self-closing fire doors. (*See also Section 6-2.*)

13-1.1.4.3 Doors in barriers required by 13-1.1.4.1 shall normally be kept closed.

Exception: Doors shall be permitted to be held open if they meet the requirements of 13-2.2.2.6.

Openings in barriers separating additions from nonconforming existing structures are limited to those that are absolutely necessary, i.e., corridors (*see 13-1.1.4.2*). Openings are required to be protected by $1\frac{1}{2}$-hour, "B"-labeled, fire door assemblies. The fire doors are required to be self-closing and are to remain closed, or they may be held open by an automatic device in accordance with 13-2.2.2.6. (*See Figure 13-1.*)

13-1.1.4.4 Conversions. Conversions shall comply with 1-7.4. A conversion from a hospital to a nursing home or from

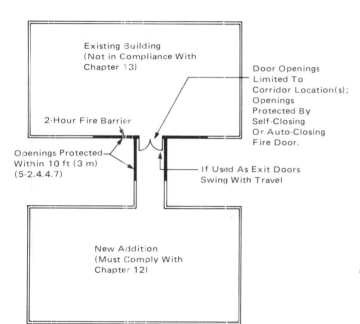

Figure 13-1. Separation of New Addition from Existing Building Not in Compliance with Chapter 13. If the addition is of fire-resistive or noncombustible (Type I or II) construction, noncombustible or limited-combustible materials must be used in the 2-hour barrier. (See NFPA 220, Standard on Types of Building Construction.)[2]

a nursing home to a hospital is not a change in occupancy or suboccupancy classification.

Any building converted to a health care facility from some other type of occupancy use (dormitory, for example) must be altered to comply with the provisions of Chapter 12 for new health care facilities. It is sometimes questioned whether the conversion of a hospital to a nursing home represents a change in occupancy. Conversion of a hospital to a nursing home or vice versa does not constitute a change in occupancy. Therefore, prior to and after such a conversion, the facility must comply with the criteria of Chapter 13 for existing health care facilities.

13-1.1.4.5* Renovations, Alterations, and Modernizations. Renovations, alterations, and modernizations shall comply, to the extent practical, with requirements for new construction in accordance with 1-5.6. Where such renovations, alterations, or modernizations are done in a nonsprinklered facility, the automatic sprinkler requirements of Chapter 12 shall apply to the smoke compartment undergoing the renovation, alteration,

or modernization. However, in such case where the building is not protected throughout by an approved automatic sprinkler system, the requirements of 13-1.6 and 13-2.3.2 shall also apply. Exception No. 2 to 12-3.7.3 shall be permitted only where adjacent smoke compartments are protected throughout by an approved supervised automatic sprinkler system in accordance with 12-3.5.2. Where minor renovations, alterations, modernizations, or repairs are done in a nonsprinklered facility, the requirements of 12-3.5.1 shall not apply, but in such cases the renovations, alterations, modernizations, or repairs shall not reduce life safety below that which existed before, nor below the requirements of Chapter 13 for nonsprinklered buildings.

A-13-1.1.4.5 The *Code* does not attempt to establish specific monetary limits or percentage values to determine "minor," as this requires judgment. It is not the intent of this paragraph to exempt significant renovations and modernization projects for which the *Code* does intend to apply the automatic sprinkler mandate.

For the purpose of this requirement, a floor that is not divided by a smoke barrier is considered one smoke compartment.

Alterations in health care facilities are regulated by 1-5.6 and 13-1.1.4.5. Alterations may not reduce the level of life safety below that which exists prior to the alterations; however, provisions in excess of the requirements for new construction are not required to be maintained. For example, an existing hospital has a 6-ft (1.8-m) wide corridor, and a portion of the hospital is to be renovated. While the hospital is an existing building, a minimum 6-ft (1.8-m) wide corridor must be maintained. Conversely, if a portion of an existing hospital that has a 10-ft (3.1-m) wide corridor is to be altered, the corridor may be reduced to 8 ft (2.4 m), which is the requirement for new construction. If alterations require replacement of a small portion of a hospital corridor wall in a nonsprinklered area, this portion of the wall should provide 1-hour fire separation in accordance with the nonsprinklered requirements for new construction contained in previous editions. However, it would not be required that the corridor width be increased to 8 ft (2.4 m) unless it was practical to do so. As a minimum, in all instances, whether or not renovations or alterations are planned, existing buildings must comply with the requirements contained in Chapter 13.

This paragraph has undergone major revisions in the 1991 *Code*. Automatic sprinkler protection is now required for all new health care facilities. The requirements of Chapter 12 contemplate complete automatic sprinkler protection, and numerous exceptions are included to eliminate redundant features of protection. Existing health care facilities may be nonsprinklered. Renovations of non-sprinklered health care facilities must comply with the requirements for new construction to the extent practical. However, Chapter 12 no longer contains a non-sprinklered option. Therefore, whenever a nonsprinklered facility undergoes alteration, and the alterations are of such a minor nature that automatic sprinklers are not required, the *Code* specifies that the level of firesafety existing prior to the renovations must be maintained. As a minimum, the requirements of Chapter 13 for non-sprinklered buildings, including fire separation of corridors, must be met.

Only that portion of a facility that is being renovated is required to comply with Chapter 12. For example, assume a floor of a hospital is subdivided into three smoke compartments and only one smoke compartment is undergoing renovation. Only the smoke compartment renovated would require compliance, to the extent practical, with Chapter 12. Accordingly, the smoke compartment undergoing alteration must be sprinklered in accordance with 12-3.5. However, where a building is only partially protected with sprinklers, the construction requirements of 13-1.6 for nonsprinklered buildings must be met, and exit capacity must be based on nonsprinklered criteria. Smoke dampers in smoke barriers may only be omitted for ducted penetrations where the smoke compartments on both sides of the barrier are fully sprinklered with quick response sprinklers in accordance with 12-3.5.2.

Although an effort should always be made to satisfy the criteria for new construction during a building alteration or the installation of new equipment, the *Code* recognizes that such modifications cannot always be achieved. Guidance for achieving equivalency to life safety is provided in Section 1-6. Regardless of circumstances, alterations or the installation of new building service equipment must be achieved in such a manner that the level of life safety that results is equivalent or superior to that prescribed for existing buildings.

13-1.1.4.6 Construction Operations. See 1-7.3 and Chapter 31 for life safety provisions during construction.

The introduction of "outside" workers and activities associated with the construction projects creates unusual risks of fire in health care occupancies. Special precautions must be taken to guard against the potential exposure created by the introduction of flammable substances or by other hazardous practices that could pose a threat to occupants. (*See 31-1.1.2.*)

Temporary fire resistant barriers should be erected to separate the new construction and associated activity from the functioning areas of the existing buildings. Care must be taken to prevent blockage of means of egress for the existing building by the construction of such barriers. Special care is also necessary to ensure that all existing equipment for fire protection and all portions of the required means of egress are maintained in full working order. (*See 1-7.3.*)

Adequate escape facilities should be provided and continuously maintained for the use of construction workers. (*See 31-1.1.1 and NFPA 241, Standard for Safeguarding Construction, Alteration, and Demolition Operations.*)[3]

13-1.1.5 Modification of Retroactive Provisions. (*See also Sections 1-5 and 1-6.*) The requirements of this chapter may be modified if their application clearly would be impractical in the judgment of the authority having jurisdiction and if the resulting arrangement could be considered as presenting minimum hazard to the life safety of the occupants. The requirements may be modified by the authority having jurisdiction to allow alternative arrangements that will secure as nearly equivalent safety to life from fire as practical.

13-1.2 Mixed Occupancies. (*See also 1-5.7.*)

13-1.2.1* Sections of health care facilities shall be permitted to be classified as other occupancies if they meet all of the following conditions:

(a) They are not intended to serve health care occupants for purposes of

(1) Housing, or

(2) Treatment, or

(3) Customary access by patients incapable of self-preservation.

(b) They are adequately separated from areas of health care occupancies by construction having a fire resistance rating of at least 2 hours.

A-13-1.2.1 Doctors' offices, treatment and diagnostic facilities intended solely for outpatient care and physically separated from facilities for the treatment or care of inpatients, but otherwise associated with the management of an institution, may be classified as business occupancy rather than health care occupancy.

13-1.2.2 Ambulatory care centers, medical clinics, and similar facilities that are contiguous to health care occupancies but are primarily intended to provide outpatient services shall be permitted to be classified as a business occupancy or ambulatory health care occupancy provided the facilities are separated from the health care occupancy by not less than 2-hour fire resistance-rated construction and the facility is not intended to provide services simultaneously for four or more health care patients who are litter-borne.

Paragraphs 13-1.2.1 and 13-1.2.2 contain criteria for classifying spaces as "other" occupancies, although they are located in buildings used primarily for health care purposes. For example, 13-1.2.1 would allow offices to be classified as business occupancies, cafeterias to be classified as assembly occupancies, or dormitories to be classified as residential occupancies if both (a) and (b) of 13-1.2.1 are met. Paragraph 13-1.2.1(a) notes that customary access by patients incapable of self-preservation is not permitted within the other occupancy. This paragraph is intended to allow an occasional ambulatory inpatient to visit a doctor's office in an adjacent business occupancy, for example, without requiring classification of the business occupancy as a health care facility. However, if either (a) or (b) is not met, then the area would be considered a mixed occupancy and require that the more restrictive life safety provisions of 1-5.7 apply. (*See 1-5.7.*)

Paragraph 13-1.2.2 addressess a subject similar to that of 13-1.2.1 but specifically covers ambulatory care centers, medical clinics, and similar areas that primarily pro-

vide outpatient services and are associated with or attached to a health care facility. If these facilities are separated by 2-hour fire-resistive construction, they may be classified as ambulatory health care centers or as business occupancies, whichever applies. If, however, four or more litter-borne inpatients are treated simultaneously, the facility must meet the requirements for health care occupancies. Conversely, three or fewer litter-borne inpatients may be present in the outpatient facility on a regular basis, and such a facility would be classified as other than health care. The provisions of business occupancies and ambulatory health care centers were written on the assumption that most people are treated on an outpatient basis.

Note that subject to certain qualifications, 13-1.2.4 allows the means of egress from health care areas using a horizontal exit to traverse non-health care spaces.

13-1.2.3 Health care occupancies in buildings housing other occupancies shall be completely separated from them by construction having a fire resistance rating of at least 2 hours as provided for additions in 13-1.1.4.

Paragraph 13-1.2.3 requires that, if a health care occupancy is located in a building of another classification (such as business, storage, mercantile, or industrial), the health care occupancy must be separated from the other occupancy by construction having a fire resistance rating of 2 hours, as detailed in 13-1.1.4. (*Also see commentary following 13-1.1.4.1.*)

Note that 13-1.2.3 deals with occupancy classification and not with hazard of contents. Hazard of contents is treated in 13-1.2.6 and 13-1.2.7.

13-1.2.4 All means of egress from health care occupancies that traverse non-health care spaces shall conform to requirements of this *Code* for health care occupancies.

Exception: It is permissible to exit through a horizontal exit into other contiguous occupancies that do not conform with health care egress provisions but that do comply with requirements set forth in the appropriate occupancy chapter of this Code as long as the occupancy does not contain high hazard contents. The horizontal exit shall comply with the requirements of 13-2.2.5.

Paragraph 13-1.2.4 specifies that the means of egress from health care occupancies that traverse non-health care spaces must conform to the requirements for health care occupancies. However, an exception is allowed where a 2-hour barrier is provided and such barrier is used as a horizontal exit. Where a 2-hour barrier serves as a horizontal exit, it is acceptable to exit into a different occupancy, if the other occupancy complies with the provisions of the *Code* that would be applicable thereto and if it does not contain high hazard contents. For example, if a horizontal exit is provided between a health care facility and a business occupancy, inpatients may exit into the business occupancy through a horizontal exit. In this instance, corridor width, corridor partitions, stairway details, and similar features must conform to the provisions of either Chapters 26 or 27, which address business occupancies. However, the horizontal exit must comply with all the requirements of 13-2.2.5.

13-1.2.5 Auditoriums, chapels, staff residential areas, or other occupancies provided in connection with health care facilities shall have means of egress provided in accordance with other applicable sections of the *Code*.

Auditoriums, chapels, and other areas separated by 2-hour construction and meeting the criteria of 13-1.2.1 and 13-1.2.2 for other occupancies are required to be designed in accordance with the appropriate occupancy chapter governing their use.

Spaces used for non-health care purposes but located within a health care facility should have means of egress features designed in accordance with the use of the space. For example, if a space located in a health care facility is used as a chapel or auditorium, assuming an occupant load in excess of 50, egress features should be designed as would be appropriate for an assembly occupancy. In such circumstances, doors in the means of egress should be side-hinged swinging doors, arranged to swing in the direction of exit travel (*see 5-2.1.4.1*), and should not be equipped with a latch or lock unless such a latch or lock is operated by panic hardware (*see 9-2.2.2.3*). Exit capacity, however, should be computed on the basis of occupant characteristics. If, for example, the space is used only by staff, visitors, and others who are mobile and otherwise capable of self-preservation, then exit capacity could

be computed in accordance with Chapter 9. However, if the space is used by health care occupants, then exit capacity should be calculated in accordance with Chapter 13, despite the fact that the occupant load might be calculated in accordance with Chapter 9.

13-1.2.6 Any area with a hazard of contents classified higher than that of the health care occupancy and located in the same building shall be protected as required in 13-3.2.

Paragraph 13-1.2.6 regulates spaces in a health care facility that, although comprising only a portion of the facility, contain more hazardous materials (in quantity or type) than are usually found in most other spaces.

Spaces such as rooms used for the storage of combustible materials, trash collection rooms, gift shops, and paint shops must be protected in accordance with 13-3.2.

13-1.2.7 Non-health care related occupancies classified as containing high hazard contents shall not be permitted in buildings housing health care occupancies.

Paragraph 13-1.2.7 prohibits another occupancy (such as storage) that contains highly hazardous contents (such as flammable liquids) from being located in a building housing health care occupancies.

This paragraph limits use, based upon occupancy classification, with regard to hazard of contents. For example, the paragraph does not intend to exclude laboratory operations from being part of a health care facility. The intent is to prevent a portion of a hospital from being converted to or designed for use as an educational or research facility (which would be classed as an educational or possibly an industrial occupancy) where laboratories use and store sizable quantities of flammable liquids.

13-1.3 Special Definitions.

(a) *Ambulatory Health Care Centers.* A building or part thereof used to provide services or treatment to four or more patients at the same time that meets the criteria of either (1) or (2) below.

(1) Those facilities that provide, on an outpatient basis, treatment for patients that would render them incapable of taking action for self-preservation under emergency conditions without assistance from others.

(2) Those facilities that provide, on an outpatient basis, surgical treatment requiring general anesthesia.

(b) *Hospital.* A building or part thereof used on a 24-hour basis for the medical, psychiatric, obstetrical, or surgical care of four or more inpatients. The term hospital, wherever used in this *Code*, shall include general hospitals, psychiatric hospitals, and specialty hospitals.

(c) *Limited Care Facility.* A building or part thereof used on a 24-hour basis for the housing of four or more persons who are incapable of self-preservation because of age, physical limitation due to accident or illness, or mental limitations such as mental retardation/developmental disability, mental illness, or chemical dependency.

(d) *Nursing Home.* A building or part thereof used on a 24-hour basis for the housing and nursing care of four or more persons who, because of mental or physical incapacity, may be unable to provide for their own needs and safety without the assistance of another person. The term nursing home, wherever used in this *Code*, shall include nursing and convalescent homes, skilled nursing facilities, intermediate care facilities, and infirmaries in homes for the aged.

Paragraph 13-1.3(a) through (d) defines the characteristics of the occupancies covered by Chapter 13. Except as discussed below for ambulatory health care, a building must house four or more people incapable of self-preservation on a 24-hour basis in order to be classed as a health care occupancy.

Occupants of hospitals or nursing homes are assumed to be nonambulatory and incapable of self-preservation. In making this judgment, due consideration should be given to the use of physical restraints and tranquilizing drugs, which can render occupants immobile. Variable staffing criteria and levels of care make differentiation between hospitals and nursing homes apparent. The difference between nursing homes and limited care facilities is less clear.

Although limited care facilities house four or more occupants incapable of self-preservation due to age or

physical or mental limitations, occupants are generally considered to be ambulatory and to require only limited assistance during emergency evacuation. Buildings that house ambulatory occupants who are mentally handicapped or undergoing treatment for alcohol or drug abuse and who can be expected to evacuate a structure with limited assistance meet the criteria for limited care facilities. Day-care facilities that provide care for the aged, children, mentally handicapped, or others would be classified as other than health care if the care or treatment is not provided on a 24-hour basis. (*See Chapter 11.*)

Although age itself is not sufficient justification for developing a separate classification for a health care occupancy, it should be recognized that the elderly pose a unique problem in the achievement of firesafety. Experiences in buildings where the elderly are housed demonstrate that the response of the elderly to a fire may not be in the interest of self-preservation. Upon discovering a fire, elderly occupants may ignore it, become transfixed by it, or seek refuge from it in their rooms and fail to notify anyone of the fire. In some cases, the elderly have resisted efforts to remove them from the building and familiar surroundings.

Terms such as "residential," "lodging and boarding," and "custodial care" previously used in 13-1.3, have been deleted to avoid confusion with a residential occupancy classification included in Chapter 21 (Chapters 22 and 23 in the 1991 *Code*), which was added to the 1985 Edition of the *Code*. Board and care facilities, personal care homes, halfway houses, or similar facilities house occupants who may require medication and personal care but do not require the close supervision and services typical of the occupants in a health care facility. Therefore, these would be classified as residential occupancies. Occupant capability must be carefully evaluated to determine whether application of health care criteria (Chapter 13) or application of lesser safeguards associated with residential occupancies (Chapter 23) is more appropriate.

Prior to the 1981 Edition of the *Code*, occupancies that offered medical services on an outpatient basis would have been regulated within the chapter covering business occupancies. The threat to life in an outpatient facility where four or more patients may be subject to medical procedures requiring general anesthesia, treatments such as hemodialysis, or freestanding emergency service is significantly greater than that typical of a business occupancy. Conversely, application of the requirements for health care facilities that contemplate 24-hour care would be inappropriate and would be unnecessarily restrictive. In establishing the occupancy classification of an ambulatory health care center, the intent was to develop requirements that fall between the restrictions applicable to business occupancies and health care facilities in terms of level of life safety achieved.

13-1.4 Classification of Occupancy. (*See Special Definitions, 13-1.3.*)

13-1.5 Classification of Hazard of Contents. The classification of hazard of contents shall be as defined in Section 4-2.

13-1.6 Minimum Construction Requirements.

13-1.6.1 For the purpose of 13-1.6, the number of stories shall be counted starting with the primary level of exit discharge and ending with the highest occupiable level. For the purposes of this section, the primary level of exit discharge of a building shall be that floor that is level with or above finished grade of the exterior wall line for 50 percent or more of its perimeter. Building levels below the primary level shall not be counted as a story in determining the height of a building.

Allowable building construction types are determined according to the number of stories in a building. The first story is considered to be the primary level of exit discharge. Only occupiable levels are counted in determining story height. For example, an unoccupied attic would not constitute a story.

Difficulties have been experienced in determining story height where a building is located on a sloping grade. Paragraph 13-1.6.1 notes that a story on a sloping site that is partially below grade should be counted as a story if the floor is level with or above grade along 50 percent or more of the perimeter of the building at the exterior wall. (*See Figure 13-2.*)

13-1.6.2 Health care occupancies shall be limited to the following types of building construction (*see 6-2.1*):

Table 13–1.6.2

Construction Type	Stories			
	1	2	3	Over 3
I (443)				
I (332)	X	X	X	X
II (222)				
II (111)	X	X†	X†	N.P.
II (000)	X†	X†	N.P.	N.P.
III (211)	X†	X†	N.P.	N.P.
III (200)	X†	N.P.	N.P.	N.P.
IV (2HH)	X†	X†	N.P.	N.P.
V (111)	X†	X†	N.P.	N.P.
V (000)	X†	N.P.	N.P.	N.P.

X: Permitted type of construction
X†: Building requires automatic sprinkler protection (*see 13–3.5.1*)
N.P.: Not Permitted

Exception*: Any building of Type I or Type II (222 or 111) construction shall be permitted to include roofing systems involving combustible supports, decking, or roofing provided: (1) the roof covering meets Class C requirements in accordance with NFPA 256, Standard Methods of Fire Tests of Roof Coverings, and (2) the roof is separated from all occupied portions of the building by a noncombustible floor assembly that includes at least 2½ in. (6.4 cm) of concrete or gypsum fill. To qualify for this exception, the attic or other space so developed shall either be unoccupied or protected throughout by an approved automatic sprinkler system.

A-13-1.6.2 **Exception.** Unoccupied space, for the purposes of this exception, is a space not normally occupied by persons, fuel-fired equipment, or hazardous areas.

Construction types permitted in existing health care facilities are indicated as a function of height in 13-1.6.2. See NFPA 220, *Standard on Types of Building Construction,*[2] for definitions of construction types.

Multistory, nonsprinklered health care facilities are required to be constructed of noncombustible materials. A minimum 2-hour fire resistance rating is required for building members of structures exceeding three stories. It is recognized that it may not be possible to move patients, and occupants of a health care facility may be required to remain in the structure for the duration of the fire. In specifying 2-hour fire resistance, it is intended that building members be adequately protected against

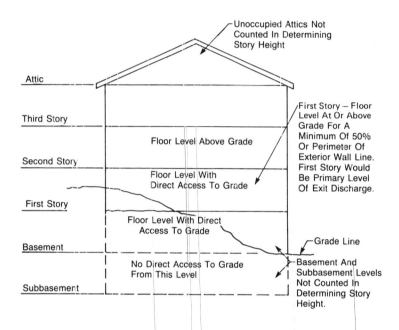

Attic

Third Story

Second Story

First Story

Basement

Subbasement

Unoccupied Attics Not
Counted In Determining
Story Height

Floor Level Above Grade

Floor Level With
Direct Access To Grade

Floor Level With Direct
Access To Grade

No Direct Access To Grade
From This Level

First Story — Floor
Level At Or Above
Grade For A
Minimum Of 50%
Or Perimeter Of
Exterior Wall Line.
First Story Would
Be Primary Level
Of Exit Discharge.

Grade Line

Basement And
Subbasement Levels
Not Counted In
Determining Story
Height.

Figure 13-2. Building Section View Illustrates Application of 13-1.6.1.

the effects of fire to ensure building stability for the projected fire duration.

Two-story buildings that use combustible elements are allowed where completely protected by automatic sprinklers. Type II (111) structures can be erected with up to three stories where a complete system of electrically supervised automatic sprinklers is provided.

In certain areas, it has been common practice to erect a building with a flat concrete roof deck. A wood deck on a wood frame peaked roof is then added for weather protection. Paragraph 13-1.6.2 contains an exception that permits, under certain conditions, construction of such a combustible roof system on a multistory building without jeopardizing the building construction (Type I or II) classification. The exception specifies that the attic space must be either unoccupied or protected with automatic sprinklers. The term "unoccupied" is meant to disallow routine regular use of the attic, which might either increase the likelihood of fire or add a "fuel load" to the non-sprinklered space. Office or combustible storage spaces, for example, would be prohibited. The term "unoccupied" is not intended to prohibit the presence of mechanical equipment, such as air-handling units, requiring periodic maintenance. (*Also see commentary following 13-3.5.1.*)

13-1.6.3 All interior walls and partitions in buildings of Type I or Type II construction shall be of noncombustible or limited-combustible materials.

Exception*: Listed fire retardant treated wood studs shall be permitted within non-load bearing 1-hour fire-rated partitions.

A-13-1.6.3   Exception There is a finish capacity in a 1-hour fire-rated partition that would be expected to prevent the generation of smoke and gases from fire retardant-treated wood studs for an extended time during fire exposure. This *Code* does not intend to allow the use of fire retardant wood studs and partitions of only 20 minutes fire resistance.

NFPA 220, *Standard on Types of Building Construction*,[2] establishes restrictions on the use of combustible building materials within structures required to be constructed of noncombustible or limited-combustible materials. NFPA 220 should be consulted for specific limitations. The terms noncombustible and limited-combustible are defined within NFPA 220 and are repeated in Chapter 3 of this *Code* for easy reference.

Note that the exception allows listed fire retardant treated wood studs within non-load bearing, 1-hour fire-rated partitions. It does not allow them in 20-minute or

30-minute partitions, since the studs would be exposed to fire sooner.

13-1.6.4 Openings for the passage of pipes or conduit in walls or partitions that are required to have fire or smoke resisting capability shall be protected in accordance with 6-2.3.6.2 or 6-3.6.1.

Fire and smoke may spread across a fire-rated barrier or fire-rated wall via openings created by the passage of pipes, conduit, or other building services. Paragraph 13-1.6.4 specifies that where such penetrations occur, suitable protection such as metal plates, masonry fill, or other products approved for the purpose should be installed to maintain the fire and smoke resisting capability of the barrier.

13-1.6.5 **Firestopping.** Each exterior wall of frame construction and interior stud partitions shall be firestopped so as to cut off all concealed draft openings, both horizontal and vertical, between any cellar or basement and the first floor. Such firestopping shall consist of wood at least 2 in. (5 cm) (nominal) thick or of suitable noncombustible material.

13-1.7 **Occupant Load.** The occupant load for which means of egress shall be provided for any floor shall be the maximum number of persons intended to occupy that floor but not less than one person for each 120 sq ft (11.1 sq m) gross floor area in health care sleeping departments, and not less than one person for each 240 sq ft (22.3 sq m) of gross floor area of inpatient health care treatment departments. Gross floor areas shall be measured within the exterior building walls with no deductions. (*See Chapter 3.*)

Paragraph 13-1.7 specifies criteria for projecting occupant loads. The minimum occupant load for which exits must be provided in all buildings cannot be less than that established by projections involving (1) a single person for each 120 sq ft (11.1 sq m) of gross floor area in health care sleeping areas, and (2) one person for each 240 sq ft (22.3 sq m) of gross floor area in inpatient health care treatment areas. However, if by actual count, the number of persons exceeds that number projected by area calculations, then the actual number of persons present

becomes the minimum occupant load for which exits must be provided.

The maximum number of people allowed to occupy a space is limited by available exit capacity and other functional considerations. It is not intended to limit populations based upon the area projections contained in this paragraph.

SECTION 13-2   Means of Egress Requirements

13-2.1* **General.** Every aisle, passageway, corridor, exit discharge, exit location, and access shall be in accordance with Chapter 5.

Exception: As modified in the following paragraphs.

A-13-2.1 The specifications in Chapter 13 for door widths are minimums based on actual door width (leaf width). The provisions in Chapter 5 for clear width, as indicated in 5-2.1.2, apply only for purposes of capacity calculations not for minimum widths as indicated in this chapter.

Means of egress details are to conform to the fundamental provisions of Chapter 5, except as modified in Chapter 13. Egress door width and capacity calculations using 13-2.3.2 must be determined using "clear width" in accordance with 5-2.1.2. Where minimum door widths are established within Chapter 13 (in 13-2.3.4, for example), door widths are determined using actual door leaf width. Where door widths are specified in Chapter 13, hinge stile and stops that project into the door opening are to be ignored, since those projections were taken into consideration when the door widths specified in Chapter 13 were developed.

13-2.2 **Means of Egress Components.**

In planning exits, arrangements should be made so that patients confined to their beds may be transferred from one section of a floor to another section of the same floor that is separated by a fire or smoke barrier. Where the building design will permit, the section of the corridor containing an entrance or elevator lobby should be separated from adjoining corridors by fire or smoke barriers. Where the lobby is centrally located, such an arrangement will produce a smoke lock, placing a double barrier between the area to which patients may be taken and the area from which they must be evacuated due to threatening smoke and fire. Note that this is not required by the *Code* but is considered to be good fire protection design.

13-2.2.1 Components of the means of egress shall be limited to the types described in 13-2.2.2 through 13-2.2.7.

13-2.2.2 Doors.

13-2.2.2.1 Doors shall comply with 5-2.1.

13-2.2.2.2 Locks shall not be permitted on patient sleeping room doors.

Exception No. 1: Key locking devices that restrict access to the room from the corridor and that are operable only by staff from the corridor side shall be permitted. Such devices shall not restrict egress from the room.

This exception allows rooms that are not being used to be secured by staff. However, in the event that the room is occupied, the *Code* requires that the lock cannot restrict egress from the room.

Exception No. 2: Door locking arrangements are permitted in health care occupancies or portions of health care occupancies where the clinical needs of the patients require specialized security measures for their safety, provided keys are carried by staff at all times.

Some health care facilities may be required to provide resident security, but the *Code* requires that staff must have immediate access to patient rooms. See also paragraph 13-2.2.2.5, which limits the number of locks per door and specifies that keys must be carried by staff at all times, or other provisions must be made for the immediate release of patients using remotely controlled locking devices.

13-2.2.2.3 Doors not in a required means of egress are permitted to be subject to locking.

13-2.2.2.4 Doors within a required means of egress shall not be equipped with a latch or lock that requires the use of a tool or key from the egress side.

Exception No. 1: Door locking arrangements are permitted in health care occupancies or portions of health care occupancies where the clinical needs of the patients require specialized security measures for their safety, provided keys are carried by staff at all times. (See 13-1.1.1.7 and 13-2.2.2.5.)

Note that 13-1.1.1.7 allows the authority having jurisdiction to make appropriate modifications to compensate for locking of egress doors. (*See commentary on 13-2.2.2.2 Exception No. 2.*)

Exception No. 2: *Special locking arrangements complying with 5-2.1.6 shall be permitted provided not more than one such device is located in any egress path.*

A-13-2.2.2.4 Exception No. 2. The intent of the provision is that a person following the natural path of the means of egress not encounter more than one delay release device along that path of travel to an exit. Thus, each door from the multiple floors of a building that opens into an enclosed stair may have its own delay release device, but an additional delay release device could not be present at the level of exit discharge on the door that discharges people from the enclosed stair to the outside.

Paragraph 5-2.1.6 specifies minimum requirements for delayed release hardware, including the requirement that the building must be protected throughout by automatic sprinklers or automatic fire detection. The exception permits the use of time-delay locks on any door. However, only one door in each means of egress for any given space may use such a feature.

13-2.2.2.5 Doors located in the means of egress that are permitted to be locked under other provisions of this chapter shall have adequate provisions made for the rapid removal of occupants by such reliable means as the remote-control of locks or by keying all locks to keys carried by staff at all times. Only one such locking device is permitted on each door.

Exception No. 1: Locks installed in accordance with 13-2.2.2.4 Exception No. 2.

Exception No. 2: More than one lock may be permitted on each door subject to approval of the authority having jurisdiction.

In buildings where it is necessary to lock doors, continuous supervision by staff must be provided. Provisions must be made for the prompt release of persons who must be restrained by equipping staff with keys or by providing remote unlocking capabilities for doors. Where staff relies on the use of keys, consideration should be given to a master key system, which would facilitate the quick release of occupants. In existing buildings, and with the approval of the authority having jurisdiction, more than one lock on a door is permitted. (*See commentary following Exception No. 2 to 13-2.2.2.2. Also see 13-1.1.1.7.*)

13-2.2.2.6* Any door in an exit passageway, stairway enclosure, horizontal exit, smoke barrier, or hazardous area enclosure shall be permitted to be held open only by an automatic release device that complies with 5-2.1.8. The automatic sprinkler system if provided, the required fire alarm system, and the systems required by 5-2.1.8(c) shall be arranged so as to initiate the closing action of all such doors by zone or throughout the entire facility.

A-13-2.2.2.6 It is desirable to keep doors in exit passageways, horizontal exits, smoke barriers, stair enclosures, and required enclosures around hazardous areas closed at all times to impede the travel of smoke and fire gases. Functionally, however, this involves decreased efficiency and limits patient supervision by the staff of a facility. To accommodate these necessities, it is practical to presume that such doors will be kept open even to the extent of employing wood chocks and other makeshift devices. Doors in exit passageways, horizontal exits, and smoke barriers should, therefore, be equipped with automatic hold-open devices actuated by the methods described regardless of whether or not the original installation of the doors was predicated on a policy of keeping them closed.

13-2.2.2.7 Where doors in a stair enclosure are held open by an automatic device as permitted in 13-2.2.2.6, initiation of a door closing action on any level shall cause all doors at all levels in the stair enclosure to close.

Fire doors protecting openings in fire resistant enclosures should preferably be maintained in the closed position. Doors protecting openings in exit enclosures, stair enclosures, horizontal exits, smoke barriers, or required enclosures for hazardous areas may be held open only by a device designed to close the door automatically (*see 13-2.2.2.6*). The automatic-closing device must close the doors upon operation of the manual fire alarm system as well as upon the activation of either a local device designed to detect smoke on either side of the opening or a complete automatic smoke detection system [*see also 5-2.1.8(d) and NFPA 72E, Standard on Automatic Fire Detectors*].[4] In addition, if the facility is sprinklered, the water flow alarm shall also initiate automatic closing of the doors.

It is especially important in health care facilities to maintain floor-to-floor separation. Doors protecting openings in a stair enclosure may be held open as permitted above. Initiation of any action that causes a door to close at one level must cause all doors at all levels in the stair enclosure to close and latch. (*See 13-2.2.2.7 and 13-3.1.2.*)

13-2.2.2.8* Health care occupancies are exempted from the provisions of 5-2.1.5.2.

A-13-2.2.2.8 Doors to the enclosures of interior stair exits should be arranged to open from the stair side at least at every third floor so that it will be possible to leave the stairway at such floor should the fire render the lower part of the stair unusable during egress or should the occupants seek refuge on another floor.

13-2.2.2.9 Horizontal sliding doors shall be permitted in a means of egress serving an occupant load of less than 50 in accordance with 5-2.1.14.2. Sliding doors that are not automatic-closing shall be limited to a single leaf and shall have a latch or other mechanism that will ensure that doors will not rebound into a partially opened position if forceably closed in an emergency.

Paragraph 13-2.2.2.9 permits horizontal sliding doors complying with 5-2.1.14.2 to be used in a means of egress where occupant loads are limited. Where sliding doors are to be closed manually, the doors must consist of a single leaf (to avoid openings at the meeting edges of the leafs), and provision must be made, by use of a latch or other means, to prevent the door from impacting the frame fully and rebounding to a partially open position when closed forcefully.

The requirements of 5-2.1.14.2 should be closely reviewed. The sliding door described is highly specialized, and all requirements of 5-2.1.14.2 must be met.

13-2.2.3 Stairs. Stairs shall comply with 5-2.2.

13-2.2.4 Smokeproof Enclosures. Smokeproof enclosures shall comply with 5-2.3.

13-2.2.5 Horizontal Exits. Horizontal exits shall comply with 5-2.4, modified as follows:

(a) At least 30 net sq ft (2.8 net sq m) per patient in a hospital or nursing home or 15 net sq ft (1.4 net sq m) per resident in a limited care facility shall be provided within the aggregated area of corridors, patient rooms, treatment rooms, lounge or dining areas, and other low hazard areas on each side of the horizontal exit. On stories not housing bed or litter patients, at least 6 net sq ft (.56 net sq m) per occupant shall be provided on each side of the horizontal exit for the total number of occupants in adjoining compartments.

(b)* A door in a horizontal exit is not required to swing with exit travel as specified in 5-2.4.3.6.

A-13-2.2.5(b) The waiver of swinging of doors in the direction of exit travel is based on the assumption that in this occupancy there will be no possibility of a panic rush that might prevent opening of doors swinging against exit travel.

A desirable arrangement, possible with corridors 8 ft (244 cm) or more in width, is to have two 42-in. (107-cm) doors, normally closed, each swinging with the exit travel (in opposite directions).

(c) The total exit capacity of the other exits (stairs, ramps, doors leading outside the building) shall not be reduced below one-third that required for the entire area of the building.

(d) Door openings in horizontal exits shall be protected by a swinging door a minimum of 34 in. (86 cm) in width or a horizontal sliding door complying with 5-2.1.14 and providing a clear opening of at least 34 in. (86 cm).

Because of practical difficulties involving vertical exit travel in health care facilities, special recognition is given to horizontal travel and the use of horizontal exits. Up to two-thirds of the total required exit capacity for a given fire area may be provided by horizontal exits [see 13-2.2.5(c)]. It should be noted, however, that every floor and every fire section must have at least one exit consisting of a door leading directly outside the building, an interior stair, an outside stair, a smokeproof enclosure, a ramp, or an exit passageway (see 13-2.4.2). No fire area can be served by horizontal exits only. In the event a horizontal exit also serves as a smoke barrier, see commentary following 13-2.4.3, and also see 13-3.7.

It is also recognized that corridors in existing health care occupancies may be 4 ft (1.2 m) wide, and it is therefore impractical in many instances to install a pair of doors in a horizontal exit. However, the 4-ft (1.2-m) corridor width will permit the opening of a single door against the flow of travel with minimal difficulty. A power-operated sliding door might be used to reduce problems associated with door swing. The *Code* permits sliding doors complying with 5-2.1.14 for the protection of openings in horizontal exits. The use of power-operated sliding doors results in an obstruction-free opening for normal traffic, while still providing adequate fire protection for openings.

In the case of a fire barrier serving as a horizontal exit for two adjoining fire areas, and where corridor widths will permit, a pair of doors arranged with each leaf to swing in a direction opposite from the other should be used. Each leaf in the pair of doors should be a minimum of 34 in. (86.4 cm) wide.

New horizontal exits in an existing facility are considered a renovation and must be installed in accordance with Chapter 12 to the extent feasible (see commentary following 13-1.1.4.5 and 1-5.6). The requirements for horizontal exits in 13-2.2.5(a) to (d) are illustrated in Figure 13-3.

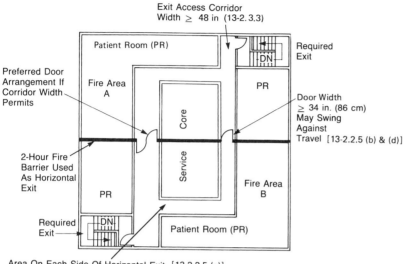

Exit Access Corridor
Width ≥ 48 in (13-2.3.3)

Patient Room (PR)

Required Exit

DN

Preferred Door Arrangement If Corridor Width Permits

Fire Area A

PR

Core

Door Width ≥ 34 in. (86 cm) May Swing Against Travel [13-2.2.5 (b) & (d)]

2-Hour Fire Barrier Used As Horizontal Exit

Service

PR

Fire Area B

Required Exit

DN

Patient Room (PR)

Area On Each Side Of Horizontal Exit [13-2.2.5 (a)] Or Smoke Barrier (13-3.7.4) Must Provide At Least 30 sq ft (2.8 sq m) (Net) For The Total Number Of Patients (Hospital And Nursing Homes), At Least 15 sq ft (1.4 sq m) (Net) For The Total Number Of Residents (Limited Care), And At Least 6 sq ft (.6 sq m) (Net) For The Total Number Of Other Occupants. Space Must Be Provided In Corridors, Patient Room, Treatment Rooms, Lounge Areas, Dining Rooms, Etc.

Figure 13-3. Horizontal Exits in an Existing Health Care Facility. If corridor width permits, the door arrangement as required by 12-2.2.5 should be provided.

Formal Interpretation 76-26
Reference: 13-2.2.5

Question: Does paragraph 13-2.2.5 intend to prohibit the use of center mullions, as is the case in paragraph 12-2.2.5(e)?

Answer: No.

Issue Edition: 1976
Reference: 10-3.2.2.5
Date: August 1977 ■

Ramps are undesirable in hospitals and nursing homes due to the potential for accidents in both normal and emergency traffic, except in the case of ramps of extremely gradual slope, which require so much space as to be impracticable in most situations. They are, however, the only practicable method of moving patients in beds from one story to another, except by elevators, which may not be available during fire conditions. The best plan is to provide for horizontal egress to another section of the building, minimizing the need for complete evacuation.

Ramps may be the best means for providing egress from doors two or three steps above or below grade level (*see 5-1.5*) and may also compensate for minor differences in floor levels between adjoining sections of buildings. Such ramps must be constructed in accordance with 13-2.2.6.

13-2.2.6 **Ramps.**

13-2.2.6.1 Ramps shall comply with 5-2.5.

13-2.2.6.2 Ramps enclosed as exits shall be of sufficient width to provide exit capacity in accordance with 13-2.3.2.

13-2.2.7 **Exit Passageways.** Exit passageways shall comply with 5-2.6.

13-2.3   Capacity of Means of Egress.

13-2.3.1   The capacity of any required means of egress shall be based on its width as defined in Section 5-3.

13-2.3.2   The capacity of means of egress providing travel by means of stairs shall be 0.6 in. (1.5 cm) per person, and the capacity of means of egress providing horizontal travel (without stairs) by means such as doors, ramps, or horizontal exits shall be 0.5 in. (1.3 cm) per person.

Exception: The capacity of means of egress in health care occupancies protected throughout by an approved supervised automatic sprinkler system in accordance with 13-3.5.2 shall be 0.3 in. (0.8 cm) per person for travel by means of stairs and 0.2 in. (0.5 cm) per person for horizontal travel without stairs.

Exit capacity is calculated using a concept of "effective width" (*see Chapter 2 of NFPA 101M, Alternative Approaches to Life Safety*).[1] This calculation method relates the usable width of an exit and the anticipated egress flow. This approach was developed using research that demonstrates that exit capacity varies with exit width and is based upon a linear relationship, rather than on the step function used in older editions of the *Code*.

Older editions of the *Code* calculated exit capacity based upon units of exit width [22 in. (55.9 cm)]. Increases in exit capacity were permitted only for minimum increases of 12 in. (30.5 cm) (½ unit of exit width). Therefore, exit capacity for a 44-in. (112-cm) stair (2 units) was computed at 44 people (22 people per unit × 2 units). No increase in capacity was allowed for stair width increases up to 11 in. (27.9 cm) [e.g., a 55-in. (139.7-cm) stair]. A 56-in. (142.2-cm) stair [44 in. (112 cm) + 12 in. (30.5 cm) = 2.5 units] had a capacity of 55 persons (22 people per unit × 2.5 units).

The method currently prescribed acknowledges that increasing the width of egress systems results in increasing the flow. The new arrangement computes stair egress capacity in nonsprinklered buildings on the basis of 0.6 in. (1.5 cm) per person. Therefore, a 44-in. (112-cm) stair provides adequate egress for 73 persons [44 in. (112 cm) ÷ 0.6 in. (1.5 cm) per person]. Similarly, a 50-in. (127-cm) stair would have a capacity of 83 persons. The capacity of level passageways and doors in nonsprinklered buildings is computed on the basis of 0.5 in. (1.3 cm) per person. Exit capacity calculations must use clear width as defined in 5-2.1.2.1 and 5-2.2.2.1. For fully sprinklered buildings, exit capacity is calculated in a similar manner using 0.3 in. (0.8 cm) per person for travel over stairs and 0.2 in. (0.5 cm) per person for horizontal travel.

Health care occupancies are the only occupancies in the *Code* that allow an increase due to automatic sprinkler protection. The increase in exit capacity is based upon the assumption that sprinklers will limit fire size, thereby allowing greater time for safe egress.

The origin of the design of exits using an exit unit concept evolved in the early part of the century. A philosophy developed used exit stair enclosures in health care facilities as areas of refuge. The capacity of health care exits was set conservatively in recognition of the slow rate of travel for patients and the fact that space had to be reserved for patients on litters and in wheelchairs.

Recent editions of the *Code* use a different concept for exit design. Life safety from fire in health care facilities relies upon a defend in place principle. Horizontal exits or smoke barriers are used to subdivide each story to provide an area of refuge on each story without requiring travel by means of stairs. Flow rates for exits (capacity) are established on the assumption that exit stairs will be used principally by able-bodied staff, visitors, and ambulatory patients for emergency evacuation. Nonambulatory patients will remain in the building, with those on the floor of fire origin being moved horizontally to an area of refuge.

	Capacity (Inches per person)	
	Nonsprinklered	Sprinklered
Stairs	0.6	0.3
Level Travel	0.5	0.2

13-2.3.3   Any required aisle, corridor, or ramp shall be not less than 48 in. (122 cm) in clear width where serving as means of egress from patient sleeping rooms. It shall be so arranged as to avoid any obstructions to the convenient removal of nonambulatory persons carried on stretchers or on mattresses serving as stretchers.

Exception: Aisles, corridors, and ramps in adjunct areas not intended for the housing, treatment, or use of inpatients shall be a minimum of 44 in. (112 cm) in clear and unobstructed width.

Figure 13-4 illustrates an exit access corridor that complies with 13-2.3.3. The specified minimum of 48 in. (122 cm) leaves little safety margin. Care is necessary to prevent carts, furnishings, and other materials from obstructing or interfering with potential occupant movement.

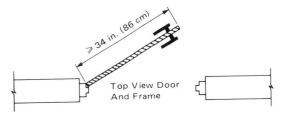

Figure 13-5. Minimum Width of Doors in Means of Egress in Existing Health Care Facilities.

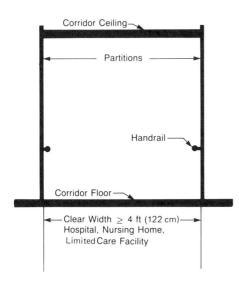

Figure 13-4. Corridor in Exit Access in Existing Health Care Occupancy. (See 13-2.3.3.)

13-2.3.4 For evacuation purposes only, the minimum width for doors in the means of egress from hospital, nursing home, limited care facility, and psychiatric hospital sleeping rooms, and diagnostic and treatment areas such as X-ray, surgery, or physical therapy shall be at least 34 in. (86 cm) wide.

Egress door width must be determined on the basis of required capacity and is measured using clear width in accordance with 5-2.1.2. Where minimum door widths are specified within Chapter 13 (in 13-2.3.4, for example), door widths are to be determined using actual door leaf widths. Where minimum door widths are specified in Chapter 13, hinge stile and stops that project into the door opening are to be ignored, since these projections were taken into account when the door widths specified in Chapter 13 were developed. (*See Figure 13-5.*)

> **Formal Interpretation 76-29**
> Reference: 13-2.3.4
>
> *Question:* Does paragraph 13-2.3.4 intend that the requirement for 34 in. wide door leaf result in a clear opening nominally 32 in. wide?
>
> *Answer:* Yes.
>
> *Issue Edition:* 1976
> *Reference:* 10-3.2.8.3
> *Date:* August 1977 ∎

13-2.4 Number of Exits.

13-2.4.1 At least two exits of the types described in 13-2.2.2 through 13-2.2.7, remotely located from each other, shall be provided for each floor or fire section of the building.

13-2.4.2 At least one exit from each floor or fire section shall be one of the following:

(a) A door leading directly outside the building, or
(b) A stair, or
(c) A smokeproof enclosure, or
(d) A ramp, or
(e) An exit passageway.

Any fire section not meeting these requirements shall be considered as part of an adjoining zone. Egress shall not require return through the zone of fire origin.

13-2.4.3* At least two exits of the types described in 13-2.2.2 through 13-2.2.7 shall be accessible from each smoke compartment. Egress shall be permitted through adjacent compartment(s), but shall not require return through the compartment of fire origin.

A-13-2.4.3 An exit is not necessary for each individual smoke compartment if there is access to an exit through other smoke compartments without passing through the smoke compartment of fire origin.

Figure 13-6 can be used to illustrate the application of 13-2.4.2 and 13-2.4.3. If both Wall I and Wall II are horizontal exits, then three fire compartments or fire sections are formed. Paragraph 13-2.4.2 would then require that Area B must also be provided with one of the five types of exits listed. Specifically, Area B must be provided with an exit other than a horizontal exit, even though two horizontal exits are already provided from that area. Without this additional exit, Area B must be considered part of one of the adjoining areas: part of Area A, where the horizontal exit of Wall I is not recognized, or part of Area C, where the horizontal exit of Wall II is not recognized. Prior to the 1985 Edition of the *Code*, this also would have applied to smoke barriers. However, the *Code* now allows egress through adjoining smoke compartments. If both Wall I and Wall II are smoke barriers, the arrangement is acceptable. If Wall I is a smoke barrier and Wall II is a horizontal exit, the arrangement is also acceptable, since Areas A and B would be one fire area and Area C would be the other fire area. Consequently, all requirements of 13-2.4.2 and 13-2.4.3 would be met.

There are two reasons for using caution in determining the number of smoke compartments that can be safely traveled before reaching the final exit. First, excessive moving of patients should be avoided, and, second, each compartment must have sufficient area to handle all the patients it serves. In the previous example, where Wall I is a smoke barrier and Wall II is a horizontal exit, each area would have to be sufficient in size to comply with 13-2.2.5(a) for horizontal exits or 13-3.7.4 for smoke barriers, based on figures calculated for the entire floor, since all three areas are an integral part of the horizontal evacuation design for the floor. This is easily justified since, if a fire started near the exit for Area A, thus requiring evacuation into Area B, ultimate evacuation could be achieved only through Area C, because there is no exit

from Area B. In such a case, Area C would have to have sufficient area to handle patients from Areas A and B as well as those patients originally in Area C.

In order to ensure that egress does not require return through the compartment of fire origin, each compartment formed must be analyzed to ensure that a path of travel to an exit other than a horizontal exit is available. (*See Figure 13-6.*)

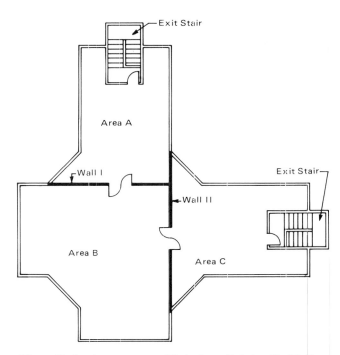

Figure 13-6. Arrangement of Exits in an Existing Health Care Occupancy Involving Smoke Barriers and Horizontal Exits. (See commentary following 13-2.4.3 for discussion of figure.)

13-2.5 **Arrangement of Means of Egress.**

13-2.5.1 Every habitable room shall have an exit access door leading directly to an exit access corridor.

Exception No. 1: If there is an exit door opening directly to the outside of the room at ground level.

Exception No. 2: Patient sleeping rooms shall be permitted to have one intervening room if the intervening room is not used to serve as an exit access for more than eight patient sleeping beds.

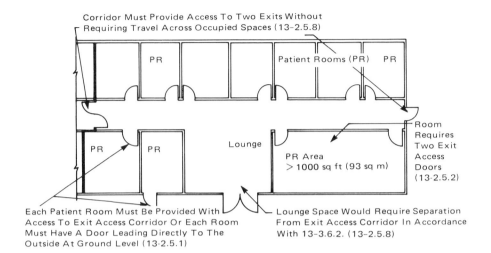

Corridor Must Provide Access To Two Exits Without Requiring Travel Across Occupied Spaces (13-2.5.8)

PR

Patient Rooms (PR) PR

PR PR

Lounge

PR Area > 1000 sq ft (93 sq m)

Room Requires Two Exit Access Doors (13-2.5.2)

Each Patient Room Must Be Provided With Access To Exit Access Corridor Or Each Room Must Have A Door Leading Directly To The Outside At Ground Level (13-2.5.1)

Lounge Space Would Require Separation From Exit Access Corridor In Accordance With 13-3.6.2. (13-2.5.8)

Figure 13-7a. *Arrangement of Exit Access in an Existing Health Care Facility. Improper lounge arrangement, as lounge must not interfere with exit access (see Figure 13-7b for proper lounge arrangement). Paragraph 13-2.5.1 Exception No. 1, 13-2.5.2, and 13-2.5.8 are also illustrated.*

Exception No. 3: Special nursing suites are permitted to have one intervening room where the arrangement allows for direct and constant visual supervision by nursing personnel.

Exception No. 4: For rooms other than patients' sleeping rooms, one or more adjacent rooms shall be permitted to intervene in accordance with 13-2.5.7.

The term "habitable room" is used in 13-2.5.1 in lieu of "patient sleeping room" to clarify that all occupied rooms in a health care facility must have access to a corridor leading to an exit. (*See commentary following 13-2.4.3.*)

Figures 13-7a and b illustrate the intent of 13-2.5.1. Figure 13-8 on the following page illustrates Exception No. 2 to 13-2.5.1.

Nursing suites and various treatment areas are frequently arranged with an intervening workroom located between the exit access corridor and a treatment room. Exception No. 4 to 13-2.5.1, in combination with 13-2.5.7, will allow egress through spaces that are closely related in function to the treatment room and, therefore, are under the immediate control of staff who, along with patients, would be forced to travel across such rooms. Where such an arrangement is used, locking hardware on doors is not permitted to restrict egress from the nursing suite or intervening room. (*See 13-2.2.2.*)

Maximum travel distance limitations to reach the exit access (corridor) door of nonsleeping suites are specified in 13-2.5.7 [*for sleeping suites, see 13-2.6.2(d)*]. Where applying Exception Nos. 2, 3, and 4 to 13-2.5.1, 13-2.5.4 prohibits intervening rooms from being hazardous areas.

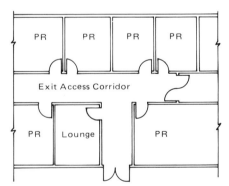

PR PR PR PR

Exit Access Corridor

PR Lounge PR

Figure 13-7b. *Proper Arrangement of Exit Access in an Existing Health Care Facility (see Figure 13-7a). Lounge is separated from exit access corridor in accordance with 13-3.6.2 as required by 13-2.5.8. (See also 13-3.6.1 Exception Nos. 1, 2, 6, and 7 where a waiting space may be open to an exit access corridor.)*

13-2.5.2 Any patient sleeping room, or any suite that includes patient sleeping rooms, of more than 1,000 sq ft (93 sq m) shall have at least two exit access doors remotely located from each other.

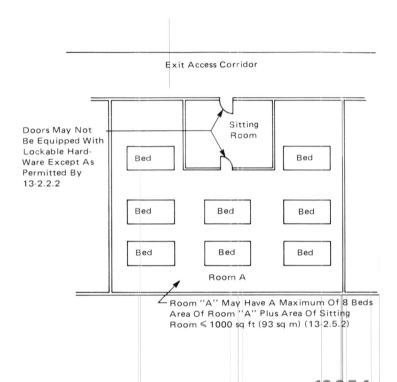

Exit Access Corridor

Doors May Not
Be Equipped With
Lockable Hard-
Ware Except As
Permitted By
13-2.2.2

Sitting
Room

Bed   Bed

Bed   Bed   Bed

Bed   Bed   Bed

Room A

Room "A" May Have A Maximum Of 8 Beds
Area Of Room "A" Plus Area Of Sitting
Room ≤ 1000 sq ft (93 sq m) (13-2.5.2)

Figure 13-8. Exit Access from a Patient Sleeping Room through an Adjacent Room in an Existing Health Care Facility. This arrangement complies with 13-2.5.1 Exception No. 2 and 13-2.5.2.

Any room or any suite of rooms, other than patient sleeping rooms, of more than 2,500 sq ft (230 sq m) shall have at least two exit access doors remotely located from each other.

Patient sleeping rooms or suites with sleeping rooms that are greater than 1,000 sq ft (93 sq m) require two exit access doors. The doors may open onto a common corridor but are required to be as remotely located from each other as possible. Rooms or suites not used for patient sleeping purposes may be up to 2,500 sq ft (230 sq m) in area and require only one door based on the premise that occupants are alert or ambulatory or are, in most instances, accompanied by staff who can assist in evacuating the space during fire or other emergency. For sleeping suites, refer to 13-2.5.1, 13-2.5.3, 13-2.5.4, and 13-2.5.5 for additional requirements. For nonsleeping suites, refer to 13-2.5.1, 13-2.5.3, 13-2.5.4, 13-2.5.6, and 13-2.5.7 for additional requirements. Figures 13-9a and 13-9b illustrate the requirements for sleeping suites. Figures 13-10a, 13-10b, and 13-10c on pages 500 and 501 illustrate the requirements for nonsleeping suites.

13-2.5.3 Any suite of rooms that complies with the requirements of this section shall be permitted to be subdivided with non-fire-rated, noncombustible or limited-combustible partitions.

13-2.5.4 Intervening rooms shall not be hazardous areas as defined by 13-3.2.

13-2.5.5 Suites of sleeping rooms shall not exceed 5,000 sq ft (460 sq m).

Paragraphs 13-2.5.1 Exception No. 3, 13-2.5.2, 13-2.5.3, 13-2.5.4, and 13-2.5.5 contain provisions for nursing suites, such as Intensive Care Units (ICU) or Coronary Care Units (CCU). Interior suite arrangements are not required to comply with 13-2.3.3 or 13-3.6 relative to corridor access to exits. For example, interior corridors within special nursing units are not required to be 48 in. (122 cm) wide. Doors to individual cubicles may be sliding doors. (*See Figures 13-9a and b.*)

13-2.5.6 Suites of rooms, other than patient sleeping rooms, shall not exceed 10,000 sq ft (930 sq m).

13-2.5.7 Suites of rooms, other than patient sleeping rooms, shall be permitted to have one intervening room if the travel distance within the suite to the exit access door is not greater than 100 ft (30 m) and shall be permitted to have two intervening rooms where the travel distance within the suite to the exit access door is not greater than 50 ft (15 m).

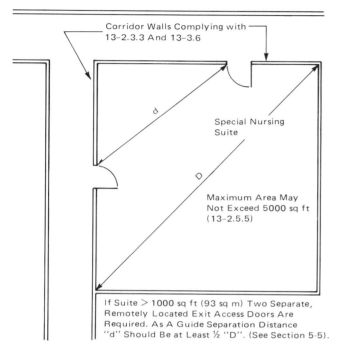

Figure 13-9a. *Suites Involving Patient Sleeping Rooms in an Existing Health Care Occupancy. The requirements of 13-2.5.1, 13-2.5.2, and 13-2.5.5 are illustrated here. The suite must comply with Figures 13-9a and b.*

The requirements of 13-2.5.1 Exception No. 4, 13-2.5.2, 13-2.5.6, and 13-2.5.7 are illustrated in Figures 13-10a, 13-10b, and 13-10c on the following pages.

13-2.5.8* Every corridor shall provide access to at least two approved exits in accordance with Section 5-4 and Section 5-5 without passing through any intervening rooms or spaces other than corridors or lobbies.

Exception: Existing dead-end corridors may be continued to be used if it is not practical and feasible to alter them so that exits will be accessible in at least two different directions from all points in aisles, passageways, and corridors.

A-13-2.5.8 Every exit or exit access should be so arranged, if practical and feasible, that no corridor, passageway, or aisle has a pocket or dead end exceeding 30 ft (9.1 m). (*Also see Table A-5-6.1.*)

Exit access corridors, aisles, and passageways should preferably be arranged so that exits will be accessible in at least two different directions from all points in the corridor, aisle, or passageway. However, in many buildings,

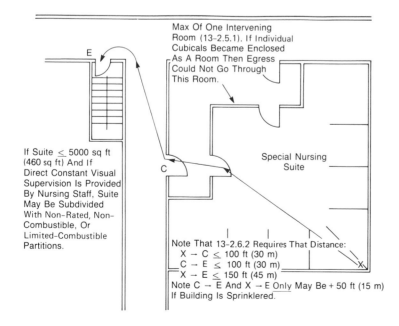

Figure 13-9b. *Suites Involving Patient Sleeping Rooms in an Existing Health Care Occupancy. The requirements of 13-2.5.1, 13-2.5.2, 13-2.5.5, and 13-2.6.2 for patient sleeping suites are illustrated. The suite must comply with Figures 13-9a and 13-9b.*

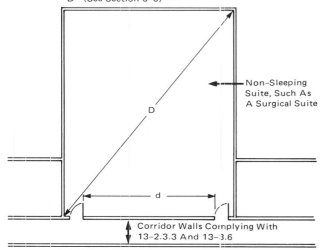

If Suite Over 2500 sq ft
(230 sq m) 2 Doors Are
Required And They
Must Be As Remote
From Each Other As
Practical. As A Guide, "d"
Should Be At Least ½
"D" (See Section 5-5)

D

Non-Sleeping
Suite, Such As
A Surgical Suite

d

Corridor Walls Complying With
13-2.3.3 And 13-3.6

Figure 13-10a. Suites Not Involving Patient Sleeping Rooms in an Existing Health Care Occupancy. This illustrates the provisions of 13-2.5.2 and 13-2.5.6. The suites must comply with Figures 13-10a and b or 13-10a and c.

dead-end corridors exist. The *Code* intends to allow dead-end corridors of moderate length to remain without alteration.

In all instances, dead-end corridors up to 30 ft (9.1 m) may remain in use without alteration. For dead-end corridors in excess of 30 ft (9.1 m), considerable judgment must be exercised in determining what constitutes an excessive dead-end pocket. Where a dead-end corridor is judged excessive, corrective action should be taken, either by provision of additional egress facilities or by provision of other safeguards that result in an equivalent degree of safety. Alternative approaches might involve application of additional smoke detectors, sprinklers, smoke control, or other means of protection.

13-2.6 Travel Distance to Exits.

13-2.6.1 Travel distance shall be measured in accordance with Section 5-6.

13-2.6.2 Travel distance:

(a) Between any room door required as exit access and an exit shall not exceed 100 ft (30 m);

(b) Between any point in a room and an exit shall not exceed 150 ft (45 m);

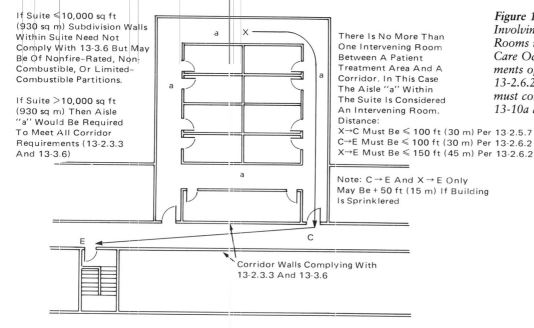

If Suite ≤ 10,000 sq ft
(930 sq m) Subdivision Walls
Within Suite Need Not
Comply With 13-3.6 But May
Be Of Nonfire-Rated, Non-
Combustible, Or Limited-
Combustible Partitions.

If Suite > 10,000 sq ft
(930 sq m) Then Aisle
"a" Would Be Required
To Meet All Corridor
Requirements (13-2.3.3
And 13-3.6)

a   X

a

a

a

There Is No More Than
One Intervening Room
Between A Patient
Treatment Area And A
Corridor. In This Case
The Aisle "a" Within
The Suite Is Considered
An Intervening Room.
Distance:
X→C Must Be ≤ 100 ft (30 m) Per 13-2.5.7
C→E Must Be ≤ 100 ft (30 m) Per 13-2.6.2
X→E Must Be ≤ 150 ft (45 m) Per 13-2.6.2

Note: C → E And X → E Only
May Be + 50 ft (15 m) If Building
Is Sprinklered

E

C

Corridor Walls Complying With
13-2.3.3 And 13-3.6

Figure 13-10b. Suites Not Involving Patient Sleeping Rooms in an Existing Health Care Occupancy. The requirements of 13-2.5.2, 13-2.5.4, and 13-2.6.2 are illustrated. The suite must comply with Figures 13-10a and b or 13-10a and c.

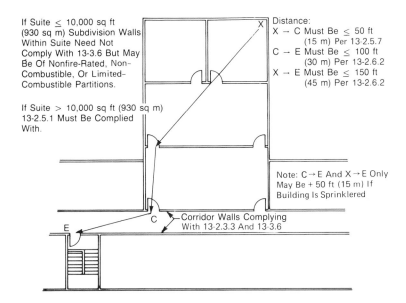

If Suite ≤ 10,000 sq ft (930 sq m) Subdivision Walls Within Suite Need Not Comply With 13-3.6 But May Be Of Nonfire-Rated, Non-Combustible, Or Limited-Combustible Partitions.

If Suite > 10,000 sq ft (930 sq m) 13-2.5.1 Must Be Complied With.

Distance:
X → C Must Be ≤ 50 ft (15 m) Per 13-2.5.7
C → E Must Be ≤ 100 ft (30 m) Per 13-2.6.2
X → E Must Be ≤ 150 ft (45 m) Per 13-2.6.2

Note: C→E And X→E Only May Be + 50 ft (15 m) If Building Is Sprinklered

Corridor Walls Complying With 13-2.3.3 And 13-3.6

Figure 13-10c. *Suites Not Involving Patient Sleeping Rooms in an Existing Health Care Occupancy. The requirements of 13-2.5.2, 13-2.5.4, and 13-2.6.2 for suites not involving patient sleeping rooms are illustrated. The suite must comply with Figures 13-10a and b or 13-10a and c.*

Exception: The maximum permitted travel distance in (a) or (b) above shall be increased by 50 ft (15 m) in buildings protected throughout by an approved supervised automatic sprinkler system.

(c) Between any point in a health care sleeping room and an exit access door of that room shall not exceed 50 ft (15 m);

(d) Between any point in a suite of sleeping rooms as permitted by 13-2.5 and an exit access door of that suite shall not exceed 100 ft (30 m) and shall meet the requirements of (b) above.

The requirements of 13-2.6.1 and 13-2.6.2 are illustrated in Figure 13-11. Travel distance is measured only to the closest exit. It is not measured to the second exit required by 13-2.4.1. It should be noted that the 50-ft (15-m) restriction within a room applies only to sleeping rooms. (*See also 13-2.5.7 and Figures 13-9 and 13-10.*)

13-2.7 Discharge from Exits.

13-2.7.1 Discharge from exits shall be arranged in accordance with Section 5-7.

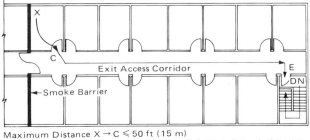

Maximum Distance X → C ≤ 50 ft (15 m)
C → E ≤ 100 ft (30 m) [150 ft (45 m) If Building Is Sprinklered]
X → E ≤ 150 ft (45 m) [200 ft (60 m) If Building Is Sprinklered]
See Figures 13-9 And 13-10 For Suites

Figure 13-11. *Travel Distance in Existing Health Care Occupancies.*

All exit stairs or exit ramps are required to discharge to the outside either directly or through an enclosed exit passageway. Where an exit passageway is used, the fire-resistive separation of the enclosure must be the same as required for the enclosure of a stair or ramp (*see 5-2.5*). Openings into the passageway must be suitably protected and limited to doors leading to spaces that are normally occupied [*see 5-1.3.1(a) through (e)*]. Under certain conditions, a maximum of 50 percent of the required exits may discharge to the outside through the level of exit discharge in accordance with 5-7.2.

13-2.8 Illumination of Means of Egress.

13-2.8.1 Means of egress shall be illuminated in accordance with Section 5-8.

13-2.9 Emergency Lighting.

13-2.9.1 Emergency lighting shall be provided in accordance with Section 5-9.

Also see 31-1.3.8.

13-2.10 Marking of Means of Egress.

13-2.10.1 Means of egress shall have signs in accordance with Section 5-10.

Exception: Where the line of exit travel is obvious, signs are not required in one story buildings with an occupancy of less than 30 persons.

13-2.11 Special Features. (Reserved.)

SECTION 13-3   Protection

13-3.1 Protection of Vertical Openings.

13-3.1.1 Any stairway, ramp, elevator hoistway, light or ventilation shaft, chute, or other vertical opening between stories shall be enclosed in accordance with Section 6-2.4 with construction having a 1-hour fire resistance rating.

Exception No. 1: Vertical openings that are not concealed within the building construction that do not connect to a corridor, do not connect more than two levels, and do not serve as a means of egress need not comply with these regulations.

Exception No. 2: Where a full enclosure of a stairway that is not a required exit is impractical, the required enclosure may be limited to that necessary to prevent a fire originating in any story from spreading to any other story.

Exception No. 3: Floor and ceiling openings for pipes or conduits where the opening around the pipes or conduits is sealed in an approved manner. (See 6-2.3.6.2.)

Exception No. 4: An atrium shall be permitted in accordance with 6-2.4.6. Exception No. 1 to 6-2.4.6(g) shall not apply to patient sleeping and treatment rooms in new or existing atriums.

Paragraph 13-3.1.1 requires that vertical shafts (including stairways, ramp enclosures, elevators, light and ventilation shafts, chutes, and other vertical openings connecting stories) must be enclosed with barriers providing a minimum fire resistance of 1 hour. Openings must be protected by approved fire doors, complete with a closing device and a positive latch. Doors in stair enclosures may be held open as specified by 13-2.2.2.6 and 13-2.2.2.7. Stairs used as an exit must be enclosed in accordance with 5-1.3.1.

Where a stairway is not used as a portion of the means of egress, and full enclosure is not possible, the enclosure may be limited to that necessary to prevent fire or smoke originating in any one story from spreading to another story. For example, in a two-story building, the stair might be enclosed at the first floor level and left open at the second floor level.

Exception No. 1 to 13-3.1.1 is illustrated in Figure 13-12. In previous editions of the *Code*, Exception No. 1 was limited to stairs. This exception has been broadened in the 1991 Edition to apply to all vertical openings. However, an additional restriction is included to prohibit unenclosed openings that are concealed in building construction. This exception would allow a light well to connect two stories or allow a stair to connect two levels of a medical library, file storage area, or an administrative office, for example. The exception would not allow omission of firestopping around pipe penetrations of a floor slab or omission of protection for duct penetrations.

Exception No. 3 will allow piping and conduit to penetrate floors without requiring an enclosed shaft. Floor penetrations, however, must be adequately protected in an approved manner to maintain the required fire resistance of the floor system. The penetrations should be sealed in a fashion that will minimize the transfer of smoke.

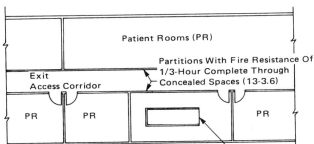

Patient Rooms (PR)

Partitions With Fire Resistance Of 1/3-Hour Complete Through Concealed Spaces (13-3.6)

Exit Access Corridor

PR   PR   PR

Open Stairs, Light Well, Or Similar Opening Leading Either Up Or Down To One Level; Connect Not More Than Two Floors

Figure 13-12. *Unprotected Vertical Openings in Accordance with 13-3.1.1 Exception No. 1 in Existing Health Care Occupancies.*

Exception No. 4 permits atriums in existing health care facilities in accordance with 6-2.4.6. Patient sleeping and treatment rooms must be separated from the atrium by partitions complying with 13-3.6. Special requirements for smoke barriers in atriums are illustrated in Figures 13-19a through 13-19d following 13-3.7.

13-3.1.2 A door in a stair enclosure shall be self-closing and shall normally be kept in a closed position.

Exception: Doors in stair enclosures held open under the conditions specified by 13-2.2.2.6 and 13-2.2.2.7.

Refer to commentary following 13-2.2.2.7 for discussion on stairway doors.

13-3.2 **Protection from Hazards.**

13-3.2.1 **Hazardous Areas.** Any hazardous areas shall be safeguarded by a fire barrier having a 1-hour fire resistance rating or provided with an automatic extinguishing system in accordance with 6-4.1. The automatic extinguishing shall be permitted to be in accordance with 13-3.5.5. Where the sprinkler option is used, the areas shall be separated from other spaces by smoke-resisting partitions and doors. The doors shall be equipped with self- or automatic-closers. Hazardous areas include, but are not restricted to, the following:

Boiler and fuel-fired heater rooms
Central/bulk laundries greater than 100 sq ft (9.3 sq m)
Repair shops
Handicraft shops

Employee locker rooms
Soiled linen rooms
Paint shops
Trash collection rooms
Rooms or spaces of more than 50 sq ft (4.6 sq m), including repair shops, used for storage of combustible supplies and equipment in quantities deemed hazardous by the authority having jurisdiction.
Laboratories employing quantities of flammable or combustible materials less than that which would be considered severe.

Hazardous areas are spaces containing materials that, due to their basic nature (as in the case of flammable liquids) or because of the quantity of combustible materials involved, represent a significantly higher hazard than would otherwise be typical in general areas of health care facilities.

A list of typical hazardous areas is included in 13-3.2.1. The list is meant to be representative, not all inclusive. The authority having jurisdiction is given the discretion to regulate any space judged to represent a hazard greater than most spaces. Hazardous areas must be separated from other areas by barriers having a 1-hour fire resistance rating, complete with approved fire doors protecting door openings; otherwise, automatic sprinkler protection must be installed. Where automatic sprinkler protection is provided, the hazardous area must still be separated from the rest of the building by nonrated barriers designed to resist the passage of smoke. (*See commentary under the exceptions to 13-3.6 for automatic sprinkler protection.*)

Provisions for the enclosure of rooms used for charging linen and waste chutes, or for the rooms into which chutes empty, are provided in Chapter 7. In addition to the fire resistant cutoff of rooms into which linen chutes and waste chutes discharge, automatic sprinkler protection is considered essential.

Where flammable liquids are handled or stored, NFPA 30, *Flammable and Combustible Liquids Code,*[5] must be consulted to establish the minimum criteria necessary to mitigate this hazard. Rooms in clinical laboratories where the unattended automatic processing of specimens with flammable solvents is likely to occur present a limited hazard that may be mitigated by use of sprinklers connected to the domestic water supply. Provisions for the use and storage of flammable gases and oxygen are covered in NFPA 99, *Standard for Health Care Facilities.*[6]

(*See commentary on 13-3.2.2 for discussion of laboratories.*)

13-3.2.2* **Laboratories.** Laboratories employing quantities of flammable, combustible, or hazardous materials that are considered as severe hazard shall be protected in accordance with NFPA 99, *Standard for Health Care Facilities.*

A-13-3.2.2 The hazard level of a laboratory is considered severe if quantities of flammable, combustible, or hazardous materials are present that are capable of sustaining a fire condition of sufficient magnitude to breach a 1-hour fire separation.

See NFPA *Fire Protection Handbook* (*see Appendix B*), Section 7, Chapter 9, for guidance.

Laboratories that contain "ordinary" combustibles and flammable liquids in sufficient quantity to threaten a 1-hour fire separation [e.g., wood-equivalent fuel loads in the range of 5 to 10 lb/sq ft (25 to 50 kg/sq m)] are considered a severe hazard]. Laboratories posing a severe hazard must be protected in accordance with NFPA 99, *Standard for Health Care Facilities.*[6] Protection would include 1-hour fire resistance separation and automatic sprinkler protection.

Where fuel loads of lesser amounts are involved and quantities of flammable liquids are limited, laboratories would simply be considered hazardous areas and would require either 1-hour separation or automatic sprinkler protection, as indicated in 13-3.2.1 and Section 6-4.

13-3.2.3 **Anesthetizing Locations.** Anesthetizing locations shall be protected in accordance with NFPA 99, *Standard for Health Care Facilities.*

13-3.2.4 **Medical Gas.** Medical gas storage and administration areas shall be protected in accordance with NFPA 99, *Standard for Health Care Facilities.*

13-3.2.5 **Gift Shops.** Gift shops shall be protected as hazardous areas where used for the storage or display of combustibles in quantities considered hazardous. Gift shops not considered hazardous and having separately protected storage shall be permitted to be:

(a) Open to a lobby or corridor if the gift shop is not greater than 500 sq ft (46.5 sq m) and is protected throughout by an approved automatic sprinkler system, or

(b) Separated from a lobby with non-fire-rated walls if the gift shop is protected throughout by an approved automatic sprinkler system, or

(c) Separated from corridors by non-fire-rated walls if the gift shop is protected throughout by an approved automatic sprinkler system.

Many gift shops, particularly those containing combustible storage and having sizable retail areas, pose a hazard well beyond that normal to patient-occupied spaces and, thus, merit special protection. However, it is recognized that many small retail areas [less than 500 sq ft (46.5 sq m), for example] constitute a relatively minor hazard that is adequately mitigated by automatic sprinkler protection. This paragraph was added to provide the authority having jurisdiction with guidance in judging the degree of hazard and offers the facility some flexibility in the design and operation of gift shops.

It should be noted that to use any of the three options offered, the gift shop must be judged nonhazardous, must be sprinklered, and must have separately protected storage areas.

13-3.2.6 **Cooking Facilities.** Cooking facilities shall be protected in accordance with 7-2.3.

Exception*: Where domestic cooking equipment is used for food warming or limited cooking, protection or segregation of food preparation facilities is not required.

A-13-3.2.6 **Exception.** This exception is intended to permit small appliances used for reheating, such as microwave ovens, hot plates, toasters, and nourishment centers, to be exempt from requirements of commercial cooking equipment.

Commercial cooking equipment must be installed and protected in accordance with NFPA 96, *Standard for the Installation of Equipment for the Removal of Smoke and Grease-Laden Vapors from Commercial Cooking Equipment.*[7] A regularly serviced, fixed, automatic fire extinguishing system would be required for the protection of cooking surfaces and exhaust and duct systems where cooking operations involve the potential for grease-laden vapors. Cooking operations that do not involve the release of smoke or grease-laden vapors are not subject to compliance with NFPA 96 and would not normally be treated as hazardous operations.

The exception notes that 13-3.2.6 would not apply to a room used as a staff lounge equipped with a domestic-type range or microwave oven. Such a room would be considered similar to a treatment room and would require separation as indicated in 13-3.6.1.

13-3.3 Interior Finish.

13-3.3.1 Existing interior finish on walls and ceilings throughout shall be Class A or Class B in accordance with Section 6-5.

Exception: In buildings protected by an approved supervised automatic sprinkler system in accordance with 12-3.5.2, Class C interior finish shall be permitted to be continued to be used on walls and ceilings within rooms separated from the exit access corridors in accordance with 13-3.6.

Existing interior finishes on walls and ceilings are limited solely on the basis of flame spread. Paragraph 6-5.3.2 exempts existing interior finishes from the limitations based upon smoke development.

Paragraph 6-5.6.1 makes provision for application of approved flame-retardant coatings for the purpose of reducing the flame spread characteristics of certain types of existing interior finish materials to an acceptable level. Refer to the commentary on 6-5.6.1 for additional guidance.

Where rooms are separated from corridors by barriers designed to retard the transfer of smoke, and the building is completely protected by an automatic sprinkler system, Class C interior finish materials may continue to be used on walls and ceilings within the rooms so separated and protected.

13-3.3.2 Newly installed interior finish on walls and ceilings throughout shall be Class A in accordance with Section 6-5.

Exception No. 1: Walls and ceilings shall be permitted to have Class A or B interior finish in individual rooms having a capacity of not more than four persons.

Exception No. 2: Corridor wall finish up to 4 ft (122 cm) in height that is restricted to the lower half of the wall shall be permitted to be Class A or B.

Alterations are required by 13-1.1.4.5 to be made, to the extent practical, in accordance with the requirements for new construction found in Chapter 12. Chapter 12 now requires automatic sprinkler protection for all new facilities and, therefore, incorporates safeguards appropriate for fully sprinklered buildings. Since new interior finish may be added to an existing nonsprinklered building, 13-3.3.2 has been added to the 1991 Edition to provide reasonable regulation of wall and ceiling finish materials in nonsprinklered existing buildings.

New interior finish on walls or ceilings is limited to Class A materials, except in small rooms having four or fewer persons, where Class B materials are allowed.

Exception No. 2 to 13-3.3.2 allows wall finish in corridors to be of Class B materials where located on the lower half of the wall. This exception recognizes fire research[8] that has shown the finish on the lower half of a wall is far less significant in its influence on early fire growth than the materials on the upper portion of a wall.

Where automatic sprinkler protection is provided, Class B materials can be used where Class A materials are normally required, and similarly, Class C materials can be used where Class B materials would otherwise be required.

Textile wall or ceiling materials are regulated by 6-5.2.3, which requires automatic sprinkler protection in conjunction with Class A materials, or such wall and ceiling materials must be proven safe by room/corner testing. Previously approved, existing Class A materials may continue to be used without sprinkler protection.

13-3.3.3 Newly installed interior floor finish in corridors and exits shall be Class I in accordance with Section 6-5. No restrictions shall apply to existing interior floor finish.

Exception: In buildings protected throughout by an approved supervised automatic sprinkler system in accordance with 12-3.5.2, no interior floor finish requirements shall apply.

This paragraph, similar to 13-3.3.2, is needed, since Chapter 12 requires all new facilities to be sprinklered. Any new interior floor finish to be installed in corridors and exits within existing nonsprinklered health care facilities is required to meet the criteria for Class I materials as indicated in 6-5.4.2. However, existing floor finish materials that have been previously evaluated and judged acceptable may continue to be used.

It has been shown that floor coverings will not spread a fire until the fire becomes large, i.e., approaches flashover (*see commentary on 6-5.4*). Automatic sprinklers will activate well in advance of any significant involvement of a floor covering. Therefore, the limitations on interior floor finish for sprinklered facilities have been deleted in the 1991 Edition.

13-3.4 Detection, Alarm, and Communication Systems.

13-3.4.1 General. Health care occupancies shall be provided with a fire alarm system in accordance with Section 7-6.

13-3.4.2 Initiation. Initiation of the required fire alarm systems shall be by manual means in accordance with 7-6.2 and by means of any detection devices or detection systems required.

Exception No. 1: Fire alarm pull stations in patient sleeping areas are not required at exits if located at all nurses' control stations or other continuously attended staff location, provided such pull stations are visible and continuously accessible and that travel distances required by 7-6.2.4 are not exceeded.

Exception No. 2: Fixed extinguishing systems protecting commercial cooking equipment in kitchens that are protected by a complete automatic sprinkler system need not initiate the fire alarm system.

Manual fire alarm systems are required for all existing health care facilities. Any required fire detection device must be connected to the fire alarm system to sound the alarm when activated. The reference to Section 7-6 would require alarm systems to be installed and maintained in accordance with appropriate NFPA standards and would specify that alarm circuits be electrically supervised and that emergency power be provided.

Exception No. 1 to 13-3.4.2 allows pull stations, with certain qualifications, to be located at continuously

---

Formal Interpretation 76-19
Reference: 13-3.4.2

Question: Does 13-3.4.2 intend to require local devices designed to detect smoke on either side of an opening as referenced in 13-2.2.2.6 to be connected to the fire alarm system?

Answer: In existing buildings, it is the intent of the Committee that required fire detection devices be connected to the fire alarm system where practical.

Issue Edition: 1976
Reference: 10-3.3.3.6
Date: August 1977 ■

---

attended staff positions in sleeping areas. This arrangement provides the opportunity for prompt notification of fire without requiring staff to leave their normal work stations. Manual pull stations should always be located so that anyone qualified to send an alarm may summon aid without having to leave the zone of their ordinary activities or pass out of view and hearing of people immediately exposed to, or in direct view of, a fire.

13-3.4.3 Notification.

13-3.4.3.1 Occupant Notification. Occupant notification shall be accomplished automatically, without delay, upon operation of any fire alarm activating device by means of an internal audible alarm in accordance with 7-6.3. Presignal systems are prohibited.

Exception: Where visual devices have been installed in patient sleeping areas in place of the audible alarm, they may be accepted by the authority having jurisdiction.

Internal, audible alarm devices are required by 13-3.4.3.1, but previously installed visual alarm devices may continue to be used in areas where patients sleep, subject to the approval of the authority having jurisdiction. This exception assumes adequate, continuous supervision by the staff to ensure that the alarm is recognized. The use of visual devices places heavy reliance upon the staff to sound the alert.

13-3.4.3.2 Emergency Forces Notification. Fire department notification shall be accomplished in accordance with 7-6.4.

Exception: Smoke detection devices or smoke detection systems equipped with reconfirmation features need not automatically notify the fire department unless the alarm condition is reconfirmed after a maximum 120-second time period.

> **Formal Interpretation 81-9**
> Reference: 13-3.4.3.2
>
> *Question:* Is it the intent of the Committee to permit the use of an automatic telephone dialer to send a pre-recorded telephone message to the local fire department in the event of a fire alarm?
>
> *Answer:* Paragraph 7-6.4 lists four acceptable means of transmitting the alarm. The method described in the question above is not one of these methods. If none of those methods are available or are impractical due to the location of the facility, any method approved by the authority having jurisdiction is acceptable.
>
> *Issue Edition:* 1981
> *Reference:* 13-3.4.4
> *Date:* February 1982 ■

The alarm must automatically transmit to a point outside the facility. Where automatic transmission of alarms to the fire department legally committed to serve the facility is not permitted, arrangements are to be made for the prompt notification of the fire department or such other assistance as may be available in the case of fire or other emergency. Paragraph 7-6.4 lists various methods acceptable for automatic notification of the fire department. The fire department should still be notified manually to verify and confirm the automatic transmission of the alarm. In larger facilities, this may be the responsibility of the facility telephone operator; in smaller facilities, it may be the responsibility of the nursing staff.

An independent study by the National Bureau of Standards indicates a high rate of false alarms for smoke detectors installed in health care facilities.[9] The study determined 4.4 false alarms occurred per 100 smoke detectors

per year. Furthermore, approximately 14 false alarms occurred for every actual alarm. Because of the high incidence of false alarms, the *Code* permits delaying fire department notification for up to 120 seconds where smoke detectors or smoke detector systems are equipped with a reconfirmation feature.

13-3.4.4 Emergency Control. Operation of any activating device in the required fire alarm system shall be arranged to automatically accomplish, without delay, any control functions to be performed by that device. (*See 7-6.5.*)

13-3.4.5 Detection.

13-3.4.5.1 Corridors. An approved automatic smoke detection system shall be installed in all corridors of limited care facilities. Such system shall be installed in accordance with Section 7-6.

Exception No. 1: Where each patient sleeping room is protected by an approved smoke detection system, and a smoke detector is provided at smoke barriers and horizontal exits, such corridor systems will not be required on the patient sleeping room floors.

Exception No. 2: Buildings protected throughout by an approved supervised automatic sprinkler system installed in accordance with 12-3.5.2.

Paragraph 13-3.4.5.1 requires smoke detectors in limited care facilities. Staffing levels in hospitals and nursing homes reasonably ensure discovery of a fire at an early stage. In existing hospitals and nursing homes, it is considered reasonable to rely on staff to sound the alert.

13-3.4.5.2 Spaces Open to Corridors. (*See 13-3.6.1.*)

13-3.5 Extinguishment Requirements.

13-3.5.1 Where required by 13-1.6, health care facilities shall be protected throughout by an approved automatic sprinkler system in accordance with Section 7-7.

Exception: In Types I and II construction, where approved by the authority having jurisdiction, alternative protection measures may be substituted for sprinkler protection in specified areas where the authority having jurisdiction has prohibited sprinklers, without causing a building to be classified as nonsprinklered.

To summarize, automatic sprinkler protection is required by 13-1.6 in any instance where combustible elements are used in the construction of a building.

Where sprinkler protection is specified, complete building coverage, in accordance with the provisions of NFPA 13, *Standard for the Installation of Sprinkler Systems,*[10] is required. The *Code* does not exempt any area of the building from protection (*see Section 7-7*). However, where automatic sprinkler protection is omitted from certain spaces at the mandate of the authority having jurisdiction, and the authority having jurisdiction approves alternative protective measures, the building is still considered fully protected throughout. Sprinklers may be omitted from isolated areas in buildings of fire-rated, noncombustible construction only. Use of alternative protective measures to automatic sprinklers should be carefully evaluated to ensure equivalent protection is achieved. Where fixed automatic fire extinguishing systems (those using Halon, for example) are used as an alternative to sprinklers for specific spaces, it is suggested that the spaces also be separated by fire resistant construction.

13-3.5.2* Where this *Code* permits exceptions for fully sprinklered health care occupancies, the sprinkler system shall be:

(a) In complete accordance with Section 7-7,
(b) Electrically connected to the fire alarm system, and
(c) Fully supervised.

Exception: In Types I and II construction, where approved by the authority having jurisdiction, alternative protection measures may be substituted for sprinkler protection in specified areas where the authority having jurisdiction has prohibited sprinklers, without causing a building to be classified as nonsprinklered.

A-13-3.5.2 It is intended that any valve that controls automatic sprinklers in the entire building or portions of the build-

ing, including sectional and floor control valves, be electrically supervised. Valves that control isolated sprinkler heads such as in laundry and trash chutes need not be electrically supervised. Appropriate means should be taken to assure that valves that are not electrically supervised remain open.

The term "fully supervised" means a distinct supervisory signal must be provided to a constantly attended location in the event of any malfunction or action that would impair sprinkler performance. Supervision must be provided, for example, for water supply and sprinkler control valves, fire pump power and running conditions, water tank levels and temperatures, pressure in pressure tanks, air pressure in dry-pipe systems, building temperature, and city water pressure. Supervision should include all sprinkler sectional control valves in addition to main control valves. Water flow alarms must actuate the building fire alarm system and notify the fire department. (*See also 7-7.2 and commentary for 13-3.5.1.*)

13-3.5.3* Where this *Code* permits exceptions for fully sprinklered buildings utilizing quick response sprinklers, the system shall be:

(a) Installed throughout the building in accordance with Section 7-7, and
(b) Electrically connected to the fire alarm system, and
(c) Fully supervised, and
(d) Equipped with listed quick response or listed residential sprinklers throughout all smoke compartments containing patient sleeping rooms.

Exception No. 1 to (d): Standard response sprinklers shall be permitted for use in areas where quick response and residential sprinklers are prohibited from being installed by their listing.

Exception No. 2 to (d): Standard response sprinklers shall be permitted for use in hazardous areas protected in accordance with Section 13-3.2.1.

A-13-3.5.3 See A-13-3.5.2.

The 1991 Edition allows deletion of a number of redundant features of protection where automatic sprinkler protection is provided and where quick response sprinklers are used throughout smoke compartments having sleeping rooms. For example, Exception No. 2 to 13-3.7.3 will permit elimination of dampers in ducts penetrating smoke barriers where compartments on both sides of the barrier are sprinkler protected under certain conditions. It will permit elimination of dampers where "nonsleeping" compartments are sprinklered using either standard or quick response sprinklers, or where compartments having sleeping rooms use quick response sprinklers, and Exception Nos. 1 and 2 allow the use of "standard" sprinklers in those isolated instances where the use of quick response sprinklers are disallowed or inappropriate. Quick response sprinklers may not be suitable for use in areas subject to elevated temperatures such as spaces under skylights or near ceiling unit heaters. Quick response sprinklers have not been evaluated for use in hazardous spaces, and, therefore, Exception No. 2 permits standard sprinklers in such locations.

13-3.5.4 For renovations or modernization projects where supervised automatic sprinkler protection is installed in smoke compartments in accordance with Section 7-7, exceptions allowed for fully sprinklered buildings shall be permitted within the sprinklered smoke compartment.

The intent of 13-3.5.4 is to allow deletion of redundant features of fire protection within an individual smoke compartment where a compartment is sprinklered. This paragraph, for example, could be used to allow higher flame spread wall/ceiling finish or could be used to allow nonrated corridor partitions within the sprinklered compartment. In addition, corridor smoke detection could be eliminated within the compartment. However, certain general building protection features must be maintained unless the building is fully sprinklered. For example, no relaxation should be granted in exit features (*see Section 13-2*) or building construction requirements (*see 13-1.6*) unless the building is fully protected by automatic sprinklers.

13-3.5.5 Isolated hazardous areas shall be permitted to be protected in accordance with 7-7.1.2. For new installations in existing buildings, where more than two sprinklers are installed in a single area, water flow detection shall be provided to sound

the building fire alarm or notify by a signal any constantly attended location, such as PBX, security, or emergency room, whereby necessary corrective action shall be directed.

13-3.5.6 Portable fire extinguishers shall be provided in all health care occupancies in accordance with 7-7.4.1.

13-3.6 Corridors.

The provisions for corridor walls are organized as follows:

Paragraph 13-3.6.1 establishes requirements for the existence and location of corridor walls.

Paragraph 13-3.6.2 establishes construction requirements for corridor walls.

Paragraph 13-3.6.3 establishes requirements for doors in corridor walls.

Paragraph 13-3.6.4 addresses transfer grilles.

The requirements of 13-3.6.1 to 13-3.6.5 essentially stipulate that all areas containing combustibles in sufficient quantity to produce a life-threatening fire must be separated from exit access corridors by partitions designed to resist the passage of smoke. The details of construction for such partitions vary, depending upon whether or not automatic sprinkler protection is provided.

13-3.6.1 Corridors shall be separated from all other areas by partitions complying with 13-3.6.2 through 13-3.6.5. (*Also see 13-2.5.8.*)

Exception No. 1: Buildings protected throughout by an approved supervised automatic sprinkler system in accordance with 13-3.5.3 shall be permitted to have spaces that are unlimited in size open to the corridor provided:

(a) The spaces are not used for patient sleeping rooms, treatment rooms, or hazardous areas, and

(b) The corridors onto which the spaces open in the same smoke compartment are protected by an electrically supervised automatic smoke detection system installed in accordance with 13-3.4, or the smoke compartment in which the space is located is protected throughout by quick response sprinklers, and

(c) The open space is protected by an electrically supervised automatic smoke detection system installed in accor-

dance with 13-3.4, or the entire space is arranged and located to permit direct supervision by the facility staff from a nurses' station or similar space, and

(d) The space does not obstruct access to required exits.

Exception No. 2: In buildings protected throughout by an approved supervised automatic sprinkler system in accordance with 13-3.5.3, waiting areas shall be permitted to be open to the corridor provided:

(a) The aggregate waiting area in each smoke compartment does not exceed 600 sq ft (55.7 sq m), and

(b) Each area is protected by an electrically supervised automatic smoke detection system installed in accordance with 13-3.4, or each area is arranged and located to permit direct supervision by the facility staff from a nursing station or similar space.

(c) The area does not obstruct access to required exits.

Exception No. 3*: Spaces for nurses' stations.

A-13-3.6.1 Exception No. 3. A typical nurses' station would normally contain one or more of the following with associated furniture and furnishings.

(a) Charting area.
(b) Clerical area.
(c) Nourishment station.
(d) Storage of small amounts of medications, medical equipment and supplies, clerical supplies, and linens.
(e) Patient monitoring and communication equipment.

Exception No. 4: Gift shops open to the corridor where protected in accordance with 13-3.2.5.

Exception No. 5: Limited care facilities in buildings protected throughout by an approved supervised automatic sprinkler system in accordance with 13-3.5.3 shall be permitted to have group meeting or multipurpose therapeutic spaces open to the corridor provided:

(a) The space is not a hazardous area, and

(b) The space is protected by an electrically supervised automatic smoke detection system installed in accordance with 13-3.4, or the space is arranged and located to permit direct supervision by the facility staff from the nurses' station or similar location, and

(c) The area does not obstruct access to required exits.

Exception No. 6: Spaces other than patient sleeping rooms, treatment rooms, and hazardous areas shall be permitted to be open to the corridor and unlimited in area provided:

(a) The space and corridors that the space opens onto in the same smoke compartment are protected by an electrically supervised automatic smoke detection system installed in accordance with 13-3.4, and

(b) Each space is located to permit direct supervision by the facility staff, and

(c)* Each space is protected by automatic sprinklers, or the furnishings and furniture in combination with all other combustibles within the area are of such a minimum quantity and are so arranged that a fully developed fire is unlikely to occur, and

(d) The space does not obstruct access to required exits.

A-13-3.6.1 Exception No. 6(c). A fully developed fire (flashover) occurs if the rate of heat release of the burning materials exceeds the capability of the space to absorb or vent that heat. The ability of common lining (wall, ceiling, and floor) materials to absorb heat is approximately 0.75 Btu (0.79 kJ) per sq ft of lining. The venting capability of open doors or windows is in excess of 20 Btu (21 kJ) per sq ft of opening. In a fire that has not reached flashover conditions, fire will spread from one furniture item to another only if the burning item is close to another furniture item. For example, if individual furniture items have heat release rates of 500 Btu per second (525 kW) and are separated by 12 in. (30.5 cm) separation or more, the fire is not expected to spread from item to item and flashover is unlikely to occur. Also see the NFPA *Fire Protection Handbook*, Section 21. (*See Appendix B.*)

Exception No. 7: Waiting areas shall be permitted to be open to the corridor provided:

(a) Each area does not exceed 600 sq ft (55.7 sq m), and

(b) The area is located to permit direct supervision by the facility staff, and

(c) The area is equipped with an electrically supervised automatic smoke detection system installed in accordance with 13-3.4, and

(d) The area does not obstruct any access to required exits.

Exception No. 8: In a limited care facility, group meeting or multipurpose therapeutic spaces, other than hazardous areas, under continuous supervision by facility staff shall be permitted to be open to the corridor provided:

(a) Each area does not exceed 1,500 sq ft (140 sq m), and

(b) Not more than one such space is permitted per smoke compartment, and

(c) The area is located to permit direct supervision by the facility staff, and

(d) The area is equipped with an electrically supervised automatic smoke detection system installed in accordance with 13-3.4, and

(e) The area does not obstruct any access to required exits.

Paragraph 13-3.6.1 requires that all spaces be separated from corridors by partitions. Exceptions allow specific areas to be open to the corridor. The intent is to limit the risk of exposing the corridor to fire. Exception Nos. 1 through 8 to 13-3.6.1 specify those areas that may be open to corridors (*see Figures 13-13a and b on the following page*). However, with the exception of limited care facilities (*see Exception Nos. 5 and 8*), patient sleeping rooms, treatment rooms, and hazardous areas must be separated by partitions.

For example, Exception No. 6 states that waiting spaces, lounges, and other similar spaces may be open to corridors on floors with rooms where patients sleep or on floors used for other purposes. Each space must be located to permit direct visual supervision by staff from a permanent staff location. Each space must also be located and arranged so that its furnishing will not interfere with or obstruct access to any required exits. The number of such areas open to the corridor in each smoke compartment is not limited. The spaces and the corridor within each smoke compartment to which the spaces open must be equipped with an electrically supervised automatic smoke detection system. The area of the open space is not limited. However, each space must be provided with automatic sprinkler protection, or the furnishings and furniture in combination with all other available fuels (combustibles) must be adequately restricted so a fire will be self-limiting. In making use of the fuel-limiting technique, combustibles must be of a minimum quantity and adequately separated so that a fire will remain confined to the object of origin. Combustibles must be arranged and limited to a type to prevent full room involvement. (*See Figure 13-13b.*)

The "direct supervision" required by Exception Nos. 1, 2, 5, 6, 7, and 8 (and assumed in Exception No. 3) is important. It allows the staff to see, hear, or smell a developing fire or to prevent the ignition of a fire by virtue of their presence. Direct visual supervision should be available from a permanent staff location. The use of closed-circuit television or mirrors does not provide for all the above and is discouraged in existing facilities. However, the use of these devices may be the most reasonable remedy to an existing installation if approved by the authority having jurisdiction. Exception Nos. 1, 2, and 5 permit smoke detection to substitute for direct supervision, since the quick response sprinkler technology is being used.

Exception Nos. 1, 2, and 5 have been added to the 1991 Edition. All three new exceptions contemplate automatic sprinkler protection using quick response sprinklers in compartments having sleeping rooms. Exception No. 1 will allow space to be of unlimited size and open to the corridor but does not permit patient sleeping, treatment, or hazardous areas to be included in the "open" area. Exception No. 5, however, will permit multipurpose treatment spaces to be open to corridors in limited care facilities. Nevertheless, the open space may not be used for hazardous operations, such as woodworking involving occupational therapy.

Exception Nos. 1, 2, and 5 parallel Exception Nos. 6, 7, and 8 but require the facility to be protected throughout with automatic sprinklers, using quick response sprinklers in smoke compartments housing patient sleeping rooms. Due to this added protection, *either* staff supervision *or* smoke detection is required, rather than both, and certain area limitations are deleted.

Areas used for charting and communication by doctors and nurses may be open to the corridor.

It is important to note that the installation of new corridor walls is considered a renovation, and such walls must comply with Chapter 12 to the extent feasible. However, such walls should be of 1-hour construction if the smoke compartment is not sprinklered. (*See* 1-5.6.)

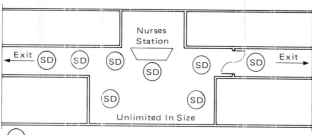

Figure 13-13a. Areas Open to Corridor. Unlimited size area open to corridor in accordance with 13-3.6.1 Exception No. 6.

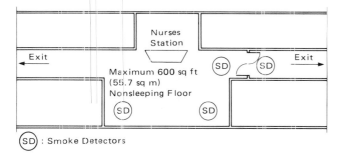

Figure 13-13b. Waiting Spaces. Waiting area complying with 13-3.6.1 Exception No. 7.

13-3.6.2 Construction of Corridor Walls.

13-3.6.2.1* Corridor walls shall be continuous from the floor to the underside of the floor or roof deck above, through any concealed spaces, such as those above the suspended ceilings, and through interstitial structural and mechanical spaces, and shall have a fire resistance rating of at least 20 minutes.

Exception No. 1: In health care occupancies protected throughout by an approved supervised automatic sprinkler system in accordance with 13-3.5.2, a corridor shall be permitted to be separated from all other areas by non-fire-rated partitions and shall be permitted to terminate at the ceiling where the ceiling is constructed to limit the transfer of smoke.

Exception No. 2: Existing corridor partitions shall be permitted to terminate at ceilings that are not an integral part of a floor construction if there exists 5 ft (152 cm) or more of space between the top of the ceiling subsystem and the bottom of the floor or roof above, provided:

(a) The ceiling shall have been tested as a part of a fire-rated assembly in accordance with NFPA 251, Standard Methods of Fire Tests of Building Construction and Materials, for a test period of 1 hour or more, and

(b) Corridor partitions form smoketight joints with the ceilings (joint filler, if used, shall be noncombustible), and

(c) Each compartment of interstitial space that constitutes a separate smoke area is vented, in case of smoke emergency, to the outside by mechanical means having sufficient capacity to provide at least two air changes per hour, but in no case having a capacity less than 5,000 cfm (2.36 cu m/s), and

(d) The interstitial space shall not be used for storage, and

(e) The space shall not be used as a plenum for supply, exhaust, or return air except as noted in (c).

Exception No. 3*: Existing corridor partitions shall be permitted to terminate at monolithic ceilings that resist the passage of smoke where there is a smoketight joint between the top of the partition and the bottom of the ceiling.

A-13-3.6.2.1 The intent of the 20-minute fire resistance rating for corridor partitions is to require a nominal fire rating, particularly where the fire rating of existing partitions cannot be documented. Examples of acceptable partition assemblies would include, but are not limited to, ½-in. (1.3-cm) gypsum board, wood lath and plaster, gypsum lath or metal lath and plaster.

A-13-3.6.2.1 Exception No. 3. Monolithic ceilings are continuous horizontal membranes composed of noncombustible or limited-combustible materials, such as plaster or gypsum board, with seams or cracks permanently sealed.

13-3.6.2.2 Corridor walls shall form a barrier to limit the transfer of smoke.

13-3.6.2.3 Fixed fire window assemblies in accordance with 6-2.3.4 shall be permitted in corridor walls.

Exception: There shall be no restrictions in area and fire resistance of glass and frames in buildings protected throughout by an approved supervised automatic sprinkler system installed in accordance with 13-3.5.2.

In nonsprinklered buildings, corridor partitions must be constructed of assemblies having a minimum fire resistance rating of 20 minutes. In setting the requirements for 20-minute partitions, it was intended to accept the separation provided by existing partitions of any substantial construction that are capable of serving as a barrier for a short period of time, without requiring documentation of a specific fire rating. The 20-minute rating is intended to permit partitions of wood lath and plaster, 1/2-in. (1.27-cm) gypsum board, and similar materials. Ordinary glass would not be permitted in nonsprinklered buildings. Materials used in the construction of partitions are limited on the basis of the construction types allowed by 13-1.6.2 and 13-1.6.3. All material used in the construction of Type I and Type II buildings must satisfy the criteria for noncombustible or limited-combustible materials. *(See 13-1.6.3.)*

Corridor partitions must be constructed to extend continuously through all concealed spaces [e.g., through to the floor or roof deck above a suspended ceiling, *(see Figure 13-14a)*]. Where a monolithic ceiling is provided that is composed of noncombustible materials, such as plaster or gypsum board having seams or cracks permanently sealed, thus forming a continuous horizontal membrane, existing partitions may be terminated at the underside of the ceiling in accordance with Exception No. 3.

Openings in corridor partitions in nonsprinklered buildings must be suitably protected to maintain corridor separation. One-quarter-in. (.65-cm) thick, fire-rated, wired glass is limited to a maximum of 1,296-sq in. (0.84-sq m) set in approved metal frames. Each wired glass panel is limited to a maximum dimension of 54 in. (140 cm). The glass should be labeled and should be well embedded in putty,

with all exposed joints between the metal and the glass struck and pointed (*see NFPA 80, Standard for Fire Doors and Windows*).[11] A number of wired glass panels may be used in a single partition, provided that each 1,296-sq in. (0.84-sq m) section is separated from adjacent panels by a steel or other approved metal mullion. Fire rated glazing, other than 1/4-in. (.65-cm) wired glass, should be installed in accordance with the manufacturer's instructions and listing. It should be recognized that the use of fire rated glazing in a partition will reduce the fire resistance capability of the partition, since there will be radiant energy transfer through the glass panel. The excessive use of glazing, therefore, should be avoided.

Where complete automatic sprinkler protection is provided, corridor partitions need not be rated but must still be constructed to resist the passage of smoke. The materials for constructing the partitions must be selected on the basis of the construction types allowed by 13-1.6.2 and 13-1.6.3. Where suspended ceilings are provided, partitions may be terminated at the suspended ceiling without any additional special protection if the suspended ceiling will resist the passage of smoke. The ability to resist the passage of smoke must be carefully evaluated (*see Figure 13-14b*). There are no restrictions in terms of area or fire resistance for glazing used in corridor partitions in sprinklered buildings.

Exception No. 2 to 13-3.6.2.1 specifies criteria for terminating existing corridor partitions at ceilings, including "lay-in" type ceilings in nonsprinklered buildings. Partitions may be terminated at a ceiling that has been tested as a portion of an assembly having a fire resistance rating of 1 hour or more. Each compartment located above such a ceiling must be equipped with an automatic mechanical smoke exhaust system capable of providing a minimum of two air changes per hour but exhausting not less than 5,000 cu ft/min (2.36 cu m/sec) [*see the additional criteria in items (a) through (e) of Exception No. 2*]. This is not a common arrangement, due to the large interstitial space needed and the energy loss resulting from the ventilation requirements.

It is important to note that the installation of new corridor walls is considered a renovation, and such walls must provide 1-hour separation in nonsprinklered areas. *(See 1-5.6 and 13-1.1.4.5.)*

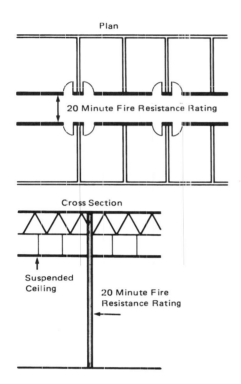

Figure 13-14a.   *Corridor Walls, Nonsprinkered Buildings. Corridor wall complying with 13-3.6.2. Note that wall must extend to the floor or roof deck above, unless complying with one of the exceptions.*

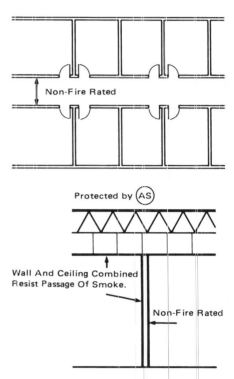

Figure 13-14b.   *Corridor Walls, Sprinklered Buildings. In buildings protected throughout by an approved automatic sprinkler system, walls may terminate at ceilings, provided the wall and ceiling together resist the passage of smoke. (See 13-3.6.2.1 Exception No. 1.)*

13-3.6.3   Corridor Doors.

13-3.6.3.1   Doors protecting corridor openings in other than required enclosures of vertical openings, exits, or hazardous areas shall be substantial doors, such as those constructed of 1¾-in. (4.4-cm) thick solid bonded core wood or of construction that will resist fire for at least 20 minutes.

Exception No. 1: In buildings protected throughout by an approved supervised automatic sprinkler system in accordance with 13-3.5.2, the door construction requirements noted above are not mandatory, but the doors shall be constructed to resist the passage of smoke.

Exception No. 2: Doors to toilet rooms, bathrooms, shower rooms, sink closets, and similar auxiliary spaces that do not contain flammable or combustible materials.

13-3.6.3.2*   Doors shall be provided with means suitable for keeping the door closed that is acceptable to the authority hav-

ing jurisdiction. The device used shall be capable of keeping the door fully closed if a force of 5 lbf (22 N) is applied at the latch edge of the door. Roller latches are prohibited on corridor doors in buildings not fully protected by an approved automatic sprinkler system in accordance with 13-3.5.1.

Exception No. 1: Existing roller latches demonstrated to keep the door closed against a force of 5 lbf (22 N) may be kept in service if acceptable to the authority having jurisdiction.

Exception No. 2: Doors to toilet rooms, bathrooms, shower rooms, sink closets, and similar auxiliary spaces that do not contain flammable or combustible materials.

A-13-3.6.3.2   While it is recognized that closed doors serve to maintain tenable conditions in a corridor and adjacent patient rooms, such doors, which under normal or fire conditions are self-closing, may create a special hazard for the personal safety of a room occupant. These closed doors may present a problem of delay in discovery, confining fire products beyond tenable conditions.

Since it is critical for responding staff members to be able to immediately identify the specific room involved, it is suggested that approved automatic smoke detection that is interconnected with the building fire alarm be considered for rooms having doors equipped with closing devices. Such detection may be located at any approved point within the room. When activated, the detector must provide warning that indicates the specific room of involvement by activation of fire alarm annunciator, nurse call system, or any other device acceptable to the authority having jurisdiction.

In existing buildings, a number of options exist to reasonably assure that patient room doors will be closed and remain closed during a fire:

(a) Doors should have positive latches, coupled with a suitable training program for staff to close the doors in an emergency.

(b) It is the intent of the *Code* that no new installations of roller latches be allowed. However, existing installations of roller latches that keep the door closed against a force of 5 lbf (22 N) and acceptable to the authority having jurisdiction, coupled with adequate maintenance and staff training, may be continued to be used.

(c) Doors protecting openings to patient sleeping or treatment rooms, or spaces having a similar combustible loading might be held closed using a closer exerting a minimum closing force of 5 lb (22 N) on the door latch stile.

13-3.6.3.3 Door-closing devices are not required on doors in corridor wall openings other than those serving required enclosures of vertical openings, exits, or hazardous areas.

13-3.6.3.4 Door frames shall be labeled or shall be of steel construction or shall be of other materials complying with the requirements of NFPA 252, *Standard Methods of Fire Tests of Door Assemblies.*

Exception: Door frames in buildings protected throughout by an approved supervised automatic sprinkler system installed in accordance with Section 7-7.

13-3.6.3.5 Fixed fire window assemblies in accordance with 6-2.3.4 shall be permitted in these doors.

Exception: There shall be no restrictions in area and fire resistance of glass and frames in buildings protected throughout by an approved supervised automatic sprinkler system installed in accordance with 13-3.5.2.

13-3.6.3.6 Dutch doors shall be permitted where they conform to 13-3.6.3, and in addition, both upper leaf and lower leaf shall be equipped with a latching device, and the meeting edges of the upper and lower leaves shall be equipped with an astragal, rabbet, or bevel.

Dutch doors protecting openings in enclosures around hazardous areas shall comply with NFPA 80, *Standard for Fire Doors and Windows.*

Doors in corridor partitions are required to resist the penetration of fire for at least 20 minutes, to be constructed of 1¾-in. (4.5-cm) thick solid bonded wood core, or be of equivalent construction. Doors must be capable of being closed and maintained closed during a fire. Where positive latches are used, doors must be equipped with a latch that cannot be held in the retracted position. The latch should be capable of holding the door in a closed position when subjected to stresses imposed by exposure to fire. Except in sprinklered buildings, roller latches are not allowed. Existing roller latches may be continued in use where maintenance is satisfactory subject to approval by the authority having jurisdiction (*see also A-13-3.6.3.2*). Such doors are required to be installed in approved metal or "heavy wood" frames. Fixed wired glass vision panels installed in these doors may not exceed an area of 1,296 sq in. (.84 sq m) [maximum dimension of 54 in. (140 cm)] and must be set in approved metal frames. Other fire rated glazing must be used in accordance with its listing. Labeled door frames and closing devices are not required except on doors protecting openings in exit enclosures, vertical openings, or required enclosures of hazardous areas.

Where complete automatic sprinkler protection is provided, doors protecting openings in corridor partitions must be installed to resist the passage of smoke, but are not required to have a fire protection rating. There are no restrictions in terms of area or fire resistance for glazing used in corridor doors in sprinklered buildings.

13-3.6.4 **Transfer Grilles.** Transfer grilles, whether or not protected by fusible link operated dampers, shall not be used in these walls or doors.

Exception: Doors to toilet rooms, bathrooms, shower rooms, sink closets, and similar auxiliary spaces that do not contain flammable or combustible materials shall be permitted to have ventilating louvers or be undercut.

The use of an exit access corridor as an exhaust, supply, or return air plenum for a building's air-handling system is prohibited. Corridor doors may not be undercut to facilitate transfer of air, nor are transfer grilles allowed in corridor partitions (*see 13-3.6.4*) or corridor doors (*see also 2-3.11.1 of NFPA 90A, Standard for the Installation of Air Conditioning and Ventilating Systems*).[12] However, sink closets, bathrooms, and toilets may have doors equipped with a fixed grille or louver to provide make-up air from the corridor for room exhaust systems. Where the door is equipped with a grille or louver, such spaces may not be used for the storage of flammable or combustible supplies. Caution must be exercised where using this exception for sink closets, as they are often used for storage of combustibles.

Air-handling ducts penetrating corridor partitions should be adequately protected to preserve the 20-minute separation of exit access routes. Any space around ducts at the point of penetration of corridor partitions should be tightly sealed with a noncombustible material.

13-3.6.5 In other than smoke compartments containing patient sleeping rooms, miscellaneous openings such as mail slots, pharmacy pass-through windows, laboratory pass-through windows, and cashier pass-through windows shall be permitted in vision panels or doors without special protection provided the aggregate area of openings per room does not exceed 20 sq in. (.0135 sq m) and the openings are installed at or below half the distance from the floor to the room ceiling.

13-3.7 **Subdivision of Building Spaces.**

13-3.7.1 Smoke barriers shall be provided to divide every story used for sleeping rooms for more than 30 patients into at least two smoke compartments. The maximum size of any such smoke compartment shall not exceed 22,500 sq ft (2,100 sq m), and the travel distance from any point to reach a required smoke barrier door shall not exceed 200 ft (60 m).

Exception No. 1: Where neither the length nor width of the smoke compartment exceeds 150 ft (45 m), the travel distance to reach the smoke barrier door shall not be limited.

Exception No. 2: The area of an atrium separated in accordance with Section 6-2.4.6 shall not be limited in size.

Paragraph 13-3.7.1 requires smoke barriers only for the purpose of subdividing stories having sleeping rooms for more than 30 patients. Subdivision is not required on treatment floors (assuming there are no sleeping rooms) regardless of area or number of patients. Patient bed capacity is to be used (*see 13-3.7.2*) to determine the number of patients per story.

Paragraph 13-3.7.1 specifies a maximum size where smoke barriers are required. The maximum area of 22,500 sq ft (2,100 sq m) [150 ft (45 m) × 150 ft (45 m)] of previous editions has been retained. However, to provide the facility and designer with flexibility in the arrangement of smoke compartments, the arbitrary 150-ft (45-m) length and width limits have been deleted in favor of a 200-ft (60-m) travel distance. Smoke compartments must be designed so a person is able to reach a smoke barrier door within a travel distance of 200 ft (60 m) or less from any point in a compartment, measured along the natural path of travel in accordance with 5-6.2.

Horizontal exits, constructed to comply with requirements for smoke barriers, may be substituted for smoke barriers.

Areas open to atriums may not be used for patient sleeping or treatment areas (*see Exception No. 4 to 13-3.1.1*). A maximum of three levels may be open to the atrium in accordance with 6-2.4.6, with additional stories separated by 1-hour partitions or glass walls with special sprinkler protection. Atrium smoke compartments complying with 6-2.4.6 are not limited in size.

13-3.7.2 For purposes of this section, the number of health care occupants shall be determined by actual count of patient bed capacity.

13-3.7.3 Any required smoke barrier shall be constructed in accordance with Section 6-3 and shall have a fire resistance rating of at least ½ hour.

Exception No. 1: Where an atrium is used, smoke barriers shall be permitted to terminate at an atrium wall constructed in accordance with Exception No. 2 to 6-2.4.6(g). A minimum of two separate smoke compartments shall be provided on each floor.

See Figures 13-19a through 13-19d on pages 520 and 521.

Exception No. 2: Dampers are not required in duct penetrations of smoke barriers in fully ducted HVAC systems where an approved supervised automatic sprinkler system in accordance with 13-3.5.3 has been provided for smoke compartments adjacent to the smoke barrier.

13-3.7.4 At least 30 net sq ft (2.8 net sq m) per patient in a hospital or nursing home or 15 net sq ft (1.4 net sq m) per resident in a limited care facility shall be provided within the aggregate area of corridors, patient rooms, treatment rooms, lounge or dining areas, and other low hazard areas on each side of the smoke barrier. On stories not housing bed or litter patients, at least 6 net sq ft (.56 net sq m) per occupant shall be provided on each side of the smoke barrier for the total number of occupants in adjoining compartments.

13-3.7.5 Openings in smoke barriers shall be protected by wired glass panels in steel frames, by doors of 20-minute fire protection rating, or by 1¾-in. (4.4-cm) thick solid bonded wood core doors as a minimum.

Exception: Doors shall be permitted to have fixed fire window assemblies in accordance with 6-2.3.4.

13-3.7.6* Doors in smoke barriers shall comply with 6-3.4 and shall be self-closing or automatic-closing in accordance with 13-2.2.2.6. Such doors in smoke barriers shall not be required to swing with exit travel. Positive latching hardware is not required.

A-13-3.7.6 Smoke barriers may include walls having door openings other than cross-corridor doors. There is no restriction in the *Code* regarding which doors or how many doors form part of a smoke barrier. For example, doors from the corridor to individual rooms may form part of a smoke barrier.

13-3.7.7 Door openings in smoke barriers shall be protected by a swinging door a minimum of 34 in. (86 cm) in width or by a horizontal sliding door complying with 5-2.1.14 and providing a clear opening of at least 34 in. (86 cm).

The requirements of 13-3.7.1 through 13-3.7.7 for subdividing building spaces through smoke barriers are illustrated in Figures 13-15 through 13-19. Paragraph 13-2.2.5 discusses horizontal exits.

During a fire, the emergency evacuation of patients in a health care facility is an inefficient, time consuming process. Realistically, if patients must be moved, sizable numbers of occupants can be relocated only through horizontal travel. Smoke barriers and horizontal exits used to subdivide a building serve three purposes fundamental to the protection of inpatients:

1. They limit the spread of fire and fire-produced contaminants,

2. They limit the number of occupants exposed to a single fire, and

3. They provide for horizontal relocation of patients by creating an area of refuge on the same floor level.

Note that the combination fire/smoke dampers required in 6-3.5 may be omitted in engineered smoke-control systems if the design of the system is such that a damper is not required at that point. Exception No. 2 to 13-3.7.3 also permits deletion of dampers in ducted penetrations of smoke barriers where compartments adjacent to the barrier are protected by automatic sprinklers. This exception would not be permitted if an engineered smoke-control system required a damper at this point. Openings for transfer grilles would require automatic-closing dampers. (*See also commentary on 13-3.5.3 and 13-3.5.4.*)

To summarize, the requirements of 13-3.7 for existing health care occupancies are as follows:

1. Only stories with sleeping accommodations for more than 30 health care occupants must be divided into at least two compartments by a smoke barrier. For application of 13-3.7.1, the number of occupants is determined by actual count of bed capacity. (*See 13-3.7.2.*)

2. Each story having more than 30 sleeping occupants must be subdivided by a smoke barrier.

3. Smoke barriers must be constructed of assemblies providing a fire resistance rating of at least ½ hour, constructed continuously from outside wall to outside wall through concealed spaces (for example, above suspended ceilings).

4. Doors protecting openings in smoke barriers must, as a minimum, have a 20-minute fire protection rating, or be of 1¾-in. (4.5-cm)-thick solid bonded wood core construction. Latching hardware is not required.

5. Openings in smoke barriers may be protected by fixed, wired glass panels set in metal frames. Such panels may not exceed a maximum of 1,296 sq in. (0.84 sq m). Other fire rated glazing may be used in accordance with its listing.

6. Doors in smoke barriers are required to be self-closing but may be held open if the criteria of 13-2.2.2.6 are satisfied. Doors in smoke barriers are not required to swing in the direction of exit travel, although this is desirable.

7. Vision panels are not required in existing smoke barrier doors. However, if provided, they must be of wired glass in approved metal frames or of other fire rated glazing.

8. The minimum area requirements for each smoke compartment are the same as for horizontal exits.

13-3.8 Special Features.

13-3.8.1 Every patient sleeping room shall have an outside window or outside door with light. The maximum allowable sill height shall not exceed 44 in. (112 cm) above the floor.

Exception No. 1: The window sill in special nursing care areas such as those housing ICU, CCU, hemodialysis, and neonatal patients shall not exceed up to 60 in. (152 cm) above the floor.

Exception No. 2: Rooms intended for occupancy for less than 24 hours, such as those housing obstetrical labor beds, recovery beds, and observation beds in the emergency department, and newborn nurseries.

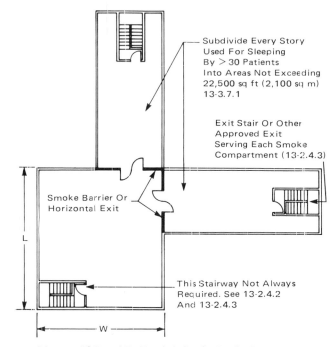

Subdivide Every Story Used For Sleeping By > 30 Patients Into Areas Not Exceeding 22,500 sq ft (2,100 sq m) 13-3.7.1

Exit Stair Or Other Approved Exit Serving Each Smoke Compartment (13-2.4.3)

Smoke Barrier Or Horizontal Exit

This Stairway Not Always Required. See 13-2.4.2 And 13-2.4.3

Distance Of Travel To Reach A Smoke Barrier Door Measured Along The Natural Path Of Travel From Any Point May Not Exceed 200 ft (60 m). The Travel Distance Is Not Limited Where Neither L Or W Exceeds 150 ft (45 m). See 13-3.7.1 Ex. No 1

Figure 13-15. Subdivision of Building Spaces in Existing Health Care Occupancies.

Exception No. 3: Windows opening into atriums where the atrium has a smoke removal system are, for the purposes of this requirement, considered outside windows.

Although 13-3.8.1 requires each patient sleeping room to have an outside window or door with glazing, the window may have a fixed sash. Security glazing should be avoided. Glazing should be of a type that can be broken out should such action become necessary in a fire emergency. Glazing should be limited to a type that, if broken out, will not develop sharp edges posing a threat to occupants located at grade outside the building.

For a discussion of Exception No. 3 and atrium windows, refer to the commentary on 13-3.1 and to Figures 13-19a through 13-19d.

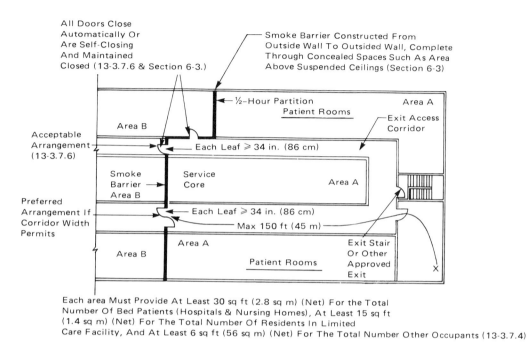

Figure 13-16. *Subdivision of Building Spaces in Existing Health Care Occupancies.*

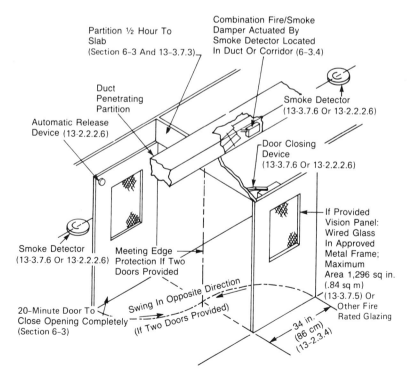

Figure 13-17. *Smoke Barrier for Existing Health Care Occupancy.*

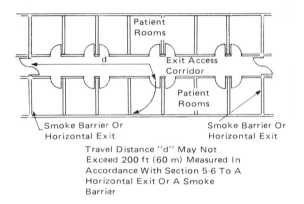

Figure 13-18. *Maximum Travel Distance to a Smoke Barrier.*

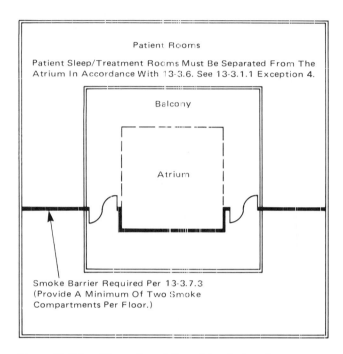

Figure 13-19b. *Illustration of Complying Atrium Arrangement in Existing Health Care Occupancies. (Also see Figures 13-19c and d.)*

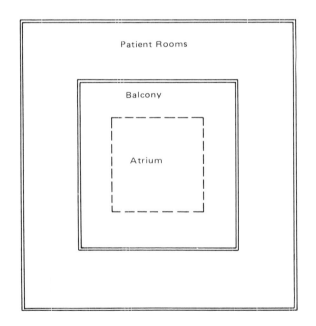

Figure 13-19a. *Illustration of a Noncomplying Atrium Arrangement in an Existing Health Care Occupancy. (See Figure 13-19b for corrected arrangement.)*

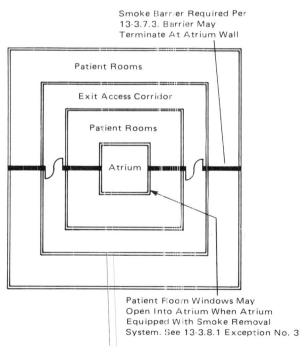

Figure 13-19c. *Existing Health Care Occupancy with Complying Atrium Arrangement.*

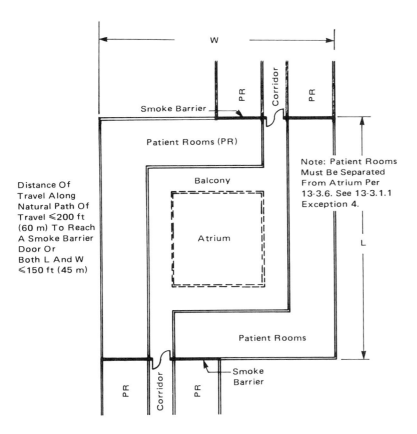

W

PR | Corridor | PR

Smoke Barrier

Patient Rooms (PR)

Balcony

Atrium

Patient Rooms

Smoke Barrier

PR | Corridor | PR

Distance Of Travel Along Natural Path Of Travel ≤200 ft (60 m) To Reach A Smoke Barrier Door Or Both L And W ≤150 ft (45 m)

Note: Patient Rooms Must Be Separated From Atrium Per 13-3.6. See 13-3.1.1 Exception 4.

L

Figure 13-19d. *Illustration of Complying Atrium Arrangement in Existing Health Care Occupancies. (Also see Figures 13-19b and c.)*

SECTION 13-4 Special Provisions

13-4.1 **Windowless Buildings.** See Section 30-7 for requirements for windowless buildings.

Windowless portions of health care facilities must comply with the requirements of Chapter 13 in addition to the criteria specified for such structures in Section 30-7. Paragraph 13-4.1 does not obviate the requirements for patient room windows contained within 13-3.8.1.

13-4.2 **High Rise Buildings.** (Reserved.)

13-4.3 **Operating Features.** (*See Chapter 31.*)

SECTION 13-5 Building Services

13-5.1 **Utilities.** Utilities shall comply with the provisions of Section 7-1.

13-5.2 **Heating, Ventilating, and Air Conditioning.**

13-5.2.1 Heating, ventilating, and air conditioning shall comply with the provisions of Section 7-2 and shall be installed in accordance with the manufacturer's specifications.

Exception: As modified in 13-5.2.2.

13-5.2.2* Any heating device other than a central heating plant shall be so designed and installed that combustible material will not be ignited by it or its appurtenances. If fuel- fired, such heating devices shall be chimney or vent connected, shall take air for combustion directly from the outside, and shall be so designed and installed to provide for complete separation of the combustion system from the atmosphere of the occupied area. Any heating device shall have safety features to immediately stop the flow of fuel and shut down the equipment in case of either excessive temperature or ignition failure.

Exception No. 1: Approved suspended unit heaters shall be permitted in locations other than means of egress and patient sleeping areas, provided such heaters are located high enough to be out of the reach of persons using the area and provided they are equipped with the safety features required above.

Exception No. 2: Fireplaces shall be permitted to be installed and used only in areas other than patient sleeping areas, provided that these areas are separated from patient sleeping spaces by construction having a 1-hour fire resistance rating and they comply with NFPA 211, Standard for Chimneys, Fireplaces, Vents, and Solid Fuel Burning Appliances. In addition thereto, the fireplace shall be equipped with a fireplace enclosure guaranteed against breakage up to a temperature of 650°F (343°C) and constructed of heat tempered glass or other approved material. If, in the opinion of the authority having jurisdiction, special hazards are present, a lock on the enclosure and other safety precautions may be required.

A-13-5.2.2   For both new and existing buildings, it is the intent of the Committee to permit the installation and use of fireplace stoves and room heaters utilizing solid fuel as defined in Chapter 8 of NFPA 211, *Standard for Chimneys, Fireplaces, Vents, and Solid Fuel Burning Appliances*, provided that all such devices are installed, maintained, and used in accordance with the appropriate provisions of that standard and all manufacturers' specifications. These requirements are not intended to permit freestanding solid fuel burning appliances such as freestanding wood-burning stoves.

Paragraphs 13-5.2.1 and 13-5.2.2 specify safeguards for air conditioning, ventilating, heating, and other service equipment in order to minimize the possibility of such devices serving as a source of ignition. Fuel-fired heating devices, except central heating systems, must be designed to provide complete separation of the combustion system from the occupied spaces. Air for combustion must be taken directly from the outside.

A major concern of the *Code* is prevention of the ignition of clothing, bedclothes, furniture, and other furnishings by a heating device. Therefore, 31-4.7 prohibits portable heating devices in areas used by patients.

13-5.3   **Elevators, Escalators, and Conveyors.** Elevators, escalators, and conveyors shall comply with the provisions of Section 7-4.

Although not counted as required exits, elevators may constitute a valuable supplemental facility for evacuating patients from health care buildings. In some cases, movement of critically ill patients or patients in restraining devices may be realistically accomplished only by an elevator.

Elevators, however, have many inherent weaknesses that tend to limit reliability. Elevator access doors are designed with operating tolerances that permit smoke transfer into the shaft. Power failure during a fire could result in trapping persons on elevators that stop between floors. Elevators may, during their descent from upper floors, stop automatically at the floor where the fire is burning, allow the doors to open, and expose the occupants to the fire.

Many of these weaknesses can be minimized by providing emergency power, separating the elevator lobby from other building spaces using rated construction, designing detection and alarm equipment to prevent elevators from stopping at a floor exposed to a fire, providing an emergency smoke control system, and by pressurizing the elevator shaft and adjacent lobbies (*see Section 7-3*). This represents good fire protection judgment but is not the result of any requirements of this *Code*.

Through emergency planning and staff training, crowding of elevators (another potential problem) may be avoided. Emergency plans may make effective use of elevators by transferring patients through a horizontal exit, for example, to a separate fire area. Within the separate fire area, a staged evacuation program could be instituted, the elevators ultimately taking patients to the outside at ground level.

13-5.4   **Rubbish Chutes, Incinerators, and Laundry Chutes.**

13-5.4.1   Any existing linen and trash chute, including pneumatic rubbish and linen systems, that opens directly onto any corridor shall be sealed by fire-resistive construction to prevent further use or shall be provided with a fire door assembly suitable for a Class B location and having a fire protection rating of 1½ hours. All new chutes shall comply with Section 7-5.

13-5.4.2 Any rubbish chute or linen chute, including pneumatic rubbish and linen systems, shall be provided with automatic extinguishing protection installed in accordance with Section 7-7. (*See Section 7-5.*)

13-5.4.3 Any trash chute shall discharge into a trash collecting room used for no other purpose and protected in accordance with Section 6-4.

13-5.4.4 Existing flue-fed incinerators shall be sealed by fire-resistive construction to prevent further use.

SECTION 13-6   Existing Ambulatory Health Care Centers

13-6.1 General Requirements.

13-6.1.1 Application.

13-6.1.1.1 Existing ambulatory health care centers shall comply with the provisions of Chapter 27 and (this) Section 13-6, whichever is more stringent. The provisions of Sections 13-2 through 13-5 shall not apply to this section unless a specific requirement is referenced by this section.

13-6.1.1.2 This section establishes life safety requirements, in addition to those required in Chapter 27, for all ambulatory health care centers and outpatient surgical centers that meet the requirements of 13-1.3(a).

Ambulatory health care centers exhibit some of the occupancy characteristics of business occupancies and some of the characteristics of health care facilities. In developing Section 13-6, it was intended to prescribe a level of life safety from fire that would be greater than that typically specified for business occupancies, but less than that typically found in health care facilities. (*See commentary for 13-1.3.*)

Ambulatory health care centers are required to comply with the provisions of Chapter 27 pertaining to business occupancies, except as more restrictive provisions are established within Section 13-6.

Ambulatory health care facilities are not identifiable as such in the national fire incident data bases. Their fires are probably recorded under those of clinics, doctors' offices, and unclassified or unknown-type facilities that care for the sick. Collectively, these properties accounted for 1,600 structure fires per year during 1984 to 1988, with 2 civilian deaths and 22 civilian injuries per year. Ambulatory health care facilities presumably account for some fraction of those totals.

13-6.1.1.3 Modification of Retroactive Provisions. The requirements of this section may be modified if their application clearly would be impractical in the judgment of the authority having jurisdiction and if the resulting arrangement could be considered as presenting minimum hazard to the life safety of the occupants. The requirements may be modified by the authority having jurisdiction to allow alternative arrangements that will secure as nearly equivalent safety to life from fire as practical.

This section is to be applied retroactively. Due consideration has been given to the practical difficulties of making alterations in existing, functioning facilities. The specified provisions, viewed as a whole, establish minimum acceptable criteria for life safety that reasonably minimize the likelihood of a life-threatening fire.

The requirements of Chapter 13 may be modified in instances of practical difficulty or where alternate, but equal, provisions are proposed. The modifications must provide an equivalent level of protection as would be achieved by compliance with the corresponding *Code* requirements.

In some cases, appreciable cost may be involved in bringing an existing occupancy into compliance with Section 13-1. Where this is true, it would be appropriate for the authority having jurisdiction to formulate a schedule, determined jointly with the owner of the facility, that allows suitable periods of time to correct various deficiencies and due consideration to the ability of the owner to secure the necessary funds. (*Also see 1-5.2, 1-5.4, Section 1-6, and 1-7.2.*)

13-6.1.2 Reserved.

13-6.1.3 Special Definitions. (*See 13-1.3.*)

13-6.1.4 Classification of Occupancy. (*See 13-1.3.*)

13-6.1.5 Reserved.

13-6.1.6 Minimum Construction Requirements.

13-6.1.6.1 For purposes of 13-6.1.6, the number of stories shall be counted starting with the primary level of exit discharge and ending with the highest occupiable level. For the purposes of this section, the primary level of exit discharge of a building shall be that floor that is level with or above finished grade of this exterior wall line for 50 percent or more of its perimeter.

Allowable building construction types are determined as a function of the number of stories in a building. In determining the number of stories, the first story is considered to be the primary level of exit discharge. Only occupiable levels are counted in determining story height. For example, an unoccupied attic would not constitute a story.

Problems have occurred in determining story height where a building is located on a sloping grade. Paragraph 13-6.1.6.1 notes that a story on a sloping site that is partially below grade should be counted as a story if the floor is level with or above grade along 50 percent or more of the perimeter of the building at the exterior wall. (*See Figure 13-20.*)

13-6.1.6.2 Buildings of one story in height housing ambulatory health care centers shall be of Type I, II, III, IV, or V construction. (*See 6-2.1.*)

13-6.1.6.3 Buildings of two or more stories in height housing ambulatory health care centers shall be of Type I (443) or (332), Type II (222) or (111), Type III (211), Type IV (2HH), or Type V (111) construction. (*See 6-2.1.*)

Exception: Buildings constructed of Type II (000), III (200), or V (000) if protected throughout by an approved supervised automatic sprinkler system in accordance with Section 7-7.

Construction types permitted in ambulatory health care centers are summarized in Table 13-1. (*See NFPA 220, Standard on Types of Building Construction.*)[2]

Table 13-1 Construction Types Permitted in Ambulatory Health Care Occupancies

Construction Type	1	Stories 2 or more
I (443), I (332), II (222), II (111) (Fire Resistive and Protected Noncombustible)	X	X
II (000) (Unprotected Noncombustible)	X	X*
III (211) (Protected Ordinary)	X	X
III (200) (Unprotected Ordinary)	X	X*
IV (2HH) (Heavy Timber)	X	X
V (111) (Protected Wood Frame)	X	X
V (000) (Unprotected Wood Frame)	X	X*

X = Construction types allowed.
* = Automatic sprinkler protection required.

13-6.1.6.4 Any level below the level of exit discharge shall be separated from the level of exit discharge by at least Type II (111), Type III (211), or Type V (111) construction. (*See 6-2.1.*)

Exception: Separation is not required for such levels if they are under the control of the ambulatory health care center and any hazardous spaces are protected in accordance with Section 6-4.

13-6.1.6.5 In existing buildings, the authority having jurisdiction may accept construction systems of lesser fire resistance than required above if it can be demonstrated to the authority's satisfaction that prompt evacuation of the center can be achieved in case of fire or that the exposing occupancies and materials of construction present no threat of fire penetration from such occupancy to the ambulatory health care center or to the collapse of the structure.

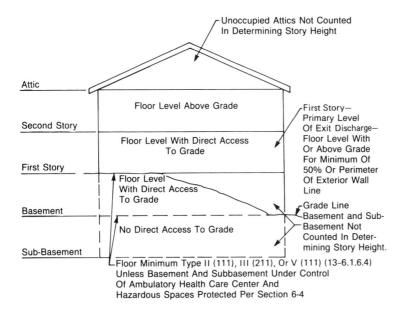

Figure 13-20. Illustration of the Application of 13-6.1.6.1 and 13-6.1.6.4.

This paragraph allows the authority having jurisdiction to accept lesser construction types than those specified above, provided it can be demonstrated that the occupants of the ambulatory health care center are capable of evacuating the building promptly. If lesser construction types are to be accepted, potential exposures from adjacent occupancies or tenants must be provided with appropriate safeguards such as sprinklers, fire detectors, or fire-resistive separation. Structural stability must be maintained for the time required to evacuate the building, plus an additional period of time as a safety margin.

13-6.1.7 Occupant Load. *(See 26-1.7.)*

13-6.2 Means of Egress Requirements.

13-6.2.1 General. Every aisle, passageway, corridor, exit discharge, exit location, and access shall be in accordance with Chapter 5.

Exception: As modified in the following paragraphs.

Means of egress details are to conform to the fundamental provisions expressed in Chapter 5, except as modified in Chapter 27 and Chapter 13. For example, egress capacity for doors must be calculated on the basis of clear width in accordance with 5-2.1.2, whereas minimum door widths specified by 13-6.2.3.3 are to be determined using actual door leaf width.

13-6.2.2 Means of Egress Components.

13-6.2.2.1 Components of means of egress shall be limited to the types described in 27-2.2.

13-6.2.2.2 Special locking arrangements complying with 5-2.1.6 are permitted on exterior doors.

Paragraph 5-2.1.6 establishes minimum requirements for delayed release hardware, including the requirement that the building must be protected throughout by an automatic sprinkler system or automatic fire detection system.

13-6.2.2.3 Any door in an exit passageway, horizontal exit, smoke barrier, stairway enclosure, or hazardous area enclosure shall be permitted to be held open only by an automatic release device that complies with 5-2.1.8. The required manual fire alarm system and the systems required by 5-2.1.8(c) shall be arranged so as to initiate the closing action of all such doors by zone or throughout the entire facility.

13-6.2.2.4   Where doors in a stair enclosure are held open by an automatic device as permitted in 13-6.2.2.3, initiation of a door closing action on any level shall cause all doors at all levels in the stair enclosure to close.

It is desirable to keep doors in exit enclosures, stair enclosures, horizontal exits, smoke barriers, and hazardous areas closed at all times to impede the spread of smoke and gases caused by a fire. However, some doors will be kept open for reasons of either operating efficiency or comfort. Where doors in required fire or smoke barriers are to be held open, such doors must be equipped with automatic devices that are designed to close the doors by the methods described within 13-6.2.2.3 and 5-2.1.8.

The automatic device must cause the doors to close upon operation of the manual fire alarm system. The doors must also be designed to close by actuation of a smoke detector located to detect smoke on either side of the door opening or by actuation of a complete automatic fire extinguishing or complete automatic fire detection system.

It is especially important in facilities providing health care to maintain floor-to-floor separation. Doors protecting openings in a stair enclosure may be held open by an automatic device only if arranged to close as specified above. Initiation of any action that causes a door to close at one level must cause all doors protecting openings within the stair enclosure to close and latch at all levels.

13-6.2.3   **Capacity of Means of Egress.**

13-6.2.3.1   The capacity of any required means of egress shall be determined in accordance with the provisions of 27-2.3 and shall be based on its width as defined in Section 5-3.

The capacity of the means of egress in ambulatory health care centers is determined on the basis of provisions in Chapter 27 that address business occupancies. Paragraph 27-2.3.1 refers to Section 5-3, which requires the capacity of level exit components to be computed on the basis of 0.2 in. (0.5 cm) per person, whereas stair capacity is computed using 0.3 in. (0.8 cm) per person. These capacities are considered reasonable based on the assumption that the majority of occupants will be ambulatory.

13-6.2.3.2   The minimum width of any corridor or passageway required for exit access shall be 44 in. (112 cm) clear.

Corridor widths greater than 44 in. (112 cm) may be required within ambulatory health care centers. However, the minimum width for public corridors used as common exit access corridors or passageways is 44 in. (112 cm). The 44-in. (112-cm) width is stipulated on the assumption that most occupants will be ambulatory.

13-6.2.3.3   Doors in the means of egress from diagnostic or treatment areas such as X-ray, surgical, or physical therapy shall be at least 34 in. (86 cm) wide.

In many instances, doors wider than 34 in. (86 cm) will be needed to operate efficiently. This paragraph intends to address doors used by the public or those doors that provide access to public hallways and corridors. The 34-in. (86-cm) minimum width is specified for doors on the assumption that most occupants will be ambulatory.

13-6.2.4   **Number of Exits.**

13-6.2.4.1   At least two exits of the types described in 27-2.2 that are remotely located from each other shall be provided for each floor or fire section of the building.

13-6.2.4.2   Any room and any suite of rooms of more than 1,000 sq ft (93 sq m) shall have at least two exit access doors remotely located from each other.

13-6.2.5   **Arrangement of Means of Egress.** (*See 27-2.5.*)

13-6.2.6   **Travel Distance to Exits.**

13-6.2.6.1   Travel distance shall be measured in accordance with Section 5-6.

13-6.2.6.2   Travel distance:

(a) Between any room door required as exit access and an exit shall not exceed 100 ft (30 m); and

(b) Between any point in a room and an exit shall not exceed 150 ft (45 m).

Exception: The maximum travel distance permitted in (a) or (b) above shall be increased by 50 ft (15 m) in buildings protected throughout by an approved automatic sprinkler system.

Travel distance is measured only to the closest exit, not to both exits required by 13-6.2.4.1. The requirements of 13-6.2.6.2 are illustrated in Figure 13-21.

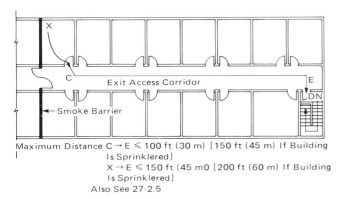

Maximum Distance C → E ≤ 100 ft (30 m) [150 ft (45 m) If Building Is Sprinklered]
X → E ≤ 150 ft (45 m0 [200 ft (60 m) If Building Is Sprinklered]
Also See 27-2.5

Figure 13-21. Travel Distance in an Existing Ambulatory Care Facility.

13-6.2.7 Discharge from Exits. (*See 27-2.7.*)

13-6.2.8 Illumination of Means of Egress. Means of egress shall be illuminated in accordance with Section 5-8.

13-6.2.9 Emergency Lighting and Essential Electrical Systems.

13-6.2.9.1 Emergency lighting shall be provided in accordance with Section 5-9.

13-6.2.9.2 Where general anesthesia or life support equipment is used, each ambulatory health care center shall be provided with an essential electrical system in accordance with NFPA 99, *Standard for Health Care Facilities.*

Exception: Where battery operated equipment is provided and acceptable to the authority having jurisdiction.

All ambulatory health care centers are required to be equipped with emergency lighting. If medical procedures requiring general anesthesia are practiced, or if life-support equipment is required, ambulatory health care centers are required to be served by electrical systems meeting the criteria for essential electrical systems as detailed in Chapter 3, "Electrical Systems," of NFPA 99, *Standard for Health Care Facilities.*[6]

A facility would not be required to have an emergency generator if the building is a freestanding unit and if, as a normal practice, (1) management maintains admitting and discharge policies that preclude the provision of care for any patient or resident who may need to be sustained by electrical life-support equipment, such as respirators or suction apparatus, and (2) no surgical treatment requiring general anesthesia is offered, and (3) battery-operated systems or equipment are provided that would maintain power to exit lights and illumination for exit corridors, stairways, medical preparation areas, and the like, for a minimum of 1½ hours. Additionally, battery power would be required to be supplied to all alarm systems.

13-6.2.10 Marking of Means of Egress. Means of egress shall have signs in accordance with Section 5-10.

13-6.2.11 Special Features. (Reserved.)

13-6.3 Protection.

13-6.3.1 Protection of Vertical Openings. (*See 27-3.1.*)

13-6.3.2 Protection from Hazards. (*See 27-3.2.*)

13-6.3.2.1 Laboratories employing quantities of flammable, combustible, or hazardous materials that are considered as severe hazard shall be protected in accordance with NFPA 99, *Standard for Health Care Facilities.*

Laboratories that contain "ordinary" combustibles and flammable liquids in sufficient quantity to threaten a 1-hour fire separation [e.g., wood-equivalent fuel loads in the range of 5 to 10 lb/sq ft (25 to 50 kg/sq m)] are considered a severe hazard. Laboratories representing a severe hazard must be protected in accordance with Chapter 10 of NFPA 99, *Standard for Health Care Facilities.*[6] Protection would include 1-hour fire resistance separation and automatic sprinkler protection.

Where fuel loads of lesser amounts are involved and quantities of flammable liquids are limited, laboratories would simply be considered hazardous areas and would require either 1-hour separation or automatic sprinkler protection as indicated within 27-3.2 and Section 6-4.

13-6.3.2.2 Anesthetizing locations shall be protected in accordance with NFPA 99, *Standard for Health Care Facilities.*

13-6.3.3 Interior Finish. (*See 27-3.3.*)

13-6.3.4 Detection, Alarm, and Communication Systems.

13-6.3.4.1 General. Centers shall be provided with a fire alarm system in accordance with Section 7-6, except as modified below.

13-6.3.4.2 Initiation. Initiation of the required fire alarm systems shall be by manual means in accordance with 7-6.2 and by means of any detection devices or detection systems required.

13-6.3.4.3 Occupant Notification. Occupant notification shall be accomplished automatically, without delay, upon operation of any fire alarm activating device by means of an internal audible alarm in accordance with 7-6.3.

Exception: The presignal system allowed by 7-6.3.2 Exception No. 1 shall not be permitted.

13-6.3.4.4 Emergency Forces Notification. Fire department notification shall be accomplished in accordance with 7-6.4.

13-6.3.4.5 Emergency Control. Operation of any activating device in the required fire alarm system shall be arranged to automatically accomplish, without delay, any control functions required to be performed by that device. (*See 7-6.5.*)

Paragraphs 13-6.3.4.1 through 13-6.3.4.5 address required fire alarm equipment. Reliability is of prime importance; therefore, electrical supervision of the system and system components is specified by the standards referenced in Section 7-6. In the event of circuit fault, component failure, or other "trouble," a continuous "trouble indication" signal is required and should be provided at a constantly attended location.

A manual fire alarm system is required by 13-6.3.4.2. Manual pull stations should be located along the natural routes of egress and located so as to adequately cover all portions of the building. Manual pull stations should always be located so that those qualified to send an alarm may summon aid without having to leave their zone of ordinary activities or pass beyond the view and hearing of people immediately exposed to, or in direct view of, a fire. The operation of a manual fire alarm station should automatically summon attendants who can assist in removing physically helpless occupants.

The system required by 13-6.3.4.2 may be incorporated into an automatic system equipped to detect a fire and initiate an alarm.

Actuation of any required fire or smoke detector, activation of a required sprinkler system, or operation of a manual pull station must automatically, without delay, sound audible alarm devices within the building. Presignal systems are not permitted.

The alarm must automatically transmit to a point outside the facility. Where automatic transmission of alarms to the fire department legally committed to serve the facility is not permitted, arrangements are to be made for the prompt notification of the fire department or such other assistance as may be available in the case of fire or other emergency. Paragraph 7-6.4 lists various methods acceptable for automatically notifying the fire department. The fire department should still be notified manually to verify and confirm the automatic transmission of the alarm. In larger facilities, this may be the responsibility of the facility telephone operator; in smaller facilities, it may be the responsibility of the nursing staff.

Actuation of the fire alarm must cause audible alerting devices to sound throughout the affected zone or building as appropriate. Visible alerting devices may be used but may not serve as a substitute for audible devices.

13-6.3.5 Extinguishment Requirements. (*See 27-3.5.*)

13-6.3.5.1 Isolated hazardous areas shall be permitted to be protected in accordance with 7-7.1.2. For new installations in existing buildings where more than two sprinklers are installed in a single area, water flow detection shall be provided to sound the building fire alarm or notify by a signal any constantly attended location, such as PBX, security, or emergency room, whereby necessary corrective action shall be directed.

13-6.3.5.2 Portable fire extinguishers shall be provided in ambulatory health care occupancies in accordance with 7-7.4.1.

13-6.3.6 Corridors.

13-6.3.6.1 In other than smoke compartments containing patient sleeping rooms, miscellaneous openings such as mail slots, pharmacy pass-through windows, laboratory pass-through windows, and cashier pass-through windows may be installed in vision panels or doors without special protection provided the aggregate area of openings per room does not exceed 20 sq in. (.013 sq cm) and the openings are installed at or below half the distance from the floor to the room ceiling.

See commentary for 13-3.6.5.

13-6.3.7 Subdivision of Building Space.

13-6.3.7.1 Ambulatory health care occupancies shall be separated from other tenants and occupancies by walls having at least a 1-hour fire resistance rating. Such walls shall extend from the floor slab below to the floor or roof slab above. Doors shall be constructed of at least 1¾-in. (4.4-cm) thick solid bonded wood core or the equivalent and shall be equipped with positive latches. These doors shall be self-closing and kept in the closed position except when in use. Any vision panels shall be of fixed fire window assemblies in accordance with 6-2.3.4.

Ambulatory health care centers are frequently located within buildings used for a variety of purposes. Location within buildings containing hazardous occupancies should be avoided. Where ambulatory health care centers are located within buildings of mixed use, the ambulatory health care center must be separated from adjacent tenants and occupancies by minimum 1-hour fire-rated partitions. Doors protecting openings in such partitions must be of at least 1¾-in. (4.5-cm) thick solid bonded wood core or of equivalent construction that will resist fire for a minimum of 20 minutes. The doors must be equipped

with positive latching hardware of a type that cannot be held in the retracted position. Roller latches cannot be used. These doors must be self-closing and normally maintained in the closed position, or, if the doors are to be held open, an automatic device must be used as specified in 13-6.2.2.3.

Glazing within doors and partitions will generally involve a maximum area of 1,296 sq in. (0.84 sq m) of wired glass, set in approved metal frames. Each wired glass panel should be limited to a maximum dimension of 54 in. (137 cm). The glass should be labeled, should be ¼-in. (0.6-cm) thick, and be well embedded in putty, with all exposed joints between the metal and the glass struck and pointed (*see NFPA 80, Standard for Fire Doors and Windows*).[11] A number of wired glass panels may be used in a single partition, provided that each 1,296-sq in. (0.84-sq m) section is separated from adjacent panels by a metal mullion. The excessive use of wired glass panels should be avoided. It should be recognized that the use of wired glass panels in a partition reduces the effectiveness of the partition due to the fact that radiant energy transfer through the glass panel will readily occur. Other fire rated glazing is available and, where used, should be installed in accordance with the manufacturer's instructions and its listing.

Partitions separating ambulatory health care centers from other occupancies must extend from the floor to the floor or roof deck above, extending completely through concealed spaces above suspended ceilings, for example. The partition must form a continuous barrier. Openings around penetrations involving building services must be adequately protected to maintain the 1-hour separation. Special attention should be paid to penetrations involving air-handling ducts. In general, steel ducts will not require a fire damper. Penetrations involving nonmetallic ducts or aluminum ducts should be carefully evaluated. Fire dampers should be provided to protect duct penetrations where the projected fire exposure is judged sufficient to jeopardize the required separation because of the duct penetration. The possible movement of air from space to space under conditions of system operation and conditions of system shutdown should be evaluated for both conditions. If there is a significant potential for the transfer of smoke from an adjacent space to the ambulatory health care center or from the ambulatory health care center to a corridor, fire dampers should be provided for duct penetrations, even though the *Code* does not specifically require such protection. (*See Figure 13-22.*)

13-6.3.7.2 The ambulatory health care facility shall be divided into at least two smoke compartments.

Exception: Facilities of less than 2,000 sq ft (185 sq m) and protected by an approved automatic smoke detection system.

13-6.3.7.3 Any required smoke barrier shall be constructed in accordance with Section 6-3 and shall have a fire resistance rating of at least 1 hour.

13-6.3.7.4 Vision panels in the smoke barrier shall be of fixed fire window assemblies in accordance with 6-2.3.4.

13-6.3.7.5 Reserved.

13-6.3.7.6* Doors in smoke barriers shall be constructed of at least 1¾-in. (4.4-cm) thick solid bonded wood core or the equivalent and shall be self-closing. A vision panel is required.

A-13-6.3.7.6 Smoke barriers may include walls having door openings other than cross-corridor doors. There is no restriction in the *Code* regarding which doors or how many doors form part of a smoke barrier. For example, doors from the corridor to individual rooms may form part of a smoke barrier.

13-6.3.7.7 Doors in smoke barriers shall normally be kept closed, or if held open, they shall be equipped with automatic devices that will release the doors upon activation of:

(a) The fire alarm system, and either

(b) A local smoke detector, or

(c) A complete automatic fire extinguishing system or complete automatic fire detection system.

The requirements of 13-6.3.7.1 through 13-6.3.7.7 for subdividing building spaces through smoke barriers are illustrated in Figures 13-22 and 13-23. Paragraph 13-2.2.5 discusses horizontal exits.

During a fire, the emergency evacuation of patients in an ambulatory health care facility can be an inefficient,

time consuming process. Realistically, if nonambulatory patients must be moved, any number of occupants can be relocated, but this can be done only through horizontal travel. Smoke barriers and horizontal exits used to subdivide a building serve three purposes fundamental to the protection of inpatients because they:

1. Limit the spread of fire and fire-produced contaminants,
2. Limit the number of occupants exposed to a single fire, and
3. Provide for horizontal relocation of patients by creating an area of refuge on the same floor level.

13-6.4 Special Provisions. (*See Section 27-4.*)

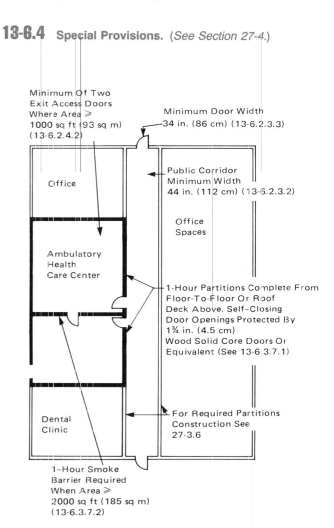

Figure 13-22. Building Subdivision in Existing Ambulatory Health Care Center.

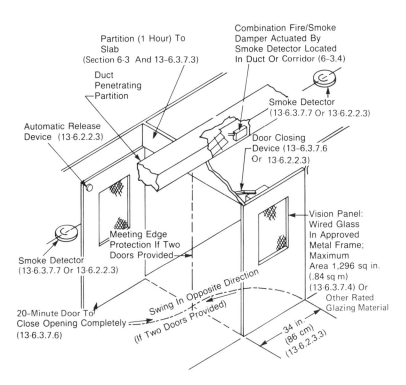

Figure 13-23.   Smoke Barrier for Existing Ambulatory Health Care Occupancy Installed in Accordance with 13-6.3.7.

13-6.5   Building Services.

13-6.5.1   Utilities. Utilities shall comply with the provisions of Section 7-1.

13-6.5.2   Heating, Ventilating, and Air Conditioning.

13-6.5.2.1   Heating, ventilating, and air conditioning shall comply with the provisions of Section 7-2 and shall be installed in accordance with the manufacturer's specifications.

Exception: As modified in 13-6.5.2.2.

13-6.5.2.2   Any heating device other than a central heating plant shall be so designed and installed that combustible material will not be ignited by it or its appurtenances. If fuel-fired, such heating devices shall be chimney or vent connected, shall take air for combustion directly from the outside, and shall be so designed and installed to provide for complete separation of the combustion system from the atmosphere of the occu-

pied area. Any heating device shall have safety features to immediately stop the flow of fuel and shut down the equipment in case of either excessive temperature or ignition failure.

Exception: Approved suspended unit heaters shall be permitted in locations other than means of egress and patient treatment areas, provided such heaters are located high enough to be out of the reach of persons using the area and provided they are equipped with the safety features called for above.

Paragraphs 13-6.5.2.1 and 13-6.5.2.2 specify safeguards for air conditioning, ventilating, heating, and other service equipment in order to minimize the possibility of such devices serving as a source of ignition. Fuel-fired heating devices, except central heating systems, must be designed to provide complete separation of the combustion system from the occupied spaces. Air for combustion must be taken directly from the outside.

A major concern of the *Code* is to prevent the ignition of clothing, bedclothes, furniture, and other furnishings by a heating device. Therefore, 31-4.7 prohibits portable heating devices in areas used by patients.

13-6.5.3 Elevators, Escalators, and Conveyors. Elevators, escalators, and conveyors shall comply with the provisions of Section 7-4.

13-6.5.4 Rubbish Chutes, Incinerators, and Laundry Chutes. Rubbish chutes, incinerators, and laundry chutes shall comply with the provisions of Section 7-5.

References Cited in Commentary

[1] NFPA 101M, *Alternative Approaches to Life Safety,* National Fire Protection Association, Quincy, MA.†

[2] NFPA 220, *Standard on Types of Building Construction,* National Fire Protection Association, Quincy, MA, 1985.

[3] NFPA 241, *Standard for Safeguarding Construction, Alteration, and Demolition Operations,* National Fire Protection Association, Quincy, MA, 1989.

[4] NFPA 72E, *Standard on Automatic Fire Detectors,* National Fire Protection Association, Quincy, MA, 1990.

[5] NFPA 30, *Flammable and Combustible Liquids Code,* National Fire Protection Association, Quincy, MA, 1990.

[6] NFPA 99, *Standard for Health Care Facilities,* National Fire Protection Association, Quincy, MA, 1990.

[7] NFPA 96, *Standard for the Installation of Equipment for the Removal of Smoke and Grease-Laden Vapors from Commercial Cooking Equipment,* National Fire Protection Association, Quincy, MA, 1991.

[8] W.J. Christian and T.E. Waterman, "Flame Spread in Corridors: Effects of Location and Area of Wall Finish," *Fire Journal,* Vol. 65, No. 4, pp. 25-32, July 1971.

[9] R.W. Bukowski and S.M. Istvan, "A Survey of Field Experience with Smoke Detectors in Health Care Facilities," NBSIR 80-2130, Center for Fire Research, National Bureau of Standards, October 1980.

[10] NFPA 13, *Standard for the Installation of Sprinkler Systems,* National Fire Protection Association Quincy, MA 1991.

[11] NFPA 80, *Standard for Fire Doors and Windows,* National Fire Protection Association, Quincy, MA, 1990.

[12] NFPA 90A, *Standard for the Installation of Air Conditioning and Ventilating Systems,* National Fire Protection Association, Quincy, MA, 1989.

---

†The edition of NFPA 101M that corresponds with the 1991 *Life Safety Code* will be published in 1992.

14

New Detention and Correctional Occupancies

(See also Chapter 31.)

In a typical year, there will be one fire fatality in a U.S. detention or correctional occupancy. However, the potential for a major incident still exists, and such incidents tend to overshadow the single-death fires. For example, the 1982 jail fire in Biloxi, Mississippi killed 29 people. This was several times the death toll for prison and jail fires combined during that decade.[1] Because the *Life Safety Code* is designed with particular emphasis on the prevention of loss of life in areas beyond the area of fire origin, this underscores the need for *Code* compliance in detention and correctional occupancies.

The 1981 Edition of the *Life Safety Code* was the first edition to include separate chapters on detention and correctional occupancies. In previous editions, these occupancies were briefly addressed in the chapter on institutional occupancies.

In 1974, the Committee on Safety to Life established a Sectional Committee on Penal Occupancies. It was, however, too late to prepare a report for the 1976 Edition of the *Code*, and in 1977, the Committee on Safety to Life was reorganized as a technical committee with associated subcommittees. The Subcommittee on Penal Occupancies was appointed, and its first working meeting took place in January, 1978. Shortly thereafter, it was renamed the Subcommittee on Detention and Correctional Occupancies. During this period, there were several major detention and correctional occupancy fires that underscored the need for the subcommittee and provided information for its use. These fires included:

Date	Place	Civilian Deaths
October 1974	Youth Correctional Center Cranston, RI	2[2]
June 1975	Seminole County Jail Sanford, FL	11[2]
November 1975	Lycoming County Jail Williamsport, PA	3[2]
June 1976	Marion State Prison Marion, NC	9[2]
June 1977	Maury County Jail Tennessee	42[3]
June 1977	St. John City Detention Center St. John, NB, Canada	21[4]

(continued)

Date	Place	Civilian Deaths
July 1977	Federal Correctional Institution Danbury, CT	5[5]
December 1979	Lancaster County Jail Lancaster, SC	11[6]

SECTION 14-1   General Requirements

14-1.1 Application.

14-1.1.1 New detention and correctional facilities shall comply with the provisions of this chapter. They shall also comply with the applicable requirements of Chapter 31.

Provisions for existing detention and correctional occupancies are contained in Chapter 15.

Chapter 31, "Operating Features," and Section 31-5 in particular, provide routine operating requirements, such as 24-hour staffing, means for resident notification of staff in an emergency, preparation and maintenance of evacuation plans, staff training in the use of portable fire extinguishers, storage of combustible personal property, presence of heat-producing appliances, control of flammability of draperies, curtains, mattresses, and upholstered furniture, and visual and tactile identification of keys necessary for unlocking doors within the means of egress. Because the locking of doors, which is necessary for the intended function of the facility, is contrary to the basic *Code* tenet that the means of egress system be under the control of building occupants, the presence of properly trained staff is paramount in the provision of a package of life safety equivalent to that provided in other occupancies. Chapter 31 requires the necessary staffing and training that, where combined with the *Code* requirements of Chapters 1 through 7 and 14, achieve the necessary level of life safety.

14-1.1.2 This chapter establishes life safety requirements for the design of all new detention and correctional facilities.

pancy. Therefore, although 14-1.1.2 states that Chapter 14 establishes life safety requirements for the design of all new detention and correctional facilities, the chapter focuses primarily on life safety requirements for the design of residential portions of new detention and correctional occupancies.

Exception No. 1: Use Condition I requirements are those stated in the applicable requirements of Chapter 16, 18, or 20.

In accordance with 14-1.4, which defines the five resident user category groups, Use Condition I provides residents with free movement from sleeping areas, and other spaces where access or occupancy is permitted, to the exterior by a means of egress system that meets the same requirements as that which would be provided for occupants of hotel, dormitory, apartment, lodging, or rooming house occupancies. Because locked doors have not been imposed on the residents of a Use Condition I detention or correctional occupancy, such a facility does not require the "protect in place strategy" and associated requirements of Chapter 14. For information on the protection of Use Condition I facilities, Exception No. 1 to 14-1.1.2 and 14-1.4.3 refer the *Code* user to Chapter 16,18, or 20 in lieu of the provisions of Chapter 14.

Exception No. 2: *Facilities determined to have equivalent safety provided in accordance with Section 1-6.*

A-14-1.1.2 Exception No. 2. In determining equivalency for conversions, modernizations, renovations, or unusual design concepts of detention and correctional facilities, the authority having jurisdiction may accept evaluations based on Chapter 4 of NFPA 101M, *Alternative Approaches to Life Safety* (*see Appendix B*), utilizing the parameters for new construction.

Exception No. 2 provides that the equivalency provisions of Section 1-6 can be used to comply with the intended level of life safety rather than having to meet the requirements of Chapter 14. The 1992 Edition of NFPA 101M, *Alternative Approaches to Life Safety*,[7] will provide information on one possible equivalency system for use in detention and correctional occupancies. Its measurement system has been calibrated against the requirements of the 1991 Edition of the *Life Safety Code*, whereas the firesafety evaluation systems contained in the

1988 Edition of NFPA 101M were calibrated against the requirements of the 1988 Edition of the *Code*.

Chapter 4 of NFPA 101M, "Firesafety Evaluation System for Detention and Correctional Occupancies," provides a method in which the user assigns numerical values to various building parameters. The individual values are totaled and compared with established values. This is a system by which alternative designs can be evaluated as options to literal *Code* compliance. The *Code* does not intend to limit acceptable equivalency evaluations solely to those based on this system. The authority having jurisdiction retains the discretion, in accordance with Section 1-6, to evaluate and approve alternative designs on the basis of appropriate supporting data.

14-1.1.3 Detention and correctional occupancies are those used for purposes such as correctional institutions, detention facilities, community residential centers, training schools, work camps, and substance abuse centers where occupants are confined or housed under some degree of restraint or security.

Both 4-1.5 and 14-1.1.3 have been updated to reflect the current terminology for various forms of detention and correctional occupancies. The use of the terms adult correctional institutions, adult local detention facilities, juvenile detention facilities, juvenile training schools, adult and juvenile community residential centers, adult and juvenile work camps, and adult and juvenile substance abuse centers have replaced terms such as reformatories and houses of correction.

14-1.1.4 Detention and correctional occupancies provide sleeping facilities for four or more residents and are occupied by persons who are generally prevented from taking self-preservation action because of security measures not under the occupants' control.

Residents of detention and correctional occupancies and patients in health care occupancies are judged to be incapable of self-preservation during a fire emergency. In the case of a health care occupancy patient, the incapability is due to physical or mental illness or infirmity. The detention and correctional occupancy resident, although most likely ambulatory or able-bodied, is incapable of self-preservation due to security measures imposed and beyond

the resident's control. In both cases, the occupants must await staff action before moving to either an exit, another fire compartment, or a smoke compartment. Impediments to adequate egress are further compounded in detention and correctional occupancies by the reluctance of staff to unlock doors leading to the outside. Thus, horizontal movement within the facility to another fire compartment or smoke compartment may be the only means of egress system that the resident is allowed to use in a fire emergency, regardless of how many exit doors to the outside are installed. Therefore, the "Total Concept" described in 14-1.1.5 is critical.

14-1.1.5   Total Concept. All detention and correctional facilities shall be so designed, constructed, maintained, and operated as to minimize the possibility of a fire emergency.

Because the safety of all occupants in detention and correctional facilities cannot be adequately assured solely by dependence on evacuation of the building, their protection from fire shall be provided by appropriate arrangement of facilities, adequate trained staff, and careful development of operating, security, and maintenance procedures composed of the following:

(a) Proper design, construction, and compartmentation,

(b) Provision for detection, alarm, and extinguishment,

(c) Fire prevention and planning, training, and drilling in programs for the isolation of fire and transfer of occupants to areas of refuge or evacuation of the building, or protection of the occupants in place, and

(d) Provision of security to the degree necessary for the safety of the public and the occupants of the facility.

The "Total Concept" establishes a "protect in place" or "defend in place" strategy. This strategy mandates requirements that minimize the need for building evacuation by restricting the development and spread of a fire emergency to the room of fire origin, because safety cannot be ensured by relying on a means of egress system that utilizes evacuation, since locks either cannot or will not be unlocked in a timely manner. The requirements (e.g., Section 31-5) first try to prevent ignition and, when fires do occur, set out to detect them (e.g., 14-3.4.4). Other requirements aim to control the speed with which a fire will develop (e.g., 14-3.3), while still others serve to confine the effects of fire. Extinguishment of fire is facilitated by sprinkler, standpipe, and portable extinguisher requirements. Provisions are made for refuge areas by encouraging the use of horizontal exits and by requiring smoke barriers. Heavy reliance is placed on staff reaction. All these requirements fit together to minimize the need for evacuation. This is the "Total Concept."

14-1.1.6   Additions. Additions shall be separated from any existing structure not conforming with the provisions of Chapter 15 by a fire barrier having at least a 2-hour fire resistance rating constructed to the requirements of the addition. Doors in these partitions shall normally be kept closed.

Exception: Doors shall be permitted to be held open if they meet the requirements of the Exception to 5-2.1.8.

Buildings that do comply with the requirements for existing detention and correctional occupancies in accordance with Chapter 15 do not require separation from new additions.

Note that, unlike similar requirements that apply to health care occupancies, the positioning of doors in the separating fire barriers is not restricted to corridors only. Doors must be kept closed unless they meet the requirements for automatic closing found in the Exception to 5-2.1.8.

Figure 14-1 illustrates the requirements of 14-1.1.6.

14-1.2*   Mixed Occupancies.

A-14-1.2   Detention and correctional facilities are a complex of structures, each serving a definite and usually different purpose. For instance, in all probability there will be represented in many institutions an example of all, or almost all, the occupancy-type classifications found in this *Code*. Exits and other features shall be governed by the type of occupancy classification and the hazard of occupancy unless specific exceptions are made.

All buildings and structures are to be classified using this chapter and Section 4-1 as a guide, subject to the ruling of the authority having jurisdiction in case of question as to the proper classification of any individual building or structure.

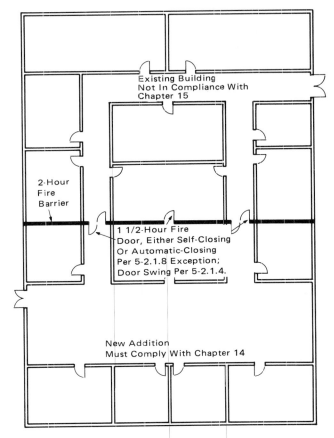

Figure 14-1.   *Separation of New Addition from an Existing Building That Does Not Comply with Chapter 15. (See 14-1.1.6.)*

Use Condition classification of the institution, as well as individual areas within the complex, are always to be considered by the authority having jurisdiction.

14-1.2.1   Egress provisions for areas of detention and correctional facilities that correspond to other occupancies shall meet the corresponding requirements of this *Code* for such occupancies. Where security operations necessitate the locking of required means of egress, necessary staff shall be provided for the supervised release of occupants during all times of use.

The requirements of Chapter 14 apply mainly to the residential portions (i.e., the sleeping and living areas) of the detention and correctional facility. Although the work areas might look much like a typical industrial occupancy, the requirements of Chapter 28, "Industrial Occupancies," cannot be applied by themselves, because doors within the required means of egress of a detention and correctional occupancy will be locked for security. Without using the requirements of Chapter 14 itself to protect the locked industrial work areas, the concepts of Chapter 14 should be implemented to ensure that the necessary trained staff who control locks is present to facilitate immediate, supervised release of occupants during all times of use in the event of fire or similar emergency.

In addition, some areas of a large facility may correspond to another occupancy classification. For example, a gymnasium would be considered an assembly occupancy (Chapter 8). If locked doors are required, prompt unlocking and release are critical.

Release of occupants may be achieved by a remotely activated system capable of unlocking all doors in the means of egress or by a sufficient number of attendants who are continuously on duty, provided with keys, and stationed in the immediate area of all locked means of egress doors. Continuous supervision is essential.

14-1.2.2 Sections of detention and correctional facilities shall be permitted to be classified as other occupancies if they meet all of the following conditions:

   (a) They are not intended to serve residents for sleeping purposes, and

   (b) They are adequately separated from areas of detention or correctional occupancies by construction having a fire resistance rating of at least 2 hours.

For example, administrative offices or maintenance areas that are not customarily used by the residents as sleeping areas and are separated by 2-hour fire resistance rated construction could be classified as business or industrial occupancies. In many cases, "trustees" may be employed in these areas. Their presence in these areas would not be considered a violation of 14-1.2.2, provided they had the freedom of egress found in an unlocked environment.

14-1.2.3 Detention and correctional occupancies in buildings housing other occupancies shall be completely separated from the other occupancies by construction having a fire resistance rating of at least 2 hours as provided for additions in 14-1.1.6.

Paragraph 14-1.2.3 requires that if a detention or correctional occupancy is located in a building of another classification, the detention or correctional occupancy must be separated from the other occupancy by construction having a fire resistance rating of 2 hours (*see 14-1.1.6*). This requirement would apply to a small detention lockup facility (at least 4 residents, per 14-1.1.4) located in a combination county courthouse/office/police building. In accordance with 31-5.1.1, the detention area must be staffed 24 hours per day. The remainder of the building, especially office areas, might not be occupied at night. A fire that originates and develops in an unoccupied area will not threaten the occupants of the detention facility as readily due to the protection provided by the required 2-hour fire resistance rated barrier.

Note that 14-1.2.3 addresses occupancy classification only, not hazard of contents. Hazard of contents is addressed in 14-1.2.5.

14-1.2.4 All means of egress from detention and correctional occupancies that traverse other use areas shall, as a minimum, conform to requirements of this *Code* for detention and correctional occupancies.

Exception: It is permissible to exit through a horizontal exit into other contiguous occupancies that do not conform to detention and correctional occupancy egress provisions, but that do comply with requirements set forth in the appropriate occupancy chapter of this Code, as long as the occupancy does not have high hazard contents. The horizontal exit shall comply with the requirements of 14-2.2.5.

The means of egress from detention and correctional occupancies that traverse nondetention and noncorrectional spaces must conform to the requirements for detention and correctional occupancies. However, if a 2-hour fire barrier and associated opening protectives located between a detention or correctional occupancy and another occupancy (e.g., business) qualify as a horizontal exit, then the means of egress system in the business occupancy need comply only with the appropriate requirements contained in Chapters 26 and 27.

14-1.2.5 Any area with a hazard of contents classified higher than that of the detention or correctional occupancy and located in the same building shall be protected as required in 14-3.2.

This paragraph regulates those spaces in a detention and correctional occupancy that contain more hazardous materials (in quantity or type) than are usually found in such an occupancy. Spaces, such as rooms used for the storage of highly combustible materials, trash collection rooms, and paint shops, must be protected in accordance with 14-3.2.

14-1.2.6 Nondetention or noncorrectional related occupancies classified as containing high hazard contents shall not be permitted in buildings housing detention or correctional occupancies.

This paragraph prohibits another occupancy containing highly hazardous materials (such as flammable liquids storage) from being located in a building housing detention and correctional occupancies. It is not the intent of this paragraph to exclude normal storage. The intent is to prevent the conversion of a portion of a detention and correctional facility to a warehouse that contains a larger quantity or a more hazardous type of combustible material than would be normally expected in a detention and correctional occupancy. This applies principally to residential areas. For example, industrial areas that are part of the overall detention and correctional facility but are located in a nonresidential-use building may have flammable liquids as part of the industrial process.

14-1.3 Special Definitions.

(a) *Direct Exit.* A direct exit is an exit that serves only one area, and the direct exit has no openings to *other* areas.

The term "direct exit" is defined here so that its particular meaning can be utilized in Exception No. 2 to 14-3.7.1, which addresses the subdivision of building spaces by means of smoke barriers.

(b) *Fire Barrier.* See Chapters 3 and 6.

(c) *Fire Compartment.* See Chapters 3 and 6.

(d) *Residential Housing Area.* Includes sleeping areas and any contiguous day room, group activity space, or other common spaces for customary access of residents.

(e) *Sally Port (Security Vestibule).* A compartment provided with two or more doors where the intended purpose is to prevent continuous and unobstructed passage by allowing the release of only one door at a time.

See 14-2.5.4.

(f) *Smoke Barrier.* See Chapters 3 and 6.

(g) *Smoke Compartment.* See Chapters 3 and 6.

14-1.4 Classification of Occupancy.

14-1.4.1* For applications of the life safety requirements that follow, the resident user category is divided into five groups:

Use Condition I — Free Egress
Free movement is allowed from sleeping areas, and other spaces where access or occupancy is permitted, to the exterior via means of egress that meet the requirements of the *Code*.

In facilities classified as Use Condition I, there are no physical restrictions on the means of egress, such as locks. The occupants are capable of self-preservation. An example is a work release center where the doors are not locked (*see Figure A-14-1.4.1*). Because the means of egress system is kept unlocked, occupants are as free to escape a fire emergency as occupants of any other residential type of occupancy. Therefore, Use Condition I detention and correctional occupancies are exempted from the requirements of Chapter 14 by 14-1.4.3 and must meet the requirements of some other occupancy chapter, such as Chapter 16 for new hotels and dormitories. (*See 14-1.4.3.*)

Use Condition II — Zoned Egress
Free movement is allowed from sleeping areas and any other occupied smoke compartment to one or more other smoke compartments.

The residents of a Use Condition II facility have the freedom to move within the building, including the freedom to move from their rooms, across the smoke barrier, and into a separate smoke compartment. Movement through the exit door in the exterior wall to the outside is impeded by locked doors that are permitted to be unlocked manually at the door. (*See Figure A-14-1.4.1.*)

Use Condition III — Zoned Impeded Egress

Free movement is allowed within individual smoke compartments, such as within a residential unit comprised of individual sleeping rooms and group activity space, with egress impeded by remote control release of means of egress from such smoke compartment to another smoke compartment.

The residents of a Use Condition III facility are free to move outside their rooms but are confined to the smoke compartment that contains their rooms. Movement to an adjoining smoke compartment is impeded by locked doors within the smoke barrier that must be equipped with remote control release. Movement through the exit door in the exterior wall to the outside is impeded by locked doors that are permitted to be unlocked manually at the door. (*See Figure A-14-1.4.1.*)

Use Condition IV — Impeded Egress

Free movement is restricted from an occupied space. Remote controlled release is provided to permit movement from all sleeping rooms, activity spaces, and other occupied areas within the smoke compartment to other smoke compartment(s).

The residents of Use Condition IV facilities are locked in their sleeping rooms. Locks on sleeping room doors must be equipped with remote control release. Movement to an adjoining smoke compartment is impeded by locked doors within the smoke barrier that must be equipped with remote control release. Movement through the exit door in the exterior wall to the outside is impeded by locked doors that are permitted to be unlocked manually at the door. (*See Figure A-14-1.4.1.*)

Use Condition V — Contained

Free movement is restricted from an occupied space. Staff controlled manual release at each door is provided to permit movement from all sleeping rooms, activity spaces, and other occupied areas within the smoke compartment to other smoke compartment(s).

In Use Condition V facilities, all locks are manually operated at the individual door. (*See Figure A-14-1.4.1.*) This places a heavy demand on staff to open the doors in an emergency. The movement of the residents of the Use Condition V facilities is severely restricted. Therefore, the most stringent requirements of Chapter 14 apply.

A-14-1.4.1 Users and occupants of detention and correctional facilities at various times can be expected to include staff, visitors, and residents. The extent and nature of facility utilization will vary according to type of facility, its function, and programs.

Figure A-14-1.4.1 illustrates the five use conditions.

As part of the definitions of Use Condition II through Use Condition V, reference is made to smoke compartments and the type of locking (none, remote release, or manual operation) used for smoke barrier doors. A facility without a smoke barrier can still qualify as meeting the requirements for one of these Use Conditions by providing for movement to a location judged to be equivalent to a smoke compartment, such as (1) a public way, (2) a building separated from the space in question by either adequate fire resistance rated construction or distance, or (3) an adequately sized outside holding area located at a safe distance. The locking operation of the door to this alternate location cannot be more stringent than that allowed for the smoke barrier door of the corresponding Use Condition (i.e., no locking for Use Condition II, remote release for Use Conditions III and IV, and manual operation for Use Condition V). (*Also see 14-3.7 and Figure 14-13.*)

Note that in Figure A-14-1.4.1, "Locked" (L) designates manual unlocking operation at the door.

14-1.4.2* To classify as Use Condition III or IV, the arrangement, accessibility, and security of the release mechanism(s) used for emergency egress shall be such that the minimum available staff, at any time, can promptly release the locks.

A-14-1.4.2 Prompt operation is intended to be accomplished in the period of time between detection of fire by either the smoke detector(s) required by 14-3.4 or by other means (whichever comes first), and the advent of intolerable conditions forcing emergency evacuation. Fire tests have indicated that the time available is a function of the volume and height of the space involved and the rate of fire development. In traditional single-story corridor arrangements, the time between detection by smoke detectors and the advent of lethal conditions down to head height can be as short as approximately 3 minutes. In addition, it should be expected that approximately

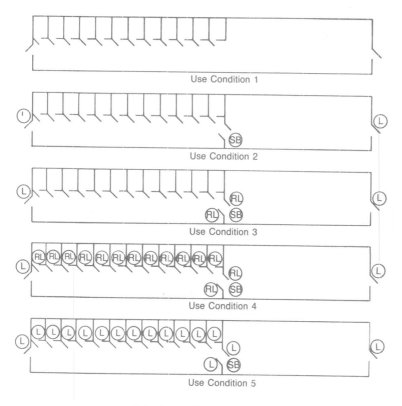

Figure A-14-1.4.1

Use Condition 1

Use Condition 2

Use Condition 3

Use Condition 4

Use Condition 5

Detention and Correctional Use Conditions

(L) Locked

(RL) Locked—Remote Release or Equivalent

(SB) Smoke Barrier or Horizontal Exit

1 minute will be required to evacuate all the occupants of a threatened smoke compartment once the locks are released. In this example, a prompt release time would be 2 minutes.

The major requirements noted in this paragraph are that the area must be under continuous supervision, and a sufficient number of staff must be present and must have the necessary keys readily available to release the locks.

14-1.4.3 Areas housing occupancies corresponding to Use Condition I — Free Egress shall conform to the requirements of residential occupancies under this *Code*.

The *Code* intends that detention and correctional occupancies in which the occupants are not locked in at any time are to be classified as residential occupancies and,

thus, meet the requirements of Chapter 16, 18, or 20, as appropriate. Those buildings that permit free egress, although used as correctional occupancies, are not classified as detention and correctional occupancies under this *Code*. A facility equipped with locking devices on its doors cannot be classified as Use Condition I, since the locks could be used in the future. Instead, depending on the locks' mode of operation (remote or manual), the corresponding Use Condition should be assigned, and the requirements of Chapter 14 followed. A facility can be classified as Use Condition I only if the locking devices are physically removed.

14-1.5 **Classification of Hazard of Contents.** The classification of hazard of contents shall be as defined in Section 4-2.

14-1.6 Minimum Construction Requirements.

14-1.6.1 For the purpose of 14-1.6, stories shall be counted starting with the primary level of exit discharge. For the purposes of this section, the primary level of exit discharge of a building shall be that floor that is level with or above finished grade on the exterior wall line for 50 percent or more of its perimeter. Building levels below the primary level shall not be counted as a story in determining the height of the building.

See Figure 14-2 for method of counting stories.

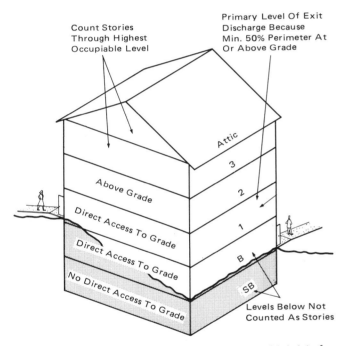

Figure 14-2. Method of Counting Stories, per 14-1.6.1, for Use with 14-1.6.3. If attic were judged to be occupiable, the figure would depict a four-story building.

14-1.6.2 A residential housing area complying with 14-3.1.2 shall be considered as a one-story building for purposes of applying 14-1.6.3.

The provisions of 14-3.1.2 address multilevel housing areas for which the vertical separation between the lowest floor level and the uppermost floor level does not exceed 13 ft (4.0 m), but the paragraph does not limit the number of levels [see *Figure A-14-3.1.2(c)*]. A multilevel housing area meeting all the requirements of

14-3.1.2 is treated as a single story in determining required building construction type in accordance with 14-1.6.3.

14-1.6.3 Detention and correctional occupancies shall be limited to the following types of building construction (*see 6-2.1*):

Table 14-1.6.3

Type of Construction	1 Story with Basement	1 Story without Basement	2 Story	3 Story	>3 Story and not more than 75 ft (23 m) in Height	>75 ft (23 m) in Height
I (443) I (332) II (222)	X	X	X	X	X	X†
II (111)	X††	X	X††	N.P.	N.P.	N.P.
III (211) IV (2HH) V (111)	X††	X††	X††	N.P.	N.P.	N.P.
II (000) III (200) V (000)	X†	X†	X†	N.P.	N.P.	N.P.

X: Permitted types of construction
X†: Permitted if the entire building is protected throughout by an approved supervised automatic sprinkler system in accordance with Section 7-7
X††: X† applies in buildings where Use Condition V is used
N.P.: Not Permitted

The Code recognizes that locked doors to the outside will be reluctantly unlocked, slowly unlocked, or never unlocked. Therefore, the *Code* relies on the "defend in place" or "protect in place" strategy contained in the commentary to 14-1.1.5. Paragraph 14-1.6.3 establishes minimum construction requirements to help ensure the structural integrity of the building for the time required to release residents to the outside or hold them in a fire compartment or smoke compartment.

Table 14-1.6.3 establishes minimum construction types for detention and correctional occupancies. Under some conditions, certain building construction types are prohibited from being occupied for detention/correctional occupancy use, even if protected by automatic sprinklers. The automatic sprinkler requirements contained in this table are based on construction type. Automatic sprinkler protection may also be required by other sections of this *Code*.

(See NFPA 220, *Standard on Types of Building Construction,*[8] for definitions of types of construction. *Also see 6-2.1 and Table A-6-2.1.*)

14-1.6.4 All interior walls and partitions in Type I or Type II construction shall be of noncombustible or limited-combustible construction.

The incapability for self-preservation of detention and correctional facility residents caused by imposed security mandates that the integrity of building construction under fire conditions be maintained. Thus, although NFPA 220, *Standard on Types of Building Construction,*[8] does not regulate the combustibility of interior nonbearing walls and partitions, 14-1.6.4 allows for credit to be taken for Type I or Type II construction in new detention and correctional occupancies only if such interior walls and partitions are of noncombustible or limited-combustible construction. For definitions of the terms noncombustible and limited-combustible, see Chapter 3 of this *Code* and NFPA 220.

14-1.7 **Occupant Load.** The occupant load for which means of egress shall be provided for any floor shall be the maximum number of persons intended to occupy that floor, but not less than one person for each 120 sq ft (11.1 sq m) gross floor area.

This paragraph establishes a factor from which an occupant load may be determined. The means of egress system must be sized to handle whichever is larger: the number of persons intended to occupy the space or the number of persons calculated by using the occupant load factor.

The *Code* intends that the occupant load factor be used only for sizing the means of egress, not for limiting the number of persons within a space. If a means of egress can accommodate an occupant load larger than that calculated using the occupant load factor provided in 14-1.7, the *Code* does not prohibit such a load. In a facility with excess means of egress capacity, plumbing codes, sanitary codes, sociological considerations, and common sense will help determine the maximum occupant load.

SECTION 14-2   Means of Egress Requirements

14-2.1 **General.** Means of egress shall comply with Chapter 5.

Exception: As otherwise provided or modified in this section.

14-2.2 **Means of Egress Components.**

14-2.2.1 Components of means of egress shall be limited to the types described in 14-2.2.2 through 14-2.2.7.

Chapter 14 recognizes the following means of egress components as described in Chapter 5: doors (5-2.1), stairs (5-2.2), smokeproof enclosures (5-2.3), horizontal exits (5-2.4), ramps (5-2.5), and exit passageways (5-2.6). However, Chapter 14 often modifies the provisions of Chapter 5 applicable to those means of egress components. For example, although the Chapter 5 provisions that apply to horizontal exits would limit a horizontal exit to providing a maximum of 50 percent of the number of exits or 50 percent of the total egress capacity, Chapter 14 encourages the voluntary use of horizontal exits by permitting up to 100 percent of the exits to be reached by way of horizontal exits if additional criteria can be met.

Chapter 5 considers escalators, moving walks, and fire escape stairs acceptable means of egress only if they are part of an existing occupancy and are specifically recognized by an occupancy chapter. They are not permitted in the means of egress system of a new detention and correctional occupancy. Fire escape ladders, alternating tread devices, and slide escapes are not recognized by Chapter 14 as part of an egress system in new detention and correctional occupancies. Areas of refuge (*see 5-2.12*) are not required. However, reference can be made to the provisons of 14-3.7, which addresses mandatory subdivision of building spaces by means of smoke barriers.

14-2.2.2 **Doors.** Doors shall comply with 5-2.1.

Exception: As provided in 14-2.11.

14-2.2.3   Stairs.

14-2.2.3.1   Stairs shall comply with 5-2.2.

Older editions of the *Code* contained an exception to 14-2.2.3.1 that exempted handrails and guards from the requirement for intermediate rails designed to keep children from falling through the spaces between rails. The exception still applies to detention and correctional occupancies but now appears as Exception No. 2 to 5-2.2.4.5(f) and Exception No. 2 to 5-2.2.4.6(c). The rationale for this exception is that these facilities are used only by adults or older juveniles, and intermediate railings may interfere with visual observation.

14-2.2.3.2   Spiral stairs complying with 5-2.2.2.7 are permitted for access to and between staff locations.

Paragraph 14-2.2.3.2 permits spiral stairs conforming to 5-2.2.2.7 for staff use only. Note that Chapter 5 restricts the use of spiral stairs to those serving an occupant load of 5 or fewer persons. Thus, these provisions prohibit a spiral stair from being part of the required means of egress system within areas occupied by residents.

14-2.2.4   Smokeproof Enclosures.   Smokeproof enclosures shall comply with 5-2.3.

This paragraph does not mandate the use of smokeproof enclosures but does recognize a smokeproof enclosure as part of the means of egress system in a detention/correctional occupancy only if the smokeproof enclosure meets the requirements of 5-2.3. An example of an occupancy requiring a smokeproof enclosure can be found in 19-2.11.1. In this example, nonsprinklered, existing, high rise apartment buildings are required to be provided with smokeproof enclosures in accordance with 5-2.3.

14-2.2.5   Horizontal Exits.   Horizontal exits shall comply with 5-2.4, modified as follows:

(a) At least 6 sq ft (.56 sq m) of accessible space per occupant shall be provided on each side of the horizontal exit for the total number of people in adjoining compartments.

Subsection 5-2.4 requires at least 3 sq ft (0.28 sq m) of accumulation space per occupant on each side of the horizontal exit. This section requires 6 sq ft (0.56 sq m) per occupant. The reasons for this requirement include possible conflicts among the residents, the anticipated time spent in the refuge area, and the fact that horizontal exits are permitted to comprise 100 percent of required exits in detention and correctional occupancies in accordance with 14-2.2.5(b).

(b) Horizontal exits shall be permitted to comprise 100 percent of the exits required provided that an exit, other than a horizontal exit, is accessible in some other (not necessarily adjacent) fire compartment without requiring return through the compartment of fire origin.

This permits horizontal exits to comprise 100 percent of the exits from any fire compartment as long as it is not necessary to travel through the compartment of fire origin in order to reach a door to the outside (i.e., the compartment is not "dead-ended").

In Figure 14-3, all compartments except compartment F satisfy the above rule. Fire compartment F would require a door to the outside in order to preclude the need to travel through compartment E, which could be the area of fire origin, to get to the outside of the building.

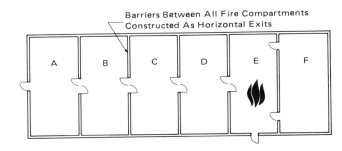

Figure 14-3.   *Horizontal Exits Correctly Comprise 100 Percent of Total Exits from Fire Compartments B, C, and D. Compartment F would require the addition of an exit door that opens directly to the outside in order to reach the outside of the building without traveling through fire compartment E. Compartments A and E comply with the Code, using one horizontal exit and one exit door directly to the exterior of the building.*

Due to the practical difficulties of using vertical exit travel to the outside in detention and correctional occupancies, including the reluctance of staff to unlock doors, special recognition is given to horizontal travel and the use of horizontal exits. One hundred percent of the total required exit capacity for a given fire area may be provided by horizontal exits, as previously explained. In the event a horizontal exit also serves as a smoke barrier, refer to 14-2.4.3 and 14-3.7.

(c)* Ducts shall be allowed to penetrate horizontal exits in accordance with Exception No. 3 to 5-2.4.3.3 if protected by combination fire dampers/smoke leakage-rated dampers that meet the smoke damper actuation requirements of 6-3.5.

The provisions of 14-2.2.5(c) are new to this edition of the *Code*. Paragraph 5-2.4.3.3 is also new to this edition and specifically states that fire barriers used in creating a horizontal exit are prohibited from penetration by ducts. To promote the use of horizontal exits in detention and correctional occupancies without burdening a facility with regard to duct pentrations, 14-2.2.5(c) and the corresponding Exception No. 3 to 5-2.4.3.3 were developed. The Committee reasoned that if smoke detection is used to shut a combination fire damper/smoke leakage-rated damper early in a fire, the fire- and smoke-resisting features of the horizontal exit can be reestablished at points where ducts penetrate the barrier.

A-14-2.2.5(c)   In order to help promote the use of horizontal exits in detention and correctional occupancies because horizontal exits provide an especially effective egress system for an occupancy where the occupants, due to security concerns, will not commonly be released to the outside. This provision offers a *Code*-specified equivalent alternative to the Chapter 5 requirement that horizontal exits not be penetrated by ducts. The intended continuity of the fire resistance-rated and smoke resisting barrier is maintained by requiring that duct penetrations of horizontal exits be protected by combination fire damper/smoke leakage-rated dampers that will close upon activation of a smoke detector and a heat actuated mechanism before the barrier's ability to resist the passage of smoke and fire is compromised.

14-2.2.6   Ramps. Ramps shall comply with 5-2.5.

This paragraph does not mandate the use of ramps but does recognize a ramp as part of the means of egress system only if the ramp meets the requirements of 5-2.5.

14-2.2.7   Exit Passageways. Exit passageways shall comply with 5-2.6.

This paragraph does not mandate the use of exit passageways but does recognize an exit passageway as part of the means of egress system only if the exit passageway meets the requirements of 5-2.6.

14-2.3   Capacity of Means of Egress.

14-2.3.1   The capacity of any required means of egress shall be in accordance with Section 5-3.

14-2.3.2   Aisles, corridors, and ramps required for access or exit shall be at least 4 ft (122 cm) in width.

14-2.3.3   For residents' sleeping room door widths, see 14-2.11.3.

14-2.4   Number of Exits. (*See also Section 5-4.*)

14-2.4.1   At least two exits of the types permitted in 14-2.2, remotely located from each other, shall be provided for each occupied story of the building.

14-2.4.2   At least two exits of the types permitted in 14-2.2, remotely located from each other, shall be accessible from each fire or smoke compartment.

14-2.4.3*   At least one approved exit shall be accessible from each fire compartment and each required smoke compartment into which residents may be moved in a fire emergency, with the exits so arranged that egress shall not require return through the zone of fire origin.

A-14-2.4.3   An exit is not necessary for each individual fire compartment or smoke compartment if there is access to an exit through other fire compartments or smoke compartments without passing through the fire compartment or smoke compartment of origin.

See commentary following 14-2.2.5(b) and Figure 14-3

14-2.5   Arrangement of Means of Egress. (*See also Section 5-5.*)

14-2.5.1 Every sleeping room shall have a door leading directly to an exit access corridor.

Exception No. 1: If there is an exit door opening directly to the outside from the room at the ground level.

Exception No. 2: One adjacent room, such as a dayroom, group activity space, or other common spaces shall be permitted to intervene. Where sleeping rooms directly adjoin a dayroom or group activity space that is utilized for access to an exitway, such sleeping rooms shall be permitted to open directly to the dayroom or space and shall be separated in elevation by a one-half or full story height. (See 14-3.1.2.)

Figure 14-4 illustrates the requirements of Exception No. 2.

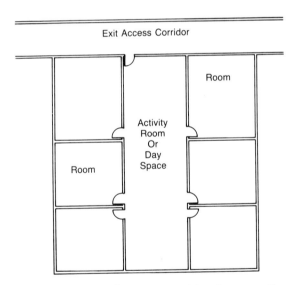

Figure 14-4.   One Adjacent Room May Intervene Between Sleeping Room and Exit Access Corridor. Sleeping rooms may be separated in elevation by ¹/₂ to 1 story. (See Exception No. 2 to 14-2.5.1.)

14-2.5.2 No exit or exit access shall contain a corridor, hallway, or aisle having a pocket or dead end exceeding 50 ft (15 m) for Use Conditions II, III, or IV and 20 ft (6.1 m) for Use Condition V.

Figure 14-5 illustrates the requirements of 14-2.5.2.

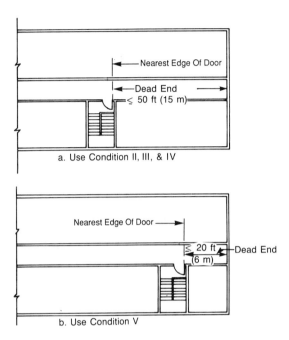

Figure 14-5.   Dead-End Corridor Requirements. (See 14-2.5.2.)

14-2.5.3 No common path of travel shall exceed 50 ft (15 m).

Exception: A common path of travel shall be permitted for the first 100 ft (30 m) in a building protected throughout by an approved automatic sprinkler system in accordance with 14-3.5.3.

The limitation on common path of travel for detention and correctional occupancies first appeared in the 1988 Edition of the *Code*. In multilevel residential housing areas (*see 14-3.1.2*) where individual levels do not constitute floors, the common path of travel limitation will dictate where a second exit access from any given level is necessary. (*See Figure 14-6.*)

14-2.5.4 A sally port shall be permitted in a means of egress where there are provisions for continuous and unobstructed travel through the sally port during an emergency exit condition.

During routine and nonfire emergency conditions, a sally port or security vestibule is designed so that the door at one end of the vestibule is securely locked whenever the door at the opposite end is open. When one door is

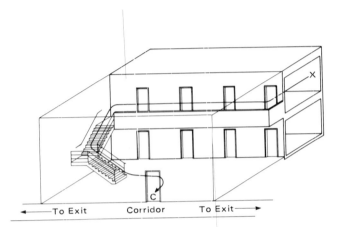

Figure 14-6. *Common Path of Travel Limitations. If distance x to c exceeds 50 ft (15 m) [100 ft (30 m) if building is sprinklered], second exit access required for upper level. If multilevel housing area is large, common path of travel limitation could require a remote, second exit access door to corridor.*

opened, the door through which entrance is made is closed and locked; the door at the opposite end is then unlocked and opened to provide exit from the vestibule. The sally port acts as a security device that prevents a continuous flow of people from "storming" the exits. Under fire conditions, it would severely restrict the exit flow of occupants and prevent hose lines from being run through the openings. Therefore, if a sally port is to be permitted as part of a required means of egress, the door controls must be overridden to allow continuous and unobstructed passage in accordance with 14-2.5.4.

Figure 14-7 illustrates the requirements of 14-2.5.4.

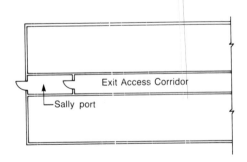

Figure 14-7. *Requirements for Sally Port or Security Vestibule. If sally port is part of required means of egress, both doors of sally port must be capable of being opened at the same time to provide unobstructed egress. (See 14-2.5.4.)*

14-2.6 Travel Distance to Exits.

14-2.6.1 Travel distance:

(a) Between any room door required as exit access and an exit shall not exceed 100 ft (30 m);

(b) Between any point in a room and an exit shall not exceed 150 ft (45 m); and

(c) Between any point in a sleeping room to the door of that room shall not exceed 50 ft (15 m).

Exception No. 1: The maximum permitted travel distance in (a) or (b) above shall be increased by 50 ft (15 m) in buildings protected throughout by an approved automatic sprinkler system or smoke control system.

Exception No. 2: The maximum permitted travel distance in (c) above shall be increased to 100 ft (30 m) in open dormitories where the enclosing walls of the dormitory space are at least of smoketight construction. Where travel distance to the exit access door from any point within the dormitory exceeds 50 ft (15 m), at least two exit access doors remotely located from each other shall be provided.

Travel distance is measured to the closest exit only, not to both exits required by 14-2.4. Figure 14-8 illustrates the requirements of 14-2.6.1.

14-2.7 Discharge from Exits.

14-2.7.1 Exits shall be permitted to discharge into a fenced or walled courtyard, provided that not more than two walls of the courtyard are the building walls from which exit is being made. Enclosed yards or courts shall be of sufficient size to accommodate all occupants at a minimum distance of 50 ft (15 m) from the building with a net area of 15 sq ft (1.4 sq m) per person.

Figures 14-9a and 14-9b illustrate 14-2.7.1.

14-2.7.2 All exits shall be permitted to discharge through the level of exit discharge. The requirements of 5-7.2 are waived provided that not more than 50 percent of the exits discharge into a single fire compartment.

The provisions of 5-7.2 establish criteria under which up to 50 percent of the required exits, in either number

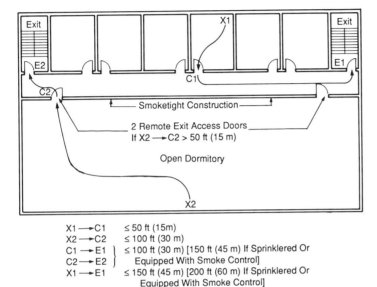

X1 ─→ C1 ≤ 50 ft (15m)
X2 ─→ C2 ≤ 100 ft (30 m)
C1 ─→ E1 } ≤ 100 ft (30 m) [150 ft (45 m) If Sprinklered Or
C2 ─→ E2 } Equipped With Smoke Control]
X1 ─→ E1 ≤ 150 ft (45 m) [200 ft (60 m) If Sprinklered Or
Equipped With Smoke Control]
X2 ─→ E2 ≤ 200 ft (60 m) [250 ft (76 m) If Sprinklered
Or Equipped With Smoke Control]

Figure 14-8. Maximum Travel Distance to Exits in New Detention and Correctional Occupancies (see 14-2.6.1). The travel distance is measured along the natural path of travel (see 5-6.2). "Sprinklered" means that the entire building is protected by a complete, approved automatic extinguishing system. "Smoke Control" means that the entire building or fire area is equipped with a system to control the movement of smoke in accordance with Section 7-3.

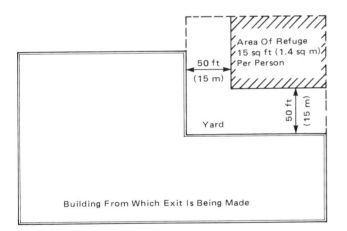

Figure 14-9a. Exit Discharge into a Fenced Yard. (See 14-2.7.1.)

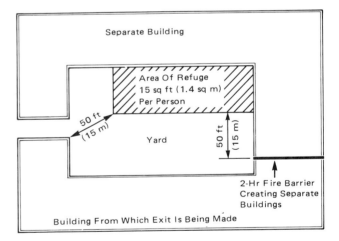

Figure 14-9b. Exit Discharge into an Enclosed Yard. (See 14-2.7.1.)

or capacity, may discharge through the level of exit discharge, with the other 50 percent required to discharge directly to the outside. Because of security concerns and the belief that doors to the exterior will not be readily unlocked in detention and correctional occupancies, 14-2.7.2 allows 100 percent of the exits to discharge through the level of exit discharge. This is permitted only if a fire separation that creates at least two fire compartments is provided on the level of exit discharge. Not more

than one-half of the exits (in number and capacity) may discharge into any one fire compartment.

14-2.8 **Illumination of Means of Egress.** Illumination shall be in accordance with Section 5-8.

14-2.9 **Emergency Lighting.** Emergency lighting shall be in accordance with Section 5-9.

14-2.10 **Marking of Means of Egress.** Exit marking shall be provided in areas accessible to the public in accordance with Section 5-10.

Exception: Exit signs are not required in sleeping areas.

The exemption of exit signs in sleeping areas of detention and correctional occupancies recognizes that persons occupying such areas are familiar with those portions of the facility and know the location of exits. Other portions of the facility may not be as familiar to residents and visitors and, thus, must have proper exit marking in accordance with 14-2.10.

14-2.11 **Special Features.**

14-2.11.1 Doors within means of egress shall be as required in Chapter 5.

Exception: As provided in 14-2.11.2 through 14-2.11.10.

14-2.11.2 Doors shall be permitted to be locked in accordance with the applicable use condition.

This provision overrides the Chapter 5 requirement that all doors within the required means of egress be unlocked from the side from which egress is to be made and, therefore, they must be fully under the control of the building occupants. It recognizes that, in order to function as intended, a detention and correctional occupancy uses various means of locking. Paragraph 14-2.11.2 allows only that means of locking appropriate to a specific use condition. Therefore, a Use Condition II facility, which has more lenient life safety requirements than a Use Condition V facility, cannot contain sleeping rooms that must be individually locked by key. A Use Condition V facility must comply with a more stringent set of requirements than a Use Condition II facility and is permitted to have individual doors manually locked by key.

14-2.11.3* Doors to resident sleeping rooms shall be at least 28 in. (71 cm) in clear width.

A-14-2.11.3 It may be necessary to provide a certain number of resident sleeping rooms with doors providing a minimum clear width of 32 in. (81 cm) (*see 5-2.1.2.1*) in order to

comply with the requirements for the physically handicapped. Such sleeping rooms should be located where there is a direct accessible access to the exterior or to an area of safe refuge. (*See 14-3.7.*)

14-2.11.4 Doors in a means of egress shall be permitted to be of the horizontal sliding type, provided the force to slide the door to its fully open position does not exceed 50 lb (222 N) with a perpendicular force against the door of 50 lb (222 N).

Paragraph 5-2.1.4.1 requires that all doors in a means of egress be side-hinged and swinging. This paragraph allows the use of sliding doors if they meet the specified requirements. In addition, Exception No. 4 to 5-2.1.4.1 recognizes the limited use of other horizontal sliding doors in accordance with the provisions of 5-2.1.14.

14-2.11.5 Doors from areas of refuge to the exterior shall be permitted to be locked with key locks in lieu of locking methods described in 14-2.11.6. The keys to unlock such doors shall be maintained and available at the facility at all times, and the locks shall be operable from the outside.

This paragraph requires that keys be maintained and available. "Available" means readily accessible to staff for use at any time for evacuation of occupants. It is important that (1) the keys required to evacuate occupants are accessible at all times, (2) the staff is trained in the location and use of keys, and (3) the staff has authorization and standing orders to immediately unlock doors that lead from areas of refuge to the exterior during fire emergency conditions. This will prevent the loss of time that can occur while waiting for authorization from administrative authorities before doors can be unlocked.

14-2.11.6* Any remote control release used in a means of egress shall be provided with reliable means of operation, remotely located from the resident living areas, to release locks on all doors.

Exception: Provisions for remote control locking and unlocking of occupied rooms in Use Condition IV are not required provided not more than ten locks are necessary to be unlocked in order to move all occupants from one smoke compartment to an area of refuge as promptly as required for remote con-

trol unlocking. Unlocking of all necessary locks shall be accomplished with no more than two separate keys. (See 14-3.7.7 for smoke barrier doors.)

A-14-2.11.6 A remote position is generally a control point where a number of doors can be unlocked simultaneously, either mechanically or electrically. In areas where there are a number of sleeping rooms, it is not practical for attendants to unlock doors individually. Doors in an exit should be unlocked prior to unlocking sleeping room doors.

This section of the *Code* does not intend to prohibit Use Condition V facilities, nor does it intend to limit Use Condition V facilities to 10 manually released locks.

"Remote" means outside the area where occupants are restrained. It is not necessary to have the remote unlocking mechanism in a separate fire area, although this may be beneficial. Doors within the exit should be unlocked prior to unlocking sleeping room doors. This will prevent jamming of the exit door caused by several persons exerting pressure on the door.

The Exception to 14-2.11.6 applies to facilities that are seeking classification as Use Condition IV but that have a need for up to ten locks that must be manually released at the door. Where remote locking is required by Use Condition IV, it must be provided, except as addressed by the exception. The exception permits up to ten manual locks in order to allow occupants to move to another fire compartment or smoke compartment while permitting the facility to qualify as having provided remote release. The use of a limited number (i.e., maximum of ten) of manual locks in addition to the possibility of hundreds of remotely released locks within the same facility does not impose a Use Condition V classification. This exception may apply in situations where there are fewer than ten doors if a door is secured with more than one lock. Figures 14-10a and 14-10b depict two typical arrangements that illustrate this exception.

This exception has been misinterpreted to mean that a Use Condition V detention/correctional facility (which, by definition, requires manual unlocking at each locked door) may have a maximum of ten such manual locks. A Use Condition V facility is permitted to have any number of manual locks. In fact, the exception applies *only*

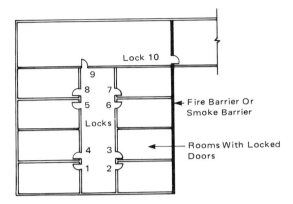

Figure 14-10a. *Maximum of Ten Manually Unlocked Doors Where Each Door is Equipped with a Single Key-Operated Lock. (See Exception to 14-2.11.6.)*

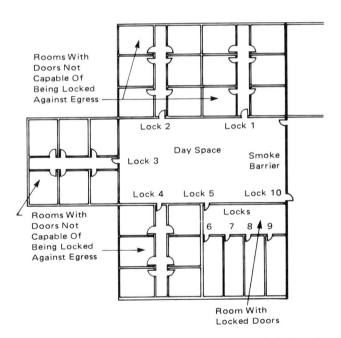

Figure 14-10b. *Maximum of Ten Manually Unlocked Locks with Multiple-Door Areas Secured by a Door with a Single Key-Operated Lock. (See Exception to 14-2.11.6.)*

to use Condition IV facilities and allows a facility to retain its classification as Use Condition IV (i.e., remote release) provided there are ten or fewer manually released locks and provided unlocking can be achieved with a maximum of two keys.

The speed with which the doors can be unlocked and the occupants removed to a safe location is critical. If the ten locks cannot be rapidly released by manual unlocking due to staffing restrictions or for any other reasons, remote unlocking must be used. If doors are equipped with locking devices, it is assumed that the locks will be used, and they must be counted as part of the total number of locks.

14-2.11.7 All remote-control release operated doors shall be provided with a redundant means of operation as follows:

(a) Power-operated sliding doors or power-operated locks shall be so constructed that in the event of power failure, a manual mechanical means to release and open the doors is provided at each door, and either emergency power in accordance with 5-9.2.3 is provided for the power operation, or a remote control manual mechanical release is provided.

(b) Mechanically operated sliding doors or mechanically operated locks shall be provided with a manual mechanical means at each door to release and open the door.

14-2.11.8 Doors unlocked by means of remote control under emergency conditions shall not automatically relock when closed unless specific action is taken at the remote control location to enable doors to relock.

Paragraph 14-2.11.8 requires that, once doors are unlocked remotely under emergency conditions, they cannot automatically relock if they reclose unless deliberate action is taken to lock them. This deliberate action can be taken at the individual door or at the remote location.

14-2.11.9 Standby emergency power shall be provided for all electrically power-operated sliding doors and power-operated locks. Power shall be arranged to automatically operate within 10 seconds upon failure of normal power and to maintain the necessary power source for at least 1½ hours.

Exception: This provision is not applicable for facilities with ten locks or less complying with the exception in 14-2.11.6.

14-2.11.10 The provisions of 5-2.1.5.2 for stairway reentry do not apply.

SECTION 14-3 Protection

14-3.1 Protection of Vertical Openings.

This subsection specifies the protection required to maintain floor-to-floor separation, which helps to prevent the products of combustion from moving vertically through the building.

14-3.1.1 Any stairway, ramp, elevator, hoistway, light or ventilation shaft, chute or other vertical opening between stories shall be enclosed in accordance with Section 6-2.

Exception No. 1: Stairs that do not connect a corridor, do not connect more than two levels, and do not serve as a means of egress.

Exception No. 2: Multilevel residential housing areas in accordance with 14-3.1.2.

Exception No. 3: In residential housing areas protected throughout by an approved automatic sprinkler system, unprotected vertical openings are permitted in accordance with the conditions of 6-2.4.5, provided that the height between the lowest and highest finished floor levels does not exceed 23 ft (7.0 m). The number of levels is not restricted. Residential housing areas subdivided in accordance with 14-3.8.1 are permitted to be considered as part of the communicating space.

Exception No. 4: Atriums in accordance with 6-2.4.6 are permitted.

The convenience stair addressed by Exception No. 1 is illustrated in Figures 14-11a and 14-11b.

Paragraph 6-2.4.5 restricts vertical openings from connecting more than three floor levels. Exception No. 3 to 14-3.1.1 addresses typical multilevel housing areas that utilize staggered partial levels as depicted in Figure 14-12. The exception modifies the three-floor restriction by allowing a 23-ft (7-m) height limitation between the lowest and highest finished floor levels so as to permit greater flexibility in the design and use of detention and correctional occupancies. The exception applies only to facilities where the residential housing areas are protected throughout by automatic sprinklers.

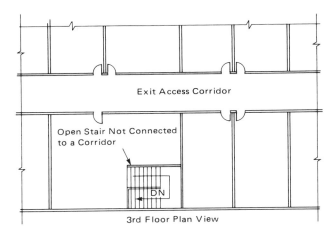

Figure 14-11a. *Plan View of Convenience Stair Allowed by Exception No. 1 to 14-3.1.1.*

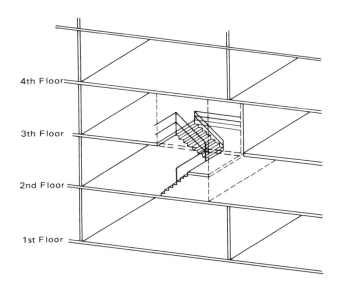

Figure 14-11b. *Open Convenience Stair as Allowed by Exception No. 1 to 14-3.1.1.*

Exception No. 3 to 14-3.1.1 has been revised in the 1991 Edition of the *Code* to clarify that a residential housing unit that complies with the requirements of Table 14-3.8.1 is considered to be part of the communicating space addressed by 6-2.4.5. This clarification prevents the *Code* user from needlessly complying with 6-2.4.5(d), which would require a fully sprinklered residential area to be separated from all rooms abutting a communicating space (e.g., a day room with a high ceiling) by means

of smoke-resisting construction. All openings, including doors, from resident sleeping rooms to the day space would be required to have smoketight opening protectives. This would place an undue burden on such facilities. Instead of requiring smoketight separations between each resident sleeping room and the day space, the Committee judged that adequate life safety is provided if the residential housing unit is subdivided in accordance with the provisions of 14-3.8.1. Also, compliance with 6-2.4.5(h) would then be impractical. Exception No. 2 was added to 6-2.4.5(d) to prevent this portion of Exception No. 3 to 14-3.1.1 from conflicting with the provisions of 6-2.4.5(d).

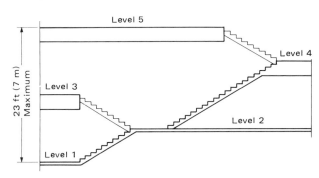

Figure 14-12. *Unprotected Vertical Openings in Sprinklered Housing Area Allowed by Exception No. 3 to 14-3.1.1.*

14-3.1.2 Multilevel residential housing areas are permitted without enclosure protection between levels, provided all the following conditions are met:

(a)* The entire normally occupied area, including all communicating floor levels, is sufficiently open and unobstructed so that it may be assumed that a fire or other dangerous condition in any part will be readily obvious to the occupants or supervisory personnel in the area.

A-14-3.1.2(a) It is not the intent of this requirement to restrict room face separations, which restrict visibility from the common space into individual sleeping rooms.

(b) Exit capacity is sufficient to provide simultaneously for all the occupants of all communicating levels and areas, with all communicating levels in the same fire area being considered as a single floor area for purposes of determination of required exit capacity.

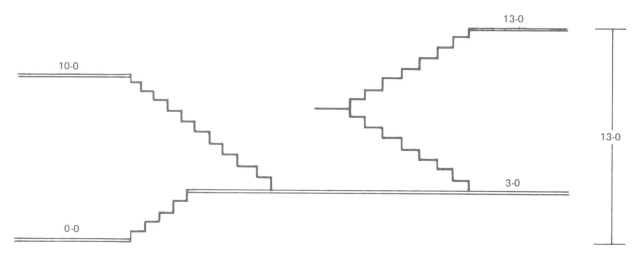

Figure A-14-3.1.2(c)

(c)* The height between the highest and lowest finished floor levels does not exceed 13 ft (4.0 m). The number of levels is not restricted.

A-14-3.1.2(c)   The maximum vertical separation between the lowest floor level and the uppermost floor level is restricted to 13 ft (4.0 m). Figure A-14-3.1.2(c) illustrates how the height is to be determined.

Whereas 14-3.1.1 Exception No. 3 allows multilevel housing areas with a maximum 23-ft (7-m) height between the lowest and the highest finished floor levels if the housing areas are fully sprinklered, 14-3.1.2 allows similar nonsprinklered multilevel housing areas but limits the height to 13 ft (4 m).

14-3.2 **Protection from Hazards.**

14-3.2.1* **Hazardous Areas.** Any hazardous area shall be protected in accordance with Section 6-4. The areas in the following table shall be protected as indicated.

Exception: When, in the opinion of the authority having jurisdiction, such areas are no longer incidental to residents' housing, they shall be separated by 2-hour fire barriers in conjunction with automatic sprinkler protection.

Area Description	Separation/Protection
Areas not incidental to resident housing	2-hr
Boiler and fuel-fired heater rooms	2-hr or 1-hr and sprinklers
Commercial cooking equipment	In accordance with 7-2.3
Commissaries	1-hr or sprinklers
Employee locker rooms	1-hr or sprinklers
Hobby/handicraft shops	1-hr or sprinklers
Central or bulk laundries over 100 sq ft (9.3 sq m)	1-hr and sprinklers
Maintenance shops	1-hr or sprinklers
Padded cells	1-hr and sprinklers
Soiled linen rooms	1-hr and sprinklers
Storage rooms > 50 sq ft (4.6 sq m) in area but <100 sq ft (9.3 sq m) in area storing combustible material	1-hr or sprinklers
Storage rooms ≥ 100 sq ft (9.3 sq m) storing combustible materials	1-hr and sprinklers
Trash collection rooms	1-hr and sprinklers

A-14-3.2.1 Furnishings are usually the first items ignited in the detention and correctional environment. The type, quantity, and arrangement of furniture and other combustibles are important factors in determining how fast the fire will develop. Furnishings, including upholstered items and wood items, such as wardrobes, desks, and bookshelves may provide sufficient fuel to result in room flashover. (Flashover refers to full fire involvement of all combustibles within a room once sufficient heat has been built up within the room.)

Combustible loading in any room opening onto a residential housing area should be limited to reduce the potential for room flashover. Rooms in which fuel loads are not controlled, thereby creating a potential for flashover, should be considered hazardous areas. If the separation option of 14-3.2.1 is selected, doors to such rooms, including sleeping rooms, should be self-closing.

It is strongly recommended that padded cells not be used due to their fire record. However, recognizing that they will be used in some cases, provisions for the protection of padded cells are provided. It is recognized that the ³⁄₄-hour fire door will be violated with the "plant on" of the padding, but a ³⁄₄-hour fire door should be the base of the assembly.

Hazardous areas in detention and correctional occupancies are spaces containing materials that, due to their nature (as in the case of flammable liquids) or because of the quantity of combustible materials involved, represent a significantly higher hazard than would otherwise be typical of detention and correctional occupancies. Paragraph 14-3.2.1 requires hazardous areas to be protected. The areas listed in 14-3.2.1 must be protected by the specified fire resistance rated separation, sprinklering, or combination of separation and sprinklering. The list of hazardous areas commonly found in this occupancy was expanded for this edition of the *Code*. The result is a format that is consistent with the -3.2 subsections of many of the other occupancy chapters.

Padded cells are considered to be severe hazard areas due to high heat release, high rate of combustion, and the quantity of smoke produced by padding materials. Therefore, padded cells must be protected by automatic sprinklers and separated by 1-hour construction. Many of the recent multiple-death fires in detention and correctional occupancies have started in padded cells.

Where flammable liquids are handled or stored, NFPA 30, *Flammable and Combustible Liquids Code*,⁹ should

be consulted to establish the minimum criteria necessary to mitigate this hazard. (*See 6-4.3.*)

Even typical housing area furnishings can provide the combustible loading that will allow room flashover to occur. The potential for flashover should be considered, particularly for nonsprinklered multilevel housing areas allowed by 14-3.1.2. Flashover on a lower level could rapidly deteriorate the tenability of conditions on upper levels, as the products of combustion bank down from the ceiling of the housing area, overcoming residents of the upper levels before they can make use of the means of egress system.

14-3.2.2 Where cooking facilities are protected in accordance with 7-2.3, kitchens shall not be required to be provided with roomwide protection.

14-3.3 **Interior Finish.**

14-3.3.1 Interior wall and ceiling finish in corridors, exits, and any space not separated from corridors and exits by a partition capable of retarding the passage of smoke shall be Class A. In all other areas, interior wall and ceiling finish shall be Class A, B, or C in accordance with Section 6-5.

Paragraph 14-3.3.1 requires only that the separating partition be capable of retarding the passage of smoke. The partition must be of substantial construction but is not required to have a fire resistance rating. (*See Chapter 3 for the definition of a smoke barrier.*)

14-3.3.2 Interior floor finish material in corridors and exits shall be Class I in accordance with Section 6-5.

14-3.4 **Detection, Alarm, and Communication Systems.**

See Supplement 2.

14-3.4.1 **General.**

14-3.4.1.1 Detention and correctional occupancies shall be provided with a fire alarm system in accordance with Section 7-6, except as modified below.

14-3.4.1.2 All required fire alarm systems shall be electrically supervised.

14-3.4.1.3 All fire alarm systems and detection systems required in this section shall be provided with a secondary power supply, and the installation shall be in accordance with NFPA 72, *Standard for the Installation, Maintenance, and Use of Protective Signaling Systems.*

14-3.4.2 **Initiation.** Initiation of the required fire alarm system shall be by manual means in accordance with 7-6.2 and by means of any detection devices or detection systems required.

Exception No. 1: Manual fire alarm boxes shall be permitted to be locked provided that staff is present within the subject area when occupied and has keys readily available to unlock the boxes.

Exception No. 2: Manual fire alarm boxes shall be permitted to be located in a staff location, provided that the staff location is attended when the building is occupied and that the staff attendant has direct supervision of the sleeping area.

14-3.4.3 **Notification.**

14-3.4.3.1 **Occupant Notification.** Occupant notification shall be accomplished automatically, without delay, upon operation of any fire alarm initiating device in accordance with 7-6.3. Presignal systems are prohibited.

Exception*: Any smoke detectors required by this chapter are permitted to be arranged to alarm at a constantly attended location only and are not required to accomplish general alarm indication.

A-14-3.4.3.1 **Exception.** The staff at the constantly attended location should have the capability to promptly initiate the general alarm function and contact the fire department or have direct communication with a control room or other location that can initiate the general alarm function and contact the fire department.

Presignal systems are prohibited by 14-3.4.3.1, which requires that notification be provided "without delay." However, the exception does exempt smoke detectors from sounding a general alarm in order to avoid numerous nuisance alarms.

14-3.4.3.2 **Emergency Forces Notification.** Fire department notification shall be accomplished in accordance with 7-6.4.

Exception: Any smoke detectors required by this chapter are not required to transmit an alarm to the fire department.

Where the fire department is not equipped to receive such alarms or where direct transmission to the fire department is not permitted, arrangements are to be made for the prompt notification of the fire department. The second best option is notification by an approved central station alarm system. Paragraph 7-6.4 provides several options for notifying the fire department automatically. Where smoke detectors are provided, they are not required to sound the fire alarm or to transmit a signal to the fire department but are required to sound an alarm at a constantly attended location, unless otherwise specified.

14-3.4.4 **Detection.** An approved automatic smoke detection system shall be installed in accordance with Section 7-6 throughout all resident housing areas.

Exception No. 1: Smoke detectors are not required in sleeping rooms with four or fewer occupants in Use Condition II or III.

Exception No. 2: In buildings protected throughout by an approved automatic sprinkler system installed in accordance with 14-3.5.3, smoke detectors are not required except in corridors, common spaces, and sleeping rooms with more than four occupants.

Exception No. 3: Other arrangements and positioning of smoke detectors shall be permitted to prevent damage or tampering, or for other purposes, provided the function for detecting any fire is fulfilled and the placement of detectors is such that the speed of detection will be equivalent to that provided by the spacing and arrangements described in Section 7-6. This may include the location of detectors in exhaust ducts from cells, behind grilles, or in other locations. The equivalent performance of the design, however, must be acceptable to the authority having jurisdiction in accordance with the equivalency concepts specified in Section 1-6 of this Code.

14-3.5 **Extinguishment Requirements.**

See Supplement 3.

14-3.5.1* High rise buildings shall comply with 14-4.3.

A-14-3.5.1 For purposes of providing control valves and water flow devices, multilevel residential housing areas complying with 14-3.1.2 are considered to be a single floor.

Paragraph 14-3.5.1 refers to 14-4.3, which in turn mandatorily references 30-8.2, which addresses those high rise building provisions applicable to automatic sprinkler systems and standpipes. In addition to the standpipe and automatic sprinkler system requirements, these provisions require that a sprinkler control valve and water flow device be provided for each floor. The appendix note to 14-3.5.1 clarifies that the levels of a multilevel housing area complying with 14-3.1.2 do not constitute multiple floors and, thus, are not required to be provided with individual control valves and water flow devices on each level.

14-3.5.2 Where required by 14-1.6, facilities shall be protected throughout by an approved supervised automatic sprinkler system in accordance with Section 7-7.

14-3.5.3 Where this *Code* permits exceptions for fully sprinklered detention and correctional occupancies, the sprinkler system shall be:

(a) In complete accordance with Section 7-7,
(b) Electrically connected to the fire alarm system, and
(c) Fully supervised.

Paragraphs 14-3.5.2 and 14-3.5.3 indicate that, where automatic sprinklers are installed to comply with the *Code*, the system shall be a complete, approved automatic sprinkler system installed in accordance with NFPA 13, *Standard for the Installation of Sprinkler Systems.*[10] The use of manually operated sprinklers is not recognized by the *Code*. Informal surveys conducted by the Committee indicate no significant problems with the installation, maintenance, and use of automatic sprinkler systems in detention and correctional facilities. The system must also be supervised in accordance with the requirements of 7-7.2 in order to comply with the *Code*.

14-3.5.4 Portable fire extinguishers shall be provided in accordance with 7-7.4.1.

Exception No. 1: *Access to portable fire extinguishers shall be permitted to be locked.*

A-14-3.5.4 Exception No. 1. Where access to portable fire extinguishers is locked, staff should be present on a 24-hour basis and have keys readily available to unlock access to the extinguishers. Where supervision of sleeping areas is from a 24-hour manned staff location, portable fire extinguishers may be provided at the staff location in lieu of other areas.

Exception No. 1 to 14-3.5.4 permits fire extinguishers to be locked. Time is critical when using extinguishers; therefore, keys must be carried by the staff or be readily accessible.

Exception No. 2: Portable fire extinguishers shall be permitted to be located at staff locations only.

14-3.5.5 Standpipe and hose systems shall be provided in accordance with 7-7.4.2 as follows:

(a) Class I standpipe systems shall be provided for any building over two stories in height, and

(b) Class III standpipe and hose systems shall be provided for all nonsprinklered buildings over two stories in height.

Exception No. 1: One-inch (2.5-cm) diameter formed hose on hose reels shall be permitted to provide Class II service.

Exception No. 2: Separate Class I and Class II systems shall be permitted in lieu of Class III.

The requirements for standpipes intend that 2½-in. (6.2-cm) hose connections be available for fire department use in any detention and correctional occupancy more than two stories in height. In addition, if such buildings are unsprinklered, there should also be 1½-in. (3.8-cm) connections and hose for occupant (i.e., staff and resident) use.

Exception No. 1 permits the use of 1-in. (2.5-cm) formed rubber hose in place of the fabric-jacket rubber-lined hose normally required in standpipe systems. The rubber hose is normally stored on reels and is somewhat easier to use.

14-3.6 Corridors. [*See 14-3.8, "Special Features (Subdivision of Resident Housing Spaces)."*]

14-3.7 Subdivision of Building Spaces.

14-3.7.1 Smoke barriers shall be provided so as to divide every story used for sleeping by residents, or any other story having an occupant load of 50 or more persons, into at least two compartments.

Exception No. 1: Protection shall be permitted to be accomplished with horizontal exits. (See 5-2.4.)

Exception No. 2: Smoke compartments having direct exit to (a) a public way, (b) a building separated from the resident housing area by a 2-hour fire resistance rating or 50 ft (15 m) of open space, or (c) a secured open area having a holding space located 50 ft (15 m) from the housing area that provides 15 sq ft (1.4 sq m) or more of refuge area for each person (resident, staff, visitors) that may be present at the time of a fire fulfills the requirements for subdivision of such spaces, provided the locking arrangement of doors involved meets the requirements for doors at the compartment barrier for the applicable use condition.*

A-14-3.7.1 Exception No. 2. A door to the outside, by itself, does not meet the intent of the exception if emergency operating procedures do not provide for the door to be unlocked when needed. In cases where use of the door is not assured, a true smoke barrier per the base requirement of 14-3.7.1 would be needed.

14-3.7.2 Where smoke barriers are required by 14-3.7.1, smoke barriers shall be provided so as:

(a) To limit the housing to a maximum of 200 residents in any smoke compartment, and

(b) To limit the travel distance to a door in a smoke barrier:

1. From any room door required as exit access to a maximum of 100 ft (30 m),

2. From any point in a room to a maximum of 150 ft (45 m).

Exception to (b): The maximum permitted travel distance shall be increased by 50 ft (15 m) in buildings protected throughout by an approved automatic sprinkler system or smoke control system.

Smoke barriers and horizontal exits used to subdivide a building serve three purposes fundamental to the protection of occupants:

1. They limit the spread of fire and fire-produced contaminants,
2. They limit the number of occupants exposed to a single fire, and
3. They provide for horizontal relocation of occupants by creating a safe area on the same floor.

The requirements of 14-3.7.1 and 14-3.7.2 for subdividing building spaces are illustrated in Figure 14-13.

Figure 14-14 illustrates the requirements of Exception No. 2 to 14-3.7.1.

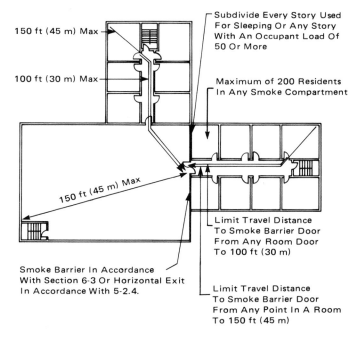

Figure 14-13. *Subdivision of Building Spaces in New Detention and Correctional Occupancies.*

14-3.7.3* Any required smoke barrier shall be constructed in accordance with Section 6-3. Barriers shall be of substantial construction and shall have structural fire resistance.

A-14-3.7.3 Structural fire resistance is defined as the ability of the assembly to stay in place and maintain structural

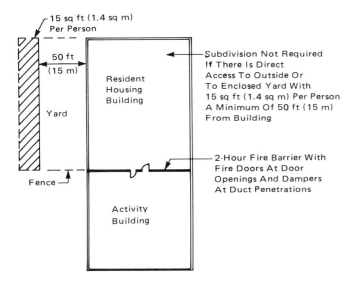

Figure 14-14.   Alternatives to Subdivision by Smoke Barriers.

integrity without consideration of heat transmission. Twelve gauge steel plate suitably framed and stiffened meets this requirement.

Paragraph 14-3.7.3 requires smoke barriers to have structural fire resistance. However, the specific fire resistance in hours is omitted. The intent is to eliminate the use of highly combustible or flimsy materials, such as plastic sheeting, which could possibly limit smoke movement but which have little structural integrity.

14-3.7.4   Openings in smoke barriers shall be protected in accordance with Section 6-3.

Exception: There is no restriction on the total number of vision panels in any barrier (e.g., a smoke barrier may consist of fire-rated glazing panels mounted in a security grille arrangement).

14-3.7.5   At least 6 net sq ft (.56 net sq m) per occupant shall be provided on each side of the smoke barrier for the total number of occupants in adjoining compartments. This space shall be readily available whenever the occupants are moved across the smoke barrier in a fire emergency.

14-3.7.6   Doors shall provide resistance to the passage of smoke. Swinging doors shall be self-latching, or the opening resistance of the door shall be a minimum of 5 lbf (22 N).

The doors in the required smoke barriers must resist the passage of smoke for the same reason the smoke barriers must resist the passage of smoke. The door constructed of materials that resist the passage of smoke will stop smoke from traveling across the door opening only if the door remains tightly closed. Therefore, 14-3.7.6 requires that the door, which 6-3.4.3 requires to be either self-closing or automatic-closing, also must be self-latching or offer a 5-lbf (22-N) resistance to opening, as a minimum. This combination of requirements should help to ensure that the door will be closed under smoke conditions and remain closed, even under the pressures generated by a fire, in order to resist the passage of smoke.

14-3.7.7   Doors in smoke barriers shall conform with the requirements for doors in means of egress as specified in Section 14-2 and shall have locking and release arrangements according to the applicable use condition. The provisions of the Exception to 14-2.11.6 shall not be used for smoke barrier doors serving a smoke compartment containing more than 20 persons.

The provisions of the Exception to 14-2.11.6 allow up to ten locks to require manual unlocking in a timely fashion and still be considered as providing the degree of remote unlocking necessary to satisfy the requirements of a Use Condition IV (as opposed to Use Conditon V) facility. However, 14-3.7.7 does not allow locks on smoke barrier doors to be part of the maximum ten manually unlocked locks where a smoke compartment houses more than 20 persons. This limitation emphasizes the importance of maintaining a means of egress system within a Use Condition IV facility (i.e., where remote release is required), with more than 20 persons per smoke compartment, that allows resident movement to another smoke compartment without having to manually release the lock on the smoke barrier door. A manually released lock on the smoke barrier door would force a reclassification of the facility to Use Condition V and subsequent compliance with the more stringent requirements applicable to that classification.

14-3.7.8   Vision panels shall be provided in smoke barriers at points where the barrier crosses an exit access corridor.

14-3.7.9 Smoke dampers shall be provided in accordance with 6-3.5.

Exception: Other arrangements and positioning of smoke detectors shall be permitted to prevent damage or tampering or may be used for other purposes, provided the function of detecting any fire is fulfilled and the placement of detectors is such that the speed of detection will be equivalent to that provided by the required spacing and arrangement.

14-3.8 **Special Features.** (Subdivision of Resident Housing Spaces.)

14-3.8.1* Subdivision of facility spaces shall comply with Table 14-3.8.1.

A-14-3.8.1 Requirements in Table 14-3.8.1 for smoketight and fire rated separations include the necessary precautions to restrict the spread of smoke through the air handling system. This, however, does not mean that smoke dampers must be provided for each opening. Smoke dampers would be one acceptable method; however, other techniques such as allowing the fans to continue to run with 100 percent supply and 100 percent exhaust would be acceptable.

Paragraph 14-3.8.1 provides for the separation of areas where residents are housed. This separation serves two basic needs: (1) it keeps a fire and its products confined to the area of origin, and (2) it protects those occupants located outside the area of origin. Table 14-3.8.1 estab-

Table 14-3.8.1

USE CONDITION	II		III		IV		V	
Feature	NS	AS	NS	AS	NS	AS	NS	AS
Room to Room Separation	NR	NR	NR	NR	ST	NR	FR(½)	ST
Room Face to Corridor Separation	ST	NR	ST	NR	ST	NR	FR	ST
Room Face to Common Space Separation	NR	NR	NR ST ≤50 ft† >50 ft† (15 m) (15m)	NR ST ≤50 ft† >50 ft† (15 m) (15 m)	ST	NR ST ≤50 ft† >50 ft† (15 m) (15 m)	FR	ST
Common Space to Corridor Separation	FR	NR	FR	NR	FR	NR	FR	ST
Total Openings in Solid Room Face	120 sq in. (.08 sq m)		120 sq in. (.08 sq m)		120 sq in. (.08 sq m)		120 sq in. (.08 sq m) Closable from inside or 120 sq in. (.08 sq m) w/smoke control	

AS: Protected by automatic sprinklers
NS: Not protected by automatic sprinklers
NR: No Requirement

ST: Smoketight
FR: Fire Rated – 1 hour
FR(½): Fire Rated – ½ hour

†This is the travel distance through the common space to the exit access corridor.
NOTE 1: Doors in openings in partitions required to be fire resistive in accordance with this chart in other than required enclosures of exits or hazardous areas shall be substantial doors and of construction that will resist fire for at least 20 minutes. Wired glass or minimum 45–min fire-rated glazing vision panels are permitted. Latches and door closers are not required on cell doors.
NOTE 2: Doors in openings in partitions required to be smoketight in accordance with this chart shall be substantial doors and of construction that will resist the passage of smoke. Latches and door closers are not required on cell doors.
NOTE 3: "Total Openings in Solid Room Face" includes all openings (undercuts, food passes, grilles, etc.), the total of which shall not exceed 120 sq in. (.08 sq m). All openings shall be 36 in. (91 cm) or less above the floor.
NOTE 4: Under Use Condition II, III, or IV, a space subdivided by open construction (any combination of grating doors and grating walls or solid walls) may be considered one room if housing not more than 16 persons. The perimeter walls of such space shall be of smoketight construction. Smoke detection shall be provided in such space. Under Use Condition IV, common walls between sleeping areas within the space shall be smoketight, and grating doors and fronts may be used. In Use Conditions II and III, open dormitories may house more than 16 persons as permitted by other sections of this chapter.

lishes individual requirements based on the Use Condition involved. Within each Use Condition classification, different provisions are required depending upon whether or not automatic sprinkler protection is provided. Where a common wall is used for different purposes, such as "room face to corridor" and "common space to corridor," the most restrictive requirement shall apply to the entire wall. Table 14-3.8.1 and its notes specify a wide variety of options in addition to the locking options previously detailed. Note 4 to Table 14-3.8.1 also allows a space that has been subdivided to be treated as a single room. In combination with the various locking options, this can be quite useful.

Formal Interpretation 81-18
Reference: Table 14-3.8.1

Question: Is it the intent of Table 14-3.8.1 that a room sidewall that faces a corridor in the arrangement shown by wall segment "Room-Corr" of the accompanying figure have the same separation requirements with respect to fire resistance rating or smoketightness as the adjacent common space to corridor separation wall (segment "Comm-Corr" on sketch)?

Answer: Yes. For example, in unsprinklered Use Condition III, both wall segments should be 1-hour fire resistance rated construction.

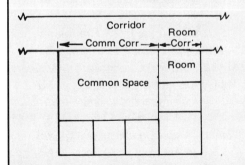

Issue Edition: 1981
Reference: Table 14-3.8.1
Date: March 1982 ■

Formal Interpretation 88-14
Reference: Tables 14-3.8.1 and 15-3.8.1

Question: Is the 120-sq in. (0.08-sq m) requirement applicable where there is no requirement for either a smoketight or fire resistant separation?

Answer: No.

Issue Edition: 1988
Reference: Tables 14-3.8.1 and 15-3.8.1
Issue Date: August 1, 1990 ■

SECTION 14-4 Special Provisions

14-4.1 Windowless Areas.

14-4.1.1* For the purposes of this chapter, a windowless area is a smoke compartment that does not contain operable windows or fixed windows that can be readily broken by impact.

A-14-4.1.1 Windows that are intended to be breakable should be capable of being broken with materials readily available to the facility staff.

14-4.1.2 Windowless areas shall be provided with vent openings, smoke shafts, or an engineered smoke control system to provide ventilation (mechanical or natural).

Paragraph 14-4.1.2 does not require venting or smoke control for those areas (smoke compartments) that are provided with operable windows or fixed windows that can be broken by impact.

14-4.2 Underground Buildings.

14-4.2.1 See Chapter 30 for requirements for underground buildings.

14-4.3 High Rise Buildings. High rise buildings shall comply with 30-8.2.

14-4.4 Operating Features. (*See Chapter 31.*)

SECTION 14-5   Building Services

14-5.1 Utilities.

14-5.1.1 Utilities shall comply with the provisions of Section 7-1.

14-5.1.2 Alarms, emergency communication systems, and the illumination of generator set locations shall be provided with emergency power in accordance with NFPA 70, *National Electrical Code*.

14-5.2 Heating, Ventilating, and Air Conditioning.

14-5.2.1 Heating, ventilating, and air conditioning equipment shall comply with the provisions of Section 7-2 and shall be installed in accordance with manufacturer's specifications.

Exception: As modified in 14-5.2.2.

14-5.2.2 Portable space heating devices are prohibited. Any heating device other than a central heating plant shall be so designed and installed that combustible material will not be ignited by it or its appurtenances. If fuel-fired, such heating devices shall be chimney or vent connected, shall take air for combustion directly from outside, and shall be so designed and installed to provide for complete separation of the combustion system from the atmosphere of the occupied area. The heating system shall have safety devices to immediately stop the flow of fuel and shut down the equipment in case of either excessive temperatures or ignition failure.

Exception: Approved suspended unit heaters shall be permitted in locations other than means of egress and sleeping areas, provided such heaters are located high enough to be out of the reach of persons using the area, and provided they are vent connected and equipped with the safety devices required above.

14-5.2.3 Combustion and ventilation air for boiler, incinerator, or heater rooms shall be taken directly from and discharged directly to the outside air.

14-5.3 Elevators, Escalators, and Conveyors. Elevators, escalators, and conveyors shall comply with the provisions of Section 7-4.

14-5.4 Rubbish Chutes, Incinerators, and Laundry Chutes.

14-5.4.1 Rubbish chutes, incinerators, and laundry chutes shall comply with the provisions of Section 7-5.

14-5.4.2 Any rubbish chute or linen chute, including pneumatic rubbish and linen systems, shall be provided with automatic extinguishing protection installed in accordance with Section 7-7.

14-5.4.3 Any trash chute shall discharge into a trash collecting room used for no other purpose and protected in accordance with Section 6-4.

14-5.4.4 Any incinerator shall not be directly flue-fed, nor shall any floor chute directly connect with the combustion chamber.

References Cited in Commentary

[1]James Bell, "Twenty-Nine Die in Biloxi, Mississippi Jail Fire," *Fire Journal*, Vol. 77, No. 6, November 1983, pp. 44-49, 52-55.

[2]"A Study of Penal Institution Fires," NFPA FR 78-1, National Fire Protection Association, Boston, MA, 1978.

[3]David Demers, "42 Die in Maury County, Tennessee, Jail Fire," *Fire Journal*, Vol. 72, No. 2, March 1978, pp. 30-33, 37.

[4]David Demers, "21 Die in Saint John, New Brunswick, Jail Fire," *Fire Journal*, Vol. 72, No. 2, March 1978, pp. 34-37.

[5]David Demers, "Five Die in Danbury, Connecticut, Federal Correctional Institution Fire," *Fire Journal*, Vol. 72, No. 2, March 1978, pp. 38-42.

[6]James Bell, "Eleven Die in Jail Fire," *Fire Journal*, Vol. 74, No. 4, July 1980, pp. 23-25, 90.

[7]NFPA 101M, *Alternative Approaches to Life Safety*, National Fire Protection Association, Quincy, MA.†

[8]NFPA 220, *Standard on Types of Building Construction*, National Fire Protection Association, Quincy, MA, 1985.

[9]NFPA 30, *Flammable and Combustible Liquids Code*, National Fire Protection Association, Quincy, MA, 1990.

[10]NFPA 13, *Standard for the Installation of Sprinkler Systems*, National Fire Protection Association, Quincy, MA, 1991.

†The edition of NFPA 101M that corresponds with the 1991 *Life Safety Code* will be published in 1992.

15

Existing Detention and Correctional Occupancies

(See also Chapter 31.)

SECTION 15-1 General Requirements

In a typical year, there will be one fire fatality in a U.S. detention or correctional occupancy. However, the potential for a major incident still exists, and such incidents tend to overshadow the single-death fires. For example, the 1982 jail fire in Biloxi, Mississippi killed 29 people. That was several times the death toll for all other prison and jail fires combined during that decade.[1] Because the *Life Safety Code* is designed with particular emphasis on the prevention of loss of life in areas beyond the area of fire origin, this underscores the need for *Code* compliance in detention and correctional occupancies.

The 1981 Edition of the *Life Safety Code* was the first edition to include separate chapters on detention and correctional occupancies. In previous editions, these occupancies were briefly addressed in the chapter on institutional occupancies.

In 1974, the Committee on Safety to Life established a Sectional Committee on Penal Occupancies. It was, however, too late to prepare a report for the 1976 Edition of the *Code*, and in 1977, the Committee on Safety to Life was reorganized as a technical committee with associated subcommittees. The Subcommittee on Penal Occupancies was appointed, and its first working meeting took place in January, 1978. Shortly thereafter, it was renamed the Subcommittee on Detention and Correctional Occupancies. During this period, there were several major detention and correctional occupancy fires that underscored the need for the subcommittee and provided information for its use. These fires included:

Date	Place	Civilian Deaths
October 1974	Youth Correctional Center Cranston, RI	2[2]
June 1975	Seminole County Jail Sanford, FL	11[2]
November 1975	Lycoming County Jail Williamsport, PA	3[2]
June 1976	Marion State Prison Marion, NC	9[2]

(continued)

Date	Place	Civilian Deaths
June 1977	Maury County Jail Tennessee	42[3]
June 1977	St. John City Detention Center St. John, NB, Canada	21[4]
July 1977	Federal Correctional Institution Danbury, CT	5[5]
December 1979	Lancaster County Jail Lancaster, SC	11[6]

15-1.1 Application.

15-1.1.1 Existing detention and correctional facilities shall comply with the provisions of this chapter. Provisions of Chapter 14 do not apply to existing detention and correctional facilities. Existing facilities shall also comply with the applicable requirements of Chapter 31.

Chapter 31, "Operating Features," and Section 31-5 in particular, provide routine operating requirements, such as 24-hour staffing, means for resident notification of staff in an emergency, preparation and maintenance of evacuation plans, staff training in the use of portable fire extinguishers, storage of combustible personal property, presence of heat-producing appliances, control of flammability of draperies, curtains, mattresses, and upholstered furniture, and visual and tactile identification of keys necessary for unlocking doors within the means of egress. Because the locking of doors, which is necessary for the intended function of the facility, is contrary to the basic *Code* tenet that the means of egress system be under the control of building occupants, the presence of properly trained staff is paramount in the provision of a package of life safety equivalent to that provided in other occupancies. Chapter 31 requires the necessary staffing and training that, where combined with the *Code* requirements of Chapters 1 through 7 and 15, achieves the necessary level of life safety.

15-1.1.2 This chapter establishes life safety requirements for all existing detention and correctional facilities.

Chapter 15 has been prepared for application solely to existing buildings.

This section is to be applied retroactively. Due consideration has been given to the practical difficulties of making alterations in existing, functioning facilities. The specified provisions, viewed as a whole, establish minimum acceptable criteria for life safety that reasonably minimize the likelihood of a life-threatening fire.

See the commentary following 15-1.2.1, which explains that the requirements of Chapter 15 apply mainly to the residential areas of a detention and correctional occupancy. Therefore, although 15-1.1.2 states that Chapter 15 establishes life safety requirements for the design of all existing detention and correctional facilities, the chapter focuses primarily on life safety requirements for the residential portions of existing detention and correctional occupancies.

Exception No. 1: Use Condition I requirements are those stated in the applicable requirements for existing buildings of Chapter 17, 19, or 20.

In accordance with 15-1.4, which defines of the five resident user category groups, Use Condition I provides residents with free movement from sleeping areas, and other spaces where access or occupancy is permitted, to the exterior by a means of egress system that meets the same requirements as that which would be provided for occupants of hotel, dormitory, apartment, lodging, or rooming house occupancies. Because locked doors have not been imposed on the residents of a Use Condition I detention or correctional occupancy, such a facility does not require the "protect in place strategy" and associated requirements of Chapter 15. For information on the protection of Use Condition I facilities, Exception No. 1 to 15-1.1.2 and 15-1.4.3 refer the *Code* user to Chapter 17, 19, or 20 in lieu of the provisions of Chapter 15.

Exception No. 2: *Facilities determined to have equivalent safety provided in accordance with Section 1-6.*

A-15-1.1.2   Exception No. 2. In determining equivalency for existing detention and correctional facilities, the authority having jurisdiction may accept evaluations based on Chapter 4 of NFPA 101M, *Alternative Approaches to Life Safety*, utilizing the parameters for existing buildings.

The requirements of Chapter 15 may be modified in instances of practical difficulty or where alternate but equal provisions are proposed. The modifications must provide a level of protection equivalent to that achieved by compliance with the corresponding *Code* provisions.

Exception No. 2 provides that the equivalency provisions of Section 1-6 can be used to comply with the intended level of life safety rather than having to meet the requirements of Chapter 15. The 1992 Edition of NFPA 101M, *Alternative Approaches to Life Safety*,[7] will provide information on a single equivalency system for use in detention and correctional occupancies. Its measurement system has been calibrated against the requirements of the 1991 Edition of the *Life Safety Code*, whereas, the firesafety evaluation systems contained in the 1988 Edition of NFPA 101M were calibrated against the requirements of the 1988 Edition of the *Code*.

Chapter 4 of NFPA 101M, "Firesafety Evaluation System for Detention and Correctional Occupancies," provides a method in which the user assigns numerical values to various building parameters. The individual values are totaled and compared with established values. This is a system by which alternative designs can be evaluated as options to literal *Code* compliance. The *Code* does not intend to limit acceptable equivalency evaluations solely to those based on this system. The authority having jurisdiction retains the discretion, in accordance with Section 1-6, to evaluate and approve existing life safety systems or alternative improvement programs on the basis of appropriate supporting data.

15-1.1.3 Detention and correctional occupancies are those used for purposes such as correctional institutions, detention facilities, community residential centers, training schools, work camps, and substance abuse centers where occupants are confined or housed under some degree of restraint or security.

Both 4-1.5 and 15-1.1.3 have been updated to reflect the current terminology for various forms of detention and correctional occupancies. The use of the terms adult correctional institutions, adult local detention facilities, juvenile detention facilities, juvenile training schools, adult and juvenile community residential centers, adult and juvenile work camps, and adult and juvenile substance abuse centers have replaced terms such as reformatories and houses of correction.

15-1.1.4 Detention and correctional occupancies provide sleeping facilities for four or more residents and are occupied by persons who are generally prevented from taking self-preservation action because of security measures not under the occupants' control.

Residents of detention and correctional occupancies and patients in health care occupancies are judged to be incapable of self-preservation during a fire emergency. In the case of a health care occupancy patient, the incapability is due to physical or mental illness or infirmity. The detention and correctional occupancy resident, although most likely ambulatory or able-bodied, is incapable of self-preservation due to security measures imposed and beyond the resident's control. In both cases, the occupants must await staff action before moving to either an exit, another fire compartment, or a smoke compartment. Impediments to adequate egress are further compounded in detention and correctional occupancies by the reluctance of staff to unlock doors leading to the outside. Thus, horizontal movement within the facility to another fire compartment or smoke compartment may be the only means of egress system that the resident is allowed to use in a fire emergency, regardless of how many exit doors to the outside are installed. Therefore, the "Total Concept" described in 15-1.1.5 is critical.

15-1.1.5 **Total Concept.** All detention and correctional facilities shall be so designed, constructed, maintained, and operated as to minimize the possibility of a fire emergency.

Because the safety of all occupants in detention and correctional facilities cannot be adequately assured solely by dependence on evacuation of the building, their protection from fire shall be provided by appropriate arrangement of facilities, adequate trained staff, and careful development of operating, security, and maintenance procedures composed of the following:

(a) Proper design, construction, and compartmentation,

(b) Provision for detection, alarm, and extinguishment,

(c) Fire prevention and planning, training, and drilling in programs for the isolation of fire and transfer of occupants to areas of refuge or evacuation of the building, or protection of the occupants in place, and

(d) Provision of security to the degree necessary for the safety of the public and the occupants of the facility.

The "Total Concept" establishes a "protect in place" or "defend in place" strategy. This strategy mandates requirements that minimize the need for building evacuation by restricting the development and spread of a fire emergency to the room of fire origin, because safety cannot be ensured by relying on a means of egress system that utilizes evacuation, since locks either cannot or will not be unlocked in a timely manner. The requirements (e.g., Section 31-5) first try to prevent ignition and, when fires do occur, set out to detect them (e.g., 15-3.4.4). Other requirements aim to control the speed with which a fire will develop (e.g., 15-3.3), while still others serve to confine the effects of fire. Extinguishment of fire is facilitated by sprinkler, standpipe, and portable extinguisher requirements. Provisions are made for refuge areas by encouraging the use of horizontal exits and by requiring smoke barriers. Heavy reliance is placed on staff reaction. All these requirements fit together to minimize the need for evacuation. This is the "Total Concept."

15-1.1.6 **Additions.** Additions shall be separated from any existing structure not conforming with the provisions of Chapter 15 by a fire barrier having at least a 2-hour fire resistance rating constructed to the requirements of the addition. Doors in these partitions shall normally be kept closed.

Exception: Doors shall be permitted to be held open if they meet the requirements of the Exception to 5-2.1.8.

Additions must comply with the provisions of Chapter 14. Paragraph 15-1.1.6 contains provisions for the separation of the new construction from the existing occupancy where the existing occupancy does not comply with Chapter 15.

Note that, unlike similar requirements that apply to health care occupancies, the positioning of doors in the separating fire barriers is not restricted to corridors only. Doors must be kept closed unless they meet the requirements for automatic closing found in the Exception to 5-2.1.8.

Figure 15-1 illustrates the requirements of 15-1.1.6.

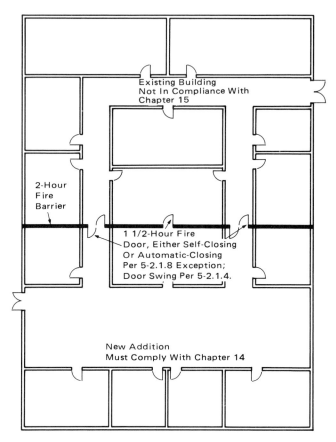

Figure 15-1.   Separation of New Addition from an Existing Building That Does Not Comply with Chapter 15. (See 15-1.1.6.)

15-1.2* **Mixed Occupancies.**

A-15-1.2 Detention and correctional facilities are a complex of structures, each serving a definite and usually different purpose. For instance, in all probability there will be represented in many institutions an example of all, or almost all, of the occupancy-type classifications found in this *Code*. Exits and other features shall be governed by the type of occupancy classification and the hazard of occupancy unless specific exceptions are made.

All buildings and structures are to be classified using this chapter and Section 4-1 as a guide, subject to the ruling of the authority having jurisdiction in case of question as to the proper classification of any individual building or structure.

Use Condition classification of the institution, as well as individual areas within the complex, are always to be considered by the authority having jurisdiction.

15-1.2.1 Egress provisions for areas of detention and correctional facilities that correspond to other occupancies shall meet the corresponding requirements of this *Code* for such occupancies. Where security operations necessitate the locking of required means of egress, necessary staff shall be provided for the supervised release of occupants during all times of use.

The requirements of Chapter 15 apply mainly to the residential portions (i.e., the sleeping and living areas) of the detention and correctional facility. Although the work areas might look much like a typical industrial occupancy, the requirements of Chapter 28, "Industrial Occupancies," cannot be applied by themselves, because doors within the required means of egress of a detention and correctional occupancy will be locked for security. Without using the requirements of Chapter 15 itself to protect the locked industrial work areas, the concepts of Chapter 15 should be implemented to ensure that the necessary trained staff who control locks is present to facilitate immediate, supervised release of occupants during all times of use in the event of fire or similar emergency.

In addition, some areas of a large facility may correspond to another occupancy classification. For example, a gymnasium would be considered an assembly occupancy (Chapter 9). If locked doors are required, prompt unlocking and release are critical.

Release of occupants may be achieved by a remotely activated system capable of unlocking all doors in the means of egress or by a sufficient number of attendants who are continuously on duty, provided with keys, and stationed in the immediate area of all locked means of egress doors. Continuous supervision is essential.

15-1.2.2 Sections of detention and correctional facilities shall be permitted to be classified as other occupancies if they meet all of the following conditions:

(a) They are not intended to serve residents for sleeping purposes, and

(b) They are adequately separated from areas of detention or correctional occupancies by construction having a fire resistance rating of at least 2 hours.

For example, administrative offices or maintenance areas that are not customarily used by the residents as

sleeping areas and are separated by 2-hour fire resistance rated construction could be classified as business or industrial occupancies. In many cases, "trustees" may be employed in these areas. Their presence in these areas would not be considered a violation of 15-1.2.2, provided they the had freedom of egress found in an unlocked environment.

15-1.2.3 Detention and correctional occupancies in buildings housing other occupancies shall be completely separated from the other occupancies by construction having a fire resistance rating of at least 2 hours as provided for additions in 15-1.1.6.

Paragraph 15-1.2.3 requires that if a detention or correctional occupancy is located in a building of another classification, the detention or correctional occupancy must be separated from the other occupancy by construction having a fire resistance rating of 2 hours (*see 15-1.1.6*). This requirement would apply to a small detention lockup facility (at least 4 residents, per 15-1.1.4) located in a combination county courthouse/office/police building. In accordance with 31-5.1.1, the detention area must be staffed 24 hours per day. The remainder of the building, especially office areas, might not be occupied at night. A fire that originates and develops in an unoccupied area will not threaten the occupants of the detention facility as readily due to the protection provided by the required 2-hour fire resistance rated barrier.

Note that 15-1.2.3 addresses occupancy classification only, not hazard of contents. Hazard of contents is addressed in 15-1.2.5.

15-1.2.4 All means of egress from detention and correctional occupancies that traverse other use areas shall, as a minimum, conform to requirements of this *Code* for detention and correctional occupancies.

Exception: It is permissible to exit through a horizontal exit into other contiguous occupancies that do not conform to detention and correctional occupancy egress provisions, but that do comply with requirements set forth in the appropriate occupancy chapter of this Code, as long as the occupancy does not have high hazard contents. The horizontal exit shall comply with the requirements of 15-2.2.5.

The means of egress from detention and correctional occupancies that traverse nondetention and noncorrectional spaces must conform to the requirements for detention and correctional occupancies. However, if a 2-hour fire barrier and associated opening protectives located between a detention or correctional occupancy and another occupancy (e.g., business) qualify as a horizontal exit, then the means of egress system in the business occupancy need comply only with the appropriate requirements contained in Chapters 26 and 27.

15-1.2.5 Any area with a hazard of contents classified higher than that of the detention or correctional occupancy and located in the same building shall be protected as required in 15-3.2.

This paragraph regulates those spaces in a detention and correctional occupancy that contain more hazardous materials (in quantity or type) than are usually found in such an occupancy. Spaces, such as rooms used for the storage of highly combustible materials, trash collection rooms, and paint shops, must be protected in accordance with 15-3.2.

15-1.2.6 Nondetention or noncorrectional related occupancies classified as containing high hazard contents shall not be permitted in buildings housing detention or correctional occupancies.

This paragraph prohibits another occupancy containing highly hazardous materials (such as flammable liquids storage) from being located in a building housing detention and correctional occupancies. It is not the intent of this paragraph to exclude normal storage. The intent is to prevent the conversion of a portion of a detention and correctional facility to a warehouse that contains a larger quantity or a more hazardous type of combustible material than would be normally expected in a detention and correctional occupancy. This applies principally to residential areas. For example, industrial areas that are part of the overall detention and correctional facility but are located in a nonresidential-use building may have flammable liquids as part of the industrial process.

15-1.3   Special Definitions.

(a) *Direct Exit.* A direct exit is an exit that serves only one area, and the direct exit has no openings to *other* areas.

The term "direct exit" is defined here so that its particular meaning can be utilized in Exception No. 2 to 15-3.7.1, which addresses the subdivision of building spaces by means of smoke barriers.

(b) *Fire Barrier.* See Chapters 3 and 6.

(c) *Fire Compartment.* See Chapters 3 and 6.

(d) *Residential Housing Area.* Includes sleeping areas and any contiguous day room, group activity space, or other common spaces for customary access of residents.

(e) *Sally Port (Security Vestibule).* A compartment provided with two or more doors where the intended purpose is to prevent continuous and unobstructed passage by allowing the release of only one door at a time.

See 15-2.5.4.

(f) *Smoke Barrier.* See Chapters 3 and 6.

(g) *Smoke Compartment.* See Chapters 3 and 6.

15-1.4   Classification of Occupancy.

15-1.4.1* For applications of the life safety requirements that follow, the resident user category is divided into five groups:

Use Condition I — Free Egress

Free movement is allowed from sleeping areas, and other spaces where access or occupancy is permitted, to the exterior via means of egress meeting the requirements of the *Code.*

In facilities classified as Use Condition I, there are no physical restrictions on the means of egress, such as locks. The occupants are capable of self-preservation. An example is a work release center where the doors are not locked (*see Figure A-15-1.4.1*). Because the means of egress system is kept unlocked, occupants are as free to escape a fire emergency as occupants of any other residential type of occupancy. Therefore, Use Condition I detention and correctional occupancies are exempted from the requirements of Chapter 15 by 15-1.4.3 and must meet the requirements of some other occupancy chapter, such as Chapter 17 for existing hotels and dormitories. (*See 15-1.4.3.*)

Use Condition II — Zoned Egress

Free movement is allowed from sleeping areas and any other occupied smoke compartment to one or more other smoke compartments.

The residents of a Use Condition II facility have the freedom to move within the building, including the freedom to move from their rooms, across the smoke barrier, and into a separate smoke compartment. Movement through the exit door in the exterior wall to the outside is impeded by locked doors that are permitted to be unlocked manually at the door. (*See Figure A-15-1.4.1.*)

Use Condition III — Zoned Impeded Egress

Free movement is allowed within individual smoke compartments, such as within a residential unit comprised of individual sleeping rooms and group activity space, with egress impeded by remote control release of means of egress from such smoke compartment to another smoke compartment.

The residents of a Use Condition III facility are free to move outside of their rooms but are confined to the smoke compartment that contains their rooms. Movement to an adjoining smoke compartment is impeded by locked doors within the smoke barrier that must be equipped with remote control release. Movement through the exit door in the exterior wall to the outside is impeded by locked doors that are permitted to be unlocked manually at the door. (*See Figure A-15-1.4.1.*)

Use Condition IV — Impeded Egress

Free movement is restricted from an occupied space. Remote controlled release is provided to permit movement from all sleeping rooms, activity spaces, and other occupied areas within the smoke compartment to other smoke compartment(s).

The residents of Use Condition IV facilities are locked in their sleeping rooms. Locks on sleeping room doors must be equipped with remote control release. Movement to an adjoining smoke compartment is impeded by locked doors within the smoke barrier that must be equipped with remote control release. Movement through the exit door in the exterior wall to the outside is impeded by locked doors that are permitted to be unlocked manually at the door. (*See Figure A-15.1.4.1.*)

Use Condition V — Contained

Free movement is restricted from an occupied space. Staff controlled manual release at each door is provided to permit movement from all sleeping rooms, activity spaces, and other occupied areas within the smoke compartment to other smoke compartment(s).

In Use Condition V facilities, all locks are manually operated at the individual door (*see Figure A-15-1.4.1*). This places a heavy demand on staff to open the doors in an emergency. The movement of the residents of Use Condition V facilities is severely restricted. Therefore, the most stringent requirements of Chapter 14 apply.

A-15-1.4.1 Users and occupants of detention and correctional facilities at various times can be expected to include staff, visitors, and residents. The extent and nature of facility utilization will vary according to type of facility, its function, and programs.

Figure A-15-1.4.1 illustrates the five use conditions.

As part of the definitions of Use Condition II through Use Condition V, reference is made to smoke compartments and the type of locking (none, remote release, or manual operation) used for smoke barrier doors. A facility without a smoke barrier can still qualify as meeting the requirements for one of these Use Conditions by providing for movement to a location judged to be equivalent to a smoke compartment, such as (1) a public way, (2) a building separated from the space in question by either adequate fire resistance rated construction or distance, or (3) an adequately sized outside holding area located at a safe distance. The locking operation of the door to this alternate location cannot be more stringent than that allowed for the smoke barrier door of the corresponding Use Condition (i.e., no locking for Use Condition II, remote release for Use Conditions III and IV, and manual operation for Use Condition V). (*Also see 15-3.7 and Figure 15-11.*)

Note that in Figure A-15-1.4.1, "Locked" (L) designates manual unlocking operation at the door.

15-1.4.2* To classify as Use Condition III or IV, the arrangement, accessibility, and security of the release mechanism(s) used for emergency egress shall be such that the minimum available staff, at any time, can promptly release the locks.

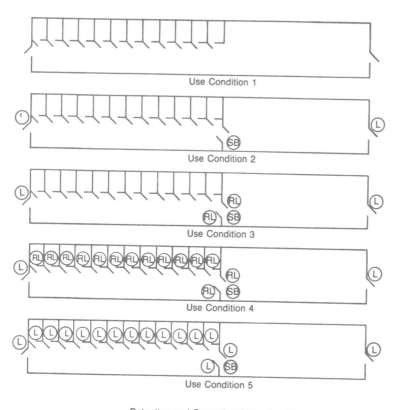

Figure A-15-1.4.1

Detention and Correctional Use Conditions

Ⓛ   Locked

ⓇⓁ Locked—Remote Release or Equivalent

ⓈⒷ Smoke Barrier or Horizontal Exit

A-15-1.4.2 Prompt operation is intended to be accomplished in the period of time between detection of fire by either the smoke detector(s) required by 15-3.4 or by other means (whichever comes first) and the advent of intolerable conditions forcing emergency evacuation. Fire tests have indicated that the time available is a function of the volume and height of the space involved and the rate of fire development. In traditional single-story corridor arrangements, the time between detection by smoke detectors and the advent of lethal conditions down to head height can be as short as approximately 3 minutes. In addition, it should be expected that approximately 1 minute will be required to evacuate all the occupants of a threatened smoke compartment once the locks are released. In this example, a prompt release time would be 2 minutes.

The major requirements noted in this paragraph are that the area must be under continuous supervision, and a sufficient number of staff must be present and must have the necessary keys readily available to release the locks.

15-1.4.3 Areas housing occupancies corresponding to Use Condition I — Free Egress shall conform to the requirements of residential occupancies under this *Code*.

The *Code* intends that detention and correctional occupancies in which the occupants are not locked in at any time are to be classified as residential occupancies and, thus, meet the requirements of Chapter 17, 19, or 20, as appropriate. Those buildings that permit free egress, although used as correctional occupancies, are not to be classified as detention and correctional occupancies under this *Code*. A facility equipped with locking devices on its doors cannot be classified as Use Condition I, since the locks could be used in the future. Instead, depending on the locks' mode of operation (remote or manual), the corresponding Use Condition should be assigned, and the requirements of Chapter 15 followed. A facility can be classified as Use Condition I only if the locking devices are physically removed.

15-1.5 Classification of Hazard of Contents. The classification of hazard of contents shall be as defined in Section 4-2.

15-1.6 Minimum Construction Requirements.

15-1.6.1 For the purpose of 15-1.6, stories shall be counted starting with the primary level of exit discharge. For the purposes of this section, the primary level of exit discharge of a building shall be that floor that is level with or above finished grade on the exterior wall line for 50 percent or more of its perimeter. Building levels below the primary level shall not be counted as a story in determining the height of the building.

See Figure 15-2 for method of counting stories.

15-1.6.2 A residential housing area complying with 15-3.1.2 shall be considered as a one-story building for purposes of applying 15-1.6.3.

The provisions of 15-3.1.2 address multilevel housing areas for which the vertical separation between the lowest floor level and the uppermost floor level does not exceed 13 ft (4.0 m), but the paragraph does not limit the number of levels [*see Figure A-15-3.1.2(c)*]. A multilevel housing area meeting all the requirements of 15-3.1.2 is treated as a single story in determining required building construction type in accordance with 15-1.6.3.

15-1.6.3 Detention and correctional occupancies shall be limited to the following types of building construction shown in Table 15-1.6.3. (*See 6-2.1.*)

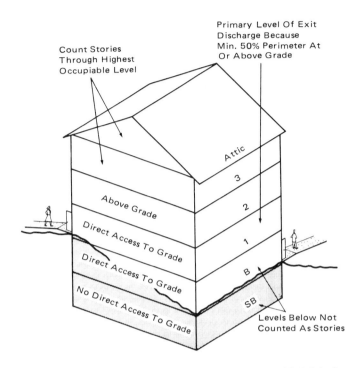

Figure 15-2. Method of Counting Stories, per 15-1.6.1, for Use with 15-1.6.3. If the attic were judged to be occupiable, the figure would depict a four-story building.

Table 15-1.6.3

Type of Construction	1 Story with Basement	1 Story without Basement	2 Story	3 Story	4 Story and Higher
I (443) I (332) II (222)	X	X	X	X	X
II (111)	X††	X	X††	X†	X†
III (211) IV (2HH) V (111)	X††	X	X††	X†	X†
II (000) III (200) V (000)	X††	X††	X†	X†	X†

X: Permitted types of construction
X†: Permitted if the entire building is protected throughout by an approved supervised automatic sprinkler system in accordance with Section 7-7
X††: X† applies in buildings where Use Condition V is used

Exception No. 1: Any building of Type I or Type II (222 or 111) construction shall be permitted to include roofing systems involving combustible or steel supports, decking, or roofing provided:

(a) The roof covering at least meets Class C requirements in accordance with NFPA 256, Standard Methods of Fire Tests of Roof Coverings, and

(b) The roof is separated from all occupied portions of the building by a noncombustible floor assembly that includes at least 2½ in. (6.4 cm) of concrete or gypsum fill. To qualify for this exception, the attic or other space so developed shall either be unoccupied or protected throughout by an approved automatic sprinkler system.

Exception No. 2: In determining building construction type, exposed steel roof members located 16 ft (4.9 m) or more above the floor of the highest cell shall be disregarded.

The Code recognizes that locked doors to the outside will be reluctantly unlocked, slowly unlocked, or never unlocked. Therefore, the *Code* relies on the "defend in place" or "protect in place" strategy contained in the commentary to 15-1.1.5. Paragraph 15-1.6.3 establishes minimum construction requirements to help ensure the structural integrity of the building for the time required to release residents to the outside or hold them in a fire compartment or smoke compartment.

Table 15-1.6.3 establishes minimum construction types for detention and correctional occupancies. In order to be occupied for detention/correctional occupancy use, certain building construction types require automatic sprinkler protection regardless of the use condition classification. Other building construction types require such sprinkler protection only for a Use Condition V detention/correctional occupancy. The automatic sprinkler requirements contained in this table are based on construction type. Automatic sprinkler protection may also be required by other sections of this *Code*.

(See NFPA 220, Standard on Types of Building Construction,[8] for definitions of types of construction. Also see 6-2.1 and Table A-6-2.1.)

15-1.7 Occupant Load. The occupant load for which means of egress shall be provided for any floor shall be the maximum number of persons intended to occupy that floor, but not less than one person for each 120 sq ft (11.1 sq m) gross floor area.

This paragraph establishes a factor from which an occupant load may be determined. The means of egress system must be sized to handle whichever is larger: the number of persons intended to occupy the space or the number of persons calculated by using the occupant load factor.

The *Code* intends that the occupant load factor be used only for sizing the means of egress, not for limiting the number of persons within a space. If a means of egress can accommodate an occupant load larger than that calculated using the occupant load factor provided in 15-1.7, the *Code* does not prohibit such a load.

In a facility with excess means of egress capacity, plumbing codes, sanitary codes, sociological considerations, and common sense will help determine the maximum occupant load.

SECTION 15-2 Means of Egress Requirements

15-2.1 General. Means of egress shall comply with Chapter 5.

Exception: As otherwise provided or modified in this section.

15-2.2 Means of Egress Components.

15-2.2.1 Components of means of egress shall be limited to the types described in 15-2.2.2 through 15-2.2.8.

Chapter 15 recognizes the following means of egress components as described in Chapter 5: doors (5-2.1), stairs (5-2.2), smokeproof enclosures (5-2.3), horizontal exits (5-2.4), ramps (5-2.5), exit passageways (5-2.6), and fire escape stairs (5-2.8). However, Chapter 15 often modifies the provisions of Chapter 5 applicable to those means of egress components. For example, although the Chapter 5 provisions that apply to horizontal exits would limit a horizontal exit to providing a maximum of 50 percent of the number of exits or 50 percent of the total egress capacity, Chapter 15 encourages the voluntary use of horizontal exits by permitting up to 100 percent of the exits to be reached by way of horizontal exits if additional criteria can be met.

Chapter 5 considers escalators and moving walks acceptable means of egress only if they are part of an existing occupancy and are specifically recognized by an occupancy chapter. They are not permitted in the means of egress system of a detention and correctional occupancy. Fire escape ladders, alternating tread devices, and slide escapes are not recognized by Chapter 15 as part of an egress system in existing detention and correctional occupancies. Areas of refuge (*see 5-2.12*) are not required. However, reference can be made to the provisons of 15-3.7, which address mandatory subdivision of building spaces by means of smoke barriers.

15-2.2.2   Doors. Doors shall comply with 5-2.1.

Exception: As provided in 15-2.11.

15-2.2.3   Stairs.

15-2.2.3.1   Stairs shall comply with 5-2.2.

Older editions of the *Code* contained an exception to 15-2.2.3.1 that exempted handrails and guards from the requirement for intermediate rails designed to keep children from falling through the spaces between rails. The exception still applies to detention and correctional occupancies but now appears as Exception No. 2 to 5-2.2.4.5(f) and Exception No. 2 to 5-2.2.4.6(c). The rationale for this exception is that these facilities are used only by adults or older juveniles, and intermediate railings may interfere with visual observation.

15-2.2.3.2   Spiral stairs complying with 5-2.2.2.7 are permitted for access to and between staff locations.

Paragraph 15-2.2.3.2 permits spiral stairs conforming to 5-2.2.2.7 for staff use only. Note that Chapter 5 restricts the use of spiral stairs to those serving an occupant load of 5 or fewer persons. Thus, these provisions prohibit a spiral stair from being part of the required means of egress system within areas occupied by residents.

15-2.2.4   Smokeproof Enclosures. Smokeproof enclosures shall comply with 5-2.3.

This paragraph does not mandate the use of smokeproof enclosures but does recognize a smokeproof enclosure as part of the means of egress system in a detention/correctional occupancy only if the smokeproof enclosure meets the requirements of 5-2.3. An example of an occupancy requiring a smokeproof enclosure can be found in 19-2.11.1. In this example, nonsprinklered, existing, high rise apartment buildings are required to be provided with smokeproof enclosures in accordance with 5-2.3.

15-2.2.5   Horizontal Exits. Horizontal exits shall comply with 5-2.4, modified as follows:

(a) At least 6 sq ft (.56 sq m) of accessible space per occupant shall be provided on each side of the horizontal exit for the total number of people in adjoining compartments.

Subsection 5-2.4 requires at least 3 sq ft (0.28 sq m) of accumulation space per occupant on each side of the horizontal exit. This section requires 6 sq ft (0.56 sq m) per occupant. The reasons for this requirement include possible conflicts among the residents, the anticipated time spent in the refuge area, and the fact that horizontal exits are permitted to comprise 100 percent of required exits in detention and correctional occupancies in accordance with 15-2.2.5(b).

(b)* Horizontal exits shall be permitted to comprise 100 percent of the exits required provided that an exit, other than a horizontal exit, is accessible in some other (not necessarily adjacent) fire compartment without requiring return through the compartment of fire origin.

A-15-2.2.5(b)   An exit is not necessary from each individual fire compartment if there is access to an exit through other fire compartments without passing through the fire compartment of origin.

This permits horizontal exits to comprise 100 percent of the exits from any fire compartment as long as it is not necessary to travel through the compartment of fire origin in order to reach a door to the outside (i.e., the compartment is not "dead-ended").

In Figure 15-3, all compartments except compartment F satisfy the above rule. Fire compartment F would require a door to the outside in order to preclude the need

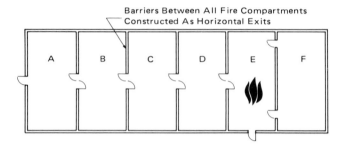

Figure 15-3. *Horizontal Exits Correctly Comprise 100 Percent of Total Exits from Fire Compartments B, C, and D. Compartment F would require the addition of an exit door that opens directly to the outside in order to reach the outside of the building without traveling through fire compartment E. Compartments A and E comply with the Code using one horizontal exit and one exit door directly to the exterior of the building.*

to travel through compartment E, which could be the area of fire origin, to get to the outside of the building.

Due to the practical difficulties of using vertical exit travel to the outside in detention and correctional occupancies, including the reluctance of staff to unlock doors, special recognition is given to horizontal travel and the use of horizontal exits. One hundred percent of the total required exit capacity for a given fire area may be provided by horizontal exits, as previously explained. In the event a horizontal exit also serves as a smoke barrier, refer to 15-2.4.3 and 15-3.7.

(c)* Ducts shall be allowed to penetrate horizontal exits in accordance with Exception No. 3 to 5-2.4.3.3 if protected by combination fire dampers/smoke leakage-rated dampers that meet the smoke damper actuation requirements of 6-3.5.

A-15-2.2.5(c)   In order to help promote the use of horizontal exits in detention and correctional occupancies because horizontal exits provide an especially effective egress system for an occupancy where the occupants, due to security concerns, will not commonly be released to the outside. This provision offers a *Code*-specified equivalent alternative to the Chapter 5 requirement that horizontal exits not be penetrated by ducts. The intended continuity of the fire resistance-rated and smoke resisting barrier is maintained by requiring that duct penetrations of horizontal exits be protected by combination fire damper/smoke leakage-rated dampers that will close upon

activation of a smoke detector and a heat actuated mechanism before the barrier's ability to resist the passage of smoke and fire is compromised.

The provisions of 15-2.2.5(c) are new to this edition of the *Code*. Paragraph 5-2.4.3.3 is also new to this edition and specifically states that fire barriers used in creating a horizontal exit are prohibited from penetration by ducts. To promote the use of horizontal exits in detention and correctional occupancies without burdening a facility with regard to duct pentrations, 15-2.2.5(c) and the corresponding Exception No. 3 to 5-2.4.3.3 were developed. The Committee reasoned that if smoke detection is used to shut a combination fire damper/smoke leakage-rated damper early in a fire, the fire- and smoke-resisting features of the horizontal exit can be reestablished at points where ducts penetrate the barrier.

(d) A door in a horizontal exit is not required to swing with travel as specified in 5-2.4.3.6.

15-2.2.6   Ramps. Ramps shall comply with 5-2.5.

This paragraph does not mandate the use of ramps but does recognize a ramp as part of the means of egress system only if the ramp meets the requirements of 5-2.5.

15-2.2.7   Exit Passageways. Exit passageways shall comply with 5-2.6.

This paragraph does not mandate the use of exit passageways but does recognize an exit passageway as part of the means of egress system only if the exit passageway meets the requirements of 5-2.6.

15-2.2.8   Fire Escape Stairs. Fire escape stairs complying with 5-2.8 are permitted.

This paragraph does not mandate the use of fire escape stairs but does recognize an existing fire escape stair as part of the means of egress system only if the existing fire escape stair meets the requirements of 5-2.8.

15-2.3   Capacity of Means of Egress.

15-2.3.1   The capacity of any required means of egress shall be in accordance with Section 5-3.

15-2.3.2 Aisles, corridors, and ramps required for access or exit shall be at least 3 ft (91 cm) wide.

Note that 14-2.3.2 for new detention and correctional occupancies requires a minimum 4-ft (122-cm) width.

15-2.3.3 For residents' sleeping room door widths, see 15-2.11.3.

15-2.4 **Number of Exits.** (*See also Section 5-4.*)

15-2.4.1 At least two exits of the types permitted in 15-2.2, remotely located from each other, shall be provided for each occupied story of the building.

15-2.4.2 At least two exits of the types permitted in 15-2.2, remotely located from each other, shall be accessible from each fire or smoke compartment.

15-2.4.3* At least one approved exit shall be accessible from each fire compartment and each required smoke compartment into which residents may be moved in a fire emergency, with the exits so arranged that egress shall not require return through the zone of fire origin.

A-15-2.4.3 An exit is not necessary from each individual fire compartment and smoke compartment if there is access to an exit through other fire sections or smoke compartments without passing through the fire section or smoke compartment of origin.

See commentary following 15-2.2.5(b) and Figure 15-3.

15-2.5 **Arrangement of Means of Egress.** (*See also Section 5-5.*)

15-2.5.1 Every sleeping room shall have a door leading directly to an exit access corridor.

Exception No. 1: If there is an exit door opening directly to the outside from the room at the ground level.

Exception No. 2: One adjacent room, such as a dayroom, group activity space, or other common spaces shall be permitted to intervene. Where sleeping rooms directly adjoin a dayroom or group activity space that is utilized for access to

an exitway, such sleeping room shall be permitted to open directly to the dayroom or space and may be separated in elevation by a one-half or full story height. (See 15-3.1.2.)

Figure 15-4 illustrates the requirements of Exception No. 2.

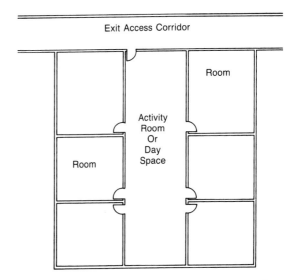

Figure 15-4. One Adjacent Room May Intervene Between Sleeping Room and Exit Access Corridor. Sleeping rooms may be separated in elevation by 1/2 to 1 story. (See Exception No. 2 to 15-2.5.1.)

15-2.5.2* Existing dead-end corridors are undesirable and shall be altered wherever possible so that exits will be accessible in at least two different directions from all points in aisles, passageways, and corridors.

A-15-2.5.2 Every exit or exit access should be so arranged, if feasible, that no corridor or aisle has a pocket or dead end exceeding 50 ft (15 m) for Use Conditions II, III, and IV and 20 ft (6.1 m) for Use Condition V.

See Figure 14-5 and the commentary following 14-2.5.2.

15-2.5.3 No common path of travel shall exceed 50 ft (15 m).

Exception No. 1: A common path of travel shall be permitted for the first 100 ft (30 m) in a building protected throughout by an approved automatic sprinkler system in accordance with 15-3.5.3.

See Figure 14-6 and the commentary following 14-2.5.3.

Exception No. 2: Multilevel residential housing units in which each floor level, considered separately, has at least one-half of its individual required exit capacity accessible by exit access leading directly out of that level without traversing another communicating floor level.

Exception No. 3: Existing excessive common paths of travel may be continued in use subject to the approval of the authority having jurisdiction and the travel distance requirements of 15-2.6.

The common path limitation of 15-2.5.3 and the associated increase allowed for sprinklered buildings in accordance with Exception No. 1 is identical to that required for new detention/correctional occupancies by 14-2.5.3 and its exception. However, Exception Nos. 2 and 3 to 15-2.5.3 introduce criteria that recognize existing common paths of travel that exceed the 50-ft (15-m) limitation contained in the base paragraph and the 100-ft (30-m) limitation allowed in sprinklered buildings by Exception No. 1. Exception No. 2 offers some relief to existing facilities with lengthy common paths of travel on individual levels of multilevel residential housing units, provided that at least half the occupant load of any level can be accommodated by exit access leading directly from that level without traveling on any other level that is open to that housing unit. This affords the residents of any level with an exit access that leads to an exit without being exposed to the fire on another level of the housing unit. Exception No. 3 permits excessively long existing common paths of travel to continue to be used only if specifically approved by the authority having jurisdiction.

15-2.5.4 A sally port shall be permitted in a means of egress where there are provisions for continuous and unobstructed travel through the sally port during an emergency exit condition.

During routine and nonfire emergency conditions, a sally port or security vestibule is designed so that the door at one end of the vestibule is securely locked whenever the door at the opposite end is open. When one door is opened, the door through which entrance is made is closed and locked; the door at the opposite end is then unlocked

and opened to provide exit from the vestibule. The sally port acts as a security device that prevents a continuous flow of people from "storming" the exits. Under fire conditions, it would severely restrict the exit flow of occupants and prevent hose lines from being run through the openings. Therefore, if a sally port is to be permitted as part of a required means of egress, the door controls must be overridden to allow continuous and unobstructed passage in accordance with 15-2.5.4.

Figure 15-5 illustrates the requirements of 15-2.5.4.

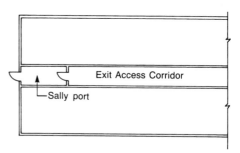

Figure 15-5. *Requirements for Sally Port or Security Vestibule. If sally port is part of required means of egress, both doors of sally port must be capable of being opened at the same time to provide unobstructed egress. (See 15-2.5.4.)*

15-2.6 **Travel Distance to Exits.**

15-2.6.1 Travel distance:

(a) Between any room door required as exit access and an exit or smoke barrier shall not exceed 100 ft (30 m);

(b) Between any point in a room and an exit or smoke barrier shall not exceed 150 ft (45 m); and

(c) Between any point in a sleeping room to the door of that room shall not exceed 50 ft (15 m).

Exception No. 1: The maximum permitted travel distance in (a) or (b) above shall be increased by 50 ft (15 m) in buildings protected throughout by an approved automatic sprinkler system or smoke control system.

Exception No. 2: The maximum permitted travel distance in (c) above shall be increased to 100 ft (30 m) in open dormitories where the enclosing walls of the dormitory space are at least of smoketight construction. Where travel distance to the exit access door from any point within the dormitory

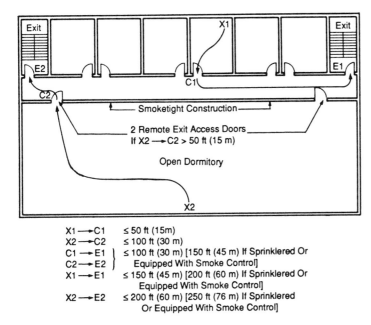

Figure 15-6. *Maximum Travel Distance to Exits in Existing Detention and Correctional Occupancies (see 15-2.6.1). The travel distance is measured along the natural path of travel (see 5-6.2). "Sprinklered" means that the entire building is protected by a complete, approved automatic extinguishing system. "Smoke Control" means that the entire building or fire area is equipped with a system to control the movement of smoke in accordance with Section 7-3.*

X1 → C1	≤ 50 ft (15m)
X2 → C2	≤ 100 ft (30 m)
C1 → E1 C2 → E2	≤ 100 ft (30 m) [150 ft (45 m) If Sprinklered Or Equipped With Smoke Control]
X1 → E1	≤ 150 ft (45 m) [200 ft (60 m) If Sprinklered Or Equipped With Smoke Control]
X2 → E2	≤ 200 ft (60 m) [250 ft (76 m) If Sprinklered Or Equipped With Smoke Control]

exceeds 50 ft (15 m), at least two exit access doors remotely located from each other shall be provided.

Travel distance is measured to the closest exit only, not to both exits required by 15-2.4. Figure 15-6 illustrates the requirements of 15-2.6.1.

15-2.7 Discharge from Exits.

15-2.7.1 Exits shall be permitted to discharge into a fenced or walled courtyard, provided that not more than two walls of the courtyard are the building walls from which exit is being made. Enclosed yards or courts shall be of sufficient size to accommodate all occupants at a minimum distance of 50 ft (15 m) from the building with a net area of 15 sq ft (1.4 sq m) per person.

Figures 15-7a and 15-7b illustrate 15-2.7.1.

15-2.7.2 All exits shall be permitted to discharge through the level of exit discharge. The requirements of 5-7.2 are waived provided that not more than 50 percent of the exits discharges into a single fire compartment.

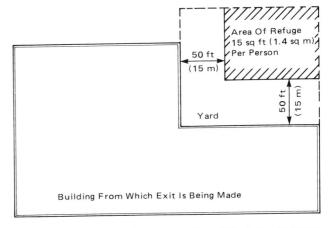

Figure 15-7a. *Exit Discharge into a Fenced Yard. (See 15-2.7.1.)*

Exception: Where all exits discharge through areas on the level of discharge, a smoke barrier shall be provided to divide that level into at least two compartments with at least one exit discharging into each compartment, and each smoke compartment shall have an exit discharge to the building exterior. The level of discharge shall be provided with automatic sprinkler protection, and any other portion of the level of discharge area

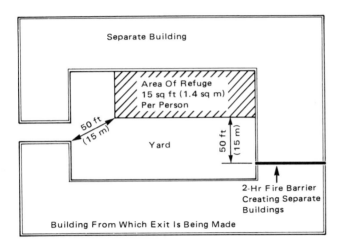

Figure 15-7b. Exit Discharge into an Enclosed Yard. (See 15-2.7.1.)

with access to the discharge area shall be provided with automatic sprinkler protection or separated from it in accordance with the requirements for the enclosure of exits. (See 5-1.3.1.)

The provisions of 5-7.2 establish criteria under which up to 50 percent of the required exits, in either number or capacity, may discharge through the level of exit discharge, with the other 50 percent required to discharge directly to the outside. Because of security concerns and the belief that doors to the exterior will not be readily unlocked in detention and correctional occupancies, 15-2.7.2 allows 100 percent of the exits to discharge through the level of exit discharge. Therefore, the Exception to 15-2.7.2 requires that a fire separation that creates at least two fire compartments be provided on the level of exit discharge. Not more than one-half of the exits (in number and capacity) may discharge into any one fire compartment.

The Exception to 15-2.7.2 allows a smoke barrier to be substituted for a fire barrier under certain conditions. The travel route along the level of exit discharge must be sprinklered, and the route must be separated from nonsprinklered portions of the level of exit discharge by fire barriers meeting the fire resistance rating requirements applicable to exit enclosures.

15-2.8   **Illumination of Means of Egress.** Illumination shall be in accordance with Section 5-8.

15-2.9   **Emergency Lighting.** Emergency lighting shall be in accordance with Section 5-9.

Exception: Emergency lighting of at least 1-hour duration may be provided.

15-2.10   **Marking of Means of Egress.** Exit marking shall be provided in areas accessible to the public in accordance with Section 5-10.

Exception: Exit signs are not required in sleeping areas.

The exemption of exit signs in sleeping areas of detention and correctional occupancies recognizes that persons occupying such areas are familiar with those portions of the facility and know the location of exits. Other portions of the facility may not be as familiar to residents and visitors and, thus, must have proper exit marking in accordance with 15-2.10.

15-2.11   **Special Features.**

15-2.11.1   Doors within means of egress shall be as required in Chapter 5.

Exception: As provided in 15-2.11.2 through 15-2.11.8.

15-2.11.2   Doors shall be permitted to be locked in accordance with the applicable use condition.

This provision overrides the Chapter 5 requirement that all doors within the required means of egress be unlocked from the side from which egress is to be made and, therefore, they must be fully under the control of the building occupants. It recognizes that, in order to function as intended, a detention and correctional occupancy uses various means of locking. Paragraph 15-2.11.2 allows only that means of locking appropriate to a specific use condition. Therefore, a Use Condition II facility, which has more lenient life safety requirements than a Use Condition V facility, cannot contain sleeping rooms that must be individually locked by key. A Use Condition V facility must comply with a more stringent set of requirements than a Use Condition II facility and is permitted to have individual doors manually locked by key.

15-2.11.3* Doors to resident sleeping rooms shall be at least 28 in. (71 cm) in clear width.

Exception: Existing doors to resident sleeping rooms housing four or fewer residents shall be permitted to be a minimum of 19 in. (48.3 cm) in clear width.

A-15-2.11.3 It may be necessary to provide a certain number of resident sleeping rooms with doors providing a minimum clear width of 32 in. (81 cm) (*see 5-2.1.2.1*) in order to comply with the requirements for the physically handicapped. Such sleeping rooms should be located where there is a direct accessible access to the exterior or to an area of safe refuge. (*See 15-3.7.*)

15-2.11.4 Doors in a means of egress shall be permitted to be of the horizontal sliding type, provided the force to slide the door to its fully open position does not exceed 50 lb (222 N) with a perpendicular force against the door of 50 lb (222 N).

Paragraph 5-2.1.4.1 requires that all doors in a means of egress be side-hinged and swinging. This paragraph allows the use of sliding doors if they meet the specified requirements. In addition, Exception No. 4 to 5-2.1.4.1 recognizes the limited use of other horizontal sliding doors in accordance with the provisions of 5-2.1.14.

15-2.11.5 Doors from areas of refuge to the exterior shall be permitted to be locked with key locks in lieu of locking methods described in 15-2.11.6. The keys to unlock such doors shall be maintained and available at the facility at all times, and the locks shall be operable from the outside.

This paragraph requires that keys be maintained and available. "Available" means readily accessible to staff for use at any time for the evacuation of occupants. It is important that (1) the keys required to evacuate occupants are accessible at all times, (2) the staff is trained in the location and use of keys, and (3) the staff has authorization and standing orders to immediately unlock doors that lead from areas of refuge to the exterior during fire emergency conditions. This will prevent the loss of time that can occur while waiting for authorization from administrative authorities before doors can be unlocked.

15-2.11.6* Any remote control release used in means of egress shall be provided with a reliable means of operation, remotely located from the resident living area, to release locks on all doors.

Exception: Provisions for remote control locking and unlocking of occupied rooms in Use Condition IV are not required provided not more than ten locks are necessary to be unlocked in order to move all occupants from one smoke compartment to an area of refuge as promptly as required for remote control unlocking. Unlocking of all necessary locks shall be accomplished with no more than two separate keys. (See 15-3.7.7 for smoke barrier doors.)

A-15-2.11.6 A remote position is generally a control point where a number of doors can be unlocked simultaneously, either mechanically or electrically. In areas where there are a number of sleeping rooms, it is not practical for attendants to unlock doors individually. Doors in an exit should be unlocked prior to unlocking sleeping room doors.

This section of the *Code* does not intend to prohibit Use Condition V facilities, nor does it intend to limit Use Condition V facilities to 10 manually released locks.

"Remote" means outside area where the occupants are restrained. It is not necessary to have the remote unlocking mechanism in a separate fire area, although this may be beneficial. Doors within the exit should be unlocked prior to unlocking sleeping room doors. This will prevent jamming of the exit door caused by several persons exerting pressure on the door.

The Exception to 15-2.11.6 applies to facilities that are seeking classification as Use Condition IV but that have a need for up to ten locks that must be manually released at the door. Where remote locking is required by Use Condition IV, it must be provided, except as addressed by the exception. The exception permits up to ten manual locks in order to allow occupants to move to another fire compartment or smoke compartment while permitting the facility to qualify as having provided remote release. The use of a limited number (i.e., maximum of ten) of manual locks in addition to the possibility of hundreds of remotely released locks within the same facility does not impose a Use Condition V classification. This exception may apply in situations where there are fewer than ten doors if a door is secured with more than one lock. Figures 15-8a and 15-8b depict two typical arrangements that illustrate this exception.

This exception has been misinterpreted to mean that a Use Condition V detention/correctional facility (which, by definition, permits manual unlocking at each locked door) may have a maximum of ten such manual locks. A Use Condition V facility is permitted to have any number of manual locks. In fact, the exception applies *only* to use Condition IV facilities and allows a facility to retain its classification as Use Condition IV (i.e., remote release) provided there are ten or fewer manually released locks and provided all unlocking can be achieved with a minimum of two keys.

The speed with which the doors can be unlocked and the occupants removed to a safe location is critical. If the ten locks cannot be rapidly released by manual unlocking due to staffing restrictions or for any other reasons, remote unlocking must be used. If doors are equipped with locking devices, it is assumed that the locks will be used, and they must be counted as part of the total number of locks.

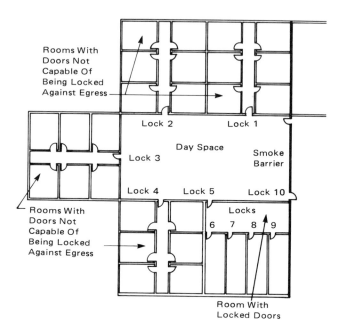

Figure 15-8b. Maximum of Ten Manually Unlocked Locks with Multiple-Door Areas Secured by a Door with a Single Key-Operated Lock. (See Exception to 15-2.11.6.)

dance with 5-9.2.3 is provided for the power operation, or a remote control manual mechanical release is provided.

Exception to (a): The combination of emergency power-operated release of selected individual doors and remote control manual mechanical ganged release shall be allowed without mechanical release means at each door.

(b) Mechanically operated sliding doors or mechanically operated locks shall be provided with a manual mechanical means at each door to release and open the door.

15-2.11.8   The provisions of 5-2.1.5.2 for stairway reentry do not apply.

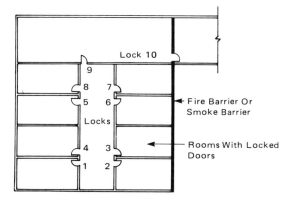

Figure 15-8a. Maximum of Ten Manually Unlocked Doors Where Each Door Is Equipped with a Single Key-Operated Lock. (See Exception to 15-2.11.6.)

15-2.11.7   All remote-control release operated doors shall be provided with a redundant means of operation as follows:

(a) Power-operated sliding doors or power-operated locks shall be so constructed that in the event of power failure, a manual mechanical means to release and open the doors is provided at each door, and either emergency power in accor-

SECTION 15-3   Protection

15-3.1   Protection of Vertical Openings.

This subsection specifies the protection required to maintain floor-to-floor separation, which helps to prevent of the products of combustion from moving vertically through the building.

15-3.1.1   Any stairway, ramp, elevator, hoistway, light or ventilation shaft, chute or other vertical opening between stories shall be enclosed in accordance with Section 6-2.

Exception No. 1: Stairs that do not connect a corridor, do not connect more than two levels, and do not serve as a means of egress.

The convenience stair addressed by Exception No. 1 is illustrated in Figures 15-9a and 15-9b.

Exception No. 2: Multilevel residential housing areas in accordance with 15-3.1.2.

Exception No. 3: In residential housing areas protected throughout by an approved automatic sprinkler system, unprotected vertical openings are permitted in accordance with the conditions of 6-2.4.5, provided that the height between the lowest and highest finished floor levels does not exceed 23 ft (7.0 m). The number of levels is not restricted. Residential housing areas subdivided in accordance with 15-3.8.1 are permitted to be considered as part of the communicating space.

Exception No. 4: Atriums in accordance with 6-2.4.6 are permitted.

Exception No. 5: Where full enclosure is impractical, the required enclosure may be limited to that necessary to prevent a fire originating in any story from spreading to any other story.

Exception No. 6: The required minimum fire resistance rating of enclosures in detention and correctional occupancies protected throughout by an approved automatic sprinkler system shall be 1 hour.

Exception No. 3 to 15-3.1.1. addresses typical multilevel housing areas that utilize staggered partial levels as depicted in Figure 15-10. Paragraph 6-2.4.5 restricts vertical openings from connecting more than three floor levels. The exception modifies the three-floor restriction by allowing a 23-ft (7-m) height limitation between the lowest and highest finished floor levels so as to permit greater flexibility in the use of detention and correctional occupancies. The exception applies only to facilities where the residential housing areas are protected throughout by automatic sprinklers.

Exception No. 3 to 15-3.1.1 has been revised in the 1991 Edition of the *Code* to clarify that a residential housing unit that complies with the requirements of Table 15-3.8.1 is considered to be part of the communicating space addressed by 6-2.4.5. This clarification prevents the *Code* user from needlessly complying with 6-2.4.5(d), which would require a fully sprinklered residential area to be separated from all rooms abutting a communicating space (e.g., a day room with a high ceiling) by means of smoke-resisting construction. All openings, including doors, from resident sleeping rooms to the day space would be required to have smoketight opening protectives.

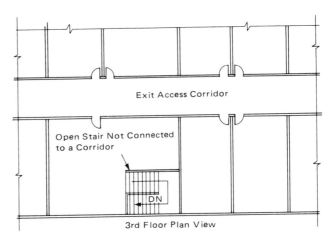

Figure 15-9a. *Plan View of Convenience Stair Allowed by Exception No. 1 to 15-3.1.1.*

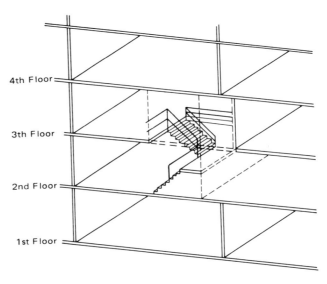

Figure 15-9b. *Open Convenience Stair as Allowed by Exception No. 1 to 15-3.1.1.*

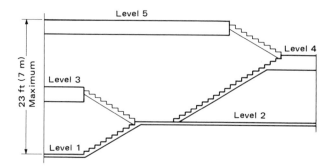

Figure 15-10. Unprotected Vertical Openings in Sprinklered Housing Area Allowed by Exception No. 3 to 15-3.1.1.

This would place an undue burden on such facilities. Instead of requiring smoketight separations between each resident sleeping room and the day space, the Committee judged that adequate life safety is provided if the residential housing unit is subdivided in accordance with the provisions of 15-3.8.1. Also, compliance with 6-2.4.5(h) would then be impractical. Exception No. 2 was added to 6-2.4.5(d) to prevent this portion of Exception No. 3 to 15-3.1.1 from conflicting with the provisions of 6-2.4.5(d).

15-3.1.2 Multilevel residential housing areas are permitted without enclosure protection between levels provided all the following conditions are met:

(a)* The entire normally occupied area, including all communicating floor levels, is sufficiently open and unobstructed so that it may be assumed that a fire or other dangerous condition in any part will be readily obvious to the occupants or supervisory personnel in the area.

A-15-3.1.2(a) It is not the intent of this requirement to restrict room face separations, which restrict visibility from the common space into individual sleeping rooms.

(b) Exit capacity is sufficient to provide simultaneously for all the occupants of all communicating levels and areas, with all communicating levels in the same fire area being considered as a single floor area for purposes of determination of required exit capacity.

(c)* The height between the highest and lowest finished floor levels does not exceed 13 ft (4.0 m). The number of levels is not restricted.

A-15-3.1.2(c) The maximum vertical separation between the lowest floor level and the uppermost floor level is restricted to 13 ft (4.0 m). Figure A-15-3.1.2(c) illustrates how the height is to be determined.

Whereas 15-3.1.1 Exception No. 3 allows multilevel housing areas with a maximum 23-ft (7-m) height between the lowest and the highest finished floor levels if the housing areas are fully sprinklered, 15-3.1.2 allows nonsprinklered multilevel housing areas without requiring sprinklering but limits the height to 13 ft (4 m).

15-3.1.3* A multitiered open cell block shall be considered as a single-story building provided that:

(a) A smoke control system is provided (*see recommended design criteria in A-15-3.1.3*) to maintain the level of smoke filling from potential cell fires at least 5 ft (152 cm) above the floor level of any occupied tier involving space that is:

1. Use Condition IV or V.

2. Use Condition III, unless all persons housed in such space can pass through a free access smoke barrier or freely pass below the calculated smoke level with not more than 50 ft (15 m) of travel from their cells, or

(b) The entire building, including cells, is provided with complete automatic sprinkler protection in accordance with 15-3.5.

A multitiered open cell block in excess of 23 ft (7.0 m) in height, measured between the lowest and highest finished floor levels, (*see Exception No. 3 to 15-3.1.1*) could not be built in compliance with the *Life Safety Code*. However, the provisions of 15-3.1.3 continue to recognize existing multitiered open cell blocks if: (1) automatic sprinkler protection is provided, or (2) smoke control is provided to deal with the limited amount of smoke that a sprinkler-controlled fire will generate. In addition to the information on smoke control provided in A-15-3.1.3, see the detailed commentary following 6-2.4.6(e) on the

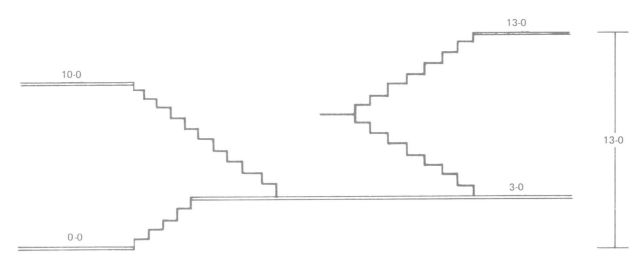

Figure A-15-3.1.2(c)

subject of atrium smoke control. The physics associated with smoke development, spread, and control in a multitiered open cell block is similar to that of an atrium.

A-15-3.1.3   A recommended method of calculating expected level of smoke in a smoke removal equipped cell block follows:

This method for calculating the expected level of smoke has been developed from data experimentally produced in full-scale burnouts of test cells. The test cells were sized, loaded with fuel, and constructed to represent severe conditions of heavily fuel loaded [approximately 6 lb/sq ft (29 kg/sq m)] cells as found in prison locations. The filling rate and temperature of the effluent gas and smoke have been calculated using the data from these tests and established formulae from plume dynamics.

The application of the method described in A-15-3.1.3 should be limited to situations where there is at least 10 ft (3 m) from the floor level to the lowest acceptable level of smoke accumulation (Z); the reservoir above the lowest acceptable level for Z is at least 20 percent of the Z dimension, the length of the cell block is at least equal to Z, and the fan is at least 10 ft (3 m) higher than the floor of the highest cell.

The determination of smoke removal requirements is based on the dimensions of the cell opening. Where more than one cell opening is involved, the larger size on the level being calculated should be used.

The fan size, temperature rating, and operations means may be determined by the following procedure:

1. *Acceptable Smoke Level.* Determine the lowest acceptable level of smoke accumulation in accordance with 15-3.1.3. The vertical distance between that level and the floor level of the lowest open cell is the value of Z to be used in connection with Figure A-15-3.1.3(a).

2. *Characteristic Cell Opening.* Determine the opening of the cell face. Where there is more than one size of cell opening, use the largest. Match the actual opening to those shown in Figure A-15-3.1.3(b), and use the corresponding curve on Figure A-15-3.1.3(a). If there is no match between the size and shape of opening and Figure A-15-3.1.3(a), then interpolate between the curves. If the opening exceeds 6 ft (183 cm) × 6 ft (183 cm), use the curve for a 6 ft (183 cm) × 6 ft (183 cm) opening. This curve is considered to represent the maximum burning situation, and increasing the size of the opening will not increase the actual burning rate.

3. *Exhaust Fan Rate.* Determine the exhaust fan capacity needed to extract smoke at a rate that will maintain the smoke level at a point higher than Z. This is the rate shown on the baseline of Figure A-15-3.1.3(a) corresponding to the level of Z on the vertical axis for the solid line (ventilation rate) curve appropriate to the cell door size. This exhaust capability must be provided at a point higher than Z.

4. *Intake Air.* Provide intake air openings that are either present or automatically provided at times of emergency smoke removal. These are to be located at or near the baseline of the cell block to allow for intake air at the rate to be

vented by the fan. The openings provided shall be suffi cient to avoid a friction load that can reduce the exhaust efficiency. Standard air handling design criteria are used in making this calculation.

5. *Fan Temperature Rating.* Determine the potential temperature of gases that the fan may be required to handle. To do this, determine the distance from the floor of the highest cell to the centerline of the fan (or fan ports if the fan is in a duct or similar arrangement). Determine the intersection of this new "Z" value with the appropriate ventilation rate curve (solid line) on Figure A-15-3.1.3(a). Estimate the temperature rise by interpolating along the appropriate ventilation rate curve and between the constant temperature rise curves (dashed lines) on Figure A-15-3.1.3(a). Provide all elements of the exhaust system that are to be above the acceptable smoke level with the capability to effectively operate with the indicated increase in temperature.

6. *Operation of Exhaust System.* The emergency exhaust system should be arranged to initiate automatically on detection of smoke, operation of a manual fire alarm system, or direct manual operation. The capability to manually start the automatic exhaust system should be provided in a guard post in the cell block and/or at another control location.

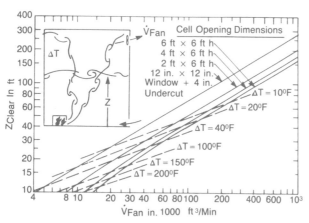

ΔT—Temperature of Upper Layer Gases Above Ambient
—Ventilation Rate Curves
— —Constant Temperature Rise Curves
V̇Fan — Fan Discharge Capacity (As Installed)
ZClear — Distance From Cell Floor to Smoke Layer

Conversion: (ft) × .3048 = (m); (cu ft/min) × .00047 = (cu m/s); (°F-32) ÷ 1.8 = °C.

Figure A-15-3.1.3(a) Cell Block Smoke Control Ventilation Curves.

When appropriate, the emergency exhaust fans may be used for comfort ventilation as well as serving their emergency purposes.

15-3.2 Protection from Hazards.

15-3.2.1* Hazardous Areas. Any hazardous area shall be protected in accordance with Section 6-4. The following areas shall be protected as indicated:

Area Description	Separation/Protection
Areas not incidental to resident housing	2-hr
Boiler and fuel-fired heater rooms	1-hr or sprinklers
Commercial cooking equipment	In accordance with 7-2.3
Commissaries	1-hr or sprinklers
Employee locker rooms	1-hr or sprinklers
Hobby/handicraft shops	1-hr or sprinklers
Central or bulk laundries over 100 sq ft (9.3 sq m)	1-hr or sprinklers
Maintenance shops	1-hr or sprinklers
Padded cells	1-hr and sprinklers
Soiled linen rooms	1-hr or sprinklers
Storage rooms > 50 sq ft (4.6 sq m) in area storing combustible material	1-hr or sprinklers
Trash collection rooms	1-hr or sprinklers

Exception: When, in the opinion of the authority having jurisdiction, such areas are no longer incidental to resident housing, they shall be separated by 2-hour fire barriers in conjunction with automatic sprinkler protection.

A-15-3.2.1 It is strongly recommended that padded cells not be used due to their fire record. However, recognizing that they will be used in some cases, provisions for the protection of padded cells are provided. It is recognized that the ¾-hour fire door will be violated with the "plant on" of the padding, but a ¾-hour fire door should be the base of the assembly.

Hazardous areas in detention and correctional occupancies are spaces containing materials that, due to their basic nature (as in the case of flammable liquids) or

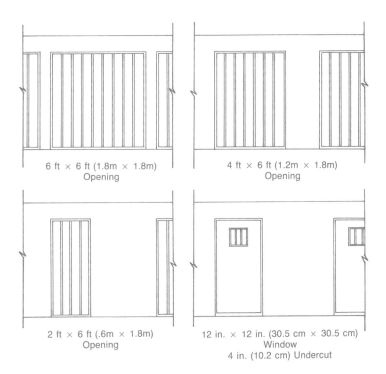

6 ft × 6 ft (1.8m × 1.8m)
Opening

4 ft × 6 ft (1.2m × 1.8m)
Opening

2 ft × 6 ft (.6m × 1.8m)
Opening

12 in. × 12 in. (30.5 cm × 30.5 cm)
Window
4 in. (10.2 cm) Undercut

Conversion: 1 in. = 2.54 cm.
Figure A-15-3.1.3(b) Typical Cell Openings.

because of the quantity of combustible materials involved, represent a significantly higher hazard than would otherwise be typical of detention and correctional occupancies. Paragraph 15-3.2.1 requires hazardous areas to be protected. The areas listed in 15-3.2.1 must be protected by the specified fire resistance rated separation, sprinklering, or combination of separation and sprinklering. The list of hazardous areas commonly found in this occupancy was expanded for this edition of the *Code*. The result is a format that is consistent with the -3.2 subsections of many of the other occupancy chapters.

Padded cells are considered to be severe hazard areas due to high heat release, high rate of combustion, and the quantity of smoke produced by padding materials. Therefore, padded cells must be protected by automatic sprinklers and separated by 1-hour construction. Many of the recent multiple-death fires in detention and correctional occupancies have started in padded cells.

Where flammable liquids are handled or stored, NFPA 30, *Flammable and Combustible Liquids Code*,[9] should be consulted to establish the minimum criteria necessary to mitigate this hazard. (*See 6-4.3.*)

15-3.2.2 Where cooking facilities are protected per 7-2.3, kitchens shall not be required to be provided with roomwide protection.

15-3.3 Interior Finish.

15-3.3.1 Interior wall and ceiling finish in corridors and exits and any space not separated from corridors and exits by a partition capable of retarding the passage of smoke shall be Class A or B. In all other areas, interior wall and ceiling finish shall be Class A, B, or C in accordance with Section 6-5.

Paragraph 15-3.3.1 requires only that the separating partition be capable of retarding the passage of smoke. The partition must be of substantial construction but is not required to have a fire resistance rating. (*See Chapter 3 for the definition of a smoke barrier.*)

15-3.3.2 Interior floor finish material in corridors and exits shall be Class II in accordance with Section 6-5.

Exception: Existing floor finish material of Class A or B in nonsprinklered buildings and Class A, B, or C in sprinklered buildings, may continue to be used provided they have been evaluated based upon tests performed in accordance with 6-5.3.1.

NFPA 255, *Standard Method of Test of Surface Burning Characteristics of Building Materials,*[10] contains the flame spread and smoke development measurement method currently used to evaluate interior wall and ceiling finish materials in accordance with the requirements of Section 6-5. Prior to the 1981 Edition of the *Code,* floor finish was tested in accordance with NFPA 255. This exception allows material that was tested and approved by this method to remain in use.

15-3.4 Detection, Alarm, and Communication Systems.

See Supplement 2.

15-3.4.1 General.

15-3.4.1.1 Detention and correctional occupancies shall be provided with a fire alarm system in accordance with Section 7-6, except as modified below.

15-3.4.1.2 All required fire alarm systems shall be electrically supervised.

Exception: Existing nonelectrically supervised systems shall be permitted in buildings protected by a complete automatic extinguishing system.

15-3.4.1.3 All fire alarm systems and detection systems required in this section shall be provided with a secondary power supply, and the installation shall be in accordance with NFPA 72, *Standard for the Installation, Maintenance, and Use of Protective Signaling Systems.*

15-3.4.2 Initiation. Initiation of the required fire alarm system shall be by manual means in accordance with 7-6.2 and by means of any detection devices or detection systems required.

Exception No. 1: Manual fire alarm boxes shall be permitted to be locked provided that staff is present within the subject area when occupied and has keys readily available to unlock the boxes.

Exception No. 2: Manual fire alarm boxes shall be permitted to be located in a staff location, provided that the staff location is attended when the building is occupied and that the staff attendant has direct supervision of the sleeping area.

15-3.4.3 Notification.

15-3.4.3.1 Occupant Notification. Occupant notification shall be accomplished automatically, without delay, upon operation of any fire alarm initiating device in accordance with 7-6.3. Presignal systems are prohibited.

Exception*: Any smoke detectors required by this chapter are permitted to be arranged to alarm at a constantly attended location only and are not required to accomplish general alarm indication.

A-15-3.4.3.1 Exception. The staff at the constantly attended location should have the capability to promptly initiate the general alarm function and contact the fire department or have direct communication with a control room or other location that can initiate the general alarm function and contact the fire department.

Presignal systems are prohibited by 15-3.4.3.1, which requires that notification be provided "without delay." However, the exception does exempt smoke detectors from sounding a general alarm in order to avoid numerous nuisance alarms.

15-3.4.3.2 Emergency Forces Notification. Fire department notification shall be accomplished in accordance with 7-6.4.

Exception No. 1: Any smoke detectors required by this chapter are not required to transmit an alarm to the fire department.

Where the fire department is not equipped to receive such alarms or where direct transmission to the fire department is not permitted, arrangements are to be made for the prompt notification of the fire department. Paragraph 7-6.4 provides several options for notifying the fire department automatically. Where smoke detectors are provided, they are not required to sound the fire alarm or to transmit a signal to the fire department but are required to sound an alarm at a constantly attended location, unless otherwise specified.

Exception No. 2: Where staff is provided at a constantly attended location that has the capability to promptly notify the fire department or has direct communication with a control room having direct access to the fire department. The fire plan as required by 31-5.1.3 shall include procedures for logging of alarms and immediate notification of the fire department.

Detention/correctional facilities that are located in rural areas are often served by fire departments that do not have the notification capabilities required by 15-3.4.3.2. The exception provides a *Code*-specified equivalent, which is based on meeting the requirements for immediate logging of alarms and immediate notification of the fire department.

15-3.4.4 Detection. An approved automatic smoke detection system shall be installed in accordance with Section 7-6 throughout all resident housing areas.

Exception No. 1: Smoke detectors are not required in sleeping rooms with four or fewer occupants in Use Condition II or III.

Exception No. 2: In buildings protected throughout by an approved automatic sprinkler system installed in accordance with 15-3.5.3, smoke detectors are not required except in corridors, common spaces, and sleeping rooms with more than four occupants.

Exception No. 3: Other arrangements and positioning of smoke detectors shall be permitted to prevent damage or tampering, or for other purposes, provided the function for detecting any fire is fulfilled and the placement of detectors is such that the speed of detection will be equivalent to that provided by the spacing and arrangements described in Section 7-6. This may include the location of detectors in exhaust ducts from cells, behind grilles, or in other locations. The equivalent performance of the design, however, must be acceptable to the authority

having jurisdiction in accordance with the equivalency concepts specified in Section 1-6 of this Code.

15-3.5 Extinguishment Requirements.

See Supplement 3.

15-3.5.1 Reserved.

15-3.5.2* Where required by 15-1.6, facilities shall be protected throughout by an approved supervised automatic sprinkler system in accordance with Section 7-7.

A-15-3.5.2 Where the openings in ceilings or partitions are 1/4 in. (.6 cm) or larger in the least dimension, where the thickness or depth of the material does not exceed the least dimension of the openings, and where such openings constitute at least 70 percent of the area of the ceiling or partition material, the disruption of sprinkler spray patterns may be disregarded.

15-3.5.3 Where this *Code* permits exceptions for fully sprinklered detention and correctional occupancies, the sprinkler system shall be:

(a) In complete accordance with Section 7-7,
(b) Electrically connected to the fire alarm system, and
(c) Fully supervised.

Paragraphs 15-3.5.2 and 15-3.5.3 indicate that, where automatic sprinklers are installed to comply with the *Code*, the system shall be a complete, approved automatic sprinkler system installed in accordance with NFPA 13, *Standard for the Installation of Sprinkler Systems.*[11] The use of manually operated sprinklers is not recognized by the *Code*. Informal surveys conducted by the Committee indicate no significant problems with the installation, maintenance, and use of automatic sprinkler systems in detention and correctional facilities. The system must also be supervised in accordance with the requirements of 7-7.2 in order to comply with the *Code*.

15-3.5.4 Portable fire extinguishers shall be provided in accordance with 7-7.4.1.

Exception No. 1*: Access to portable fire extinguishers shall be permitted to be locked.

A-15-3.5.4 **Exception No. 1.** Where access to portable fire extinguishers is locked, staff should be present on a 24-hour basis and have keys readily available to unlock access to the extinguishers. Where supervision of sleeping areas is from a 24-hour manned staff location, portable fire extinguishers may be provided at the staff location in lieu of within the sleeping area.

Exception No.1 to 15-3.5.4 permits fire extinguishers to be locked. Time is critical when using extinguishers; therefore, keys must be carried by the staff or be readily accessible.

Exception No. 2: Portable fire extinguishers shall be permitted to be located at staff locations only.

15-3.5.5 Standpipe and hose systems shall be provided in accordance with 7-7.4.2 as follows:

(a) Class I standpipe systems shall be provided for any building over two stories in height, and

(b) Class III standpipe and hose systems shall be provided for all nonsprinklered buildings over two stories in height.

Exception No. 1: One-inch (2.5-cm) diameter formed hose on hose reels shall be permitted to provide Class II service.

Exception No. 2: Separate Class I and Class II systems shall be permitted in lieu of Class III.

The requirements for standpipes intend that 2$\frac{1}{2}$-in. (6.2-cm) hose connections be available for fire department use in any detention and correctional occupancy more than two stories in height. In addition, if such buildings are unsprinklered, there should also be 1$\frac{1}{2}$-in. (3.8-cm) connections and hose for occupant (i.e., staff and resident) use.

Exception No. 1 permits the use of 1-in. (2.5-cm) formed rubber hose in place of the fabric-jacket rubber-lined hose normally required in standpipe systems. The rubber hose is normally stored on reels and is somewhat easier to use.

15-3.6 **Corridors.** *[See 15-3.8, "Special Features (Subdivision of Resident Housing Spaces)."]*

15-3.7 **Subdivision of Building Spaces.**

15-3.7.1* Smoke barriers shall be provided so as to divide every story used for sleeping by ten or more residents, or any other story having an occupant load of 50 or more persons, into at least two compartments.

A-15-3.7.1 Consideration can be given for large open areas which may function as smoke sinks as an alternative to the installation of more than one smoke barrier as required by this section. Vertical movement downward to an area of refuge may be accepted by the authority having jurisdiction in lieu of horizontal movement.

Exception No. 1: Protection shall be permitted to be accomplished with horizontal exits. (See 5-2.4.)

Exception No. 2*: Smoke compartments having direct exit to (a) a public way, (b) a building separated from the resident housing area by a 2-hour fire resistance rating or 50 ft (15 m) of open space, or (c) a secured open area having a holding space located 50 ft (15 m) from the housing area that provides 15 sq ft (1.4 sq m) or more of refuge area for each person (resident, staff, visitors) that may be present at the time of a fire fulfills the requirements for subdivision of such spaces, provided the locking arrangement of doors involved meets the requirements for doors at the compartment barrier for the applicable use condition.

A-15-3.7.1 **Exception No. 2.** A door to the outside, by itself, does not meet the intent of the exception if emergency operating procedures do not provide for the door to be unlocked when needed. In cases where use of the door is not assured, a true smoke barrier per the base requirement of 15-3.7.1 would be needed.

15-3.7.2 Where smoke barriers are required by 15-3.7.1, smoke barriers shall be provided so as:

(a) To limit the housing to a maximum of 200 residents in any smoke compartment, and

(b)* To limit the travel distance to a door in a smoke barrier:

1. From any room door required as exit access to a maximum of 100 ft (30 m),

2. From any point in a room to a maximum of 150 ft (45 m).

Exception to (b): The maximum permitted travel distance shall be increased by 50 ft (15 m) in buildings protected throughout by an approved automatic sprinkler or smoke control system.

A-15-3.7.2(b) Consideration should be given to increasing the travel distance to a smoke barrier to coincide with existing range lengths and exits.

Smoke barriers and horizontal exits used to subdivide a building serve three purposes fundamental to the protection of occupants:

1. They limit the spread of fire and fire-produced contaminants,
2. They limit the number of occupants exposed to a single fire, and
3. They provide for horizontal relocation of occupants by creating a safe area on the same floor.

The requirements of 15-3.7.1 and 15-3.7.2 for subdividing building spaces are illustrated in Figures 15-11 and 15-12.

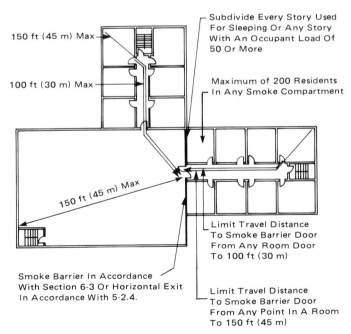

Figure 15-11. Subdivision of Building Spaces in Existing Detention and Correctional Occupancies.

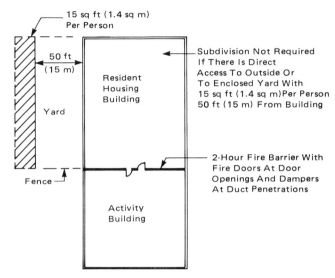

Figure 15-12. Alternatives to Subdivision by Smoke Barriers.

15-3.7.3* Any required smoke barrier shall be constructed in accordance with Section 6-3. Barriers shall be of substantial construction and shall have a structural fire resistance.

A-15-3.7.3 Structural fire resistance is defined as the ability of the assembly to stay in place and maintain structural integrity without consideration of heat transmission. Twelve gage steel plate suitably framed and stiffened meets this requirement.

Paragraph 15-3.7.3 requires smoke barriers to have structural fire resistance. However, the specific fire resistance in hours is omitted. The intent is to eliminate the use of highly combustible or flimsy materials, such as plastic sheeting, which could possibly limit smoke movement but which have little structural integrity.

15-3.7.4 Openings in smoke barriers shall be protected in accordance with Section 6-3.

Exception: There is no restriction on the total number of vision panels in any barrier (e.g., a smoke barrier may consist of fire-rated glazing panels mounted in a security grille arrangement.

15-3.7.5 At least 6 net sq ft (.56 net sq m) per occupant shall be provided on each side of the smoke barrier for the total number of occupants in adjoining compartments. This space shall be readily available whenever the occupants are moved across the smoke barrier in a fire emergency.

15-3.7.6 Doors shall provide resistance to the passage of smoke. Swinging doors shall be self-latching, or the opening resistance of the door shall be a minimum of 5 lbf (22 N). Such doors are not required to swing with exit travel.

The doors in the required smoke barriers must resist the passage of smoke for the same reason the smoke barriers must resist the passage of smoke. The door constructed of materials that resist the passage of smoke will stop smoke from traveling across the door opening only if the door remains tightly closed. Therefore, 15-3.7.6 requires that the door, which 6-3.4.3 requires to be either self-closing or automatic-closing, also must be self-latching or offer a 5-lbf (22-N) resistance to opening, as a minimum. This combination of requirements should help to ensure that the door will be closed under smoke conditions and remain closed, even under the pressures generated by a fire, in order to resist the passage of smoke.

15-3.7.7 Doors in smoke barriers shall conform with the requirements for doors in means of egress as specified in Section 15-2 and shall have locking and release arrangements according to the applicable use condition. The provisions of the Exception to 15-2.11.6 shall not be used for smoke barrier doors serving a smoke compartment containing more than 20 persons.

The provisions of the exception to 15-2.11.6 allow up to ten locks to require manual unlocking in a timely fashion and still be considered as providing the degree of remote unlocking necessary to satisfy the requirements of a Use Condition IV (as opposed to a Use Conditon V) facility. However, 15-3.7.7 does not allow locks on smoke barrier doors to be part of the maximum ten manually unlocked locks where a smoke compartment houses more than 20 persons. This limitation emphasizes the importance of maintaining a means of egress system within a Use Condition IV facility (i.e., where remote release is required) with more than 20 persons per smoke compartment, that allows resident movement to another smoke

compartment without having to manually release the lock on the smoke barrier door. A manually released lock on the smoke barrier door would force a reclassification of the facility to Use Condition V and subsequent compliance with the more stringent requirements applicable to that classification.

15-3.7.8 Vision panels shall be provided in smoke barriers at points where the barrier crosses an exit access corridor.

15-3.7.9 Smoke dampers shall be provided in accordance with 6-3.5.

Exception: Other arrangements and positioning of smoke detectors shall be permitted to prevent damage or tampering or may be used for other purposes, provided the function of detecting any fire is fulfilled, and the placement of detectors is such that the speed of detection will be equivalent to that provided by the required spacing and arrangement.

15-3.8 **Special Features.** (Subdivision of Resident Housing Spaces.)

15-3.8.1* Subdivision of facility spaces shall comply with Table 15-3.8.1 found on the following page.

A-15-3.8.1 Requirements in Table 15-3.8.1 for smoketight and fire rated separations include taking the necessary precautions to restrict the spread of smoke through the air handling system. This, however, does not mean that smoke dampers must be provided for each opening. Smoke dampers would be one acceptable method; however, other techniques such as allowing the fans to continue to run with 100 percent supply and 100 percent exhaust would be acceptable.

Paragraph 15-3.8.1 provides for the separation of areas where residents are housed. This separation serves two basic needs: (1) it keeps a fire and its products confined to the area of origin, and (2) it protects those occupants located outside the area of origin. Table 15-3.8.1 establishes individual requirements based on the Use Condition involved. Within each Use Condition classification, different provisions are required depending upon whether or not automatic sprinkler protection is provided. Where

Table 15-3.8.1

USE CONDITION	II		III				IV				V	
Feature	NS	AS	NS		AS		NS	AS			NS	AS
Room to Room Separation	NR	NR	NR		NR		ST	NR			ST	ST††
Room Face to Corridor Separation	NR	NR	ST†††		NR		ST†††	NR			FR†††	ST††
Room Face to Common Space Separation	NR	NR	NR ≤50 ft† (15 m)	ST††† >50 ft† (15 m)	NR ≤50 ft† (15 m)	ST†† >50 ft† (15 m)	ST†††	NR ≤50 ft† (15 m)	ST††† >50 ft† (15 m)		ST†††	ST††
Common Space to Corridor Separation	ST	NR	ST		NR		ST	NR			FR	ST††
Total Openings in Solid Room Face	120 sq in. (.08 sq m)		120 sq in. (.08 sq m)				120 sq in. (.08 sq m)				120 sq in. (.08 sq m) Closable from inside or 120 sq in. (.08 sq m) w/smoke control	

AS: Protected by automatic sprinklers   ST: Smoketight

NS: Not protected by automatic sprinklers   FR: Fire Rated — 1 hour

NR: No Requirement

† This is the travel distance through the common space to the exit access corridor.

†† May be NR where there is either:

   (a) An approved automatic smoke detection system installed in all corridors and common spaces, or

   (b) Multitiered cell blocks meeting the requirements of 15–3.1.3.

††† May be NR in multitiered open cell blocks meeting the requirements of 15–3.1.3.

NOTE 1:   Doors in openings in partitions required to be fire resistive in accordance with this chart in other than required enclosures of exits or hazardous areas shall be substantial doors and of construction that will resist fire for at least 20 minutes. Wired glass or minimum 45–min fire-rated glazing vision panels are permitted. Latches and door closers are not required on cell doors.

NOTE 2:   Doors in openings in partitions required to be smoketight in accordance with the chart shall be substantial doors and of construction that will resist the passage of smoke. Latches and door closers are not required on cell doors.

NOTE 3:   "Total Openings in Solid Room Face" includes all openings (undercuts, food passes, grilles, etc.), the total of which shall not exceed 120 sq in. (.08 sq m). All openings shall be 36 in. (91 cm) or less above the floor.

NOTE 4:   Under Use Condition II, III, or IV, a space subdivided by open construction (any combination of grating doors and grating walls or solid walls) may be considered one room if housing not more than 16 persons. The perimeter walls of such space shall be of smoketight construction. Smoke detection shall be provided in such space. Under Use Condition IV, common walls between sleeping areas within the space shall be smoketight, and grating doors and fronts may be used. In Use conditions II and III, open dormitories may house more than 16 persons as permitted by other sections of this chapter.

a common wall is used for different purposes, such as "room face to corridor" and "common space to corridor," the most restrictive requirement shall apply to the entire wall. Table 15-3.8.1 and its associated notes specify a wide variety of options in addition to the locking options previously detailed. Note 4 to Table 15-3.8.1 also allows a space that has been subdivided to be treated as a single room. In combination with the various locking options, this can be quite useful.

Formal Interpretation 88-14
Reference: Tables 14-3.8.1 and 15-3.8.1

Question: Is the 120-sq in. (0.08-sq m) requirement applicable where there is no requirement for either a smoketight or fire resistant separation?

Answer: No.

Issue Edition: 1988
Reference: Tables 14-3.8.1 and 15-3.8.1
Issue Date: August 1, 1990 ∎

SECTION 15-4   Special Provisions

15-4.1 Windowless Areas.

15-4.1.1* For purposes of this chapter, a windowless area is a smoke compartment that does not contain operable windows or fixed windows that can be readily broken by impact.

A-15-4.1.1 Windows that are intended to be breakable should be capable of being broken with materials readily available to the facility staff.

15-4.1.2 Windowless areas shall be provided with vent openings, smoke shafts, or an engineered smoke control system to provide ventilation (mechanical or natural).

Paragraph 15-4.1.2 does not require venting or smoke control for those areas (smoke compartments) that are provided with operable windows or fixed windows that can be broken by impact.

15-4.2 Underground Buildings.

15-4.2.1 See Chapter 30 for requirements for underground buildings.

15-4.3 High Rise Buildings. (Reserved.)

15-4.4 Operating Features. (*See Chapter 31.*)

SECTION 15-5   Building Services

15-5.1 Utilities.

15-5.1.1 Utilities shall comply with the provisions of Section 7-1.

15-5.1.2 Alarms, emergency communication systems, and the illumination of generator set installations shall be provided with emergency power in accordance with NFPA 70, *National Electrical Code.*

Exception: Systems complying with earlier editions of NFPA 70 and not presenting a life safety hazard may be continued in use.

15-5.2 Heating, Ventilating, and Air Conditioning.

15-5.2.1 Heating, ventilating, and air conditioning equipment shall comply with the provisions of Section 7-2 and shall be installed in accordance with the manufacturer's specifications.

Exception No. 1: As modified in 15-5.2.2.

Exception No. 2: Systems complying with earlier editions of the applicable codes and not presenting a life safety hazard may be continued in use.

15-5.2.2 Portable space heating devices are prohibited. Any heating device other than a central heating plant shall be so designed and installed that combustible material will not be ignited by it or its appurtenances. If fuel-fired, such heating devices shall be chimney or vent connected, shall take air for combustion directly from outside, and shall be so designed and installed to provide for complete separation of the combustion system from the atmosphere of the occupied area. The heating system shall have safety devices to immediately stop the flow of fuel and shut down the equipment in case of either excessive temperatures or ignition failure.

Exception: Approved suspended unit heaters shall be permitted in locations other than means of egress and sleeping areas, provided such heaters are located high enough to be out of reach of persons using the area, and provided they are vent connected and equipped with the safety devices required above.

15-5.2.3 Combustion and ventilation air for boiler, incinerator, or heater rooms shall be taken directly from and discharged directly to the outside air.

15-5.3 Elevators, Escalators, and Conveyors. Elevators, escalators, and conveyors shall comply with the provisions of Section 7-4.

15-5.4 Rubbish Chutes, Incinerators, and Laundry Chutes.

15-5.4.1 Rubbish chutes, incinerators, and laundry chutes shall comply with the provisions of Section 7-5.

15-5.4.2 Any rubbish chute or linen chute, including pneumatic rubbish and linen systems, shall be provided with automatic extinguishing protection installed in accordance with Section 7-7.

15-5.4.3 Any trash chute shall discharge into a trash collecting room used for no other purpose and protected in accordance with Section 6-4.

15-5.4.4 Any incinerator shall not be directly flue-fed, nor shall any floor chute directly connect with the combustion chamber.

References Cited in Commentary

[1] James Bell, "Twenty-Nine Die in Biloxi, Mississippi Jail Fire," *Fire Journal*, Vol. 77, No. 6, November 1983, pp. 44-49, 52-55.

[2] "A Study of Penal Institution Fires," NFPA FR 78-1, National Fire Protection Association, Boston, MA, 1978.

[3] David Demers, "42 Die in Maury County, Tennessee, Jail Fire," *Fire Journal*, Vol. 72, No. 2, March 1978, pp. 30-33, 37.

[4] David Demers, "21 Die in Saint John, New Brunswick, Jail Fire," *Fire Journal*, Vol. 72, No. 2, March 1978, pp. 34-37.

[5] David Demers, "Five Die in Danbury, Connecticut, Federal Correctional Institution Fire," *Fire Journal*, Vol. 72, No. 2, March 1978, pp. 38-42.

[6] James Bell, "Eleven Die in Jail Fire," *Fire Journal*, Vol. 74, No. 4, July 1980, pp. 23-25, 90.

[7] NFPA 101M, *Alternative Approaches to Life Safety*, National Fire Protection Association, Quincy, MA.†

[8] NFPA 220, *Standard on Types of Building Construction*, National Fire Protection Association, Quincy, MA, 1985.

[9] NFPA 30, *Flammable and Combustible Liquids Code*, National Fire Protection Association, Quincy, MA, 1990.

[10] NFPA 255, *Standard Method of Test of Surface Burning Characteristics of Building Materials*, National Fire Protection Association, Quincy, MA, 1990.

[11] NFPA 13, *Standard for the Installation of Sprinkler Systems*, National Fire Protection Association, Quincy, MA, 1991.

---

† The edition of NFPA 101M that corresponds with the 1991 *Life Safety Code* will be published in 1992.

16

New Hotels and Dormitories

(See also Chapter 31.)

Hotels and dormitories are one of five residential occupancy types addressed by the *Life Safety Code*. Other residential occupancies include one- and two-family dwellings, apartment buildings, lodging and rooming houses, and residential board and care facilities. Sleeping accommodations are a feature common to all residential occupancies.

Paragraph 4-1.6 highlights the common principle of life safety with which the *Code* is concerned as applied to all residential occupancies addressed by Chapters 16 through 23. Paragraph 4-1.6 states: "Residential occupancies are those occupancies in which sleeping accommodations are provided for normal residential purposes and include all buildings designed to provide sleeping accommodations." This use of residential occupancies is central to the *Code* provisions of Chapters 16 through 23, since occupants who are asleep will be unaware of a rapidly developing fire and, when alerted to the emergency, may be somewhat confused due to being awakened suddenly.

Other factors on which the provisions of Chapters 16 through 23 are based are the presence of hazards (such as cooking and heating equipment) in residential occupancies and the degree of familiarity of the occupants with their living space. Occupants may have little or no familiarity, as in the case of transient residents of hotels, or they may have the total familiarity of residents of a one-family dwelling.

Unfamiliar surroundings and the possibility of being asleep when a fire occurs put hotel guests in particular jeopardy. Hotels pose an additional problem, because the typical hotel building configuration requires escaping guests to traverse an interior corridor, which subsequently exposes them to the heat and smoke of potential corridor and room fires. In recognition of these potential hazards, the 1991 Edition of the *Code* now requires most new hotels and dormitories to be protected throughout by an approved supervised automatic sprinkler system.

Hotels and motels averaged 8,300 structure fires a year as reported to U.S. fire departments from 1984 to 1988. These fires caused an average of 49 civilian deaths and 405 civilian injuries per year. These figures do not include lodging and rooming houses and residential board and care facilities (defined for fire reporting purposes as facilities limited to fewer than 16 occupants).

The primary causes of hotel and motel fires are careless handling of smoking materials and arson (including suspected arson). Collectively, they account for nearly half of all hotel and motel fires, two-thirds of associated deaths, and more than half of associated injuries. Nevertheless, nearly half of all people killed in hotel and motel fires from 1980 to 1988 were not in the room of fire origin. Therefore, the potential for fire protection is considerable.

More than two-thirds of hotel and motel fires during 1988 occurred where smoke detectors were used. The usage of smoke detectors in hotels and motels probably exceeds the percentage documented as a result of reported fires. Nearly half of all hotels were sprinklered as of 1988. The growth in the usage of these and other fire protection features in the 1980s helps explain a steady downward trend in fires, deaths, and injuries in these occupancies.

In spite of the increase in protection, hotels and motels were the site of the two deadliest fires in the U.S. and its possessions in the 1980s: the MGM Grand Hotel fire in 1980,[5] which killed 85 people, and the DuPont Plaza Hotel fire in 1986,[1] which killed 97 people. These and other large, multiple-death fires in hotels and motels have served to emphasize the importance of systematic fire protection in accordance with the provisions of the *Life Safety Code*.

The following is a brief list representing hotel fires that have not only emphasized the need for changes in the *Code* but have also focused attention on the need for compliance with the *Code*:

Date	Place	Civilian Deaths
December 1986	DuPont Plaza San Juan, PR	97 dead[1]
March 1982	Hilton Hotel Houston, TX	12 dead[2]
February 1981	Hilton Hotel Las Vegas, NV	8 dead[3]
December 1980	Stouffer's Inn Harrison, NY	26 dead[3]
November 1980	MGM Grand Hotel Las Vegas, NV	85 dead[3,5]
December 1946	Winecoff Hotel Atlanta, GA	119 dead[3]
June 1946	LaSalle Hotel Chicago, IL	61 dead[3]

The following multiple fatality dormitory fires occurred within the past decade:

Date	Place	Civilian Deaths
June 1980	Migrant Labor Camp Barracks Clinton, NC	5 dead
October 1985	Fraternity House Fort Collins, CO	4 dead
Sept. 1990	Fraternity House Berkeley, CA	3 dead

SECTION 16-1 General Requirements

16-1.1 Application.

16-1.1.1 This chapter establishes life safety requirements for all new hotels and for modified buildings according to the provisions of Section 1-5. (*See Chapter 31 for operating features.*)

Hotels and dormitories are defined in 16-1.3.1. It should be noted that lodging or rooming houses that contain more than 16 people are considered hotels and must comply with Chapter 16. Existing hotels are covered in Chapter 17.

16-1.1.2 New dormitories shall comply with the requirements for new hotels.

Exception: Any dormitory divided into suites of rooms, with one or more bedrooms opening into a living room or study that has a door opening into a common corridor serving a number of suites, shall be classified as an apartment building.

The Exception to 16-1.1.2 recognizes that the popular dormitory design in which a group of bedrooms opens into a living room duplicates a typical apartment design in which several bedrooms open into a living room (or kitchen). Since the design and the risk of fire are the same, the *Code* treats this arrangement as that of an apartment building. (*See Figure 16-1.*)

16-1.2 Mixed Occupancies.

16-1.2.1 Where another type of occupancy occurs in the same building as a residential occupancy, the requirements of 1-5.7 of this *Code* shall be applicable.

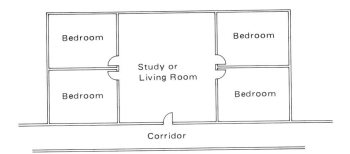

Figure 16-1. Arrangement of Dormitory Suite Treated as an Apartment Under the Exception to 16-1.1.2. More than one bedroom opens into a study or living room that has a door opening into a corridor. The corridor serves a number of suites.

16-1.2.2 For requirements on mixed mercantile and residential occupancies, see 24-1.2; for mixed assembly and residential, see 8-1.2; and for mixed business and residential, see 26-1.2.

The *Code* previously provided requirements to ensure the integrity of the residential means of egress in mixed residential/mercantile occupancies. The 1991 Edition now applies this safeguard to assembly and business occupancies.

16-1.2.3 Any ballroom, assembly or exhibition hall, and other space used for purposes of public assembly shall be in accordance with Chapter 8. Any dining area having a capacity of 50 or more persons shall be treated as an assembly occupancy.

Most larger hotels are made up of several occupancies that include Hotel, Assembly (ballrooms, restaurants, lounges), Business (large administrative areas), Mercantile (large shopping areas), and others. Unless these areas are adequately separated and protected, the complex is considered a mixed occupancy, and the most stringent provisions of the various occupancies must be applied. Note that small administrative areas and small gift shops or newsstands are not subject to mixed occupancy requirements. This can be very important with regard to construction and sprinkler requirements for assembly occupancies and sprinkler requirements for mercantile occupancies. (*See commentary following 16-1.6, 16-3.2, and 16-3.5.*)

16-1.3 Definitions.

16-1.3.1 Terms applicable to this chapter are defined in Chapter 3 of this *Code*; where necessary, other terms will be defined in the text as they may occur.

Dormitories. Dormitories include buildings or spaces in buildings where group sleeping accommodations are provided for more than 16 persons who are not members of the same family in one room or a series of closely associated rooms under joint occupancy and single management, with or without meals, but without individual cooking facilities. Examples are college dormitories, fraternity houses, and military barracks.

In 16-1.3.1, the phrase "without individual cooking facilities" refers to the absence of cooking equipment in any room or unit of a dormitory. If this equipment is present throughout a facility, the occupancy should be classed as an apartment building. The phrase "with or without meals" indicates the *Code's* acceptance of a central cafeteria used to serve meals for the occupants of a dormitory.

Hotels. Hotels include buildings or groups of buildings under the same management in which there are more than 16 sleeping accommodations primarily used by transients (those who occupy accommodations for less than 30 days) for lodging with or without meals, whether designated as a hotel, inn, club, motel, or by any other name. So-called apartment hotels shall be classified as hotels because they are potentially subject to the same transient occupancy as hotels.

Lodging or rooming houses containing more than 16 people are treated as hotels. The parenthetical reference to a 30-day time period has been added to better define "transient." Where units have individual cooking facilities, the *Code* classifies the occupancy as an apartment building (*see 18-1.3*). However, where the authority having jurisdiction believes that the potential for hazards associated with both a hotel (unfamiliarity with surroundings) and an apartment building (higher fuel load, greater number of ignition sources, and travel through multiple rooms) are present, it may be appropriate to classify the building as a mixed occupancy (hotel and apartment).

16-1.4 Classification of Occupancy. (*See 16-1.3.*)

16-1.5 Classification of Hazard of Contents.

16-1.5.1 The contents of residential occupancies shall be classified as ordinary hazard in accordance with Section 4-2. For the design of automatic sprinkler systems, the classification of contents in NFPA 13, *Standard for the Installation of Sprinkler Systems*, shall apply.

NFPA 13, *Standard for the Installation of Sprinkler Systems,*[4] would classify the contents as "light hazard" for the purpose of designing extinguishing systems. The difference in classification is based on the threat to life or life safety (ordinary) versus the threat to the extinguishing capability of the automatic sprinkler system (light).

16-1.6 Minimum Construction Requirements. No special requirements.

Although this chapter does not establish minimum construction requirements, if the hotel contains an assembly occupancy, Chapter 8 does establish minimum construction requirements based on the location of the assembly occupancy.

16-1.7 Occupant Load.

16-1.7.1* The occupant load in numbers of persons for whom exits are to be provided shall be determined on the basis of one person per 200 sq ft (18.6 sq m) gross floor area or the maximum probable population of any room or section under consideration, whichever is greater. The occupant load of any open mezzanine or balcony shall be added to the occupant load of the floor below for the purpose of determining exit capacity.

A-16-1.7.1 Dormitory-type occupancy, particularly where 2- or 3-tier bunks are used with close spacing, may produce an occupant load substantially greater than one person per 200 sq ft (18.6 sq m) gross floor area. However, even though sleeping areas are densely populated, the building as a whole may not necessarily exceed one person per 200 sq ft (18.6 sq m) gross area, owing to the space taken for toilet facilities, halls, closets, and living rooms not used for sleeping purposes.

The requirements of this paragraph do not preclude the need for providing exit capability from concentrated sleeping areas (bunk rooms) based on the "maximum probable population" rather than on the floor area. If the actual population of a bunk room exceeds 1 person per 200 sq ft (18.6 sq m), the exit capacity features (door widths, etc.) will have to be designed based on the actual population load. See 5-3.1 for further details on the use of occupant load for determining capacity of the means of egress.

The occupant loads for areas of hotels used for non-residential purposes are based on the use of the area. Occupant loads are calculated in accordance with the -1.7 subsection of each occupancy chapter (e.g., 8-1.7 for assembly areas, 24-1.7 for mercantile areas).

SECTION 16-2   Means of Egress Requirements

16-2.1 General.

16-2.1.1 Means of egress from guest rooms/guest suites to the outside of the building shall be in accordance with Chapter 5 and this chapter. Means of escape within the guest room/guest suite shall comply with the provisions of Section 21-2 for one- and two-family dwellings. For the purpose of application of the requirements of Chapter 21, guest room/guest suite is synonymous with dwelling or living unit.

A general reference is made to Chapter 5 in place of repeating many of its provisions. Many of the requirements contained in Section 16-2 are Chapter 5 provisions that are options for the occupancy chapters, such as the Exception to 16-2.2.2.2, which allows the use of special locking arrangements per 5-2.1.6; or that prohibit the use of an item if it is not listed (note that alternating tread devices are not listed in 16-2.2); or that establish restrictions based on criteria provided in Chapter 5, such as the limits placed on dead-end corridors found in 16-2.5.3.

Paragraph 16-2.1.1 requires that every guest room/suite comply with Section 21-2 of Chapter 21, which addresses one- and two-family dwellings. This requirement is important for several reasons. First, it establishes two means of escape from every sleeping room and living area of a guest room/suite having two rooms or more. Paragraph 21-2.1.2 establishes several acceptable types of "second means of escape," the most common of which is the operable window. A second means of escape is exempted if a guest room/suite is protected by an automatic sprinkler system. Note that this does not require the entire building to be sprinklered but only the guest room/suite that is not in compliance with the secondary means of escape.

A second important provision of Section 21-2 is that the means of egress provisions in Chapter 5 do not apply unless specifically referenced. For example, the minimum widths of doors within a guest room/suite are reduced to 28 in. (71 cm) from the 32 in. (81 cm) in width specified by Chapter 5. This does not apply to the door into the room or suite as this is where the standard means of egress begins under the concept. Chapter 21 also allows the use of winders and spiral stairs within a guest room/suite, and the provisions of Chapter 21 for headroom apply within the guest room/suite, superseding those of Chapter 5. (*See commentary on Chapter 21 for additional information on means of escape from living units.*)

16-2.2 Means of Egress Components.

16-2.2.1 General.

16-2.2.1.1 Components of means of egress shall be limited to the types described in 16-2.2.2 through 16-2.2.7.

16-2.2.1.2 In buildings protected throughout by an approved supervised automatic sprinkler system installed in accordance with 16-3.5, exit enclosures shall have a fire resistance rating of not less than 1 hour, and the fire protection rating of doors shall be not less than 1 hour.

In recognition of the relatively low fuel loads in hotels, the fire resistance rating for exit enclosures, as well as for other vertical openings (*see 16-3.1.1 Exception No. 4*), need not exceed 1 hour; however, as a safeguard, this is permitted only in buildings protected throughout by automatic sprinklers.

Since the *Code* currently requires most new hotels to be protected throughout by an approved automatic sprin-

kler system, a 1-hour exit enclosure is the minimum requirement, regardless of building height, for fully sprinklered buildings. However, if the Exception to 16-3.5.2 exempting certain building arrangements from the sprinkler requirement is exercised, then 16-2.2.1.2 cannot be applied. This subsequently dictates a default to the Chapter 5 exit enclosure requirements, which are based upon the number of stories connected by the exit enclosure. (*See 5-1.3.1.*)

This 1-hour rating is not permitted for assembly occupancies or business occupancies and, therefore, cannot be utilized where mixed occupancies are involved; nor can it be used for stairways or vertical openings located in or passing through other occupancies. In facilities where occupancies are adequately separated and treated independently, a 1-hour enclosure in the hotel portion and a 2-hour enclosure elsewhere could be permitted. (*See Figure 16-2.*)

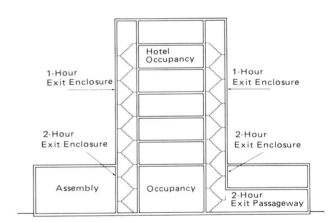

Figure 16-2. Protection of Exit Enclosures and Other Vertical Openings in a Fully Sprinklered Hotel. The provision for the 1-hour enclosure does not apply to other occupancies in a hotel complex or to mixed occupancies.

16-2.2.2 Doors.

16-2.2.2.1 Doors shall comply with 5-2.1.

16-2.2.2.2* No door in any means of egress shall be locked against egress when the building is occupied.

Exception: Special locking arrangements complying with 5-2.1.6 are permitted.

A-16-2.2.2.2 It is the intent of this requirement that security measures, where installed, should not prevent egress.

Paragraph 16-2.2.2.2 prohibits a hotel from having any door locked "against egress" while the building is occupied. This requirement permits a door to be equipped with a locking device that allows the door to be opened from within the building for the purpose of egress but does not allow the door to be opened from outside the building. Ordinary double cylinder locks and chain locks do not meet these provisions, since they require keys for operation. Several tragic multiple-death fires have occurred where these devices could not be unlocked because no key could be found.

The language of 5-2.1.5.1 is clear: "Locks, if provided, shall not require the use of a key, tool, special knowledge, or effort for operation from the inside of the building." This eliminates double cylinder locks and chain locks that require a key to be operated from the inside. Paragraph 5-2.1.5.3 requires the use of a simple operation to open a door; locks that require two-handed knob and similar operations are specifically prohibited.

Chapter 5 specifically recognizes the need for security chains or rods as well as locks on hotel room doors and allows one additional releasing device. The typical hotel room door has three devices: a latch, a lock, and a security chain or rod. However, the *Code* allows only two releasing actions for new installations. This requirement is met by using a latch and lock set equipped with a lock bolt that automatically retracts when the latch handle is turned from the inside; thus, only one releasing action is needed for the two devices. The second action is the release of the security chain or rod. However, neither device can require the use of a key, tool, special knowledge, or effort.

The Exception to 16-2.2.2.2 recognizes the use of a delay release lock provided for in 5-2.1.6. Use of a delay release lock requires that the building either be protected throughout by automatic sprinklers or be equipped throughout with a fire detection system. The 15- or 30-second delay permitted by 5-2.1.6 does not affect the immediate release of the lock upon activation of sprinklers or detectors or upon loss of power to the lock. This delay device provides the security needed for doors or

stairs that are used infrequently. At the same time, the door remains available for use. Chains and padlocks are unable to provide these features.

16-2.2.2.3* Every stairwell door shall allow reentry from the stairwell to the interior of the building, or an automatic release shall be provided to unlock all stairwell doors to allow reentry. Such automatic release shall be actuated with the initiation of the building fire alarm system. Also, stairwell doors shall unlock upon loss of power controlling the lock or locking mechanism.

A-16-2.2.2.3 This arrangement makes it possible to leave the stairway at any floor should the fire render the lower part of the stair unusable during egress or should the occupants seek refuge on another floor.

The provisions of 16-2.2.2.3 are more stringent than those of Chapter 5, since the provisions of Exception No. 1 to 5-2.1.5.2 cannot be applied to hotels. The Committee reasoned that hotels are not subject to the circumstance experienced by business occupancies in which tenants lease an entire floor with no public corridor arrangement. Therefore, the exception is unwarranted. If hotels wish to restrict normal movement in stairs, the automatic release system can be used. Numerous fatalities occurred in stairways at the MGM Grand Hotel in Las Vegas in 1980,[5] where people were trapped in smoke-filled stairways and were locked out of floors.

16-2.2.2.4 Revolving doors complying with 5-2.1.10 are permitted.

16-2.2.2.5 Horizontal sliding doors in accordance with 5-2.1.14 shall be permitted in a means of egress serving a room or area with an occupant load of less than 50. Such doors shall not be used across corridors.

Note that 16-2.2.2.5 restricts the use of these special doors to a greater extent than Chapter 5. Paragraph 16-2.2.2.5 prohibits cross-corrridor installation or location in a means of egress serving 50 or more people. This overrides some of the general provisions of 5-2.1.14.

16-2.2.3 **Stairs.** Stairs shall comply with 5-2.2.

16-2.2.4 Smokeproof Enclosures. Smokeproof enclosures shall comply with 5-2.3.

16-2.2.5 Horizontal Exits. Horizontal exits shall comply with 5-2.4.

16-2.2.6 Ramps. Ramps shall comply with 5-2.5.

16-2.2.7 Exit Passageways. Exit passageways shall comply with 5-2.6.

16-2.3 Capacity of Means of Egress.

16-2.3.1 The capacity of means of egress shall be in accordance with Section 5-3.

16-2.3.2 Street floor exits shall be sufficient for the occupant load of the street floor plus the required capacity of stairs and ramps discharging onto the street floor.

When upper floor occupants discharge through the street floor (in accordance with 5-7.2) and mix with street floor occupants attempting egress, the result is an increased demand upon street floor exits. Therefore, the *Code* requires that street floor exits be sized to handle the combined capacity.

Figure 16-3 illustrates the traditional grand lobby design found in many hotels in which multiple exit stairs and street floor exits converge at one or two exterior door locations.

16-2.3.3 The minimum corridor width shall be sufficient to accommodate the required occupant load, but not less than 44 in. (112 cm).

Exception*: Corridors within individual guest rooms or individual guest suites.

A-16-2.3.3 **Exception.** This provision applies to corridors within an individual room or suite and does not apply where a suite can be subdivided and rented separately.

16-2.4 Number of Exits. (*See also Section 5-4.*)

16-2.4.1 Not less than two exits shall be accessible from every floor, including floors below the level of exit discharge and occupied for public purposes.

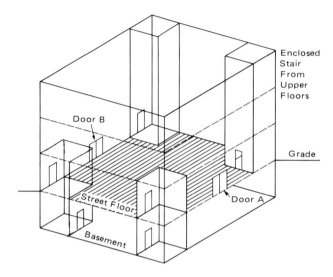

Figure 16-3. *Capacity of Means of Egress in Accordance with 16-2.3.2. Required widths of Doors A and B are based on the number of people expected to use them. Assuming that the street floor has an occupant load of 500, that each upper floor has an occupant load of 200, and that the basement has an occupant load of 100, the required exit capacity for the street floor would be calculated as follows:*
500 (street floor) + 200 ÷ 2 (upper floor max 50% per 5-7.2) + 100 ÷ 2 (basement max 50% per 5-7.2) = 650 total using exits on street floor × 0.2 in. (0.5 cm) of door per person = 130 in. (325 cm) ÷ 2 exits = 65 in. (163 cm) at A and at B.

Paragraph 5-4.1.2 will require a greater number of exits for floors with a capacity of more than 500 people. This will probably have little effect on hotels, since floors large enough to accommodate more than 500 people would probably need additional exits to meet travel distance limitations.

16-2.5 Arrangement of Exits.

16-2.5.1 Access to all required exits shall be in accordance with Section 5-5.

16-2.5.2 No common path of travel shall exceed 35 ft (10.7 m). Travel within a guest room or suite shall not be included when calculating common path of travel.

Exception: In buildings protected throughout by an approved supervised automatic sprinkler system in accordance with 16-3.5, common path of travel shall not exceed 50 ft (15 m).

16-2.5.3 No dead-end corridor shall exceed 35 ft (10.7 m).

Exception: In buildings protected throughout by an approved supervised automatic sprinkler system in accordance with 16-3.5, dead-end corridors shall not exceed 50 ft (15 m).

Common path of travel is normally measured from the most remote point subject to occupancy (*see 5-5.1.2 and the definition of common path of travel in Section 3-2*); therefore, this provides a modified common path of travel, as measurement does not extend into the guest room or suite. Common path of travel within the suite is essentially regulated by 16-2.5.4, which limits single exit access to suites under 2,000 sq ft (185 sq m).

Since the dead-end limits of 16-2.5.3 are the same as the modified common path of travel limitations, it is difficult to envision an excessive modified common path of travel that is not also in violation of the dead-end provision. (*See Figure 16-4.*)

Although part of the Exception to 16-2.5.3, the 50-ft (15-m) common path and dead-end limitations are now the standard minimums, since 16-3.5.2 requires most new buildings to be protected throughout by an approved supervised sprinkler system. However, if a building can comply with the Exception to 16-3.5.2, which exempts sprinklers, the 35-ft(10.7-m) common path and dead-end limitations would then be applied.

16-2.5.4 Any room or any suite of rooms in excess of 2,000 sq ft (185 sq m) shall be provided with at least two exit access doors remotely located from each other.

16-2.6 Travel Distance to Exits.

16-2.6.1 Any exit as indicated in 16-2.4.1 shall be such that it will not be necessary to travel more than 100 ft (30 m) from the door of any room to reach the nearest exit. Travel distance to exits shall be measured in accordance with Section 5-6.

Exception No. 1: Maximum permitted travel distance to exits shall be 200 ft (60 m) for exterior ways of exit access arranged in accordance with 5-5.3.

Exception No. 2: Maximum permitted travel distance to exits shall be 200 ft (60 m) if the exit access and any portion of the building that is tributary to the exit access are protected

throughout by an approved supervised automatic sprinkler system in accordance with 16-3.5. In addition, the portion of the building in which the 200-ft (60-m) travel distance is permitted shall be separated from the remainder of the building by construction having a fire resistance rating of not less than 1 hour for buildings not more than three stories in height, and 2 hours for buildings more than three stories in height.

See Figure 16-5.

16-2.6.2 Travel distance within a room or suite to a corridor door shall not exceed 75 ft (23 m).

Exception: One hundred twenty-five-ft (38-m) travel distance is allowed in buildings protected by an approved supervised automatic sprinkler system in accordance with 16-3.5.

The 1988 Edition of the *Code* revised Section 5-6 so that travel distance is measured from the most remote point subject to occupancy. In order to coordinate with Section 5-6, the Committee revised the method of measuring travel distance in hotels. The travel distance within a room or suite was increased by 25 ft (7.5 m) as compensation. If the travel distance within a room or suite is excessive, an additional remote door to the corridor must be added. (*See 16-2.5.4. Also see Figure 16-5.*)

16-2.7 Discharge from Exits.

16-2.7.1 Exit discharge shall comply with Section 5-7.

16-2.7.2* Any required exit stair that is so located that it is necessary to pass through the lobby or other open space to reach the outside of the building shall be continuously enclosed down to a level of exit discharge or to a mezzanine within a lobby at a level of exit discharge.

A-16-2.7.2 Where open stairways are permitted, they are considered as exit access to exits rather than as exits, and requirements for distance to exits include the travel on such stairs. (*See 5-6.4.*)

16-2.7.3 The distance of travel from the termination of the exit enclosure to an exterior door leading to a public way shall not exceed 100 ft (30 m).

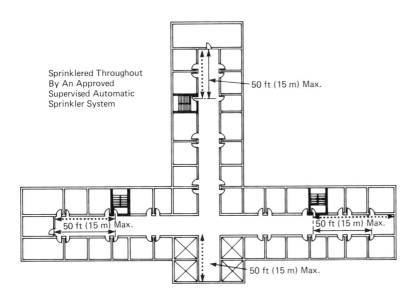

Sprinklered Throughout
By An Approved
Supervised Automatic
Sprinkler System

50 ft (15 m) Max.

50 ft (15 m) Max.

50 ft (15 m) Max.

50 ft (15 m) Max.

Figure 16-4. *Common Path of Travel (Modified) and Dead-End Limitations in a Hotel Sprinklered throughout by an Approved Supervised Automatic Sprinkler System. Modified common paths of travel are indicated by ⟷ and dead ends are indicated by ⟨--⟩. Note that it is possible to have a dead end that is not a common path of travel. However, it is difficult to envision a realistic situation where a modified common path of travel is not also a dead end.*

Figure 16-5. *Travel Distance in Hotels.*

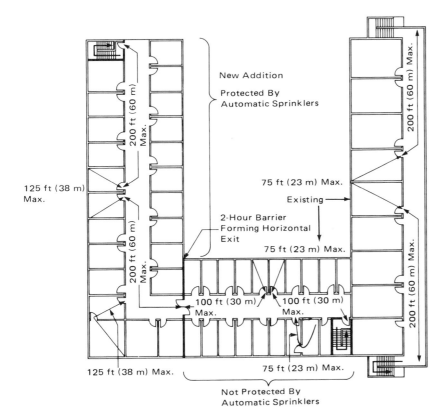

New Addition

Protected By
Automatic Sprinklers

200 ft (60 m) Max.

200 ft (60 m) Max.

125 ft (38 m) Max.

75 ft (23 m) Max.

Existing

2-Hour Barrier
Forming Horizontal
Exit

75 ft (23 m) Max.

200 ft (60 m) Max.

200 ft (60 m) Max.

100 ft (30 m) Max.

100 ft (30 m) Max.

125 ft (38 m) Max.

75 ft (23 m) Max.

Not Protected By
Automatic Sprinklers

Section 5-7 does allow a maximum of 50 percent of the number and capacity of exits to discharge through the street floor under limited conditions (*see 5-7.2*). Paragraph 16-2.7.2 modifies the restrictions of Section 5-7 by including a mezzanine within the lobby. Therefore, 50 percent of the exits can discharge onto a mezzanine. Occupants then travel across the mezzanine, downstairs to the lobby level, and outside. However, 16-2.7.3 contains a provision not included in 5-7.2. It restricts the distance from the termination of the exit enclosure to the exterior door to a maximum of 100 ft (30.5 m).

(*See Figures 16-6 and 16-7. Also see commentary on 5-7.2.*)

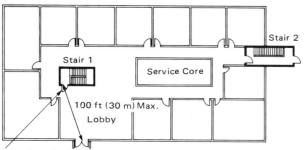

Route from Stair through Lobby to Exterior Must be Readily Visible, Identified, Clear, and Unobstructed.

Figure 16-6. Arrangement of Means of Egress in Accordance with 16-2.7 (see Section 5-7). Stair 1 (50 percent of the total number and capacity of exits) discharges through the first floor. Stair 2 discharges directly to the exterior (it may discharge through an exit passageway) are not separated from the path that an occupant leaving Stair 1 must follow in order to exit through the lobby, the entire first floor must be completely sprinklered. However, 16-3.5.2 now requires most new hotels to be fully sprinklered.

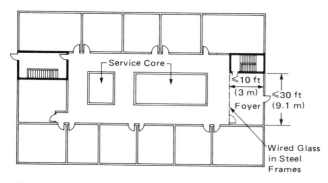

Figure 16-7. Foyer Constructed in Compliance with 16-2.7 (see 5-7.2). The foyer must serve only as a means of egress.

16-2.8 Illumination of Means of Egress.

16-2.8.1 Means of egress shall be illuminated in accordance with Section 5-8.

16-2.9 Emergency Lighting.

16-2.9.1 Emergency lighting in accordance with Section 5-9 shall be provided in all buildings with more than 25 rooms.

Exception: Where each guest room or suite has an exit direct to the outside of the building at street or ground level.

The Exception to 16-2.9.1 applies only to those rooms or suites with doors directly to grade. It does not apply to motels with exterior balconies and stairs.

16-2.10 Marking of Means of Egress.

16-2.10.1 Means of egress shall have signs in accordance with Section 5-10.

16-2.11 Special Features. (Reserved.)

SECTION 16-3   Protection

16-3.1 Protection of Vertical Openings.

16-3.1.1 Every stairway, elevator shaft, and other vertical opening shall be enclosed or protected in accordance with 6-2.4.

Exception No. 1: Unprotected vertical openings connecting not more than three floors in accordance with 6-2.4.5 shall be permitted.

Exception No. 2: An atrium in accordance with 6-2.4.6 shall be permitted.

Exception No. 3: Stairway enclosures shall not be required where a one-story stair connects two levels within a single dwelling unit, guest room, or suite.

Exception No. 4: In buildings protected throughout by an approved supervised automatic sprinkler system installed in accordance with 16-3.5, fire resistance of walls shall be not less than 1 hour and fire protection rating of doors shall be not less than 1 hour.

All new hotels must be sprinklered throughout by an approved supervised automatic sprinkler system unless they qualify for application of the Exception to 16-3.5.2 (i.e., those buildings, other than high rise, where all guest sleeping rooms have a door to the exterior at grade or to an exterior exit access balcony). Therefore, most new hotels, by virtue of their compliance with the sprinkler requirements of 16-3.5.2, may use 1-hour vertical enclosure protection in accordance with Exception No. 4 to 16-3.1.1, regardless of the number of stories connected. *(Also see commentary following 16-2.1.1.)*

16-3.1.2 No floor below the level of exit discharge used only for storage, heating equipment, or purposes other than residential occupancy shall have unprotected openings to floors used for residential purposes.

16-3.2 Protection from Hazards.

16-3.2.1 Any room containing high-pressure boilers, refrigerating machinery, transformers, or other service equipment subject to possible explosion shall not be located directly under or directly adjacent to exits. All such rooms shall be effectively cut off from other parts of the building as specified in Section 6-4.

16-3.2.2 Hazardous Areas. Any hazardous area shall be protected in accordance with Section 6-4. The areas in the following table shall be protected as indicated. Where sprinkler protection without fire rated separation is used, areas shall be separated from other spaces by partitions complying with 6-3.2 and with doors complying with 6-3.4.

This paragraph has been completely rewritten for the 1991 *Code*. Protection for the typical hazardous areas found in hotels and dormitories has been specifically provided. Note that the areas protected by sprinklers still require walls and self-closing doors that resist the passage of smoke unless the first footnote applies.

While the list that appears in 16-3.2.2 provides specific direction for certain hazardous areas, it is not all-inclusive. Other areas that are hazardous need to comply

with the appropriate level of protection in accordance with Section 6-4.

Hazardous Area	Separation/Protection
Boiler and fuel-fired heater rooms serving more than a single guest room or suite.	1-hr and sprinklers
Employee locker rooms	1-hr or sprinklers
Gift or retail shops	1-hr or sprinklers
Bulk laundries	1-hr and sprinklers
Guest laundries not more than 100 sq ft (9.3 sq m) outside of guest rooms or suites	1-hr or sprinklers[1]
Guest laundries more than 100 sq ft (9.3 sq m) outside of guest rooms or suites	1-hr and sprinklers
Maintenance shops	1-hr and sprinklers
Storage rooms[2]	1-hr or sprinklers
Trash rooms	1-hr and sprinklers

[1]Where automatic sprinkler protection is provided, no enclosure is required.
[2]Where storage areas not exceeding 24 sq ft (2.2 sq m) are directly accessible from the guest room or suite, no separation/protection is required.

16-3.3 Interior Finish.

16-3.3.1 Interior finish on walls and ceilings in accordance with Section 6-5 shall be as follows:

(a) Exit enclosures — Class A.
(b) Corridors and lobbies — Class A or B.
(c) All other spaces — Class A, B, or C.

16-3.3.2 Interior floor finish in corridors and exits shall be Class I or Class II in accordance with Section 6-5.

The provisions for interior finish found in 16-3.3 were rewritten for the 1976 Edition of the *Code* to reflect the elimination of the Class D and E categories of interior finish and to better specify where these requirements apply in hotel occupancies. In the 1981 Edition, the interior floor finish requirements were modified to reflect critical radiant flux requirements. Section 6-5 contains strict limitations on the use of textile or carpetlike materials on walls or ceilings.

16-3.4 Detection, Alarm, and Communication Systems.

See Supplement 2.

16-3.4.1 General. A fire alarm system in accordance with Section 7-6 shall be provided.

16-3.4.2 Initiation. The required fire alarm system shall be initiated by:

(a) Manual means in accordance with 7-6.2, and

(b) A manual fire alarm station located at the hotel desk or other convenient central control point under continuous supervision by responsible employees, and

(c) Any automatic sprinkler system, and

(d) Any required automatic detection system.

Exception to (d): Sleeping room smoke detectors are not required to initiate the building fire alarm system.

The *Code* requires that, in addition to the normal distribution of manual fire alarm stations (*see 7-6.2*), the front desk, telephone operator's location, or similar location must also be equipped with a manual pull station. The intent is to have a pull station available at the location where guests phone in an emergency.

The *Code* exempts sleeping room smoke detectors from activating the building fire alarm system. The detectors installed in sleeping rooms are usually single station or multiple station detectors and are not a part of a "required automatic detection system" and, therefore, are automatically exempted. The exception emphasizes this point but clarifies that, if detectors are part of a system, they are not required to initiate the building fire alarm system. The *Code* does not prohibit room detectors from activating the system; however, this is discouraged to prevent numerous activations, which could pose a particular problem in large hotels. The purpose of the sleeping room detector is to warn the occupants of that room. There are detectors available that annunciate at a central point, alert the occupants of the room, and notify management of a problem in that room without sounding an alarm throughout the facility. (*Also see commentary following 16-3.4.4.2.*)

16-3.4.3 Notification.

16-3.4.3.1 Occupant notification shall be provided automatically, without delay, by internal audible alarm in accordance with 7-6.3.

Exception: A presignal system (see 7-6.3.2 Exception No. 1) may be used only in buildings protected throughout by an approved supervised automatic sprinkler system, and then only where permitted by the authority having jurisdiction.

The distribution of audible alarm devices in hotels must be thoroughly reviewed. In most new construction, corridor walls are of such character (soundproof) that a sounding device would be required in each room/suite to provide an audible alarm; without the use of a sounding device in each room/suite, the corridor alarm would have to approach dangerous decibel levels in order to awaken guests in their rooms. (*See Supplement 2.*)

Presignal systems have repeatedly been involved in delaying alarms in multiple-death fires. However, the occurrence of false alarms in hotels is very real. Therefore, as a result of the excellent life loss record in sprinklered hotels, the *Code* allows presignal systems in sprinklered hotels, but the authority having jurisdiction can establish how such a system is to be arranged. If the presignal is to be transmitted to a building staff location (i.e., front desk), Exception No.1 to 7-6.3.2 specifies that it must be received by trained staff. Therefore, hotel employees assigned to signal receiving locations must be well educated regarding fire alarm signals and proper staff response to an alarm.

16-3.4.3.2 An annunciator panel connected with the fire alarm system shall be provided. The location of the annunciator shall be approved by the authority having jurisdiction.

Exception: Buildings not greater than two stories in height and with not more than 50 rooms.

16-3.4.3.3* Provisions shall be made for the immediate notification of the public fire department by telephone or other means in case of fire. Where there is no public fire department, this notification shall be made to the private fire brigade.

A-16-3.4.3.3 The provision for immediate notification of the public fire department is intended to include, but not be limited to, all of the arrangements listed in 7-6.4, "Emergency Forces Notification." Other arrangements that depend on a clerk or other member of the staff to notify the fire department may also be acceptable. In such case, however, it is essential that a trained staff member and an immediately available means of calling the fire department are continuously available. If a telephone is to be used, it should not be of any type or arrangement that requires a coin or the unlocking of a device to contact the fire department.

This paragraph does not require a direct fire alarm connection to the fire department; however, this is the best method of complying with 16-3.4.3.3. The telephone required must be equipped for direct outside dial without going through a switchboard and is not permitted to be a pay phone.

16-3.4.4 Detection.

16-3.4.4.1 A corridor smoke detection system in accordance with Section 7-6 shall be provided.

Exception: Buildings protected throughout by an approved supervised automatic sprinkler system installed in accordance with 16-3.5.

16-3.4.4.2* Each sleeping room and each living area within a guest room or suite shall be provided with an approved single station smoke detector, in accordance with 7-6.2.9, powered from the building electrical system.

A-16-3.4.4.2 Caution must be exercised in locating smoke detectors with regard to their proximity to bathrooms, cooking facilities, and HVAC outlets in order to prevent nuisance alarms.

This paragraph provides for house-powered, single station or multiple station smoke detectors in each sleeping room and living area located in a guest room or suite. These detectors are intended to alert the occupant of the room to the presence of a fire originating in that room or suite. Normally, the detectors are not tied into the building fire alarm [*see the Exception to 16-3.4.2(d).*] When an occupant leaves the room, the door shuts behind the occupant (*see 16-3.6.3*), and the occupant pulls a manual alarm station. If the occupant fails to sound the alarm manually, compensation is provided by corridor smoke detectors or by automatic sprinklers.

The requirement for single station detectors in each sleeping room was new to the 1985 Edition of the *Code*. In this edition of the *Code*, this requirement was expanded

to include each living area within the guest room or suite. The coverage is expanded for two reasons: (1) the living area is often used for sleeping, even if this was not the original intent, and (2) most sleeping rooms are designed in such a way that a fire in the living area will rapidly block escape from the sleeping area.[*See 16-3.4.4.1. Also see commentary following 16-3.4.2(d).*]

16-3.5 Extinguishment Requirements.

See Supplement 3.

16-3.5.1* Where an automatic sprinkler system is installed, either for total or partial building coverage, the system shall be installed in accordance with Section 7-7. In buildings up to and including four stories in height, systems installed in accordance with NFPA 13R, *Standard for the Installation of Sprinkler Systems in Residential Occupancies up to and Including Four Stories in Height*, shall be permitted.

Exception: In guest rooms and in guest room suites, sprinkler installations are not required in closets not over 24 sq ft (2.2 sq m) and bathrooms not over 55 sq ft (5.1 sq m).

A-16-3.5.1 Although not required by the *Code*, the use of residential sprinklers or quick response sprinklers is encouraged for new installations of sprinkler systems within dwelling units, apartments, and guest rooms. Caution must be used, as the system must be designed for the sprinkler being used.

16-3.5.2 All buildings shall be protected throughout by an approved supervised automatic sprinkler system installed in accordance with 16-3.5.1.

Exception: Buildings other than high rise, where all guest sleeping rooms have a door that opens directly to the outside at street or ground level or to exterior exit access arranged in accordance with 5-5.3.

All new hotel and dormitory buildings must be protected throughout by an approved supervised automatic sprinkler system, unless they are low rise buildings in which all guest rooms have doors to the exterior at grade or to exterior exit access balconies. In recognition of the disproportionate percentage of deaths associated with residential occupancies (82 percent)[6] and the conditions precipitating these fatalities in hotel settings (e.g., sleeping occupants must wake and become alert once notified of a fire and subsequently attempt escape in unfamiliar surroundings), the *Code* now mandates that this residential occupancy type be sprinklered. (*See the commentary at the beginning of this chapter. Also see Chapter 3 for the definition of high rise.*)

16-3.5.3 Open air parking structures complying with NFPA 88A, *Standard for Parking Structures*, need not be sprinklered under this *Code*.

Since open air parking structures are a part of many hotels, the Committee reasoned that, for Life Safety *Code* purposes only, an exemption for these structures was warranted. However, should sprinkler protection be required by other codes or by the *Life Safety Code* for reasons other than those found in 16-3.5, sprinkler protection must then be provided in these structures.

16-3.5.4 Portable fire extinguishers shall be provided in hazardous areas. Where provided, portable fire extinguishers shall be installed and maintained in accordance with 7-7.4.1.

16-3.6 Minimum Fire Resistance Requirements for Protection of Guest Rooms (Corridors).

16-3.6.1 Interior corridor walls shall consist of fire barriers in accordance with 6-2.3 having at least a 1-hour fire resistance rating.

Exception: In buildings protected throughout by an approved supervised automatic sprinkler system installed in accordance with 16-3.5, corridor walls shall have at least a ¹/₂-hour fire resistance rating.

The criteria in 16-3.6 reflect the Committee's concern for providing safety for those who are occupying their rooms during a fire. The focus of this concern is the presence of sleeping accommodations that can be used by occupants 24 hours a day. This minimum fire resistance rating for corridor wall construction will either prevent fire movement from the corridor to a room or prevent fire in a room from spreading to the corridor.

While the reduction to ¹/₂-hour fire resistance would have little benefit in new construction, it can play a major role in rehabilitation, renovations, or conversions of exist-

ing structures that are required to meet the provisions for new construction (*see 1-5.6*). Most existing lath and plaster walls provide 20- to 30-minute fire resistance ratings. If automatic sprinkler protection is provided throughout the building, the walls do not have to be replaced.

16-3.6.2 Each guest room door that opens onto an interior corridor shall have a fire protection rating of at least 20 minutes.

The door required by 16-3.6.2 provides a level of protection commensurate with the expected fuel load in the room and the fire resistance of the corridor wall construction. The purpose is to box a fire out of a room or to box it within the room by means of corridor wall and door construction (*see 16-3.6.3*). In fuel load studies conducted by the National Bureau of Standards, it has been demonstrated that residential occupancies will have fuel loads in the 20- to 30-minute range.

16-3.6.3 Each guest room door that opens onto an interior corridor shall be self-closing and shall meet the requirements of 16-3.6.2.

Since 16-3.6.2 requires guest room doors to have a 20-minute fire protection rating, NFPA 80, *Standard for Fire Doors and Windows*,[7] requires the door to be self-closing; however, the Committee believes that this requirement is important enough to be repeated in 16-3.6.3 rather than relying only on the reference document. Numerous hotel fires have resulted in multiple fatalities due to the absence or poor maintenance of door closures.

16-3.6.4 Unprotected openings shall be prohibited in partitions of corridors serving as exit access from guest rooms.

16-3.6.5 No transom, louver, or transfer grille shall be installed in partitions or doors separating the corridors from guest rooms.

Paragraph 2-3.11.1 of NFPA 90A, *Standard for the Installation of Air Conditioning and Ventilating Systems*,[8] prohibits public corridors from being used as a portion of the supply, return, or exhaust air system.

Transoms have been prohibited in hotels for many years due to tragic multiple-death fires that resulted when their presence led to the transmission of fire and smoke through corridors and directly into occupied rooms.

Figure 16-8 illustrates the requirements of 16-3.6.

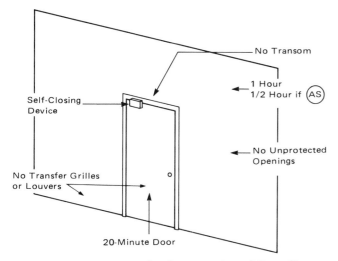

Figure 16-8. *Provisions for the Protection of Guest Rooms (Corridors) in New Hotels. The need for the self-closing 20-minute fire-rated door cannot be overemphasized. There are no exceptions or options to the self-closing door.*

16-3.7 Subdivision of Building Spaces.

16-3.7.1 Every guest room floor shall be divided into at least two smoke compartments of approximately the same size, with smoke barriers in accordance with Section 6-3. Smoke dampers are not required.

Additional smoke barriers shall be provided such that the maximum travel distance from a guest room corridor door to a smoke barrier shall not exceed 150 ft (45 m).

Exception No. 1: Buildings protected throughout by an approved supervised automatic sprinkler system installed in accordance with 16-3.5.

Exception No. 2: Where each guest room is provided with exterior ways of exit access arranged in accordance with 5-5.3.

Exception No. 3: Smoke barriers are not required where the aggregate corridor length on each floor is not more than 150 ft (45 m).

This requirement was new to the 1985 Edition of the *Code.* It should be noted that, since the 1991 Edition of the *Code* requires hotels and dormitories either to be pro-

tected throughout by automatic sprinklers or to have exterior exit access, this paragraph is always exempted. Since no fire rating is required for the barrier and smoke dampers are not required, the requirement is not overly burdensome in typical hotel or dormitory construction.

16-3.8 Special Features. (Reserved.)

SECTION 16-4   Special Provisions

16-4.1* **Operable Windows.** Each guest room shall be provided with at least one outside window. Such windows shall be openable from the inside, without the use of tools, and provide a clear opening of not less than 20 in. (50.8 cm) in width, 24 in. (61 cm) in height, and 5.7 sq ft (.53 sq m) in area. The bottom of the opening shall not be more than 44 in. (112 cm) above the floor.

Exception No. 1: Buildings protected throughout by an approved supervised automatic sprinkler system installed in accordance with 16-3.5.

Exception No. 2: Where a guest room has a door leading directly to the outside of building.

Exception No. 3: Buildings provided with an approved engineered smoke control system in accordance with Section 7-3.

A-16-4.1 Windows may serve as a means of emergency escape, particularly where ladders can be raised by fire fighters or others. Even where the location is such as to preclude the use of windows for escape purposes, they may provide air for breathing in a smoke-filled room while trapped occupants are awaiting rescue. Windows should have sills not too high above the floor; windows lower than 44 in. (112 cm) above the floor are preferable.

Where awning- or hopper-type windows are used, they should be so hinged or subdivided as to provide a clear opening of at least 5.7 sq ft (.53 sq m). Where storm windows, screens, or burglar guards are used, these should be provided with quick-opening devices so that they may be readily opened from the inside for emergency egress.

Several recent multiple-death hotel fires have graphically illustrated the problem of guest rooms equipped with nonoperable windows in both low rise and high rise buildings. An operable window allows an occupant access to fresh air and/or rescue. An operable window can be opened and then shut if smoke is drawn into a room; an inoperable window that has been broken cannot.

The windows specified in this paragraph are identical to those specified for other residential occupancies and schools. Although not stated in the language of 16-4.1, reason dictates that an occupant should be able to open the rescue/ventilation window without any special knowledge, particularly in a hotel. Because it is assumed that occupants of a hotel will not be familiar with their surroundings, the method of opening the window should be readily apparent, especially under those conditions that may demand its accessibility (i.e., lack of light, smoke, and increasing level of heat).

The door described in Exception No. 2 does not have to be an exit access door but can be a door to a balcony, as this serves the same function as a window. For reasons of security, most hotels are reluctant to use operable windows; therefore, Exception No. 1 is often applied. Application of Exception No. 3 is not practical in most hotels due to the design of typical hotel HVAC systems.

Since most new buildings are now required to be sprinklered, Exception No. 1 eliminates the need for operable windows in many new hotels.

Exception No. 2 exempts the requirement for the operable window if each guest room has a door leading directly to the outside. This appears to match the language that eliminates the requirement to sprinkler certain buildings, which would exempt the requirement for operable windows in new construction. However, a careful review of the wording clarifies that sprinklers are not required in buildings other than high rise if *each sleeping room* has a door that opens to the outside at ground level or to an exterior exit access balcony. By contrast, the operable window is exempted from guest rooms that have doors leading to the outside. Therefore, non sprinklered hotels are required to have operable windows in all guest rooms not used for sleeping (with the exception of bathrooms).

In accordance with the modernization and renovation provision of 1-5.6, where windows are replaced in existing hotels the operable window requirement should be complied with as nearly as practicable.

16-4.2   **High Rise Buildings.** High rise buildings shall comply with Section 30-8. The Exception to 16-3.5.1 shall be permitted.

16-4.3   **Operating Features.** (*See Chapter 31.*)

SECTION 16-5   Building Services

16-5.1   **Utilities.** Utilities shall comply with the provisions of Section 7-1.

16-5.2   **Heating, Ventilating, and Air Conditioning.** Heating, ventilating, and air conditioning equipment shall comply with the provisions of Section 7-2, except as otherwise required in this chapter.

16-5.3*   **Elevators, Escalators, and Conveyors.** Elevators, escalators, and conveyors shall comply with the provisions of Section 7-4. In high rise buildings, one elevator shall be provided with a protected power supply and be available for use by the fire department in case of emergency.

A-16-5.3   "Protected power supply" means a source of electrical energy of sufficient capacity to permit proper operation of the elevator and its associated control and communications systems and whose point of origin, system of distribution, type and size of overcurrent protection, degree of isolation from other portions of the building electrical system, and degree of mechanical protection are such that it is unlikely that the supply would be disrupted at any but the advanced stages of building fire involvement or by structural collapse.

A protected power supply should provide at least the level of reliability associated with, and may consist of, an electrical distribution system whose service equipment is located and installed in accordance with Sections 230-72(b) and 230-82, Exception No. 5 of NFPA 70, *National Electrical Code* (*see Appendix B*), and that has no other connection to the "normal" building electrical distribution system. A protected power supply need not incorporate two sources of energy or automatic transfer capability from a "normal" to an "emergency" source, e.g., an alternate set of service conductors.

The number and type of elevators to be connected to a protected power supply should be limited, or the characteristics of the protected power supply should be selected, so as to ensure conformance with Section 230-95 of NFPA 70, *National Electrical Code* (*see Appendix B*), without the provision of ground fault protection for the supply.

An elevator installation supplied by a protected power supply should comply with Article 620 of NFPA 70, *National Electrical Code* (*see Appendix B*), except that the "energy absorption means" required by Section 620-91 should always be connected on the load side of the disconnecting means and should not consist of loads likely to become inoperative or disconnected under the conditions assumed to exist where the elevator is under the control of fire department personnel, e.g., light and power loads external to the elevator equipment room.

16-5.4 **Rubbish Chutes, Incinerators, and Laundry Chutes.** Rubbish chutes, incinerators, and laundry chutes shall comply with the provisions of Section 7-5.

The 1985 Edition of the *Code* eliminated the special section on dormitories. Dormitories are now covered as hotels. The section was deleted due to several changes in hotel requirements affecting windows, alarms, and building subdivisions. These changes rendered special requirements for dormitories unnecessary.

References Cited in Commentary

[1]Thomas J. Klem, Investigation Report on the DuPont Plaza Hotel Fire, National Fire Protection Association, Quincy, MA, 1987.

[2]J.R. Bell, T.J. Klem, and A.E. Willey, Investigation on the Westchase Hilton Hotel Fire, National Fire Protection Association, Quincy, MA, 1982.

[3]Jon C. Jones, "A Brief Look at the Hotel Fire Record," *Fire Journal*, Vol. 75, No. 3, May 1981, pp. 38-47.

[4]NFPA 13, *Standard for the Installation of Sprinkler Systems*, National Fire Protection Association, Quincy, MA, 1991.

[5]Richard Best, and David P. Demers, Investigation Report on the MGM Grand Hotel Fire, Las Vegas, Nevada, National Fire Protection Association, Quincy, MA, NFPA No. LS-4, 1982.

[6]Michael J. Karter, Jr., "Fire Loss in the United States During 1989, *Fire Journal*, Vol. 84, No. 5, pp. 56-67, September/October 1990.

[7]NFPA 80, *Standard for Fire Doors and Windows*, National Fire Protection Association, Quincy, MA, 1990.

[8]NFPA 90A, *Standard for the Installation of Air Conditioning and Ventilating Systems*, National Fire Protection Association, Quincy, MA, 1989.

17

Existing Hotels and Dormitories

(See also Chapter 31.)

Hotels and dormitories are one of five residential occupancy types addressed by the *Life Safety Code*. Other residential occupancies include one- and two-family dwellings, apartment buildings, lodging and rooming houses, and residential board and care facilities. Sleeping accommodations are a feature common to all residential occupancies.

Paragraph 4-1.6 highlights the common principle of life safety with which the *Code* is concerned as applied to all residential occupancies addressed by Chapters 16 through 23. Paragraph 4-1.6 states: "Residential occupancies are those occupancies in which sleeping accommodations are provided for normal residential purposes and include all buildings designed to provide sleeping accommodations." This use of residential occupancies is central to the *Code* provisions of Chapters 16 through 23, since occupants who are asleep will be unaware of a rapidly developing fire and, when alerted to the emergency, may be somewhat confused due to being awakened suddenly.

Other factors on which the provisions of Chapters 16 through 23 are based are the presence of hazards (such as cooking and heating equipment) in residential occupancies and the degree of familiarity of the occupants with their living space. Occupants may have little or no familiarity, as in the case of transient residents of hotels, or they may have the total familiarity of residents of a single-family dwelling.

Hotels and motels averaged 8,300 structure fires a year as reported to U.S. fire departments from 1984 to 1988. These fires caused an average of 49 civilian deaths and 405 civilian injuries per year. These figures do not include lodging and rooming houses and residential board and care facilities (defined for fire reporting purposes as facilities limited to fewer than 16 occupants).

The primary causes of hotel and motel fires are careless handling of smoking materials and arson (including suspected arson). Collectively, they account for nearly half of all hotel and motel fires, two-thirds of associated deaths, and more than half of associated injuries. Nevertheless, nearly half of all people killed in hotel and motel fires from 1980 to 1988 were not in the room of fire origin. Therefore, the potential for fire protection is considerable.

More than two-thirds of hotel and motel fires during 1988 occurred where smoke detectors were used. The usage of smoke detectors in hotels and motels probably exceeds the percentage documented as a result of reported fires. Nearly half of all hotels were sprinklered as of 1988. The growth in the usage of these and other fire protection features in the 1980s helps explain a steady downward trend in fires, deaths, and injuries in these occupancies.

In spite of the increase in protection, hotels and motels were the site of the two deadliest fires in the U.S. and its possessions in the 1980s: the MGM Grand Hotel fire in 1980,[5] which killed 85 people, and the DuPont Plaza Hotel fire in 1986,[1] which killed 97 people. These and other large, multiple-death fires in hotels and motels have served to emphasize the importance of systematic fire protection, in accordance with the provisions of the *Life Safety Code*.

The following is a brief list representing hotel fires that have not only emphasized the need for changes in the *Code*, but have also focused attention on the need for compliance with the *Code*:

Date	Place	Civilian Deaths
December 1986	DuPont Plaza San Juan, PR	97[1]
March 1982	Hilton Hotel Houston, TX	12[2]
February 1981	Hilton Hotel Las Vegas, NV	8[3]
December 1980	Stouffer's Inn Harrison, NY	26[3]
November 1980	MGM Grand Hotel Las Vegas, NV	85[3]
December 1946	Winecoff Hotel Atlanta, GA	119[3]
June 1946	LaSalle Hotel Chicago, IL	61[3]

The following multiple fatality dormitory fires occurred within the past decade:

Date	Place	Civilian Deaths
June 1980	Migrant Labor Camp Barracks Clinton, NC	5
October 1985	Fraternity House Fort Collins, CO	4
Sept. 1990	Fraternity House Berkeley, CA	3

SECTION 17-1   General Requirements

17-1.1   Application.

17-1.1.1   This chapter establishes life safety requirements for all existing hotels. (*See Chapter 31 for operating features.*)

Hotels and dormitories are defined in 17-1.3.1. It should be noted that lodging or rooming houses that contain more than 16 people are considered hotels and must comply with Chapter 17. New hotels are covered in Chapter 16.

Renovations, modernizations, and similar work must comply with 1-5.6, which states that such work must comply with Chapter 16 to the extent practical.

17-1.1.2   Existing dormitories shall comply with the requirements for existing hotels.

Exception: Any dormitory divided into suites of rooms, with one or more bedrooms opening into a living room or study that has a door opening into a common corridor serving a number of suites, shall be classified as an apartment building.

The Exception to 17-1.1.2 recognizes that the popular dormitory design in which a group of bedrooms opens into a living room duplicates a typical apartment design in which several bedrooms open into a living room (or kitchen). Since the design and the risk of fire are the same, the *Code* treats this arrangement as that of an apartment building. (*See Figure 17-1.*)

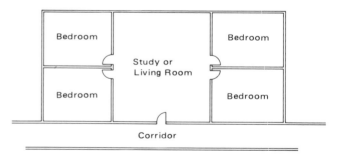

Figure 17-1.   Arrangement of Dormitory Suite Treated as an Apartment Under the Exception to 17-1.1.2. More than one bedroom opens into a study or living room that has a door opening into a corridor. The corridor serves a number of suites.

17-1.2 Mixed Occupancies.

17-1.2.1 Where another type of occupancy occurs in the same building as a residential occupancy, the requirements of 1-5.7 of this *Code* shall be applicable.

17-1.2.2 For requirements on mixed mercantile and residential occupancies, see 25-1.2; for mixed assembly and residential occupancies, see 9-1.2.

The *Code* previously provided requirements to ensure the integrity of the residential means of egress in mixed residential/mercantile occupancies. The 1991 Edition now applies this safeguard to assembly occupancies.

17-1.2.3 Any ballroom, assembly or exhibition hall, and other space used for purposes of public assembly shall be in accordance with Chapter 9. Any dining area having a capacity of 50 or more persons shall be treated as an assembly occupancy.

Most larger hotels are made up of several occupancies that include Hotel, Assembly (ballrooms, restaurants, lounges), Business (large administrative areas), Mercantile (large shopping areas), and others. Unless these areas are adequately separated and protected, the complex is considered a mixed occupancy, and the most stringent provisions of the various occupancies must be applied. Note that small administrative areas and small gift shops or newsstands are not subject to mixed occupancy requirements. This can be very important with regard to construction and sprinkler requirements for assembly occupancies and sprinkler requirements for mercantile occupancies. (*See commentary following 17-1.6, 17-3.2, and 17-3.5.*)

17-1.3 Definitions.

17-1.3.1 Terms applicable to this chapter are defined in Chapter 3 of this *Code*; where necessary, other terms will be defined in the text as they may occur.

Dormitories. Dormitories include buildings or spaces in buildings where group sleeping accommodations are provided for more than 16 persons who are not members of the same family in one room or a series of closely associated rooms under joint occupancy and single management, with or without meals, but without individual cooking facilities. Examples are college dormitories, fraternity houses, and military barracks.

In 17-1.3.1, the phrase "without individual cooking facilities" refers to the absence of cooking equipment in any room or unit of a dormitory. If this equipment is present throughout a facility, the occupancy should be classed as an apartment building. The phrase "with or without meals" indicates the *Code's* acceptance of a central cafeteria used to serve meals for the occupants of a dormitory.

Hotels. Hotels include buildings or groups of buildings under the same management in which there are more than 16 sleeping accommodations primarily used by transients (those who occupy accommodations for less than 30 days) for lodging with or without meals, whether designated as a hotel, inn, club, motel, or by any other name. So-called apartment hotels shall be classified as hotels because they are potentially subject to the same transient occupancy as hotels.

Lodging or rooming houses containing more than 16 people are treated as hotels. The parenthetical reference to a 30-day time period has been added to better define "transient." Where units have individual cooking facilities, the *Code* classifies the occupancy as an apartment building (*see 19-1.3*). However, where the authority having jurisdiction believes that the potential for hazards associated with both a hotel (unfamiliarity with surroundings) and an apartment building (higher fuel load, greater number of ignition sources, and travel through multiple rooms) are present, it may be appropriate to classify the building as a mixed occupancy (hotel and apartment).

17-1.4 Classification of Occupancy. (*See 17-1.3.*)

17-1.5 Classification of Hazard of Contents.

17-1.5.1 The contents of residential occupancies shall be classified as ordinary hazard in accordance with Section 4-2. For the design of automatic sprinkler systems, the classification of contents in NFPA 13, *Standard for the Installation of Sprinkler Systems*, shall apply.

NFPA 13, *Standard for the Installation of Sprinkler Systems*,[4] would classify the contents as "light hazard" for the purpose of designing extinguishing systems. The difference in classification is based on the threat to life or life safety (ordinary) versus the threat to the extinguishing capability of the automatic sprinkler system (light).

17-1.6 Minimum Construction Requirements. No special requirements.

Although this chapter does not establish minimum construction requirements, if the hotel contains an assembly occupancy, Chapter 9 does establish minimum construction requirements based on the location of the assembly occupancy.

17-1.7 Occupant Load.

17-1.7.1* The occupant load in numbers of persons for whom exits are to be provided shall be determined on the basis of one person per 200 sq ft (18.6 sq m) gross floor area or the maximum probable population of any room or section under consideration, whichever is greater. The occupant load of any open mezzanine or balcony shall be added to the occupant load of the floor below for the purpose of determining exit capacity.

A-17-1.7.1 Dormitory-type occupancy, particularly where 2- or 3-tier bunks are used with close spacing, may produce an occupant load substantially greater than one person per 200 sq ft (18.6 sq m) gross floor area. However, even though sleeping areas are densely populated, the building as a whole may not necessarily exceed one person per 200 sq ft (18.6 sq m) gross area, owing to the space taken for toilet facilities, halls, closets, and living rooms not used for sleeping purposes.

The requirements of this paragraph do not preclude the need for providing exit capability from concentrated sleeping areas (bunk rooms) based on the "maximum probable population" rather than on the floor area. If the actual population of a bunk room exceeds 1 person per 200 sq ft (18.6 sq m), the exit capacity features (door widths, etc.) will have to be designed based on the actual population load. See 5-3.1 for further details on the use of occupant load for determining capacity of the means of egress.

The occupant loads for areas of hotels used for non-residential purposes are based on the use of the area. Occupant loads are calculated in accordance with the -1.7 subsection of each occupancy chapter (e.g., 9-1.7 for assembly areas, 25-1.7 for mercantile areas).

SECTION 17-2   Means of Egress Requirements

17-2.1 General.

17-2.1.1 Means of egress from guest rooms/guest suites to the outside of the building shall be in accordance with Chapter 5 and this chapter. Means of escape within the guest room/guest suite shall comply with the provisions of Section 21-2 for one- and two-family dwellings. For the purpose of application of the requirements of Chapter 21, guest room/guest suite is synonymous with dwelling or living unit.

A general reference is made to Chapter 5 in place of repeating many of its provisions. Many of the requirements contained in Section 17-2 are Chapter 5 provisions that are options for the occupancy chapters, such as the Exception to 17-2.2.2.2, which allows the use of special locking arrangements per 5-2.1.6; or that prohibit the use of an item if it is not listed (note that alternating tread devices are not listed in 17-2.2); or that establish restrictions based on criteria provided in Chapter 5, such as the limits placed on dead-end corridors found in 17-2.5.3.

Paragraph 17-2.1.1 requires that every guest room/suite comply with Section 21-2 of Chapter 21, which addresses one- and two-family dwellings. This requirement is important for several reasons. First, it establishes two means of escape from every sleeping room and living area of a guest room/suite having two rooms or more. Paragraph 21-2.1.2 establishes several acceptable types of "second means of escape," the most common of which is the operable window. A second means of escape is exempted if a guest room/suite is protected by an automatic sprinkler system. Note that this does not require the entire building to be sprinklered but only the guest room/suite that is not in compliance with the secondary means of escape.

A second important provision of Section 21-2 is that the means of egress provisions in Chapter 5 do not apply unless specifically referenced. For example, the minimum widths of doors within a guest room/suite are reduced to 28 in. (71 cm) from the 32 in. (81 cm) in width specified by Chapter 5. Chapter 21 also allows the use of winders and spiral stairs within a guest room/suite, and the provisions of Chapter 21 for headroom apply within the guest room/suite, superseding those of Chapter 5. (*See commentary on Chapter 21 for additional information on means of escape from living units.*)

17-2.2 Means of Egress Components.

17-2.2.1 General.

17-2.2.1.1 Components of means of egress shall be limited to the types described in 17-2.2.2 through 17-2.2.9.

17-2.2.1.2 In buildings protected throughout by an approved automatic sprinkler system installed in accordance with 17-3.5, exit enclosures shall have a fire resistance rating of not less than 1 hour, and the fire protection rating of doors shall be not less than 1 hour.

In recognition of the relatively low fuel loads in hotels, the fire resistance rating for exit enclosures, as well as for other vertical openings (*see 17-3.1.1 Exception No. 4*), need not exceed 1 hour; however, as a safeguard, this is permitted only in buildings protected throughout by automatic sprinklers.

This 1-hour rating is not permitted for assembly occupancies or business occupancies and, therefore, cannot be utilized where mixed occupancies are involved; nor can it be used for stairways or vertical openings located in or passing through other occupancies. In facilities where occupancies are adequately separated and treated independently, a 1-hour enclosure in the hotel portion and 2-hour enclosure elsewhere could be permitted. (*See Figure 17-2.*)

17-2.2.2 Doors.

17-2.2.2.1 Doors shall comply with 5-2.1.

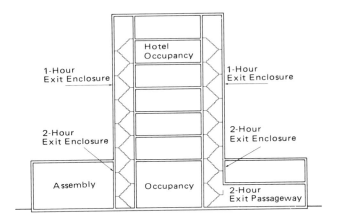

Figure 17-2. Protection of Exit Enclosures and Other Vertical Openings in a Fully Sprinklered Hotel. The provision for the 1-hour enclosure does not apply to other occupancies in a hotel complex or to mixed occupancies.

17-2.2.2.2* No door in any means of egress shall be locked against egress when the building is occupied.

Exception: Special locking arrangements complying with 5-2.1.6 are permitted.

A-17-2.2.2.2 It is the intent of this requirement that security measures, where installed, should not prevent egress.

Paragraph 17-2.2.2.2 prohibits a hotel from having any door locked "against egress" while the building is occupied. This requirement permits a door to be equipped with a locking device that allows the door to be opened from within the building for the purpose of egress but does not allow the door to be opened from outside the building. Ordinary double cylinder locks and chain locks do not meet these provisions, since they require keys for operation. Several tragic multiple-death fires have occurred where these devices could not be unlocked because no key could be found.

The language of 5-2.1.5.1 is clear: "Locks, if provided, shall not require the use of a key, tool, special knowledge, or effort for operation from the inside of the building." This eliminates double cylinder locks and chain locks that require a key to operate from the inside. Paragraph 5-2.1.5.3 requires the use of a simple operation to open a door; locks that require two-handed knob and similar operations are specifically prohibited.

Chapter 5 specifically recognizes the need for security chains or rods as well as locks on hotel room doors and allows two additional releasing devices for existing installations. The typical hotel room door has three devices: a latch, a lock, and a security chain or rod. The *Code* prefers only two releasing actions (*see commentary following 16-2.2.2.2*) but recognizes the existence of thousands of installations that require the use of three actions. Where new installations are made in an existing hotel, the *Code* requires (*see 1-5.6*) that the installation comply with Chapter 16.

The Exception to 17-2.2.2.2 recognizes the use of a delay release lock provided for in 5-2.1.6. Use of a delay release lock requires that the building either be protected throughout by automatic sprinklers or be equipped throughout with a fire detection system. The 15- or 30-second delay permitted by 5-2.1.6 does not affect the immediate release of the lock upon activation of sprinklers or detectors or upon loss of power to the lock. This delay device provides the security needed for doors or stairs that are used infrequently. At the same time, the door remains available for use. Chains and padlocks are unable to provide these features.

17-2.2.2.3* Every stairwell door shall allow reentry from the stairwell to the interior of the building, or an automatic release shall be provided to unlock all stairwell doors to allow reentry. Such automatic release shall be actuated with the initiation of the building fire alarm system. Also, stairwell doors shall unlock upon loss of power controlling the lock or locking mechanism.

A-17-2.2.2.3 This arrangement makes it possible to leave the stairway at any floor should the fire render the lower part of the stair unusable during egress or should the occupants seek refuge on another floor.

The provisions of 17-2.2.2.3 are more stringent than those of Chapter 5, since the provisions of Exception No. 1 to 5-2.1.5.2 cannot be applied to hotels. The Committee reasoned that hotels are not subject to the circumstance experienced by business occupancies in which tenants lease an entire floor with no public corridor arrangement. Therefore, the exception is unwarranted. If hotels wish to restrict normal movement in stairs, the

automatic release system can be used. Numerous fatalities occurred in stairways at the MGM Grand Hotel in Las Vegas in 1980,[5] where people were trapped in smoke-filled stairways and were locked out of floors.

17-2.2.2.4 Revolving doors complying with 5-2.1.10 are permitted.

17-2.2.2.5 Horizontal sliding doors in accordance with 5-2.1.14 shall be permitted in a means of egress serving a room or area with an occupant load of less than 50. Such doors shall not be used across corridors.

Note that 17-2.2.2.5 restricts the use of these special doors to a greater extent than Chapter 5. Paragraph 16-2.2.2.5 prohibits cross-corridor installation or location in a means of egress serving 50 or more people. This overrides some of the general provisions of 5-2.1.14.

17-2.2.3 **Stairs.** Stairs shall comply with 5-2.2.

17-2.2.4 **Smokeproof Enclosures.** Smokeproof enclosures shall comply with 5-2.3.

17-2.2.5 **Horizontal Exits.** Horizontal exits shall comply with 5-2.4.

17-2.2.6 **Ramps.** Ramps shall comply with 5-2.5.

17-2.2.7 **Exit Passageways.** Exit passageways shall comply with 5-2.6.

17-2.2.8* **Escalators.** Escalators previously approved as a component in the means of egress may continue to be given credit.

A-17-2.2.8 Due to the nature of escalators, they are no longer acceptable as a component in the means of egress. However, since many escalators have been used for exit access and exit discharge in the past, credit may be continued. Very few escalators have ever been installed in a manner to qualify as an exit. For information on escalator protection and requirements, the reader is referred to previous editions of the *Code*.

17-2.2.9 **Fire Escape Stairs.** Fire escape stairs complying with 5-2.8 are permitted.

17-2.3 Capacity of Means of Egress.

17-2.3.1 The capacity of means of egress shall be in accordance with Section 5-3.

17-2.3.2 Street floor exits shall be sufficient for the occupant load of the street floor plus the required capacity of stairs and ramps discharging onto the street floor.

When upper floor occupants discharge through the street floor (in accordance with 5-7.2) and mix with street floor occupants attempting egress, the result is an increased demand upon street floor exits. Therefore, the *Code* requires that street floor exits be sized to handle the combined capacity.

Figure 17-3 illustrates the traditional grand lobby design found in many hotels in which multiple exit stairs and street floor exits converge at one or two exterior door locations.

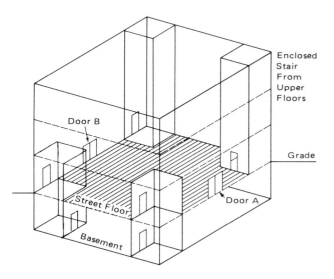

Figure 17-3. Capacity of Means of Egress in Accordance with 17-2.3.2. Required widths of Doors A and B are based on the number of people expected to use them. Assuming that the street floor has an occupant load of 500, that each upper floor has an occupant load of 200, and that the basement has an occupant load of 100, the required exit capacity for the street floor would be calculated as follows:

500 (street floor) + 200 ÷ 2 (upper floor max 50% per 5-7.2) + 100 ÷ 2 (basement max 50% per 5-7.2) = 650 total using exits on street floor × 0.2 in. (0.5 cm) of door per person = 130 in. (325 cm) ÷ 2 exits = 65 in. (163 cm) at A and at B.

17-2.4 Number of Exits. *(See also Section 5-4.)*

17-2.4.1 Not less than two exits shall be accessible from every floor, including floors below the level of exit discharge and occupied for public purposes.

Paragraph 5-4.1.2 will require a greater number of exits for floors with a capacity of more than 500 people. This will probably have little effect on hotels, since floors large enough to accommodate more than 500 people would probably need additional exits to meet travel distance limitations.

17-2.5 Arrangement of Exits.

17-2.5.1 Access to all required exits shall be in accordance with Section 5-5.

17-2.5.2 No common path of travel shall exceed 35 ft (10.7 m). Travel within a guest room or suite shall not be included when calculating common path of travel.

Exception: In buildings protected throughout by an approved supervised automatic sprinkler system in accordance with 17-3.5, common path of travel shall not exceed 50 ft (15 m).

17-2.5.3 No dead-end corridor shall exceed 50 ft (15 m).

Common path of travel is normally measured from the most remote point subject to occupancy (*see 5-5.1.2 and the definition of common path of travel in Section 3-2*); therefore, this provides a modified common path of travel, as measurement does not extend into the guest room or suite. Since existing buildings have limits for common path and dead end that are different from those of new buildings, the arrangement shown in Figure 17-4 is acceptable and does not violate either provision.

17-2.6 Travel Distance to Exits.

17-2.6.1 Any exit as indicated in 17-2.4.1 shall be such that it will not be necessary to travel more than 100 ft (30 m) from the door of any room to reach the nearest exit. Travel distance to exits shall be measured in accordance with Section 5-6.

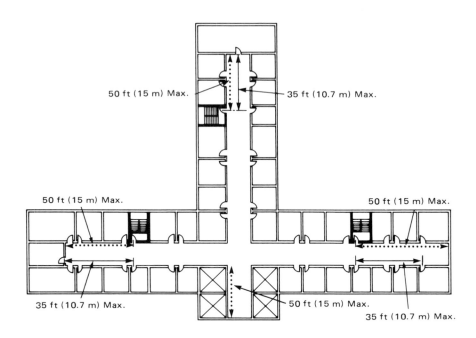

Figure 17-4. Common Path of Travel (Modified) and Dead-End Limitations in a Nonsprinklered Hotel. Modified common paths of travel are indicated by ⟷ and dead ends are indicated by ⟜⟶ .

Exception No. 1: Maximum permitted travel distance to exits shall be 200 ft (60 m) for exterior ways of exit access arranged in accordance with 5-5.3.

Exception No. 2: Maximum permitted travel distance to exits shall be 200 ft (60 m) if the exit access and any portion of the building that is tributary to the exit access are protected throughout by an approved automatic sprinkler system in accordance with 17-3.5. In addition, the portion of the building in which the 200-ft (60-m) travel distance is permitted shall be separated from the remainder of the building by construction having a fire resistance rating of not less than 1 hour for buildings not more than three stories in height, and 2 hours for buildings more than three stories in height.

See Figure 17-5.

17-2.6.2   Travel distance within a room or suite to a corridor door shall not exceed 75 ft (23 m).

Exception: One hundred twenty-five-ft (38-m) travel distance is allowed in buildings protected by an automatic sprinkler system in accordance with 17-3.5.

The 1988 Edition of the *Code* revised Section 5-6 so that travel distance is measured from the most remote point subject to occupancy. In order to coordinate with

Section 5-6, the Committee revised the method of measuring travel distance in hotels. The travel distance within a room or suite was increased by 25 ft (7.5 m) as compensation. If the travel distance within a room or suite is excessive, an additional remote door to the corridor must be added. (*See Figure 17-5.*)

17-2.7   Discharge from Exits.

17-2.7.1   Exit discharge shall comply with Section 5-7.

17-2.7.2*   Any required exit stair that is so located that it is necessary to pass through the lobby or other open space to reach the outside of the building shall be continuously enclosed down to a level of exit discharge or to a mezzanine within a lobby at a level of exit discharge.

A-17-2.7.2   Where open stairways or escalators are permitted, they are considered as exit access to exits rather than as exits, and requirements for distance to exits include the travel on such stairs. (*See 5-6.4.*)

17-2.7.3   The distance of travel from the termination of the exit enclosure to an exterior door leading to a public way shall

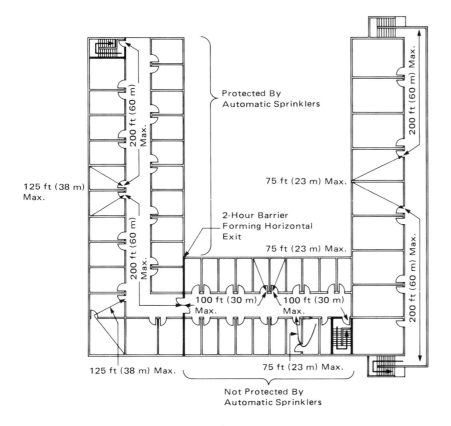

Figure 17-5. *Travel Distance in Hotels.*

not exceed 150 ft (45 m) in buildings protected throughout by an approved automatic sprinkler system in accordance with 17-3.5 and shall not exceed 100 ft (30 m) in all other buildings.

Section 5-7 does allow a maximum of 50 percent of the number and capacity of exits to discharge through the street floor under limited conditions (*see* 5-7.2). Paragraph 17-2.7.2 modifies the restrictions of Section 5-7 by including a mezzanine within the lobby. Therefore, 50 percent of the exits can discharge onto a mezzanine. Occupants then travel across the mezzanine, downstairs to the lobby level, and outside. However, 17-2.7.3 contains a provision not included in 5-7.2. It restricts the distance from the termination of the exit enclosure to the exterior door to a maximum of 100 ft (30.5 m) in nonsprinklered buildings and 150 ft (45 m) in buildings that are fully sprinklered.

(*See Figures 17-6 and 17-7. Also see commentary on 5-7.2.*)

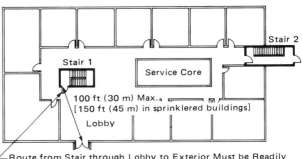

Figure 17-6. *Arrangement of Means of Egress in Accordance with 17-2.7 (see Section 5-7.2). Stair 1 (50 percent of the total number and capacity of exits) discharges through the first floor. Stair 2 discharges directly to the exterior (it may discharge through an exit passageway to the exterior). Since other areas on the first floor (the level of exit discharge) are not separated from the path that an occupant leaving Stair 1 must follow in order to exit through the lobby, the entire first floor must be completely sprinklered. If the rest of the floor were separated (to the extent required for the stair enclosure), only the path to the exit discharge would have to be sprinklered.*

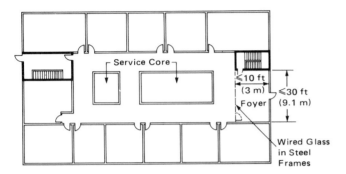

Figure 17-7. *Foyer Constructed in Compliance with 17-2.7 (see 5-7.2). The foyer must serve only as a means of egress.*

17-2.8 Illumination of Means of Egress.

17-2.8.1 Means of egress shall be illuminated in accordance with Section 5-8.

17-2.9 Emergency Lighting.

17-2.9.1 Emergency lighting in accordance with Section 5-9 shall be provided in all buildings with more than 25 rooms.

Exception: Where each guest room or suite has an exit direct to the outside of the building at street or ground level.

The Exception to 17-2.9.1 applies only to those rooms or suites with doors directly to grade. It does not apply to motels with exterior balconies and stairs.

17-2.10 Marking of Means of Egress.

17-2.10.1 Means of egress shall have signs in accordance with Section 5-10.

17-2.11 Special Features. (Reserved.)

SECTION 17-3   Protection

17-3.1 Protection of Vertical Openings.

17-3.1.1 Every stairway, elevator shaft, and other vertical opening shall be enclosed or protected in accordance with

6-2.4 or provide means of satisfying the requirements of Section 2-9.

Exception No. 1: Unprotected vertical openings connecting not more than three floors in accordance with 6-2.4.5 shall be permitted.

Exception No. 2: An atrium in accordance with 6-2.4.6 shall be permitted.

Exception No. 3: Stairway enclosures shall not be required where a one-story stair connects two levels within a single dwelling unit, guest room, or suite.

Exception No. 4: In any building protected throughout by an approved automatic sprinkler system in accordance with 17-3.5, and where exits and required ways of travel thereto are adequately safeguarded against fire and smoke within the building or where every individual room has direct access to an exterior exit without passing through any public corridor, the protection of vertical openings not part of required exits may be waived by the authority having jurisdiction to such extent as such openings do not endanger required means of egress.

Exception No. 5: In existing buildings not more than two stories in height, unprotected openings may be permitted by the authority having jurisdiction if the building is protected throughout by an approved automatic sprinkler system in accordance with 17-3.5.

Paragraph 17-3.1.1 requires the enclosure of vertical openings in existing hotels by means of a performance approach (i.e., either they must be in accordance with enclosed 6-2.2 or they must satisfy the objectives of Section 2-9).

It should be noted when applying Exception No. 1 that 6-2.4.5 requires automatic sprinkler protection for ordinary hazard occupancies, which include hotels.

Where making use of Exception No. 2, it should also be recognized that 6-2.4.6 requires buildings with atriums to be protected throughout by automatic sprinklers.

Exception No. 4 allows unprotected openings under the following conditions:

1. They are approved by the authority having jurisdiction;
2. The building is totally sprinklered;

3. Exits and exit accesses are adequately separated from the remainder of the building;
4. In lieu of condition 3, every room has direct access to an exterior exit that does not require travel through a public corridor; and
5. Shafts enclosing required exit stairs are protected.

Exception No. 5 allows unprotected vertical openings under the following conditions:

1. They are approved by the authority having jurisdiction;
2. The building is a two-story building;
3. The building is totally sprinklered.

Therefore, unless the unprotected vertical opening complies with Exception No. 3, the building that contains the opening is required to be either fully sprinklered or at least partially sprinklered. (*See 6-2.4.5.*)

17-3.1.2 No floor below the level of exit discharge used only for storage, heating equipment, or purposes other than residential occupancy shall have unprotected openings to floors used for residential purposes.

17-3.2 Protection from Hazards.

17-3.2.1 Any room containing high pressure boilers, refrigerating machinery, transformers, or other service equipment subject to possible explosion shall not be located directly under or directly adjacent to exits. All such rooms shall be effectively cut off from other parts of the building as specified in Section 6-4.

17-3.2.2 Hazardous Areas. Any hazardous area shall be protected in accordance with Section 6-4. The areas in the following table shall be protected as indicated. Where sprinkler protection without fire rated separation is used, areas shall be separated from other spaces by partitions complying with 6-3.2 and with doors complying with 6-3.4.

This paragraph has been completely rewritten for the 1991 *Code*. Protection for typical hazardous areas found in hotels and dormitories has been specifically provided. Note that the areas protected by sprinklers still require walls and self-closing doors that resist the passage of smoke unless the first footnote applies.

Hazardous Area	Separation/Protection
Boiler and fuel-fired heater rooms serving more than a single guest room or suite.	1-hr and sprinklers
Employee locker rooms	1-hr or sprinklers
Gift or retail shops more than 100 sq ft (9.3 sq m)	1-hr or sprinklers[1]
Bulk laundries	1-hr and sprinklers
Guest laundries more than 100 sq ft (9.3 sq m) outside of guest rooms or suites	1-hr or sprinklers[1]
Maintenance shops	1-hr and sprinklers
Rooms or spaces used for storage of combustible supplies and equipment in quantities deemed hazardous by the authority having jurisdiction[2]	1-hr or sprinklers
Trash rooms	1-hr and sprinklers

[1] Where sprinkler protection is provided, no enclosure is required.
[2] Where storage areas not exceeding 24 sq ft (2.2 sq m) are directly accessible from the guest room or suite, no separation/protection is required.

While the list that appears in 17-3.2.2 provides specific direction for certain hazardous areas, it is not all-inclusive. Other areas that are hazardous need to comply with the appropriate level of protection in accordance with Section 6-4.

17-3.3 Interior Finish.

17-3.3.1 Interior finish on walls and ceilings, in accordance with Section 6-5, shall be as follows:

(a) Exit enclosures — Class A or B.
(b) Corridors and lobbies that are part of an exit access — Class A or B.
(c) All other spaces — Class A, B, or C.

17-3.3.2 Interior floor finish in corridors and exits shall be Class I or Class II in accordance with Section 6-5.

Exception: Previously installed floor coverings may be continued in use subject to the approval of the authority having jurisdiction.

The provisions for interior finish in 17-3.3 were rewritten for the 1976 Edition of the *Code* to reflect the elimination of the Class D and E categories of interior finish and to better specify where these requirements apply in hotel occupancies. In the 1981 Edition, the interior floor finish requirements were modified to reflect critical radiant flux requirements. Section 6-5 contains strict limitations on the use of textile or carpetlike materials on walls or ceilings.

17-3.4 Detection, Alarm, and Communication Systems.

See Supplement 2.

17-3.4.1 General. A fire alarm system in accordance with Section 7-6, except as modified below, shall be provided.

Exception: Buildings where each guest room has exterior exit access in accordance with 5-5.3, and the building is not greater than three stories in height.

17-3.4.2 Initiation. The required fire alarm system shall be initiated by:

(a) Manual means in accordance with 7-6.2, and

Exception to (a): Manual means as specified in 7-6.2, other than as required by (b) below, shall not be required where there are other effective means (such as complete automatic sprinkler or automatic detection systems) to activate the fire alarm system.

(b) A manual fire alarm station located at the hotel desk or other convenient central control point under continuous supervision by responsible employees, and

(c) Any required automatic sprinkler system, and

(d) Any required detection system.

Exception to (d): Sleeping room smoke detectors are not required to initiate the building fire alarm system.

The *Code* requires that, in addition to the normal distribution of manual fire alarm stations (*see 7-6.2*), the front desk, telephone operator's location, or similar loca-

tion must also be equipped with a manual pull station. The intent is to have a pull station available at the location where guests phone in an emergency.

Paragraph 17-3.4.2 eliminates the requirements for fire alarm pull stations located so that all portions of a building are within 200 ft (60 m) of a box (*see Section 7-6*) in occupancies where an automatic sprinkler system or an automatic detection system is provided throughout the building. The alarm system is still required; only the requirement for additional manual fire alarm stations is eliminated.

The *Code* exempts sleeping room smoke detectors from activating the building fire alarm system. The detectors installed in sleeping rooms are usually single station or multiple station detectors and are not a part of a "required automatic detection system" and, therefore, are automatically exempted. The exception emphasizes this point but clarifies that, if detectors are part of a system, they are not required to initiate the building fire alarm system. The *Code* does not prohibit room detectors from activating the system; however, this is discouraged to prevent numerous activations, which could pose a particular problem in large hotels. The purpose of the sleeping room detector is to warn the occupants of that room. There are detectors available that annunciate at a central point, alert the occupants of the room, and notify management of a problem in that room without sounding an alarm throughout the facility. (*Also see commentary following 17-3.4.4.*)

17-3.4.3 Notification.

17-3.4.3.1 Occupant notification shall be provided automatically, without delay, by internal audible alarm in accordance with 7-6.3.

Exception: A presignal system (see 7-6.3.2 Exception No. 1) may be used only where permitted by the authority having jurisdiction.

The distribution of audible alarm devices in hotels must be thoroughly reviewed. Often alarm devices in corridors cannot be heard in rooms or, if heard, are not loud enough to waken guests. Survivors of several multiple-death hotel fires have reported either failure to hear alarms or failure to distinguish the alarm from that of a neighbor's clock. (*See Supplement 2.*)

Presignal systems have repeatedly been involved in delaying alarms in multiple-death fires. However, the occurrence of false alarms in hotels is very real. Therefore, the *Code* allows presignal systems in hotels, but the authority having jurisdiction can establish how such a system is to be arranged. If the presignal is to be transmitted to a building staff location (i.e., front desk), Exception No. 1 to 7-6.3.2 specifies that it must be received by trained staff. Therefore, hotel employees assigned to signal receiving locations must be well educated regarding fire alarm signals and proper staff response to an alarm.

17-3.4.3.2* Provisions shall be made for the immediate notification of the public fire department by telephone or other means in case of fire. Where there is no public fire department, this notification shall be made to the private fire brigade.

A-17-3.4.3.2 The provision for immediate notification of the public fire department is intended to include, but not be limited to, all of the arrangements listed in 7-6.4, "Emergency Forces Notification." Other arrangements that depend on a clerk or other member of the staff to notify the fire department may also be acceptable. In such case, however, it is essential that a trained staff member and an immediately available means of calling the fire department are continuously available. If a telephone is to be used, it should not be of any type or arrangement that requires a coin or the unlocking of a device to contact the fire department.

This paragraph does not require a direct fire alarm connection to the fire department; however, this is the best method of complying with 17-3.4.3.2. The telephone required must be equipped for direct outside dial without going through a switchboard and is not permitted to be a pay phone.

17-3.4.4 **Detection.** Each sleeping room shall be provided with an approved single station smoke detector, in accordance with 7-6.2.9, powered from the building electrical system.

Prior to the 1985 Edition of the *Code*, neither corridor nor room smoke detectors were required in existing hotels (in the 1981 Edition, existing dormitories were

required to have one or the other). However, new hotels were required to have corridor smoke detectors. In 1985, new hotels were required to have both corridor and room detectors. However, for existing hotels, the *Code* required that either corridor detectors or room detectors be provided. By allowing either protection method, the Committee was not implying that both perform a similar function, but was recognizing that many hotels were equipped with corridor detectors in accordance with prior editions of the *Code*. In this edition of the *Code*, the option has been deleted. Single station smoke detectors must be provided in all sleeping rooms. If a corridor smoke detection system is provided, it must be maintained, since this is a requirement for new construction unless the building is sprinklered. Removal of the system would be considered a renovation, and renovations must be done in conformance with the requirements for new construction to the extent practical.

17-3.5 **Extinguishment Requirements.**

See Supplement 3.

17-3.5.1* Where an automatic sprinkler system is installed, either for total or partial building coverage, the system shall be installed in accordance with Section 7-7. In buildings up to and including four stories in height, systems installed in accordance with NFPA 13R, *Standard for the Installation of Sprinkler Systems in Residential Occupancies up to and Including Four Stories in Height*, shall be permitted.

Exception: In guest rooms and in guest room suites, sprinkler installations are not required in closets not over 24 sq ft (2.2 sq m) and bathrooms not over 55 sq ft (5.1 sq m).

A-17-3.5.1 Although not required by the *Code*, the use of residential sprinklers or quick response sprinklers is encouraged for new installations of sprinkler systems within dwelling units, apartments, and guest rooms. Caution must be used, as the system must be designed for the sprinkler being used.

This paragraph does not require sprinklers but specifies requirements for such systems where they are installed. The *Code* provides significant incentive to install sprinklers with regard to: exit enclosures (17-2.2.1.2); common path of travel (17-2.5.2); travel distance (17-2.6.1 and 17-2.6.2); exit discharge (17-2.7); vertical openings (17-3.1); hazardous areas (17-3.2); interior finish (17-3.3); corridor walls (17-3.6.1); and smoke barriers (17-3.7.1). High rise hotels are required to be sprinklered unless each guest room or suite has exterior exit access (*see 17-3.5.2*). (*Also see commentary following 17-1.2.*) (*See Supplement 3.*)

17-3.5.2   All high rise buildings shall be protected throughout by an approved supervised automatic sprinkler system installed in accordance with 17-3.5.1.

Exception: Where each guest room or suite has exterior exit access in accordance with 5-5.3.

The provision that requires the installation of an approved supervised automatic sprinkler system throughout many existing high rise hotels is new to the 1991 Edition of the *Code*. Because of the poor record of life loss in residential occupancies (*see Chapter 17 introduction*), Chapter 17 retroactively requires the installation of sprinklers in existing high rise hotels, with the exception of those high rise hotels in which each guest room has exterior exit access. (*See the definition of high rise in Section 3-2.*)

The exception allows high rise hotels to remain non-sprinklered as long as every guest room/suite has exterior exit access. This eliminates traversing the corridor, which is one of the significant factors that contributes to multiple-death hotel fires.

17-3.5.3   Portable fire extinguishers shall be provided in hazardous areas. Where provided, portable fire extinguishers shall be installed and maintained in accordance with 7-7.4.1.

17-3.6   **Minimum Fire Resistance Requirements for Protection of Guest Rooms (Corridors).**

17-3.6.1   Interior corridor walls shall consist of fire barriers in accordance with 6-2.3 having at least a 30-minute fire resistance rating.

Exception No. 1: In buildings protected throughout by an approved automatic sprinkler system in accordance with 17-3.5, no fire resistance rating shall be required, but the walls and all openings therein shall resist the passage of smoke.

Exception No. 2: Where interior corridor walls have openings from transfer grilles, see 17-3.6.6.

The criteria in 17-3.6 reflect the Committee's concern for providing safety for those who are occupying their rooms during a fire. The focus of this concern is the presence of sleeping accommodations that can be used by occupants 24 hours a day. This minimum fire resistance rating for corridor wall construction will either prevent fire movement from the corridor to a room or prevent fire in a room from spreading to the corridor. Corridor partitions in both sprinklered and nonsprinklered facilities are intended to be constructed to resist the passage of smoke.

The required 30-minute fire-resistive rating for corridor partitions is intended to provide a nominal fire rating, particularly where the fire rating of existing partitions cannot be documented. Examples of acceptable partition assemblies would include, but are not limited to, $1/2$-in. (1.3-cm) gypsum board, wood lath and plaster, gypsum lath, or metal lath and plaster.

17-3.6.2   Each guest room door that opens onto an interior corridor shall have a fire protection rating of at least 20 minutes.

Exception No. 1: Previously approved 1¾-in. (4.4-cm) thick solid bonded wood core doors shall be permitted to remain in use.

Exception No. 2: Where automatic sprinkler protection is provided in the corridor in accordance with 19-3.5.2 through 19-3.5.4, doors shall not be required to have a fire protection rating but shall resist the passage of smoke. Doors shall be equipped with latches for keeping doors tightly closed.

Formal Interpretation 81-16
Reference: 17-3.6.2

Question: Is it the intent of 17-3.6.2, Exception No. 1 that 1¾-in. thick solid bonded wood core doors with ornate carvings (for aesthetic reasons) on either one or both sides, that reduce the effective thickness of the door to less than 1¾ in. qualify as 1¾-in. thick doors and thus meet the exception?

Answer: No.

Issue Edition: 1981
Reference: 17-3.6.2
Date: April 1982 ∎

The door required by 17-3.6.2 provides a level of protection commensurate with the expected fuel load in the room and the fire resistance of the corridor wall construction. The purpose is to box a fire out of a room or to box it within the room by means of corridor wall and door construction (*see 17-3.6.3*). In fuel load studies conducted by the National Bureau of Standards, it has been demonstrated that residential occupancies will have fuel loads in the 20- to 30-minute range.

Exception No. 2 would allow a non-rated door that resists the passage of smoke in buildings that are fully sprinklered or that have sprinklers installed in accordance with Option 3 for apartment buildings. (*See 19-3.5.2 and the commentary following 19-3.5.2 for information on Option 3 sprinkler requirements.*)

17-3.6.3 Each guest room door that opens onto an interior corridor shall be self-closing and shall meet the requirements of 17-3.6.2.

Since 16-3.6.2 requires guest room doors to have a 20-minute fire protection rating, NFPA 80, *Standard for Fire Doors and Windows*,[6] requires the door to be self-closing; however, the Committee believes that this requirement is important enough to be repeated in 17-3.6.3 rather than relying only on the reference document. Numerous hotel fires have resulted in multiple fatalities due to the absence or poor maintenance of door closures.

17-3.6.4 Unprotected openings shall be prohibited in partitions of interior corridors serving as exit access from guest rooms.

17-3.6.5 Existing transoms installed in corridor partitions of sleeping rooms shall be fixed in the closed position and shall be covered or otherwise protected to provide a fire resistance rating at least equivalent to that of the wall in which they are installed.

Transoms have been prohibited in hotels for many years due to tragic multiple-death fires that resulted when their presence led to the transmission of fire and smoke through corridors and directly into occupied rooms.

17-3.6.6 No louver or transfer grille shall be permitted in partitions or doors separating the corridor from guest rooms.

Exception No. 1: Where a corridor smoke detection system is provided that, when sensing smoke, will sound the building alarm and shut down return or exhaust fans that draw air into the corridor from the guest rooms. The grilles shall be located in the lower one-third of the wall or door height.

Exception No. 2: Buildings protected throughout by an approved automatic sprinkler system complying with 17-3.5 or in accordance with 19-3.5.2 through 19-3.5.4, and where the transfer grille is located in the lower one-third of the wall or door height.

Paragraph 2-3.11.1 of NFPA 90A, *Standard for the Installation of Air Conditioning and Ventilating Systems*,[7] prohibits public corridors from being used as a portion of the supply, return, or exhaust air system. However, very old hotels (built prior to 1950) often use corridors for supply or return air. The *Code* recognizes this and sets criteria for their continued existence under limited conditions.

Exception No. 2 is based on the Option 3 corridor sprinkler system for apartment buildings.

Figure 17-8 illustrates the requirements of 17-3.6.

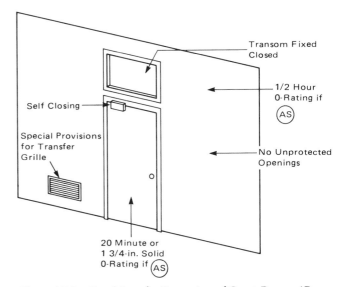

Figure 17-8. Provisions for Protection of Guest Rooms (Corridors) in Existing Hotels. The need for the self-closing door cannot be overemphasized. There are no exceptions or options to the self-closing door. Although no rating is required where sprinkler protection is provided, the wall shall be substantial and shall resist the passage of smoke.

17-3.7 Subdivision of Building Spaces.

17-3.7.1 Every guest room floor shall be divided into at least two smoke compartments of approximately the same size with smoke barriers in accordance with Section 6-3. Smoke dampers are not required.

Additional smoke barriers shall be provided such that the maximum travel distance from a guest room corridor door to a smoke barrier shall not exceed 150 ft (45 m).

Exception No. 1: Buildings protected throughout by an approved automatic sprinkler system installed in accordance with 17-3.5 or a sprinkler system conforming to 19-3.5.2 through 19-3.5.4.

Exception No. 2: Where each guest room is provided with exterior ways of exit access arranged in accordance with 5-5.3.

Exception No. 3: Smoke barriers are not required where the aggregate corridor length on each floor is not more than 150 ft (45 m).

This requirement was new to the 1985 Edition of the *Code*. It requires all but relatively small floors to be subdivided into two smoke compartments. This provides for horizontal movement of people and limits the number of rooms and, therefore, the number of people exposed to a single fire that may be blocking a corridor. Since no fire rating is required for the barrier and smoke dampers are not required, the requirement is not overly burdensome in typical hotel or dormitory construction. The exception for automatic sprinklers reflects the excellent life loss record of buildings equipped with this form of protection.

A horizontal exit may be used to comply with 17-3.7.1 and thereby serve more than one function.

17-3.8 Special Features. (Reserved.)

SECTION 17-4   Special Provisions

17-4.1 Operating Features. *(See Chapter 31.)*

17-4.2 High Rise Buildings. *(See 17-3.5.2.)*

SECTION 17-5   Building Services

17-5.1 Utilities. Utilities shall comply with the provisions of Section 7-1.

17-5.2 Heating, Ventilating, and Air Conditioning.

17-5.2.1 Heating, ventilating, and air conditioning equipment shall comply with the provisions of Section 7-2, except as otherwise required in this chapter.

17-5.2.2 Unvented fuel-fired heaters shall not be used.

17-5.3 Elevators, Escalators, and Conveyors. Elevators, escalators, and conveyors shall comply with the provisions of Section 7-4.

17-5.4 Rubbish Chutes, Incinerators, and Laundry Chutes. Rubbish chutes, incinerators, and laundry chutes shall comply with the provisions of Section 7-5.

The 1985 Edition of the *Code* eliminated the special section on dormitories. Dormitories are now covered as hotels. The section was deleted due to several changes in hotel requirements affecting windows, alarms, and building subdivisions. These changes rendered special requirements for dormitories unnecessary.

References Cited in Commentary

[1]Thomas J. Klem, Investigation Report on the DuPont Plaza Hotel Fire, National Fire Protection Association, Quincy, MA, 1987.

[2]J.R. Bell, T.J. Klem, and A.E. Willey, Investigation on the Westchase Hilton Hotel Fire, National Fire Protection Association, Quincy, MA, 1982.

[3]Jon C. Jones, "A Brief Look at the Hotel Fire Record," *Fire Journal*, Vol. 75, No. 3, May 1981, pp. 38-47.

[4]NFPA 13, *Standard for the Installation of Sprinkler Systems*, National Fire Protection Association, Quincy, MA, 1991.

[5]Richard Best and David P. Demers, Investigation Report on the MGM Grand Hotel Fire, Las Vegas,

Nevada, National Fire Protection Association, Quincy, MA, NFPA No. LS-4, 1982.

[6]NFPA 80, *Standard for Fire Doors and Windows*, National Fire Protection Association, Quincy, MA, 1990.

[7]NFPA 90A, *Standard for the Installation of Air Conditioning and Ventilating Systems*, National Fire Protection Association, Quincy, MA, 1989.

18

New Apartment Buildings

(See also Chapter 31.)

Apartment buildings are one of five residential occupancy types addressed by the *Life Safety Code*. Other residential occupancies considered include one- and two-family dwellings, hotels, lodging and rooming houses, and residential board and care facilities. Sleeping accommodations are a feature common to all residential occupancies.

Paragraph 4-1.6 highlights a common principle of life safety with which the *Code* is concerned as applied to all residential occupancies addressed by Chapters 16 through 23. Paragraph 4-1.6 states: "Residential occupancies are those occupancies in which sleeping accommodations are provided for normal residential purposes and include all buildings designed to provide sleeping accommodations." This use of residential occupancies is central to the *Code* provisions of Chapters 16 through 23, since occupants who are sleeping will be unaware of a rapidly developing fire and, when alerted to the emergency, may be somewhat confused due to being awakened suddenly.

Other factors on which the provisions of Chapters 16 through 23 are based are the presence of hazards (such as cooking and heating equipment) and the degree of familiarity of the occupants with their living space. Occupants may have little or no familiarity, as in the case of transient residents of hotels, or they may have the total familiarity of residents of a one-family dwelling.

Apartments, townhouses, flats, and condominiums accounted for 116,300 structure fires per year as reported to U.S. fire departments from 1984 to 1988. There were 906 civilian deaths and 5,966 civilian injuries per year. Fifty-seven deaths per year took place in properties with one or two apartments over a business, 352 per year in properties with three to six apartments, 212 per year in properties with more than twenty apartments, 8 per year in properties of unclassified size, and 74 per year in properties of unreported size.

Five percent of all home fire deaths that took place from 1984 to 1988 occurred in apartment buildings with twenty or more units. These apartment buildings accounted for 7 percent of all occupied housing units in 1986. The discrepency between the two percentages may be related to lower risk or other factors, such as average household size.

Half of all those who died in apartment fires from 1980 to 1988 were outside the room of fire origin; this does not mean that they were outside the apartment unit of origin. That distinction cannot be made using the existing data.

There were six apartment building fires in the 1980s that resulted in 10 or more fatalities:

Date	Place	Civilian Deaths
1980	Utah	12
1980	Illinois	10
1981	New Jersey	11
1982	Connecticut	14
1985	Pennsylvania	11
1989	Tennessee	16

The 1985 fire incident in Pennsylvania was unique, since it was caused by the use of explosives by police in a siege situation. Of the other five incidents, one involved a building over five stories in height. Few, if any, of the victims were in the apartment of fire origin. In one case, the area of origin was not an apartment unit. These incidents indicated a lack of fire protection systems and features. Other contributing factors were incendiary fire origin, early involvement of the primary or only means of egress, and the existence of doors that had been propped open.

These incidents demonstrate the importance of the *Life Safety Code* to apartment firesafety.

SECTION 18-1   General Requirements

18-1.1   Application.

18-1.1.1 This chapter establishes life safety requirements for all new apartment buildings and for renovations, alterations, or modernizations according to the provisions of Section 1-5. (*See Chapter 31 for operating features.*)

Previous editions of the *Life Safety Code* provided four life safety packages that were considered equivalent. In order to provide a *Code*-specified minimum level of apartment building life safety, one of the four alternatives could be chosen (Option 1: no suppression or detection, Option 2: total automatic detection, Option 3: partial sprinkler protection, and Option 4: protection throughout by means of an approved supervised automatic sprinkler system) and then the appropriate requirements for the option selected would be applied. In recognition of the life safety benefits associated with a properly installed and maintained sprinkler system (*see commentary on 18-3.5.2*), the *Code* provided alternatives based upon the use of Option 4 (i.e., increased travel distance, reduction in corridor fire resistance ratings, decreased interior finish requirements, and elimination of the smoke barrier requirement). The intent was to encourage the installation of an approved supervised automatic sprinkler system.

Due to the disproportionate percentage of deaths associated with residential occupancies (82 percent)[2] the *Code*, with some exceptions, now mandates the sprinkler protection of new apartment buildings. Therefore, the 1991 Edition of the *Code* is now structured to resemble the former Option 4 package of requirements.

18-1.2   Mixed Occupancies.

18-1.2.1 Where another type of occupancy occurs in the same building as a residential occupancy, the requirements of 1-5.7 of this *Code* shall apply.

18-1.2.2 For requirements on mixed mercantile and residential occupancies, see 24-1.2; for mixed assembly and residential occupancies, see 8-1.2; and for mixed business and residential occupancies, see 26-1.2.

18-1.3   Definitions.

18-1.3.1 Terms applicable to this chapter are defined in Chapter 3 of this *Code*; where necessary, other terms will be defined in the text as they occur.

Apartment Buildings.* Apartment buildings include buildings containing three or more living units with independent cooking and bathroom facilities, whether designated as apartment houses, tenements, garden apartments, or by any other name.

A-18-1.3.1 The *Code* specifies that whenever there are three or more living units in a building, the building is considered an apartment building and must comply with either Chapter 18 or 19 as appropriate. "Townhouse" units are considered to be an apartment building if there are three or more units in the building. The type of wall required between units in order to consider them to be separate buildings is normally established by the authority having jurisdiction. Should the units be separated by a wall of sufficient fire resistance and structural integrity to be considered as separate buildings, then the provisions of Chapter 21 apply to each townhouse. "Condominium" is a form of ownership, not occupancy; for example, there are condominium warehouses, condominium apartments, and condominium offices.

This new appendix note was added to the 1991 *Code* to clarify occupancy classification for townhouse-type apartments, particularly those under condominium ownership. It is often mistakenly believed that condominiums are a form of occupancy rather than a form of ownership.

18-1.4 **Classification of Occupancy.** (*See 18-1.3.1.*)

18-1.5 **Classification of Hazard of Contents.**

18-1.5.1 The contents of residential occupancies shall be classified as ordinary hazard in accordance with Section 4-2.

NFPA 13, *Standard for the Installation of Sprinkler Systems*,[1] would classify the contents as "light hazard" for the purpose of designing extinguishing systems. The difference in classification is based on the threat to life or life safety (ordinary) as opposed to the threat to the extinguishing capability of the automatic sprinkler system (light).

18-1.6 **Minimum Construction Requirements.** No special requirements.

18-1.7 **Occupant Load.**

18-1.7.1* The occupant load in numbers of persons for whom exits are to be provided shall be determined on the basis of one person per 200 sq ft (18.6 sq m) gross floor area or the maximum probable population of any room or section under consideration, whichever is greater. The occupant load of any open mezzanine or balcony shall be added to the occupant load of the floor below for the purpose of determining exit capacity.

A-18-1.7.1 Dormitory-type occupancy, particularly where 2- or 3-tier bunks are used with close spacing, may produce an occupant load substantially greater than one person per 200 sq ft (18.6 sq m) gross floor area. However, even though sleeping areas are densely populated, the building as a whole may not necessarily exceed one person per 200 sq ft (18.6 sq m) gross area, owing to the space taken for toilet facilities, halls, closets, and living rooms not used for sleeping purposes.

See 5-3.1 for further details on the use of the occupant load for determining the capacity of the means of egress.

SECTION 18-2 Means of Egress Requirements

18-2.1 **General.**

18-2.1.1 Means of egress from living units to the outside of the building shall be in accordance with Chapter 5 and this chapter. Means of escape within the living unit shall comply with the provisions of Section 21-2 for one- and two-family dwellings.

A general reference to Chapter 5 is made in place of repeating many of its provisions. Many of the requirements found in Section 18-2 are Chapter 5 provisions that serve as options for the occupancy chapters, such as Exception No. 1 to 18-2.2.2.2, which allows the use of special locking arrangements in accordance with 5-2.1.6. Other provisions prohibit the use of an item if it is not listed (note that alternating tread devices are not listed in 18-2.2) or establish restrictions based on criteria provided in Chapter 5, such as the dead-end limits for corridors found in 18-2.5.3.

This paragraph requires that every living unit (apartment) comply with Section 21-2 of Chapter 21, which addresses one- and two-family dwellings. This requirement is important for several reasons. First, it establishes two means of escape from every sleeping room and living area of a living unit (apartment) having two rooms or more (this exempts efficiency-type apartments). Paragraph 21-2.1.2 establishes several types of "second means of escape" that can be used, the most common of which is the operable window; however, Chapter 21 also sets certain requirements for operable windows in addition to those specifying minimum size and arrangement. The window must be located within 20 ft (6.1 m) of grade or be accessible by fire department rescue apparatus or must open onto a balcony. If this requirement cannot be met, a second means of escape complying with one of the other three types listed in 21-2.1.2 must be provided. A second means of escape is exempted if the dwelling unit is protected by an automatic sprinkler system in accordance with either NFPA 13, *Standard for the Installation of Sprinkler Systems,*[1] or NFPA 13D, *Standard for the Installation of Sprinkler Systems in One- and Two-Family Dwellings and Mobile Homes,*[2] or NFPA 13R, *Standard for the Installation of Sprinkler Systems in Residential Occupancies up to and Including Four Stories in Height.*[3] Note that this would not require that the entire apartment building be sprinklered, but only the living unit that is not in compliance with the secondary means of escape.

A second important provision of Section 21-2 is that the means of egress provisions of Chapter 5 do not apply unless specifically referenced. For example, the minimum width of doors within the dwelling unit is reduced to 28 in. (71 cm) from the 32-in. (81-cm) width specified by Chapter 5. Section 21-2 also allows the use of winders and spiral stairs within the living unit, and the headroom requirements of Chapter 5 do not apply within the living unit. (*See commentary on Chapter 21 for additional information on means of escape from living units.*)

18-2.2 Means of Egress Components.

18-2.2.1 General.

18-2.2.1.1 Components of means of egress shall be limited to the types described in 18-2.2.2 through 18-2.2.7.

18-2.2.1.2 In buildings protected throughout by an approved supervised automatic sprinkler system installed in accordance with 18-3.5, exit enclosures shall have a fire resistance rating of not less than 1 hour with doors having a fire protection rating of not less than 1 hour.

In recognition of the relatively low fuel loads in apartment buildings, the fire resistance rating for exit enclosures, as well as for other vertical openings (*see 18-3.1.1 Exception No. 3*), need not exceed 1 hour; however, as a safeguard, this is permitted only in buildings protected throughout by automatic sprinklers. This is not permitted in assembly occupancies or business occupancies and, therefore, cannot be utilized where mixed occupancies are involved; nor can it be used for stairways or vertical openings that are part of or pass through other occupancies.

In facilities where occupancies are adequately separated and treated independently, it may be feasible to have a 1-hour enclosure in the apartment portion of the facility and a 2-hour enclosure elsewhere.

18-2.2.2 Doors.

18-2.2.2.1 Doors shall comply with 5-2.1.

18-2.2.2.2* No door in any means of egress shall be locked against egress when the building is occupied.

Exception: Special locking arrangements complying with 5-2.1.6 are permitted.

A-18-2.2.2.2 It is the intent of this requirement that security measures, when installed, should not prevent egress.

Paragraph 18-2.2.2.2 prohibits an apartment building from having any door locked "against egress" while the building is occupied. This requirement permits a door to have a locking device that allows the door to be opened from within the building for the purpose of egress but does not allow the door to be opened from outside the building. Ordinary double cylinder locks and chain locks do not meet these provisions. Several tragic multiple-death fires occurred when the key needed to unlock these devices could not be found.

The language of 5-2.1.5.1 is clear: "Locks, if provided, shall not require the use of a key, tool, special knowledge, or effort for operation from the inside of the building." This eliminates double cylinder locks and chain locks that require a key in order to be to operated from the inside. Paragraph 5-2.1.5.3 requires the use of a simple operation to open a door; locks that require two-handed knob and similar operations are explicitly prohibited.

Chapter 5 now specifically recognizes the need for security chains or rods on apartment doors and allows one additional releasing device. The typical apartment door has three devices: a latch, a lock, and a security chain or rod. However, the *Code* allows only two releasing actions for new installations. This requirement is met by using a latch and lock set equipped with a lock bolt that automatically retracts when the latch handle is turned from the inside; thus, only one action is needed to release the two devices. The second action is the release of the security chain or rod. However, neither device can require the use of a key, tool, special knowledge, or effort.

The Exception to 18-2.2.2.2 recognizes the use of the delay release lock provided for in 5-2.1.6. This requires that the building either be protected throughout by automatic sprinklers or be equipped throughout with a fire detection system. The 15- or 30-second delay permitted by 5-2.1.6 does not affect the immediate release of the lock upon activation of the sprinklers or detectors, or upon loss of power to the lock. This device helps provide the security needed for infrequently used doors or stairs in apartment buildings. At the same time, the door remains available for use. Chains and padlocks are unable to provide this feature.

The former Exception No. 2 to 18-2.2.2.2, which allowed the so-called "captive key" type of lock permitted by Exception No. 3 to 5-2.1.5.1, has been removed from the 1991 Edition of the *Code*.

18-2.2.2.3 Revolving doors complying with 5-2.1.10 are permitted.

18-2.2.2.4 Horizontal sliding doors in accordance with 5-2.1.14 shall be permitted in a means of egress serving a room or area with an occupant load of less than 50. Such doors shall not be located for use across corridors.

Note that 18-2.2.2.4 is more restrictive regarding the use of these special doors than is Chapter 5, since they cannot be installed across corridor or be located in a means of egress serving 50 or more people. This overrides some of the general provisions of 5-2.1.14.

18-2.2.3 Stairs.

18-2.2.3.1 Stairs shall comply with 5-2.2.

18-2.2.3.2 Within any individual living unit, stairs more than one story above or below the entrance floor level of the living unit shall not be permitted.

This paragraph requires that no level of an apartment be located farther than one story away from an entrance. This would usually restrict an apartment from having more than three stories: main level, upper, and lower. However, if an apartment has entrances at more than one level, more than three stories are permitted. However, 18-3.1.1 allows only two levels to be open to each other; the third level must be protected in accordance with 6-2.4.

18-2.2.3.3 Spiral stairs complying with 5-2.2.2.7 are permitted within a single living unit.

18-2.2.3.4 Winders complying with 5-2.2.2.8 are permitted within a single living unit.

18-2.2.4 Smokeproof Enclosures. Smokeproof enclosures shall comply with 5-2.3.

18-2.2.5 Horizontal Exits. Horizontal exits shall comply with 5-2.4.

18-2.2.6 Ramps. Ramps shall comply with 5-2.5.

18-2.2.7 Exit Passageways. Exit passageways shall comply with 5-2.6.

18-2.3 Capacity of Means of Egress.

18-2.3.1 The capacity of means of egress shall be in accordance with Section 5-3.

18-2.3.2 Street floor exits shall be sufficient for the occupant load of the street floor plus the required capacity of stairs and ramps discharging onto the street floor.

Paragraph 18-2.3.2 requires street floor exit designs that have sufficient width to accommodate the convergence of occupants discharging through exits from the street floor with those discharging down from the upper floors and up from the lower floors. This constitutes the traditional grand lobby design in which stairs and street floor exits converge at one or two exterior door locations. Similar commentary on this issue is found in Chapter 16. Paragraph 5-7.2 restricts the number and arrangement of stairs that are used to discharge through the street floor.

Figure 18-1 shows a typical arrangement of multiple exits discharging on the street floor.

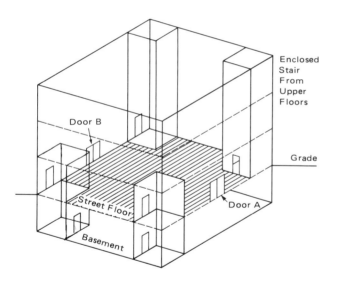

Figure 18-1. Capacity of Means of Egress in Accordance with 18-2.3.2. Required widths of Doors A and B are based on the anticipated number of people using them. Assuming that the street floor has an occupant load of 500, that each upper floor has an occupant load of 200, and that the basement has an occupant load of 100, the required exit capacity for the street floor would be calculated as follows:

500 (street floor) + 200 ÷ 2 (upper floor max 50% per 5-7.2) + 100 ÷ 2 (basement max 50% per 5-7.2) = 650 total using exits on street floor × 0.2 in. (0.5 cm) of door width per person = 130 in. (325 cm) ÷ 2 exits = 65 in. (163 cm) at A and at B.

18-2.3.3 The minimum corridor width shall be sufficient to accommodate the required occupant load, but not less than 44 in. (112 cm).

Exception: Corridors with a required capacity not greater than 50 as defined in Section 5-3 shall be not less than 36 in. (91 cm) in width.

18-2.4 **Number of Exits.** *(See also Section 5-4.)*

18-2.4.1 Every living unit shall have access to at least two separate exits remotely located from each other as required by 5-5.1.

Exception No. 1: Any living unit shall be permitted to have a single exit provided:

(a) That living unit has an exit door opening directly to the street or yard at ground level, or

(b) That living unit has direct access to an outside stair complying with 5-2.2 that serves a maximum of two units located on the same floor, or

(c) That living unit has direct access to an interior stair serving only that unit and separated from all other portions of the building by fire barriers having a 1-hour fire resistance rating with no opening therein.

Exception No. 1 allows a single exit under three arrangements: (1) The living unit has an exit leading directly to the street or yard at ground level. This is common in a townhouse or row house arrangement. Under this arrangement, the front door is the only required exit, and, therefore, there are no requirements for a rear door. If a rear door is provided, it does not have to meet the requirements of the *Code*; more importantly, it does not have to meet the locking requirements of the *Code*. (2) The apartment has direct access to an outside stair and serves a maximum of two apartments, and both these apartments must be on the same floor. (3) The single exit is a 1-hour enclosed private stairway serving that apartment only. Note that this stairway need only be separated from other spaces by the required 1-hour construction; it is not required to be separated from the unit that it serves. It is also important to note that changes to the 1991 Edition of the *Code* also require each sleeping room to be protected with either residential (or quick response) sprinklers or detectors to ensure rapid notification of occu-

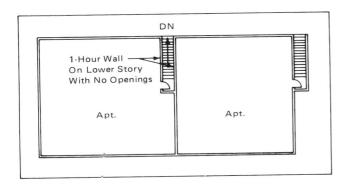

Figure 18-2. *Two Methods of Complying with Exception No. 1 to 18-2.4.1 to Allow a Single Exit. The enclosed stairway is allowed to be open to the unit it serves.*

pants. Therefore, a degree of redundancy has been provided. Conditions (b) and (c) of Exception No. 1 are illustrated in Figure 18-2.

Exception No 2: Any building protected throughout by an approved supervised automatic sprinkler system complying with 18-3.5 having four stories or less with not more than four living units per floor shall be permitted to have a single exit under the following conditions:

(a) The stairway is completely enclosed by barriers having a fire resistance rating of at least 1 hour with self-closing

1-hour fire protection rated doors protecting all openings between the stairway enclosure and the building.

(b) The stairway does not serve more than one-half story below the level of exit discharge.

(c) All corridors serving as access to exits have at least a 1-hour fire resistance rating.

(d) There is not more than 35 ft (10.7 m) of travel distance from the entrance door of any living unit to an exit.

(e) One-half hour fire rated horizontal and vertical separation between living units is provided.

Exception No. 2 to 18-2.4.1 provides the basic design approach used for "garden" apartments where the apartment entrances open onto a single enclosed stair. Often, the stair is open to the exterior or is glass-enclosed on the front of the building. The exception allows a single exit under this arrangement. Not only must the building be sprinklered in accordance with 18-3.5, but the stairway must also be separated from the building by construction of at least a 1-hour fire resistance rating. Doors must be 1-hour rated and self-closing. A frequent violation of this exception is the noncomplying construction of the door and the lack of a door closer.

Figure 18-3 illustrates one potential method for application of Exception No. 2.

Figure 18-3. *Single Exit Arrangement Complying with Exception No. 2 to 18-2.4.1.*

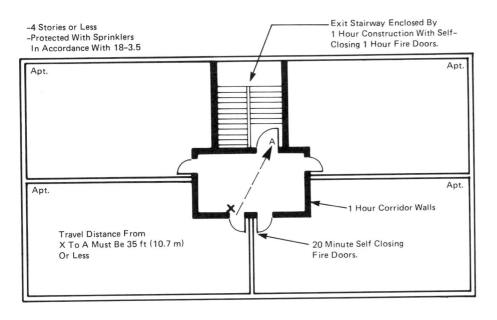

18-2.5 Arrangement of Exits.

18-2.5.1 Access to all required exits shall be in accordance with Section 5-5.

18-2.5.2 No common path of travel shall exceed 35 ft (10.7 m). Travel within a dwelling unit shall not be included when calculating common path of travel.

Exception: In buildings protected throughout by an approved supervised automatic sprinkler system in accordance with 18-3.5, common path of travel shall not exceed 50 ft (15 m).

Common path of travel is normally measured from the most remote point subject to occupancy (*see 5-5.1.2 and the definition of common path of travel in Section 3-2*); therefore, 18-2.5.2 describes a modified common path of travel, as measurement does not extend into the living unit.

Since the dead-end limits of 18-2.5.3 are the same as those of 18-2.5.2, it is difficult to envision an excessive, modified common path of travel that is not also in violation of the dead-end provision. (*See Figure 18-4.*)

18-2.5.3 No dead-end corridor shall exceed 35 ft (10.7 m).

Exception: In buildings protected throughout by an approved supervised automatic sprinkler system in accordance with 18-3.5, dead-end corridors shall not exceed 50 ft (15 m).

18-2.6 Travel Distance to Exits.

18-2.6.1 Travel distance within a living unit (apartment) to a corridor door shall not exceed 75 ft (23 m).

Exception: In buildings protected throughout by an approved supervised automatic sprinkler system in accordance with 18-3.5, the travel distance shall not exceed 125 ft (38 m).

Revision to Section 5-6 of the 1988 Edition of the *Code* require that travel distance be measured from the most remote point subject to occupancy. The provision exempting rooms occupied by six or fewer people and having 50 ft (15 m) or less travel distance was deleted. In order to be consistent with Section 5-6, the Committee revised the method of measuring travel distance in apartment buildings. The distances allowed within the unit were increased as compensation. If the travel distance within a unit is excessive, another remotely located door to the corridor must be added.

18-2.6.2 The travel distance from a living unit (apartment) entrance door to the nearest exit shall not exceed 100 ft (30 m).

Exception No. 1: In buildings protected throughout by an approved supervised automatic sprinkler system installed in accordance with 18-3.5, the travel distance shall not exceed 200 ft (60 m).

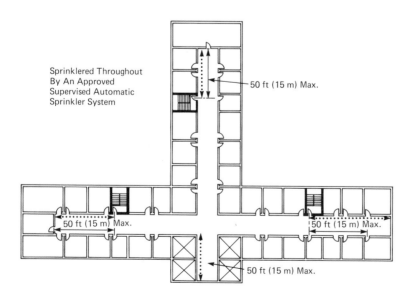

Figure 18-4. *Common Path of Travel (Modified) and Dead-End Limitations in a Sprinklered Apartment Building. Modified common paths of travel are indicated by ⟷ and dead ends are indicated by ⟨---⟩. Note that it is possible to have a dead end that is not a common path of travel, but it is difficult to envision a realistic situation in which a modified common path of travel is not also a dead end.*

Exception No. 2: Travel distance to exits shall not exceed 200 ft (60 m) for exterior ways of exit access arranged in accordance with 5-5.3.

18-2.7 Discharge from Exits.

18-2.7.1 Exit discharge shall comply with Section 5-7.

Section 5-7 does allow a maximum of 50 percent of the number and capacity of exits to discharge through the level of exit discharge (street floor) under limited conditions (*see 5-7.2*). Two permitted arrangements are illustrated in Figures 18-5 and 18-6.

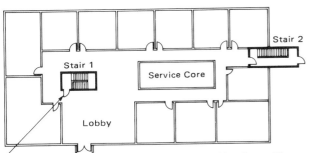

Route from Stair through Lobby to exterior Must be readily Visible, Identified, Clear, and Unobstructed.

Figure 18-5. Arrangement of Means of Egress in Accordance with 5-7.2. Stair 1 (50 percent of the total number and capacity of exits) discharges through the first floor. Stair 2 discharges directly to the exterior (it may discharge through an exit passageway to the exterior). Since other areas on the first floor (the level of exit discharge) are not separated from the path a person leaving Stair 1 must use to exit through the lobby, the entire first floor must be completely sprinklered. If the rest of the floor is separated (to the extent required for the stair enclosure), only the path to the exit discharge must be sprinklered.

18-2.8 Illumination of Means of Egress.

18-2.8.1 Means of egress shall be illuminated in accordance with Section 5-8.

18-2.9 Emergency Lighting.

18-2.9.1 Emergency lighting in accordance with Section 5-9 shall be provided in all buildings with greater than 12 living units or greater than three stories in height.

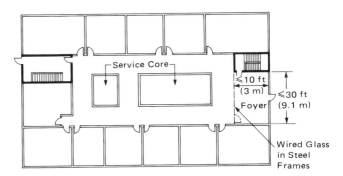

Figure 18-6. Foyer Constructed in Compliance with 5-7.2. The foyer must serve only as a means of egress.

Exception: Where every living unit has a direct exit to the outside of the building at grade level.

This exception does not apply to all buildings with exterior exit access but only to those where each unit has direct exit to grade.

18-2.10 Marking of Means of Egress.

18-2.10.1 Means of egress shall have signs in accordance with Section 5-10 in all buildings requiring more than one exit.

18-2.11 Special Features. (Reserved.)

SECTION 18-3 Protection

18-3.1 Protection of Vertical Openings.

18-3.1.1 Every stairway, elevator shaft, and other vertical opening shall be enclosed or protected in accordance with 6-2.4.

Exception No. 1: Stairway enclosures shall not be required where a one-story stair connects two levels within a single dwelling unit, guest room, or suite.

Exception No. 1 permits an unenclosed stair to be located within a dwelling unit for the purpose of connecting adjacent stories. This addresses typical two-story apartment configurations. However, in the case of a three-story dwelling unit, only two of the three stories may be connected by the open stair. The stair connecting the third story must be enclosed in accordance with 6-2.4.

Exception No. 2: An atrium shall be permitted in accordance with 6-2.4.6.

Exception No. 3: In buildings protected throughout by an approved supervised automatic sprinkler system installed in accordance with 18-3.5, the fire resistance of walls shall be not less than 1 hour, and the fire protection rating of doors shall be not less than 1 hour.

In recognition of the relatively low fuel loads in apartment buildings, the fire protection rating of required enclosure of vertical openings need not exceed 1 hour. Similar provisions are made for exit enclosures (*see 18-2.2.1.2*). However, as a safeguard, this is permitted only in buildings protected throughout by automatic sprinklers . Essentially, the level of protection required by Exception No. 3 becomes the *Code*-specified minimum for those buildings provided with sprinkler protection in accordance with 18-3.5.2. Only those apartment buildings complying with the Exception to 18-3.5.2 must apply the provisons of 6-4.2 for vertical opening protection. (*Also see commentary following 18-2.2.1.2.*)

Exception No. 4: There shall be no unprotected vertical opening in any building or fire section with only one exit.

18-3.1.2 No floor below the level of exit discharge used only for storage, heating equipment, or purposes other than residential occupancy open to the public shall have unprotected openings to floors used for residential purposes.

18-3.2 **Protection from Hazards.**

18-3.2.1 **Hazardous Areas.** Any hazardous area shall be protected in accordance with Section 6-4. The following areas shall be protected as indicated. Where sprinkler protection without fire rated separation is used, areas shall be separated from other spaces by partitions complying with 6-3.2 with doors complying with 6-3.4.

Hazardous Area	Separation/Protection
Boiler and fuel-fired heater rooms serving more than a single living unit.	1-hr and sprinklers
Employee locker rooms	1-hr or sprinklers
Gift or retail shops	1-hr or sprinklers
Bulk laundries	1-hr and sprinklers
Laundries not more than 100 sq ft (9.3 sq m) outside of living units	1-hr or sprinklers[1]
Laundries more than 100 sq ft (9.3 sq m) outside of living units	1-hr and sprinklers
Maintenance shops	1-hr and sprinklers
Storage rooms outside of living units	1-hr or sprinklers
Trash rooms	1-hr and sprinklers

[1] Where sprinklers are provided, separation is not required.

This paragraph has been totally rewritten for the 1991 *Code*. Protection for the typical hazardous areas found in apartment buildings has been specifically provided. Note that the areas protected by sprinklers still require walls and self-closing doors that resist the passage of smoke unless the footnote applies.

While the list that appears in 18-3.2.1 provides specific direction for certain hazardous areas, it is not all-inclusive. Other areas that are hazardous need to comply with the appropriate level of protection in accordance with Section 6-4.

18-3.3 **Interior Finish.**

18-3.3.1 Interior finish on walls and ceilings in accordance with Section 6-5, shall be as follows:

(a) Exit enclosures — Class A.
(b) Lobbies and corridors — Class A or B.
(c) All other spaces — Class A, B, or C.

18-3.3.2 **Interior Floor Finish.** Interior floor finish in corridors and exits shall be Class I or Class II in accordance with Section 6-5.

See the commentary in Section 6-5, particularly the discussion on interior floor finish. Paragraph 6-5.2.3 establishes stringent requirements regarding the use of textile or carpetlike material on walls and ceilings. The interior finish for walls and ceilings, other than textile or carpetlike material, can be lowered one class (e.g., A to B, B to C) in sprinklered buildings. *(See 6-5.7.)*

18-3.4 Detection, Alarm, and Communication Systems.

See Supplement 2.

18-3.4.1 General. Apartment buildings with more than three stories or with more than 11 living units shall be provided with a fire alarm system in accordance with Section 7-6.

Exception: Where each living unit is separated from other contiguous living units by fire barriers (see Section 6-2) having a fire resistance rating not less than 1¾ hour, and where each living unit has either its own independent exit or its own independent stairway or ramp discharging at grade.

The intent of this exception is to eliminate the requirement for a fire alarm system in a "townhouse" type apartment building.

18-3.4.2 Initiation.

18-3.4.2.1 Initiation of the required fire alarm system shall be by manual means in accordance with 7-6.2.

18-3.4.2.2 In buildings protected throughout by an approved supervised automatic sprinkler system installed in accordance with 18-3.5, required fire alarm systems shall be initiated upon operation of the automatic sprinkler system.

18-3.4.3 Notification.

18-3.4.3.1 An annunciator panel connected with the required fire alarm system shall be provided. The location of the annunciator panel shall be approved by the authority having jurisdiction.

Exception: Buildings not greater than two stories in height and having not more than 50 living units.

18-3.4.3.2 Occupant notification shall be accomplished automatically, without delay, by an internal audible alarm signal in accordance with 7-6.3. Presignal systems are prohibited.

18-3.4.4 Detection.

18-3.4.4.1* Approved single station or multiple station smoke detectors continuously powered from the building electrical system shall be installed in accordance with 7-6.2.9 in every living unit within the apartment building regardless of the number of stories or number of apartments. When activated, the detector shall initiate an alarm that is audible in the sleeping rooms of that unit. This individual unit detector shall be in addition to any sprinkler system or other detection system that may be installed in the building.

A-18-3.4.4.1 Previous editions of the *Code* allowed the single station smoke detector required by this section to be omitted from each apartment where a total automatic smoke detection system was installed throughout the building. With such a system, when one detector is activated, an alarm is sounded throughout the building. Experience with complete systems in apartment buildings has shown that numerous false alarms are likely to occur. Where there is a problem with frequent false alarms, occupants either ignore the alarm, or the system is either disconnected or otherwise rendered inoperative.

The detector(s) required by 18-3.4.4.1 should usually be located in the hall area(s) providing access to rooms used for sleeping. In multilevel living units, the detector covering the upper level should normally be located at the top of the stairs. The detector(s) should be mounted on the ceiling or on the wall within 12 in. (30.5 cm) of, but no closer than 6 in. (15.2 cm) to, the ceiling. The detector should be remotely located from the cooking area. Where unusual factors such as room configuration, air movement, or stagnant air pockets must be considered, the authority having jurisdiction and the designer should determine the placement of the detectors. (*See NFPA 74, Standard for the Installation, Maintenance, and Use of Household Fire Warning Equipment,*[4] *for additional details.*)

Note that the detector must be powered by "house current." This should be achieved by direct wiring of the detector or by using plug-in type detectors. Battery-powered units will not meet the requirements of 18-3.4.4.1.

It is not the intent of the paragraph to prohibit interconnecting detectors (multiple station versus single station) within a single apartment if the apartment needs more than one detector; in fact, this is probably required by the second sentence of the paragraph.

Also note that this requirement must be met in addition to any other detection or suppression system required.

18-3.4.4.2   Approved single station smoke detectors continuously powered by the building electrical system shall be installed in accordance with 7-6.2.9 in every sleeping room. When activated, the detectors shall initiate an alarm in that sleeping room.

Exception: In buildings protected throughout by an approved supervised automatic sprinkler system installed in accordance with 18-3.5.

While 18-3.4.4.1 requires the installation of smoke detectors within individual living units, 18-3.4.4.2 requires the installation of detectors within *every sleeping room* of each unit to provide rapid notification to those occupants intimate with the fire origin. A review of this exception and the Exception to 18-3.5.2 will make the applicability of this requirement apparent for those buildings with apartments having direct access to the exterior or otherwise exempted from the sprinkler requirements of 18-3.5.2 (*see commentary to A-18-3.5.1*). The Committee is not equating sprinklers and smoke detectors but is saying that, in nonsprinklered buildings, additional smoke detection is needed in addition to the exits direct to grade.

18-3.5   **Extinguishment Requirements.**

See Supplement 3.

18-3.5.1*   Where an automatic sprinkler system is installed, either for total or partial building coverage, the system shall be installed in accordance with Section 7-7. In buildings up to and including four stories in height, systems installed in accordance with NFPA 13R, *Standard for the Installation of Sprinkler Systems in Residential Occupancies up to and Including Four Stories in Height*, shall be permitted.

Exception: In individual living units, sprinkler installation is not required in closets not over 12 sq ft (1.1 sq m) and bathrooms not over 55 sq ft (5.1 sq m). Closets that contain equipment such as washers, dryers, furnaces, or water heaters shall be sprinklered regardless of size.

A-18-3.5.1   Although not required by the *Code*, the use of residential sprinklers or quick response sprinklers is encouraged for new installations of sprinkler systems within dwelling units, apartments, and guest rooms. Caution must be used, as the system must be designed for the sprinkler being used.

The 1991 *Code* includes a new reference to NFPA 13R, *Standard for the installation of Sprinkler Systems in Residential Occupancies up to and Including Four Stories in Height*.[3] Paragraph 2-4.5.1 of NFPA 13R requires the installation of listed residential sprinklers inside dwelling units. However, an exception permits the use of other listed sprinklers only if smoke detectors are provided in each sleeping room.

The Exception to 18-3.5.1 was carefully reworded for the 1988 *Code*. First, the closet size was reduced due to the potential fuel load in large closets within an apartment building (as compared to a normal load in a hotel). Second, the spaces exempted were limited to those within a living unit; public areas are not exempted. Finally, the last sentence was added to clarify that the intent of this exception applies to regular closets and bathrooms, not closets that contain equipment.

The appendix note encourages sprinklers within dwelling units to be approved residential or quick response sprinklers. The intent is to obtain the quick response provided by these sprinklers as well as the high spray pattern provided by residential sprinklers. Designers of sprinkler systems must use caution, as these sprinklers cannot always be installed on a system designed for standard sprinklers. There are also situations where residential sprinklers are not currently listed for use, such as for vaulted ceilings. In such cases, the designer needs to provide the best alternative sprinkler.

18-3.5.2 All buildings shall be protected throughout by an approved supervised automatic sprinkler system installed in accordance with 18-3.5.1.

Exception: Buildings where every living unit has either:

(a) An exit door opening directly to the street or yard at ground level, or

(b) Direct access to an outside stair complying with 5-2.2 that serves a maximum of two units located on the same floor, or

(c) Direct access to an interior stair serving only that unit and separated from all other portions of the building by fire barriers having a 1-hour fire resistance rating with no openings therein.

Those features that define residential occupancies also contribute to their associated poor life loss statistics. Approximately 82 percent of all fire deaths that occurred in the U.S. during 1989 took place in residential settings. More specifically, almost 15 percent of all deaths took place in apartment building fires. In recognition of America's fire problem in residential occupancies and the proven life safety benefit of properly installed and maintained sprinkler systems, the *Code* now requires sprinklers in new apartment buildings unless the Exception to 18-3.5.2 can be applied.

The exception can be applied only under the following conditions: Each and every living unit within a building must have either (1) a door opening to the outside at grade level, or (2) direct access to an outside stair (however, that stair may serve no more than two units and both those units must be located on the same level), or (3) access to an interior stair serving only that unit and properly separated from the remainder of the building. The direct access required from each living unit to the outside, in combination with the early warning provided by the sleeping room smoke detectors required by 18-3.4.4.2, provides an acceptable alternative to sprinklers. The conditions under which this exception is permitted are equivalent to those that allow a single exit in accordance with Exception No. 1 to 18-2.4.1. (*See Figure 18-7.*)

18-3.5.3 Portable fire extinguishers shall be provided in hazardous areas. Where provided, portable fire extinguishers shall be installed and maintained as specified 7-7.4.1.

18-3.5.4 Open air parking structures complying with NFPA 88A, *Standard for Parking Structures*, need not be sprinklered under this *Code*.

Since many apartment buildings contain open air parking structures, the Committee believed that, for *Life Safety Code* purposes only, an exemption for these structures was warranted. However, if sprinkler protection is required by other codes or by the *Life Safety Code* for reasons other than those found in 16-3.5, sprinkler protection must then be provided in these structures.

18-3.6 Corridors.

18-3.6.1 Exit access corridors shall be constructed of fire barriers in accordance with 6-2.3 having not less than a 1-hour fire resistance rating.

Exception: In buildings protected throughout by an approved supervised automatic sprinkler system installed in accordance with 18-3.5, corridor walls shall have a fire resistance rating of not less than 1/2 hour.

The criteria in 18-3.6 reflect the Committee's concern for providing safety for occupants in their apartments during a fire. The focus of this concern is the presence of occupants 24 hours a day in facilities that provide sleeping accommodations. The minimum corridor wall construction required by 18-3.6.1 will either prevent fire movement from the corridor to an apartment or prevent fire in an apartment from entering the corridor. (*Also see 18-5.2.*)

Although the reduction to 1/2-hour fire resistance in new construction would have little benefit, it can play a major role in the rehabilitation, renovation, or conversion of existing structures that are required to meet the provisions for new construction (*see 1-5.6*). Most existing lath and plaster walls provide 20- to 30-minute fire resistance ratings. If automatic sprinkler protection is provided throughout the building, the walls will not have to be replaced.

18-3.6.2 Doors between apartments and corridors shall be self-closing.

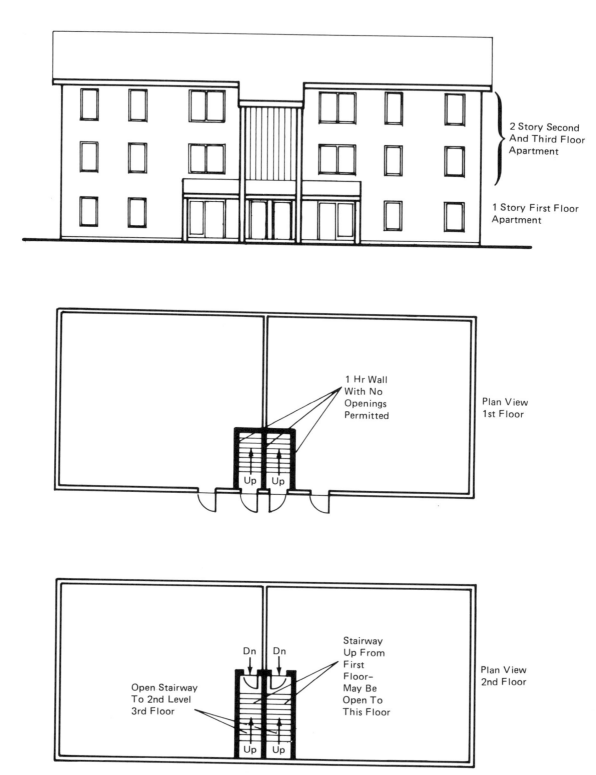

Figure 18-7. *Potential Arrangement for a Three-Story Apartment Building without Sprinkler Protection. Each apartment has its own egress system direct to ground. Every sleeping and living area must be provided with smoke detection. (See 18-3.4.4.2.)*

The requirements for self-closing doors between apartments and corridors may lead to a significant reduction in fatalities caused by fire in apartment buildings. Studies of typical apartment fires indicate that fire spreads beyond the apartment or room of origin because doors are left open as occupants escape.

In other cases, fatalities occur when occupants who suspect a fire open the door to a room fully involved with fire or cause full involvement of the room by introducing oxygen through the open door. Spring-loaded hinges or closers will cause these doors to close, preventing smoke or fire from spreading down the corridor and exposing other occupants.

18-3.6.3* The fire protection rating of doors that open from living units onto corridors shall be not less than 20 minutes.

A-18-3.6.3 Longer ratings may be required where doors are provided for property protection as well as life safety.

This does not require a listed or labeled assembly, but addresses only the door.

Figure 18-8 illustrates the provisions of 18-3.6.

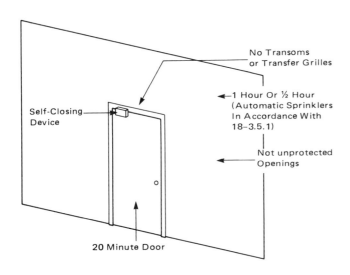

No Transoms
or Transfer Grilles

Self-Closing
Device

1 Hour Or ½ Hour
(Automatic Sprinklers
In Accordance With
18–3.5.1)

Not unprotected
Openings

20 Minute Door

Figure 18-8. *The Corridor and Wall Provisions of 18-3.6.*

18-3.7 Subdivisions of Building Spaces. (Reserved.)

18-3.8 Special Features. (Reserved.)

SECTION 18-4   Special Provisions

18-4.1 Windows for Rescue and Ventilation. (*See 18-2.1.1.*)

Exception: In buildings protected throughout by an approved supervised automatic sprinkler system installed in accordance with 18-3.5.

18-4.2 High Rise Buildings. High rise buildings shall comply with Section 30-8. The Exception to 18-3.5.1 shall be permitted.

18-4.3 Operating Features. (*See Chapter 31.*)

SECTION 18-5   Building Services

18-5.1 Utilities. Utilities shall comply with the provisions of Section 7-1.

18-5.2 Heating, Ventilating, and Air Conditioning. Heating, ventilating, and air conditioning equipment shall comply with the provisions of Section 7-2.

Paragraph 2-3.11.1 of NFPA 90A, *Standard for the Installation of Air Conditioning and Ventilating Systems,*[5] prohibits the use of public corridors in residential occupancies as part of the supply, return, or exhaust air system.

18-5.3 Elevators, Escalators, and Conveyors. Elevators, escalators, and conveyors shall comply with the provisions of Section 7-4.

18-5.4 Rubbish Chutes, Incinerators, and Laundry Chutes. Rubbish chutes, incinerators, and laundry chutes shall comply with the provisions of Section 7-5.

References Cited in Commentary

[1]NFPA 13, *Standard for the Installation of Sprinkler Systems,* National Fire Protection Association, Quincy, MA, 1991.

[2]NFPA 13D, *Standard for the Installation of Sprinkler Systems in One- and Two-Family Dwellings and Mobile Homes,* National Fire Protection Association, Quincy, MA, 1991.

[3]NFPA 13R, *Standard for the Installation of Sprinkler Systems in Residential Occupancies up to and Including Four Stories in Height,* National Fire Protection Association, Quincy, MA, 1991.

[4]NFPA 74, *Standard for the Installation, Maintenance, and Use of Household Fire Warning Equipment,* National Fire Protection Association, Quincy, MA, 1989.

[5]NFPA 90A, *Standard for the Installation of Air Conditioning and Ventilating Systems,* National Fire Protection Association, Quincy, MA, 1989.

19

Existing Apartment Buildings

(See also Chapter 31.)

Apartment buildings are one of five residential occupancy types addressed by the *Life Safety Code*. Other residential occupancies considered include one- and two-family dwellings, hotels, lodging and rooming houses, and residential board and care facilities. Sleeping accommodations are a feature common to all residential occupancies.

Paragraph 4-1.6 highlights a common principle of life safety with which the *Code* is concerned as applied to all residential occupancies addressed by Chapters 16 through 23. Paragraph 4-1.6 states: "Residential occupancies are those occupancies in which sleeping accommodations are provided for normal residential purposes and include all buildings designed to provide sleeping accommodations." This use of residential occupancies is central to the *Code* provisions of Chapters 16 through 23, since occupants who are sleeping will be unaware of a rapidly developing fire and, when alerted to the emergency, may be somewhat confused due to being awakened suddenly.

Other factors on which the provisions of Chapters 16 through 23 are based are the presence of hazards (such as cooking and heating equipment) and the degree of familiarity of the occupants with their living space. Occupants may have little or no familiarity, as in the case of transient residents of hotels, or they may have the total familiarity of residents of a one-family dwelling.

Apartments, townhouses, flats, and condominiums accounted for 116,300 structure fires per year as reported to U.S. fire departments from 1984 to 1988. There were 906 civilian deaths and 5,966 civilian injuries per year. Fifty-seven deaths per year took place in properties with one or two apartments over a business, 352 per year in properties with three to six apartments, 212 per year in properties with more than twenty apartments, 8 per year in properties of unclassified size, and 74 per year in properties of unreported size.

Five percent of all home fire deaths that took place from 1984 to 1988 occurred in apartment buildings with twenty or more units. These apartment buildings accounted for 7 percent of all occupied housing units in 1986. The discrepancy between the two percentages may be related to lower risk or other factors, such as average household size.

Half of all those who died in apartment fires from 1980 to 1988 were outside the room of fire origin; this does not mean that they were outside the apartment unit of origin. That distinction cannot be made using the existing data.

There were six apartment fires in the 1980s that resulted in 10 or more fatalities:

Date	Location	Civilian Deaths
1980	Utah	12 dead
1980	Illinois	10 dead
1981	New Jersey	11 dead
1982	Connecticut	14 dead
1985	Pennsylvania	11 dead
1989	Tennessee	16 dead

The 1985 fire incident in Pennsylvania was unique, since it was caused by the use of explosives by police in a siege situation. Of the other five incidents, one involved a building over five stories. Few, if any, of the victims were in the apartment of fire origin. In one case, the area of origin was not an apartment unit. These incidents indicated a lack of fire protection systems and features. Other contributing factors were incendiary fire origin, early involvement of the primary or only means of egress, and the existence of doors that had been propped open.

These incidents demonstrate the importance of the *Life Safety Code* to apartment firesafety.

SECTION 19-1   General Requirements

19-1.1 Application.

19-1.1.1 All existing buildings classified as apartment buildings by 19-1.3 shall conform to the provisions of this chapter and shall meet the requirements of one of the following options:

Option 1:   Buildings without fire suppression or detection systems;

Single station smoke detectors in each unit are required per 19-3.4.4.1.

Option 2:   Buildings provided with a complete automatic fire detection and notification system;

Option 3:   Buildings provided with automatic sprinkler protection in selected areas;

Option 4:   Buildings protected throughout by an approved automatic sprinkler system.

Paragraph 19-1.1.1 identifies four options for apartment buildings to comply with the *Code*:

Option 1: Buildings without fire suppression or detection systems;

Option 2: Buildings with an automatic fire detection system;

Option 3: Buildings provided with an automatic sprinkler system in corridors only; and

Option 4 Buildings protected by a total automatic sprinkler system.

In the 1976 Edition of the *Code*, Section 11-3 covered both new and existing apartment buildings. Paragraphs 11-3.1 through 11-3.4 provided general requirements for all apartment buildings, and 11-3.5, 11-3.6, 11-3.7, and 11-3.8 each covered one of the four options. In that edition, every apartment building was required to meet the provisions of 11-3.1 through 11-3.4 and any one of the requirements of 11-3.5 through 11-3.8. This format resulted in a considerable amount of cross-referencing in Sections 11-1, 11-2, and Chapter 6, as well as in Section 11-3. When the 1981 Edition underwent extensive editorial revision to create separate chapters for new and existing buildings and break the residential chapter into chapters covering individual facilities, it was decided to reorganize the chapters on apartments for easier use and to eliminate cross-referencing where possible. As a result of this restructuring, all sections of Chapter 19 then applied to all existing apartment buildings. Since the 1991 Edition has adopted mandatory sprinkler requirements for *new* apartment buildings, Chapter 18 has dropped Options 1 through 4. However, the four options remain in Chapter 19. There are various paragraphs and portions of paragraphs that apply to different options. Every apartment building must meet one of the four options.

In recognition of the equivalency provisions found in Section 1-6 of the *Code*, the Committee saw a need to establish, in advance, four equivalent schemes that provide a high degree of flexibility while remaining in compliance with the *Code*. The equivalencies developed were based on the Committee's professional judgment, the results of full-scale fire tests conducted at the National Bureau of Standards, and a review of current fire experiences. These options are considered to be equivalent to each other in providing a minimum level of life safety provisions for existing apartments. Because some systems have additional protective capability (detectors, automatic sprinklers, etc.), greater building heights and larger building areas are permitted. Where the building provides only the minimum level of safety required by the *Code*, lower building heights and smaller building areas are specified.

This comprehensive approach provides one of the first attempts at "system" design to be codified. While a total system would consist of many alternatives, this is a more limited, or bounded, system, since there are only four options available. However, an owner can identify the most appropriate option based on the building's size, height, and arrangement. This provides the owner an opportunity to coordinate a safety approach that best fits the building, rather than adapting a building to a single codified criterion.

19-1.2   Mixed Occupancies.

19-1.2.1   Where another type of occupancy occurs in the same building as a residential occupancy, the requirements of 1-5.7 of this *Code* shall apply.

19-1.2.2   For requirements on mixed mercantile and residential occupancies, see 25-1.2; for mixed assembly and residential occupancies, see 9-1.2.

19-1.3   Definitions.

19-1.3.1   Terms applicable to this chapter are defined in Chapter 3 of this *Code*; where necessary, other terms will be defined in the text as they occur.

Apartment Buildings.*   Apartment buildings include buildings containing three or more living units with independent cooking and bathroom facilities, whether designated as apartment houses, tenements, garden apartments, or by any other name.

A-19-1.3.1   The *Code* specifies that whenever there are three or more living units in a building, the building is considered an apartment building and must comply with either Chapter 18 or 19 as appropriate. "Townhouse" units are considered to be an apartment building if there are three or more units in the building. The type of wall required between units in order to consider them to be separate buildings is normally established by the authority having jurisdiction. Should the units be separated by a wall of sufficient fire resistance and structural integrity to be considered as separate buildings, then the provisions of Chapter 21 apply to each townhouse. "Condominium" is a form of ownership; not occupancy; for example, there are condominium warehouses, condominium apartments, and condominium offices.

This new appendix note was added to the 1991 *Code* to clarify occupancy classification for townhouse-type apartments, particularly those under condominium ownership. It is often mistakenly believed that condominiums are a form of occupancy rather than a form of ownership.

19-1.4   Classification of Occupancy. (*See 19-1.3.1.*)

19-1.5   Classification of Hazard of Contents.

19-1.5.1   The contents of residential occupancies shall be classified as ordinary hazard in accordance with Section 4-2.

NFPA 13, *Standard for the Installation of Sprinkler Systems*,[1] would classify the contents as "light hazard" for the purpose of designing extinguishing systems. The difference in classification is based on the threat to life or life safety (ordinary) as opposed to the threat to the extinguishing capability of the automatic sprinkler system (light).

19-1.6   Minimum Construction Requirements. No special requirements.

19-1.7 Occupant Load.

19-1.7.1* The occupant load in numbers of persons for whom exits are to be provided shall be determined on the basis of one person per 200 sq ft (18.6 sq m) gross floor area or the maximum probable population of any room or section under consideration, whichever is greater. The occupant load of any open mezzanine or balcony shall be added to the occupant load of the floor below for the purpose of determining exit capacity.

A-19-1.7.1 Dormitory-type occupancy, particularly where 2- or 3-tier bunks are used with close spacing, may produce an occupant load substantially greater than one person per 200 sq ft (18.6 sq m) gross floor area. However, even though sleeping areas are densely populated, the building as a whole may not necessarily exceed one person per 200 sq ft (18.6 sq m) gross area, owing to the space taken for toilet facilities, halls, closets, and living rooms not used for sleeping purposes.

See 5-3.1 for further details on the use of the occupant load for determining the capacity of the means of egress.

SECTION 19-2 Means of Egress Requirements

19-2.1 General.

19-2.1.1 Means of egress from living units to the outside of the building shall be in accordance with Chapter 5 and this chapter. Means of escape within the living unit shall comply with the provisions of Section 21-2 for one- and two-family dwellings.

A general reference to Chapter 5 is made in place of repeating many of its provisions. Many of the requirements found in Section 19-2 are Chapter 5 provisions that serve as options for the occupancy chapters, such as Exception No. 1 to 19-2.2.2.2, which allows the use of special locking arrangements in accordance with 5-2.1.6. Other provisions prohibit the use of an item if it is not listed (note that alternating tread devices are not listed in 19-2.2) or establish restrictions based on criteria provided in Chapter 5, such as the dead-end limits for corridors found in 19-2.5.3.

This paragraph requires that every living unit (apartment) comply with Section 21-2 of Chapter 21, which addresses one- and two-family dwellings. This requirement is important for several reasons. First, it establishes two means of escape from every sleeping room and living area of a living unit (apartment) having two rooms or more (this exempts efficiency-type apartments). Paragraph 21-2.1.2 establishes several types of "second means of escape" that can be used, the most common of which is the operable window; however, Chapter 21 also sets certain requirements for operable windows in addition to those specifying minimum size and arrangement. The window must be located within 20 ft (6.1 m) of grade or be accessible by fire department rescue apparatus or must open onto a balcony. If this requirement cannot be met, a second means of escape complying with one of the other three types listed in 21-2.1.2 must be provided. A second means of escape is exempted if the dwelling unit is protected by an automatic sprinkler system in accordance with either NFPA 13, *Standard for the Installation of Sprinkler Systems,*[1] or NFPA 13D, *Standard for the Installation of Sprinkler Systems in One- and Two-Family Dwellings and Mobile Homes,*[2] or NFPA 13R, *Standard for the Installation of Sprinkler Systems in Residential Occupancies up to and Including Four Stories in Height.*[3] Note that this would not require that the entire apartment building be sprinklered, but only the living unit that is not in compliance with the secondary means of escape.

A second important provision of Section 21-2 is that the means of egress provisions of Chapter 5 do not apply unless specifically referenced. For example, the minimum width of doors within the dwelling unit is reduced to 28 in. (71 cm) from the 32-in. (81-cm) width specified by Chapter 5. Section 21-2 also allows the use of winders and spiral stairs within the living unit, and the headroom requirements of Chapter 5 do not apply within the living unit (apartment). (*See commentary on Chapter 21 for additional information on means of escape from living units.*)

19-2.2 Means of Egress Components.

19-2.2.1 General.

19-2.2.1.1 Components of means of egress shall be limited to the types described in 19-2.2.2 through 19-2.2.9.

19-2.2.1.2 In buildings utilizing Option 4, exit enclosures shall have a fire resistance rating of not less than 1 hour with doors having a fire protection rating of not less than 1 hour.

In recognition of the relatively low fuel loads in apartment buildings, the fire resistance rating for exit enclosures, as well as for other vertical openings (*see 19-3.1.1 Exception No. 3*), need not exceed 1 hour; however, as a safeguard, this is permitted only in buildings protected throughout by automatic sprinklers (Option 4). This is not permitted in assembly occupancies or business occupancies and, therefore, cannot be utilized where mixed occupancies are involved; nor can it be used for stairways or vertical openings that are part of or pass through other occupancies.

In facilities where occupancies are adequately separated and treated independently, it may be feasible to have a 1-hour enclosure in the apartment portion of the facility and 2-hour enclosure elsewhere.

19-2.2.2 Doors.

19-2.2.2.1 Doors shall comply with 5-2.1.

19-2.2.2.2* No door in any means of egress shall be locked against egress when the building is occupied.

Exception: Special locking arrangements complying with 5-2.1.6 are permitted.

A-19-2.2.2.2 It is the intent of this requirement that security measures, when installed, should not prevent egress.

Paragraph 19-2.2.2.2 prohibits an apartment building from having any door locked "against egress" while the building is occupied. This requirement permits a door to have a locking device that allows the door to be opened from within the building for the purpose of egress but does not allow the door to be opened from outside the building. Ordinary double cylinder locks and chain locks do not meet these provisions. Several tragic multiple-death fires occurred when a key needed to unlock these devices could not be found.

The language of 5-2.1.5.1 is clear: "Locks, if provided, shall not require the use of a key, tool, special knowledge, or effort for operation from the inside of the building."

This eliminates double cylinder locks and chain locks that require a key in order to be operated from the inside. Paragraph 5-2.1.5.3 requires the use of a simple operation to open a door; locks that require two-handed knob and similar operations are explicitly prohibited.

Chapter 5 now specifically recognizes the need for security chains or rods on apartment doors as well as a lock and allows two additional releasing devices. The typical apartment door has three devices: a latch, a lock, and a security chain or rod. The *Code* prefers only two releasing actions (*see commentary following 18-2.2.2.2*); however, it recognizes the existence of thousands of installations that require the use of three actions. Where new installations are being made in an existing apartment building, the *Code* requires the installation to comply with Chapter 18. (*See 1-5.6.*)

The Exception to 19-2.2.2.2 recognizes the use of the delay release lock provided for in 5-2.1.6. This requires that the building either be protected throughout by automatic sprinklers or be equipped throughout with a fire detection system. The 15- or 30-second delay permitted by 5-2.1.6 does not affect the immediate release of the lock upon activation of the sprinklers or detectors, or upon loss of power to the lock. This device helps provide the security needed for infrequently used doors or stairs in apartment buildings. At the same time, the door remains available for use. Chains and padlocks are unable to provide this feature.

The former Exception No. 2 to 18-2.2.2.2, which allowed the so-called "captive key" type of lock permitted by Exception No. 3 to 5-2.1.5.1, has been removed from the 1991 Edition of the *Code*.

19-2.2.2.3 Revolving doors complying with 5-2.1.10 are permitted.

19-2.2.2.4 Horizontal sliding doors in accordance with 5-2.1.14 shall be permitted in a means of egress serving a room or area with an occupant load of less than 50. Such doors shall not be located for use across corridors.

Note that 19-2.2.2.4 is more restrictive regarding the use of these special doors than is Chapter 5, since they cannot be installed across corridors or be located in a means of egress serving 50 or more people. This overrides some of the general provisions of 5-2.1.14.

19-2.2.3 **Stairs.**

19-2.2.3.1 Stairs shall comply with 5-2.2.

19-2.2.3.2 Within any individual living unit, stairs more than one story above or below the entrance floor level of the living unit shall not be permitted.

This paragraph requires that no level of an apartment be located farther than one story away from an entrance. This would usually restrict an apartment from having more than three stories: main level, upper, and lower. However, if an apartment has entrances at more than one level, more than three stories are permitted. However, 19-3.1.1 allows only two levels to be open to each other; the third level must be protected in accordance with 6-2.4.

19-2.2.3.3 Spiral stairs complying with 5-2.2.2.7 are permitted within a single living unit.

19-2.2.3.4 Winders complying with 5-2.2.2.8 are permitted.

19-2.2.4 **Smokeproof Enclosures.** Smokeproof enclosures shall comply with 5-2.3. (*See also 19-2.11.1.*)

19-2.2.5 **Horizontal Exits.** Horizontal exits shall comply with 5-2.4.

19-2.2.6 **Ramps.** Ramps shall comply with 5-2.5.

19-2.2.7 **Exit Passageways.** Exit passageways shall comply with 5-2.6.

19-2.2.8* **Escalators.** Escalators previously approved as a component in the means of egress may continue to be given credit for compliance.

A-19-2.2.8 Due to the nature of escalators, they are no longer acceptable as a component in the means of egress. However, since many escalators have been used for exit access and exit discharge in the past, credit may be continued. Very few escalators have ever been installed in a manner to qualify as an exit. For information on escalator protection and requirements, the reader is referred to previous editions of the *Code*.

19-2.2.9 **Fire Escape Stairs.** Fire escape stairs complying with 5-2.8 are permitted.

19-2.3 **Capacity of Means of Egress.**

19-2.3.1 The capacity of means of egress shall be in accordance with Section 5-3.

19-2.3.2 Street floor exits shall be sufficient for the occupant load of the street floor plus the required capacity of stairs and ramps discharging onto the street floor.

Paragraph 19-2.3.2 requires street floor exit designs that have sufficient width to accommodate the convergence of occupants discharging through exits from the street floor with those discharging down from the upper floors and up from the lower floors. This constitutes the traditional grand lobby design in which stairs and street floor exits converge at one or two exterior door locations. Similar commentary on this issue is found in Chapter 17. Paragraph 5-7.2 restricts the number and arrangement of stairs that are used to discharge through the street floor.

Figure 19-1 shows a typical arrangement of multiple exits discharging on the street floor.

19-2.4 **Number of Exits.** (*See also Section 5-4.*)

19-2.4.1 Every living unit shall have access to at least two separate exits remotely located from each other as required by 5-5.1.

Exception No. 1: Any living unit shall be permitted to have a single exit provided:

(a) That living unit has an exit door opening directly to the street or yard at ground level, or

(b) That living unit has direct access to an outside stair complying with 5-2.2 that serves a maximum of two units located on the same floor, or

(c) That living unit has direct access to an interior stair serving only that unit and separated from all other portions of the building by fire barriers having a 1-hour fire resistance rating with no opening therein.

Exception No. 1 allows a single exit under three arrangements: (1) The living unit has an exit leading

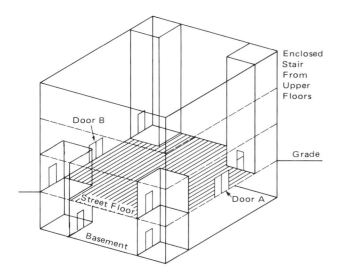

Figure 19-1. *Capacity of Means of Egress in Accordance with 19-2.3.2. Required widths of Doors A and B are based on the anticipated number of people using them. Assuming that the street floor has an occupant load of 500, that each upper floor has an occupant load of 200, and that the basement has an occupant load of 100, the required exit capacity for the street floor would be calculated as follows:*

500 (street floor) + 200 ÷ 2 (upper floor max 50% per 5-7.2) + 100 ÷ 2 (basement max 50% per 5-7.2) = 650 total using exits on street floor × 0.2 in. (0.5 cm) of door per person = 130 in. (325 cm) ÷ 2 exits = 65 in. (163 cm) at A and at B.

directly to the street or yard at ground level. This is common in a townhouse or row house arrangement. Under this arrangement, the front door is the only required exit, and, therefore, there are no requirements for a rear door. If a rear door is provided, it does not have to meet the requirements of the *Code;* more importantly, it does not have to meet locking requirements of the *Code.* (2) The apartment has direct access to an outside stair and serves not more than two apartments, and both must be on the same floor. (3) The single exit is a 1-hour enclosed private stairway serving that apartment only. Note that this stairway need only be separated from other spaces by the required 1-hour construction; it is not required to be separated from the unit that it serves. Conditions (b) and (c) of Exception No. 1 are illustrated in Figure 19-2.

Exception No. 2: Any building of three stories or less shall be permitted to have a single exit under the following conditions:

(a) The stairway is completely enclosed by barriers having a fire resistance rating of at least 1 hour with self-closing

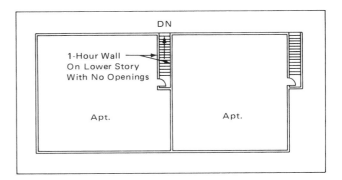

Figure 19-2. *Two Methods of Complying with Exception No. 1 to 19-2.4.1 to Allow a Single Exit. The enclosed stairway is allowed to be open to the unit it serves.*

1-hour fire protection rated doors protecting all openings between the stairway enclosure and the building.

(b) The stairway does not serve more than one-half story below the level of exit discharge.

(c) All corridors serving as access to exits have at least a 1-hour fire resistance rating.

(d) There is not more than 35 ft (10.7 m) of travel distance from the entrance door of any living unit to an exit.

(e) Three-quarter hour fire rated horizontal and vertical separation between living units is provided.

Exception No. 2 to 19-2.4.1 provides the basic design approach used for "garden" apartments where apartment entrances open onto a single enclosed stair. Often, the stair is open to the exterior or is glass-enclosed on the front of the building. The exception allows a single exit under this arrangement. Note that the stairway must be separated from the building by construction of at least a 1-hour fire resistance rating, and the doors must be 1-hour rated and self-closing. A frequent violation of this exception is the noncomplying construction of the door and the lack of a door closer.

Figure 19-3 illustrates one potential method for application of Exception No. 2.

Exception No. 3: A building of any height with not more than four living units per floor, with a smokeproof enclosure or outside stair in accordance with the requirements of 5-2.3 as the exit, immediately accessible to all living units served thereby, shall be permitted to have a single exit. ["Immediately accessible" means there are not more than 20 ft (6.1 m) of travel distance from the entrance door of any living unit to an exit.]

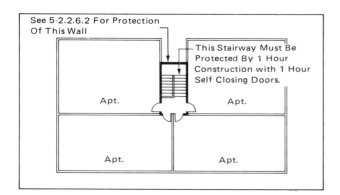

Figure 19-3. One Method of Complying with Exception No. 2 to 19-2.4.1.

Exception No. 3 does not describe a common arrangement. Note that there are no height limitations, but only four units per floor are permitted. Apartments must have immediate access to a smokeproof enclosure or an outside stair that meets the requirements of a smokeproof enclosure. The exemptions found under the requirements for outside stairs in Chapter 5 for unprotected openings exposing a stair would not be applicable in this case, since the *Code* specifically references 5-2.3 on smokeproof enclosures. Paragraph 5-2.3 does not permit unprotected openings exposing the stair.

The three exceptions to 19-2.4.1 apply to any of the four options.

19-2.5 Arrangement of Exits.

19-2.5.1 Access to all required exits shall be in accordance with Section 5-5.

19-2.5.2 No common path of travel shall exceed 35 ft (10.7 m). Travel within a dwelling unit shall not be included when calculating common path of travel.

Exception: In buildings protected throughout by an approved supervised automatic sprinkler system in accordance with 19-3.5, common path of travel shall not exceed 50 ft (15 m).

Common path of travel is normally measured from the most remote point subject to occupancy (see 5-5.1.2 and the definition of common path of travel in Section 3-2); therefore, 19-2.5.2 describes a modified common path of travel, as measurement does not extend into the living unit. Since the limits for common path and dead end differ for existing buildings, the arrangement shown in Figure 19-4 is possible without violating either provision.

19-2.5.3 No dead-end corridor shall exceed 50 ft (15 m).

19-2.6 Travel Distance to Exits.

19-2.6.1 Travel distance within a living unit (apartment) to a corridor door shall not exceed the following limits:

(a) For buildings using Option 1 or 3 — 75 ft (23 m).
(b) For buildings using Option 2 or 4 — 125 ft (38 m).

Revisions to Section 5-6 of the 1988 Edition of the *Code* require that travel distance be measured from the most remote point subject to occupancy. The provision exempting rooms occupied by six or fewer people and having 50 ft (15 m) or less travel distance was deleted. In order to be consistent with Section 5-6, the Committee revised the method of measuring travel distance in apartment buildings. The distances allowed within the unit were increased as compensation. If the travel distance within a unit is excessive, another remotely located door to the corridor must be added.

19-2.6.2 The travel distance from a living unit (apartment) entrance door to the nearest exit shall not exceed the following limits:

(a) For buildings using Option 1 — 100 ft (30 m).
(b) For buildings using Option 2 or 3 — 150 ft (45 m).
(c) For buildings using Option 4 — 200 ft (60 m).

Exception: Travel distance to exits shall not exceed 200 ft (60 m) for exterior ways of exit access arranged in accordance with 5-5.3.

19-2.7 Discharge from Exits.

19-2.7.1 Exit discharge shall comply with Section 5-7.

19-2.7.2 Any required exit stair that is located so that it is necessary to pass through the lobby or other open space to reach

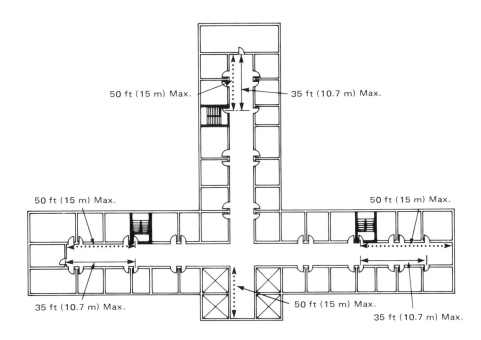

50 ft (15 m) Max.

35 ft (10.7 m) Max.

50 ft (15 m) Max.

50 ft (15 m) Max.

35 ft (10.7 m) Max.

50 ft (15 m) Max.

35 ft (10.7 m) Max.

Figure 19-4. Common Path of Travel (Modified) and Dead-End Limitations in a Nonsprinklered Apartment Building. Modified common paths of travel are indicated by ⟷ and dead ends are indicated by ⟵-⟶.

the outside of the building shall be continuously enclosed to a level of exit discharge or to a mezzanine within a lobby at a level of exit discharge.

19-2.7.3 The distance of travel from the termination of the exit enclosure to an exterior door leading to a public way shall not exceed 150 ft (45 m) in buildings protected throughout by an approved automatic sprinkler system and shall not exceed 100 ft (30 m) in all other buildings.

Section 5-7 does allow a maximum of 50 percent of the number and capacity of exits to discharge through the street floor under limited conditions (*see* 5-7.2). Paragraph 19-2.7.2 slightly modifies these conditions by including a mezzanine within the lobby. Therefore, 50 percent of the exits can discharge onto a mezzanine with occupants then traveling across the mezzanine, downstairs to the lobby level, and outside. However, 19-2.7.3 includes a provision not found in 5-7.2. It restricts the distance from the termination of the exit enclosure to the exterior door to a maximum of 100 ft (30.5 m) in non-sprinklered buildings and 150 ft (45 m) in buildings that are fully sprinklered.

See Figures 19-5 and 19-6. (*Also see discussion of 5-7.2.*)

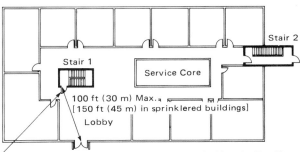

Stair 2

Stair 1

Service Core

100 ft (30 m) Max.
[150 ft (45 m) in sprinklered buildings]

Lobby

└─Route from Stair through Lobby to Exterior Must be Readily Visible, Identified, Clear, and Unobstructed.

Figure 19-5. Arrangement of Means of Egress in Accordance with 5-7.2. Stair 1 (50 percent of the total number and capacity of exits) discharges through the first floor. Stair 2 discharges directly to the exterior (it may discharge through an exit passageway to the exterior). Since other areas on the first floor (the level of exit discharge) are not separated from the path a person leaving Stair 1 must use to exit through the lobby, the entire first floor must be completely sprinklered. If the rest of the floor is separated (to the extent required for the stair enclosure), only the path to the exit discharge must be sprinklered.

19-2.8 Illumination of Means of Egress.

19-2.8.1 Means of egress shall be illuminated in accordance with Section 5-8.

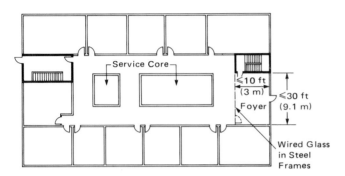

Figure 19-6. *Foyer Constructed in Compliance with 5-7.2. The foyer must serve only as a means of egress.*

19-2.9 Emergency Lighting.

19-2.9.1 Emergency lighting in accordance with Section 5-9 shall be provided in all buildings with greater than 12 living units or greater than three stories in height.

Exception: Where every living unit has a direct exit to the outside of the building at grade level.

This exception does not apply to all buildings with exterior exit access but only to those where each unit has direct exit to grade.

19-2.10 Marking of Means of Egress.

19-2.10.1 Means of egress shall have signs in accordance with Section 5-10 in all buildings requiring more than one exit.

19-2.11 Special Features.

19-2.11.1* In high rise buildings using Option 1, 2, or 3, smokeproof enclosures shall be provided in accordance with 5-2.3.

A-19-2.11.1 The Committee recognizes the need to provide smoke control in existing buildings. Smokeproof enclosures can be accomplished without the use of a vestibule in accordance with 5-2.3.

This paragraph has critical impact on nonsprinklered high rise apartment buildings. If smokeproof enclosures are not already provided, it may be much more realis-

tic to add sprinkler protection than to modify stairs into smokeproof enclosures. A common question regarding this paragraph concerns whether or not stairs served by an exterior exit access balcony can be considered as smokeproof enclosures. If the stairs are enclosed, the intent of 5-2.3.1 is obviously met; however, if the stairs are open and outside, the specific arrangement will need to be reviewed by the authority having jurisdiction. If the outside stairs are protected from the building (i.e., they do not utilize Exception No. 1 to 5-2.2.6.3), it could easily be argued that the intent of 5-2.3.2 is met.

SECTION 19-3 Protection

19-3.1 Protection of Vertical Openings.

19-3.1.1 Every stairway, elevator shaft, and other vertical opening shall be enclosed or protected in accordance with 6-2.4 or provide means of satisfying the requirements of Section 2-9.

Exception No. 1: Stairway enclosures shall not be required where a one-story stair connects two levels within a single dwelling unit, guest room, or suite.

Exception No. 1 permits an unenclosed stair to be located within a dwelling unit for the purpose of connecting adjacent stories. This addresses typical two-story apartment configurations. However, in the case of a three-story dwelling unit, only two of the three stories may be connected by the open stair. The stair connecting the third story must be enclosed in accordance with 6-2.4.

Exception No. 2: An atrium shall be permitted in accordance with 6-2.4.6.

Since 6-2.4.6 requires total automatic sprinkler protection, atriums can be used only in buildings using Option 4.

Exception No. 3: In buildings using Option 4, fire resistance of walls shall be not less than ³/₄ hour for buildings of one to three stories and 1 hour for buildings greater than three stories; and fire protection rating of doors shall be not less than ³/₄ hour for buildings up to three stories and 1 hour for buildings greater than three stories.

In recognition of the relatively low fuel loads in apartment buildings, the fire protection rating of required enclosure of vertical openings need not exceed 1 hour. Similar provisions are made for exit enclosures (*see 19-2.2.1.2*). However, as a safeguard, this is permitted only in buildings protected throughout by automatic sprinklers (Option 4). (*Also see commentary following 19-2.2.1.2.*)

Exception No. 4: Unprotected vertical openings connecting not more than three floors shall be permitted in accordance with the conditions of 6-2.4.5.

Since 6-2.4.5 requires automatic sprinkler protection, the exception will most likely be used only in buildings using Option 4.

Exception No. 5: In any building protected throughout by an approved automatic sprinkler system in accordance with 19-3.5, and where exits and required ways of travel thereto are adequately safeguarded against fire and smoke within the building, or where every individual room has direct access to an exterior exit without passing through any public corridor, the protection of vertical openings not part of required exits may be waived by the authority having jurisdiction to such extent as such openings do not endanger required means of egress.

19-3.1.2 No floor below the level of exit discharge used only for storage, heating equipment, or purpose other than residential occupancy open to the public shall have unprotected openings to floors used for residential purposes.

19-3.2 **Protection from Hazards.**

19-3.2.1 **Hazardous Areas.** Any hazardous area shall be protected in accordance with Section 6-4. The areas in the following table shall be protected as indicated. Where sprinkler protection without fire rated separation is used, areas shall be separated from other spaces by partitions complying with 6-3.2, with doors complying with 6-3.4.

This paragraph has been totally rewritten for the 1991 *Code*. Protection for the typical hazardous areas found in apartment buildings has been specifically provided. Note that the areas protected by sprinklers still require walls and self-closing doors that resist the passage of smoke unless the footnote applies.

Hazardous Area	Separation/Protection
Boiler and fuel-fired heater rooms serving more than a single living unit.	1-hr or sprinklers
Employee locker rooms	1-hr or sprinklers
Gift or retail shops more than 100 sq ft (9.3 sq m)	1-hr or sprinklers[1]
Bulk laundries	1-hr or sprinklers
Laundries more than 100 sq ft (9.3 sq m) outside of dwelling units	1-hr or sprinklers[1]
Maintenance shops	1-hr or sprinklers
Rooms or spaces used for storage of combustible supplies and equipment in quantities deemed hazardous by the authority having jurisdiction	1-hr or sprinklers
Trash rooms	1-hr or sprinklers[1]

[1] Where sprinklers are provided, separation is not required.

While the list that appears in 19-3.2.1 provides specific direction for certain hazardous areas, it is not all-inclusive. Other areas that are hazardous need to comply with the appropriate level of protection in accordance with Section 6-4.

19-3.3 **Interior Finish.**

19-3.3.1 Interior finish on walls and ceilings in accordance with Section 6-5 shall be as follows:

(a) Exit enclosures — Class A or B.
(b) Lobbies and corridors — Class A or B.
(c) All other spaces — Class A, B, or C.

19-3.3.2 **Interior Floor Finish.** In buildings using Option 1 or 2, interior floor finish in corridors and exits shall be Class I or Class II in accordance with Section 6-5.

Exception: Previously installed floor coverings may be continued in use, subject to the approval of the authority having jurisdiction.

See the commentary in Section 6-5, particularly the discussion on interior floor finish. Paragraph 6-5.2.3 establishes stringent requirements regarding the use of textile or carpetlike material on walls and ceilings. The interior finish for walls and ceilings, other than textile or carpetlike material, can be lowered one class (e.g., A to B, B to C) in Option 4 buildings and in corridors of Option 3 buildings. (*See 6-5.7.*)

19-3.4 **Detection, Alarm, and Communication Systems.**

See Supplement 2.

19-3.4.1 **General.** Apartment buildings with more than three stories or with more than 11 living units shall be provided with a fire alarm system in accordance with Section 7-6.

Exception: Where each living unit is separated from other contiguous living units by fire barriers (see Section 6-2) having a fire resistance rating not less than ³/₄ hour, and where each living unit has either its own independent exit or its own independent stairway or ramp discharging at grade.

The intent of this exception is to eliminate the requirement for a fire alarm system in a "townhouse" type apartment building.

19-3.4.2 **Initiation.**

19-3.4.2.1 Initiation of the required fire alarm system shall be by manual means in accordance with 7-6.2.

19-3.4.2.2 In buildings using Option 2, the required fire alarm system shall be initiated by the automatic fire detection system in addition to the manual initiation means of 19-3.4.2.1.

19-3.4.2.3 In buildings using Option 3, the required fire alarm system shall be initiated upon operation of the automatic sprinkler system in addition to the manual initiation means of 19-3.4.2.1.

19-3.4.2.4 In buildings using Option 4, the required fire alarm system shall be initiated upon operation of the automatic sprinkler system in addition to the manual initiation means of 19-3.4.2.1.

19-3.4.3 **Notification.**

19-3.4.3.1 An annunciator panel connected with the required fire alarm system shall be provided. The location of the annunciator panel shall be approved by the authority having jurisdiction.

Exception: Buildings not greater than two stories in height and having not more than 50 living units.

19-3.4.3.2 Occupant notification shall be by an internal audible alarm signal in accordance with 7-6.3.

19-3.4.4 **Detection.**

19-3.4.4.1 Approved single station or multiple station smoke detectors continuously powered from the building electrical system shall be installed in accordance with 7-6.2.9 in every living unit within the apartment building regardless of the number of stories or number of apartments. When activated, the detector shall initiate an alarm that is audible in the sleeping rooms of that unit. This individual unit detector shall be in addition to any sprinkler system or other detection system that may be installed in the building.

Exception: The single station smoke detector is not required where the building is equipped with an existing total automatic smoke detection system throughout.

The detector(s) required by 19-3.4.4.1 should usually be located in the hall area(s) providing access to rooms used for sleeping. In multilevel living units, the detector covering the upper level should normally be located at the top of the stairs. The detector(s) should be mounted on the ceiling or on the wall within 12 in. (30.5 cm) of, but no closer than 6 in. (15.2 cm) to, the ceiling. The detector should be remotely located from the cooking area. Where unusual factors such as room configuration, air movement, or stagnant air pockets must be considered, the authority having jurisdiction and the designer should determine the placement of the detectors. (*See NFPA 74, Standard for the Installation, Maintenance, and Use of Household Fire Warning Equipment,*[4] *for additional details.*)

Note that the detector must be powered by "house current." This should be achieved by direct wiring of the detector or by using plug-in type detectors. Battery-powered units will not meet the provision of 19-3.4.4.1.

It is not the intent of the paragraph to prohibit inter-connecting detectors (multiple station vs. single station) within a single apartment if the apartment needs more than one detector; in fact, this is probably required by the second sentence of the paragraph.

Also note that this requirement must be met in addition to any other detection or suppression system required.

19-3.4.4.2 In buildings using Option 2, a total automatic fire detection system is required. An automatic fire detection system is one that is designed to provide complete coverage using fire detectors in accordance with the spacings and layouts required by NFPA 72E, *Standard on Automatic Fire Detectors*, and laboratory test data. It is a system in which the detectors are tied together to initiate the alarm and other automatic fire protection devices.

In buildings utilizing Option 2, a total automatic fire detection system is required, and this system must be interconnected with the building fire alarm system in accordance with 19-3.4.2.2. This system is required in addition to the single station or multiple station smoke detectors required by 19-3.4.4.1. Note that this paragraph does not specify smoke detectors but instead allows the use of either heat detectors or smoke detectors. Heat detectors are allowed by this paragraph, since they are to be used in addition to the smoke detectors as stated above. The Committee believes that the single station or multiple station smoke detectors will alert occupants within an apartment of a fire originating within that unit. When an occupant leaves the apartment, the door shuts behind the occupant (*see 19-3.6.2*), and the occupant pulls a manual alarm station. If the occupant fails to sound the alarm manually and the fire continues to develop in the apartment, the heat detectors activate and sound the building fire alarm system prior to the fire becoming a threat to other apartment units. This system has proved very effective where used. In addition, since the system is required to be tied into the building fire alarm system, it would eliminate many false alarms that might occur if the entire building were protected by automatic smoke detection.

19-3.5 Extinguishment Requirements.

See Supplement 3.

19-3.5.1* Where an automatic sprinkler system is installed, either for total or partial building coverage, the system shall be installed in accordance with Section 7-7. In buildings up to and including four stories in height, systems installed in accordance with NFPA 13R, *Standard for the Installation of Sprinkler Systems in Residential Occupancies up to and Including Four Stories in Height*, shall be permitted.

Exception: In individual living units, sprinkler installation is not required in closets not over 24 sq ft (2.2 sq m) and bathrooms not over 55 sq ft (5.1 sq m). Closets that contain equipment such as washers, dryers, furnaces or water heaters shall be sprinklered regardless of size.

A-19-3.5.1 Although not required by the *Code*, the use of residential sprinklers or quick response sprinklers is encouraged for new installations of sprinkler systems within dwelling units, apartments, and guest rooms. Caution must be used as the system must be designed for the sprinkler being used.

This paragraph does not require the installation of sprinklers but sets provisions for their installation where required. The *Code* provides numerous incentives to encourage the installation of sprinklers. Some of the more significant incentives offered that apply to existing buildings are provided in 19-2.11.1, 19-3.6.1, and 19-3.7.1. Also see 19-3.5.6 for sprinkler requirements in high rise buildings. The appendix note encourages sprinklers within dwelling units to be approved residential or quick response sprinklers. The intent is to obtain the quick response provided by these sprinklers as well as the high spray pattern provided by residential sprinklers. Designers of sprinkler systems must use caution, as these sprinklers cannot always be installed on a system designed for standard sprinklers. There are also situations where residential or quick response sprinklers are not currently listed for use, such as for vaulted ceilings. In such cases, the designer could provide the best alternative sprinkler.

The 1991 *Code* includes a new reference to NFPA 13R, *Standard for the installation of Sprinkler Systems in Residential Occupancies up to and Including Four Stories in Height*.[3] Paragraph 2-4.5.1 of NFPA 13R requires the installation of listed residential sprinklers inside dwelling units. However, an exception permits the use of other listed sprinkler heads only if smoke detectors are provided in each sleeping room.

The Exception to 19.3.5.1 was carefully reworded for the 1988 *Code*. The spaces exempted are limited to those within a living unit; public areas are not exempted. The last sentence was added to clarify that the intent of this exception applies to regular closets and bathrooms, not closets that contain equipment.

19-3.5.2 In buildings using Option 3, automatic sprinklers shall be installed in corridors along the corridor ceiling, and one sprinkler head shall be opposite the center of and inside any living unit door that opens into the corridor.

Exception: The sprinkler head inside living units shall not be required if the door to the living unit has a fire protection rating of at least 20 minutes and is self-closing.

Figure 19-7 illustrates typical sprinkler location as required by 19.3.5.2.

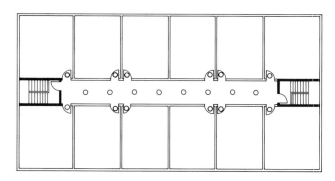

Figure 19-7.   Typical Sprinkler Locations That Comply with the Sprinkler Location Requirements of Option 3.

19-3.5.3 The sprinkler installation required in 19-3.5.2 shall meet the requirements of Section 7-7 in terms of workmanship and materials.

19-3.5.4 The installation of the corridor sprinklers required in 19-3.5.2 shall not exceed the maximum spacing and protection area requirements of Section 7-7.

19-3.5.5 Buildings using Option 4 shall be protected throughout by an approved automatic sprinkler system complying with 19-3.5.1. The automatic sprinkler system shall meet the requirements of Section 7-7 for supervision for buildings greater than six stories in height.

19-3.5.6 All high rise buildings shall be protected throughout by an approved supervised automatic sprinkler system installed in accordance with 19-3.5.1.

Exception No. 1: Where every living unit has exterior exit access in accordance with 5-5.3.

Exception No. 2: Buildings in which an engineered life safety system has been approved by the authority having jurisdiction.*

A-19-3.5.6   Exception No. 2. This system may consist of a combination of any or all of the following systems:

(a)   Partial automatic sprinkler protection.
(b)   Smoke detection alarms.
(c)   Smoke control.
(d)   Compartmentation and/or other approved systems.

The provision requiring approved supervised sprinkler systems to be installed throughout high rise apartment buildings is new to the 1991 Edition. However, the *Code* does provide two alternatives. The first exempts sprinklers throughout if each living unit has direct access to exterior exit access. In lieu of installing sprinklers throughout, the *Code* also permits the application of an approved, engineered life safety system. Although not required, the appendix note suggests that this engineered life safety system should include some combination of automatic sprinkler protection, detection, smoke control, and compartmentation. The *Code* further requires that this alternative approach be approved by the authority having jurisdiction. The enforcing agency should be consulted during the planning phase in order to judge "acceptable" systems. (*See definition of high rise in Section 3-2.*)

19-3.5.7 Portable fire extinguishers shall be provided in hazardous areas. Where provided, portable fire extinguishers shall be installed and maintained as specified in 7-7.4.1.

19-3.6   Corridors.

19-3.6.1*   Exit access corridors shall be constructed of fire barriers in accordance with 6-2.3 having a fire resistance rating of not less than 30 minutes.

A-19-3.6.1   The intent of the Committee is to recognize that existing partitions of sound wood-lath and plaster, wire-lath and plaster, or gypsum lath and plaster construction have demonstrated the ability to contain most room fires. Recent data on archaic construction methods has established the fire resistance "rating" of such construction at about 20 minutes. Such construction meets the intent of this section.

The criteria in 19-3.6 reflect the Committee's concern for providing safety for occupants in their apartments during a fire. The focus of this concern is the presence of occupants 24 hours a day in facilities that provide sleeping accommodations. The minimum corridor wall construction required by 19-3.6.1 will either prevent fire movement from the corridor to an apartment or prevent fire in an apartment from entering the corridor. Most existing lath and plaster walls provide 20- to 30-minute fire resistance ratings.

19-3.6.2   Doors between living units and corridors shall be self-closing. Doors shall be equipped with latches for keeping doors tightly closed.

The requirement for self-closing doors between apartments and corridors may lead to a significant reduction in fatalities caused by fire in apartment buildings. Studies of typical apartment fires indicate that fire spreads beyond the apartment or room of origin because doors are left open as occupants escape.

In other cases, fatalities occur when occupants who suspect fire open the door to a room fully involved with fire or cause full involvement of the room by introducing oxygen through the open door. Spring-loaded hinges or closers cause these doors to close, preventing smoke or fire from spreading down the corridor and exposing other occupants.

19-3.6.3*   The fire protection rating of doors that open from living units onto corridors shall be not less than 20 minutes.

Exception No. 1: Previously approved 1¾-in. (4.4-cm) thick solid bonded wood core doors.

Exception No. 2: In buildings using Option 3 or 4, doors shall be so constructed as to resist the passage of smoke.

A-19-3.6.3   This does not require a listed or labeled assembly, but addresses only the door.

The door required by 19-3.6.3 provides a level of protection commensurate with the expected fuel load in the room and the fire resistance of the corridor wall construction. The purpose is to box a fire out of a room or to box it within the room by means of corridor wall and door construction. Fuel load studies conducted by the National Bureau of Standards demonstrate that residential occupancies will have fuel loads in the 20- to 30-minute range.

19-3.6.4   Transfer grilles, whether protected by fusible link operated dampers or not, shall not be permitted in these walls or doors.

Paragraph 2-3.11.1 of NFPA 90A, *Standard for the Installation of Air Conditioning and Ventilating Systems,*[5] prohibits the use of public corridors in residential occupancies as part of the supply, return, or exhaust air system.

Figure 19-8 illustrates the requirements of 19-3.6.

19-3.7   Subdivision of Building Spaces.

19-3.7.1   Smoke Barriers.   Smoke barriers in accordance with Section 6-3 shall be provided in exit access corridors to establish at least two compartments approximately equal in size. The maximum length of each smoke compartment measured along the corridor shall not exceed 200 ft (60 m). Smoke dampers are not required.

Exception No. 1: Buildings using Option 4.

Exception No. 2: Exterior exit access in accordance with 5-5.3 that provides access to two exits.

Exception No. 3: Buildings allowed to comply with 19-2.4.1 Exceptions No. 1, 2, or 3.

Exception No. 4: Buildings with exits not more than 50 ft (15 m) apart.

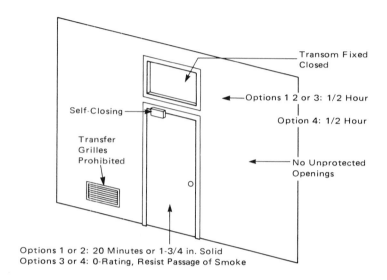

Figure 19-8. The Corridor Wall and Door Provisions of 19-3.6.

Transom Fixed Closed

Options 1 2 or 3: 1/2 Hour

Option 4: 1/2 Hour

Self-Closing

Transfer Grilles Prohibited

No Unprotected Openings

Options 1 or 2: 20 Minutes or 1-3/4 in. Solid
Options 3 or 4: 0-Rating, Resist Passage of Smoke

Exception No. 5: Where each dwelling unit has direct access to the exterior at grade.

The smoke barriers required by 19-3.7.1 are relatively easy to provide, since no fire resistance rating is required and smoke dampers are exempted. In most cases, installing a set of cross-corridor doors with smoke actuated automatic closures will meet the requirement. This can be achieved in conjunction with horizontal exits. Exemptions to the requirement include sprinklered buildings (Exception No. 1), buildings with a single exit (Exception No. 3), and buildings that do not utilize corridors as required exit access (Exception Nos. 2 and 5).

It should be noted that Exception No. 4 does not require smoke barriers every 50 ft (15 m), but exempts a smoke barrier only where the stair spacing is less than 50 ft (15 m) apart.

19-3.8 Special Features. (Reserved.)

SECTION 19-4   Special Provisions

19-4.1 Windows for Rescue and Ventilation. *(See 19-2.1.1.)*

Exception: Buildings using Option 4.

19-4.2 High Rise Buildings. *(See 19-2.11.1 and 19-3.5.6.)*

19-4.3 Operating Features. *(See Chapter 31.)*

SECTION 19-5   Building Services

19-5.1 Utilities. Utilities shall comply with the provisions of Section 7-1.

19-5.2 Heating, Ventilating, and Air Conditioning.

Paragraph 2-3.11.1 of NFPA 90A, *Standard for the Installation of Air Conditioning and Ventilating Systems,*[5] prohibits the use of public corridors in residential occupancies as part of the supply, return, or exhaust air system.

19-5.2.1 Heating, ventilating, and air conditioning equipment shall comply with the provisions of Section 7-2.

19-5.2.2 Unvented fuel-fired heaters shall not be used.

19-5.3 Elevators, Escalators, and Conveyors. Elevators, escalators, and conveyors shall comply with the provisions of Section 7-4.

19-5.4 Rubbish Chutes, Incinerators, and Laundry Chutes.
Rubbish chutes, incinerators, and laundry chutes shall comply with the provisions of Section 7-5.

References Cited in Commentary

[1]NFPA 13, *Standard for the Installation of Sprinkler Systems*, National Fire Protection Association, Quincy, MA, 1991.

[2]NFPA 13D, *Standard for the Installation of Sprinkler Systems in One- and Two-Family Dwellings and Mobile Homes*, National Fire Protection Association, Quincy, MA, 1991.

[3]NFPA 13R, *Standard for the Installation of Sprinkler Systems in Residential Occupancies up to and Including Four Stories in Height*, National Fire Protection Association, Quincy, MA, 1991.

[4]NFPA 74, *Standard for the Installation, Maintenance, and Use of Household Fire Warning Equipment*, National Fire Protection Association, Quincy, MA, 1989.

[5]NFPA 90A, *Standard for the Installation of Air Conditioning and Ventilating Systems*, National Fire Protection Association, Quincy, MA, 1989.

20

Lodging or Rooming Houses

SECTION 20-1 General Requirements

Lodging and rooming houses are one of five residential occupancy types addressed by the *Life Safety Code*. Other residential occupancies considered include one- and two-family dwellings, apartment buildings, hotels and dormitories, and residential board and care facilities. Sleeping accommodations are one of the features common to all residential occupancies.

Paragraph 4-1.6 highlights a common principle of life safety with which the *Code* is concerned as applied to all residential occupancies addressed by Chapters 16 through 23. Paragraph 4-1.6 states: "Residential occupancies are those occupancies in which sleeping accommodations are provided for normal residential purposes and include all buildings designed to provide sleeping accommodations." This use of residential occupancies is central to the *Code* provisions of Chapters 16 through 23, since occupants who are sleeping will be unaware of a rapidly developing fire and, when alerted to the emergency, may be somewhat confused due to being awakened suddenly.

Other factors on which the provisions of Chapters 16 through 23 are based are the presence of hazards (such as cooking and heating equipment) and the degree of familiarity of the occupants with their living space. Occupants may have little or no familiarity, as in the case of transient residents of hotels, or they may have the familiarity of residents of a one-family dwelling.

Lodging and rooming houses accounted for 1,900 structure fires per year as reported to U.S. fire departments from 1984 to 1988. There were 62 civilian deaths and 164 civilian injuries per year. Two-thirds of these fatalities from 1980 to 1988 were outside the room of fire origin. This is one of the highest percentages of any property class.

Part of the problem associated with these properties lies with those facilities that house older adults or the mentally handicapped. Because of their physical or mental limitations, these individuals would be safer living in a residential board and care home or nursing home. The deadliest lodging and rooming house fire that occurred during the 1980s killed 15 residents in a 1984 Massachusetts rooming house fire.

20-1.1 Application.

20-1.1.1 This chapter applies to buildings that provide sleeping accommodations for a total of 16 or fewer persons on either a transient or permanent basis, with or without meals, but without separate cooking facilities for individual occupants except as provided in Chapter 21.

If sleeping accommodations for more than 16 people are provided, the occupancy should be classified as a hotel. The reference to Chapter 21 concerns the provision allowing rooms to be rented to a maximum of three "outsiders" in one- and two-family dwellings. It should be noted that there are many facilities that house more than three but fewer than sixteen persons that ordinarily might not be considered lodging and rooming houses but that do, in fact, meet the definition; a fire house or a coast guard station that has a bunk room are examples. These would normally be considered a mixed occupancy depend-

ing upon the arrangement of the facility. (*See Figure 20-1. See commentary following 1-5.7.*)

20-1.1.2 The requirements of this chapter are applicable to new buildings and to existing or modified buildings according to the provisions of Section 1-5 of this *Code*.

20-1.2 Mixed Occupancies.

20-1.2.1 Where another type of occupancy occurs in the same building as a residential occupancy, the requirements of 1-5.7 of this *Code* shall be applicable.

Also see commentary following 20-1.1.1.

20-1.2.2 For requirements on mixed mercantile and residential occupancies, see 24-1.2 or 25-1.2; for mixed assembly and residential occupancies, see 8-1.2 or 9-1.2; and for mixed business and residential occupancies, see 26-1.2.

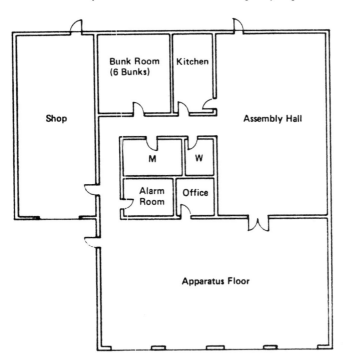

Figure 20-1(a). A New Fire Station Consisting of a Mixed Occupancy (Storage, Assembly, and Lodging or Rooming House). This facility is required to be sprinklered throughout per 20-3.5.2. Adding a door that leads directly to the outside from the bunk room will eliminate the sprinkler requirement unless mandated by the assembly occupancy requirements. (See 8-1.6 and 8-3.5.)

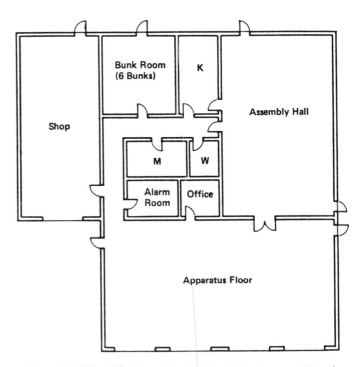

Figure 20-1(b). The Same Fire Station is No Longer a Mixed Occupancy. By adding an exit from the bunk room, the assembly hall, and the apparatus floor and separating the assembly hall, each occupancy can be considered independently.

Since the *Code* previously provided requirements to ensure the integrity of the residential evacuation system in mixed residential/mercantile occupancies, the 1991 Edition applies this safeguard to assembly and new business occupancies.

20-1.3 Definitions.

20-1.3.1 Terms applicable to this chapter are defined in Chapter 3 of this *Code*; where necessary, other terms will be defined in the text as they may occur.

20-1.4 Classification of Occupancy. (*See 20-1.1.1.*)

20-1.5 Classification of Hazard of Contents.

20-1.5.1 The contents of residential occupancies shall be classified as ordinary hazard in accordance with Section 4-2.

NFPA 13, *Standard for the Installation of Sprinkler Systems*,[1] would classify the contents as "light hazard" for the purpose of designing extinguishing systems. The difference in classification is based on the threat to life or life safety (ordinary) as opposed to the threat to the extinguishing capability of the automatic sprinkler system (light).

20-1.6 Minimum Construction Requirements. No special requirements.

20-1.7 Occupant Load. (*See 20-1.1.1.*)

SECTION 20-2 Means of Escape

20-2.1 Number and Means of Escape.

20-2.1.1 Every sleeping room and living area shall have access to a primary means of escape complying with Chapter 21 so located as to provide a safe path of travel to the outside of the building without traversing any corridor or space exposed to an unprotected vertical opening. Where the sleeping room is above or below the level of exit discharge, the primary means of escape shall be an enclosed interior stair, an exterior stair, a horizontal exit, or an existing fire escape stair.

In 20-2.1.1, the phrase "means of escape" is separate and distinct from means of egress and indicates the Committee's acceptance of a means of egress for a lodging or rooming house that falls slightly short of compliance with Chapter 5. Note that the *Code* requires at least one means of escape from levels above or below the level of exit discharge to be an enclosed interior stairway, an exterior stairway, or a horizontal exit (or an existing fire escape). The Committee intended at least one means of escape to be of a high degree of quality but was reluctant to tie the criteria directly to Chapter 5, since most rooming or lodging houses are converted homes that rarely have an exit arrangement complying with Chapter 5. However, the Committee recognized the issue of public liability associated with lodging guests and intended a level of escape quality higher than that normally found in a single-family home.

The protection of vertical openings as required by 20-2.1.1, 20-2.2, and 20-3.1.1 is the major distinction between one- or two-family dwellings and lodging and rooming houses (*also see 20-3.5.2 for new construction*). By eliminating exposure to unprotected vertical openings (normally found in single-family dwellings), the *Code* requires an exit arrangement that provides a level of safety above that normally found in a single-family dwelling. Figures 20-2, 20-3, 20-4, and 20-5 illustrate four possible methods of complying with 20-2.1.1.

20-2.1.2 In addition to the primary route, each sleeping room and living area shall have a second means of escape in accordance with 21-2.2.3.

Exception: If the sleeping room or living area has a door leading directly outside the building with access to grade or to a stairway that meets the requirements for exterior stairs in 20-2.1.1, that exit shall be considered as meeting all of the exit requirements for that sleeping room or living area.

Those editions of the *Code* prior to 1985 required two means of escape but did not specify acceptable criteria for the secondary escapes other than windows for the level of exit discharge. In order to clarify its requirements, the *Code* specifies that the secondary escape must comply

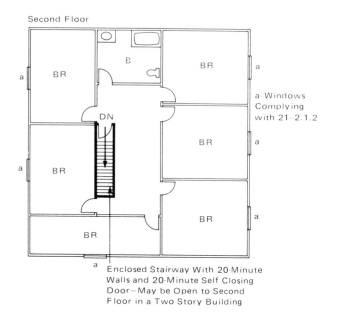

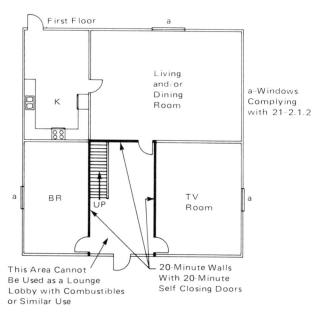

Figure 20-2. *Means of Escape—Existing Lodging and Rooming House—Example 1. This example illustrates an enclosed interior stair discharging directly outside. Access to the interior stair is via an interior corridor that is not exposed to an unprotected vertical opening. The second means of escape may be windows acceptable to the authority having jurisdiction in accordance with 20-2.1.2. The enclosure at the bottom of the stair can be achieved in several ways; this is only one example.*

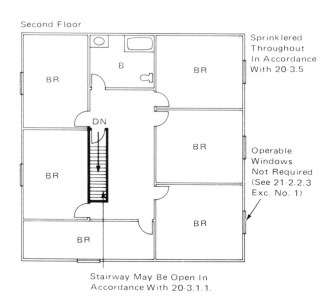

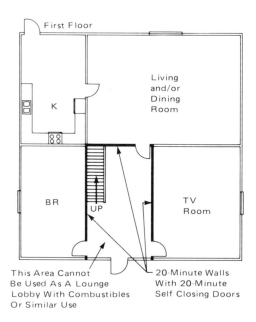

Figure 20-3. *Means of Escape—Sprinklered Lodging and Rooming House—Example 2. This example illustrates one method of providing a Code-complying arrangement in a new or existing lodging or rooming house protected with sprinklers in accordance with 20-3.5.*

Outside Stair (Fire Escape-Existing Only)

a-Windows Complying with 21-2.1.2-Secondary Means of Escape May be Omitted in Sprinklered Buildings (See 21-2.2.3)

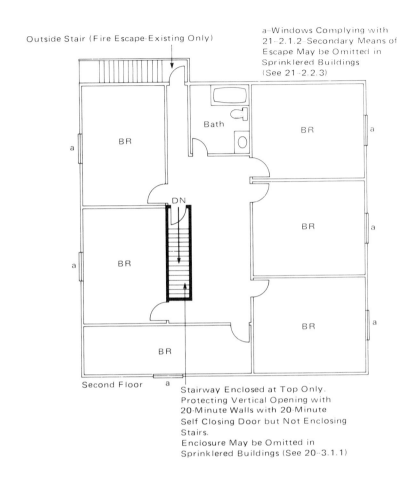

DN

BR

BR

BR

Bath

BR

BR

BR

BR

a
a
a
a
a
a
a

Second Floor

Stairway Enclosed at Top Only. Protecting Vertical Opening with 20-Minute Walls with 20-Minute Self Closing Door but Not Enclosing Stairs. Enclosure May be Omitted in Sprinklered Buildings (See 20-3.1.1)

Figure 20-4 (top). *Means of Escape—Lodging and Rooming House—Example 3. Illustration of an exterior stair complying with 5-2.5 (see 20-2.1.1). The exterior stair is accessed via the interior corridor, which is not exposed to an unprotected vertical opening. The second means of escape is via windows complying with 20-2.1.2. If the building is sprinklered, the stairway is not required to be enclosed, and the escape windows are not required.*

Figure 20-5 (below). An outside stair with exterior exit access complying with 5-2.5 (see 20-2.1.1). Access is not by way of the interior corridor, which is exposed by the open stair. This arrangement meets exit requirements for each sleeping room. Therefore, secondary means of escape is not necessary (see Exception to 20-2.1.2). If each first floor sleeping room has direct access to the exterior, similar to the second floor, then a new lodging and rooming house of this design would also be exempt from the requirement for full sprinklering. (See 20-3.5.2.)

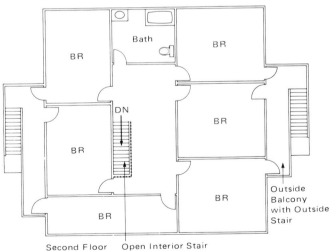

BR

Bath

BR

DN

BR

BR

BR

BR

Outside Balcony with Outside Stair

Second Floor   Open Interior Stair

Figure 20-5. Means of Escape—Lodging and Rooming House—Example 4.

with 21-2.2.3. It should be noted that 21-2.2.3 exempts a secondary escape if the building is sprinklered in accordance with either NFPA 13, *Standard for the Installation of Sprinkler Systems,*[1] NFPA 13D, *Standard for the Installation of Sprinkler Systems in One- and Two-Family Dwellings and Mobile Homes,*[2] or NFPA 13R, *Standard for the Installation of Sprinkler Systems in Residential Occupancies up to and Including Four Stories in Height.*[3] It is important to note that, since the 1991 Edition of the *Code* requires most new lodging and rooming houses to be protected with sprinklers in accordance with 20-3.5.2, this exception now mandates the minimum requirement for those facilities installed with sprinklers. However, in conjunction with the Exception to 20-2.1.3, the Exception to 20-3.1.1, Exception No. 2 to 20-3.3.2, and the Exception to 20-3.4, this exemption makes sprinklering an existing lodging or rooming house a viable alternative.

20-2.1.3   Every story of every lodging or rooming house that is greater than 2,000 sq ft (185 sq m) or where the travel distance to the primary means of escape is greater than 75 ft (23 m) shall be provided with two primary means of escape remotely located from each other.

Exception No. 1: Existing buildings.

Exception No. 2: Buildings protected throughout by an approved supervised automatic sprinkler system in accordance with 20-3.5.

20-2.2   Interior stairways shall be enclosed by 20-minute fire barriers with all openings protected with smoke-actuated automatic-closing or self-closing doors having a fire resistance comparable to that required for the enclosure. The stairway shall comply with 5-2.2.6.5.

Also see 20-2.1.1 and 20-3.1.1.

Exception No. 1: Stairs connecting two levels only shall be permitted to be open to other than the street floor.

Exception No. 2: Stairways shall be permitted to be unprotected in accordance with the Exception to 20-3.1.1.

Figure 20-6 illustrates the use of Exception No. 1. In writing this exception, the Committee was considering a stairway connecting the street floor to the basement or second floor, not a stairway connecting the second and third floor.

20-2.3   No door or path of travel to a means of egress shall be less than 28 in. (71 cm) wide.

Exception: Bathroom doors shall be not less than 24 in. (61 cm) wide.

20-2.4   Every closet door latch shall be such that it can be readily opened from the inside in case of emergency.

20-2.5   Every bathroom door shall be designed to allow opening from the outside during an emergency when locked.

20-2.6   Winders in accordance with 5-2.2.2.8 are permitted.

20-2.7*   No door in any means of egress shall be locked against egress when the building is occupied.

Exception: Special locking arrangements complying with 5-2.1.6 are permitted.

A-20-2.7   It is the intent of this requirement that security measures, where installed, should not prevent egress.

Paragraph 20-2.7 prohibits a lodging or rooming house from having any door locked "against egress" while the building is occupied. This requirement permits a door to have a locking device that allows the door to be opened from within the building for the purpose of egress but does not allow the door to be opened from outside the building. Ordinary double cylinder locks and chain locks do not meet these provisions. Several tragic multiple-death fires have occurred when the key needed to unlock these devices could not be found.

The language of 5-2.1.5.1 is clear: "Locks, if provided, shall not require the use of a key, tool, special knowledge, or effort for operation from the inside of the building." This eliminates double cylinder locks and chain locks that require a key in order to be operated from the inside. Paragraph 5-2.1.5.3 requires the use of a simple operation to open a door; locks that require a two-handed knob and similar operations are specifically prohibited.

Chapter 5 now specifically recognizes the need for security chains or rods on guest room doors and allows one additional releasing device. The typical guest room door has three devices: a latch, a lock, and a security chain or rod. However, the *Code* allows only two releasing actions for new installations. This requirement is met by using a latch and lock set equipped with a lock bolt that automatically retracts when the latch handle is turned from the inside; therefore, only one releasing action is needed for the two devices. The second action is the release of the security chain or rod. However, neither device can require the use of a key, tool, special knowledge, or effort. In existing installations, three actions are permitted: the latch, the lock, and the security device.

The Exception to 20-2.7 recognizes the use of the delay release lock provided for in 5-2.1.6. This requires that the building either be protected throughout by automatic sprinklers or be equipped throughout with a fire detection system. The 15- or 30-second delay permitted by 5-2.1.6 does not affect the immediate release of the lock upon activation of the sprinklers or detectors, or upon

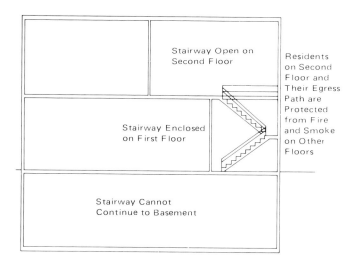

Stairway Open on Second Floor

Residents on Second Floor and Their Egress Path are Protected from Fire and Smoke on Other Floors

Stairway Enclosed on First Floor

Stairway Cannot Continue to Basement

Figure 20-6. A Stairway That Connects Two Levels May Be Open to a Floor Other than the Street Floor. (Also see Figures 20-3 and 20-4.)

loss of power to the lock. This device helps provide the security needed for infrequently used doors or stairs in lodging and rooming houses. At the same time, doors remain available for use. Chains and padlocks are unable to provide this protection.

20-2.8 Doors serving a single dwelling unit shall be permitted to be provided with a lock in accordance with 5-2.1.5.1 Exception No. 3.

SECTION 20-3   Protection

20-3.1 Protection of Vertical Openings.

20-3.1.1 Vertical openings shall be protected so that no primary exit route is exposed to an unprotected vertical opening. The vertical opening is considered protected if the opening is cut off and enclosed in a manner that provides a smoke and fire resisting capability of not less than 20 minutes. Any doors or openings shall have fire and smoke resisting capability equivalent to that of the enclosure and shall be automatic-closing on detection of smoke or shall be self-closing.

Exception: In buildings three stories or less in height that are protected throughout by an approved automatic sprinkler system installed in accordance with 20-3.5, unprotected vertical openings are permitted. However, in such case, there shall still remain a primary means of exit from each sleeping area that does not require occupants to pass through a portion of a lower floor, unless that route is separated from all spaces on that floor by construction having a 20-minute fire resistance rating.

This provision coordinates with 20-2.1.1. (*See commentary following 20-2.1.1.*)

20-3.1.2 Exterior stairs shall be reasonably protected against blockage caused by fire that would simultaneously expose both the interior and exterior means of escape. This may be accomplished through separation by physical distance, arrangement of the stairs, protection of the openings exposing the stairs, or other means acceptable to the authority having jurisdiction.

20-3.2 Interior Finish. Interior finish on walls and ceilings of occupied spaces shall be Class A, B, or C as defined in Section 6-5. There are no requirements for interior floor finish.

20-3.3 Detection, Alarm, and Communication Systems.

See Supplement 2.

20-3.3.1 General. Lodging and rooming houses shall be provided with a fire alarm system in accordance with Section 7-6.

Exception: Buildings that have a smoke detection system meeting or exceeding the requirements of 20-3.3.4 and where that detection system includes at least one manual fire alarm station per floor arranged to initiate the smoke detection alarm.

This exception allows a multiple station smoke detector "system" with manual pull stations to substitute for a "standard" fire alarm system in accordance with NFPA 72, *Standard for the Installation, Maintenance, and Use of Protective Signaling Systems.*[4]

20-3.3.2 Initiation. Initiation of the required fire alarm system shall be by manual means in accordance with 7-6.2.

Exception: Buildings protected throughout by an approved automatic sprinkler system installed in accordance with 20-3.5, with alarm initiation in accordance with 7-6.2.1(c).

20-3.3.3 Notification. Occupant notification shall be provided automatically, without delay, by internal audible alarm in accordance with 7-6.3. Presignal systems are prohibited.

20-3.3.4 Detection. Approved single station or multiple station smoke detectors powered by the building electrical service shall be installed in accordance with 7-6.2.9 on every level. In addition, approved single station smoke detectors powered by the building electrical service shall be provided in each sleeping room.

Exception: Existing battery powered detectors, rather than house electric service powered detectors, shall be accepted where, in the opinion of the authority having jurisdiction, the facility has demonstrated testing, maintenance, and battery replacement programs that ensure reliability of power to the detectors.

This paragraph has been revised in the 1991 Edition and now requires the installation of a smoke detector in each sleeping room. It should be noted that this requirement applies retroactively to existing lodging and rooming houses.

While the exception allows existing battery powered smoke detectors to remain in place if approved by the authority having jurisdiction, newly installed smoke detectors must be powered by the building electrical service for both new and existing lodging and rooming houses.

NFPA analysis of reported fires indicates that about one-third of all smoke detectors installed in homes are inoperative. A landmark study by the IAFC Foundation found that, when detectors are nonoperational, the usual reason is dead or missing batteries. Since 85 percent of U.S. homes had at least one detector in 1989, the percentage of homes with detectors that are inoperative now exceeds the percentage of homes with no detectors (although far more fires occur in the latter situation).

Therefore, increasing the successful record of smoke detectors in U.S. homes depends nearly as much on reducing the problem of dead and missing batteries as it does on promoting their use in all homes.

20-3.4 Separation of Sleeping Rooms. All sleeping rooms shall be separated from escape route corridors by walls and doors that are smoke resistant. There shall be no louvers or operable transoms or other air passages penetrating the wall except properly installed heating and utility installations other than transfer grilles. Transfer grilles are prohibited. Doors shall be provided with latches or other mechanisms suitable for keeping the doors closed. No doors shall be arranged so as to prevent the occupant from closing the door. Doors shall be self-closing or automatic-closing upon detection of smoke.

Exception: Door closing devices are not required in buildings protected throughout by an approved automatic sprinkler system installed in accordance with 20-3.5.

The requirement is similar to the corridor requirements of hotels and apartment buildings; however, no fire resistance rating is required. Unlike hotels and apartment buildings, door closures are exempted in sprinklered lodging or rooming houses. (*See Figure 20-7.*)

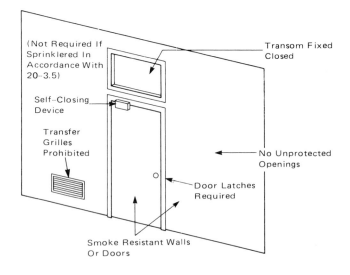

Figure 20-7. Sleeping Room/Escape Route Separation Provisions of 20-3.4.

20-3.5 Extinguishment Requirements.

See Supplement 3.

20-3.5.1* Where an automatic sprinkler system is required or is used as an alternative method of protection, either for total or partial building coverage, the system shall be installed in accordance with Seection 7-7, and shall actuate the fire alarm system in accordance with Section 7-6.

Exception No. 1: Sprinkler installations are not required in closets not over 12 sq ft (1.1 sq m) and bathrooms not over 55 sq ft (5.1 sq m).

Exception No. 2: In existing lodging and rooming houses, sprinkler installations are not required in closets not over 24 sq ft (2.2 sq m) and bathrooms not over 55 sq ft (5.1 sq m).

A-20-3.5.1 Although not required by the *Code*, the use of residential sprinklers or quick response sprinklers is encouraged for new installations of sprinkler systems within dwelling units, apartments, and guest rooms. Caution must be used, as the system must be designed for the sprinkler being used.

The *Code* recognizes the potential application of NFPA 13D, *Standard for the Installation of Sprinkler Systems in One- and Two-Family Dwellings and Mobile Homes*, to lodging and rooming houses inasmuch as these occupancies can usually be considered similar in character to one- and two-family dwellings.

Rather than referring directly to NFPA 13D, *Standard for the Installation of Sprinkler Systems in One- and Two-Family Dwellings and Mobile Homes*,[2] an appendix reference is made. This is because some lodging or rooming houses may be similar to a one- or two-family dwelling, whereas others are not. For example, it would be quite reasonable for the authority having jurisdiction to allow the use of NFPA 13D for the protection of a single-family dwelling that is now being used as a bed and breakfast (lodging or rooming house), but not for a fire station with a bunk room.

Section 7-7 of the 1991 Edition has been revised to include a reference to NFPA 13R, *Standard for the Installation of Sprinkler Systems in Residential Occupancies up to and Including Four Stories in Height*.[3] However,

Section 7-7 requires that NFPA 13R be specifically referenced by an occupancy chapter. It is apparent that NFPA 13R is appropriate for many lodging and rooming establishments. It should be noted that, because of procedural details involved in processing the 1991 Edition of the *Code*, the specific reference to NFPA 13R for Chapter 20 was not included. Nevertheless, it is the *Code's* intent that NFPA 13R be referenced where appropriate for lodging and rooming houses.

Although not required by NFPA 13, *Standard for the Installation of Sprinkler Systems*,[1] both NFPA 13D and NFPA 13R require the installation of residential-type sprinklers in all sleeping rooms with limited exceptions. (*See 2-4.5 in NFPA 13R and NFPA 13D, Section 3-5*).

20-3.5.2 All new lodging or rooming houses shall be protected throughout by an approved automatic sprinkler system. Such system shall be installed in accordance with 20-3.5.1.

Exception: If every sleeping room has a door opening directly to the outside of the building at street or ground level, or has a door opening directly to the outside leading to an exterior stairway that meets the requirements of 20-2.1.1.

With the exception of those occupancies in which each sleeping room has a door providing direct access to the exterior at grade or to an exterior stairway, all new lodging and rooming establishments shall be protected throughout with an approved automatic sprinkler system. This requirement is in recognition of the disproportionate percentage of deaths associated with residential occupancies (82 percent).[5] (*See the discussion at the beginning of this chapter.*)

If the lodging and rooming house is part of another occupancy and is treated as a mixed occupancy, the entire mixed occupancy is required to be sprinklered. In order to waive this requirement, the occupancies would have to be arranged so that the lodging and rooming house is treated as a separate occupancy. This would require that the egress system for each occupancy be separate. Usually this is achieved by a door that opens directly to the outside from the lodging and rooming house section. [*See Figures 20-1(a) and (b).*]

SECTION 20-4   Special Provisions

20-4.1 **Operating Features.** (*See Chapter 31.*)

SECTION 20-5   Building Services

20-5.1 **Utilities.** Utilities shall comply with the provisions of Section 7-1.

20-5.2 **Heating, Ventilating, and Air Conditioning.**

20-5.2.1 Heating, ventilating, and air conditioning equipment shall comply with the provisions of Sections 7-2.1 and 7-2.2.

20-5.2.2 No stove or combustion heater shall be so located as to block escape in case of fire caused by the malfunction of the stove or heater.

20-5.2.3 Unvented fuel-fired heaters shall not be used.

20-5.3 **Elevators, Escalators, and Conveyors.** Elevators, escalators, and conveyors shall comply with the provisions of Section 7-4.

References Cited in Commentary

[1]NFPA 13, *Standard for the Installation of Sprinkler Systems*, National Fire Protection Association, Quincy, MA, 1991.

[2]NFPA 13D, *Standard for the Installation of Sprinkler Systems in One- and Two-Family Dwellings and Mobile Homes*, National Fire Protection Association, Quincy, MA, 1991.

[3]NFPA 13R, *Standard for the Installation of Sprinkler Systems in Residential Occupancies up to and Including Four Stories in Height*, National Fire Protection Association, Quincy, MA, 1991.

[4]NFPA 72, *Standard for the Installation, Maintenance, and Use of Protective Signaling Systems*, National Fire Protection Association, Quincy, MA, 1990.

[5]Michael J. Karter, Jr., "Fire Loss in the United States During 1989," *Fire Journal*, Vol. 84, No. 5, pp. 56-67, September/October 1990.

21

One- and Two-Family Dwellings

The requirements of Chapter 21 are important even if they are not enforced in one- and two-family dwellings. Chapters 16 and 17, which address hotels and dormitories, and Chapters 18 and 19, which address apartment buildings, require that all living units (guest rooms/suites and apartments respectively) comply with Section 21-2. In addition, Chapter 20, which covers lodging or rooming houses, adopts the means of escape requirements of Chapter 21 for each living and sleeping area. Chapters 22 and 23 require board and care facilities to comply with the escape window requirements of 21-2.2.3.

21-1.1 Application.

21-1.1.1* This chapter establishes life safety requirements for all one- and two-family dwellings. One- and two-family dwellings include buildings containing not more than two dwelling units in which each living unit is occupied by members of a single family with no more than three outsiders, if any, accommodated in rented rooms.

A-21-1.1.1 The *Code* specifies that whenever there are three or more living units in a building, the building is considered an apartment building and must comply with either Chapter 18 or 19 as appropriate. "Townhouse" units are considered to be an apartment building if there are three or more units in the building. The type of wall required between units in order to consider them to be separate buildings is normally established by the authority having jurisdiction. Should the units be separated by a wall of sufficient fire resistance and structural integrity to be considered as separate buildings, then the provisions of Chapter 22 apply to each townhouse. "Condominium" is a form of ownership, not occupancy; for example, there are condominium warehouses, condominium apartments, and condominium offices.

If more than three outsiders are accommodated, the requirements of Chapter 20 apply.

21-1.1.2 The requirements of this chapter are applicable to new buildings and to existing or modified buildings according to the provisions of Section 1-5 of this *Code*.

21-1.2 Mixed Occupancies.

21-1.2.1 Where another type of occupancy occurs in the same building as a residential occupancy, the requirements of 1-5.7 of this *Code* shall be applicable.

Formal Interpretation 76-138
Reference: 21-1.1.1

Question 1: Is it to be interpreted that "occupied by members of a single family" literally means all the people living in the same house; household?

Answer 1: See response below.

Question 2: Is it the intent of the Committee that "occupied by members of a single family" be literally interpreted as a social unit consisting of parents and children that they rear; the children of the same parents; and one's husband (or wife) and children?

Answer 2: See response below.

Question 3: Is it the intent of the Committee that "occupied by members of a single family" be literally interpreted as a group of people related by ancestry or marriage; relatives?

Answer 3: See response below.

Question 4: Is it the intent of the Committee that "occupied by members of a single family" be literally interpreted as all those claiming descent from a common ancestor; tribe or clan; lineage?

Answer 4: See response below.

Question 5: Was it the intent of the Committee when publishing NFPA 101, *Life Safety Code*, 21-1.1.1, to include as a member of a single family a person who is: a longtime friend, not of blood or marriage relationship, not paying rent, but who contributes or has contributed monies to the owner of the house, thus subsidizing house operation expenses?

Answer 5: See response below.

Formal Interpretation 76-138 (continued)

Response: It is the intent of the Committee that "occupied by members of a single family" be literally interpreted as a social unit consisting of parents and children that they rear, the children of the same parents, and one's husband (or wife) and including children they adopt. It should be noted, however, that 21-1.1.1 does allow for up to three outsiders to be accommodated.

Issue Edition: 1976
Reference: 11-1.3.1(e)
Date: September 1980 ■

21-1.2.2 For requirements on mixed mercantile and residential occupancies, see 24-1.2 or 25-1.2; for mixed assembly and residential occupancies, see 8-1.2 or 9-1.2; for mixed business and residential occupancies, see 26-1.2.

Since the *Code* previously provided requirements to ensure the integrity of the residential means of egress in mixed residential/mercantile occupancies, the 1991 Edition applies this safeguard to assembly and new business occupancies.

21-1.3 Definitions.

21-1.3.1 Terms applicable to this chapter are defined in Chapter 3 of this *Code*; where necessary, other terms will be defined in the text as they may occur.

21-1.4 Classification of Occupancy. (*See 21-1.1.1.*)

21-1.5 Classification of Hazard of Contents.

21-1.5.1 The contents of residential occupancies shall be classified as ordinary hazard in accordance with 4-2.1.

NFPA 13, *Standard for the Installation of Sprinkler Systems*,[1] would classify the contents as "light hazard" for the purpose of designing extinguishing systems. The difference in classification is based on the threat to life or life safety (ordinary) as opposed to the threat to the extinguishing capability of the automatic sprinkler system (light).

It is not the intent of this paragraph to prohibit the use of NFPA 13D, *Standard for the Installation of Sprinkler Systems in One- and Two-Family Dwellings and Mobile Homes.*[2]

21-1.6   **Minimum Construction Requirements.** No special requirements.

21-1.7   **Occupant Load.** No requirements.

SECTION 21-2   Means of Escape Requirements

A-21-2   The Committee has adopted the phrase "means of escape" to indicate a way out of a residential unit that does not conform to the strict definition of means of egress but does meet the intent of the definition by providing an alternative way out of a building. (*See A-5-1.1.1.*)

21-2.1   **General.** The provisions of Chapter 5 are not applicable to means of escape unless specifically referenced in this chapter.

The Committee, recognizing that it is rare to find an exit that complies with Chapter 5 (or an enclosed vertical opening) in a single-family dwelling, requires the quality of egress that is normally found in dwelling design. Therefore, as stated in 21-2.1, unless Chapter 21 specifically references a means of egress provision of Chapter 5, only the means of escape requirements of Chapter 21 must be met.

21-2.2   **Number and Types of Means of Escape.**

21-2.2.1   **Number of Means of Escape.** In any dwelling or living unit of two rooms or more, every sleeping room and every living area shall have at least one primary means of escape and one secondary means of escape.

See definition of living area in Chapter 3.

21-2.2.2   **Primary Means of Escape.** The primary means of escape shall be a door, stairway, or ramp providing a means of unobstructed travel to the outside of the dwelling unit at street or ground level.

Note that a "door or stairway providing a means of unobstructed travel to the outside" addresses nearly every egress arrangement currently found in a dwelling.

Paragraph 21-2.2.2 does not permit the addition of a bedroom or den in an attic if the space is accessible only by a trap door or folding ladder. Direct stair access is required. (*See Exception No. 1 to 21-2.5.1.*)

21-2.2.3*   **Secondary Means of Escape.** The secondary means of escape shall be one of the following:

(a)   A door, stairway, passage, or hall providing a way of unobstructed travel to the outside of the dwelling at street or ground level that is independent of and remote from the primary means of escape.

(b)   A passage through an adjacent nonlockable space independent of and remote from the primary means of escape to any approved means of escape.

(c)   An outside window or door operable from the inside without the use of tools and providing a clear opening of not less than 20 in. (50.8 cm) in width, 24 in. (61 cm) in height, and 5.7 sq ft (.53 sq m) in area. The bottom of the opening shall not be more than 44 in. (112 cm) off the floor. Such means of escape shall be acceptable if:

1.   The window is within 20 ft (6.1 m) of grade, or

2.   The window is directly accessible to fire department rescue apparatus as approved by the authority having jurisdiction, or

3.   The window or door opens onto an exterior balcony.

Exception No. 1: A secondary means of escape is not required:

(a)   If the bedroom or living area has a door leading directly to the outside of the building at or to grade level, or

(b)   If the dwelling unit is protected throughout by an approved automatic sprinkler system in accordance with NFPA 13, Standard for the Installation of Sprinkler Systems, or NFPA 13D, Standard for the Installation of Sprinkler Systems in One- and Two-Family Dwellings and Mobile Homes, or NFPA 13R, Standard for the Installation of Sprinkler Systems in Residential Occupancies up to and Including Four Stories in Height, as applicable.

Exception No. 2: Existing approved means of escape may continue to be used.

A-21-2.2.3 For use of emergency escape devices, refer to A-5-1.1.1.

The provisions of 21-2.2.3 require that every bedroom and every living area (living room, family room, den, etc.) be provided with a secondary means of escape above and beyond that provided in compliance with 21-2.2.2.

There are only two exceptions to the requirement for a secondary means of escape from each bedroom or living area: (1) if the bedroom or living area has a door opening directly to the outside of the building (this is an uncommon arrangement, but it may occur); or (2) where the dwelling unit is protected throughout by an approved automatic sprinkler system in accordance with NFPA 13, *Standard for the Installation of Sprinkler Systems,*[1] NFPA 13D, *Standard for the Installation of Sprinkler Systems in One- and Two-Family Dwellings and Mobile Homes,*[2] or NFPA 13R, *Standard for the Installation of Sprinkler Systems in Residential Occupancies up to and Including Four Stories in Height.*[3] The latter exception is probably the most practical and common way to avoid the requirement for a second means of escape; for example, in an underground dwelling without windows or a dwelling with noncomplying windows, or in an apartment building containing a unit(s) that does not have windows complying with item (c). These types of dwellings could be protected in accordance with NFPA 13, which allows the use of NFPA 13D within the apartment, or in accordance with NFPA 13R. Note that this does not require the entire apartment building to be sprinklered, but only the apartment unit that does not have windows that comply with the *Code.*

The fundamental purpose of the secondary means of escape is to provide an occupant with an alternate escape route when fire and/or smoke blocks the normal means of egress from the dwelling unit. Paragraph 21-2.2.3 (a) through (c) provides three types of second means of escape.

1. It is the intent of item (a) that this door, stairway, passage, or hall be independent of and remote from the primary means of escape required in 21-2.2.2. If a room has a second door leading to the same hallway

in the dwelling unit as the first door, little, if any, additional safety is provided, since a fire in the living room or other common space of the dwelling unit would block egress from both these doors at approximately the same time. If the corridor within the dwelling unit is separated from all living spaces and leads to two separate ways out of the dwelling unit, it may be judged that it does, in fact, lead to two separate, independent, and remote means of escape. Although two doors leading out of a sleeping room may not be practical or effective in a single-family dwelling, Figure 21-2 illustrates a method that may utilize this provision within an apartment building. (*See Figures 21-1 and 21-2.*)

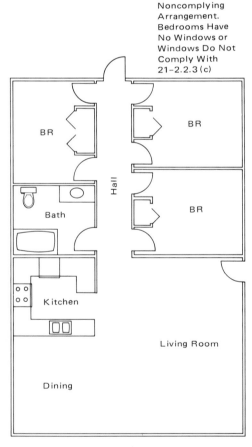

Figure 21-1. A Noncomplying Arrangement. Although each bedroom has two doors, both doors lead to the same hall, which would be affected by a single fire in the living room, dining room, or kitchen. The second door from each bedroom adds little, if any, life safety. This arrangement, which may be found in an underground dwelling, would require sprinkler protection.

2. Item (b) was new to the 1985 Edition of the *Code*; however, it could have been interpreted as a subpart of item (a) in previous editions. Figure 21-3 illustrates an example of how this provision may be used.

3. The use of an operable window of the minimum dimensions specified in item (c) has been allowed in prior editions of the *Code* and continues to be permitted in the 1991 Edition. Figure 21-4 illustrates the minimum dimensions allowed for escape windows. Note that it is not possible to use the two minimum dimensions and still comply with the minimum area dimension. The 1985 Edition of the *Code* added restrictions to the use of the outside window. These restrictions

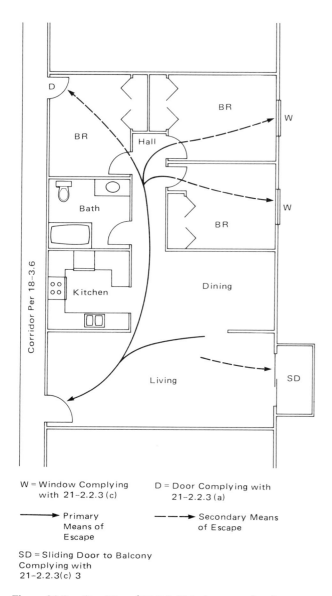

W = Window Complying with 21-2.2.3 (c)
D = Door Complying with 21-2.2.3 (a)

→ Primary Means of Escape
--→ Secondary Means of Escape

SD = Sliding Door to Balcony Complying with 21-2.2.3(c) 3

Figure 21-2. One Use of 21-2.2.3(a). An example of an apartment that has a bedroom (see upper left corner) without a window or where the window does not comply with 21-2.2.3(c). The second means of escape from the other bedrooms and living room in this apartment complies with 21-2.2.3(c).

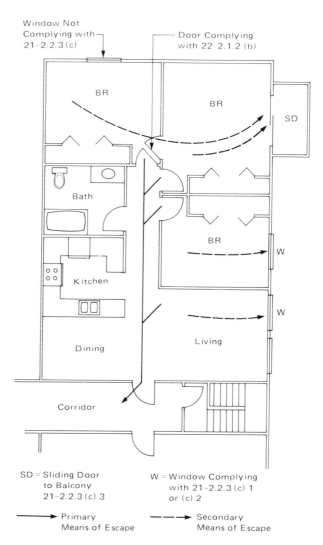

SD = Sliding Door to Balcony 21-2.2.3 (c) 3
W = Window Complying with 21-2.2.3 (c) 1 or (c) 2

→ Primary Means of Escape
--→ Secondary Means of Escape

Figure 21-3. One Use of 21-2.2.3(b). An example of an apartment unit in which the bedroom has a window that does not comply with 21-2.2.3(c) and in which there is no door to the corridor (as in Figure 21-2).

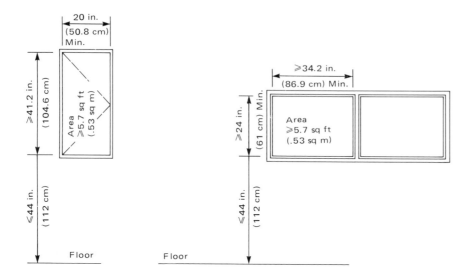

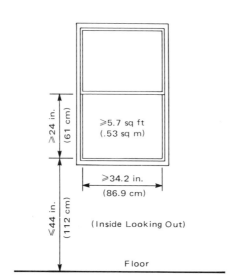

Figure 21-4.   Minimum Size and Dimensions of Outside Windows Used as a Second Means of Escape in Accordance with 21-2.2.3(c).

will have relatively little impact on the typical one- and two-family dwelling but will have significant impact on apartment buildings.

The outside window must comply with one of the following three methods. The first method makes it possible to jump from the window [the window must be within 20 ft (6.1 m) of grade]. The second method allows the fire department to rescue an occupant from a win-

dow. This can be achieved either by means of aerial ladder apparatus or ground ladders or by other means acceptable to the authority having jurisdiction. Depending on fire department vehicle access and equipment available to the fire department, a low rise apartment building could utilize standard operable windows as a secondary means of escape from apartment unit bedrooms and living areas. The third method allows an occupant to reach an exterior balcony to breathe fresh air while awaiting either rescue or fire extinguishment. This method could be utilized either in low rise or high rise apartment buildings. (*See Figures 21-2 and 21-3.*)

Exception No. 2 to 21-2.2.3 allows an existing means of escape, approved by the authority having jurisdiction, to continue to be used. With the exception of those instances where the means of escape is of extremely poor quality, this limits the impact on existing buildings where they are required to comply with 21-2.2.3.

21-2.2.4 Every story of every dwelling or living unit that is greater than 2,000 sq ft (185 sq m) or that has a travel distance to the primary means of escape greater than 75 ft (23 m) shall be provided with two primary means of escape remotely located from each other.

Exception No. 1: Existing buildings.

Exception No. 2: Buildings protected throughout by an approved supervised automatic sprinkler system in accordance with Section 7-7.

21-2.3 **Arrangements of Means of Escape.**

21-2.3.1 No required path of travel from any room to the outside shall be through another room or apartment not under the immediate control of the occupant of the first room or through a bathroom or other space subject to locking.

Paragraph 21-2.3.1 was drafted in response to the fact that one- and two-family dwellings could have up to three rooms rented to outsiders or could be arranged so that a second family must egress through the living space of the first family (this is often found in older homes not originally built as duplexes but later converted to this design). In either case, egress for the tenants or for the second family must be independent of any other family's living space.

21-2.4 **Doors.**

21-2.4.1 No door in the path of travel of a means of escape shall be less than 28 in. (71 cm) wide.

Exception: Bathroom doors shall be not less than 24 in. (61 cm) wide.

Although Chapter 5 requires 32-in. (81-cm) wide doors in new construction and 28-in. (71-cm) wide doors in existing buildings, 21-2.4.1 allows the use of 28-in. (71-cm) wide doors [24 in. (61 cm) for bathrooms] in both new and existing buildings (*see Figure 21-5*). This applies to doors in one- and two-family dwellings and those within apartments (dwelling units).

The 28-in. (71-cm) wide doors specified in 21-2.4.1 are found in dwelling designs, but ease of access and the need to move furniture and appliances usually dictate a larger size and reflect prudent architectural design.

21-2.4.2 Doors shall be a minimum of 6 ft 6 in. (198 cm) in nominal height.

21-2.4.3 Every closet door latch shall be such that children can open the door from inside the closet.

21-2.4.4 Every bathroom door shall be designed to allow opening from the outside during an emergency when locked.

Paragraphs 21-2.4.3 and 21-2.4.4 reflect the fact that, during a fire, young children will often seek refuge in bathrooms, in closets, or under beds. Provisions for unlocking bathroom and closet doors permit ease of rescue by the fire department or by parents.

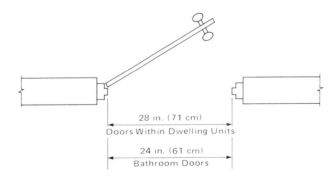

Figure 21-5. Minimum Width of Doors Within a Dwelling Unit per 21-2.4.1. Note that bathroom doors may be 4 in. (10.2 cm) smaller than the specified minimum. Closet doors that are not normally part of the means of escape are not regulated.

21-2.4.5 Doors shall be swinging or sliding.

21-2.4.6* No door in any means of escape shall be locked against egress when the building is occupied. All locking devices that impede or prohibit egress or that cannot be easily disengaged shall be prohibited.

A-21-2.4.6 It is the intent of this requirement that security measures, where installed, should not prevent egress.

Paragraph 21-2.4.6 prohibits a one- or two-family dwelling (or a dwelling unit) from having any door locked "against egress" while the building is occupied. This requirement permits a door to have a locking device that allows the door to be opened from within the building for the purpose of egress but does not allow the door to be opened from outside the building. Ordinary double cylinder locks and chain locks do not meet these provisions. Several tragic multiple-death fires have occurred when a key could not be found to unlock these devices.

Although not specifically referenced, the language of 5-2.1.5.1 is appropriate: "Locks, if provided, shall not require the use of a key, tool, special knowledge, or effort for operation from the inside of the building." This eliminates double cylinder locks and chain locks that require a key in order to be operated from the inside. Paragraph 5-2.1.5.3 requires the use of a simple operation to open a door; locks that require two-handed knob and similar operations are specifically prohibited. (*See the Exception to 5-2.1.5.3 for additional information on latches and locks.*)

This applies only to doors or windows that are part of the required escape system. Often the rear door of a dwelling is not part of the required escape system and, therefore, is permitted to be equipped with a double cylinder lock.

21-2.5 Stairs, Landings, Ramps, Balconies, or Porches.

21-2.5.1 Stairs, ramps, guards, and handrails shall be in accordance with 5-2.2 for Class B stairs. A handrail shall be provided on at least one side of stairways of four or more ris-

ers. Spiral stairs and winders in accordance with 5-2.2.2.7 and 5-2.2.2.8 shall be permitted within a single living unit. The minimum clear width of stairs, landings, ramps, balconies, and porches shall be 36 in. (91 cm) measured in accordance with 5-3.2.

Exception No. 1: Existing means of escape shall be permitted to be continued in use. However, guards and handrails shall be provided, and no sleeping rooms or living area shall be accessible by only a ladder, stair ladder, folding stairs, or through a trap door.

Exception No. 2: The provisions of 5-2.2.3 shall not apply to stairs within a dwelling unit.

Although Class B stairs are listed in Chapter 5 as applying only to existing facilities, Chapter 21 requires their installation as a minimum within a dwelling unit. Existing means of escape stair components are excepted. The language requiring a handrail to be provided on at least one side of the stair is new to the 1991 Edition. Note that this requirement also applies to existing stairs. The requirements for guards and handrails in Chapter 5 should be reviewed when using Chapter 21, since many significant revisions have been made to these two important features.

21-2.6 Hallways. The minimum width of hallways shall be 36 in. (91 cm). The minimum height shall be not less than 7 ft (213 cm) nominal height with projections from the ceiling providing not less than 6 ft 8 in. (203 cm) nominal height.

Exception: Existing approved hallways shall be permitted to be continued in use.

Within the dwelling unit, headroom is only regulated in the hallways.

SECTION 21-3   Protection

21-3.1 Protection of Vertical Openings. No requirements.

21-3.2 Interior Finish.

21-3.2.1 Interior finish on walls and ceilings of occupied spaces shall be Class A, B, or C as defined in Section 6-5.

Note that Class D interior finish (flame spread 200-500) is no longer permitted in one- and two-family dwellings. It was the intent of the Committee that this restriction on combustible finishes increase the level of life safety from fire in dwellings. The use of high flame spread interior decorative paneling has been a factor in many fatal residential fires.

21-3.2.2 Interior Floor Finish. No requirements.

See Supplement 2.

21-3.3 Detection, Alarm, and Communication Systems.

21-3.3.1 Detection. Approved single station or multiple station smoke detectors continuously powered by the house electrical system shall be installed in accordance with 7-6.2.9.

Exception No. 1: Dwelling units protected by an approved smoke detection system installed in accordance with Section 7-6, having an approved means of occupant notification.

Exception No. 2: In existing construction, approved smoke detectors powered by batteries shall be permitted.

Note that directly wired or plug-in type detectors are required in lieu of battery units. However, existing dwellings are permitted to use battery-powered units.

The detector(s) should usually be located in the hall area(s) giving access to rooms used for sleeping. In multilevel living units, the detector that covers the upper level should usually be located at the top of the stairs. The detector(s) should be mounted on the ceiling or on the wall within 12 in. (30.5 cm) of, but not closer than 6 in. (15.2 cm) to, the ceiling. The detector should be remotely located from the cooking area. Where unusual factors such as room configuration, air movement, or stagnant air pockets require consideration, the authority having jurisdiction and the designer should determine the placement of the detectors. See NFPA 74, *Standard for the Installation, Maintenance, and Use of Household Fire Warning Equipment.*[4]

NFPA analysis of reported fires indicates that about one-third of smoke detectors installed in homes are inoperative. A landmark study by the IAFC Foundation found that, when detectors are non-operational, the usual reason is dead or missing batteries. Since 85 percent of U.S. homes had at least one detector in 1989, the percentage of homes with detectors that are inoperative now exceeds the percentage of homes with no detectors (although far more fires occur in the latter situation). Therefore, increasing the success record of smoke detectors in U.S. homes depends nearly as much on reducing the problem of dead and missing batteries as it does on promoting their use in all homes.

SECTION 21-4 (Reserved)

SECTION 21-5 Building Services

21-5.1 Heating Equipment. No stove or combustion heater shall be so located as to block escape in case of fire caused by the malfunction of the stove or heater.

Formal Interpretation 81-32
Reference: 21-5

Question 1: Is it the intent of the Committee to allow wall-mounted natural gas or LP-Gas fueled heating units that are vented to the exterior in a hallway that is the primary means of egress?

Answer: No.

Question 2: If the answer to Question 1 above is no, is it the intent of the Committee to allow central heating units that use natural gas or LP-Gas fuel, that are properly vented to the exterior and have combustion air, in separate enclosed closets in a hallway that is a primary means of egress?

Answer: Yes.

Issue Edition: 1981
Reference: 22-5
Date: April 1984 ∎

This requirement takes on added significance in light of today's high energy costs, which have resulted in the use of alternative fuels in the home.

References Cited in Commentary

[1]NFPA 13, *Standard for the Installation of Sprinkler Systems*, National Fire Protection Association, Quincy, MA, 1991.

[2]NFPA 13D, *Standard for the Installation of Sprinkler Systems in One- and Two-Family Dwellings and Mobile Homes*, National Fire Protection Association, Quincy, MA, 1991.

[3]NFPA 13R, *Standard for the Installation of Sprinkler Systems in Residential Occupancies up to and Including Four Stories in Height*, National Fire Protection Association, Quincy, MA, 1991.

[4]NFPA 74, *Standard for the Installation, Maintenance, and Use of Household Fire Warning Equipment*, National Fire Protection Association, Quincy, MA, 1989.

22

New Residential Board and Care Occupancies

SECTION 22-1 General Requirements

22-1.1 Application.

It is intended that this chapter be applied to all new residential board and care facilities. However, such facilities will rarely include the designation "residential board and care facility" as part of their official name. They will operate under a variety of names, and they may house a variety of occupants. Therefore, it is important to understand the distinction between this type of occupancy and others that provide sleeping accommodations, such as lodging houses, hotels, nursing homes, and hospitals. The definitions found in 22-1.3 will be helpful in making this distinction. Additional help in recognizing types of facilities that are covered by this chapter can be found in A-22-1.3. The list is not all-inclusive.

The fire fatality problem in buildings of this occupancy classification is well documented.[1] Prior to 1985, it was not uncommon to find a multiple-death board and care fire reported in the NFPA *Fire Journal*. The following is extracted from a memo to state fire marshals, state training directors, and provincial fire marshals from NFPA regarding boarding house firesafety. It was dated July 10, 1984.

Boarding homes are known by a variety of names: board and care homes, halfway houses, retirement homes, rooming houses, or community living facilities. Regardless of what the facilities are called, an estimated 300,000 boarding homes house 2,000,000 people in the U.S.[2] The facilities range from specially designed and constructed buildings to converted single-family homes and dormitories.

The residents of boarding homes are often unable to meet the demands of independent living and are at a greater risk from fire than the general population. Typically, the victims of boarding home fires are the elderly or former mental health patients who have been released from various institutions. These residents may not require daily medical care but nonetheless may have disabilities that reduce their ability to save themselves in a fire.

The policy of deinstitutionalizing chronic mental patients began in the mid-1950s. The nation's mental hospital population from a peak of over half a million in the mid-1950s, dropped to roughly half that number by the mid-1960s, and roughly one fourth the peak figure by 1980. The National Institute of Mental Health estimated in 1980 that 800,000 chronic mental patients were both deinstitutionalized and living in sorely lacking conditions.[3] The chronic mental patients released in the late 1970s also included a higher percentage of physically handicapped individuals, and these patients have been less likely to maintain outpatient follow-up care.

Since 1978, multiple-death boarding home fires (those that kill three or more persons) have resulted in 296 deaths. Compared to the estimated boarding home population, this indicates that the risk of dying in a multiple-death fire is roughly five times as high in a boarding home than in all other residential occupancies combined. Many multiple-death boarding home fires kill at least half the tenants of the properties involved.

An analysis of recent fatal boarding home fires reveals the lack of basic fire protection provisions in these buildings, including: inadequate means of egress, combustible interior finishes, unenclosed stairways, lack of automatic detection or sprinkler systems, or lack of emergency training for staff and residents. Many of the facilities were either licensed for an occupancy other than a boarding home (such as a hotel) or were unlicensed, underground "boarding homes." None of the facilities were provided with automatic sprinkler protection.

There is no particular mystery about how to reduce the number of fatal boarding home fires. Provision of enclosed stairs, provision of two means of egress, avoidance of the use of combustible interior finishes, compartmentation, provision of automatic detection and sprinkler systems, and instruction of staff and residents in emergency procedures would greatly reduce the number of fatalities.

Comprehensive fire incident reporting systems in the U.S.A. were developed before the emergence of residential board and care facilities. Therefore, the overall fire experience of these occupancies cannot be readily isolated.

Rooming, boarding and lodging houses averaged 62 fire deaths per year from 1984 to 1988, and residential hotels averaged 4 deaths per year during the same period. This compares with 49 deaths per year for hotels. Facilities that care for the aged averaged 19 fire deaths a year in the same period, and facilities that care for the sick averaged 11 deaths a year.

Beginning in the 1970s, NFPA's major-fires data base developed a special code to identify board and care homes. Board and care homes were defined as facilities designed to provide only lodging for residents with substantial limitations, primarily those age 65 and over and former mental patients. This data base devoted particular attention to tracking fires in these facilities where 3 or more persons had died. Multiple-death fires in board and care facilities killed 214 persons from 1971 to 1989. Primarily because of these fires, the fatality rate in multiple-death fires (3 or more deaths) in all boarding homes (including board and care facilities) from 1978 to 1984, relative to the population in such facilities, was roughly five times the comparable multiple-death rate in other residential properties. The rate has diminished since that time, but five multiple-death fires in board-and-care homes from 1984 to 1989 prove that the problem still exists.

The deadliest of these fires that occurred from 1971 to 1989 were a 1981 fire in New Jersey in what was called a sheltered care boarding facility (31 deaths), a 1979 fire in Missouri in what was called a boarding house (25 deaths), and a 1980 fire in New Jersey in what was called a hotel (24 deaths). Analysis of the circumstances in multiple-death board and care home fires reveals a general lack of fire protection, including an absence of sprinklers, an absence or insufficiency of detection/alarm provisions, inadequate means of egress, unenclosed stairways, combustible interior finishes, and a lack of emergency training for staff and residents.

The provisions of this chapter address the basic fire protection features identified above while maintaining the ability to operate such a facility in a noninstitutional environment. The requirements for small board and care facilities are similar to the provisions for one- and two-family dwellings and lodging and rooming houses. The requirements for large facilities, other than those that are large and impractical to evacuate, are similar to the requirements for new hotels. Large, impractical facilities, as required by 22-3.1.2.2, shall comply with the requirements of Chapter 12, "New Health Care Occupancies." While the provisions of Chapter 22 may be similar to other residential occupancies, there are requirements that differ due to the unique characteristics of these facilities, such as the degree to which occupants are able to respond to a fire emergency.

This chapter follows the same outline as the other occupancy chapters within the *Code*. However, because there are four major sections (22-1, 22-2, 22-3, and 22-4), the standard chapter outline begins with the next digit. For example, the "-3.1" subsection of each occupancy chapter (e.g., 18-3.1) usually contains the requirements for vertical opening protection. In Chapter 22, 22-2.3.1 and 22-3.3.1 contain the vertical opening provisions.

A partial list of multiple-death board and care fires since 1979 appears in Table 22-1.

22-1.1.1* All new facilities classified as residential board and care occupancies shall conform to the requirements of this chapter. This chapter is divided into four sections as follows:

(a) Section 22-1 — General Requirements.

(b) Section 22-2 — Small Facilities (i.e., sleeping accommodations for not more than 16 residents).

(c) Section 22-3 — Large Facilities (i.e., sleeping accommodations for more than 16 residents).

(d) Section 22-4 — Suitability of an Apartment Building to House a Board and Care Occupancy.

A-22-1.1.1 The requirements in this chapter are designed to accommodate typical changes in the capabilities of the resident, such as those due to accidents, temporary illness, cyclical variations in capabilities, and gradual aging. This is based on the assumption that the capabilities of the resident will be evaluated at least annually, and for residents with geriatric problems or degenerative diseases, at least every six months. Also, residents should be reevaluated after each accident or illness that requires hospitalization.

The requirements of this chapter are based on two main concepts:

Table 22-1. Major Residential Board and Care Multiple-Death Fires

Date	Occupancy	Civilians Killed	Civilians Injured
4/1/79	Marietta Foster Home Connellsville, PA	10	2
4/2/79	Wayside Inn Boarding House Farmington, MO	25	9
4/11/79	1715 Lamont Street Washington, DC	10	4
11/11/79	Coats Boarding Home Pioneer, OH	14	0
7/26/80	Brinley Inn Boarding Home* Bradley Beach, NJ	24	4
11/30/80	Donahue Foster Home Detroit, MI	5	0
1/9/81	Beachview Rest Home* Keansburg, NJ	31	10
10/28/82	Perrys' Domiciliary Care Home* Pittsburgh, PA	5	1
2/7/83	Silver Leaves Group Home* Eau Claire, WI	6	0
3/13/83	Shannons Foster Care Home* Gladstone, MI	5	3
4/19/83	Central Community Home* Worcester, MA	7	2
8/31/83	Anandale Village* Lawrenceville, GA	8	0
12/5/83	Dana House Cincinnati, OH	6	4
11/20/84	708 Hill Rise Court Lexington, KY	5	0
6/25/86	138 Pingree Boarding Home Detroit, MI	4	19

* These are incidents in which NFPA has evidence that elderly occupants or former mental health patients were tenants.

(a) Larger buildings, which are more difficult to evacuate, require more built-in fire protection than smaller buildings.

(b) Occupants who are more difficult to evacuate require more built-in fire protection than occupants who are easier to evacuate.

It is also anticipated that a small facility typically will be located in a structure that has the appearance of and operates in a similar manner to a dwelling. The operation and size of a small facility also demands unique consideration with respect to the fire protection features provided. Certain fire protection features that are appropriate for large facilities, such as smoke barriers, may not be appropriate and may not provide adequate protection in small facilities.

22-1.1.2 The requirements of this chapter are applicable to new construction according to the provisions of Section 1-5 of this *Code*.

It should be noted that several sections contain exceptions for conversions. For the purposes of the *Code*, "conversion" refers to a building that was previously occupied as another occupancy (i.e., hotel, nursing home, dwelling, etc.) and is then converted to a board and care facility. In accordance with 1-7.4, such change of use must comply with the requirements for new construction. However, certain modifications are made in this chapter to eliminate undue hardship while maintaining a reasonable degree of life safety.

22-1.2 **Mixed Occupancies.** Where another type of occupancy occurs in the same building as a residential board and care occupancy, the requirements of 1-5.7 of this *Code* shall apply.

Exception No. 1: Occupancies that are completely separated from all portions of the building used for a residential board and care facility and its egress system by construction having a fire resistance rating of at least 2 hours.

Exception No. 1 specifically requires that the residential board and care facility and its exit system be separated from the other occupancy. Therefore, if the residential board and care facility is located on the second floor and Exception No. 1 is to be applied, the exit stair must have a 2-hour fire-rated enclosure, regardless of the fact that 5-1.3.1 would permit a 1-hour fire-rated enclosure. Where the residential board and care facility is located on the same floor as the other occupancy, the occupancy separation may also serve as a horizontal exit, if the provisions of 5-2.4 are met.

Exception No. 2: Apartment buildings housing residential board and care occupancies in conformance with Section 22-4. In such facilities, any safeguards required by Section 22-4 that

are more restrictive than those for other housed occupancies apply only to the extent prescribed by Section 22-4.

Exception No. 2 clarifies that board and care facilities located within an apartment building need not comply with the requirements for mixed occupancies. The provisions of Section 22-4 apply to the entire building and supplement the provisions of Chapter 18, "New Apartment Buildings." The board and care facility itself must comply with the provisions of Section 22-2.

22-1.3 **Definitions.**

A number of key concepts are defined in this chapter, arguably the most important of which are "personal care," "evacuation capability," and "point of safety."

Evacuation Capability.* Evacuation capability is the ability of the occupants, residents, and staff as a group either to evacuate a building or to relocate from the point of occupancy to a point of safety. Following are the levels of evacuation capability covered by this chapter:

(a) *Prompt.* Evacuation capability equivalent to the capability of the general population where applying the requirements for residential occupancies covered by Chapters 16, 18, 20, and 21.

(b) *Slow.* Evacuation capability of a group to move to a point of safety in a timely manner, with some of the residents requiring assistance from the staff.

(c) *Impractical.* A group that, even with staff assistance, cannot reliably move to a point of safety in a timely manner.

A-22-1.3 **Evacuation Capability.** The evacuation capability of the residents and staff is a function of both the ability of the residents to evacuate and the assistance provided by the staff. It is intended that the evacuation capability be determined by the procedure acceptable to the authority having jurisdiction. It is also intended that the timing of drills, the rating of residents, and similar actions related to determining the evacuation capability be performed by persons approved by or acceptable to the authority having jurisdiction. The evacuation capability can be determined by the use of the definitions in 22-1.3, the application of NFPA 101M, *Alternative Approaches to Life Safety*, Chapter 5 (*see Appendix B*), or a program of drills (timed).

Where drills are used, in determining evacuation capability, it is suggested that the facility conduct and record fire drills 12 times per year (4 times per year on each shift), and that the facility conduct the drills in consultation with the authority having jurisdiction. Records should indicate the time taken to reach a point of safety, date and time of day, location of simulated fire origin, the escape paths used, along with comments relating to residents who resisted or failed to participate in the drills.

Translation of drill times to evacuation capability may be determined as: (a) 3 minutes or less, Prompt; (b) over 3 minutes, but not in excess of 13 minutes, Slow; and (c) more than 13 minutes, Impractical.

Evacuation capability in all cases is based on the time of day or night when evacuation of the facility would be most difficult (i.e., sleeping residents or fewer staff present).

Where the facility management does not furnish an evacuation capability determination acceptable to the authority having jurisdiction, the evacuation capability should be classified as impractical. However, evacuation capability should be considered slow if the following conditions are met:

(a) All residents able to travel to centralized dining facilities without continuous staff assistance, and

(b) There is continuous staffing whenever there are residents in the facility.

Evacuation capability is a factor in all the *Code* chapters. However, in most chapters, the *Code* assumes that the building occupants have similar evacuation capabilities, and the requirements are based on the ability of occupants to reach safety by means of exits. In the "institutional occupancy" chapters, the *Code* assumes that many of the building occupants will be completely incapable of evacuating the building, and the protection of life from fire is achieved by the "defend in place" method. In large residential buildings (hotels and apartment buildings), where evacuation capability may be poor due to the large size of the building, substantial built-in fire protection is required.

In this chapter, evacuation capability is not assumed. Occupants of residential board and care facilities do not have the same evacuation capability. This should be apparent due to the numerous and diverse types of facilities that are included in this occupancy type. For example, in an orphanage, a shelter for battered women, a group home for high-functioning mentally handicapped persons, or a halfway house for prison parolees, the occupants may have normal evacuation capability. In facilities housing elderly, physically impaired persons, occupants may be slow-moving or may need assistance in recognizing the need for evacuation. In some facilities, evacuation of the building may not be practical at all.

Evacuation capability for an entire facility is not determined on the basis of that resident who is least capable. A facility that houses one impaired resident may have excellent evacuation capability if the staff or a resident "buddy" is able to provide the assistance needed to effect a prompt evacuation of the entire group without jeopardizing the safety of the other residents. It should also be noted that evacuation capability is based on the ability to relocate to a point of safety that is not necessarily a public way. (*See the definition of point of safety.*)

The protection features required by this chapter are intended to coordinate with the evacuation capability of the occupants. As such, the fire endurance of the structure, interior finish materials, types and arrangement of means of escape and exits, as well as corridor enclosure provisions, vary based on whether a facility houses occupants who are prompt, slow, or impractical to evacuate. Facilities that are impractical to evacuate utilize the "defend in place" concept. In small facilities, this is achieved by improving the protection of vertical openings. In large facilities, this is achieved by referencing the provisions of Chapter 12.

Guidance in determining the evacuation capability of a specific facility is provided in A-22-1.3.

Hazardous Area.   A hazardous area is any space where there is storage or activity having fuel conditions exceeding that of a one- or two-family dwelling and that possesses the potential for a fully involved fire. Hazardous areas include, but are not limited to, areas for cartoned storage, food or household maintenance items in wholesale or institutional-type quantities and concentrations, or mass storage of residents' belongings. Areas containing approved, properly installed and maintained furnaces and heating equipment, furnace rooms, and cooking and laundry facilities are not classed as hazardous areas solely on the basis of such equipment.

Hazardous areas are spaces containing materials that, because of their basic nature (as in the case of flammable liquids) or because of the quantity of combustible materials involved, represent a significantly greater fire hazard than would otherwise be typical of residential board and care occupancies. The mere presence of heat-producing appliances, such as furnaces, cooking equipment, or dryers, does not constitute a hazardous area. To be considered a hazardous area, the contents should be of such character that a fire or explosion could develop and pose a danger of propagating to adjacent spaces unprotected by a fire barrier.

Personal Care. "Personal care" means protective care of residents who do not require chronic or convalescent medical or nursing care. Personal care involves responsibility for the safety of the resident while inside the building. Personal care may include daily awareness by the management of the resident's functioning and whereabouts, making and reminding a resident of appointments, the ability and readiness for intervention in the event of a resident experiencing a crisis, supervision in the areas of nutrition and medication, and actual provision of transient medical care.

Personal care is a significant concept because the occupants of a board and care facility require care. This is not true medical care, as might be provided in a hospital or nursing home, but rather a form of assistance in meeting the demands of daily living. The term "transient medical care" refers to the kind of medical care that is normally provided in the home by one family member for another, not skilled nursing or acute medical care.

Point of Safety. A point of safety is a location that meets one of the following criteria:

(a) It is located exterior to and away from the building.

(b) It is located within a building of any type construction protected throughout by an approved automatic sprinkler system and is either:

1. Located within an exit enclosure meeting the requirements of this *Code*, or

2. Located within another portion of the building that is separated by smoke barriers in accordance with Section 6-3, with at least a 20-minute fire resistance rating, and that portion of the building has access to a means of escape or exit

that conforms to the requirements of this *Code* and that does not require return to the area of fire involvement.

(c) It is located within a building of Type I, Type II (222) or (111), Type III (211), Type IV, or Type V (111) construction (*see 6-2.1*) and is either:

1. Located within an exit enclosure meeting the requirements of this *Code*, or

2. Located within another portion of the building that is separated by smoke barriers in accordance with Section 6-3, with at least a 20-minute fire resistance rating, and that portion of the building has access to a means of escape or exit that conforms to the requirements of this *Code* and that does not require return to the area of fire involvement.

"Point of safety" is another *Code* concept that is specifically defined in this chapter. It is well recognized that there are many buildings from which evacuation of all occupants to the outdoors cannot be achieved within a reasonable amount of time, regardless of their capability. This chapter establishes the criteria for a point of safety within the building. Essentially, this is the point at which residents can remain in safety until the fire is extinguished or until outside assistance can arrive to complete evacuation to the exterior.

Resident. A person who is receiving personal care and resides in a residential board and care facility.

Residential Board and Care Occupancy.* A building or part thereof that is used for lodging and boarding of four or more residents, not related by blood or marriage to the owners or operators for the purpose of providing personal care services.

A-22-1.3   Residential Board and Care Occupancy. Following are examples of facilities that may be classified as residential board and care occupancies.

(a) A group housing arrangement for physically or mentally handicapped persons who normally may attend school in the community, attend church in the community, or otherwise use community facilities.

(b) A group housing arrangement for physically or mentally handicapped persons who are undergoing training in preparation for independent living, for paid employment, or for other normal community acitivities.

(c) A group housing arrangement for the elderly that provides personal care services but that does not provide nursing care.

(d) Facilities for social rehabilitation, alcoholism, drug abuse, or mental health problems that contain a group housing arrangement and that provide personal care services but do not provide acute care.

(e) Other group housing arrangements that provide personal care services but not nursing care.

Staff.   A person who provides personal care services, supervision, or assistance.

Thermal Barrier.*   A material that will limit the average temperature rise of the unexposed surface to not more than 250°F (120°C) for a specified fire exposure complying with the standard time temperature curve of NFPA 251, *Standard Methods of Fire Tests of Building Construction and Materials.*

A-22-1.3   **Thermal Barrier.** Finish ratings as published in the UL Fire Resistance Directory are one way of determining thermal barrier.

In previous editions of the *Code,* several sections referred to a finish rating of 15 or 20 minutes. The term "finish rating" is not as widely used as the term "thermal barrier." For this reason, the chapter now uses this term in lieu of "finish rating" for the protection of structural elements and the separation of areas where automatic sprinkler protection may be omitted. As noted in A-22-1.3, finish ratings may be used to determine a material's acceptability as a thermal barrier.

22-1.4   **Acceptability of Means of Egress or Escape.** No means of escape or means of egress shall be considered as complying with the minimum criteria for acceptance unless emergency evacuation drills are regularly conducted using that route in accordance with the requirements of 31-7.3.

Exits and means of escape are worthless unless residents are familiar with them and feel comfortable using them. An exit or means of escape that is never used in drills will probably not be used in an emergency evacuation. This does not mean that if windows serve as a secondary means of escape that a resident must use the window.

However, during drills it would be important to identify the appropriate windows and ensure that residents are familiar with the operation of the windows and their proper use during escape.

SECTION 22-2   Small Facilities

See Table 22-2 on page 690 for a summary of the major requirements.

22-2.1   **General.**

22-2.1.1   **Scope.** This section applies to residential board and care occupancies providing sleeping accommodations for not more than 16 residents. Where there are sleeping accommodations for more than 16 residents, the occupancy shall be classed as a large facility. The requirements for large facilities are found in Section 22-3.

22-2.1.2   **Requirements Based on Evacuation Capability.**

22-2.1.2.1   Small facilities shall comply with the requirements of Section 22-2 as indicated for the appropriate evacuation capability.

Exception: Facilities where the authority having jurisdiction has determined equivalent safety is provided in accordance with Section 1-6.

A-22-2.1.2.1   **Exception.** In determining equivalency for conversions, modernizations, renovations, or unusual design concepts, the authority having jurisdiction may accept evaluations based on NFPA 101M, *Alternative Approaches to Life Safety,* Chapter 6. (*See Appendix B.*)

The 1988 Edition of NFPA 101M was designed for use with the 1988 Edition of NFPA 101 and cannot be used to evaluate facilities under the 1991 *Life Safety Code.* At the time this *Handbook* went to press, the Committee on Safety to Life was preparing the 1992 Edition of NFPA 101M to use in conjunction with the 1991 *Life Safety Code.*

Table 22-2.   Summary of Major Requirements for New Small Facilities

Parameter	Evacuation Capability		
	Prompt	Slow	Impractical
1. Construction 22-2.1.3	No Requirements	20-Minute Fire Resistant or Sprinklered (See No. 8)	1-Hour Fire-Rated or Sprinklered (See No. 8)
2. Means of Escape 22-2.2	1 Primary and 1 Emergency Route	2 Remote Routes	2 Remote Routes
3. Vertical Openings 22-2.3.1	20-Minute Fire Resitant	20-Minute Fire Resistant	20-Minute Fire Resistant
4. Protection of Hazardous Areas 22-2.3.2	Defines 2 Levels	Defines 2 Levels	Defines 2 Levels
5. Interior Finish 22-2.3.3	Class A,B,C No Req. for Floor Finish	Class A, B, or C due to Sprinklers No Req. for Floor Finish	Class A, B, or C due to Sprinklers No Req. for Floor Finish
6. Manual F.A. 22-2.3.4.1	Section 7-6 Local	Section 7-6 Local	Section 7-6 Local
7. Smoke Detection 22-2.3.4.2, 22-2.3.4.3	Sleeping Rooms or 1 Each Level + Each Living and Day Room	Sleeping Rooms or 1 Each Level + Each Living and Day Room	Sleeping Rooms or 1 Each Level + Each Living and Day Room
8. Sprinklers 22-2.3.5	Required with Quick-Response or Residential Sprinklers	Required with Quick-Response or Residential Sprinklers	Required with Quick-Response or Residential Sprinklers
9. Separation of Sleeping Rooms 22-2.3.6	Smoke-Resisting	Smoke Resistant due to Sprinkers	Smoke Resistant due to Sprinklers

This table summarizes major items. See specific requirements for additional details and exceptions.

22-2.1.3 Minimum Construction Requirements.

22-2.1.3.1 Prompt. No special requirements.

22-2.1.3.2 Slow. The facility shall be housed in a building where the interior is fully sheathed with lath and plaster or other material providing a 15-minute thermal barrier, including all portions of bearing walls, bearing partitions, floor construction, and roofs. All columns, beams, girders, and trusses shall be similarly encased or otherwise provide a minimum of at least a 20-minute fire resistance rating.

Exception No. 1: Exposed steel or wood columns, girders, and beams (but not joists) located in the basement.

Exception No. 2: Buildings of Type I, Type II (111) or (222), Type III (211), Type IV, or Type V (111) construction. (See 6-2.1.)

Exception No. 3: Areas protected by approved automatic sprinkler systems in accordance with 22-2.3.5.

Exception No. 4: Unfinished, unused, and essentially inaccessible loft, attic, or crawl spaces.

Exception No. 5: Where the facility can demonstrate to the authority having jurisdiction that the group is capable of evac-

uating the building in eight minutes or less or achieves an E-Score of three or less using Chapter 5 of NFPA 101M, Alternative Approaches to Life Safety.

See Figure 22-1 for examples of some acceptable construction types.

Since 22-2.3.5.2 requires automatic sprinkler protection, the construction requirements in most areas will not be applicable in accordance with Exception No. 3. The construction requirements of 22-2.1.3.2 and 22-2.1.3.3 apply to the entire building, whereas the mandatory sprinkler provisions of 22-2.3.5.2 apply to the facility. Therefore, in buildings with multiple, non-mixed occupancies, the construction requirements of 22-2.1.3.2 or 22-2.1.3.3 apply to the building unless the entire building is sprinklered. Exception No. 5 is intended to allow unsheathed, wood frame construction in facilities that house groups capable of evacuation to a point of safety within eight minutes. For such groups, the additional evacuation time provided by fire resistant sheathing is not an absolute necessity.

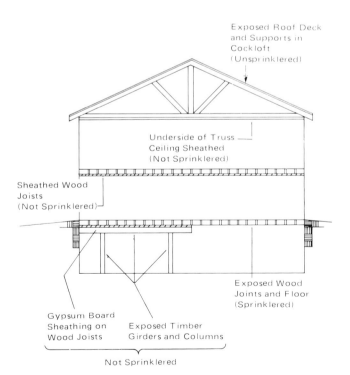

Figure 22-1. A Few Permissible Types of Construction. These may be mixed within a single building. Note that the non-sprinklered areas are still shown, since 22-2.3.5 permits the omission of sprinklers from certain areas.

22-2.1.3.3 **Impractical.** Buildings shall be of any construction type in accordance with Section 6-2 other than Type II (000), Type III (200), or Type V (000) construction.

Exception: Buildings protected throughout by an approved supervised automatic sprinkler system in accordance with 22-2.3.5 shall be of any type of construction.

Paragraph 22-2.3.5.2 mandates that all small residential board and care facilities be protected with a supervised automatic sprinkler system. The exception is permitted only if the entire building and not just the residential board and care facility is protected with a supervised automatic sprinkler system.

22-2.2 **Means of Escape.**

22-2.2.1 **Number of Means of Escape.** Every facility shall have at least two remotely located means of escape that do not involve using windows from each normally occupied story. At least one of these means of escape shall comply with 22-2.2.2.

Exception No. 1: In prompt facilities, one means of escape shall be permitted to involve windows complying with 22-2.2.3(c).

Exception No. 2: A second means of escape from each story is not required where the entire building is protected throughout by an approved automatic sprinkler system complying with 22-2.3.5, and the facility has two means of escape. This exception cannot be used in conjunction with 22-2.2.3 Exception No. 2.

Paragraph 22-2.2.1 as well as 22-2.2.2 and 22-2.2.3 establish the criteria for acceptable means of escape in small facilities. This paragraph mandates that each *story* of the facility be provided with at least two means of escape. If the entire building housing the residential board and care facility is protected throughout by an automatic sprinkler system in accordance with 22-2.3.5, if the facility itself has at least two means of escape, and if each sleeping room has a secondary means of escape or alternate protection, then each story is required to have only one means of escape. In this instance, the single means of escape shall meet the criteria for a primary means of escape. (*See 22-2.2.2.*)

The paragraph permits the use of windows only as a means of escape from a prompt facility. It should be noted, however, that this restriction applies to the means of escape from the facility and not the secondary means of escape required from each sleeping room (22-2.2.3). Where a window is considered as a means of escape, the window shall meet the criteria established in 22-2.2.3(c). Windows are not permitted to be considered as a primary means of escape.

22-2.2.2 Primary Means of Escape.

22-2.2.2.1 Every sleeping room and living area shall have access to a primary means of escape so located as to provide a safe path of travel to the outside of the building without traversing any corridor or other space exposed to unprotected vertical openings. Where sleeping rooms or living areas are above or below the level of exit discharge, the primary means of escape shall be an enclosed interior stair, exterior stair, or horizontal exit.

This paragraph requires at least one means of escape from every sleeping room and living area to be protected from vertical openings. Therefore, the primary means of escape provides some degree of quality and reliability but may not meet the criteria of an exit. If the primary means of escape is at a level other than the level of exit discharge, it must be an enclosed stairway, an exterior stairway, or possibly a horizontal exit.

22-2.2.2.2 In slow and impractical facilities, the primary means of escape for each sleeping room shall not be exposed to common living spaces such as living rooms and kitchens.

Exception: Buildings equipped with quick response or residential sprinklers throughout. Standard response sprinklers shall be permitted for use in hazardous areas in accordance with 22-2.3.2.

In slow and impractical facilities, the primary means of escape is further restricted, since it cannot be exposed to common living spaces. Therefore, the primary means of escape from a sleeping room is not permitted to include travel through a day room, common use space, or space that is open to a common living space. The objective of this requirement is to reduce the probability that smoke

and heat from a fire in a common use area will affect the primary means of escape. This provision is based in part on historical fire experience, which indicates that fires in residential board and care facilities frequently originate in common living spaces.

In recognition of the protection provided by an automatic sprinkler system and the response capabilities of quick response and residential sprinklers, the primary means of escape may be exposed to common living areas where such protection is provided. However, the *Code* does not permit the primary means of escape to be exposed and to also include an unprotected vertical opening (22-2.2.4). In addition, the exception permits the use of standard response sprinklers in hazardous areas that are required to be separated from other parts of the building by Section 22-2.3.3 in accordance with listing limitations on the use of residential and quick response sprinklers. (*See 22-2.3.5.2.*)

(*For additional information, see commentary following 20-2.2.1.*)

22-2.2.3 Secondary Means of Escape. In addition to the primary route, each sleeping room shall have a second means of escape or alternate protection that consists of one of the following:

(a) A door, stairway, passage, or hall providing a way of unobstructed travel to the outside of the dwelling at street or ground level that is independent of and remotely located from the primary means of escape.

(b) A passage through an adjacent nonlockable space, independent of and remotely located from the primary means of escape, to any approved means of escape.

(c) An outside window or door operable from the inside without the use of tools and providing a clear opening of not less than 20 in. (50.8 cm) in width, 24 in. (61 cm) in height, and 5.7 sq ft (.53 sq m) in area. The bottom of the opening shall be no more than 44 in. (112 cm) off the floor. Such means of escape shall be acceptable if:

1. The window is within 20 ft (6.1 m) of grade, or
2. The window is directly accessible to fire department rescue apparatus as approved by the authority having jurisdiction, or
3. The window or doors open onto an exterior balcony.

(d) The sleeping room shall be separated from all other parts of the facility by construction having a fire resistance rating of at least 20 minutes and shall be equipped with a door that resists passage of fire for at least 20 minutes and is designed and installed to minimize smoke leakage. A means of providing smoke venting and fresh air to the occupants shall be provided.

Exception No. 1: If the sleeping room has a door leading directly to the outside of the building with access to grade or to a stairway that meets the requirements of exterior stairs in 22-2.3.1.2, that means of escape shall be considered as meeting all the escape requirements for the sleeping room.

Exception No. 2: A second means of escape or alternate protection from each sleeping room is not required where the facility is protected throughout by an approved automatic sprinkler system complying with 22-2.3.5.

The provisions of 22-2.2.3 require that every sleeping room be provided with a secondary means of escape in addition to the primary means of escape required by 22-2.2.2. The only two exceptions to the requirement for a secondary means of escape are (1) if the sleeping room has a door leading directly to the outside of the building; or (2) where the residential board and care facility is protected throughout with an automatic sprinkler system in accordance with 22-2.3.5. Although either case is an acceptable alternative, Exception No. 2 may be the more practical method to use in order to avoid a required second means of escape. For example, if the facility is housed in an apartment building without windows that comply with item (c), an automatic sprinkler system can be installed within the facility in lieu of retrofitting complying windows for the sleeping rooms. Exception No. 2 may not be used in conjunction with Exception No. 2 to 22-2.2.1, since the result would be a single means of escape from each room and a single means of escape from each floor. Therefore, the secondary means of escape from sleeping rooms is not required only if a secondary means of escape is provided from each floor and the facility is protected by an automatic sprinkler system (22-2.3.5.2).

The primary purpose for the secondary means of escape is to allow the occupants to have some reasonable escape alternative when fire or smoke blocks the primary means

of escape. Paragraph 22-2.2.3(a) through (d) outlines four acceptable methods for providing a secondary means of escape or alternate protection:

(1) It is the intent of item (a) that the door, stairway, passage, or hall be independent of and remotely located from the primary means of escape required in 22-2.2.2. If the sleeping room has a second door that leads to the same hallway as the door serving as a primary means of escape, little additional protection is provided, since fire or smoke could affect both of the doors at approximately the same time. If the corridor within the facility into which a sleeping room door opens is separated from all common living spaces (as required by 22-2.2.2.2 for slow and impractical facilities located in buildings that are not protected throughout by an automatic sprinkler system using quick response or residential sprinklers), it may be determined that the arrangement is acceptable, provided the corridor does actually lead to two separate, independent, and remote means of escape. This arrangement is similar to that permitted in other occupancies in which protected corridors are provided. In such a case, little, if any, additional safety would be provided by requiring two doors from the sleeping room to the corridor.

(2) Figure 22-2 illustrates an example of how the secondary means of escape may pass through an adjacent space, such as another sleeping room, provided the occupant has free and unobstructed access to the space in accordance with item (b).

(3) The use of an operable window of the minimum dimensions specified in item (c) is permitted as a secondary means of escape from a story in prompt facilities only (22-2.2.1) but is permitted as the secondary means of escape for each sleeping room in all facilities. Figure 22-3 illustrates the minimum dimensions required for escape windows. Note that it is not possible to use the minimum dimensions for width and height and still comply with minimum area dimension. In addition to the minimum size of the window, the utility of the window must be ensured by one of three alternatives.

First, the window must be within 20 ft (61 m) of grade so that jumping is possible, if necessary. The second alternative permits fire department rescue of the occupant from the window. The authority having jurisdiction must determine the acceptable means of fire department rescue (e.g., aerial ladder apparatus, ground ladders, etc.) and the additional criteria necessary for approval of the alternative, such as fire department vehicle accessibility. The third alternative allows the occupant to reach an exterior balcony to breathe fresh air while awaiting either rescue or fire extinguishment.

(4) Item (d) is actually another alternative to the secondary means of escape. In lieu of the secondary means of escape, the sleeping room must be completely separated from all other parts of the building (not only the corridor). In addition, a means of smoke venting and access to fresh air must be provided. A window to the outside that does not comply with item (c) may be an acceptable means of providing smoke venting and fresh air if the window is of substantial enough size to serve as a reasonable vent.

(For additional information, see commentary following 21-2.1.2.)

22-2.2.4 Enclosed Interior Stairs. Interior stairways shall be enclosed with 20-minute fire barriers with all openings equipped with smoke actuated automatic-closing or self-closing devices on doors having a fire resistance comparable to that required for the enclosure. Stairways shall comply with 5-2.2.6.5.

Exception No. 1: Stairs connecting two levels only shall be permitted to be open to other than the street floor.

Exception No. 2: For prompt and slow facilities in buildings three stories or less in height having an approved automatic sprinkler system using quick response or residential sprinklers, stair enclosures shall not be required provided there still remains a primary means of escape from each sleeping area that does not require occupants to pass through a portion of a lower floor, unless that route is separated from all spaces on that floor by construction having a 20-minute fire resistance rating.

The need to protect interior stairs has been well documented by historical fire experience. The exceptions do permit unprotected or partially protected stairs in limited instances. For example, a stair between the first and second floor may be open to the second floor, or a stair between the basement and first level may be open to the

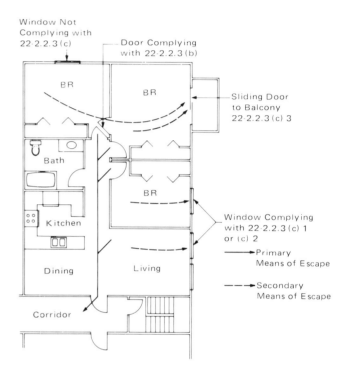

Figure 22-2.   One Potential Use of 22-2.2.3(b). An example of a board and care facility within an apartment building in which a sleeping room has a window that does not comply with 22-2.2.3(c) and in which there is no door to the corridor. The balcony door in the upper right bedroom is not required if the facility is sprinklered (see commentary on 22-2.3.5.1) or if the sleeping room in question is protected in accordance with 22-2.2.3(d).

basement, provided the stair is enclosed on the street floor. However, it is not the intent of Exception No. 1 to allow an open stair that connects a second and third floor, for example, to qualify as an "enclosed interior stair."

In prompt and slow facilities located in buildings three stories or less in height, stairs need not be enclosed if the building is protected throughout with an automatic sprinkler system using quick response or residential sprinklers. However, there must be a primary means of escape that does not require occupants to pass through another level unless the path through that level is separated by construction having a minimum 20-minute fire resistance rating.

Therefore, if a board and care facility that has been determined to be prompt or slow is located in a typical two-story dwelling in which the stairway is not enclosed, the following options exist:

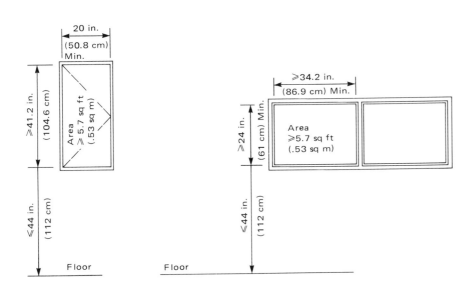

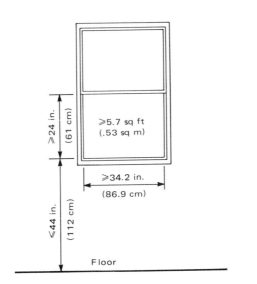

Figure 22-3. *Minimum Size and Dimensions of Outside Windows Used as a Second Means of Escape in Accordance with 22-2.2.3(c).*

1. Stairs must be enclosed with construction having a 20-minute fire resistance rating in accordance with 22-2.2.4.

2. Sprinkler protection must be provided using quick response or residential sprinklers as required by 22-2.3.5, and a primary means of escape must be provided from the second floor that does not require travel through the first floor. In this case, there is no need for a separation at the top or bottom of the stair (Exception No. 2).

3. Sprinkler protection must be provided using quick response or residential sprinklers as required by 22-2.3.5, and the stair may be used as the primary means of escape. However, in this instance, travel area on the first floor must be separated from all other spaces by construction having a fire resistance rating of at least 20 minutes. Therefore, rooms that are typically open to the stair, such as the living and dining rooms, must be separated from the stair. (*Also see 22-2.2.1 and 22-2.2.2.*)

Figure 22-4 illustrates the use of Exception No. 1 to 22-2.2.4.

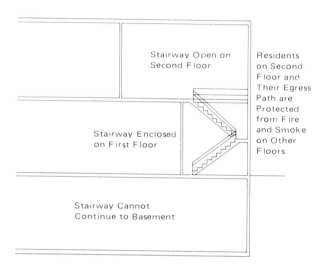

Stairway Open on Second Floor

Residents on Second Floor and Their Egress Path are Protected from Fire and Smoke on Other Floors

Stairway Enclosed on First Floor

Stairway Cannot Continue to Basement

Figure 22-4. *A Stairway That Connects the First Floor to the Second Floor May Be Open to the Second Floor.*

22-2.2.5 Doors.

22-2.2.5.1 No door or path of travel to a means of escape shall be less than 32 in. (81 cm) wide.

Exception No. 1: In conversions, 28-in. (71-cm) doors shall be permitted to be continued in use.

Exception No. 2: Bathroom doors shall be a minimum of 24 in. (61 cm) wide.

22-2.2.5.2 Every closet door latch shall be such that it can be readily opened from the inside in case of an emergency.

22-2.2.5.3 Every bathroom door shall be designed to allow opening from the outside during an emergency when locked.

22-2.2.5.4 No door in any means of escape shall be locked against egress when the building is occupied.

Paragraph 22-2.2.5.4 prohibits a residential board and care facility from having any door in the means of egress locked against egress while the building is occupied. This is consistent with a fundamental principle of the *Code*. This

requirement permits a door to have a locking device that allows the door to be opened from within the facility for the purpose of egress but does not allow the door to be opened from outside the facility. Ordinary double cylinder locks and chain locks do not meet these provisions.

The language of 5-2.1.5.1 is clear: "Locks, if provided, shall not require the use of a key, tool, special knowledge, or effort for operation from the inside of the building." This eliminates double cylinder locks and chain locks that require a key in order to be operated from the inside. Paragraph 5-2.1.5.3 requires doors to be opened by means of a simple operation; two-handed knob and other features are specifically prohibited.

It is important to remember that the resident sleeping room doors are doors in the means of egress. However, 5-2.1.5.3 permits the sleeping room doors to have additional releasing actions. (*See 5-2.1.5.3 for details.*)

22-2.2.6 The width, riser, and treads of every stair shall comply with the minimum requirements for Class B stairs as described in 5-2.2.

Exception: In conversions, existing noncomplying stairs may continue to be used subject to the approval of the authority having jurisdiction.

Note that this allows the use of Class B stairs even in new construction.

22-2.2.7 Winders in accordance with 5-2.2.2.8 are permitted.

22-2.3 Protection.

22-2.3.1 Protection of Vertical Openings.

22-2.3.1.1 Vertical openings shall be protected so that no primary exit route is exposed to an unprotected vertical opening. The vertical opening is considered protected if the opening is cut off and enclosed in a manner that provides a fire resisting capability of not less than 20 minutes and resists the passage of smoke. Any doors or openings shall have fire and smoke resisting capability equivalent to that of the enclosure and be self-closing or automatic-closing in accordance with 5-2.1.8.

Exception: For prompt and slow facilities in buildings three stories or less in height having an approved automatic sprinkler system using quick response or residential sprinklers, stair enclosures shall not be required provided there still remains a primary means of escape from each sleeping area that does not require occupants to pass through a portion of a lower floor, unless that route is separated from all spaces on that floor by construction having a 20-minute fire resistance rating.

This provision coordinates with 22-2.2.2 and 22-2.2.4. The lack of vertical opening protection has been identified as a contributing factor in many of the multiple-death fires in residential board and care facilities.

See commentary on 22-2.2.4 for a further description of the protection of stairways in new board and care facilities.

22-2.3.1.2 Exterior stairs shall be reasonably protected against blockage caused by fire that would simultaneously expose both the interior and the exterior means of escape. This shall be accomplished through separation by physical distance, arrangement of the stairs, protection of the openings exposing the stairs, or other means acceptable to the authority having jurisdiction.

This paragraph does not mandate compliance with the provisions of Chapter 5 for exterior stairs. However, if the exterior stair is to be used as a primary means of escape, protection should be provided to reduce the likelihood that a fire within the facility will render the stair useless. While this provision applies to small facilities, it should be noted that 5-2.2.3.2 does exempt outside stairs serving a two-story building from the protection requirements of that section if a remotely located second exit is provided. In this case, a remote secondary means of escape may eliminate the need to protect the exterior stair.

22-2.3.2 **Hazardous Areas.** Any hazardous area shall be protected in accordance with the following:

(a) Any hazardous area that is on the same floor as, and is in or abuts a primary means of escape or a sleeping room, shall be protected by either:

1. An enclosure with a fire resistance rating of at least 1 hour with a self-closing or automatic-closing fire door in accordance with 5-2.1.8 having a fire resistance rating of at least ¾ hour, or

2. Automatic sprinkler protection, in accordance with 22-2.3.5 of the hazardous area and a separation that will resist the passage of smoke between the hazardous area and the sleeping area or primary exit route. Any doors in such separation shall be self-closing or automatic-closing in accordance with 5-2.1.8.

(b) Other hazardous areas shall be protected by either:

1. An enclosure having a fire resistance rating of at least 20 minutes with a self-closing or automatic-closing door in accordance with 5-2.1.8 equivalent to at least a 1¾-in. (4.4-cm) thick solid bonded wood core construction, or

2. Automatic sprinkler protection, in accordance with 22-2.3.5, of the hazardous area regardless of enclosure.

The protection of hazardous areas is based on the potential impact a fire in the area would have on a primary means of escape or on sleeping rooms. If the hazardous area is located on the same floor as sleeping rooms or a primary means of escape, and a room or means of escape is exposed to the hazardous area, the construction shall be capable of containing a fire, or automatic sprinkler protection shall be provided to control a fire, and the construction shall be capable of resisting smoke spread outside the area. If the hazardous area is on a different floor or does not abut a primary means of escape or sleeping rooms, the construction shall be capable of containing a fire for a limited time, or automatic sprinkler protection shall be provided to control a fire.

For example, if a basement in a wood frame residence is used for the storage of combustible materials, the basement is not a required means of escape. If the basement storage area does not abut a sleeping area on the same floor, sheathing the ceiling to provide fire resistance is not required if the basement is sprinklered. In applying the provisions of this section, the mandatory sprinkler requirements of 22-2.3.5.1 should be considered.

22-2.3.3 **Interior Finishes.** Interior wall and ceiling finish shall be Class A or Class B in accordance with Section 6-5. There are no requirements for interior floor finish.

Exception: Class C interior wall and ceiling finish is permitted in prompt facilities.

The 1985 Edition contained an exception for structural elements of heavy timber. The issue is now addressed by similar language in 6-5.3.4.

22-2.3.4 Detection, Alarm, and Communication Systems.

See Supplement 2.

22-2.3.4.1 Fire Alarm Systems.
A manual fire alarm system shall be provided in accordance with Section 7-6. Presignal systems are prohibited.

Exception No. 1: If there are interconnected smoke detectors meeting the requirements of 22-2.3.4.2 and there is at least one manual fire alarm station per floor arranged to continuously sound the smoke detector alarms.

Exception No. 2: Other manually activated continuously sounding alarms acceptable to the authority having jurisdiction.

A means of manually initiating the fire protective signaling system is required. If there is a "system" of interconnected multiple station smoke detectors, the manual fire alarm station requirement can be met by providing a manual station on each floor that is integrated with the smoke detectors. However, Exception No. 2 recognizes that, in a small building, a sophisticated fire protective signaling system that employs components "listed" for use in fire protective signaling systems may not be necessary. The requirements can be satisfied by the installation of electric bells activated by a clearly identified switch on each floor where approved by the authority having jurisdiction.

22-2.3.4.2 Smoke Detectors.
Approved smoke detectors shall be installed in accordance with 7-6.2.9. These shall be powered from the building electrical system and, when activated, shall initiate an alarm that is audible in all sleeping areas. Detectors shall be installed on all levels, including basements, but excluding crawl spaces and unfinished attics. Additional detectors shall be installed for living rooms, dens, day rooms, and similar spaces.

Exception: Detectors are not required in buildings protected throughout by an approved automatic sprinkler system in accordance with 22-2.3.5 using quick response or residential sprinklers.

This paragraph does not specifically require a "system" of smoke detectors in a small facility. If the building is small enough, single station detectors may be able to meet the criterion of audibility in all sleeping areas. However, if the building is of significant size or consists of multiple levels, interconnected multiple station detectors will probably be needed. Additional detectors are required in living rooms and day rooms because fire statistics indicate that most multiple-death fires in board and care homes start in such rooms. In order to waive the requirement for detectors as permitted by the exception, the entire building must be protected with an automatic sprinkler system using quick response or residential sprinklers in accordance with 22-2.3.5.

22-2.3.4.3 Smoke Detectors.
Each sleeping room shall be provided with an approved single station smoke detector in accordance with 7-6.2.9 that is powered from the building electrical system.

Exception: Rooms protected by quick response sprinklers or residential sprinklers in buildings protected throughout by an approved supervised automatic sprinkler system in accordance with 22-2.3.5. The Exception to 22-2.3.4.2 shall not be used in conjunction with this exception.

Single station detectors shall be provided in every sleeping room in a new board and care facility unless the sleeping rooms are protected by quick response or residential sprinklers; the entire building is protected with an automatic sprinkler system; and the interconnected smoke detectors required in 22-2.3.4.2 are provided. Therefore, in sprinklered buildings, the *Code* requires either that detectors be provided on every level and in every common space (22-2.3.4.2) or that individual room detectors be provided (22-2.3.4.3). The room detectors may be single station detectors and need not initiate any alarm outside a sleeping room. It is anticipated that an occupant will hear the detector and initiate the fire alarm system by the manual means required in Section 22-2.3.4.1. The smoke detectors must be powered from the building electrical system to ensure reliability.

The exception recognizes the ability of quick response and residential sprinklers to maintain tenability from most fire scenarios in the room of origin.

Table 22-3 illustrates the smoke detector coverage options.

Table 22-3. Options for Smoke Detector Locations

Sprinkler Protection	Room Detectors (House Current)	Corridor and Common Space Detectors (House Powered)
QRS or RS in rooms	Not required	Required
QRS or RS throughout	{ Required or Not provided	Not provided Required

22-2.3.5 Automatic Extinguishing Systems.

See Supplement 3.

22-2.3.5.1* Where an automatic sprinkler system is installed, for either total or partial building coverage, the system shall be in accordance with Section 7-7 and shall activate the fire alarm system in accordance with 22-2.3.4.1.

Exception No. 1: In prompt and slow facilities, a sprinkler system complying with NFPA 13D, Standard for the Installation of Sprinkler Systems in One- and Two-Family Dwellings and Mobile Homes, shall be permitted. Automatic sprinklers are not required in closets not exceeding 24 sq ft (2.7 sq m) and bathrooms not exceeding 55 sq ft (5.1 sq m) provided such spaces are finished with lath and plaster or material with a 15-minute thermal barrier.

Exception No. 2: In impractical facilities, a sprinkler system complying with NFPA 13D Standard for the Installation of Sprinkler Systems in One- and Two-Family Dwellings and Mobile Homes, with a 30-minute water supply, shall be permitted. All habitable areas and closets shall be sprinklered.

Exception No. 3: In prompt and slow facilities, where an automatic sprinkler system is installed in accordance with NFPA 13, Standard for the Installation of Sprinkler Systems, automatic sprinklers are not required in closets not exceeding

24 sq ft (2.7 sq m) and bathrooms not exceeding 55 sq ft (5.1 sq m) provided such spaces are finished with lath and plaster or material with a 15-minute thermal barrier.

A-22-2.3.5.1 The decision to allow the use of the criteria from NFPA 13D, *Standard for the Installation of Sprinkler Systems in One- and Two-Family Dwellings and Mobile Homes*, in these occupancies is based on: (1) the desire of the Committee to obtain a level of fire suppression and control approximately the same as that delivered by residential facilities protected by such systems (*see the appendix statement in NFPA 13D*), and (2) the fact that potential fire exposure and challenge to the suppression system in a small board and care facility is of the same nature and no more severe than that found in residences.

This section establishes the criteria to be followed for the installation of automatic sprinklers systems.

NFPA 13R, *Standard for the Installation of Sprinkler Systems in Residential Buildings up to and Including Four Stories in Height,*[6] is not specifically referenced as required by 7-7.1.1. However, virtually all NFPA 13R systems, where properly designed and installed, would also comply with NFPA 13D, *Standard for the Installation of Sprinkler Systems in One- and Two-Family Dwellings and Mobile Homes.*[5] One exception is that NFPA 13R does permit the use of standard sprinklers where smoke detectors are provided within a room. However, in accordance with 22-2.3.5.2, quick response or residential sprinklers would still be required. Furthermore, since 22-3.3.5.1 permits compliance with NFPA 13R in large facilities, it is reasonable to accept such systems in small facilities as well.

The omission of sprinklers in bathrooms and closets as permitted in Exception No. 1 is intended to reinforce the exemption for sprinklers in these areas. All the exceptions for sprinkler coverage permitted by NFPA 13D, *Standard for the Installation of Sprinkler Systems in One- and Two-Family Dwellings and Mobile Homes,*[5] (and NFPA 13R, *Standard for the Installation of Sprinkler Systems in Residential Buildings up to and Including Four Stories in Height*[6]) are applicable. However, contrary to NFPA 13D (and NFPA 13R), the combustibility of plumbing fixtures is not an issue. NFPA 13D (and NFPA 13R) address the combustibility of plumbing fixtures, not because they are viewed as a source of ignition, but because frequently wall finish materials are not installed behind prefabricated enclosures. Therefore, the exception clearly states that the bathroom must be finished with plaster or materials providing a 15-minute thermal barrier. This includes the area behind a prefabricated enclosure. Exception No. 3 provides similar exceptions for a sprinkler system in accordance with NFPA 13, *Standard for the Installation of Sprinkler Systems.*[4]

Exception No. 2 recognizes the "defend in place" concept utilized in impractical facilities by increasing the duration of the water supply and by mandating sprinklers in all habitable areas, including closets. Therefore, those areas in which sprinklers are not required by NFPA 13D (and NFPA 13R) are greatly reduced.

22-2.3.5.2 All facilities shall be protected throughout by an approved automatic sprinkler system installed in accordance with 22-2.3.5.1. Quick response or residential sprinklers shall be provided.

Exception No. 1: Standard response sprinklers shall be permitted for use in areas where quick response and residential sprinklers are prohibited to be installed by their listing.

Exception No. 2: Standard response sprinklers shall be permitted for use in hazardous areas in accordance with 22-2.3.2.

This paragraph requires that the automatic sprinkler system include the use of quick response or residential sprinklers. This requirement recognizes the ability of quick response and residential sprinklers to maintain tenability in the room of origin during most fire scenarios. However, these sprinklers do have some limitations associated with their listing regarding clearances from heat sources and ceiling slopes. When such a situation is encountered, standard sprinklers must be installed. Standard sprinklers may also be installed in hazardous areas, since such areas are not occupied by sleeping residents.

If sprinkler protection is provided only in the board and care facility, and not throughout the building, the exceptions for sprinklers that require building protection (i.e., 22-2.1.3.3, 22-2.2.1, 22-2.2.2.2, 22-2.2.4, 22-2.3.1.1, 22-2.3.4.2, 22-2.3.4.3, and 22-2.3.6.4) may not be used.

22-2.3.5.3 Automatic sprinkler systems installed in impractical facilities shall be supervised in accordance with Section 7-7.

The importance of the role of the sprinkler system in defending occupants in place requires that sprinkler systems in impractical facilities be supervised as defined in 7-7.2. Note that this requires electrical supervision of control valves and the transmission of water flow alarms to a monitoring station. It should also be noted that NFPA 13D, *Standard for the Installation of Sprinkler Systems in One- and Two-Family Dwellings and Mobile Homes,*[5] and NFPA 13R, *Standard for the Installation of Sprinkler Systems in Residential Buildings up to and Including Four Stories in Height,*[6] permit the sprinkler systems to be installed with the domestic water supply valve as the only means to shut off the sprinklers; there are no valves that control only the sprinkler system. This arrangement could satisfy the supervision requirements of 7-7.2; however, the water flow would still need to be transmitted to a monitoring station.

In prompt and slow facilities, the sprinkler systems shall be supervised as required by the installation standard. While electrical supervision is permitted, locking of valves in the open position is also allowed.

22-2.3.5.4 Sprinkler piping serving not more than six sprinklers for any isolated hazardous area shall be permitted to be installed in accordance with 7-7.1.2. In new installations, where more than two sprinklers are installed in a single area, water flow detection shall be provided to sound the fire alarm system required by 22-2.3.4.1. Duration of water supplies shall be as required by 22-2.3.5.1.

Paragraph 7-7.1.2 provides a sprinkler design specification of 0.15 gpm/sq ft (6.1 L/m/sq m) for systems using six sprinklers or less where protecting an isolated area. In areas where the connection to the domestic water supply results in unlimited duration due to the presence of public water, duration is not an issue. However, facilities that utilize a private water system (well) are not as fortunate. Therefore, the duration criteria of 22-2.3.5.1 is specified.

22-2.3.6 Construction of Corridor Walls.

22-2.3.6.1 The separation walls of sleeping rooms shall be capable of resisting fire for at least 20 minutes. This is considered to be achieved if the partitioning is finished on both sides with lath and plaster or material providing a 15-minute thermal barrier. Sleeping room doors shall be substantial doors, such as those of 1¾-in. (4.4-cm) thick solid bonded wood core construction or of other construction of equal or greater stability and fire integrity. Any vision panels shall be of wired glass not exceeding 1,296 sq in. (0.84 sq m) each in area, and installed in approved frames.

The intent of the 20-minute fire resistance rating is to require a nominal fire rating, particularly where the fire rating of existing partitions cannot be documented, as in the case of conversions. Examples of acceptable partition assemblies include, but are not limited to, ½-in. (1.3-cm) gypsum board, wood lath and plaster, gypsum lath, or metal lath, and plaster.

Exception No. 1: In prompt facilities, all sleeping rooms shall be separated from the escape route by walls and doors that are at least smoke resistant.

Exception No. 2: Corridor walls and doors that are capable of resisting the passage of smoke and that are protected by automatic sprinklers in accordance with 22-2.3.5 on both sides of the wall and door. In such instances, there is no limitation on the type or size of glass panels.

In essence, the intent of the exception is that the fire resistance requirements shall not apply where sprinkler protection is provided on both sides of the wall and door. Complete sprinkler protection as required by 22-2.3.5.2 would clearly meet this criteria. Therefore, the exception represents the most typical case.

Exception No. 3: Sleeping arrangements that are not located in sleeping rooms are permitted for nonresident staff members provided the audibility of the alarm in the sleeping area is sufficient to waken staff who may be sleeping.

It is recognized that there are many board and care homes that employ "sleep-in" staff. The exception is intended to allow staff members to sleep in locations that are not separated from the corridors by construction meeting the minimum requirements for construction of corridor walls. The placement of a staff cot in the supervisor's station, living room, or other room is not intended to reclassify that room as a sleeping room.

22-2.3.6.2 There shall be no louvers or operable transoms or other air passages penetrating the wall except properly installed heating and utility installations other than transfer grilles. Transfer grilles are prohibited.

22-2.3.6.3 Doors shall be provided with latches or other mechanisms suitable for keeping the doors closed. No doors shall be arranged so as to prevent the occupant from closing the door.

22-2.3.6.4 Doors shall be self-closing or automatic-closing in accordance with 5-2.1.8.

Exception: Door closing devices are not required in buildings protected throughout by an approved automatic sprinkler system in accordance with 22-2.3.5.1.

This exception differs from Exception No. 2 to 22-2.3.6.1. In order for the door-closing device to be waived under this exception, the entire building must be protected throughout by an approved automatic sprinkler system.

22-2.4 **Operating Features.** (*See Chapter 31.*)

22-2.5 **Building Services.**

22-2.5.1 **Utilities.** Utilities shall comply with Section 7-1.

22-2.5.2 **Heating, Ventilating, and Air Conditioning Equipment.**

22-2.5.2.1 Heating, ventilating, and air conditioning equipment shall comply with the provisions of 7-2.1 and 7-2.2 except as otherwise required in this chapter.

22-2.5.2.2 No stove or combustion heater shall be so located as to block escape in case of fire caused by the malfunction of the stove or heater.

22-2.5.2.3 Unvented fuel-fired heaters shall not be used in any residential board and care facility.

This paragraph prohibits the use of the typical kerosene portable heater, as well as other fuel-fired, nonvented heaters.

22-2.5.3 Elevators, Escalators, and Conveyors. Any elevators, escalators, and conveyors installed shall comply with the provisions of Section 7-4.

SECTION 22-3 Large Facilities

See Table 22-4 for summary of major requirements.

22-3.1 General.

22-3.1.1 Scope. This section applies to residential board and care occupancies providing sleeping accommodations for more than 16 residents. Facilities having sleeping accommodations for not more than 16 residents shall be evaluated in accordance with Section 22-2, "Small Facilities."

22-3.1.2 Requirements Based on Evacuation Capability.

22-3.1.2.1 Prompt and Slow. Large facilities shall comply with the requirements of Section 22-3 as indicated for the appropriate evacuation capability.

Exception: *Facilities where the authority having jurisdiction has determined equivalent safety is provided in accordance with Section 1-6.*

A-22-3.1.2.1 Exception. In determining equivalency for conversions, modernizations, renovations, or unusual design concepts, the authority having jurisdiction may accept evaluations based on NFPA 101M, *Alternative Approaches to Life Safety*, Chapter 6. (*See Appendix B.*)

The 1988 Edition of NFPA 101M was designed for use with the 1988 Edition of NFPA 101 and cannot be used to evaulate facilities under the 1991 *Life Safety Code*. At the time this *Handbook* went to press, the Committee on Safety to Life was preparing the 1992 Edition of NFPA 101M to use in conjunction with the 1991 *Life Safety Code*.

22-3.1.2.2 Impractical. Facilities housing groups of persons classed as impractical to evacuate shall meet the requirements for limited care facilities in Chapter 12.

Exception: *Facilities where the authority having jurisdiction has determined equivalent safety is provided in accordance with Section 1-6.*

A-22-3.1.2.2 Exception. In determining equivalency for conversions, modernizations, renovations, or unusual design concepts, the authority having jurisdiction may accept evaluations based on NFPA 101M, *Alternative Approaches to Life Safety*, Chapter 3 (*see Appendix B*), using the mandatory safety requirements for nursing homes.

The difficulty in evacuating this type of facility is comparable to that of a health care facility. Therefore, reference should be made to Chapter 12, "New Health Care Occupancies." Due to this difficulty in evacuation and the fact that residents of these facilities will typically require additional care, a staff level that more closely approximates that of a health care facility is anticipated.

The 1988 Edition of NFPA 101M was designed for use with the 1988 Edition of NFPA 101 and cannot be used to evaluate facilities under the 1991 *Life Safety Code*. At the time this *Handbook* went to press, the Committee on Safety to Life was preparing the 1992 Edition of NFPA 101M to use in conjunction with the 1991 *Life Safety Code*.

22-3.1.3 Minimum Construction Requirements.

22-3.1.3.1 Construction requirements for large facilities shall be as required by this section. Where noted as "fully sheathed," the interior shall be covered with lath and plaster or materials providing a 15-minute thermal barrier.

22-3.1.3.2 For the purpose of construction requirements, stories shall be counted starting with the primary level of exit discharge and ending with the highest occupied level. For the purpose of this section, the primary level of exit discharge of a building shall be that floor that is level with or above finished grade of the exterior wall line for 50 percent or more of its perimeter. Building levels below the primary level shall not be counted as a story in determining the height of the building.

22-3.1.3.3 The minimum construction requirements (*see 6-2.1*), based on the highest story normally used by board and care residents, are:

Table 22-4. Summary of Major Requirements for New Large Facilities

Parameter	Evacuation Capability		
	Prompt	Slow	Impractical
1. Construction 22-3.1.4	See Table 22-3	See Table 22-3	12-1.6
2. Means of Egress 22-3.2	2 Exits per Floor	2 Exits per Floor	Section 12-2
3. Vertical Openings 22-3.3.1	6-2.4	6-2.4	12-3.1
4. Protection of Hazardous Areas 22-3.3.2	Sprinklers as Required by No. 8	Sprinklers as Required by No. 8	12-3.2
5. Interior Finish 22-3.3.3	Class A in Exits, B with Sprinklers. Class A or B in other locations, C with Sprinklers. No Requirement for Floor Finish due to Sprinklers.	Class A in Exits, B with Sprinklers. Class A or B in other locations, C with Sprinklers. No Requirement for Floor Finish due to Sprinklers.	12-3.3
6. Manual F.A. 22-3.3.4	Local	Local	12-3.4
7. Smoke Detection 22-3.3.4.7, 22-3.3.4.8	Sleeping Rooms—Single Station	Sleeping Rooms—Single Station	12-3.4
8. Sprinklers 22-3.3.5	Required with Quick Response or Residential Sprinklers	Required with Quick-Response or Residential Sprinklers	Required with Quick Response or Residential Sprinklers (12-3.5)
9. Separation of Sleeping Rooms 22-3.3.6.2	New—30-Min. Conversion Smoke Resistant (due to Sprinklers)	New—30-Min. Conversion Smoke Resistant (due to Sprinklers)	12.3.6
10. Smoke Control 22-3.3.7	Not Required due to Sprinklers	Not Required due to Sprinklers	12-3.7

(a) *One- or Two-Story Facilities.* Any construction type that meets the requirements for 1-hour or greater fire resistance rating, or is Type IV (2HH), or is fully sheathed, or is protected throughout by an approved automatic sprinkler system in accordance with 22-3.3.5.

Exception to (a): One-story facilities having 30 or fewer residents that house groups capable of prompt evacuation may be of any type construction.

(b) *Three- to Six- Story Facilities.* Type I, II, or III construction that meets the requirements for 1-hour or greater fire resistance rating, and Type IV construction that is protected throughout by an approved automatic sprinkler system in accordance with 22-3.3.5, or any other type of construction that is both sheathed and protected throughout by an approved automatic sprinkler system in accordance with 22-3.3.5, other than Type V (000).

Exception to (b): Three- to four-story facilities of Type V (000) construction that are both fully sheathed and protected throughout by an approved supervised automatic sprinkler system in accordance with 22-3.3.5.

(c) *Facilities More Than Six Stories High.* Any Type I or Type II (222) construction. Any Type II (111), Type III (211), or Type IV (2HH) construction that is protected throughout by an approved automatic sprinkler system in accordance with 22-3.3.5.

Exception to (a), (b), and (c): Any building of Type I or Type II (111) or (222) construction may include roofing systems involving combustible supports, decking, or roofing provided:

1. The roof covering meets Class A requirements in accordance with NFPA 256, Standard Methods of Fire Tests of Roof Coverings, and

2. The roof is separated from all occupied portions of the building by a noncombustible floor assembly having at least a 2-hour fire resistance rating that includes at least 2½ in. (6.4 cm) of concrete or gypsum fill. To qualify for this exception, the attic or other space so developed shall be either unused or protected throughout by an approved automatic sprinkler system in accordance with 22-3.3.5.1.

Minimum construction requirements are necessary, since this chapter requires evacuation only to a "point of safety." Therefore, the residents of a large facility will frequently remain inside the building during a fire emergency. Consequently, the stability of the building must be maintained by the required automatic sprinkler system (22-3.3.5.1) and, in some cases, the use of fire resistant construction (*see Table 22-5 for a summary of permissible construction types*). Note that, in the Exception to (a), buildings from which there is a reasonable expectation of prompt evacuation to the exterior of the building are exempted from the minimum construction requirements.

22-3.1.4 Occupant Load. The occupant load in numbers of persons for whom exits are to be provided shall be determined on the basis of one person per 200 sq ft (18.6 sq m) gross floor area or the maximum probable population of any room or section under consideration, whichever is greater. The occupant load of any open mezzanine or balcony shall be added to the occupant load of the floor below for the purpose of determining exit capability.

Table 22-5. Minimum Construction Standards for Large Facilities with Prompt and Slow Evacuation Capability

Construction Type	Number of Stories						
	1	2	3	4	5	6	7+
Type I	X	X	X	X	X	X	X
Type II (222)	X	X	X	X	X	X	X
Type II (111)	X	X	X	X	X	X	(AS)
Type II (000)†	*/(AS)	*/(AS)	*(AS)	*(AS)	*(AS)	*(AS)	NP
Type III (211)	X	X	X	X	X	X	(AS)
Type III (200)†	*/(AS)	*/(AS)	*(AS)	*(AS)	*(AS)	*(AS)	NP
Type IV (2HH)	X	X	(AS)	(AS)	(AS)	(AS)	(AS)
Type V (111)	X	X	*(AS)	*(AS)	*(AS)	*(AS)	NP
Type V (000)†	*/(AS)	*/(AS)	*(AS)	*(AS)	NP	NP	NP

X = Permitted
NP = Not permitted
(AS) = Permitted if sprinklered as required by 22-3.3.5
*(AS) = Permitted if sheathed *and* sprinklered
*/(AS) = Permitted if sheathed *or* sprinklered (Note: Sprinklers required by 22-3.3.5)
† = Permitted up to 1 story high, unsheathed and unsprinklered if housing 30 or fewer residents with prompt evacuation capability.

If the actual occupant load of the facility exceeds one person per 200 sq ft (18.6 sq m), the exit capacity must be designed to meet the anticipated occupant load. The determination of actual occupant load should be based on the total number of residents, staff, and visitors. However, the minimum exit capacity must not be less than that required for a density of one person per 200 sq ft (18.6 sq m).

Since mezzanines need not have their own exits, the occupant load of the mezzanine must be included with the occupant load of the floor below.

22-3.2 Means of Egress.

22-3.2.1 All means of egress shall be in accordance with Chapter 5.

A general reference is made to Chapter 5 in place of repeating many of its provisions. Many of the requirements contained in Section 22-3.2 are Chapter 5 provisions that are options for the occupancy chapters, such as the Exception to 22-3.2.2.2(b), which allows the use of special locking arrangements per 5-2.1.6; or that prohibit the use of an item if it is not listed (note that alternating tread devices are not listed in 22-3.2.2); or that establish restrictions based on criteria provided in Chapter 5, such as the limits placed on travel distance in 22-3.2.6.

22-3.2.2 Means of Egress Components.

22-3.2.2.1 Components of means of egress shall be limited to the types described in 22-3.2.2.2 through 22-3.2.2.7.

22-3.2.2.2 Doors.

(a) Doors shall comply with 5-2.1.

(b) No door in any means of egress shall be locked against egress when the building is occupied.

Paragraph 22-3.2.2.2(b) prohibits a facility from having any door locked "against egress" while the building is occupied. This is consistent with a fundamental principle of the *Code*. This requirement permits a door to be equipped with a locking device that allows the door to be opened from within the building for the purpose of egress but does not allow the door to be opened from outside the building. Ordinary double cylinder locks and chain locks do not meet these provisions since they require keys for operation.

The language of 5-2.1.5.1 is clear: "Locks, if provided, shall not require the use of a key, tool, special knowledge, or effort for operation from the inside of the building." This eliminates double cylinder locks and chain locks that require a key to be operated from the inside. Paragraph 5-2.1.5.3 requires the use of a simple operation to open the door; locks that require two-handed knob and similar operations are specifically prohibited.

It is important to remember that the resident sleeping room doors are doors in the means of egress. However, 5-2.1.5.3 permits the sleeping room doors to have additional releasing actions. (*See 5-2.1.5.3 for details.*)

Exception to (b): Special locking requirements complying with 5-2.1.6 are permitted.

The exception does permit the use of special locking arrangements that comply with 5-2.1.6. This requires that the building either be protected throughout by automatic sprinklers or be equipped throughout with a fire detection system. The 15- or 30-second delay permitted by 5-2.1.6 does not affect the immediate release of the lock upon activation of the sprinklers or detectors, or upon loss of power to the lock. This device helps provide security for infrequently used doors or stairs in board and care facilities, while doors remain available for use. Chains and padlocks are unable to provide this feature.

(c) Every stairwell door shall allow reentry from the stairwell to the interior of the building, or an automatic release shall be provided to unlock all stairwell doors to allow reentry. Such automatic release shall be activated with the initiation of the building fire alarm system. Also, doors shall unlock upon loss of power controlling the lock or locking mechanism.

The provisions of 22-3.2.2.2(c) are more stringent than those of Chapter 5, since the provisions of Exception No. 1 to 5-2.1.5.2 (selected reentry doors) are not allowed. The Committee reasoned that board and care facilities are not subject to the circumstance experienced by business occupancies in which tenants lease an entire floor with no public corridor arrangement. Therefore, the exception is unwarranted. If a board and care facility wishes to restrict normal movement in stairs, the automatic release system can be used.

(d) Revolving doors complying with 5-2.1.10 are permitted.

(e) Horizontal sliding doors in accordance with 5-2.1.14 shall be permitted to be used in a means of egress serving an occupant load of less than 50.

22-3.2.2.3 Stairs. Stairs shall comply with 5-2.2.

22-3.2.2.4 Smokeproof Enclosures. Smokeproof enclosures shall comply with 5-2.3.

22-3.2.2.5 Horizontal Exits. Horizontal exits shall comply with 5-2.4.

22-3.2.2.6 Ramps. Ramps shall comply with 5-2.5.

22-3.2.2.7 Exit Passageways. Exit passageways shall comply with 5-2.6.

22-3.2.3 Capacity of Means of Egress.

22-3.2.3.1 The capacity of means of egress shall be in accordance with Section 5-3.

22-3.2.3.2 Street floor exits shall be sufficient for the occupant load of the street floor plus the required capacity of stairs and ramps discharging onto the street floor.

Paragraph 22-3.2.3.2 requires street floor exit designs that have sufficient width to accommodate for the convergence of occupants discharging through exits from the street floor with those discharging down from the upper floors and up from the lower floors. Section 5-7 restricts the number and arrangement of stairs that are used to discharge through the street floor.

Figure 22-5 shows an arrangement of multiple exits discharging on the street floor.

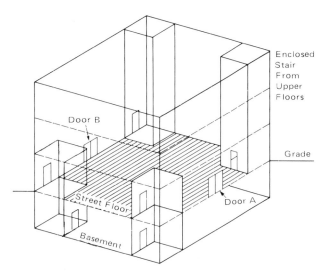

Figure 22-5. Capacity of Means of Egress in Accordance with 22-3.2.3.2. Required widths of Doors A and B are based on the anticipated number of people using them. There should be 0.2 in. (0.5 cm) allowed for each person on the street floor and for every person traveling down from the upper floors and up from the lower floors who must traverse the street floor to exit.

22-3.2.3.3 The width of corridors shall be sufficient for the occupant load served, but not less than 44 in. (112 cm).

Exception: Corridors serving an occupant load less than 50 shall not be less than 36 in. (91 cm) in width.

22-3.2.4 Number of Exits. Not fewer than two exits shall be accessible from every floor, including floors below the level of exit discharge and occupied for public purposes.

This paragraph contains provisions similar to those for hotels. There are no exceptions to permit a building with a single exit. It should also be noted that 5-4.1.2 will require a greater number of exits for floors with more than 500 people. This will probably have minimal impact on board and care facilities, since such large floors would probably need additional exits to meet travel distance limitations.

22-3.2.5 Arrangement of Exits.

22-3.2.5.1 Access to all required exits shall be in accordance with Section 5-5.

22-3.2.5.2 Exits shall be so arranged that, from any corridor room door, exits shall be accessible in at least two different directions.

Exception: Up to the first 35 ft (10 m) of exit travel from a corridor room door may be within a corridor with access only in one direction.

Note that this exception actually describes a modified dead end and modified common path of travel. This dead end is not always measured as a true dead end, since the room door may not be located at the end of the corridor; neither is it a true common path of travel, since the distance is measured from the corridor room door and not the most remote point. Figure 22-6 illustrates the method of measuring in accordance with the Exception to 22-3.2.5.2.

22-3.2.5.3 Any room or any suite of rooms in excess of 2,000 sq ft (185 sq m) shall be provided with at least two exit access doors remotely located from each other.

22-3.2.6 Travel Distance to Exits.

22-3.2.6.1 Any exit shall be such that it will not be necessary to travel more than 100 ft (30 m) from the door of any room to reach the nearest exit. Travel distance to exits shall be measured in accordance with Section 5-6.

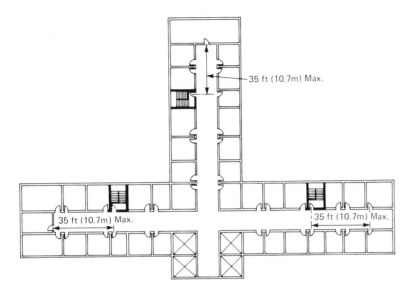

Figure 22-6. *The "Modified" Dead End Used in Board and Care Occupancies Is Illustrated by this Figure. Note that, where a room door is not located at the end of the corridor, the actual dead end is longer. Since the elevator lobby has no room doors, it has no "modified" dead end.*

Exception No. 1: Travel distance to exits shall not exceed 200 ft (60 m) for exterior ways of exit access arranged in accordance with 5-5.3.

Exception No. 2: Travel distance to exits shall not exceed 200 ft (60 m) if the exit access and any portion of the building that is tributary to the exit access are protected throughout by approved automatic sprinkler systems. In addition, the portion of the building in which the 200-ft (60-m) travel distance is permitted shall be separated from the remainder of the building by construction having a fire resistance rating of not less than 1 hour for buildings not greater than three stories in height and 2 hours for buildings greater than three stories in height.

See Figure 22-7.

22-3.2.6.2 Travel distance within a room or suite or living unit to a corridor door shall not exceed 75 ft (23 m).

Exception: Travel distance shall not exceed 125 ft (48 m) in buildings protected throughout by an approved automatic sprinkler system in accordance with 22-3.3.5.

Paragraph 22-3.2.6.2 limits the travel distance permitted within a room or suite. Note that the travel distance may be increased by 50 ft (15 m) in buildings protected throughout by an automatic sprinkler system as required by 22-3.3.5.1.

22-3.2.7 **Discharge from Exits.**

22-3.2.7.1 Exit discharge shall comply with Section 5-7.

22-3.2.8 **Illumination of Means of Egress.**

22-3.2.8.1 Means of egress shall be illuminated in accordance with Section 5-8.

22-3.2.9 **Emergency Lighting.**

22-3.2.9.1 Emergency lighting in accordance with Section 5-9 shall be provided in all buildings with more than 25 rooms.

Exception: Where each guest room has a direct exit to the outside of the building at ground level, no emergency lighting shall be required.

The Exception to 22-3.2.9.1 does not apply to facilities with exterior balconies and stairs, but applies only to those that have doors opening directly to grade.

22-3.2.10 **Marking of Means of Egress.**

22-3.2.10.1 Means of egress shall be marked in accordance with Section 5-10.

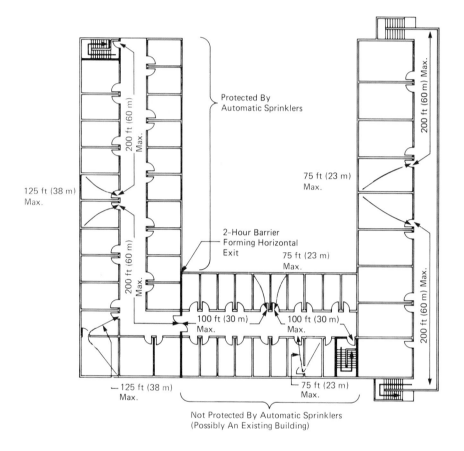

Figure 22-7. *Travel Distance in Large Facilities.*

Protected By Automatic Sprinklers

200 ft (60 m) Max.

125 ft (38 m) Max.

200 ft (60 m) Max.

2-Hour Barrier Forming Horizontal Exit

75 ft (23 m) Max.

75 ft (23 m) Max.

200 ft (60 m) Max.

100 ft (30 m) Max.

100 ft (30 m) Max.

125 ft (38 m) Max.

75 ft (23 m) Max.

Not Protected By Automatic Sprinklers (Possibly An Existing Building)

22-3.2.11 Special Features. (Reserved.)

22-3.3 Protection.

22-3.3.1 Protection of Vertical Openings.

22-3.3.1.1 Every stairway, elevator shaft, and other vertical opening shall be enclosed or protected in accordance with 6-2.4.

Exception No. 1: Unprotected vertical openings connecting not more than three floors shall be permitted in accordance with 6-2.4.5.

Since 22-3.3.5.1 requires a building sprinkler system, the communicating space may be separated from the remainder of the building by a smoke barrier in accordance with 6-2.4.5.

Exception No. 2: Atriums in accordance with 6-2.4.6 shall be permitted.

22-3.3.1.2 No floor below the level of exit discharge used only for storage, heating equipment, or purposes other than residential occupancy shall have unprotected openings to floors used for residential occupancy.

22-3.3.2 Protection from Hazards.

22-3.3.2.1 Any room containing high-pressure boilers, refrigerating machinery, transformers, or other service equipment subject to possible explosion shall not be located directly under or adjacent to exits. All such rooms shall be effectively cut off from other parts of the building as specified in Section 6-4.

22-3.3.2.2 Every hazardous area shall be separated from other parts of the building by construction having a fire resistance rating of at least 1 hour, and communicating openings shall be protected by approved self-closing fire doors, or such area shall be equipped with automatic fire extinguishing systems. Hazardous areas include, but are not limited to:

Boiler and heater rooms	Rooms or spaces used for storage of combustible supplies and equipment in quantities deemed hazardous by the authority having jurisdiction.
Laundries	
Repair shops	

The list that appears in 22-3.3.2.2 is not all-inclusive. Hazardous areas are those that contain materials that, because of their basic nature or because of the quantity of combustible materials involved, represent a significantly higher hazard than would otherwise be typical in residential board and care facilities. In applying these requirements, the mandatory sprinkler requirements of 22-3.3.5.1 should be considered.

22-3.3.3 Interior Finish. Interior wall and ceiling finish within exit enclosures shall be Class A. In all other areas, interior walls and ceiling finish shall be Class A or Class B in accordance with Section 6-5. Interior floor finish shall be Class I or Class II in corridors and exits.

22-3.3.4 Detection, Alarm, and Communication Systems.

See Supplement 2.

22-3.3.4.1 General. A fire alarm system in accordance with Section 7-6 shall be provided.

22-3.3.4.2 Initiation. Initiation of the required fire alarm system shall be by:

(a) Manual means in accordance with 7-6.2, and

(b) A manual fire alarm station located at a convenient central control point under continuous supervision of responsible employees, and

(c) Any automatic sprinkler system, and

(d) Any required detection system.

Exception to (d): Sleeping room smoke detectors are not required to initiate the building fire alarm system.

Paragraph 22-3.3.4.2(b) requires that, in addition to the normal distribution of manual fire alarm stations (*see 7-6.2*), locations such as that of the telephone operator must also be equipped with a manual fire alarm station. The intent is to have a manual fire alarm station available at the location where residents phone in an emergency.

The *Code* exempts sleeping room smoke detectors from activating the building fire protective signaling system. The detectors installed in the sleeping rooms are usually single station or multiple station detectors and are not part of a "required automatic detection system" and, therefore, are automatically exempted (22-3.3.4.7). The exception emphasizes this point but clarifies that, if detectors are part of a system, they are not required to initiate the building fire protective signaling system. The *Code* does not prohibit room detectors from activating the system; however, this is discouraged to prevent numerous activations, which could pose a particular problem in large board and care facilities. The purpose of the sleeping room detector is to warn the occupants of that room. The notification of the management and other occupants is the responsibility of the occupant and, as such, should be emphasized in the required training for residents.

22-3.3.4.3 Annunciator Panel. An annunciator panel connected with the fire alarm system shall be provided. The location of the annunciator shall be approved by the authority having jurisdiction.

Exception: Buildings not greater than two stories in height and with not more than 50 sleeping rooms.

22-3.3.4.4 Occupant Notification. Occupant notification shall be provided automatically, without delay, by internal audible alarm in accordance with 7-6.3. Presignal systems shall be prohibited.

The distribution of audible alarm-notification appliances in residential board and care facilities must be thoroughly reviewed. In most new construction, corridor walls are of such character (soundproof) that a sounding device would be required in each room to provide an audible alarm; without the use of a sounding device in each room, the corridor alarm would have to approach dangerous decibel levels in order to awaken residents in their rooms.

22-3.3.4.5 High rise buildings shall be provided with an approved means of voice communication in accordance with 7-6.3.

Exception: Buildings equipped with a public address system.

22-3.3.4.6*   Fire Department Notification. In case of a fire, provisions shall be made for the immediate notification of the public fire department by either telephone or other means. Where there is no public fire department, this notification shall be made to the private fire brigade.

A-22-3.3.4.6 *(See A-16-3.4.3.4.)*

This paragraph does not require a direct fire alarm connection to the fire department, although that is the best method of compliance. If a telephone is provided, the telephone must be equipped for direct outside dial without going through a switchboard and is not permitted to be a pay phone.

22-3.3.4.7   Smoke Detectors. Each sleeping room shall be provided with an approved single station smoke detector in accordance with 7-6.2.9, powered from the building electrical system.

The purpose of placing detectors in each room is to alert the occupants of a sleeping room to the presence of a fire originating in that room. The detectors are not normally tied into the building fire protective signaling system [*see the Exception to 22-3.3.4.2(d).*] When an occupant leaves the room, the door shuts behind the occupant (*see 22-3.3.6.6*), and the occupant pulls a manual fire alarm station. If the occupant fails to sound the alarm manually, compensation is provided by corridor smoke detectors or by automatic sprinklers. (*See 22-3.3.4.8 and 22-3.3.5.*)

22-3.3.4.8   Smoke Detection Systems. All corridors and common spaces shall be provided with smoke detectors in accordance with NFPA 72E, *Standard on Automatic Fire Detectors*, arranged to initiate an alarm that is audible in all sleeping areas.

Exception No. 1: Detectors are not required in common spaces in facilities protected throughout by an approved automatic sprinkler system in accordance with 22-3.3.5.

Exception No. 2: Unenclosed corridors, passageways, balconies, colonnades, or other arrangements where one or more sides along the long dimension are fully or extensively open to the exterior at all times.

A system of smoke detectors is required in the corridors and all common spaces of any facility that is not fully sprinklered. Note that the exception for sprinklers does not apply to 22-3.3.4.7. The Committee has specifically emphasized in its discussion of this issue that it is not equating sprinklers and smoke detectors, but it does believe that a fully sprinklered building is an adequate alternative to smoke detectors in common spaces. It should be noted that, since 22-3.3.5.1 requires automatic sprinkler protection, smoke detectors in corridor and common spaces will not typically be required. If the facility is built "motel style," using exterior access corridors, smoke detection is not required in the exterior corridors.

22-3.3.5   Extinguishment Requirements.

See Supplement 3.

22-3.3.5.1* All buildings shall be protected throughout with an approved automatic sprinkler system installed in accordance with Section 7-7. Quick response or residential sprinklers shall be provided throughout. Such systems shall activate the fire alarm system in accordance with Section 7-6.

Exception No. 1: In buildings not more than four stories in height, a sprinkler system complying with NFPA 13R, Standard for the Installation of Sprinkler Systems in Residential Occupancies up to and Including Four Stories in Height, shall be permitted.

Exception No. 2: Automatic sprinklers are not required in bathrooms not exceeding 55 sq ft (5.1 sq m) provided such spaces are finished with lath and plaster or materials providing a 15-minute thermal barrier.

This exception applies to sprinkler systems installed in accordance with NFPA 13R, *Standard for the Installation of Sprinkler Systems in Residential Buildings up to and Including Four Stories in Height,*[6] and NFPA 13, *Standard for the Installation of Sprinkler Systems.*[4] It should be noted that the combustibility of plumbing fixtures is not an issue. NFPA 13R and NFPA 13 address the combustibility of plumbing fixtures, not because they are viewed as a source of ignition, but because frequently wall finish materials are not installed behind prefabricated enclosures. Therefore, the exception clearly states that the bathroom must be finished with plaster or materials providing a 15-minute thermal barrier. This includes the area behind a prefabricated enclosure.

Exception No. 3: Automatic sprinklers are not required in small clothes closets where the smallest dimension does not exceed 3 ft (0.9 m) and the area does not exceed 24 sq ft (2.2 sq m) and the walls and ceiling are finished with noncombustible or limited-combustible materials.

Exception No. 4: Standard response sprinklers shall be permitted for use in areas where quick response and residential sprinklers are prohibited to be installed by their listing.

Exception No. 5: Standard response sprinklers shall be permitted for use in hazardous areas in accordance with 22-3.3.2.

Quick response and residential sprinklers do have some limitations associated with their listing regarding clearances from heat sources and ceiling slopes. When such a situation is encountered, standard sprinklers must installed. Standard sprinklers may also be installed in hazardous areas, since such areas are not occupied by sleeping residents.

A-22-3.3.5.1 It is intended that this requirement applies to existing small facilities that are converted to large facilities.

This paragraph requires the installation of automatic sprinklers throughout the building, as well as in the facility itself. The paragraph also establishes the criteria to be used for the installation of sprinkler systems. While NFPA 13R, *Standard for the Installation of Sprinkler Systems in Residential Buildings up to and Including Four Stories in Height,*[6] is referenced, such systems may not be used in large, impractical facilities, since they must comply with Chapter 12, which does not recognize NFPA 13R.

This paragraph recognizes the ability of quick response and residential sprinklers to maintain tenability in the room of origin during most fire scenarios.

22-3.3.5.2 Automatic sprinkler systems installed in high rise buildings shall be supervised in accordance with Section 7-7.

22-3.3.5.3 **Portable Fire Extinguishers.** Portable fire extinguishers in accordance with Section 7-7 shall be provided near hazardous areas.

22-3.3.6 **Corridors and Separation of Sleeping Rooms.**

22-3.3.6.1 Access shall be provided from every resident use area to at least one means of egress that is separated from all other rooms or spaces by fire barriers complying with 22-3.3.6.3 through 22-3.3.6.6.

Exception No. 1: Rooms or spaces, other than sleeping rooms, if those rooms or spaces are protected throughout by an approved automatic sprinkler system installed in accordance with 22-3.3.5.

Exception No. 2: Rooms or spaces, other than sleeping rooms, if those rooms or spaces are provided with a smoke detection and alarm system connected to activate the building evacuation alarm. Furnishings, finishes, and furniture, in combination with all other combustibles within the spaces, if of such minimum quantity and so arranged that a fully developed fire is unlikely to occur.

Exception No. 3: Facilities housing groups capable of prompt evacuation in buildings not over two stories in height that have at least two remotely located means of egress not involving windows. The arrangement shall be such that there is at least one such means of egress from each sleeping room that provides a path of travel to the outside without traversing any corridor or other spaces exposed to unprotected vertical openings or common living spaces, such as living rooms and kitchens.

Under some circumstances, it is permissible to have access to an exit that passes through a sitting room, television room, living room, or other common use space. However, because numerous multiple-death fires have originated in such locations, this paragraph is intended to preclude exposing all exit access paths to a fire in such a space. Exceptions are provided that permit egress paths to be exposed to the common use space where the space is sprinklered as required by 22-3.5.1.1. Therefore, Exceptions Nos. 2 and 3 provide minimal benefit. (*See Figure 22-8 for examples.*)

22-3.3.6.2 Sleeping rooms shall be separated from corridors and other common spaces by fire barriers complying with 22-3.3.6.3 through 22-3.3.6.6.

22-3.3.6.3 Fire barriers required by 22-3.3.6.1 or 22-3.3.6.2 shall have a fire resistance rating of not less than 1 hour.

X Through Sketch Indicates Arrangement is Prohibited

Figure 22-8. Examples of Permitted and Prohibited Arrangements.

Examples of Permitted and Prohibited Arrangements

Exception No. 1: In buildings protected throughout by an approved automatic sprinkler system installed in accordance with 22-3.3.5, such barriers shall have a fire resistance rating of not less than 30 minutes, and in conversions, no fire resistance rating is required, but it shall resist the passage of smoke.

Exception No. 2: In buildings housing groups capable of prompt evacuation, not greater than two stories in height, and with a maximum of 30 residents, such barriers shall have a fire resistance rating of not less than 30 minutes.

Exception No. 3: In conversions, such fire barriers shall have a fire resistance rating of not less than 20 minutes.

In general, sleeping rooms in new facilities must be separated from corridors by construction having a fire resistance rating of at least 1 hour. If the building is protected throughout by an automatic sprinkler system as required by 22-3.5.1, or if it is a moderately sized prompt facility (Exception No. 2), the corridor walls may have a 30-minute fire resistance rating.

In buildings that are converted to board and care facilities, which also must be sprinklered (22-3.3.5.1), sleeping rooms must be separated from corridors by construction that resists the passage of smoke, but no fire resistance rating is required. Therefore, existing hotels and health care facilities can be converted to board and care facilities without requiring replacement of corridor walls if the hotel or health care facility has complied with the applicable provisions of the *Code.* Due to the mandatory sprinkler provisions of 22-3.3.5.1, Exceptions Nos. 2 and 3 are of minimal benefit.

22-3.3.6.4 Doors in fire barriers required by 22-3.3.6.1 or 22-3.3.6.2 shall have a fire protection rating of not less than 20 minutes.

Exception No. 1: In conversions, existing 1¾-in. (4.4-cm) thick solid bonded wood core doors shall be permitted to be continued in use.

Exception No. 2: In buildings protected throughout by an approved automatic sprinkler system installed in accordance with 22-3.3.5, existing doors in renovations and conversions that are nonrated shall be permitted to be continued in use.

Exception No. 3: Walls that are required only to resist the passage of smoke, without a fire resistance rating, shall be permitted to have doors that resist the passage of smoke without a fire protection rating.

The intent of Exception Nos. 1 and 2 is to minimize the impact of converting from a health care facility or hotel to a board and care facility. It is intended that even the existing 1¾-in. (4.4-cm) thick solid bonded wood core doors and the nonrated room doors should have a reliable means to keep the door closed. Such doors may also be required to be self-closing or automatic-closing in accordance with 22-3.3.6.6.

22-3.3.6.5 Walls and doors required by 22-3.3.6.1 and 22-3.3.6.2 shall be constructed to resist the passage of smoke. There shall be no louvers, transfer grilles, operable transoms, or other air passages penetrating such walls or doors except properly installed heating and utility installations.

22-3.3.6.6 Doors in walls required by 22-3.3.6.1 and 22-3.3.6.2 shall be self-closing or automatic-closing in accordance with 5-2.1.8. Doors in walls separating sleeping rooms from corridors shall be automatic-closing in accordance with 5-2.1.8.

Exception No. 1: Doors to sleeping rooms that have occupant control locks such that access is normally restricted to the occupants or staff personnel shall be permitted to be self-closing.

Exception No. 2: In buildings protected throughout by an approved automatic sprinkler system installed in accordance with 22-3.3.5, doors, other than doors to hazardous areas, vertical openings, and exit enclosures are not required to be self-closing or automatic-closing.

A reliable means of closing sleeping room doors during a fire is required unless the building is sprinklered as required by 22-3.3.5.1. Generally, automatic, smoke-activated closers will be required. In facilities in which the residents control the privacy lock on their own sleeping room doors, a simple self-closer (e.g., spring hinges or a hydraulic door check) is acceptable. This is because, in practice, such doors are usually kept closed. Therefore, the likelihood that the door will be chocked or held open is minimized. In accordance with 22-3.3.6.4, a reliable means to keep the doors closed should also be provided.

22-3.3.7 Subdivision of Building Spaces.

22-3.3.7.1 Every sleeping room floor shall be divided into at least two smoke compartments of approximately the same size, with smoke barriers in accordance with Section 6-3. Smoke dampers are not required.

Additional smoke barriers shall be provided such that the maximum travel distance from a sleeping room corridor door to a smoke barrier shall not exceed 150 ft (45 m).

Exception No. 1: Buildings protected throughout by an approved automatic sprinkler system in accordance with 22-3.3.5.

Exception No. 2: Where each sleeping room is provided with exterior ways of exit access arranged in accordance with 5-5.3.

Exception No. 3: Smoke barriers are not required where the aggregate corridor length on each floor is not more than 150 ft (45 m).

The smoke barrier provides for horizontal movement of occupants and limits the number of rooms (and, therefore, occupants) exposed to a single fire that may block a corridor. Since no fire rating is required for the barrier and smoke dampers are not required, the provision of smoke barriers is not overly burdensome. The exception for buildings equipped with automatic sprinklers reflects the excellent life loss record associated with this protection.

A horizontal exit may be used to comply with 22-3.3.7 and therefore may serve more than one function.

Due to the mandatory sprinkler provisions of 22-3.3.5.1, smoke barriers typically will not be required.

22-3.4 Special Provisions.

22-3.4.1* Operable Windows. Each sleeping room shall be provided with at least one outside window. Such windows shall be openable from the inside without the use of tools and shall provide clear opening of not less than 20 in. (50.8 cm) in width, 24 in. (61 cm) in height, and 5.7 sq ft (.53 sq m) in area. The bottom of the opening shall not be more than 44 in. (112 cm) above the floor.

Exception No. 1: Buildings protected throughout by an approved automatic sprinkler system in accordance with 22-3.3.5.

Exception No. 2: Where the sleeping room has a door leading directly to the outside of the building.

Exception No. 3: Buildings provided with an approved engineered smoke control system in accordance with Section 7-3.

Exception No. 4: In conversions, the openable clear height, width, and area of windows may be modified to the dimensions as approved by the authority having jurisdiction.

A-22-3.4.1 Windows may serve as a means of emergency escape, particularly where ladders can be raised by fire fighters or others. Even where the location is such as to preclude the use of windows for escape purposes, they may provide air for breathing in a smoke-filled room while trapped occupants are awaiting rescue.

Where awning- or hopper-type windows are used, they should be so hinged or subdivided as to provide a clear opening of at least 5.7 sq ft (.53 sq m). Where storm windows, screens, or burglar guards are used, these should be provided with quick-opening devices so that they may be readily opened from the inside for emergency egress.

An operable window allows an occupant access to fresh air and/or rescue. If an operable window is opened and smoke is drawn into the room, it can be closed; a fixed window that has been broken cannot be closed. The win-

dows specified are the same as those required in other residential occupancies and in schools. The door described in Exception No. 2 does not have to be an exit access door but can be a door to a balcony, as this would serve the same purpose as a window. Since 22-3.3.5.1 requires sprinklers throughout all buildings, the requirement for operable windows is typically not applicable.

22-3.4.2 Operating Features. (*See Chapter 31.*)

22-3.5 Building Services.

22-3.5.1 Utilities. Utilities shall comply with provisions of Section 7-1.

22-3.5.2 Heating, Ventilating, and Air Conditioning.

22-3.5.2.1 Heating, ventilating, and air conditioning equipment shall comply with the provisions of Section 7-2.

22-3.5.2.2 No stove or combustion heater shall be so located as to block escape in case of fire caused by the malfunction of the stove or heater.

22-3.5.2.3 Unvented fuel-fired heaters shall not be used in any board and care occupancy.

This paragraph prohibits the use of the typical kerosene portable heater, as well as other fuel-fired, non-vented heaters.

22-3.5.3 Elevators, Dumbwaiters, and Vertical Conveyors.

22-3.5.3.1 Elevators, dumbwaiters, and vertical conveyors shall comply with the provisions of Section 7-4.

22-3.5.3.2* In high rise buildings, one elevator shall be provided with a protected power supply and be available for use by the fire department in case of emergency.

A-22-3.5.3.2 (*See A-16-5.3.*)

22-3.5.4 Rubbish Chutes, Incinerators, and Laundry Chutes. Rubbish chutes, incinerators, and laundry chutes shall comply with the provisions of Section 7-5.

SECTION 22-4*   Suitability of an Apartment Building to House a Board and Care Occupancy

A-22-4   Board and care occupancies in apartment buildings will usually be small facilities housing 16 or fewer residents. It is intended that the board and care occupancy be made to conform to the requirements of Section 22-2 for small board and care facilities. In the unusual case where an apartment houses a large board and care facility, it would be reasonable for the authority having jurisdiction, using 1-5.3, to apply the provisions of Section 22-3 to the apartment. In addition, the apartment building in which the facility is housed is required to comply with the requirements for apartment buildings in Chapters 18 and 19 and the additional criteria presented in this section.

Board and care occupancies in apartment buildings are usually small facilities housing 16 or fewer residents. It is intended that the board and care occupancy conform to the requirements of Section 22-2 for small board and care facilities. In the unusual case where an apartment houses a large board and care facility, it is reasonable for the authority having jurisdiction, in accordance with 1-5.3, to apply the provisions of Section 22-3 to the apartment. In addition, the apartment building in which the facility is housed is required to comply with the requirements for new apartment buildings in Chapter 18 and the additional criteria provided in this section. Note that Chapter 18 requirements are referenced even though the apartment building itself may be an existing structure.

22-4.1   General.

22-4.1.1   Scope. This section applies to apartment buildings that have one or more individual apartments used as a board and care occupancy. This section determines the suitability of such buildings to house a residential board and care facility. The suitability of such buildings for apartments not used for board and care occupancies is covered in Chapter 18.

22-4.1.2   Requirements for individual apartments used as a residential board and care occupancy are specified in Section

22-2, "Small Facilities." Egress from the apartment into the common building corridor shall be considered acceptable egress from the board and care facility.

See commentary following the section title.

22-4.1.3   Requirements Based on Evacuation Capability.

22-4.1.3.1   Apartment buildings housing board and care facilities shall comply with the requirements of Section 22-4.

Exception*: Facilities where the authority having jurisdiction has determined that equivalent safety for housing a residential board and care facility is provided in accordance with Section 1-6.

A-22-4.1.3.1   Exception. In determining equivalency for conversions, modernizations, renovations, or unusual design concepts, the authority having jurisdiction may accept evaluations based on NFPA 101M, *Alternative Approaches to Life Safety*, Chapter 6. (*See Appendix B.*)

22-4.1.3.2   All facilities shall meet the requirements of Chapter 18 and the additional requirements of Section 22-4.

22-4.1.4   Minimum Construction Requirements. In addition to the requirements of Chapter 18, apartment buildings housing residential board and care facilities that house groups classed as prompt or slow shall meet the construction requirements of 22-3.1.3, and those housing groups classed as impractical to evacuate shall meet the construction requirements of 12-1.6. In applying the construction requirements, the height shall be determined by the height of the residential board and care facility above the primary level of exit discharge.

22-4.2   Means of Egress. The requirements of Section 18-2 apply only to parts of the means of egress serving the apartment(s) used as residential board and care occupancy.

22-4.3   Protection.

22-4.3.1   Interior Finish. The requirements of 18-3.3 apply only to the parts of means of egress serving the apartment(s) used as a residential board and care occupancy.

22-4.3.2 **Construction of Corridor Walls.** The requirements of 18-3.6 apply only to corridors serving the residential board and care facility, including that portion of the corridor wall separating the residential board and care facility from the common corridor.

22-4.3.3 **Subdivision of Building Spaces.** The requirements of 18-3.7 apply to those stories with an apartment(s) used as a residential board and care occupancy.

22-4.4 **Operating Features.** *(See Chapter 31.)*

References Cited in Commentary

[1]*Fire Safety in Boarding Homes*, NFPA SPP-76, Quincy, MA, 1982.

[2]Boarding Home Fires: New Jersey, Hearing before the Select Committee on Aging, House of Representatives, Ninety-seventh Congress, Comm. Pub. No. 97-304, March 9, 1981.

[3]Toward a National Plan for the Chronically Mentally Ill, Bethesda, MD, National Institute of Mental Health, 1980.

[4]NFPA 13, *Standard for the Installation of Sprinkler Systems*, National Fire Protection Association, Quincy, MA, 1991.

[5]NFPA 13D, *Standard for the Installation of Sprinkler Systems in One- and Two- Family Dwellings and Mobile Homes*, National Fire Protection Association, Quincy, MA 1991.

[6]NFPA 13R, *Standard for the Installation of Sprinkler Systems in Residential Buildings up to and Including Four Stories in Height*, National Fire Protection Association, Quincy, MA, 1991.

23

Existing Residential Board and Care Occupancies

SECTION 23-1 General Requirements

23-1.1 Application.

It is intended that this chapter be applied to all existing residential board and care facilities. However, such facilities will rarely include the designation "residential board and care facility" as part of their official name. They will operate under a variety of names, and they may house a variety of occupants. Therefore, it is important to understand the distinction between this type of occupancy and others that provide sleeping accommodations, such as lodging houses, hotels, nursing homes, and hospitals. The definitions found in 23-1.3 will be helpful in making this distinction. Additional help in recognizing types of facilities that are covered by this chapter can be found in A-23-1.3. The list is not all-inclusive.

The fire fatality problem in buildings of this occupancy classification is well documented.[1] Prior to 1985, it was not uncommon to find a multiple-death board and care fire reported in the NFPA *Fire Journal*. The following is extracted from a memo to state fire marshals, state training directors, and provincial fire marshals from NFPA regarding boarding house firesafety. It was dated July 10, 1984.

Boarding homes are known by a variety of names: board and care homes, halfway houses, retirement homes, rooming houses, or community living facilities. Regardless of what the facilities are called, an estimated 300,000 boarding homes house 2,000,000 people in the U.S.[2] The facilities range from specially designed and constructed buildings to converted single-family homes and dormitories.

The residents of boarding homes are often unable to meet the demands of independent living and are at a greater risk from fire than the general population. Typically, the victims of boarding home fires are the elderly or former mental health patients who have been released from various institutions. These residents may not require daily medical care but nonetheless may have disabilities that reduce their ability to save themselves in a fire.

The policy of deinstitutionalizing chronic mental patients began in the mid-1950s. The nation's mental hospital population from a peak of over half a million in the mid-1950s, dropped to roughly half that number by the mid-1960s, and roughly one fourth the peak figure by 1980. The National Institute of Mental Health estimated in 1980 that 800,000 chronic mental patients were both deinstitutionalized and living in sorely lacking conditions.[3] The chronic mental patients released in the late 1970s also included a higher percentage of physically handicapped individuals, and these patients have been less likely to maintain outpatient follow-up care.

Since 1978, multiple-death boarding home fires (those that kill three or more persons) have resulted in 296 deaths. Compared to the estimated boarding home population, this indicates that the risk of dying in a multiple-death fire is roughly five times as high in a boarding home than in all other residential occupancies combined. Many multiple-death boarding home fires kill at least half the tenants of the properties involved.

An analysis of recent fatal boarding home fires reveals the lack of basic fire protection provisions in these buildings, including: inadequate means of egress, combustible interior finishes, unenclosed stairways, lack of automatic detection or sprinkler systems, or lack of emergency training for staff and residents. Many of the facilities were either licensed for an occupancy other than a boarding home (such as a hotel) or were unlicensed, underground "boarding homes." None of the facilities were provided with automatic sprinkler protection.

There is no particular mystery about how to reduce the number of fatal boarding home fires. Provision of enclosed stairs, provision of two means of egress, avoidance of the use of combustible interior finishes, compartmentation, provision of automatic detection and sprinkler systems, and instruction of staff and residents in emergency procedures would greatly reduce the number of fatalities.

Comprehensive fire incident reporting systems in the U.S.A. were developed before the emergence of residential board and care facilities. Therefore, the overall fire experience of these occupancies cannot be readily isolated.

Rooming, boarding and lodging houses averaged 62 fire deaths per year from 1984 to 1988, and residential hotels averaged 4 deaths per year during the same period. This compares with 49 deaths per year for hotels. Facilities that care for the aged averaged 19 fire deaths a year in the same period, and facilities that care for the sick averaged 11 deaths a year.

Beginning in the 1970s, NFPA's major-fires data base developed a special code to identify board and care homes. Board and care homes were defined as facilities designed to provide only lodging for residents with substantial limitations, primarily those age 65 and over and former mental patients. This data base devoted particular attention to tracking fires in these facilities where 3 or more persons had died. Multiple-death fires in board and care facilities killed 214 persons from 1971 to 1989. Primarily because of these fires, the fatality rate in multiple-death fires (3 or more deaths) in all boarding homes (including board and care facilities) from 1978 to 1984, relative to the population in such facilities, was roughly five times the comparable multiple-death rate in other residential properties. The rate has diminished since that time, but five multiple-death fires in board-and-care homes from 1984 to 1989 prove that the problem still exists.

The deadliest of these fires that occurred from 1971 to 1989 were a 1981 fire in New Jersey in what was called a sheltered care boarding facility (31 deaths), a 1979 fire in Missouri in what was called a boarding house (25 deaths), and a 1980 fire in New Jersey in what was called a hotel (24 deaths). Analysis of the circumstances in multiple-death board and care home fires reveals a general lack of fire protection, including an absence of sprinklers, an absence or insufficiency of detection/alarm provisions, inadequate means of egress, unenclosed stairways, combustible interior finishes, and a lack of emergency training for staff and residents.

The provisions of this chapter address the basic fire protection features identified above while maintaining the ability to operate such a facility in a noninstitutional environment. The requirements for small board and care facilities are similar to the provisions for one- and two-family dwellings and lodging and rooming houses. The requirements for large facilities, other than those that are large and impractical to evacuate, are similar to the requirements for existing hotels. Large, impractical facilities, as required by 23-3.1.2.2, shall comply with the requirements of Chapter 13, "Existing Health Care Occupancies." While the provisions of Chapter 23 may be similar to other residential occupancies, there are requirements that differ due to the unique characteristics of these facilities, such as the degree to which occupants are able to respond to a fire emergency.

This chapter follows the same outline as the other occupancy chapters within the *Code*. However, because there are four major sections (23-1, 23-2, 23-3, and 23-4) the standard chapter outline begins with the next digit. For example, the "-3.1" subsection of each occupancy chapter (e.g., 19-3.1) usually contains the requirements for vertical opening protection. In Chapter 23, 23-2.3.1 and 23-3.3.1 contain the vertical opening provisions.

A partial list of multiple-death board and care fires since 1979 appears in Table 23-1.

23-1.1.1* All existing facilities classified as residential board and care occupancies shall conform to the requirements of this chapter. This chapter is divided into four sections as follows:

(a) Section 23-1 — General Requirements.

(b) Section 23-2 — Small Facilities (i.e., sleeping accommodations for not more than 16 residents).

(c) Section 23-3 — Large Facilities (i.e., sleeping accommodations for more than 16 residents).

(d) Section 23-4 — Suitability of an Apartment Building to House a Board and Care Occupancy.

A-23-1.1.1 The requirements in this chapter are designed to accommodate typical changes in the capabilities of the resident, such as those due to accidents, temporary illness, cyclical variations in capabilities, and gradual aging. This is based on the assumption that the capabilities of the resident will be evaluated at least annually, and for residents with geriatric problems or degenerative diseases, at least every six months. Also, residents should be reevaluated after each accident or illness that requires hospitalization.

The requirements of this chapter are based on two main concepts:

(a) Larger buildings, which are more difficult to evacuate, require more built-in fire protection than smaller buildings.

(b) Occupants who are more difficult to evacuate require more built-in fire protection than occupants who are easier to evacuate.

It is also anticipated that a small facility typically will be located in a structure that has the appearance of and

Table 23-1. Major Residential Board and Care Multiple-Death Fires

Date	Occupancy	Civilians Killed	Civilians Injured
4/1/79	Marietta Foster Home Connellsville, PA	10	2
4/2/79	Wayside Inn Boarding House Farmington, MO	25	9
4/11/79	1715 Lamont Street Washington, DC	10	4
11/11/79	Coats Boarding Home Pioneer, OH	14	0
7/26/80	Brinley Inn Boarding Home* Bradley Beach, NJ	24	4
11/30/80	Donahue Foster Home Detroit, MI	5	0
1/9/81	Beachview Rest Home* Keansburg, NJ	31	10
10/28/82	Perrys' Domiciliary Care Home* Pittsburgh, PA	5	1
2/7/83	Silver Leaves Group Home* Eau Claire, WI	6	0
3/13/83	Shannons Foster Care Home* Gladstone, MI	5	3
4/19/83	Central Community Home* Worcester, MA	7	2
8/31/83	Anandale Village* Lawrenceville, GA	8	0
12/5/83	Dana House Cincinnati, OH	6	4
11/20/84	708 Hill Rise Court Lexington, KY	5	0
6/25/86	138 Pingree Boarding Home Detroit, MI	4	19

* These are incidents in which NFPA has evidence that elderly occupants or former mental health patients were tenants.

operates in a similar manner to a dwelling. The operation and size of a small facility also demands unique consideration with respect to the fire protection features provided. Certain fire protection features that are appropriate for large facilities, such as smoke barriers, may not be appropriate and may not provide adequate protection in small facilities. For this reason, the exception that permits small facilities to comply with the requirements for large facilities (23-2.1.2.1) applies only to those facilities that have previously complied with the exception. The 1985 Edition of the *Code* permitted small facilities to comply with the requirements for large facilities in lieu of the provisions for small facilities. As stated in Exception No. 2 to 23-2.1.2.1, a small facility that has previously been approved based on the requirements for a large facility may continue to be evaluated in this manner. However, any other small facility must meet the provisions for a small facility and may not use the provisions for a large facility as an alternative.

23-1.1.2 The requirements of this chapter are applicable to existing buildings according to the provisions of Section 1-5 of this *Code*.

23-1.2 **Mixed Occupancies.** Where another type of occupancy occurs in the same building as a residential board and care occupancy, the requirements of 1-5.7 of this *Code* shall apply.

Exception No. 1: Occupancies that are completely separated from all portions of the building used for a residential board and care facility and its egress system by construction having a fire resistance rating of at least 2 hours.

Exception No. 1 specifically requires that the residential board and care facility and its exit system be separated from the other occupancy. Therefore, if the residential board and care facility is located on the second floor and Exception No. 1 is to be applied, the exit stair must have a 2-hour fire-rated enclosure, regardless of the fact that 5-1.3.1 would permit a 1-hour fire-rated enclosure. Where the residential board and care facility is located on the same floor as the other occupancy, the occupancy separation may also serve as a horizontal exit, if the provisions of 5-2.4 are met.

Exception No. 2: Apartment buildings housing residential board and care occupancies in conformance with Section 23-4. In such facilities, any safeguards required by Section 23-4 that are more restrictive than those for other housed occupancies apply only to the extent prescribed by Section 23-4.

Exception No. 2 clarifies that board and care facilities located within an apartment building need not comply with the requirements for mixed occupancies. The provisions of Section 23-4 apply to the entire building and supplement the provisions of Chapter 19, "Existing Apartment Buildings." The board and care facility itself must comply with the provisions of Section 23-2.

23-1.3 **Definitions.**

A number of key concepts are defined in this chapter, arguably the most important of which are "personal care," "evacuation capability," and "point of safety."

Evacuation Capability.* Evacuation capability is the ability of the occupants, residents, and staff as a group either to evacuate a building or to relocate from the point of occupancy to a point of safety. Following are the levels of evacuation capability covered by this chapter:

(a) *Prompt.* Evacuation capability equivalent to the capability of the general population where applying the requirements for residential occupancies covered by Chapters 17, 19, 20, and 21.

(b) *Slow.* Evacuation capability of a group to move to a point of safety in a timely manner, with some of the residents requiring assistance from the staff.

(c) *Impractical.* A group that, even with staff assistance, cannot reliably move to a point of safety in a timely manner.

A-23-1.3 **Evacuation Capability.** The evacuation capability of the residents and staff is a function of both the ability of the residents to evacuate and the assistance provided by the staff. It is intended that the evacuation capability be determined by the procedure acceptable to the authority having jurisdiction. It is also intended that the timing of drills, the rating of residents, and similar actions related to determining the evacuation capability be performed by persons approved by or acceptable to the authority having jurisdiction. The evacuation capability can be determined by the use of the definitions in 23-1.3, the application of NFPA 101M, *Alternative Approaches to Life Safety*, Chapter 5, or a program of drills (timed).

Where drills are used, in determining evacuation capability, it is suggested that the facility conduct and record fire drills 12 times per year (4 times per year on each shift), and that the facility conduct the drills in consultation with the authority having jurisdiction. Records should indicate the time to reach a point of safety, date and time of day, location of simulated fire origin, the escape paths used, along with comments relating to residents who resisted or failed to participate in the drills.

Translation of drill times to evacuation capability may be determined as: (a) 3 minutes or less, Prompt; (b) over 3 minutes, but not in excess of 13 minutes, Slow; and (c) more than 13 minutes, Impractical.

Evacuation capability in all cases is based on the time of day or night when evacuation of the facility would be most difficult (i.e., sleeping residents or fewer staff present).

Where the facility management does not furnish an evacuation capability determination acceptable to the authority having jurisdiction, the evacuation capability should be classified as impractical. However, evacuation capability should be considered slow if the following conditions are met:

(a) All residents are able to travel to centralized dining facilities without continuous staff assistance, and

(b) There is continuous staffing whenever there are residents in the facility.

Evacuation capability is a factor in all the *Code* chapters. However, in most chapters, the *Code* assumes that the building occupants have similar evacuation capabilities, and the requirements are based on the ability of occupants to reach safety by means of exits. In the "institutional occupancy" chapters, the *Code* assumes that many of the building occupants will be incapable of evacuating the building, and the protection of life from fire is achieved by the "defend in place" method. In large residential buildings (hotels and apartment buildings), where evacuation capability may be poor due to the large size of the building, substantial built-in fire protection is required.

In this chapter, evacuation capability is not assumed. Occupants of all residential board and care facilities do not have the same evacuation capability. This should be apparent due to the numerous and diverse types of facilities that are included in this occupancy type. For example, in an orphanage, a shelter for battered women, a group home for high-functioning mentally handicapped persons, or a halfway house for prison parolees, the occupants may have normal evacuation capability. In facilities housing elderly, physically impaired persons, occupants may be slow-moving or may need assistance in recognizing the need for evacuation. In some facilities, evacuation of the building may not be practical at all.

Evacuation capability for an entire facility is not determined on the basis of that resident who is least capable. A facility that houses one impaired resident may have excellent evacuation capability if the staff or a resident "buddy" is able to provide the assistance needed to effect a prompt evacuation of the entire group without jeopardizing the safety of the other residents. It should also be noted that evacuation capability is based on the ability to relocate to a point of safety and not necessarily a public way. (*See the definition of point of safety.*)

The protection features required by this chapter are intended to coordinate with the evacuation capability of the occupants. As such, the fire endurance of the structure, interior finish materials, types and arrangement of means of escape and exits, as well as corridor enclosure provisions, vary based on whether a facility houses occupants who are prompt, slow, or impractical to evacuate. Facilities that are impractical to evacuate utilize the "defend in place" concept. In small facilities, this is achieved by improving the protection of vertical openings and by mandating the installation of automatic sprinkler systems. In large facilities, this is achieved by referencing the provisions of Chapter 13.

Guidance in determining the evacuation capability of a specific facility is provided in A-23-1.3.

Hazardous Area. A hazardous area is any space where there is storage or activity having fuel conditions exceeding that of a one- or two-family dwelling and that possesses the potential for a fully involved fire. Hazardous areas include, but are not limited to, areas for cartoned storage, food or household maintenance items in wholesale or institutional-type quantities and concentrations, or mass storage of residents' belongings. Areas containing approved, properly installed and maintained furnaces and heating equipment, furnace rooms, and cooking and laundry facilities are not classed as hazardous areas solely on the basis of such equipment.

Hazardous areas are spaces containing materials that, because of their basic nature (as in the case of flammable liquids) or because of the quantity of combustible materials involved, represent a significantly greater fire hazard than would otherwise be typical of residential board and care occupancies. The mere presence of heat-producing appliances, such as furnaces, cooking equipment, or dryers, does not constitute a hazardous area. To be considered a hazardous area, the contents should be of such character that a fire or explosion could develop and pose a danger of propagating to adjacent spaces unprotected by a fire barrier or automatic sprinkler system.

Personal Care. "Personal care" means protective care of residents who do not require chronic or convalescent medical or nursing care. Personal care involves responsibility for the safety of the resident while inside the building. Personal care may include daily awareness by the management of the resident's functioning and whereabouts, making and reminding a resident of appointments, the ability and readiness for intervention in the event of a resident experiencing a crisis, supervision in the areas of nutrition and medication, and actual provision of transient medical care.

Personal care is a significant concept because the occupants of a board and care facility require care. This is not true medical care, as might be provided in a hospital or nursing home, but rather a form of assistance in meeting the demands of daily living. The term "transient medical care" refers to the kind of medical care that is normally provided in the home by one family member for another, not skilled nursing or acute medical care.

Point of Safety. A point of safety is a location that meets one of the following criteria:

(a) It is located exterior to and away from the building.

(b) It is located within a building of any type construction protected throughout by an approved automatic sprinkler system and is either:

1. Located within an exit enclosure meeting the requirements of this *Code*, or

2. Located within another portion of the building that is separated by smoke barriers in accordance with Section 6-3, with at least a 20-minute fire resistance rating, and that portion of the building has access to a means of escape or exit that conforms to the requirements of this *Code* and that does not require return to the area of fire involvement.

(c) It is located within a building of Type I, Type II (222) or (111), Type III (211), Type IV, or Type V (111) construction (*see 6-2.1*) and is either:

1. Located within an exit enclosure meeting the requirements of this *Code*, or

2. Located within another portion of the building that is separated by smoke barriers in accordance with Section 6-3, with at least a 20-minute fire resistance rating, and that portion of the building has access to a means of escape or exit that conforms to the requirements of this *Code* and that does not require return to the area of fire involvement.

"Point of safety" is another *Code* concept that is specifically defined in this chapter. It is well recognized that there are many buildings from which evacuation of all occupants to the outdoors cannot be achieved within a reasonable amount of time, regardless of their capability. This chapter establishes the criteria for a point of safety within the building. Essentially, this is the point at which residents can remain in safety until the fire is extinguished or until outside assistance can arrive to complete evacuation to the exterior.

Resident. A person who is receiving personal care and resides in a residential board and care facility.

Residential Board and Care Occupancy.* A building or part thereof that is used for lodging and boarding of four or more residents, not related by blood or marriage to the owners or operators for the purpose of providing personal care services.

A-23-1.3 Residential Board and Care Occupancy. Following are examples of facilities that may be classified as residential board and care occupancies:

(a) A group housing arrangement for physically or mentally handicapped persons who normally may attend school in the community, attend church in the community, or otherwise use community facilities.

(b) A group housing arrangement for physically or mentally handicapped persons who are undergoing training in preparation for independent living, for paid employment, or for other normal community activities.

(c) A group housing arrangement for the elderly that provides personal care services but that does not provide nursing care.

(d) Facilities for social rehabilitation, alcoholism, drug abuse, or mental health problems that contain a group housing arrangement and that provide personal care services but do not provide acute care.

(e) Other group housing arrangements that provide personal care services but not nursing care.

Staff. A person who provides personal care services, supervision, or assistance.

Thermal Barrier.* A material that will limit the average temperature rise of the unexposed surface to not more than 250°F (120°C) for a specified fire exposure complying with the standard time temperature curve of NFPA 251, *Standard Methods of Fire Tests of Building Construction and Materials.*

A-23-1.3 **Thermal Barrier.** Finish ratings as published in the UL *Fire Resistance Directory* are one way of determining thermal barrier.

In previous editions of the *Code*, several sections referred to a finish rating of 15 or 20 minutes. The term "finish rating" is not as widely used as the term "thermal barrier." For this reason, the chapter now uses this term in lieu of "finish rating" for the protection of structural elements and the separation of areas where automatic sprinkler protection may be omitted. As noted in A-23-1.3, finish ratings may be used to determine a material's acceptability as a thermal barrier.

23-1.4 **Acceptability of Means of Egress or Escape.** No means of escape or means of egress shall be considered as complying with the minimum criteria for acceptance unless emergency evacuation drills are regularly conducted using that route in accordance with the requirements of 31-7.3.

Exits and means of escape are worthless unless residents are familiar with them and feel comfortable using them. An exit or means of escape that is never used in drills will probably not be used in an emergency evacuation. This does not mean that if windows serve as a secondary means of escape that a resident must use the window. However, during drills it would be important to identify the appropriate windows and ensure that residents are familiar with the operation of the windows and their proper use during escape.

SECTION 23-2 Small Facilities

See Table 23-2 on page 724 for a summary of the major requirements.

23-2.1 **General.**

23-2.1.1 **Scope.** This section applies to residential board and care occupancies providing sleeping accommodations for not more than 16 residents. Where there are sleeping accommodations for more than 16 residents, the occupancy shall be classed as a large facility. The requirements for large facilities are in Section 23-3.

23-2.1.2 **Requirements Based on Evacuation Capability.**

23-2.1.2.1 Small facilities shall comply with the requirements of Section 23-2 as indicated for the appropriate evacuation capability.

Exception No. 1: *Facilities where the authority having jurisdiction has determined equivalent safety is provided in accordance with Section 1-6.*

A-23-2.1.2.1 **Exception No. 1.** In determining equivalency for existing buildings, conversions, modernizations, renovations, or unusual design concepts, the authority having jurisdiction may accept evaluations based on NFPA 101M, *Alternative Approaches to Life Safety*, Chapter 6.

The 1988 Edition of NFPA 101M was designed for use with the 1988 Edition of NFPA 101 and cannot be used to evaluate facilities under the 1991 *Life Safety Code*. At

Table 23-2.   Summary of Major Requirements for Existing Small Facilities

Parameter	Evacuation Capability		
	Prompt	Slow	Impractical
1. Construction 23-2.1.3	No Requirements	20-Minute Fire Resistant or Sprinklered	1-Hour Fire-Rated or Sprinklered
2. Means of Escape 23-2.2	1 Primary and 1 Emergency Route	2 Remote Routes	2 Remote Routes
3. Vertical Openings 23-2.3.1	20-Minute Fire Resitant	20-Minute Fire Resistant	20-Minute Fire Resistant
4. Protection of Hazardous Areas 23-2.3.2	Defines 2 Levels	Defines 2 Levels	Defines 2 Levels
5. Interior Finish 23-2.3.3	Class A,B, or C No Req. for Floor Finish	Class A or B No Req. for Floor Finish	Class A or B No Req. for Floor Finish
6. Manual F.A. 23-2.3.4.1	Section 7-6 Local	Section 7-6 Local	Section 7-6 Local
7. Smoke Detection 23-2.3.4.2, 23-2.3.4.3	Sleeping Rooms or 1 Each Level + Each Living and Day Room	Sleeping Rooms or 1 Each Level + Each Living and Day Room	Sleeping Rooms or 1 Each Level + Each Living and Day Room
8. Sprinklers 23-2.3.5	Not Required	Not Required	Required
9. Separation of Sleeping Rooms 23-2.3.6	Smoke-Resisting Self-Closing Door	20-Minute Fire Resistant and Self-Closing Door	20-Minute Fire Resistant and Self-Closing Door

This table summarizes major items. See specific requirements for additional details and exceptions.

the time this *Handbook* went to press, the Committee on Safety to Life was preparing the 1992 Edition of NFPA 101M to use in conjunction with the 1991 *Life Safety Code*.

Exception No. 2: Facilities that were previously approved as complying with the requirements for a large facility having the same evacuation capability.

An exception included in the 1985 *Code* that permitted small facilities to comply with the requirements for large facilities has been restricted to apply to previously approved facilities only (Exception No. 2). The protection features applicable to large facilities may not necessarily provide protection for small facilities. In the case of "prompt" and "slow" facilities, the requirements are such that the application of the exception would provide no benefit to the user of the *Code*.

23-2.1.3 Minimum Construction Requirements.

23-2.1.3.1 Prompt. No special requirements.

23-2.1.3.2 Slow. The facility shall be housed in a building where the interior is fully sheathed with lath and plaster or other material providing a 15-minute thermal barrier, including all portions of bearing walls, bearing partitions, floor construction, and roofs. All columns, beams, girders, and trusses shall be similarly encased or otherwise provide a minimum of a 20-minute fire resistance rating.

Exception No. 1: Exposed steel or wood columns, girders, and beams (but not joists) located in the basement.

Exception No. 2: Buildings of Type I, Type II (111) or (222), Type III (211), Type IV, or Type V (111) construction. (See 6-2.1.)

Exception No. 3: Areas protected by approved automatic sprinkler systems in accordance with 23-2.3.5.

Exception No. 4: Unfinished, unused, and essentially inaccessible loft, attic, or crawl spaces.

Exception No. 5: Where the facility can demonstrate to the authority having jurisdiction that the group is capable of evacuating the building in eight minutes or less or achieves an E-Score of three or less using Chapter 5 of NFPA 101M, Alternative Approaches to Life Safety.

See Figure 23-1 for examples of some acceptable construction types.

Exception No. 5 is intended to allow unsheathed, unsprinklered wood frame construction in facilities that house groups capable of evacuation to a point of safety within eight minutes. For such groups, the additional evacuation time provided by fire resistant sheathing is not an absolute necessity.

23-2.1.3.3 **Impractical.** Buildings shall be of any construction type in accordance with Section 6-2 other than Type II (000), Type III (200), or Type V (000) construction.

Exception: Buildings protected throughout by an approved supervised automatic sprinkler system in accordance with 23-2.3.5 shall be of any type of construction.

Paragraph 23-2.3.5.2 mandates that all small residential board and care facilities that are impractical to evacuate be protected with a supervised automatic sprinkler system. The exception is permitted only if the entire building and not just the residential board and care facility is protected with a supervised automatic sprinkler system.

23-2.2 **Means of Escape.**

23-2.2.1 **Number of Means of Escape.** Every facility shall have at least two remotely located means of escape that do

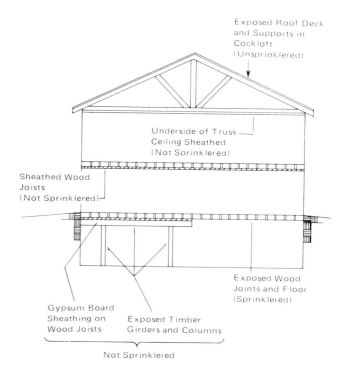

Figure 23-1. *A Few Permissible Types of Construction. These may be mixed within a single building.*

not involve using windows from each normally occupied story. At least one of these means of escape shall comply with 23-2.2.2.

Exception No. 1: In prompt facilities, one means of escape shall be permitted to involve windows complying with 23-2.2.3(c).

Exception No. 2: A second means of escape from each story is not required where the entire building is protected throughout by an approved automatic sprinkler system complying with 23-2.3.5, and the facility has two means of escape. This exception cannot be used in conjunction with 23-2.2.3 Exception No. 2.

Paragraph 23-2.2.1 as well as 23-2.2.2 and 23-2.2.3 establish the criteria for acceptable means of escape in small facilities. This paragraph mandates that each *story* of the facility be provided with at least two means of escape. If the entire building housing the residential board and care facility is protected throughout by an automatic sprinkler system in accordance with 23-2.3.5, if the facility itself has at least two means of escape, and if each sleeping room has a secondary means of escape or alternate protection, then each story is required to have only one means of escape. In this instance, the single means of escape from the story shall meet the criteria for a primary means of escape. (*See 23-2.2.2.*)

The paragraph permits the use of windows only as a means of escape from a prompt facility. It should be noted, however, that this restriction applies to the means of escape from the facility and not the secondary means of escape required from each sleeping room (23-2.2.3). Where a window is considered as a means of escape, the window shall meet the criteria established in 23-2.2.3(c). Windows are not permitted to be considered as a primary means of escape.

23-2.2.2 Primary Means of Escape.

23-2.2.2.1 Every sleeping room and living area shall have access to a primary means of escape so located as to provide a safe path of travel to the outside of the building without traversing any corridor or other space exposed to unprotected vertical openings. Where sleeping rooms or living areas are above or below the level of exit discharge, the primary means of escape shall be an enclosed interior stair, exterior stair, horizontal exit, or existing fire escape stair.

This paragraph requires at least one means of escape from every sleeping room and living area to be protected from vertical openings. Therefore, the primary means of escape provides some degree of quality and reliability but may not meet the criteria of an exit. If the primary means of escape is at a level other than the level of exit discharge, it must be an enclosed stairway, an exterior stairway, an existing fire escape, or possibly a horizontal exit.

23-2.2.2.2 In slow and impractical facilities, the primary means of escape for each sleeping room shall not be exposed to common living spaces such as living rooms and kitchens.

Exception: Buildings equipped with quick response or residential sprinklers throughout. Standard response sprinklers shall be permitted for use in hazardous areas in accordance with 23-2.3.2.

In slow and impractical facilities, the primary means of escape is further restricted, since it cannot be exposed to common living spaces. Therefore, the primary means of escape from a sleeping room is not permitted to include travel through a day room, common use space, or space that is open to a common living space. The objective of this requirement is to reduce the probability that smoke and heat from a fire in a common use area will affect the primary means of escape. This provision is based in part on historical fire experience, which indicates that fires in residential board and care facilities frequently originate in common living spaces.

In recognition of the protection provided by an automatic sprinkler system and the response capabilities of quick response and residential sprinklers, the primary means of escape may be exposed to common living areas where such protection is provided. However, the *Code* does not permit the primary means of escape to be exposed and to also include an unprotected vertical opening (23-2.2.4). In addition, the exception permits the use of standard response sprinklers in hazardous areas that are required to be separated from other parts of the building by Section 23-2.3.3 in accordance with listing limitations on the use of residential and quick response sprinklers.

(*For additional information, see commentary following 20-2.2.1.*)

23-2.2.3 Secondary Means of Escape. In addition to the primary route, each sleeping room shall have a second means of escape or alternate protection that consists of one of the following:

(a) A door, stairway, passage, or hall providing a way of unobstructed travel to the outside of the dwelling at street or ground level that is independent of and remotely located from the primary means of escape.

(b) A passage through an adjacent nonlockable space, independent of and remotely located from the primary means of escape, to any approved means of escape.

(c) An outside window or door operable from the inside without the use of tools and providing a clear opening of not less than 20 in. (50.8 cm) in width, 24 in. (61 cm) in height, and 5.7 sq ft (.53 sq m) in area. The bottom of the opening shall be no more than 44 in. (112 cm) off the floor. Such means of escape shall be acceptable if:

1. The window is within 20 ft (6.1 m) of grade, or

2. The window is directly accessible to fire department rescue apparatus as approved by the authority having jurisdiction, or

3. The window or doors open onto an exterior balcony.

(d) The sleeping room shall be separated from all other parts of the facility by construction having a fire resistance rating of at least 20 minutes and shall be equipped with a door that resists passage of fire for at least 20 minutes and is designed and installed to minimize smoke leakage. A means of providing smoke venting and fresh air to the occupants shall be provided.

Exception No. 1: If the sleeping room has a door leading directly to the outside of the building with access to grade or to a stairway that meets the requirements of exterior stairs in 23-2.3.1.2, that means of escape shall be considered as meeting all the escape requirements for the sleeping room.

Exception No. 2: A second means of escape or alternate protection from each sleeping room is not required where the facility is protected throughout by an approved automatic sprinkler system complying with 23-2.3.5.

Exception No. 3: Existing approved means of escape may be continued to be used.

The provisions of 23-2.2.3 require that every sleeping room be provided with a secondary means of escape in addition to the primary means of escape required by 23-2.2.2. The only two exceptions to the requirement for a secondary means of escape are (1) if the sleeping room has a door leading directly to the outside of the building; or (2) where the residential board and care facility is protected throughout with an automatic sprinkler system in accordance with 23-2.3.5. Although either case is an acceptable alternative, Exception No. 2 may be the more practical method to use in order to avoid a required secondary means of escape. For example, if the facility is housed in an apartment building without windows that comply with item (c), an automatic sprinkler system can be installed within the facility in lieu of retrofitting complying windows for the sleeping rooms. Exception No. 2 may not be used in conjunction with Exception No. 2 to 23-2.2.1, since the result would be a single means of escape from each room and a single means of escape from each floor. Therefore, the secondary means of escape from sleeping rooms is not required only if a secondary means of escape is provided from each floor and the facility is protected by an automatic sprinkler system (23-2.3.5).

The primary purpose for the secondary means of escape is to allow the occupants to have some reasonable escape alternative when fire or smoke blocks the primary means of escape. Paragraphs 23-2.2.3(a) through (d) outlines four acceptable methods for providing a secondary means of escape or alternate protection:

(1) It is the intent of item (a) that the door, stairway, passage, or hall be independent of and remotely located from the primary means of escape required in 23-2.2.2. If the sleeping room has a second door that leads to the same hallway as the door serving as a primary means of escape, little additional protection is provided, since fire or smoke could affect both of the doors at approximately the same time. If the corridor within the facility into which a sleeping room door opens is separated from all common living spaces (as required by 23-2.2.2.2 for slow and impractical facilities located in buildings that are not protected throughout by an automatic sprinkler system using quick response or residential sprinklers), it may be determined that the arrangement is acceptable, provided the corridor does actually lead to two separate, independent, and remote means of escape. This arrangement is similar to that permitted in other occupancies in which protected corridors are provided. In such a case, little, if any, additional safety would be provided by requiring two doors from the sleeping room to the corridor.

(2) Figure 23-2 illustrates an example of how the secondary means of escape may pass through an adjacent space, such as another sleeping room, provided the occupant has free and unobstructed access to the space in accordance with item (b).

(3) The use of an operable window of the minimum dimensions specified in item (c) is permitted as a secondary means of escape from a story in prompt facilities only (23-2.2.1) but is permitted as the secondary means of escape for each sleeping room in all facilities. Figure 23-3 illustrates the minimum dimensions required for escape windows. Note that it is not possible to use the minimum dimensions for width and height and still comply with minimum area dimension. In addition to the minimum

size of the window, the utility of the window must be ensured by one of three alternatives.

First, the window must be within 20 ft (6.1 m) of grade so that jumping is possible, if necessary. The second alternative permits fire department rescue of the occupant from the window. The authority having jurisdiction must determine the acceptable means of fire department rescue (e.g., aerial ladder apparatus, ground ladders, etc.) and the additional criteria necessary for approval of the alternatives, such as fire department vehicle accessibility. The third alternative allows the occupant to reach an exterior balcony to breathe fresh air while awaiting either rescue or fire extinguishment.

(4) Item (d) is, actually, another alternative to the secondary means of escape. In lieu of the secondary means of escape, the sleeping room must be completely separated from all other parts of the building (not only the corridor). In addition, a means of smoke venting and access to fresh air must be provided. A window to the outside that does not comply with item (c) may be an acceptable means of providing smoke venting and fresh air if the window is of substantial enough size to serve as a reasonable vent.

(*For additional information, see commentary following 21-2.1.2.*)

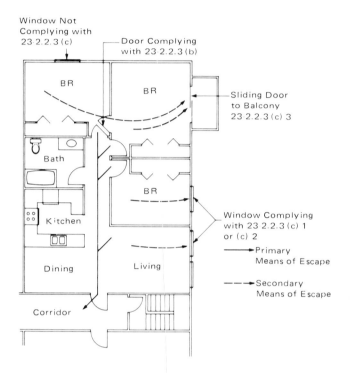

Figure 23-2. *One Potential Use of 23-2.2.3(b). An example of a board and care facility within an apartment building in which a sleeping room has a window that does not comply with 23-2.2.3(c) and in which there is no door to the corridor. The balcony door in the upper right bedroom is not required if the facility is sprinklered (see commentary on 23-2.3.5.1) or if the sleeping room in question is protected in accordance with 23-2.2.3(d).*

23-2.2.4   Enclosed Interior Stairs. Interior stairways shall be enclosed with 20-minute fire barriers with all openings equipped with smoke actuated automatic-closing or self-closing doors having a fire resistance comparable to that required for the enclosure. Stairways shall comply with 5-2.2.6.5.

Exception No. 1: Stairs connecting two levels only shall be permitted to be open to other than the street floor.

Exception No. 2: For prompt and slow facilities in buildings three stories or less in height having an approved automatic sprinkler system using quick response or residential sprinklers, stair enclosures shall not be required provided there still remains a primary means of escape from each sleeping area that does not require occupants to pass through a portion of a lower floor, unless that route is separated from all spaces on that floor by construction having a 20-minute fire resistance rating.

Exception No. 3: In prompt and slow facilities, stairways shall be permitted to be unprotected in accordance with Exception No. 2 to 23-2.3.1.1.

The need to protect interior stairs has been well documented by historical fire experience. The exceptions do permit unprotected or partially protected stairs in limited instances. For example, a stair between the first and second floor may be open to the second floor, or a stair between the basement and first level may be open to the basement, provided the stair is enclosed on the street floor. However, it is not the intent of Exception No. 1 to allow an open stair that connects a second and third floor, for example, to qualify as an "enclosed interior stair."

In prompt and slow facilities located in buildings three stories or less in height, stairs need not be enclosed if the

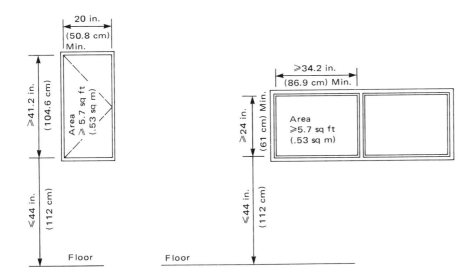

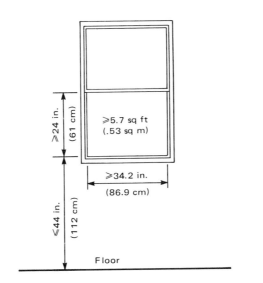

Figure 23-3. Minimum Size and Dimensions of Outside Windows Used as a Secondary Means of Escape in accordance with 23-2.2.3(c).

building is protected throughout with an automatic sprinkler system using quick response or residential sprinklers. However, there must be a primary means of escape that does not require occupants to pass through another level unless the path through that level is separated by construction having a minimum 20-minute fire resistance rating.

Therefore, if an existing board and care facility that has been determined to be prompt or slow is located in a typical two-story dwelling in which the stairway is not enclosed, the following options exist:

1. Stairs must be enclosed with construction having a 20-minute fire resistance rating in accordance with 23-2.2.4.
2. Sprinkler protection must be provided, and a primary means of escape from the second floor that is not exposed to the unprotected vertical opening must also be provided. This is usually achieved by means of a separation at the top or bottom of the stair. The separation must have a fire resistance rating of at least 20 minutes (Exception No. 3).

3. Sprinkler protection must be provided using quick response or residential sprinklers, and a primary means of escape must be provided from the second floor that does not require travel through the first floor. In this case, there is no need for a separation at the top or bottom of the stair (Exception No. 2).

4. Sprinkler protection must be provided using quick response or residential sprinklers, and the stair may be used as the primary means of escape. However, in this instance, travel area on the first floor must be separated from all other spaces by construction having a fire resistance rating of at least 20 minutes. Therefore, rooms that are typically open to the stair, such as the living and dining rooms, must be separated from the stair. (*Also see 23-2.2.1 and 23-2.2.2.*)

Figure 23-4 illustrates the use of Exception No. 1 to 23-2.2.4

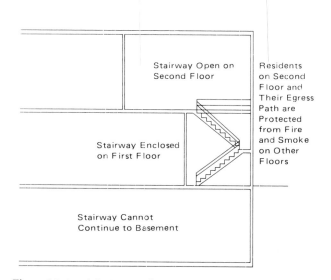

Stairway Open on Second Floor

Residents on Second Floor and Their Egress Path are Protected from Fire and Smoke on Other Floors

Stairway Enclosed on First Floor

Stairway Cannot Continue to Basement

Figure 23-4.   A Stairway That Connects the First Floor to the Second Floor May Be Open to the Second Floor.

23-2.2.5 Doors.

23-2.2.5.1 No door or path of travel to a means of escape shall be less than 28 in. (71 cm) wide.

Exception: Bathroom doors shall be a minimum of 24 in. (61 cm) wide.

23-2.2.5.2 Every closet door latch shall be such that it can be readily opened from the inside in case of an emergency.

23-2.2.5.3 Every bathroom door shall be designed to allow opening from the outside during an emergency when locked.

23-2.2.5.4 No door in any means of escape shall be locked against egress when the building is occupied.

Paragraph 23-2.2.5.4 prohibits a residential board and care facility from having any door in the means of egress locked against egress while the building is occupied. This is consistent with a fundamental principle of the *Code*. This requirement permits a door to have a locking device that allows the door to be opened from within the facility for the purpose of egress but does not allow the door to be opened from outside the facility. Ordinary double cylinder locks and chain locks do not meet these provisions.

The language of 5-2.1.5.1 is clear: "Locks, if provided, shall not require the use of a key, tool, special knowledge, or effort for operation from the inside of the building." This eliminates double cylinder locks and chain locks that require a key in order to be operated from the inside. Paragraph 5-2.1.5.3 requires doors to be opened by means of a simple operation; two-handed knobs and other features are specifically prohibited.

It is important to remember that the resident sleeping room doors are doors in the means of egress. However, 5-2.1.5.3 permits the sleeping room doors to have additional releasing actions. (*See 5-2.1.5.3 for details.*)

23-2.2.6 The width, riser, and treads of every stair shall comply with the minimum requirements for Class B stairs as described in 5-2.2.

Exception: Existing noncomplying stairs may be continued to be used subject to the approval of the authority having jurisdiction.

23-2.2.7 Winders in accordance with 5-2.2.2.8 are permitted.

23-2.3 Protection.

23-2.3.1 Protection of Vertical Openings.

23-2.3.1.1 Vertical openings shall be protected so that no primary exit route is exposed to an unprotected vertical opening. The vertical opening is considered protected if the opening is cut off and enclosed in a manner that provides a fire resisting capability of not less than 20 minutes and resists the passage of smoke. Any doors or openings shall have fire and smoke resisting capability equivalent to that of the enclosure and be self-closing or automatic-closing in accordance with 5-2.1.8.

Exception No. 1: For prompt and slow facilities in buildings three stories or less in height having an approved automatic sprinkler system using quick response or residential sprinklers, stair enclosures shall not be required provided there still remains a primary means of escape from each sleeping area that does not require occupants to pass through a portion of a lower floor, unless that route is separated from all spaces on that floor by construction having a 20-minute fire resistance rating.

Exception No. 2: In buildings three or fewer stories in height that house prompt and slow facilities protected throughout by an approved automatic sprinkler system in accordance with 23-2.3.5, unprotected vertical openings are permitted. Access to a primary means of escape from each sleeping room and living area that complies with 23-2.2.2 shall remain.

This provision coordinates with 23-2.2.2 and 23-2.2.4. The lack of vertical opening protection has been identified as a contributing factor in many of the multiple-death fires in residential board and care facilities. Note that Exception No. 1 allows the egress to pass through an unprotected vertical opening but requires quick response or residential sprinklers. Exception No. 2 requires the egress path to be protected but allows any type of sprinkler.

See commentary for 23-2.2.4 for a further description of the protection of stairways in existing board and care facilities.

23-2.3.1.2 Exterior stairs shall be reasonably protected against blockage caused by fire that would simultaneously expose both the interior and the exterior means of escape. This shall be accomplished through separation by physical distance, arrangement of the stairs, protection of the openings exposing the stairs, or other means acceptable to the authority having jurisdiction.

This paragraph does not mandate compliance with the provisions of Chapter 5 for exterior stairs. However, if the exterior stair is to be used as a primary means of escape, protection should be provided to reduce the likelihood that a fire within the facility will render the stair useless. While this provision applies to small facilities, it should be noted that 5-2.2.3.2 does exempt outside stairs serving an existing three-story building from the protection requirements of that section if a remotely located second exit is provided. In this case, a remote secondary means of escape may eliminate the need to protect the exterior stair.

23-2.3.2 **Hazardous Areas.** Any hazardous area shall be protected in accordance with the following:

(a) Any hazardous area that is on the same floor as, and is in or abuts, a primary means of escape or a sleeping room shall be protected by either:

1. An enclosure with a fire resistance rating of at least 1 hour with a self-closing or automatic-closing fire door in accordance with 5-2.1.8 having a fire protection rating of at least ¾ hour, or

2. Automatic sprinkler protection, in accordance with 23-2.3.5, of the hazardous area and a separation that will resist the passage of smoke between the hazardous area and the sleeping area or primary exit route. Any doors in such separation shall be self-closing or automatic-closing in accordance with 5-2.1.8.

(b) Other hazardous areas shall be protected by either:

1. An enclosure having a fire resistance rating of at least 20 minutes with a self-closing or automatic-closing door in accordance with 5-2.1.8 equivalent to at least a 1¾-in. (4.4-cm) thick solid bonded wood core construction, or

2. Automatic sprinkler protection, in accordance with 23-2.3.5, of the hazardous area regardless of enclosure.

The protection of hazardous areas is based on the potential impact a fire in the area would have on a primary means of escape or on sleeping rooms. If the hazardous area is located on the same floor as sleeping rooms or a primary means of escape, and a room or means of escape is exposed to the hazardous area, the construction shall be capable of containing a fire, or automatic sprinkler protection shall be provided to control a fire, and the construction shall be capable of resisting smoke spread outside the area. If the hazardous area is on a different floor or does not abut a primary means of escape or sleeping rooms, the construction shall be capable of containing a fire for a limited time, or automatic sprinkler protection shall be provided to control a fire.

For example, if a basement in a wood frame residence is used for the storage of combustible materials, the basement is not a required means of escape. If the basement storage area does not abut a sleeping area on the same floor, sheathing the ceiling to provide fire resistance is not required if the basement is sprinklered.

23-2.3.3 Interior Finishes. Interior wall and ceiling finish shall be Class A or Class B in accordance with Section 6-5. There are no requirements for interior floor finish.

Exception: Class C interior wall and ceiling finish is permitted in prompt facilities.

The 1985 Edition contained an exception for structural elements of heavy timber. The issue is now addressed by similar language in 6-5.3.4.

23-2.3.4 Detection, Alarm, and Communication Systems.

See Supplement 2.

23-2.3.4.1 Fire Alarm Systems. A manual fire alarm system shall be provided in accordance with Section 7-6. Presignal systems are prohibited.

Exception No. 1: If there are interconnected smoke detectors meeting the requirements of 23-2.3.4.2 and there is at least one manual fire alarm station per floor arranged to continuously sound the smoke detector alarms.

Exception No. 2: Other manually activated continuously sounding alarms acceptable to the authority having jurisdiction.

A means of manually initiating the fire protective signaling system is required. If there is a "system" of interconnected multiple station smoke detectors, the manual fire alarm station requirement can be met by providing a manual station on each floor that is integrated with the smoke detectors. However, Exception No. 2 recognizes that, in a small building, a sophisticated fire protective

signaling system that employs components "listed" for use in fire protective signaling systems may not be necessary. The requirements can be satisfied by the installation of electric bells activated by a clearly identified switch on each floor where approved by the authority having jurisdiction.

23-2.3.4.2* Smoke Detectors. Approved smoke detectors shall be installed in accordance with 7-6.2.9. These shall be powered from the building electrical system and, when activated, shall initiate an alarm that is audible in all sleeping areas. Detectors shall be installed on all levels, including basements, but excluding crawl spaces and unfinished attics. Additional detectors shall be installed for living rooms, dens, day room, and similar spaces.

Exception: Detectors are not required in buildings protected throughout by an approved automatic sprinkler system in accordance with 23-2.3.5 using quick response or residential sprinklers.

A-23-2.3.4.2 Most often detectors sounding an alarm at 85 dBA or greater, installed outside the bedroom area, will meet the intent of this requirement. Detectors remotely located from the bedroom may not be loud enough to awaken the average person. In such cases, it is recommended that detectors be interconnected so that the activation of any detector will cause all detectors to alarm.

This paragraph does not specifically require a "system" of smoke detectors in a small facility. If the building is small enough, single station detectors may be able to meet the criterion of audibility in all sleeping areas. However, if the building is of significant size or consists of multiple levels, interconnected multiple station detectors will probably be needed. Additional detectors are required in living rooms and day rooms because fire statistics indicate that most multiple-death fires in board and care homes start in such rooms. In order to waive the requirement for detectors as permitted by the exception, the entire building must be protected with an automatic sprinkler system using quick response or residential sprinklers in accordance with 23-2.3.5.

23-2.3.4.3 Smoke Detectors. Each sleeping room shall be provided with an approved single station smoke detector in accordance with 7-6.2.9 that is powered from the building electrical system.

Exception No. 1: Rooms protected by quick response sprinklers or residential sprinklers in buildings protected throughout by an approved supervised automatic sprinkler system in accordance with 23-2.3.5. The Exception to 23-2.3.4.2 shall not be used in conjunction with this exception.

Exception No. 2: Existing battery-powered detectors, rather than building electrical service-powered detectors, shall be accepted where, in the opinion of the authority having jurisdiction, the facility has demonstrated testing, maintenance, and battery replacement programs that ensure the reliability of power to the detectors.

Exception No. 3: Buildings equipped with smoke detectors installed in accordance with 23-2.3.4.2. The Exception to 23-2.3.4.2 shall not be used in conjunction with this exception.

Single station detectors shall be provided in every sleeping room in an existing board and care facility unless the smoke detectors required in Section 23-2.3.4.2 are provided. Therefore, the *Code* requires either that detectors be provided on every level and in every common space (23-2.3.4.2) or that individual room detectors be provided (23-2.3.4.3). The room detectors may be single station detectors and need not initiate any alarm outside a sleeping room. It is anticipated that an occupant will hear the detector and initiate the fire alarm system by the manual means required in Section 23-2.3.4.1.

In lieu of smoke detectors powered from the building electrical system, battery-powered smoke detectors are acceptable only if they are existing detectors. If an existing board and care facility does not currently have the smoke detectors required by 23-2.3.4.2 and does not currently have sleeping room detectors, detectors must be added. The facility has the option of complying with either 23-2.3.4.2 or 23-2.3.4.3; however, the detectors must be connected to the building electrical system or another power supply permitted in NFPA 74, *Standard for the Installation, Maintenance, and Use of Household Fire Warning Equipment.*[7] The *Code* does not permit newly installed detectors to be battery-powered.

In addition to the restriction on battery-powered detectors, the facility must provide satisfactory docu-

mentation to the authority having jurisdiction confirming that the detectors are tested and maintained, and that the batteries are replaced by a regular program to ensure reliability.

Since smoke detection for common spaces in accordance with 23-2.3.4.2 is allowed to omit sleeping room detectors where quick response or residential sprinklers are used, Exception No. 1 is of minimal value because of similar allowances in Exception No. 3. Table 23-3 illustrates the smoke detector coverage options.

Table 23-3. Options for Smoke Detector Locations

Sprinkler Protection	Room Detectors (House Powered or Battery Powered, if Existing)		Corridor/Common Area Detectors (House Powered)
None or Not QRS	NR		Required
RS—QRS in rooms	NR		Required
RS—QRS throughout	Required	or	Required

23-2.3.5 Automatic Extinguishing Systems

See Supplement 3.

23-2.3.5.1* Where an automatic sprinkler system is installed, for either total or partial building coverage, the system shall be in accordance with Section 7-7 and shall activate the fire alarm system in accordance with 23-2.3.4.1.

Exception No. 1: In prompt and slow facilities, a sprinkler system complying with NFPA 13D, Standard for the Installation of Sprinkler Systems in One- and Two-Family Dwellings and Mobile Homes, shall be permitted. Automatic sprinklers are not required in closets not exceeding 24 sq ft (2.2 sq m) and bathrooms not exceeding 55 sq ft (5.1 sq m) provided such spaces are finished with lath and plaster or materials providing a 15-minute thermal barrier.

Exception No. 2: In impractical facilities, a sprinkler system complying with NFPA 13D, Standard for the Installation of Sprinkler Systems in One- and Two-Family Dwellings and Mobile Homes, with a 30-minute water supply shall be permitted. All habitable areas and closets shall be sprinklered. Automatic sprinklers are not required in bathrooms not exceeding 55 sq ft (5.1 sq m) provided such spaces are finished with lath and plaster or material providing a 15-minute thermal barrier.

Exception No. 3: In prompt and slow facilities, where an automatic sprinkler system is installed in accordance with NFPA 13, Standard for the Installation of Sprinkler Systems, sprinklers are not required in closets not exceeding 24 sq ft (2.2 sq m) and bathrooms not exceeding 55 sq ft (5.1 sq m) provided such spaces are finished with lath and plaster or materials providing a 15-minute thermal barrier.

A-23-2.3.5.1 The decision to allow the use of the criteria from NFPA 13D, *Standard for the Installation of Sprinkler Systems in One- and Two-Family Dwellings and Mobile Homes,* in these occupancies is based on: (1) the desire of the Committee to obtain a level of fire suppression and control approximately the same as that delivered by residential facilities protected by such systems (*see the appendix statement in NFPA 13D*), and (2) the fact that potential fire exposure and challenge to the suppression system in a small board and care facility are of the same nature and no more severe than that found in residences.

This paragraph does not require the installation of automatic sprinklers. The purpose of this section is to establish the criteria to be followed if the facility chooses to use the sprinkler alternatives provided in this chapter.

It is recognized that NFPA 13R, *Installation of Sprinkler Systems in Residential Occupancies up to and Including Four Stories in Height,*[6] is not specifically referenced as required by 7-7.1.1. However, virtually all NFPA 13R systems, where properly designed and installed, would also comply with NFPA 13D, *Standard for the Installation of Sprinkler Systems in One- and Two-Family Dwellings and Mobile Homes.*[5] One exception is that NFPA 13R does permit the use of standard sprinklers where smoke detectors are provided within a room. Furthermore, since 23-3.3.5.1 permits compliance with NFPA 13R in large facilities, it is reasonable to accept such systems in small facilities as well.

The omission of sprinklers in bathrooms and closets as permitted in Exception No. 1 is intended to reinforce

the exemption for sprinklers in these areas. All the exceptions for sprinkler coverage permitted by NFPA 13D, *Standard for the Installation of Sprinkler Systems in One- and Two-Family Dwellings and Mobile Homes,*[5] (and NFPA 13R, *Standard for the Installation of Sprinkler Systems in Residential Occupancies up to and Including Four Stories in Height*[6]) are applicable. However, contrary to NFPA 13D (and NFPA 13R), the combustibility of plumbing fixtures is not an issue. NFPA 13D (and NFPA 13R) address combustibility of plumbing fixtures, not because they are viewed as a source of ignition but because frequently wall finish materials are not installed behind prefabricated enclosures. Therefore, the exception clearly states that the bathroom must be finished with plaster or materials providing a 15-minute thermal barrier. This includes the area behind a prefabricated enclosure. Exception No. 3 provides similar exceptions for a sprinkler system in accordance with NFPA 13, *Standard for the Installation of Sprinkler Systems.*[4]

Exception No. 2 recognizes the "defend in place" concept utilized in impractical facilities by increasing the duration of the water supply and by mandating sprinklers in all habitable areas, including closets. Therefore, those areas in which sprinklers are not required by NFPA 13D (and NFPA 13R) are greatly reduced.

23-2.3.5.2 **Impractical.** All impractical facilities shall be protected throughout by an approved supervised automatic sprinkler system in accordance with 23-2.3.5.1.

This paragraph requires that all small facilities housing occupants classed as impractical to evacuate be fully sprinklered. If sprinkler protection is provided only in the board and care facility, and not throughout the building, the exceptions for sprinklers that require building protection (i.e., 23-2.1.3.3, 23-2.2.1, 23-2.2.2.2, 23-2.2.4, 23-2.3.1.1, 23-2.3.4.2, 23-2.3.4.3, and 23-2.3.6.4) may not be used.

23-2.3.5.3 Sprinkler piping serving not more than six sprinklers for any isolated hazardous area shall be permitted to be installed in accordance with 7-7.1.2. In new installations, where more than two sprinklers are installed in a single area, water flow detection shall be provided to sound the fire alarm system required by 23-2.3.4.1. Duration of water supplies shall be as required by 23-2.3.5.1.

Paragraph 7-7.1.2 provides a sprinkler design specification of 0.15 gpm/sq ft (6.1 L/m/sq m) for systems using six sprinklers or less where protecting an isolated area. In areas where the connection to the domestic water supply results in unlimited duration due to the presence of public water, duration is not an issue. However, facilities that utilize a private water system (well) are not as fortunate. Therefore, the duration criteria of 23-2.3.5.1 is specified.

23-2.3.6 Construction of Corridor Walls.

23-2.3.6.1 The separation walls of sleeping rooms shall be capable of resisting fire for at least 20 minutes. This is considered to be achieved if the partitioning is finished on both sides with the lath and plaster or material providing a 15-minute thermal barrier. Sleeping room doors shall be substantial doors, such as those of 1¾-in. (4.4-cm) thick solid bonded wood core construction or of other construction of equal or greater stability and fire integrity. Any vision panels shall be of wired glass not exceeding 1,296 sq in. (0.84 sq m) each in area and installed in approved frames.

The intent of the 20-minute fire resistance rating is to require a nominal fire rating, particularly where the fire rating of existing partitions cannot be documented. Examples of acceptable partition assemblies include, but are not limited to, ½-in. (1.3-cm) gypsum board, wood lath and plaster, gypsum lath, or metal lath, and plaster.

Exception No. 1: In prompt facilities, all sleeping rooms shall be separated from the escape route by walls and doors that are at least smoke resistant.

Exception No. 2: Corridor walls and doors that are capable of resisting the passage of smoke and that are protected by automatic sprinklers in accordance with 23-2.3.5 on both sides of the wall and door. In such instances, there is no limitation on the type or size of glass panels.

In essence, the intent of the exception is that the fire resistance requirements shall not apply where sprinkler protection is provided on both sides of the wall and door.

Exception No. 3: Sleeping arrangements that are not located in sleeping rooms are permitted for nonresident staff members provided the audibility of the alarm in the sleeping area is sufficient to waken staff who may be sleeping.

It is recognized that there are many board and care homes that employ "sleep-in" staff. The exception is intended to allow staff members to sleep in locations that are not separated from the corridors by construction meeting the minimum requirements for construction of corridor walls. The placement of a staff cot in the supervisor's station, living room, or other room is not intended to reclassify that room as a sleeping room.

Exception No. 4: In previously approved facilities where the facility has demonstrated to the authority having jurisdiction that the group is capable of evacuating the building in eight minutes or less or achieves an E-score of three or less using Chapter 5 of NFPA 101M, Alternative Approaches to Life Safety, sleeping rooms shall be separated from escape routes by walls and doors that are at least smoke resistant.

This exception applies only where previously approved. It can no longer be used to evaluate facilities.

23-2.3.6.2 There shall be no louvers or operable transoms or other air passages penetrating the wall except properly installed heating and utility installations other than transfer grilles. Transfer grilles are prohibited.

23-2.3.6.3 Doors shall be provided with latches or other mechanisms suitable for keeping the doors closed. No doors shall be arranged so as to prevent the occupant from closing the door.

23-2.3.6.4 Doors shall be self-closing or automatic-closing in accordance with 5-2.1.8.

Exception: Door closing devices are not required in buildings protected throughout by an approved automatic sprinkler system in accordance with 23-2.3.5.1.

This exception differs from Exception No. 2 to 23-2.3.6.1. In order for the door-closing device to be waived under this exception, the entire building must be protected throughout by an approved automatic sprinkler system.

23-2.4 Operating Features. (*See Chapter 31.*)

23-2.5 Building Services.

23-2.5.1 Utilities. Utilities shall comply with Section 7-1.

23-2.5.2 Heating, Ventilating, and Air Conditioning Equipment.

23-2.5.2.1 Heating, ventilating, and air conditioning equipment shall comply with the provisions of 7-2.1 and 7-2.2 except as otherwise required in this chapter.

23-2.5.2.2 No stove or combustion heater shall be so located as to block escape in case of fire caused by the malfunction of the stove or heater.

23-2.5.2.3 Unvented fuel-fired heaters shall not be used in any residential board and care facility.

This paragraph prohibits the use of typical kerosene portable heaters, as well as other fuel-fired, nonvented heaters.

SECTION 23-3 Large Facilities

See Table 23-4 on page 737 for summary of major requirements.

23-3.1 General.

23-3.1.1 Scope. This section applies to residential board and care occupancies providing sleeping accommodations for more than 16 residents. Facilities having sleeping accommodations for not more than 16 residents shall be evaluated in accordance with Section 23-2, "Small Facilities." However, existing facilities meeting the requirements of this section are considered to meet the requirements of Section 23-2 for prompt evacuation capability or slow evacuation capability.

23-3.1.2 Requirements Based on Evacuation Capability.

23-3.1.2.1 Prompt and Slow. Large facilities shall comply with the requirements of Section 23-3 as indicated for the appropriate evacuation capability.

Exception No. 1*: Facilities where the authority having jurisdiction has determined equivalent safety is provided in accordance with Section 1-6.

A-23-3.1.2.1 Exception No. 1. In determining equivalancy for existing buildings, conversions, modernizations, renovations, or unusual design concepts, the authority having jurisdiction may accept evaluations based on NFPA 101M, *Alternative Approaches to Life Safety*, Chapter 6.

The 1988 Edition of NFPA 101M was designed for use with the 1988 Edition of NFPA 101 and cannot be used to evaluate facilities under the 1991 *Life Safety Code*. At the time this *Handbook* went to press, the Committee on Safety to Life was preparing the 1992 Edition of NFPA 101M to use in conjunction with the 1991 *Life Safety Code*.

Exception No. 2: Facilities that were previously approved as complying with 23-3.1.2.2.

Exception No. 2 has been restricted to facilities that were previously approved as having complied with the criteria for impractical facilities. It is anticipated that the staffing level in prompt and slow facilities is not the same as that which is typically found in health care facilities or impractical facilities.

23-3.1.2.2 Impractical. Facilities housing groups of persons classed as impractical to evacuate shall meet the requirements for limited care facilities in Chapter 13.

Exception*: Facilities where the authority having jurisdiction has determined equivalent safety is provided in accordance with Section 1-6.

A-23-3.1.2.2 Exception. In determining equivalency for existing buildings, the authority having jurisdiction may accept evaluations based on NFPA 101M, *Alternative Approaches to Life Safety*, Chapter 6, using the following mandatory safety requirements:

ZONE LOCATION	CONTAIN-MENT S_a	ENTINGUISH-MENT S_b	PEOPLE MOVEMENT S_c
FIRST FLOOR	5	6	3
ABOVE OR BELOW FIRST FLOOR	9	8	5
OVER 75 ft (23 m) IN HEIGHT	9	8	5

Table 23-4. **Summary of Major Requirements for Existing Large Facilities**

Parameter	Evacuation Capability		
	Prompt	Slow	Impractical
1. Construction 23-3.1.4	See Table 23-3	See Table 23-3	13-1.6
2. Means of Egress 23-3.2	2 Exits per Floor	2 Exits per Floor	Section 13-2
3. Vertical Openings 23-3.3.1	6-2.4	6-2.4	13-3.1
4. Protection of Hazardous Areas 23-3.3.2	1 hour enclosure or sprinklers	1 hour enclosure or sprinklers	13-3.2
5. Interior Finish 23-3.3.3	Class A and B Class I and II Corr. and Exit Floor	Class A and B Class I and II Corr. and Exit Floor	13-3.3
6. Manual F.A. 23-3.3.4	Local	Local	13-3.4
7. Smoke Detection 23-3.3.4.5, 23-3.3.4.6	Sleeping Rooms—Single Station and Corridors and Common Areas per NFPA 72E	Sleeping Rooms—Single Station and Corridors and Common Areas per NFPA 72E	13-3.4
8. Sprinklers 23-3.3.5	Not Required (*Also see Table 23-3*)	Not Required (*Also see Table 23-3*)	Required Except Certain Type I and II (222) Bldgs. 13-3.5
9. Separation of Sleeping Rooms 23-3.3.6.2	20 minutes	20 minutes	13-3.6
10. Smoke Control 23-3.3.7	Smoke Barrier	Smoke Barrier	13-3.7

The difficulty in evacuating this type of facility is comparable to that of a health care facility. Therefore, reference should be made to Chapter 13, "Existing Health Care Occupancies." Due to this difficulty in evacuation and the fact that residents of these facilities will typically require additional care, a staff level that more closely approximates that of a health care facility is anticipated.

The 1988 Edition of NFPA 101M was designed for use with the 1988 Edition of NFPA 101 and cannot be used to evaluate facilities under the 1991 *Life Safety Code*. At the time this *Handbook* went to press, the Committee on Safety to Life was preparing the 1992 Edition of NFPA 101M to use in conjunction with the 1991 *Life Safety Code*.

23-3.1.3 Minimum Construction Requirements.

23-3.1.3.1 Construction requirements for large facilities shall be as required by this section. Where noted as "fully sheathed," the interior shall be covered with lath and plaster or materials providing a 15-minute thermal barrier.

23-3.1.3.2 For the purpose of construction requirements, stories shall be counted starting with the primary level of exit discharge and ending with the highest occupied level. For the purpose of this section, the primary level of exit discharge of a building shall be that floor that is level with or above finished grade of the exterior wall line for 50 percent or more of its perimeter. Building levels below the primary level shall not be counted as a story in determining the height of the building.

23-3.1.3.3 The minimum construction requirements (*see Section 6-2*), based on the highest story normally used by board and care residents, are:

(a) *One- or Two-Story Facilities.* Any construction type that meets the requirements for 1-hour or greater fire resistance rating, or is Type IV (2HH), or is fully sheathed, or is protected throughout by an approved automatic sprinkler system in accordance with 23-3.3.5.

Exception to (a): One-story facilities having 30 or fewer residents that house groups capable of prompt evacuation shall be of any type construction.

(b) *Three- to Six-Story Facilities.* Type I, II, or III construction that meets the requirements for 1-hour or greater fire resistance rating and Type IV construction that is protected throughout by an approved automatic sprinkler system in accordance with 23-3.3.5, or any other type of construction that is both sheathed and protected throughout by an approved automatic sprinkler system in accordance with 23-3.3.5, other than Type V (000).

Exception to (b): Three- to four-story facilities of Type V (000) construction that are both fully sheathed and protected throughout by an approved supervised automatic sprinkler system in accordance with 23-3.3.5.

(c) *Facilities More Than Six Stories High.* Any Type I or Type II (222) construction. Any Type II (111), Type III (211), or Type IV (2HH) construction that is protected throughout by an approved automatic sprinkler system in accordance with 23-3.3.5.

Exception to (a), (b), and (c): Any building of Type I or Type II (111) or (222) construction may include roofing systems involving combustible supports, decking, or roofing provided:

1. The roof covering meets Class A requirements in accordance with NFPA 256, Standard Methods of Fire Tests of Roof Coverings, and

2. The roof is separated from all occupied portions of the building by a noncombustible floor assembly having at least a 2-hour fire resistance rating that includes at least 2½ in.

(6.4 cm) of concrete or gypsum fill. To qualify for this exception, the attic or other space so developed shall be either unused or protected throughout by an approved automatic sprinkler system in accordance with 23-3.3.5.1.

Minimum construction requirements are necessary, since this chapter requires evacuation only to a "point of safety." Therefore, the residents of a large facility will frequently remain inside the building during a fire emergency. Consequently, the stability of the building must be maintained either by the use of fire resistant construction or by automatic suppression of a fire initiated before it can threaten the stability of the building (*see Table 23-5 for a summary of permissible construction types*). Note that, in the Exception to (a), buildings from which there is a reasonable expectation of prompt evacuation to the exterior of the building are exempted from the minimum construction requirements.

23-3.1.4 **Occupant Load.** The occupant load in numbers of persons for whom exits are to be provided shall be determined on the basis of one person per 200 sq ft (18.6 sq m) gross floor area or the maximum probable population of any room or section under consideration, whichever is greater. The occupant load of any open mezzanine or balcony shall be added to the occupant load of the floor below for the purpose of determining exit capability.

If the actual occupant load of the facility exceeds one person per 200 sq ft (18.6 sq m), the exit capacity must be designed to meet the anticipated occupant load. The determination of actual occupant load should be based on the total number of residents, staff, and visitors. However, the minimum exit capacity must not be less than that required for a density of one person per 200 sq ft (18.6 sq m).

Since mezzanines need not have their own exits, the occupant load of the mezzanine must be included with the occupant load of the floor below.

23-3.2 **Means of Egress.**

23-3.2.1 All means of egress shall be in accordance with Chapter 5.

Table 23-5. Minimum Construction Standards for Large Facilities with Prompt and Slow Evacuation Capability

Construction Type	Number of Stories						
	1	2	3	4	5	6	7+
Type I	X	X	X	X	X	X	X
Type II (222)	X	X	X	X	X	X	X
Type II (111)	X	X	X	X	X	X	(AS)
Type II (000)†	*/(AS)	*/(AS)	*(AS)	*(AS)	*(AS)	*(AS)	NP
Type III (211)	X	X	X	X	X	X	(AS)
Type III (200)†	*/(AS)	*/(AS)	*(AS)	*(AS)	*(AS)	*(AS)	NP
Type IV (2HH)	X	X	(AS)	(AS)	(AS)	(AS)	(AS)
Type V (111)	X	X	*(AS)	*(AS)	*(AS)	*(AS)	NP
Type V (000)†	*/(AS)	*/(AS)	*(AS)	*(AS)	NP	NP	NP

X = Permitted
NP = Not permitted
(AS) = Permitted if sprinklered
*(AS) = Permitted if sheathed *and* sprinklered
*/(AS) = Permitted if sheathed *or* sprinklered
† = Permitted up to 1 story high, unsheathed and unsprinklered if housing 30 or fewer residents with prompt evacuation capability.

A general reference is made to Chapter 5 in place of repeating many of its provisions. Many of the requirements contained in Section 23-3.2 are Chapter 5 provisions that are options for the occupancy chapters, such as the Exception to 23-3.2.2.2(b), which allows the use of special locking arrangements per 5-2.1.6; or that prohibit the use of an item if it is not listed (note that alternating tread devices are not listed in 23-3.2.2); or that establish restrictions based on criteria provided in Chapter 5, such as the limits placed on travel distance in 23-3.2.6.

23-3.2.2 Means of Egress Components.

23-3.2.2.1 Components of means of egress shall be limited to the types described in 23-3.2.2.2 through 23-3.2.2.7.

23-3.2.2.2 Doors.

(a) Doors shall comply with 5-2.1.

(b) No door in any means of egress shall be locked against egress when the building is occupied.

Paragraph 23-3.2.2.2(b) prohibits a facility from having any door locked "against egress" while the building is occupied. This is consistent with a fundamental principle of the *Code*. This requirement permits a door to be equipped with a locking device that allows the door to be opened from within the building for the purpose of egress but does not allow the door to be opened from outside the building. Ordinary double cylinder locks and chain locks do not meet these provisions since they require keys for operation.

The language of 5-2.1.5.1 is clear: "Locks, if provided, shall not require the use of a key, tool, special knowledge, or effort for operation from the inside of the building." This eliminates double cylinder locks and chain locks that require a key to be operated from the inside. Paragraph 5-2.1.5.3 requires the use of a simple operation to open the door; locks that require a two-handed knob and similar operations are specifically prohibited.

It is important to remember that the resident sleeping room doors are doors in the means of egress. However, 5-2.1.5.3 permits the sleeping room doors to have additional releasing actions. (*See 5-2.1.5.3 for details.*)

Exception to (b): Special locking requirements complying with 5-2.1.6 are permitted.

The exception does permit the use of special locking arrangements that comply with 5-2.1.6. This requires that the building either be protected throughout by automatic sprinklers or be equipped throughout with a fire detection system. The 15- or 30-second delay permitted by 5-2.1.6 does not affect the immediate release of the lock upon activation of the sprinklers or detectors, or upon loss of power to the lock. This device helps provide security for infrequently used doors or stairs in board and care facilities, while doors remain available for use. Chains and padlocks are unable to provide this feature.

(c) Every stairwell door shall allow reentry from the stairwell to the interior of the building, or an automatic release shall be provided to unlock all stairwell doors to allow reentry. Such automatic release shall be activated with the initiation of the building fire alarm system. Also, the doors shall unlock upon loss of power controlling the lock or locking mechanism.

The provisions of 23-3.2.2.2(c) are more stringent than those of Chapter 5 since the provisions of Exception No. 1 to 5-2.1.5.2 (selected reentry doors) are not allowed in board and care facilities. The Committee reasoned that board and care facilities are not subject to the circumstance experienced by business occupancies in which tenants lease an entire floor with no public corridor arrangement. Therefore, the exception is unwarranted. If a board and care facility wishes to restrict normal movement in stairs, the automatic release system can be used.

(d) Revolving doors complying with 5-2.1.10 are permitted.

(e) Horizontal sliding doors in accordance with 5-2.1.14 shall be permitted to be used in a means of egress serving an occupant load of less than 50.

23-3.2.2.3 **Stairs.** Stairs shall comply with 5-2.2.

23-3.2.2.4 **Smokeproof Enclosures.** Smokeproof enclosures shall comply with 5-2.3.

23-3.2.2.5 **Horizontal Exits.** Horizontal exits shall comply with 5-2.4.

23-3.2.2.6 **Ramps.** Ramps shall comply with 5-2.5.

23-3.2.2.7 **Exit Passageways.** Exit passageways shall comply with 5-2.6.

23-3.2.3 **Capacity of Means of Egress.**

23-3.2.3.1 The capacity of means of egress shall be in accordance with Section 5-3.

23-3.2.3.2 Street floor exits shall be sufficient for the occupant load of the street floor plus the required capacity of stairs and ramps discharging onto the street floor.

Paragraph 23-3.2.3.2 requires street floor exit designs that have sufficient width to accommodate the convergence of occupants discharging through exits from the street floor with those discharging down from the upper floors and up from the lower floors. Section 5-7 restricts the number and arrangement of stairs that are used to discharge through the street floor.

Figure 23-5 shows an arrangement of multiple exits discharging on the street floor.

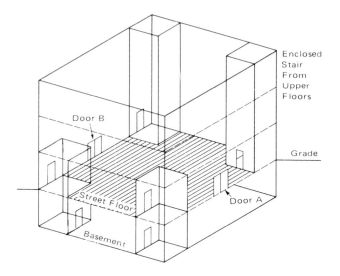

Figure 23-5. *Capacity of Means of Egress in Accordance with 23-3.2.3.2. Required widths of Doors A and B are based on the anticipated number of people using them. There should be 0.2 inches (0.5 cm) allowed for each person on the street floor and for every person traveling down from the upper floors and up from the lower floors who must traverse the street floor to exit.*

23-3.2.3.3 The width of corridors shall be sufficient for the occupant load served, but not less than 44 in. (112 cm).

Exception: Corridors serving an occupant load less than 50 shall not be less than 36 in. (91 cm) in width.

23-3.2.4 **Number of Exits.** Not fewer than two exits shall be accessible from every floor, including floors below the level of exit discharge and occupied for public purposes.

This paragraph contains provisions similar to those for hotels. There are no exceptions to permit a building with a single exit. It should also be noted that 5-4.1.2 will require a greater number of exits for floors with more than 500 people. This will probably have minimal impact on board and care facilities, since such large floors would probably need additional exits to meet travel distance limitations.

23-3.2.5 **Arrangement of Exits.**

23-3.2.5.1 Access to all required exits shall be in accordance with Section 5-5.

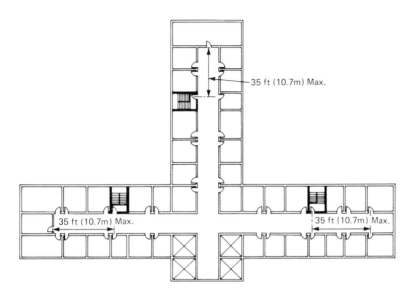

35 ft (10.7m) Max.

35 ft (10.7m) Max.

35 ft (10.7m) Max.

23-3.2.5.2 Exits shall be so arranged that, from any corridor room door, exits shall be accessible in at least two different directions.

Exception: Up to the first 35 ft (10 m) of exit travel from a corridor room door may be within a corridor with access only in one direction.

Note that this exception actually describes a modified dead end and modified common path of travel. This dead end is not always measured as a true dead end, since the room door may not be located at the end of the corridor; neither is it a true common path of travel, since the distance is measured from the corridor room door and not the most remote point. Figure 23-6 illustrates the method of measuring in accordance with the Exception to 22-3.2.5.2.

23-3.2.6 **Travel Distance to Exits.**

23-3.2.6.1 Any exit shall be such that it will not be necessary to travel more than 100 ft (30 m) from the door of any room to reach the nearest exit. Travel distance to exits shall be measured in accordance with Section 5-6.

Exception No. 1: Travel distance to exits shall not exceed 200 ft (60 m) for exterior ways of exit access arranged in accordance with 5-5.3.

Exception No. 2: Travel distance to exits shall not exceed 200 ft (60 m) if the exit access and any portion of the building that is tributary to the exit access are protected throughout by approved automatic sprinkler systems. In addition, the portion of the building in which the 200-ft (60-m) travel distance is permitted shall be separated from the remainder of the building by construction having a fire resistance rating of not less than 1 hour for buildings not greater than three stories in height and 2 hours for buildings greater than three stories in height.

See Figure 23-7.

23-3.2.6.2 Travel distance within a room or suite or living unit to a corridor door shall not exceed 75 ft (23 m).

Exception: Travel distance shall not exceed 125 ft (48 m) in buildings protected throughout by an approved automatic sprinkler system in accordance with 23-3.3.5.

Paragraph 23-3.2.6.2 limits the travel distance permitted within a room or suite. Note that the travel distance may be increased by 50 ft (15 m) in buildings protected throughout by an automatic sprinkler system.

23-3.2.7 **Discharge from Exits.**

23-3.2.7.1 Exit discharge shall comply with Section 5-7.

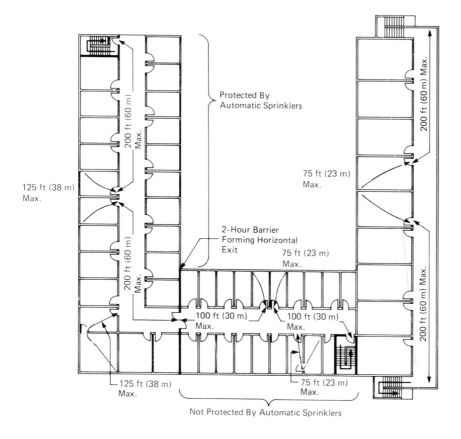

Figure 23-7. *Travel Distance in Large Facilities.*

23-3.2.8 Illumination of Means of Egress.

23-3.2.8.1 Means of egress shall be illuminated in accordance with Section 5-8.

23-3.2.9 Emergency Lighting.

23-3.2.9.1 Emergency lighting in accordance with Section 5-9 shall be provided in all buildings with more than 25 rooms.

Exception: Where each guest room has a direct exit to the outside of the building at ground level, no emergency lighting shall be required.

The Exception to 23-3.2.9.1 does not apply to facilities with exterior balconies and stairs, but applies only to those that have doors opening directly to grade.

23-3.2.10 Marking of Means of Egress.

23-3.2.10.1 Means of egress shall be marked in accordance with Section 5-10.

23-3.2.11 Special Features. (Reserved.)

23-3.3 Protection.

23-3.3.1 Protection of Vertical Openings.

23-3.3.1.1 Every stairway, elevator shaft, and other vertical opening shall be enclosed or protected in accordance with 6-2.4.

Exception No. 1: Unprotected vertical openings connecting not more than three floors shall be permitted in accordance with 6-2.4.5.

Exception No. 2: Atriums in accordance with 6-2.4.6 shall be permitted.

Exception No. 3: In buildings protected throughout by an approved automatic sprinkler system in accordance with 23-3.3.5, and where exits and required ways of travel thereto are adequately safeguarded against fire and smoke within the building, or where every individual room has direct access to an exterior exit without passing through a public corridor, the protection of vertical openings not part of required exits may be waived by the authority having jurisdiction to the extent that such openings do not endanger required means of egress.

Exception No. 4: In buildings not more than two stories in height, unprotected vertical openings may be permitted by the authority having jurisdiction if the building is protected throughout by an approved automatic sprinkler system in accordance with 23-3.3.5.1.

Exception No. 1 is the only condition under which an unprotected vertical opening may be permitted without automatic sprinkler protection throughout the building. However, 6-2.4.5 does require automatic sprinkler protection in a communicating space containing ordinary hazard contents, and the space must be separated from the remainder of the building by a 1-hour fire barrier.

23-3.3.1.2 No floor below the level of exit discharge used only for storage, heating equipment, or purposes other than residential occupancy shall have unprotected openings to floors used for residential occupancy.

23-3.3.2 **Protection from Hazards.**

23-3.3.2.1 Any room containing high-pressure boilers, refrigerating machinery, transformers, or other service equipment subject to possible explosion shall not be located directly under or adjacent to exits. All such rooms shall be effectively cut off from other parts of the building as specified in Section 6-4.

23-3.3.2.2 Every hazardous area shall be separated from other parts of the building by construction having a fire resistance rating of at least 1 hour, and communicating openings shall be protected by approved self-closing fire doors, or such area shall be equipped with automatic fire extinguishing systems. Hazardous areas include, but are not limited to:

Boiler and heater rooms
Laundries
Repair shops

Rooms or spaces used for storage of combustible supplies and equipment in quantities deemed hazardous by the authority having jurisdiction.

The list that appears in 23-3.3.2.2 is not all-inclusive. Hazardous areas are those that contain materials that, because of their basic nature or because of the quantity of combustible materials involved, represent a significantly higher hazard than would otherwise be typical in residential board and care facilities.

23-3.3.3 **Interior Finish.** Interior wall and ceiling finish shall be Class A or Class B in accordance with Section 6-5. Interior floor finish shall be Class I or Class II in corridors and exits.

Exception: Previously installed floor coverings, subject to the approval of the authority having jurisdiction.

23-3.3.4 **Detection, Alarm, and Communication Systems.**

See Supplement 2.

23-3.3.4.1 **General.** A fire alarm system in accordance with Section 7-6 shall be provided.

Exception: Where each sleeping room has exterior exit access in accordance with 5-5.3, and the building is not greater than three stories in height.

23-3.3.4.2 **Initiation.** Initiation of the required fire alarm system shall be by:

(a) Manual means in accordance with 7-6.2, and

Exception to (a): A manual means, as specified in 7-6.2, in excess of the alarm station at a constantly attended location per (b) below is not required where there are other effective means (such as a complete automatic sprinkler or automatic detection system) for notification of fire as required.

(b) A manual fire alarm station located at a convenient central control point under continuous supervision of responsible employees, and

(c) Any automatic sprinkler system, and

Exception to (c): Automatic sprinkler systems that are not required by another section of this Code are not required to initiate the fire alarm system.

(d) Any required detection system.

Exception to (d): Sleeping room smoke detectors are not required to initiate the building fire alarm system.

Paragraph 23-3.3.4.2(b) requires that, in addition to the normal distribution of manual fire alarm stations (*see* 7-6.2), locations such as that of the telephone operator must also be equipped with a manual fire alarm station. The intent is to have a manual fire alarm station available at the location where residents would phone in an emergency.

The Exception to 23-3.3.4.2(a) waives the requirements for manual fire alarm stations located at each exit and arranged so that all portions of a building are within 200 feet (60m) of a manual fire alarm station (*see Section 7-6*) if an automatic sprinkler system or an automatic detection system is provided throughout the building. This does not waive the need for a fire protective signaling system; it only deletes the requirements for manual fire alarm stations beyond the location where residents would phone in an emergency.

The *Code* exempts sleeping room smoke detectors from activating the building fire protective signaling system. The detectors installed in the sleeping rooms are usually single or multiple station detectors and are not part of a "required automatic detection system" and, therefore, are automatically exempted (23-3.3.4.5). The exception emphasizes this point but clarifies that, if detectors are part of a system, they are not required to initiate the building fire protective signaling system. The *Code* does not prohibit room detectors from activating the system; however, this is discouraged to prevent numerous activations, which could pose a particular problem in large board and care facilities. The purpose of the sleeping room detector is to warn the occupants of that room. The notification of the management and other occupants is the responsibility of the occupant and, as such, should be emphasized in the required training for residents.

23-3.3.4.3 **Occupant Notification.** Occupant notification shall be provided automatically, without delay, by internal audible alarm in accordance with 7-6.3. Presignal systems shall be prohibited.

The distribution of audible alarm-notification appliances in residential board and care facilities must be thoroughly reviewed. Corridor walls may be of such character (soundproof) that a sounding device would be required in each room to provide an audible alarm; without the use of a sounding device in each room, the corridor alarm would have to approach dangerous decibel levels in order to awaken residents in their rooms.

23-3.3.4.4* **Fire Department Notification.** In case of a fire, provisions shall be made for the immediate notification of the public fire department by either telephone or other means. Where there is no public fire department, this notification shall be made to the private fire brigade.

A-23-3.3.4.4 (See A-17-3.4.3.2.)

This paragraph does not require a direct fire alarm connection to the fire department, although that is the best method of compliance. If a telephone is provided, the telephone must be equipped for direct outside dial without going through a switchboard and is not permitted to be a pay phone.

23-3.3.4.5 **Smoke Detectors.** Each sleeping room shall be provided with an approved single station smoke detector in accordance with 7-6.2.9, powered from the building electrical system.

Exception No. 1: Existing battery-powered detectors, rather than building electrical service-powered detectors, shall be accepted where, in the opinion of the authority having jurisdiction, the facility has demonstrated testing, maintenance, and battery replacement programs that ensure the reliability of power to the detectors.

Exception No. 2: Facilities having an existing corridor smoke detection system in accordance with Section 7-6, connected to the building fire alarm system.

The purpose of placing detectors in each room is to alert the occupants of a sleeping room to the presence of a fire originating in that room. The detectors are not normally tied into the building fire protective signaling system [see the Exception to 23-3.3.4.2(d).] Upon an occupant's leaving the room, the door shuts behind the occupant (see 23-3.3.6.6), and the occupant pulls a manual fire alarm station. If the occupant fails to sound the alarm manually, compensation is provided by corridor smoke detectors or by automatic sprinklers. (See 23-3.3.4.6 and 23-3.3.5.)

Exception No. 1 applies to existing battery-powered detectors only, and not to all existing facilities. Battery-powered detectors are to be permitted only if they already exist and the facility can document that they are properly maintained and tested to ensure their reliability.

Exception No. 2 recognizes that this was the previous requirement of the Code. Note that the installation of a corridor smoke detection system does not waive the need for single station smoke detectors in each room. However, if a building already has a corridor smoke detection system, then single station smoke detectors are not required to be added. (See Table 23-6.)

23-3.3.4.6 Smoke Detection Systems.
All corridors and common spaces shall be provided with smoke detectors in accordance with NFPA 72E, Standard on Automatic Fire Detectors, arranged to initiate an alarm that is audible in all sleeping areas.

Exception No. 1: Detectors are not required in common spaces in facilities protected throughout by an approved automatic sprinkler system in accordance with 23-3.3.5.

Exception No. 2: Unenclosed corridors, passageways, balconies, colonnades, or other arrangements where one or more sides along the long dimension are fully or extensively open to the exterior at all times.

A system of smoke detectors is required in the corridors and all common spaces of any facility that is not fully sprinklered. Note that the exception for sprinklers does not apply to 23-3.3.4.5 and does not apply to the corridor detectors; it only applies to the common spaces. The Committee has specifically emphasized in its discussion of this issue that it is not equating sprinklers and smoke

detectors, but it does believe that a fully sprinklered building is an adequate alternative to smoke detectors in common spaces. If the facility is built "motel style," using exterior access corridors, smoke detection is not required in the exterior corridors. (See Table 23-6.)

Table 23-6. Options for Smoke Detector Locations

Sprinkler Protection	Room Detectors (House Powered or Battery Powered, if Existing)	Corridor Detectors (Per NFPA 72E)
None	Required[1]	Required
Complete sprinklers	Required[1]	Not Required

[1] Room detectors not required if building is already protected with corridor detectors.

23-3.3.5 Extinguishment Requirements.

See Supplement 3.

23-3.3.5.1* Automatic Extinguishment Systems.
Where an automatic sprinkler system is installed either for total or partial building coverage, the system shall be installed in accordance with Section 7-7 and shall activate the fire alarm system in accordance with Section 7-6.

Exception No. 1: In buildings not greater than four stories in height, a sprinkler system complying with NFPA 13R, Standard for the Installation of Sprinkler Systems in Residential Occupancies up to and Including Four Stories in Height, shall be permitted.

Exception No. 2: Automatic sprinklers are not required in closets not exceeding 24 sq ft (2.2 sq m) and bathrooms not exceeding 55 sq ft (5.1 sq m) provided such spaces are finished with lath and plaster or material with a 15-minute thermal barrier.

A-23-3.3.5.1
It is intended that this requirement applies to existing small facilities that are converted to large facilities.

This paragraph does not require the installation of automatic sprinklers. The purpose of the paragraph is to establish the criteria to be followed if the facility chooses to use the sprinkler alternatives provided in this chapter. The Code does provide significant incentives for the installation of sprinklers associated with: building construction (23-3.1.3.3); travel distance (23-3.2.6.1 and 23-3.2.6.2); exit discharge (23-3.2.7); vertical openings (23-3.3.1); hazardous areas (23-3.3.2.2); interior finish (23-3.3.3); corridor smoke detection (23-3.3.4.6); corridor walls (23-3.3.6.1); corridor doors (23-3.3.6.4); door closers (23-3.3.6.6); and smoke barriers (23-3.3.7.1).

While NFPA 13R, *Standard for the Installation of Sprinkler Systems in Residential Occupancies up to and Including Four Stories in Height,*[6] is referenced in Exception No. 1, such systems may not be used in large, impractical facilities, since such facilities must comply with Chapter 13, which does not recognize NFPA 13R.

Exception No. 2 applies to sprinkler systems installed in accordance with NFPA 13R, *Standard for the Installation of Sprinkler System in Residential Occupancies up to and Including Four Stories in Height,*[6] and NFPA 13, *Standard for the Installation of Sprinkler Systems.*[4] It should be noted that the combustibility of plumbing fixtures is not an issue. NFPA 13R and NFPA 13 address the combustibility of plumbing fixtures, not because they are viewed as a source of ignition, but because frequently wall finish materials are not installed behind prefabricated enclosures. Therefore, the exception clearly states that the bathroom must be finished with plaster or materials providing a 15-minute thermal barrier. This includes the area behind a prefabricated enclosure.

23-3.3.5.2 Sprinkler piping serving not more than six sprinklers for any isolated hazardous area in accordance with 7-7.1.2 shall be permitted. In new installations where more than two sprinklers are installed in a single area, water flow detection shall be provided to sound the fire alarm system required by 23-3.3.4.1.

23-3.3.5.3 Portable Fire Extinguishers. Portable fire extinguishers in accordance with Section 7-7 shall be provided near hazardous areas.

23-3.3.6 Corridors and Separation of Sleeping Rooms.

23-3.3.6.1 Access shall be provided from every resident use area to at least one means of egress that is separated from all other rooms or spaces by fire barriers complying with 23-3.3.6.3 through 23-3.3.6.6.

Exception No. 1: Rooms or spaces, other than sleeping rooms, if those rooms or spaces are protected throughout by an approved automatic sprinkler system installed in accordance with 23-3.3.5.

Exception No. 2: Rooms or spaces, other than sleeping rooms, if those rooms or spaces are provided with a smoke detection and alarm system connected to activate the building evacuation alarm. Furnishings, finishes, and furniture, in combination with all other combustibles within the spaces, if of such minimum quantity and so arranged that a fully developed fire is unlikely to occur.

Exception No. 3: Facilities housing groups capable of prompt evacuation in buildings not over two stories in height that have at least two remotely located means of egress not involving windows. The arrangement shall be such that there is at least one such means of egress from each sleeping room that provides a path of travel to the outside without traversing any corridor or other spaces exposed to unprotected vertical openings or common living spaces, such as living rooms and kitchens.

Under some circumstances, it is permissible to have access to an exit that passes through a sitting room, television room, living room, or other common use space. However, because numerous multiple-death fires have originated in such locations, this paragraph is intended to preclude exposing all exit access paths to a fire in such a space. Exceptions are provided that permit egress paths to be exposed to the common use space where the space is furnished and finished with materials that will not result in flashover and where early warning smoke detection is provided or the space is sprinklered. (*See Figure 23-8 for examples.*)

23-3.3.6.2 Sleeping rooms shall be separated from corridors and other common spaces by fire barriers complying with 23-3.3.6.3 through 23-3.3.6.6.

23-3.3.6.3 Fire barriers required by 23-3.3.6.1 or 23-3.3.6.2 shall have a fire resistance rating of not less than 20 minutes.

Exception No. 1: In buildings protected throughout by an approved automatic sprinkler system installed in accordance with 23-3.3.5, no fire resistance rating is required, but it shall resist the passage of smoke.

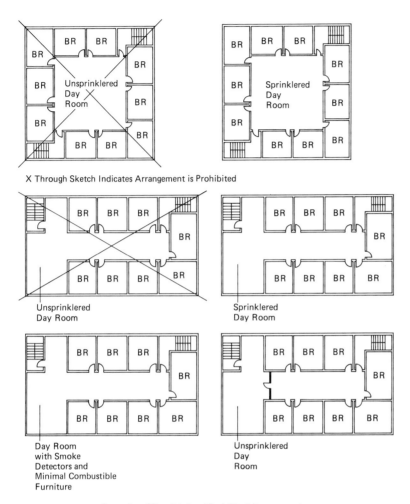

Figure 23-8. *Examples of Permitted and Prohibited Arrangements.*

X Through Sketch Indicates Arrangement is Prohibited

Unsprinklered
Day Room

Sprinklered
Day Room

Day Room
with Smoke
Detectors and
Minimal Combustible
Furniture

Unsprinklered
Day
Room

Examples of Permitted and Prohibited Arrangements

Exception No. 2: In buildings housing groups capable of prompt evacuation, not greater than two stories in height, and with a maximum of 30 residents, no fire resistance rating is required, but barriers shall resist the passage of smoke.

In general, sleeping rooms must be separated from corridors by construction having a fire resistance rating of at least 20 minutes. If the building is protected throughout by an automatic sprinkler system or if it is a moderately sized prompt facility (Exception No. 2), the corridor walls are not required to have a fire resistance rating and must only be capable of resisting the passage of smoke.

23-3.3.6.4 Doors in fire barriers required by 23-3.3.6.1 or 23-3.3.6.2 shall have a fire protection rating of not less than 20 minutes.

Exception No. 1: Existing 1¾-in. (4.4-cm) thick solid bonded wood core doors shall be permitted to be continued in use.

Exception No. 2: In buildings protected throughout by an approved automatic sprinkler system installed in accordance with 23-3.3.5, doors that are nonrated shall be permitted to be continued in use.

Exception No. 3: Walls that are required only to resist the passage of smoke, without a fire resistance rating, shall be permitted to have doors that resist the passage of smoke but no fire resistance rating is required.

It is intended that even the existing 1¾-in. (4.4-cm) thick solid bonded wood core doors and the nonrated room doors should have a reliable means to keep the door closed. Such doors may also be required to be self-closing or automatic-closing in accordance with 23-3.3.6.6.

23-3.3.6.5 Walls and doors required by 23-3.3.6.1 and 23-3.3.6.2 shall be constructed to resist the passage of smoke. There shall be no louvers, transfer grilles, operable transoms, or other air passages penetrating such walls or doors except properly installed heating and utility installations.

23-3.3.6.6 Doors in walls required by 23-3.3.6.1 and 23-3.3.6.2 shall be self-closing or automatic-closing in accordance with 5-2.1.8. Doors in walls separating sleeping rooms from corridors shall be automatic-closing in accordance with 5-2.1.8.

Exception No. 1: Doors to sleeping rooms that have occupant control locks such that access is normally restricted to the occupants or staff personnel shall be permitted to be self-closing.

Exception No. 2: In buildings protected throughout by an approved automatic sprinkler system installed in accordance with 23-3.3.5, doors, other than doors to hazardous areas, vertical openings, and exit enclosures are not required to be self-closing or automatic-closing.

A reliable means of closing sleeping room doors during a fire is required unless the building is sprinklered. Generally, automatic, smoke-activated closers will be required. In facilities in which the residents control the privacy lock on their own sleeping room doors, a simple self-closer (e.g., spring hinges or a hydraulic door check) is acceptable. This is because, in practice, such doors are usually kept closed. Therefore, the likelihood that the door will be chocked or held open is minimized. In accordance with 23-3.3.6.4, a reliable means to keep the doors closed should also be provided.

23-3.3.7 **Subdivision of Building Spaces.**

23-3.3.7.1 Every sleeping room floor shall be divided into at least two smoke compartments of approximately the same size, with smoke barriers in accordance with Section 6-3. Smoke dampers are not required.

Additional smoke barriers shall be provided such that the maximum travel distance from a sleeping room corridor door to a smoke barrier shall not exceed 150 ft (45 m).

Exception No. 1: Buildings protected throughout by an approved automatic sprinkler system in accordance with 23-3.3.5.

Exception No. 2: Where each sleeping room is provided with exterior ways of exit access arranged in accordance with 5-5.3.

Exception No. 3: Smoke barriers are not required where the aggregate corridor length on each floor is not more than 150 ft (45 m).

The smoke barrier provides for horizontal movement of occupants and limits the number of rooms (and, therefore, the number of occupants) exposed to a single fire that may block a corridor. Since no fire rating is required for the barrier and smoke dampers are not required, the provision of smoke barriers is not overly burdensome. The exception for buildings equipped with automatic sprinklers reflects the excellent life loss record associated with this protection.

A horizontal exit may be used to comply with 23-3.3.7 and therefore may serve more than one function. In addition, if the smoke barrier has at least a 20-minute fire resistance rating, protection is provided by an automatic sprinkler system throughout the building, and the smoke compartment has access to an exit that does not require return to the fire area, the smoke compartment may be considered a point of safety. (*See definition of point of safety.*)

23-3.4 **Special Provisions.** (Reserved.)

23-3.4.1 **Operating Features.** (*See Chapter 31.*)

23-3.5 Building Services.

23-3.5.1 Utilities. Utilities shall comply with provisions of Section 7-1.

23-3.5.2 Heating, Ventilating, and Air Conditioning.

23-3.5.2.1 Heating, ventilating, and air conditioning equipment shall comply with the provisions of Section 7-2.

23-3.5.2.2 No stove or combustion heater shall be so located as to block escape in case of fire caused by the malfunction of the stove or heater.

23-3.5.2.3 Unvented fuel-fired heaters shall not be used in any board and care occupancy.

This paragraph prohibits the use of the typical kerosene portable heater, as well as other fuel-fired, nonvented heaters.

23-3.5.3 Elevators, Dumbwaiters, and Vertical Conveyors.

23-3.5.3.1 Elevator, dumbwaiters, and vertical conveyors shall comply with the provisions of Section 7-4.

23-3.5.4 Rubbish Chutes, Incinerators, and Laundry Chutes. Rubbish chutes, incinerators, and laundry chutes shall comply with the provisions of Section 7-5.

SECTION 23-4* Suitability of an Apartment Building to House a Board and Care Occupancy

A-23-4 Board and care occupancies in apartment buildings will usually be small facilities housing 16 or fewer residents. It is intended that the board and care occupancy be made to conform to the requirements of Section 23-2 for small board and care facilities. In the unusual case where an apartment houses a large board and care facility, it would be reasonable for the authority having jurisdiction, using 1-5.3, to apply the provisions of Section 23-3 to the apartment. In addition, the apartment build-

ing in which the facility is housed is required to comply with the requirements for apartment buildings in Chapters 18 and 19 and the additional criteria presented in this section.

Board and care occupancies in apartment buildings are usually small facilities housing 16 or fewer residents. It is intended that the board and care occupancy conform to the requirements of Section 23-2 for small board and care facilities. In the unusual case where an apartment houses a large board and care facility, it is reasonable for the authority having jurisdiction, in accordance with 1-5.3, to apply the provisions of Section 23-3 to the apartment. In addition, the apartment building in which the facility is housed is required to comply with the requirements for existing apartment buildings in Chapter 19 and the additional criteria provided in this section.

23-4.1 General.

23-4.1.1 Scope. This section applies to apartment buildings that have one or more individual apartments used as a board and care occupancy. This section determines the suitability of such buildings to house a residential board and care facility. The suitability of such buildings for apartments not used for board and care occupancies is covered in Chapter 19.

23-4.1.2 Requirements for individual apartments used as a residential board and care occupancy are specified in Section 23-2, "Small Facilities." Egress from the apartment into the common building corridor shall be considered acceptable egress from the board and care facility.

See commentary following the section title.

23-4.1.3 Requirements Based on Evacuation Capability.

23-4.1.3.1 Apartment buildings housing board and care facilities shall comply with the requirements of Section 23-4.

Exception: Facilities where the authority having jurisdiction has determined that equivalent safety for housing a residential board and care facility is provided in accordance with Section 1-6.

A-23-4.1.3.1 Exception. In determining equivalency for existing buildings, conversions, modernizations, renovations, or unusual design concepts, the authority having jurisdiction may accept evaluations based on NFPA 101M, *Alternative Approaches to Life Safety*, Chapter 6.

23-4.1.3.2 All facilities shall meet the requirements of Chapter 19 and the additional requirements of Section 23-4.

23-4.1.4 Minimum Construction Requirements. In addition to the requirements of Chapter 19, apartment buildings housing residential board and care facilities that house groups classed as prompt or slow shall meet the construction requirements of 23-3.1.3, and those housing groups classed as impractical to evacuate shall meet the construction requirements of 13-1.6. In applying the construction requirements, the height shall be determined by the height of the residential board and care facility above the primary level of exit discharge.

23-4.2 Means of Egress. The requirements of Section 19-2 apply only to parts of the means of egress serving the apartment(s) used as residential board and care occupancy.

23-4.3 Protection.

23-4.3.1 Interior Finish. The requirements of 19-3.3 apply only to the parts of means of egress serving the apartment(s) used as a residential board and care occupancy.

23-4.3.2 Construction of Corridor Walls. The requirements of 19-3.6 apply only to corridors serving the residential board and care facility, including that portion of the corridor wall separating the residential board and care facility from the common corridor.

23-4.3.3 Subdivision of Building Spaces. The requirements of 19-3.7 apply to those stories with an apartment(s) used as a residential board and care occupancy.

23-4.4 Operating Features. (*See Chapter 31.*)

References Cited in Commentary

[1]*Fire Safety in Boarding Homes*, NFPA SPP-76, Quincy, MA, 1982.

[2]Boarding Home Fires: New Jersey, Hearing before the Select Committee on Aging, House of Representatives, Ninety-seventh Congress, Comm. Pub. No. 97-304, March 9, 1981.

[3]Toward a National Plan for the Chronically Mentally Ill, Bethesda, MD, National Institute of Mental Health, 1980.

[4]NFPA 13, *Standard for the Installation of Sprinkler Systems*, National Fire Protection Association, Quincy, MA 1991.

[5]NFPA 13D, *Standard for the Installation of Sprinkler Systems in One- and Two- Family Dwellings and Mobile Homes*, National Fire Protection Association, Quincy, MA 1991.

[6]NFPA 13R, *Standard for the Installation of Sprinkler Systems in Residential Occupancies up to and Including Four Stories in Height*, National Fire Protection Association, Quincy, MA 1991.

[7]NFPA 74, *Standard for the Installation, Maintenance, and Use of Household Fire Warning Equipment*, National Fire Protection Association, Quincy, MA 1989.

24

New Mercantile Occupancies

(See also Chapter 31.)

Mercantile occupancies include stores, markets, and other rooms, buildings, or structures used for the display and sale of merchandise. Included in this occupancy group are:

Supermarkets	24-Hour convenience stores
Department stores	Video sales and rentals stores
Drugstores	Flea markets and crafts centers
Auction rooms	Building materials/supplies centers
Shopping centers/malls	Rental equipment centers
Hardware stores	Automobile sales showrooms

Minor merchandising operations in buildings consisting predominantly of other occupancies, such as a newsstand in an office building, must meet the *Life Safety Code* requirements of the predominant occupancy.

Documentation of fires that have occurred in occupancies that the *Life Safety Code* would classify as mercantile occupancies (*see 4-1.7*) are grouped and stored in the national fire incident data bases under the category of stores. Although this category covers more uses than those that the *Life Safety Code* would define as mercantile, including occupancies such as those used as vehicle repair facilities, the fire statistics applicable to stores provide a general guideline for the yearly death toll and fire incident frequency in mercantile occupancies. Stores accounted for 28,100 structure fires per year as reported to U.S. fire departments from 1984 to 1988, with an associated 25 civilian (i.e., non-fire-service personnel) deaths and 569 civilian injuries per year. Nearly half of those who died in store fires during the period from 1980 to 1988 were not in the room of fire origin when the fire began. In addition, the fire records indicate that most stores in which fires occurred did not have sprinkler systems or fire detection systems.

In the 1980s, only one store fire killed 10 or more people, and it occurred in a natural gas company repair facility, which likely would not have been classified as a mercantile occupancy by the *Life Safety Code*. Fires in service stations and vehicle repair facilities typically accounted for the largest share of fire deaths in stores.

SECTION 24-1   General Requirements

24-1.1 Application.

24-1.1.1 New mercantile occupancies shall comply with the provisions of Chapter 24. (*See Chapter 31 for operating features.*)

Existing mercantile occupancies must comply with Chapter 25 of the *Code*.

24-1.1.2 This chapter establishes life safety requirements for all new mercantile buildings. Specific requirements for sub-occupancy groups, such as Class A, B, and C stores and covered malls, are contained in paragraphs pertaining thereto.

For the definitions of Class A, B, and C stores, see 24-1.4.2 and its associated commentary, including Table 24-1.

24-1.1.3 Additions to existing buildings shall conform to the requirements for new construction. Existing portions of the structure need not be modified, provided that the new construction has not diminished the firesafety features of the facility. Existing portions shall be upgraded if the addition results in a change of mercantile subclassification. (*See 24-1.4.2.*)

Paragraph 24-1.1.3 specifies that additions to existing mercantile occupancies conform to the requirements for new construction, but the existing portion of the occupancy generally may continue in use without an upgrade to meet the requirements for new construction if the facility complies with the provisions for existing mercantile occupancies contained in Chapter 25 of the *Code*. However, if the addition results in a change in the mercantile occupancy subclassification (*see 24-1.4.2*), such as a change from Class C to Class B or from Class B to Class A, the existing portion of the enlarged overall facility, as well as the newly constructed portion, must be upgraded to meet the provisions applicable to new construction. The provisions of 24-1.1.3 are illustrated in the following paragraphs and in Figure 24-1, Parts a, b, and c.

In Figure 24-1a, the new construction, which includes 10,000 sq ft (930 sq m) of additional sales area and approximately 2000 sq ft (186 sq m) of new storage area,

is added to an existing Class B mercantile occupancy with 5000 sq ft (465 sq m) of existing sales area. The size and placement of the new addition neither change the Class B mercantile subclassification of the enlarged overall facility nor diminish the firesafety features of the existing portion of the facility. Therefore, the addition is constructed in accordance with the requirements of Chapter 24, "New Mercantile Occupancies," and the existing portion of the building is allowed to continue to be used, without upgrade, if it meets the requirements of Chapter 25, "Existing Mercantile Occupancies." If the existing portion of the building does not meet the requirements of Chapter 25, it must be upgraded to meet those requirements.

Figure 24-1b illustrates new construction identical to that described in the preceding paragraph, which is added to an existing Class B mercantile occupancy with 14,000 sq ft (1300 sq m) of existing sales area. Although the size of the addition does not change the Class B mercantile subclassification of the overall facility, the placement of the new addition appears to have diminished the firesafety of the existing portion of the building with respect to travel distance. The broken line in Figure 24-1b represents what had previously been an exterior wall and exit door in the existing mercantile occupancy prior to construction of the addition. The door had allowed occupants in the upper left portion of the existing building to reach an exit within the allowable 150-ft (45-m) travel distance specified for nonsprinklered existing mercantile occupancies in accordance with 25-2.6. Without the exit door, occupants of the existing portion of the building must be able to reach an exit (i.e., one of the three doors in the perimeter of the enlarged facility) within the same 150-ft (45-m) travel distance limitation. If this is not possible, an additional exit within that distance must be constructed, or the building must be sprinklered in order to increase the allowable travel distance to 200 ft (60 m). Since the new construction must meet the provisions of Chapter 24, the entire building (new and existing portions) must be sprinklered in accordance with 24-3.5.1, because the building exceeds 12,000 sq ft (1,100 sq m) in gross area. [*See 24-3.5.1(b).*]

Figure 24-1c illustrates new construction identical to that described in the two preceding paragraphs, which is added to an existing Class B mercantile occupancy with 21,000 sq ft (1950 sq m) of existing sales area. The size of the new sales area, when added to that of the existing mercantile occupancy, exceeds 30,000 sq ft (2,800 sq m) and results in a change of mercantile sub-classification from Class B to Class A [*see 24-1.4.2.1(a)*]. In accordance with the provisions of the first and last sentences of 24-1.1.3, the entire building (new and existing portions) must meet the requirements for new mercantile occupancies as detailed in this chapter.

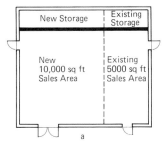

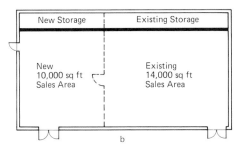

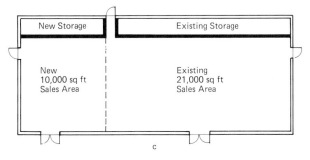

Figure 24-1a, b, and c. Examples of Additions to Existing Mercantile Occupancies. (See commentary associated with 24-1.1.3.) 1 sq ft = 0.093 sq m

24-1.2 Mixed Occupancies.

24-1.2.1 Mixed occupancies shall comply with 1-5.7.

24-1.2.2 Combined Mercantile and Residential Occupancies.

24-1.2.2.1 No dwelling unit shall have its sole means of egress through any mercantile occupancy in the same building.

24-1.2.2.2 No multiple dwelling occupancy shall be located above a mercantile occupancy.

Exception No. 1: Where the dwelling occupancy and exits therefrom are separated from the mercantile occupancy by construction having a fire resistance rating of at least 1 hour.

Exception No. 2: Where the mercantile occupancy is protected throughout by an approved automatic sprinkler system in accordance with Section 7-7.

The requirements for mixed occupancies were developed to address a once common (but now less prevalent) occupancy arrangement: the corner tavern, grocery store, or retail store that has one or two dwelling units located on the upper floors. The *Code* separates this type of combined occupancy into two classes.

Where there is a single dwelling unit located above or adjacent to the mercantile occupancy, the *Code* prohibits (*see 24-1.2.2.1*) the dwelling unit from having its sole means of egress pass through the mercantile occupancy in the same building. If the dwelling unit has a means of egress that passes through the mercantile occupancy, it must have access to a second means of egress that is independent of and does not pass through the mercantile occupancy.

The *Code* prohibits multiple dwelling units from being located above a mercantile occupancy unless one of the following conditions is met:

1. The dwelling units and their means of egress are separated from the mercantile occupancy by construction with a fire resistance rating of at least 1 hour, or
2. The mercantile occupancy is protected by an automatic sprinkler system. Sprinkler systems have proven to be an excellent alternative to 1-hour fire resistance rated construction under these circumstances. (*See Section 7-7 of the Code; NFPA 13, Standard for the Installation of Sprinkler Systems*;[1] *and NFPA 13A, Recommended Practice for the Inspection, Testing, and Maintenance of Sprinkler Systems*.)[2]

The *Code* established these requirements because of the long historical record of deaths and injuries that have occurred where fire originated in mercantile occupancies and spread to dwelling units located above the mercantile occupancies.

24-1.2.3 **Combined Mercantile Occupancies and Parking Structures.** Walls separating parking structures from mercantile occupancies shall have a fire resistance rating of not less than 2 hours.

Exception: In enclosed parking structures that are protected throughout with an approved automatic sprinkler system in accordance with Section 7-7 or in open-air parking structures, nonrated glazing and opening protectives shall be permitted if all of the following conditions are met:

(a) The openings do not exceed 25 percent of the area of the wall in which they are located, and

(b) The openings are used for main entrance and associated sidelight functions, and

(c) The enclosed connecting mercantile building is protected throughout by an approved automatic sprinkler system in accordance with Section 7-7, and

(d) The floor elevation of the mercantile use is at least 4 in. (10.2 cm) above the floor level of the parking structure, and

(e) No vehicle is able to park or drive within 10 ft (3 m) of the openings, and

(f) The openings have a minimum of a glass membrane, and

(g) Any doors in the glass membrane are self-closing.

The provisions of 24-1.2.3 are new to this edition of the *Code* and, although they address combined mercantile occupancies and parking structures, are very similar to the new requirements of 26-1.2.2, which address combined business occupancies and parking structures. It is common for multistory mercantile occupancies (e.g., department stores and shopping mall buildings) and multistory business occupancies (e.g., office buildings) to be attached to multistory parking garages. Such garages provide access to the occupancy at multiple levels. In order to allow flexibility in the number and type of openings and in the degree of stringency required for opening protectives such as fire doors and fire windows, the

Exception to 24-1.2.3 outlines a set of provisions that, when applied in total, will safely allow a reduction in the 2-hour fire resistance rating required by 24-1.2.3. The reduction allows the use of nonrated glazing and nonrated opening protectives. This permits the use of glass doors and glass sidelights in the barrier between the mercantile occupancy and the garage. Security in the garage is thereby increased, since customers can view the area through the glass doors or sidelights.

Note that all eight requirements mandated by the Exception to 24-1.2.3 [i.e., the sprinkler requirement for the garage in the base paragraph and the seven requirements of subparts (a) through (g)] must be met as a whole in order to apply the exception to the rule. Otherwise, a 2-hour fire resistance rated separation between the mercantile occupancy and the parking structure is required.

24-1.3 **Special Definitions.**

(a) **Anchor Store.** A department store or major merchandising center having direct access to the covered mall but having all required means of egress independent of the covered mall.

From a merchandising point of view, a shopping mall developer or operator may refer to any of the major tenants that have vast expanses of floor space and instant name recognition and that are often positioned at the ends and corners of the covered mall building as anchor stores. However, the *Code* reserves the use of this term for those stores having means of egress independent from the covered mall. (*See Figure 24-2.*)

(b) **Class A Stores.** [*See 24-1.4.2.1(a).*]

(c) **Class B Stores.** [*See 24-1.4.2.1(b).*]

(d) **Class C Stores.** [*See 24-1.4.2.1(c).*]

(e) **Covered Mall.** A covered or roofed interior area used as a pedestrian way and connected to a building(s) or portions of a building housing single or multiple tenants.

The definition of "covered mall" is differentiated from that of "covered mall building," since certain requirements apply only to the covered pedestrian way (i.e., the covered mall) while other requirements apply to the entire building, including all tenant spaces and common areas (i.e., the covered mall building). See the commentary

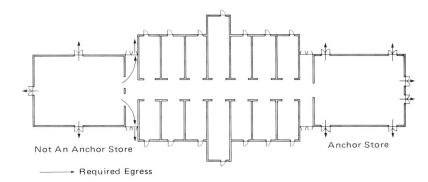

Figure 24-2. Anchor Store. This figure illustrates the difference between an anchor store and a store that, while large, is not an anchor store. Note that required egress from an anchor store cannot pass through the covered mall.

immediately following, which addresses 24-1.3(f), "Covered Mall Building." A portion of a building can be considered a covered mall even if it is open to the outside elements at one or more points.

(f) **Covered Mall Building.** A building, including the covered mall, enclosing a number of tenants and occupancies, such as retail stores, drinking and dining establishments, entertainment and amusement facilities, offices, and other similar uses, wherein two or more tenants have a main entrance into the covered mall.

The definition of "covered mall building" is differentiated from that of "covered mall," since certain requirements apply to the entire building, including all tenant spaces and common areas(i.e., the covered mall building) while other requirements apply only to the covered pedestrian way (i.e., the covered mall). For example, the provisions of 24-4.4 require automatic sprinkler protection throughout the entire covered mall building but require an alarm system and, under certain conditions, a smoke control system only within the covered mall.

(g) **Gross Leasable Area.** The total floor area designated for tenant occupancy and exclusive use, expressed in square feet (square meters), measured from centerlines of adjoining partitions and exteriors of outside walls.

The term "gross leasable area" is defined in order to provide a criterion under which an occupant load can be calculated for use in sizing the means of egress system for just the covered mall [*see 24-1.3(e)*]. [*See 24-1.7.1(g), Figure 24-1.7.1(g), and associated commentary.*]

(h) **Open-Air Mercantile Operations.** Operations conducted outside of all structures with the operations area devoid of all walls and roofs except for small, individual, weather canopies.

See the provisions of 24-4.3 and the associated commentary applicable to open-air mercantile operations.

24-1.4 Classification of Occupancy.

24-1.4.1 Mercantile occupancies shall include all buildings and structures or parts thereof with occupancy as described in 4-1.7.

It is important to review the *Code's* definition (*see 4-1.7*) of a mercantile occupancy. Note that this definition does not include "minor merchandising operations in buildings predominantly of other occupancies, such as a newsstand in an office building... ." Paragraph 4-1.7 requires that such occupancies be subject to the requirements of the predominant (i.e., major) occupancy. For example, a newsstand that is located in an office building would be treated under the same business occupancy requirements (Chapter 26 or 27) as the office building.

24-1.4.2 Subclassification of Occupancy.

24-1.4.2.1 Mercantile occupancies shall be subclassified as follows:

(a) *Class A.* All stores having aggregate gross area of more than 30,000 sq ft (2,800 sq m) or utilizing more than three levels, excluding mezzanines, for sales purposes.

(b) *Class B*. All stores of more than 3,000 sq ft (280 sq m) but not more than 30,000 sq ft (2,800 sq m) aggregate gross area, or utilizing floors above or below the street floor level for sales purposes. Mezzanines are permitted. *(See 24-1.4.2.3.)*

Exception to (b): If more than three floors, excluding mezzanines, are utilized, the store shall be Class A regardless of area.

(c) *Class C*. All stores of not more than 3,000 sq ft (280 sq m) gross area used for sales purposes on one story only, excluding mezzanines.

Mezzanines allowed by the one-third area rule of 24-1.4.2.3 do not constitute a story and, therefore, are not a factor in determining mercantile occupancy subclassification based on number of floors used for sales purposes. The area of such mezzanines used for sales purposes (*see 24-1.4.2.2*) is, however, a factor in determining occupancy subclassification based on floor area devoted to sales. For example, a store with a 2,100-sq ft (195-sq m) main sales floor and a 700-sq ft (65-sq m) sales mezzanine is a Class C mercantile occupancy, while a store with a 2,400-sq ft (225-sq m) main sales floor and a 800-sq ft (75-sq m) sales mezzanine is a Class B mercantile occupancy. In each case, the mezzanine meets the maximum one-third area rule and is not treated as a story. In the second case, the area of the 800-sq ft (75-sq m) sales mezzanine, when added to the 2,400-sq ft (225-sq m) main sales floor, exceeds the maximum 3,000-sq ft (280-sq m) sales area for Class C mercantile occupancies and is, therefore, a Class B mercantile occupancy.

Mezzanines with areas in excess of the maximum one-third area rule constitute stories and, thus, sales levels. Therefore, they must be considered as such when determining mercantile occupancy subclassification. For example, a set of plans might show a proposed store with three floor levels of 8,000 sq ft (740 sq m) each that are used for sales purposes and a single 4,000-sq ft (370-sq m) sales "mezzanine." The store will actually use four floor levels for sales purposes, because the so-called "mezzanine" is not a mezzanine based on the maximum one-third area rule of 24-1.4.2.3. Although the 30,000-sq ft (2,800-sq m) sales area limitation associated with Class A mercantile occupancies is not exceeded, the four floor levels used for sales purposes result in a Class A mercan-

tile occupancy subclassification in accordance with the definition contained in 24-1.4.2.1(a).

To qualify as a Class A, B, or C mercantile occupancy, a store must meet the requirements of 24-1.4.2.1 summarized in Table 24-1. The classification process is important because specific life safety requirements vary for each mercantile class. The criteria vary in degree of stringency depending upon a store's classification, which, while based directly on the size of the sales areas, is indirectly a measure of the number of occupants at risk from any given fire.

Table 24-1.   Subclassification of Mercantile Occupancies

Store Class	By Height		By Aggregate Gross Area† (sq ft)
A	>3 Stories‡	or	>30,000
B	≤3 Stories‡	and	>3,000 and ≤30,000
C	One Story Only§	and	≤3,000

† Sections of floors not used are not counted in the area classification.
‡ Stories not used for sales above or below sales floor are not counted in the height classification.
§ A mezzanine < ⅓ the area of the floor below is permitted.

Formal Interpretation: 88-10
Reference: Chapters 24 and 25

Question 1: Is it the intent of the *Code* to permit a store with more than 30,000 sq ft (2,800 sq m) used for sales purposes and many separate tenants or companies operating within it to be classified as a Class A store?

Answer: Yes.

Question 2: Is it the intent of the *Code* to permit a designer to select at his/her option if a building with more than 30,000 sq ft (2,800 sq m) used for sales purposes is to be classified as a Covered Mall Building or a Class A Mercantile Occupancy?

Answer: Yes.

Issue Edition: 1988
Reference: Chapters 24 and 25
Issue Date: June 11, 1990 ■

24-1.4.2.2 For the purpose of the classification required in 24-1.4.2.1, the aggregate gross area shall be the total gross area of all floors used for mercantile purposes and, where a store is divided into sections, regardless of fire separation, shall include the area of all sections used for sales purposes. Areas of floors not used for sales purposes, such as an area used only for storage and not open to the public, shall not be counted for the purposes of the above classifications, but exits shall be provided for such nonsales areas in accordance with their occupancy as specified by other chapters of this *Code*.

Some mercantile occupancies locate their sales and storage areas together (e.g., furniture warehouse sales areas). In such cases, the mercantile occupancy subclassification should be determined using all aggregate gross area open to public use.

24-1.4.2.3 The floor area of a mezzanine or the aggregate floor area of multiple mezzanines shall not exceed one-third of the floor area of the room or story in which the mezzanines are located. A mezzanine or aggregated mezzanines in excess of the one-third area limitation shall be treated as a story or stories.

Examples of mezzanine arrangements to which the maximum one-third area rule of 24-1.4.2.3 can be applied are illustrated in Figure 24-3 (a) through (f). For purpose of illustration, assume that all the mezzanines as well as the entire main floor level are used for sales purposes. Parts (a), (b), (c), and (d) of Figure 24-3 illustrate only a single story or single floor level with mezzanine because the aggregate areas of the mezzanines [i.e., 3,000 sq ft (280 sq m)] do not exceed one-third of the floor area [i.e., 10,000 sq ft (930 sq m)] of the room or story in which the mezzanine is located.

In Part (e), the single 4,000-sq ft (370-sq m) intermediate level referred to by occupants as a mezzanine exceeds the one-third area rule. Therefore, it is not a mezzanine for *Life Safety Code* purposes but is a story by itself. Part (e) of Figure 24-3, therefore, depicts a two-story mercantile occupancy.

In Part (f), one of the 3,000-sq ft (280-sq m) mezzanines fits within the maximum one-third area allowance and can be called a mezzanine without constituting a floor level. The other mezzanine, although of the same size and, thus, by itself not in excess of the one-third area rule, does

create a story, because the sum of the areas of the two mezzanines [i.e., 6,000 sq ft (560 sq m)] exceeds one-third of the 10,000-sq ft (930-sq m) lower floor level. Thus, the figure shows a two-story mercantile occupancy with a mezzanine.

Although the mezzanines in Parts (a) through (d) of Figure 24-3 do not establish separate stories, their areas, because they are used for sales, are included in the total gross sales area against which the Class A, B, and C mercantile occupancy subclassification definitions of 24-1.4.2.1 are applied. Parts (a) through (d) each show 13,000 sq ft (1,200 sq m) of sales area and would be classified as Class B mercantile occupancies.

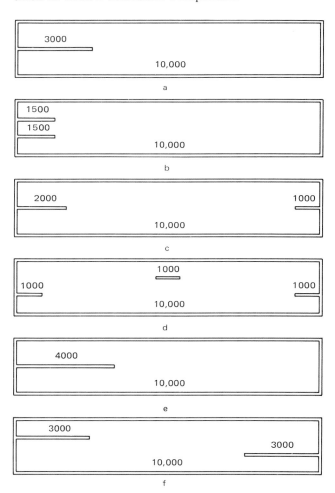

Figure 24-3 a, b, c, d, e, and f. *Examples of Mercantile Occupancy Mezzanine Arrangement Elevation Views (see commentary associated with 24-1.4.2.3). All values are expressed in square feet. For metric values, 1 sq ft = 0.093 sq m.*

In addition to the maximum one-third area limitation of 24-1.4.2.3, the provisions of 6-2.5 (which are new to this edition of the *Code*) are also applicable to mezzanines. For example, a mezzanine used for sales purposes that meets the one-third area rule, although it would not affect the mercantile occupancy subclassification with respect to number of stories used for sales purposes, would have to be sufficiently open in accordance with 6-2.5.3 to avoid treatment as a separate floor in terms of number of means of egress (*see 24-2.4.1*) and other egress arrangement requirements applicable to floors or stories.

24-1.4.2.4 Where a number of stores under different management are located in the same building, the aggregate gross area of all such stores shall be used in determining classification per 24-1.4.2.1.

Exception No. 1: Where individual stores are separated by fire barriers with a 2-hour fire resistance rating.

Note that, for existing mercantile occupancies (*see Exception No. 1 to 25-1.4.2.4*), the fire resistance rated separation required to waive aggregate gross area is 1-hour rather than the 2-hour rating of the basic rule.

Exception No. 2: Covered mall buildings. (See 24-4.4.)

Paragraphs 24-1.4.2.1 through 24-1.4.2.4 further clarify the subclassification of stores as Class A, B, or C. Most of these provisions are included in the footnotes to Table 24-1. The following should be noted for emphasis:

1. The aggregate gross area is the sum of the gross areas of all floors used for mercantile (sales) purposes.
2. If the store is divided so that some portions are not used for sales purposes, such as shipping/receiving/storage areas, only the sales areas should be included in the aggregate gross area.
3. With the exception of covered mall buildings (*see 24-4.4*), where stores are contiguous to one another (even if under different ownership or management and occupying numerous buildings) or where there are sections or floors used for sales within any building that are considered as separate stores (because, for example, they are under different management), and these

contiguous or intermixed stores are not separated from each other by at least 2-hour fire resistance rated fire barriers, the aggregate gross area of all such stores must be used in subclassifying the mercantile occupancy as Class A, B, or C.

24-1.5 **Classification of Hazard of Contents.** The contents of mercantile occupancies shall be classed as ordinary hazard in accordance with Section 4-2.

Exception: Mercantile occupancies shall be classified as high hazard if high hazard commodities are displayed or handled without protective wrappings or containers, in which case the following additional provisions shall apply:

(a) Exits shall be located so that not more than 75 ft (23 m) of travel from any point is required to reach the nearest exit.

(b) From every point there shall be at least two exits accessible by travel in different directions (no common path of travel).

(c) All vertical openings shall be enclosed.

Most occupancy chapters refer to Section 4-2 for classification of hazard of contents. However, the requirement of 24-1.5 emphasizes that, unless an extraordinarily hazardous situation exists, the contents of mercantile occupancies must be classed as ordinary hazard. This wording is intended to prevent the user from classifying the hazard of contents as high hazard unless a situation equivalent to dispensing explosives in bulk is present. Since the total package of life safety provided by the chapter's requirements anticipates the display of significant quantities of combustibles, these requirements should provide an acceptable level of safety without making it necessary to classify the typical mercantile occupancy environment as highly hazardous. Specifically, the chapter's requirements should be adequate without imposing the stringent high hazard contents requirements of the Exception to 24-1.5 on all but the most hazardous of mercantile occupancies.

Some procedures that would require classification of a mercantile occupancy as highly hazardous include dispensing gunpowder or other explosives in bulk or dispensing gasoline or flammable solvents by pouring them into open containers. The sale of flammable liquids such as camp stove fuel and rubbing alcohol should be controlled by NFPA 30, *Flammable and Combustible Liquids Code,*[3] with regard to display configuration, total amount, and separation from ignition sources.

Figure 24-4 illustrates an arrangement of exits from a highly hazardous area of a mercantile occupancy that meets the requirements of subparts (a) and (b) of the Exception to 24-1.5, which address limited travel distance and the exclusion of common path of travel. Although mercantile occupancy requirements are generally lenient in allowing vertical openings (*see 24-3.1*), all vertical openings in high hazard mercantile occupancies are required to be fully enclosed (*see 6-2.4*) in accordance with subpart (c) of the Exception to 24-1.5.

24-1.6   Minimum Construction Requirements. No special requirements.

The phrase "minimum construction" is used in the *Code* to describe the construction of the building housing the occupancy. Some occupancy chapters such as Chapters 12 and 13, which address the life safety needs of nonambulatory occupants of health care occupancies,

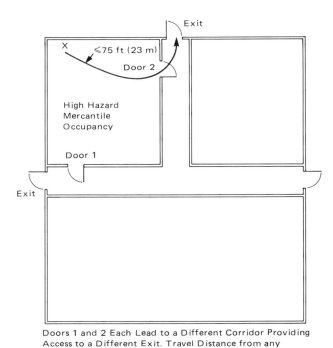

Doors 1 and 2 Each Lead to a Different Corridor Providing Access to a Different Exit. Travel Distance from any Point to an Exit Must not Exceed 75 ft (23 m)

Figure 24-4.   Exit Arrangement from an Area of a Mercantile Occupancy Defined as Highly Hazardous by 24-1.5.

require a minimum building construction type to help ensure structural integrity for a prolonged evacuation or for safe refuge within the building. Because mercantile occupancies characteristically are used by ambulatory customers and employees and do not provide sleeping accommodations, there are no minimum construction requirements imposed. Since there are no special requirements, the provisions of a local or state building code, if applicable, would need to be met.

24-1.7   Occupant Load.

24-1.7.1* For purposes of determining required exits, the occupant load of mercantile buildings or parts of buildings used for mercantile purposes shall be not less than required in the following:

(a) Street floor: One person for each 30 sq ft (2.8 sq m) gross floor area of sales space. In stores with no street floor, as defined in Chapter 3, but with access directly from the street by stairs or escalators, the principal floor at the point of entrance to the store shall be considered the street floor.

Exception to (a): In stores where, due to differences in grade of streets on different sides, there are two or more floors directly accessible from streets (not including alleys or similar back streets), for the purpose of determining occupant load, each such floor shall be considered a street floor. The occupant load factor shall be one person for each 40 sq ft (3.7 sq m) gross floor area of sales space.

(b) Sales floors below the street floor: Same as street floor.

(c) Upper floors used for sales: One person for each 60 sq ft (5.6 sq m) gross floor area of sales space.

(d) Floors or portions of floors used only for offices: One person for each 100 sq ft (9.3 sq m) gross floor area of office space.

(e) Floors or portions of floors used only for storage, receiving, shipping, and not open to the general public: One person per each 300 sq ft (27.9 sq m) gross area of storage, receiving, or shipping space.

(f) Floors or portions of floors used for assembly purposes: Occupant load determined in accordance with Chapter 8 for such assembly occupancies.

(g)* Covered mall buildings: Determined in accordance with 24-1.7.1(a) through (f).

Exception: The portions of the covered mall, where considered a pedestrian way (see Exception to 24-4.4.1) and not used as gross leasable area, shall not be assessed an occupant load. However, means of egress from a covered mall shall be provided for an occupant load determined by dividing the gross leasable area (not including anchor stores) by the appropriate lowest whole number occupant load factor from Figure 24-1.7.1(g).

Each individual tenant space shall have means of egress to the outside or to the covered mall based on occupant loads figured by using 24-1.7.1(a) through (f).

Each individual anchor store shall have means of egress independent of the covered mall.

A-24-1.7.1   These figures were established on the basis of counts of the population of typical store buildings during periods of maximum occupancy, such as before Christmas or during special sales. In some cases, the actual occupancy may be more dense than indicated by these figures, but it may reasonably be assumed that in any large mercantile building, all areas will not be similarly crowded at the same time, and the average occupant load should seldom exceed these figures.

In some types of stores, the occupant load will normally be much less than indicated: for example, in furniture stores. However, the character of mercantile operations is subject to such rapid changes that it is not prudent in designing exit facilities to assume that any store will never be crowded, and for this reason, the same load figures are used for all types of stores.

A-24-1.7.1(g)   The figure used in determining the occupancy load for covered mall shopping centers of varying sizes is arrived at empirically in surveying over 270 covered mall shopping centers, in the study of mercantile occupancy parking requirements, and in observing the number of occupants per vehicle during peak seasons.

These studies show that with an increase in shopping center size, there is a decrease in the number of occupants per square foot of gross leasable area.

This phenomenon is explained when one considers that above a certain shopping center gross leasable area [approx. 600,000 sq ft (56,000 sq m)], a multiplicity of the same types of stores starts to occur: the purpose is to increase the choices available to a customer for any given type of merchandise. Therefore, when shopping center size increases, the occupant load increases as well, but at a declining rate. In using the figure, the occupant load factor is applied to only the gross leasable area utilizing the covered mall as a means of egress.

Figure 24-1.7.1(g)

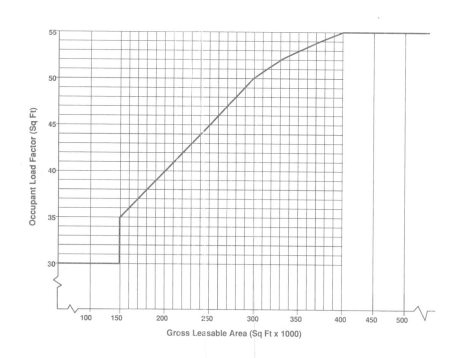

The occupant load factors specified for mercantile occupancies are based on the observation that, during normal use of a mercantile occupancy, the public will usually congregate on the street floor or in a basement sales area. In assigning a higher occupant load to the street floor, the *Code* recognizes merchandising techniques that arrange merchandise to take advantage of the heavy flow of traffic on the street floor. Customers are attracted to merchandise displays as they walk through portions of the street floor to reach escalators, elevators, and stairs to other floors. Thus, larger numbers of occupants are expected to be present on the street floor.

The street floor, as distinguished from other sales floors, is any floor that has an entrance/exit that is directly accessible from the street with not more than three risers of ascent or descent (*see Section 3-2 for definition of street floor*). If differences in the ground level on different sides of a store create several floors of this nature, the *Code* treats them all as street floors; however, a slightly different occupant load factor is used in accordance with the Exception to 24-1.7.1(a). It is important to note that, if the only access to a store from the street is by means of stairs or escalators, the principal sales floor rather than the street level must be considered the street floor for the purpose of choosing an occupant load factor and calculating the occupant load.

Since the terms "covered mall" and "covered mall building" have different meanings [*see commentary following 24-1.3(e) and (f)*], the intent of 24-1.7.1(g) and its exception is that the egress capacity of the overall covered mall building be sized to handle a number of occupants. This is calculated in two steps. First, the occupant load is calculated individually for each store and tenant space using the occupant load factors of 24-1.7.1(a) through (f). Second, the required egress capacity for the covered mall itself (i.e., the covered pedestrian way) is calculated using the values shown in Figure 24-1.7.1(g). Each store or tenant space must have sufficient egress capacity for its occupant load. The covered mall must have egress capacity based on 24-1.7.1(g), which, in effect, automatically accounts for those persons who are in the covered mall (i.e., the covered pedestrian walkway) and those persons discharged from stores into the covered mall as part of the stores' means of egress.

For example, consider a covered mall building with 21 tenant stores, all located on the "street floor." Each has 6,000 sq ft (560 sq m) of sales area from the 7,500 sq ft (700 sq m) of gross leasable area [assume that the other 1,500 sq ft (140 sq m) is storage area]. Using an occupant load factor of 30 sq ft (2.8 sq m) per person for the sales areas in accordance with 24-1.7.1(a) and 300 sq ft (27.9 sq m) for the storage areas in accordance with 24-1.7.1(e), each store must size its means of egress system to handle 205 persons (6,000 ÷ 30 + 1,500 ÷ 300 = 200 + 5 = 205). Store occupants can be sent into the covered mall as part of the required means of egress from each store. Based on the 21 tenant stores, each with 7,500 sq ft (700 sq m) of gross leasable area, the covered mall has 21 × 7,500 sq ft (700 sq m) or 157,500 sq ft (14,700 sq m) of gross leasable area that forms the basis on which the means of egress from the covered mall must be sized. Using Figure 24-1.7.1(g), for a gross leasable area of 157,500 sq ft (14,700 sq m), an occupant load factor of 36 sq ft (3.3 sq m) per person is indicated by the graph. The covered mall must provide a means of egress system for 157,500 sq ft (14,700 sq m) ÷ 36 sq ft per person (3.3 sq m per person) or 4,375 persons.

SECTION 24-2 Means of Egress Requirements

24-2.1 General.

24-2.1.1 All means of egress shall be in accordance with Chapter 5 and this chapter.

24-2.1.2 No inside open stairway or ramp may serve as a component of the required means of egress system for more than one floor.

This provision prohibits the use of unenclosed interior stairs or unenclosed interior ramps as exit access for more than one floor; it does not establish permission for the existence of an open stairway or ramp. See 24-3.1, "Protection of Vertical Openings," to determine if the stairway or ramp may be unenclosed.

24-2.1.3 Where there are two or more floors below the street floor, the same stair or other exit may serve all floors, but all required exits from such areas shall be independent of any open stairways between the street floor and the floor below it.

24-2.1.4 Where a level, outside exit from upper floors is possible owing to hills, such outside exits may serve instead of horizontal exits. If, however, such outside exits from the upper floor also serve as an entrance from a principal street, the upper floor shall be classed as a street floor in accordance with the definition in Chapter 3 and is subject to the requirements of this section for street floors.

Paragraph 24-2.1.4 reconfirms the requirements of 24-1.7.1(a) for classification of floors as street floors. Figure 24-5 illustrates a case where two floors qualify as street floors because each has one side located at a ground level. Note, however, that each floor has its other sides located either above or below the building's other ground level. As a result, these floors must have their exits arranged to allow horizontal travel to the exterior at one end of the floor and vertical travel (either up or down to ground level) at the other end of the floor. The exit capacity of the doors to the exterior on Floor 1 must accommodate that portion of the occupant load from an upper floor that is expected to travel down to and through the exits to the exterior from Floor 1 in addition to the portion of the Floor 1 occupant load assigned. The reverse is true for Floor 2, which must increase the size of its exterior exit capacity to accommodate occupants traveling up from Floor 1 as well as those traveling down to and through the exterior exits on Floor 2. Paragraphs 5-3.1.4, 5-3.1.5, and 24-2.3.2 explain how to add exit capacity based on the number of occupants expected to discharge from floors above and below the street floor. Figure 24-9 provides an example of how to calculate exit capacity for a street floor as illustrated by Floor 2 in Figure 24-5.

24-2.1.5 For special considerations with contents of high hazard, see 24-1.5.

24-2.2 Means of Egress Components.

24-2.2.1 Components of means of egress shall be limited to the types described in 24-2.2.2 through 24-2.2.9.

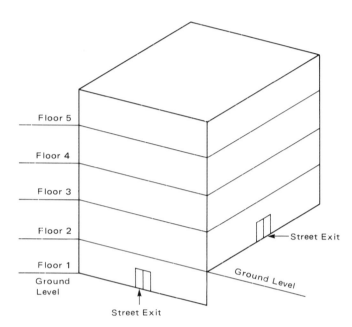

Figure 24-5. *Mercantile Occupancy with Two Street Floors. The exit capacity of each street floor must comply with 24-2.3.2. (Also see Figure 24-9.)*

24-2.2.2 Doors.

24-2.2.2.1 Doors shall comply with 5-2.1.

24-2.2.2.2* Locks complying with 5-2.1.5.1 Exception No. 2 shall be permitted only on principal entrance/exit doors.

A-24-2.2.2.2 The term "principal entrance/exit doors" is intended to imply doors that the authority having jurisdiction can be reasonably assured will be unlocked in order for the facility to do business.

This provision permits only the principal entrance/exit doors of a mercantile occupancy to be equipped with the special key-operated dead bolt lock described by the provisions of Exception No. 2 to 5-2.1.5.1, which must be easily determined to be locked by means such as a flag indicator that can be seen at some distance from the door. Other doors along the perimeter of the building are prohibited from being equipped with a key-operated dead bolt, because it cannot be guaranteed that these locks will be disengaged simultaneously when the principal entrance/exit door is unlocked each day at the opening of business. (*See Figure 24-6.*)

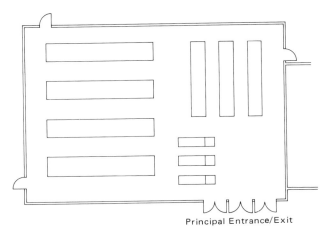

Figure 24-6. Principal Entrance/Exit. The concept of a principal entrance/exit as used in 24-2.2.2.2 is illustrated here.

24-2.2.2.3 Selected doors on stairwells shall be permitted to be equipped with hardware that prevents reentry in accordance with 5-2.1.5.2 Exception No. 1.

If the application of Exception No. 1 to 5-2.1.5.2 were not specifically recognized by this paragraph, the basic requirements of 5-2.1.5.2 would have been the only options offered for achieving reentry to the building from stairwells. This would have compelled new mercantile occupancies to provide either reentry from the stairwell back onto all floors at any time or similar reentry following automatic release of locking devices initiated by the building fire alarm system. Exception No. 1 to 5-2.1.5.2 allows some stairwell doors to remain locked from the stairwell side of the door to provide building security, while other doors must allow reentry. The location and number of reentry points provide the same overall level of life safety for this type of occupancy as that intended by the base provisions of 5-2.1.5.2.

24-2.2.2.4 Special locking arrangements in accordance with 5-2.1.6 are permitted.

Use of the delayed release locking device covered by 5-2.1.6 is allowed on any door in recognition of the security needs of a mercantile occupancy. The building must be protected throughout by an approved automatic sprinkler system or automatic fire detection system in order

to apply the delayed release locking provisions. In effect, the allowable 15- or 30- second delay will be experienced only under nonfire conditions or very early in a fire's growth, since the door must be usable immediately upon sprinkler operation, smoke or heat detection, or loss of power that controls the locking mechanism.

24-2.2.2.5 Where horizontal or vertical security grilles or doors are used as a part of the required means of egress from a tenant space, such grilles or doors shall comply with 5-2.1.4.1 Exception No. 3.

Although Exception No. 3 to 5-2.1.4.1 establishes provisions for the arrangement and use of horizontal or vertical security grilles or doors, it requires that an occupancy chapter specifically recognize the use of such security grilles or doors. Paragraph 24-2.2.2.5 provides this recognition for mercantile occupancies.

24-2.2.2.6 All doors at the foot of stairs from upper floors or at the head of stairs leading to floors below the street floor shall swing with the exit travel.

This provision suppplements the conditions of 5-2.1.4 by requiring doors that otherwise would not have to swing in the direction of egress travel to do so, based on their location. The queuing and accumulation of people at doors in locations such as at the foot of stairs from upper floors makes it difficult for occupants to step back to allow the door to swing inward.

24-2.2.2.7 Revolving doors shall comply with 5-2.1.10.

The provisions of 5-2.1.10 specify that the use of a revolving door, regardless of whether it is permitted as part of the required means of egress, requires a conforming side-hinged swinging door to be positioned and usable within the same wall as, and located within 10 ft (3 m) of, the revolving door. This helps to ensure that, once people move toward the door, if the collapsibility and other safety features of the door should fail and render it unusable, egress from the vicinity would still be possible without retracing steps and perhaps traveling toward the fire.

24-2.2.3 Stairs.

24-2.2.3.1 Stairs shall comply with 5-2.2.

24-2.2.3.2 Spiral stairs complying with 5-2.2.2.7 are permitted.

Note that 5-2.2.2.7 permits spiral stairs to serve only an occupant load of five or fewer persons. Spiral stairs may be effectively used in mercantile occupancies in storage areas having a small occupant load.

24-2.2.4 Smokeproof Enclosures. Smokeproof enclosures shall comply with 5-2.3.

This paragraph does not mandate the use of smokeproof enclosures, but it does recognize a smokeproof enclosure as part of the means of egress system in a mercantile occupancy only if the smokeproof enclosure meets the requirements of 5-2.3. For an example of an occupancy requiring a smokeproof enclosure, see 19-2.11.1, in which nonsprinklered, existing, high rise apartment buildings are required to be provided with smokeproof enclosures in accordance with 5-2.3.

24-2.2.5 Horizontal Exits. Horizontal exits shall comply with 5-2.4.

This paragraph does not mandate the use of horizontal exits, but it does recognize a horizontal exit as part of the means of egress system in a mercantile occupancy only if the horizontal exit meets the requirements of 5-2.4.

24-2.2.6 Ramps. Ramps shall comply with 5-2.5.

This paragraph does not mandate the use of ramps in mercantile occupancies, but it does recognize a ramp as part of the means of egress system only if the ramp meets the requirements of 5-2.5.

24-2.2.7 Exit Passageways. Exit passageways shall comply with 5-2.6.

Exception*: In lieu of the provisions of 5-2.6.4, an exit passageway in a covered mall building shall be permitted to independently accommodate:

(a) Its assigned occupant load from only the covered mall/pedestrian way, and

(b) The largest occupant load assigned to it from a single tenant space/store.

Exit passageways are frequently used within the means of egress system of covered mall buildings as a way of meeting the travel distance limitations or as a method of avoiding numerous exit doors along exterior walls located at the rear of tenant spaces. In effect, the exit passageway labeled A in Figure 24-7 moves the exit closer to the occupants to create a building arrangement that would otherwise require occupants to travel farther than allowable in order to reach an exit door in an exterior wall. The exit passageway labeled B in Figure 24-7 runs along the rear of multiple tenant spaces and provides access to the exterior only at each end of the exit passageway for security reasons. In both cases, the exit passageway is a *Code*-complying exit in accordance with 5-2.6 and is considered to provide the same degree of safety that an exit stair enclosure would provide an occupant of an upper floor in a multistory building.

A-24-2.2.7 Exception. To design exits from a covered mall building, the following steps should be used:

(1) The covered mall/pedestrian way has been assigned no occupant load, but it must be provided with means of egress sized to accommodate the total occupant load of the covered mall building based on the gross leasable area. The exits for the covered mall/pedestrian way can be provided by a combination of exterior exit doors and exit passageways.

(2) After completion of step (1), each tenant space (i.e., store) is to be judged individually for occupant load and exits. This step normally sends some portion of the store's occupant load into the covered mall and the remainder through the back of the store into an exit passageway that may serve multiple tenant stores and the covered mall.

(3) The exit passageway must be sized for the most restrictive of the following conditions:

(a) Minimum 66 in. per 24-4.4.1 Exception (b), or

(b) The portion of the exit capacity from the largest single tenant store being served by the exit passageway, or

(c) The portion of the exit capacity from the covered mall being provided by the exit passageway.

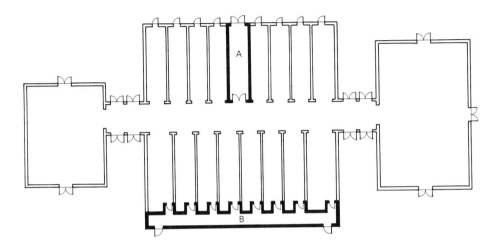

Figure 24-7. *Examples of Typical Uses of Exit Passageways in Covered Mall Buildings. (See 24-2.2.7.)*

The concepts used in the above steps include:

(1) After proper egress capacity is provided for the covered mall/pedestrian way, each store must then independently provide egress capacity for its occupants.

(2) The covered mall and the store's required exit passageway width need not be added together.

(3) The required exit passageway width for a tenant store need not be added to that of other stores using the same exit passageway.

Although the provisions of 5-2.6.4 require an exit passageway to be sized to accommodate the aggregate required capacity of all means of egress discharging through the exit passageway, the Exception to 24-2.2.7 allows some reduction in the required width of exit passageways in covered mall buildings. The exception recognizes that the sizing of the means of egress from the covered mall, calculated in accordance with the provisions of 24-1.7.1(g), provides egress capacity for occupants of the covered mall and occupants of the adjoining tenant spaces within the covered mall building. To require an exit passageway in a covered mall building to be of sufficient size to accommodate both the occupant load assigned to it from the covered mall and the occupant load of all tenant spaces discharging through the exit passageway would be the equivalent of counting a portion of the building's occupants twice, thereby oversizing the means of egress system.

24-2.2.8 **Fire Escape Ladders.** Fire escape ladders complying with 5-2.9 are permitted.

24-2.2.9 **Alternating Tread Devices.** Alternating tread devices complying with 5-2.11 are permitted.

In accordance with the provisions of 24-2.2.8 and 24-2.2.9, both fire escape ladders and alternating tread devices are allowed within the means of egress of new mercantile occupancies, but only as permitted by the relatively narrow provisions of 5-2.9 and 5-2.11. The provisions of 5-2.11, in effect, restrict the use of alternating tread devices to locations where the *Code* recognizes the use of fire escape ladders. (*See 24-2.2.8 and 5-2.9.*)

24-2.3 **Capacity of Means of Egress.**

24-2.3.1 The capacity of means of egress shall be in accordance with Section 5-3.

The mercantile occupancy chapters of prior editions of the *Code* specified requirements mandating that the occupant load of a mezzanine be added to that of the floor below the mezzanine for the purpose of determining the total size of the required means of egress system from the combined mezzanine and associated floor beneath. In the 1991 Edition, those requirements have been dropped from the mercantile occupancy chapters, because a similar requirement now appears in 5-3.1.6. The new wording in Chapter 5 mandates that any required egress capacity from a mezzanine that passes through the room below must be added to the required egress capacity of that room through which the egress passes.

Figure 24-8 illustrates a case in which a mezzanine is open to the street floor. The exits from the street floor must accommodate (1) the occupant load of the street floor, (2) the occupant load of the mezzanine in accordance with 5-3.1.6, and (3) the required capacity provided by the stairs from other floors discharging through the street floor in accordance with 24-2.3.2.

To determine the exit capacity for the street floor, the occupant load of the mezzanine (1,000) is added to the occupant load of the street floor (2,000). In addition, because one-half of the exits from the upper floors discharge through the street floor, the exit capacity of the street floor must accommodate the capacity of the exit stair enclosure that discharges through that floor. The maximum occupant load on any upper floor is 2,000 (second floor), and 24-2.7.2 permits a maximum of one-half of the exits or the exit capacity to discharge through the street floor, provided that the building is sprinklered. Therefore, the street floor must be provided with egress capacity for 4,000 persons or 800 in. (2,030 cm) of exit width using the factor of 0.2 in. (0.5 cm) per person for level exit components found in 5-3.3.1 (2,000 for street floor + 1,000 for mezzanine + 1,000 for upper floors = 4,000).

24-2.3.2 In Class A and Class B stores, street floor exits shall be sufficient for the occupant load of the street floor plus the required capacity of stairs and ramps discharging through the street floor.

Paragraph 24-2.3.2 requires that the exits for the street floor of a Class A or B mercantile occupancy have sufficient capacity to handle the occupant load of the street floor and the capacity of the exits discharging through the street floor, such as an enclosed exit stair that accommodates occupants who, when exiting the building during an emergency, must travel up from the basement sales area or down from the upper sales floors and mix with the customers already occupying the street floor.

Since people move more quickly in the horizontal direction than in the vertical direction, it is permissible to provide less door width than stair width. For example, in mercantile occupancies, in accordance with the egress capacity factors of 5-3.3.1, in mercantile occupancies, level components and ramps require only 0.2 in. (0.5 cm) of width per person, whereas stairs require 0.3 in. (0.8 cm) of width per person. As a rough approximation, for every 44 in. (112 cm) of stair discharging through the street floor, an additional 30 in. (76 cm) of door width opening to the outside must be added from the street floor. Figure 24-9 provides an example of the proper calculation method for determining the required exit capacity for the street floor.

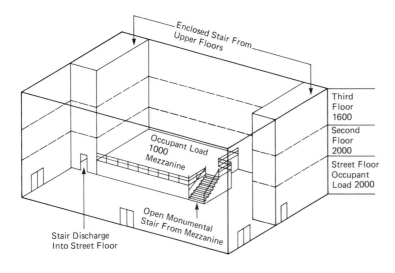

Figure 24-8. *Mercantile Occupancy with a Mezzanine Open to the Street Floor. (See second paragraph of commentary to 24-2.3.1 above.)*

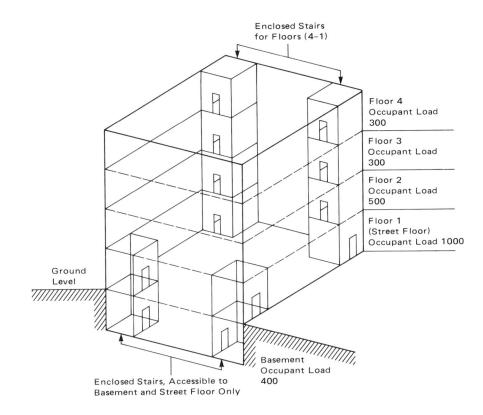

Enclosed Stairs
for Floors (4-1)

Floor 4
Occupant Load
300

Floor 3
Occupant Load
300

Floor 2
Occupant Load
500

Floor 1
(Street Floor)
Occupant Load 1000

Ground
Level

Basement
Occupant Load
400

Enclosed Stairs, Accessible to
Basement and Street Floor Only

Figure 24-9. Calculation of Exit Capacity Required for a Street Floor in Accordance with 24-2.3.2.

Street floor occupant load alone	1000
plus maximum upper floor occupant load discharging back through street floor (500 ÷ 2)	250
plus basement occupant load discharging back through street floor (400 ÷ 2)	200

1450 persons × 0.2 in. (0.5 cm) per person for level exit components per 5-3.3.1 =290 in. (737 cm) of exit width required from the street floor egress system.

24-2.4 **Number of Exits.** (*See also Section 5-4.*)

24-2.4.1 At least two separate exits shall:

(a) Be provided on every story, and

(b) Be accessible from every part of every story or mezzanine.

Exception to (b): Exit access travel shall be permitted to be common for the distances allowed as common path of travel by 24-2.5.3.

Exception No. 1: A single means of egress shall be permitted in a Class C mercantile occupancy provided that one of the following conditions is met:

(a) The travel distance does not exceed 75 ft (23 m) to the exit or to a covered mall (if it is considered a pedestrian way), or

(b) The travel distance does not exceed 100 ft (30 m) to the exit or to a covered mall (if it is considered a pedestrian way), and the story on which the occupancy is located and

all communicating levels that must be traversed to reach the exit or covered mall are protected throughout by an approved automatic sprinkler system in accordance with Section 7-7.

Exception No. 2: A single means of egress to an exit or to a covered mall (if it is considered a pedestrian way) shall be permitted from a mezzanine within any Class A, B, or C mercantile occupancy, provided that the common path of travel does not exceed 75 ft (23 m) or 100 ft (30 m) if protected throughout by an approved automatic sprinkler system in accordance with Section 7-7.

The provisions of 24-2.4, which apply to the required number of exits for mercantile occupancies, have been revised for this edition of the *Code* to clarify that any level that constitutes a story must have at least two exits located on that story. This means that the occupants of the story must be able to enter an exit (e.g., an enclosed exit stair on an upper floor of a multistory building) without having to travel to some other story to reach the entrance to the exit. Since a mezzanine that meets the maximum one-third area rule of 24-1.4.2.3 does not constitute a story (*see the commentary following 24-1.4.2.3*), two exits are not required on the mezzanine, but (1) the criteria of 24-2.4.1(b) must be met with respect to providing access to two separate exits, or (2) the provisions of the Exception to (b) or Exception No. 2 must be met.

The Exception to (b) applies only to subpart (b) of 24-2.4.1, which requires access to two separate exits from every part of every level (i.e., story or mezzanine). The exception indicates that 24-2.5.3 allows the occupant to travel in one direction for a maximum distance (i.e., the common path allowance) before requiring access in two separate directions. Therefore, although the story or mezzanine must eventually provide access to two exits in accordance with 24-2.4.1(b), that access need only be available at the point where the allowable common path is expended.

Although the basic requirement of 24-2.4.1 mandates that a mercantile occupancy be provided with at least two remotely located exits, Exception No. 1 permits a single exit for small facilities, i.e., Class C mercantile stores, such as tobacco shops, newsstands, and small 24-hour convenience stores. If the travel distance from any point in such a store to an exit is 75 ft (23 m) or less, the likelihood that a fire might surprise and overcome the customers before they could escape is low (*see Figure 24-10*). Furthermore, by allowing a single exit in these small mercantile occupancies if there is no more than 100 ft (30 m) of travel to an exit (or to a covered mall that qualifies as a pedestrian way in accordance with the provisions of the Exception to 24-4.4.1, which include an automatic sprinkler system requirement for the entire covered mall building), the exception provides additional flexibility and a potential increase in security for those small stores protected by means of automatic sprinkler installations within the store and in those portions of the overall building that occupants must traverse to reach an exit or pedestrian way.

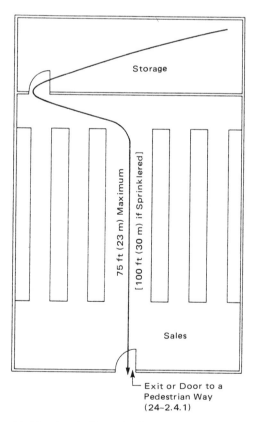

Figure 24-10.   Single Exit. A Class C mercantile occupancy may be provided with a single exit if travel distance is limited. (See Exception No. 1 to 24-2.4.1.)

While the Exception to (b) allows common access to the two required means of egress for some limited distances, Exception No. 2 exempts the facility from providing a point where access to two exits is available if the single means of egress leads to an exit or to a covered mall that qualifies as a pedestrian way in accordance with the provisions of the Exception to 24-4.4.1, which include an automatic sprinkler system requirement for the entire covered mall building. The exit or covered mall must be located within the same limited distances as those allowed for common path of travel. [*See the Exception to 24-2.4.1(b) and the Exception to 24-2.5.3.*]

24-2.5 Arrangement of Means of Egress.

24-2.5.1 Exits shall be arranged in accordance with Section 5-5.

24-2.5.2* No dead-end corridor shall exceed 20 ft (6.1 m).

Exception: In buildings protected throughout by an approved supervised automatic sprinkler system, dead-end corridors shall not exceed 50 ft (15 m).

A-24-2.5.2 The purpose of this paragraph is to avoid pockets or dead ends of such size that they pose an undue danger of persons becoming trapped in case of fire.

The Exception to 24-2.5.2 recognizes the additional level of safety to life provided by a complete automatic sprinkler system and permits added flexibility when designing the location of corridors and exits in buildings where approved sprinkler systems are installed by allowing the dead end corridor pocket to be as deep as 50 ft (15 m).

24-2.5.3* No common path of travel shall exceed 75 ft (23 m).

Exception: A common path of travel shall be permitted for the first 100 ft (30 m) in a building protected throughout by an approved supervised automatic sprinkler system in accordance with Section 7-7.

A-24-2.5.3 The common path of travel requirement permits small areas such as rooms or alcoves with only one way out where the distance is small enough so that there is little likelihood that a fire might develop to such proportions as to block escape before the occupants become aware of the fire and make their way out.

See the commentary following 5-5.1.6 for a detailed discussion on common path of travel. Also see the commentary following the Exception to 24-2.4.1(b), which allows a portion of the access to a single exit or multiple exits to be common.

Prior to 1988, the maximum common path of travel allowed by the *Code* in mercantile occupancies was 50 ft (15 m) [75 ft (23 m) if protected by smoke detectors or 100 ft (30 m) if sprinklered]. A special provision of Chapter 5 that specified the point where measurement of travel distance and common path begins for small rooms [i.e., distance within room was not counted if there was a maximum occupant load of 6 and a maximum 50 ft (15 m) of travel within the room] was deleted from the *Code* in 1988. The allowable common path of travel was increased in 1988 without either reducing the level of safety to life or imposing a hardship on designers.

24-2.5.4 Aisles leading to each exit are required. The aggregate width of such aisles shall be equal to at least the required width of the exit.

These provisions are intended to prevent constrictions in the means of egress system that would delay egress of building occupants. The aggregate width of aisles leading to an exit are required to provide egress width equal to that required of the exit to which they lead. Without this provision, occupants could be forced to squeeze through a relatively narrow aisle or similar constriction before reaching, for example, an expansive bank of doors to the outside. The exit capacity at the doors, rather than providing simultaneous egress for the large number of occupants assigned to that exit, would not be fully utilized. Occupants would move through the doors a few at a time as they passed slowly through the constriction. This requirement is illustrated in Figure 24-11 in the upper left and right corners of the floor plan of the mercantile occupancy.

24-2.5.5 In no case shall any required aisle be less than 36 in. (91 cm) in clear width.

The minimum 36-in. (91-cm) aisle width requirement is illustrated in Figure 24-11 and is consistent with the minimum 36-in. (91-cm) exit access width requirement of 5-3.4.1.

24-2.5.6 In Class A stores, at least one aisle of 5 ft (152 cm) minimum width shall lead directly to an exit.

The intent of 24-2.5.4 through 24-2.5.6 is to ensure that the interior arrangement of counters, racks, and displays of merchandise does not block or obscure accesses to an exit. Figure 24-11 illustrates an arrangement that meets the requirements for a Class A store. Essentially, the width of the exit determines the minimum width of the aisles, with the exception that one of the aisles must be at least 5 ft (152 cm) wide and lead directly to an exit.

24-2.5.7 If the only means of customer entrance is through one exterior wall of the building, two-thirds of the required exit width shall be located in this wall.

In establishing the requirements of 24-2.5.7, the *Code* demonstrates its concern regarding the arrangement of many discount and variety stores, which have one large main exit/entrance located in the front of the store and the other exits (which cannot be used as entrances) situated at points unfamiliar to the public. In such occupancies, the wall containing the main exit/entrance must be sized to handle two-thirds of the required exit capacity of the store since, due to its familiarity, most of the customers will use this exit under emergency conditions. This requirement is illustrated in Figure 24-11.

24-2.5.8 At least one-half of the required exits shall be so located as to be reached without passing through checkout stands. In no case shall checkout stands or associated railings or barriers obstruct exits, required aisles, or approaches thereto.

This is one of the most frequently violated provisions of Chapter 24. It is necessary in many supermarkets and discount and variety stores to pass through checkout counters, around shopping carts, and through turnstiles in order to exit the facility. This causes congestion or

blockage during an emergency. The *Code* requires at least one-half of all exits to be located so that occupants can avoid passing through or around these impediments to egress.

24-2.5.9* Where wheeled carts or buggies are used by customers, adequate provision shall be made for the transit and parking of such carts to minimize the possibility that they may obstruct means of egress.

A-24-2.5.9 In order to eliminate the obstruction to the means of egress of the interior exit access and the exterior exit discharge, it is the intent to provide adequate area for transit and parking of wheeled carts or buggies used by customers. This includes corral areas adjacent to exits that are constructed to restrict the movement of wheeled carts or buggies therefrom.

In states where returnable beverage bottle legislation has been enacted, stores and markets have had to create space for the collection of empty bottles and the refund of deposit charges. The area most commonly used is

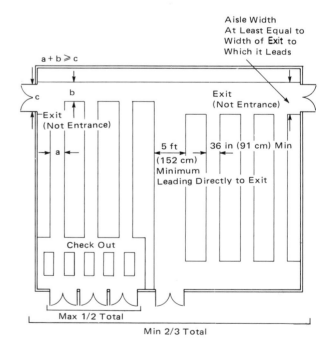

Figure 24-11. *Means of Egress Arrangement in a Mercantile Occupancy. The conditions described in the commentary associated with the requirements of 24-2.5.4 through 24-2.5.8 are illustrated here.*

located near the entrance/exit where wheeled shopping carts were formerly stored to be clear of the path of egress travel. The displaced carts are now often stored so that they obstruct the means of egress. This illustrates a situation where a properly designed, installed, and complying means of egress can be compromised abruptly by unexpected changes.

24-2.5.10* Exit access in all Class C stores and exit access in Class B stores that have an occupant load not exceeding 200 and are protected throughout by an approved automatic sprinkler system shall be permitted to pass through storerooms provided the following conditions are met:

(a) Not more than 50 percent of exit access is provided through the storeroom.

(b) The storeroom is not subject to locking.

(c) The main aisle through the storeroom shall be not less than 44 in. (112 cm) wide.

(d) The path of travel, defined with fixed barriers, through the storeroom shall be direct and continuously maintained in an unobstructed condition.

In 24-2.5.10 (a), the storeroom is limited to providing a maximum of 50 percent of the store's exit access, either in number of exits or exit capacity. Therefore, since two exits are required, neither of the following limits can be exceeded:

1. Only one of the two required exits can be reached by exit access travel through the storeroom, and
2. A maximum of half of the store's occupant load is permitted to egress through the storeroom.

In addition to allowing exit access in all Class C stores to pass through storerooms, 24-2.5.10 allows exit access in some Class B stores to pass through storerooms where that store is protected throughout by an approved automatic sprinkler system. This is permitted in recognition of the increased safety to life that a sprinkler system provides.

Figures 24-12 and 24-13 illustrate the application of the provisions of 24-2.5.10.

A-24-2.5.10 It is not the intent to allow exit access through Class A mercantile occupancy storerooms.

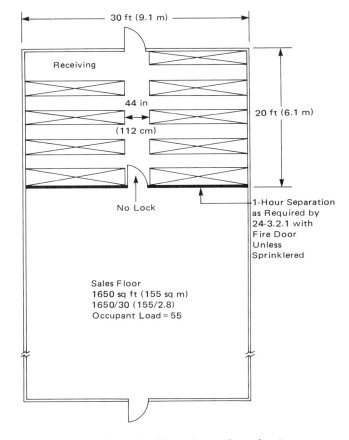

Figure 24-12. *Example of Exit Access through a Storeroom as Permitted by 24-2.5.10. The aisle within the storeroom must be defined by fixed barriers, such as those formed by the ends of shelving. The aisle must be kept unobstructed.*

24-2.6 **Travel Distance to Exits.** Travel distance to exits, measured in accordance with Section 5-6, shall be no more than 100 ft (30 m).

Exception: Travel distance shall not exceed 200 ft (60 m) in buildings protected throughout by an approved automatic sprinkler system in accordance with Section 7-7.

In accordance with of Section 5-6, travel distance requirements apply to only the first (or nearest) exit from a given point in the building. In other words, the 100-ft (30-m) travel distance limit requires that at least one exit must be located within 100 ft (30 m) of a point in the building; it does not require that all exits must be within 100 ft (30 m) of that same point in the building.

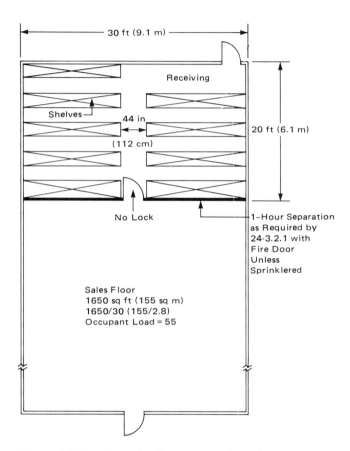

Figure 24-13. *Example of Exit Access through a Storeroom That Will Be Problematic Because of Its Relationship to the Receiving Area.*

Prior to 1988, the maximum travel distance allowed by the *Code* in sprinklered, mercantile occupancies was 150 ft (45 m). A special provision of Chapter 5 that specified the point where measurement of travel distance begins for small rooms [i.e., distance within room was not counted if there was a maximum occupant load of 6 and a maximum 50 ft (15 m) of travel within the room] was deleted from the *Code* in 1988. The allowable travel distance for sprinklered mercantile occupancies was increased to 200 ft (60 m) in 1988 without either reducing the level of safety to life or imposing a hardship on designers. For nonsprinklered mercantile occupancies, the maximum 100-ft (30-m) travel distance was not similarly increased. This was due, in part, to recognition of the high combustible load characteristic of mercantile occupancies, which is associated with displayed merchandise.

24-2.7 Discharge from Exits.

24-2.7.1 Exit discharge shall comply with Section 5-7 except as modified by 24-2.7.2.

24-2.7.2* Fifty percent of the exits shall be permitted to discharge through the level of exit discharge in accordance with 5-7.2 only where the building is protected throughout by an approved automatic sprinkler system in accordance with Section 7-7, and the distance of travel from the terminiation of the exit enclosure to an outside street door shall not exceed 50 ft (15 m).

A-24-2.7.2 The basis for the exception to the general rule on complete enclosure of exits up to their point of discharge to the outside of the building is that, with the specified safeguards, reasonable safety is maintained.

A stairway is not considered to discharge through the street floor area if it leads to the street through a fire resistance rated enclosure (exit passageway) separating it from the main area, even though there are doors between the first floor stairway landing and the main area.

The provisions of 24-2.7.2 should not be confused with open stairways as permitted by 24-3.1 Exception No. 1.

This arrangement is restricted to prevent more than 50 percent of the exits from any floor from discharging through the street floor. Furthermore, it is permitted only where the building is sprinklered throughout. Note that the path of travel on the first floor from the stair enclosure to the outside door cannot exceed 50 ft (15 m). The remaining 50 percent of the exits must discharge directly to the exterior.

The requirements of 24-2.7.2 are more stringent than those of 5-7.2, since they mandate automatic sprinkler protection throughout the building; set a 50-ft (15-m) travel limit on the street floor; and require that the street floor have an exit capacity that accommodates the street floor and the stairs discharging through the street floor. These requirements are not mandated by 5-7.2. The added requirements are imposed in recognition of the high combustible load of merchandise that may be on display, which is characteristic of mercantile occupancies.

24-2.8 **Illumination of Means of Egress.** Means of egress shall be illuminated in accordance with Section 5-8.

Note that illumination for the means of egress is not the same as emergency lighting; failure of the building power supply may cause failure of the means of egress illumination system, which is not required to have a back-up, auxiliary, or secondary power supply unless required by 24-2.9.

24-2.9 **Emergency Lighting.** Class A and Class B stores shall have emergency lighting facilities in accordance with Section 5-9.

Class C stores, due to their small size and small occupant load, are not required by the *Code* to have emergency lighting facilities.

24-2.10 **Marking of Means of Egress.** Means of egress shall have signs in accordance with Section 5-10.

Exception: Where an exit is immediately apparent from all portions of the sales area, the exit marking is not required.

The intent of the exception to the provision for marking the means of egress is to avoid requiring exit signs in small areas where the exit is readily apparent. For example, exit signs would not be required in the office of a service station, the purchase and eating areas of a small fast food restaurant, or in a Class C store whose size and arrangement comply with Exception No. 1 to 24-2.4.1.

24-2.11 **Special Features.** (Reserved.)

SECTION 24-3 Protection

24-3.1 **Protection of Vertical Openings.** Each stairway, elevator shaft, escalator opening, or other vertical opening shall be enclosed or protected in accordance with Section 6-2.

Exception No. 1: In Class A or Class B mercantile occupancies protected throughout by an approved supervised automatic sprinkler system in accordance with Section 7-7, unprotected vertical openings shall be permitted as follows:

(a) Between any two floors, or

(b) Between the street floor and the first adjacent floor below and the first adjacent floor (or mezzanines) above, or

(c) In accordance with 6-2.4.5.

Exception No. 2: In Class C mercantile occupancies, unprotected openings shall be permitted between the street floor and mezzanine.

Exception No. 3: Atriums in accordance with 6-2.4.6 are permitted.

Follow the provisions of 24-1.7 to assess properly the occupant load in order to provide sufficient egress capacity for a store in which floors or mezzanines are open to the street floor. Exception No. 1 to 24-3.1 specifies conditions under which such openings are permitted in sprinklered Class A and Class B stores.

Item (a) allows unprotected vertical openings between any two floors, regardless of floor level within the building.

Item (b) allows the floor (or mezzanine) immediately above, and the floor immediately below, the street floor to be simultaneously open to the street floor.

In lieu of item (b), item (c) allows a store that is fully sprinklered to have three contiguous levels open to each other under the provisions of 6-2.4.5. The requirement of Exception No. 1 to 24-3.1 for fully sprinklering the building is in excess of the requirements of 6-2.4.5, which mandate that only the open or communicating spaces must be sprinklered.

Exception No. 2 to 24-3.1 recognizes the limited size and probable small occupancy of Class C stores. For these reasons, a Class C store may have unprotected openings to a mezzanine.

Exception No. 3 permits an atrium in accordance with 6-2.4.6.

24-3.2 **Protection from Hazards.**

24-3.2.1 Hazardous areas, including but not limited to areas used for general storage, boiler or furnace rooms, fuel storage, janitor closets, maintenance shops including woodworking and painting areas, shall:

(a) Be separated from other parts of the building by fire barriers having a fire resistance rating of not less than 1 hour with all openings therein protected by ¾-hour fire protection rated self-closing fire doors, or

(b) The area shall be protected by an automatic extinguishing system in accordance with Section 7-7.

Exception: In general storage and stock areas protected by an automatic extinguishing system in accordance with Section 7-7, an enclosure, if provided, is exempt from the provisions of 6-4.1.

Paragraph 6-4.1 has been revised in the 1991 Edition of the *Code* to include a concept that previously applied only to assembly and educational occupancies. Specifically, where a hazardous area was protected by automatic sprinklers, rather than by enclosure with fire barriers of 1-hour fire resistance rating and doors of 45-minute fire protection rating, the hazardous area had to be enclosed by walls and doors that were at least smoke resisting. The Exception to 24-3.2.1 now allows the hazardous areas comprised of general storage and stock areas in a mercantile occupancy to be protected by automatic sprinklers without the need for the smoke resisting enclosure.

24-3.2.2 Areas with high hazard contents as defined in Section 4-2 shall be provided with both fire-resistive separation and automatic sprinkler protection.

Paragraphs 24-3.2.1 and 24-3.2.2 reflect the intent of Section 6-4, which (1) requires separation of a hazardous area from the remainder of the occupancy by means of suitable construction, or (2) mandates the installation of an automatic sprinkler system in a hazardous area, or (3) requires both where the hazard is severe.

24-3.3 Interior Finish.

24-3.3.1 Interior finish on walls and ceilings shall be Class A or B in accordance with Section 6-5.

24-3.3.2 Interior Floor Finish. No requirements.

24-3.4 Detection, Alarm, and Communication Systems.

24-3.4.1 General. Class A mercantile occupancies shall be provided with a fire alarm system in accordance with Section 7-6.

Class B and C mercantile occupancies are not required to have a fire alarm system.

24-3.4.2 Initiation. Initiation of the required fire alarm system shall be by manual means per 7-6.2.1(a).

Exception No. 1: Initiation shall be permitted to be by means of an approved automatic fire detection system in accordance with 7-6.2.1(b) that provides protection throughout the building.

Exception No. 2: Initiation shall be permitted to be by means of an approved automatic sprinkler system in accordance with 7-6.2.1(c) that provides protection throughout the building.

Since all Class A stores must be sprinklered based on gross floor area (*see 24-3.5.1*), it is logical that the method described in Exception No. 2 will be used most commonly to activate the fire alarm system, because the requirement for manual pull stations is waived if the sprinkler water flow activates the fire alarm system. Nuisance alarms might be reduced by eliminating the manual pull stations and satisfying the initiation requirements by means of water flow through the sprinkler system.

24-3.4.3 Notification.

24-3.4.3.1 During all times that the store is occupied (*see 5-2.1.1.3*), the required fire alarm system shall:

(a) Sound a general audible alarm throughout the store, or

(b) Sound an audible alarm in a continuously attended location for purposes of initiating emergency action.

Note that the *Code* provides a choice between two methods of notification. Many Class A stores do have a continuously attended location, and item (b) can be used; if such a location is not provided or not considered reliable by the authority having jurisdiction, item (a) must be applied.

24-3.4.3.2 Occupant Notification. Occupant notification shall be by means of live voice public address system announcement originating from the attended location where the alarm signal is received. (*See 24-3.4.3.1.*) The system shall be permitted to be used for other announcements. (*See 7-6.3.9 Exception No. 2.*)

Exception: Any other occupant notification means allowed by 7-6.3 shall be permitted in lieu of live voice public address system announcement.

This exception allows a system in accordance with 24-3.4.3.1(a) to use an automatic voice alarm or regular alarm sounding devices in lieu of the live voice alarm.

24-3.4.3.3 Emergency Forces Notification. Emergency forces notification shall include notifying:

(a) The fire department in accordance with 7-6.4, and

(b) The local fire brigade, if provided, via the attended location where the alarm signal is received. (*See 24-3.4.3.1.*)

Paragraph 7-6.4 allows for several different methods of automatically notifying the fire department.

24-3.5 Extinguishment Requirements.

24-3.5.1 Mercantile occupancies shall be protected throughout by an approved automatic sprinkler system in accordance with Section 7-7 as follows:

(a) In all buildings three or more stories in height.

(b) In all buildings exceeding 12,000 sq ft (1,100 sq m) in gross area.

(c) Throughout stories below the level of exit discharge where such stories have an area exceeding 2,500 sq ft (230 sq m) where used for the sale, storage, or handling of combustible goods and merchandise.

For information on the proper criteria for an approved automatic sprinkler system, see NFPA 13, *Standard for the Installation of Sprinkler Systems*;[1] NFPA 13A, *Recommended Practice for the Inspection, Testing, and Maintenance of Sprinkler Systems*;[2] and *Automatic Sprinkler and Standpipe Systems*.[4]

Item (a) requires that all buildings with three or more stories be protected with a complete automatic sprinkler system.

Under the provisions of item (b), a building with a total gross area in excess of 12,000 sq ft (1,100 sq m) is required to be protected with a complete automatic sprinkler system.

In effect, items (a) and (b) require that all Class A stores and larger Class B stores be protected by automatic sprinklers.

Item (c) ensures that all basement areas larger than 2,500 sq ft (230 sq m) (regardless of whether the space is used for sales, storage, or the handling of combustible merchandise) be sprinklered to avoid the potential threat to occupants of the floors above. Studies have shown that there is a higher rate of fire incidence in basements than in other areas of stores. Because smoke and heat rise, a fire in a basement can quickly render exits and exit discharges located on the street floor unusable. This danger is especially acute in mercantile occupancies, where allowances for various vertical openings in accordance with the provisions of 24-3.1 and its exceptions are more lenient than those for other occupancies.

24-3.5.2 Automatic sprinkler systems in Class A stores shall be supervised in accordance with 7-7.2.

24-3.5.3 Portable fire extinguishers shall be provided in all mercantile occupancies in accordance with 7-7.4.1.

Portable extinguishers are to be used by properly trained employees of the mercantile occupancy as required by 31-8.2.

24-3.6 Corridors.

24-3.6.1 Where access to exits is limited to corridors, such corridors shall be separated from use areas by fire barriers in accordance with 6-2.3 having a fire resistance rating of at least 1 hour.

Exception No. 1: Where exits are available from an open floor area.

Exception No. 2 Corridors need not have a fire resistance rating within a space occupied by a single tenant.

Exception No. 3: Corridors need not have a fire resistance rating within buildings protected throughout by an approved automatic sprinkler system.

Where access to exits is limited to corridors, separation requirements are specified. Similar requirements apply to business occupancies. (*Also see 26-3.6.1.*)

24-3.6.2 Openings in corridor partitions required to have a fire resistance rating in accordance with 24-3.6.1 shall be protected in accordance with 6-2.3.

24-3.7 **Subdivision of Building Spaces.** No special requirements.

24-3.8 **Special Features.**

24-3.8.1 Nonrated glazing and opening protectives per 24-1.2.3 Exception shall be permitted between mercantile occupancies and parking structures.

See the commentary following 24-1.2.3.

SECTION 24-4   Special Provisions

24-4.1 **Windowless or Underground Buildings.** (*See Section 30-7.*)

24-4.2 **High Rise Buildings.** High rise buildings shall comply with the automatic sprinkler requirements of 30-8.2.1.

The provisions of Section 30-8, "High Rise Buildings," whether applied singly, in various combinations, or in total, must be mandated by specific occupancy chapter requirements. In new high rise mercantile occupancies, 24-4.2 requires only the provisions of 30-8.2.1 (i.e., an approved, supervised, automatic sprinkler system with an additional sprinkler control valve and water flow device on each floor). The high rise mercantile occupancy must have a sprinkler system in accordance with 24-3.5.1 and the associated system supervision requirement of 24-3.5.2 for Class A stores regardless of the reference to 30-8.2.1.

24-4.3 **Open-Air Mercantile Operations.**

24-4.3.1 Open-air mercantile operations, such as open-air markets, gasoline filling stations, roadside stands for the sale of farm produce, and other outdoor mercantile operations shall be so arranged and conducted as to maintain free and unobstructed ways of travel at all times to permit prompt escape from any point of danger in case of fire or other emergency, with no dead ends in which persons might be trapped due to display stands, adjoining buildings, fences, vehicles, or other obstructions.

Paragraph 24-4.3.1 is virtually an open-ended provision that provides guidance for the arrangement, use, and display of merchandise for sale in open-air mercantile operations. The phrase "ways of travel" is purposely used to avoid confusion with "means of egress." "Means of egress" is strictly defined, and its use implies the application of the minimum requirements of Chapter 5. "Ways of travel" is not defined and implies no specific minimum *Code* provisions. Most open-air mercantile operations have unlimited means of entering and evacuating the areas used to display goods. For this reason, it is not necessary to provide specific *Code* requirements beyond the precautionary measures expressed in this paragraph.

24-4.3.2 If mercantile operations are conducted in roofed-over areas, they shall be treated as mercantile buildings, provided that canopies over individual small stands to protect merchandise from the weather shall not be construed to constitute buildings for the purpose of this *Code.*

The intent of 24-4.3.2 is to exempt small merchandise stands with canopies from classification as mercantile buildings. All other "roofed-over" areas should be treated as buildings, classified by area and height as Class A, B, or C mercantile occupancies, and subject to the appropriate provisions of Chapter 24.

24-4.4 **Covered Mall Buildings.** The purpose of this section is to establish minimum standards of life safety for covered mall buildings having not more than three levels.

The provisions for new covered mall buildings contained in 24-4.4 apply only to buildings up to three stories in height. For covered mall buildings with more than three stories, the equivalency concept of Section 1-6 should be used to engineer a unique life safety system that meets the intent of the *Code*.

Formal Interpretation 81-25
Reference: 1-5.7, 8-1.6, 24-4.4.1

Given that, per 8-1.6, a 3-story shopping mall with a food park (restaurant) on the third level is required to be of fire-resistive construction under the criteria for a Class A place of assembly above grade level.

Question 1: Is it possible to construct an anchor store of a different construction type from the mall building by separating it from the mall building by a 3-hour fire wall?

Question 2: Are 3-hour fire doors required for openings in this 3-hour wall between the mall and the anchor store?

Question 3: If the answer to Question 2 is no, is any type of opening protection required for openings between the mall and anchor store?

Answer: With only a few exceptions, the *Life Safety Code* sets no specific occupancy separation requirements. The authority having jurisdiction determines what separation is needed, if any, based on 1-5.7 and the 1.2 section of each occupancy chapter. The local building code or the model building codes may be consulted by the authority having jurisdiction in making this determination, keeping life safety rather than property protection in mind.

Issue Edition: 1981
Reference: 1-4.5, 8-1.6, 24-4.3.1
Date: October 1982 ■

24-4.4.1 The covered mall building shall be treated as a single building for the purpose of calculation of means of egress and shall be subject to the requirements for appropriate occupancies. The covered mall shall be at least of sufficient clear width to accommodate egress requirements as set forth in other sections of this *Code*.

Exception: The covered mall shall be permitted to be considered a pedestrian way, in which case the distance of travel within a tenant space to an exit or to the covered mall shall be a maximum of 200 ft (60 m) (see Exception to 24-2.6), or shall be the maximum for the appropriate occupancy; plus, an additional 200 ft (60 m) shall be permitted for travel through the covered mall space if all the following requirements are met:

(a) The covered mall shall be at least of sufficient clear width to accommodate egress requirements as set forth in other sections of this chapter, but in no case less than 20 ft (6.1 m) wide in its narrowest dimension.

(b)* On each side of the mall floor area, the covered mall shall be provided with an unobstructed exit access of not less than 10 ft (3 m) in clear width parallel to and adjacent to the mall tenant front. Such exit access shall lead to an exit having a minimum of 66 in. (168 cm) in width. (See 24-4.4.2.)

A-24-4.4.1 Exception (b). The minimum requirement for terminating mall exit access in not less than 66 in. (168 cm) width relates to the minimum requirement for at least one aisle in Class A stores [30,000 sq ft (2,800 sq m) or greater] to be 5 ft (152 cm) in width.

(c) The covered mall and all buildings connected thereto shall be protected throughout by an approved electrically supervised automatic sprinkler system in accordance with Section 7-7.

(d) Walls dividing stores from each other shall extend from the floor to the underside of the roof deck or floor deck above. No separation is required between a tenant space and the covered mall.

(e)* The covered mall shall be provided with a smoke control system.

A-24-4.4.1 Exception (e). Fire experience in covered mall shopping centers indicates that the most likely place of fire origin is in the tenant space where the combustible fire loading is far greater than in the covered mall proper.

Furthermore, any fires resulting from the comparatively low fire loading in the covered mall proper are far more likely to be detected and extinguished in their incipient stages because of the nature of the covered mall proper as a high traffic pedestrian way, thus producing far less smoke development in a far greater volume of space than in the much more confined adjacent tenant space.

Smoke control systems that address the foregoing are necessary in order to:

(a) Assure the integrity of the covered mall as a pedestrian way by maintaining it reasonably free of the products of combustion for at least the duration required to evacuate the building,

(b) Confine the products of combustion to the area of origin, and

(c) Remove the products of combustion with a minimum of migration of such products of combustion from one tenant to another.

Systems or combinations of systems that can be engineered to accomplish this include:

(a) Separate mechanical exhaust or control systems.

(b) Mechanical exhaust or control systems in conjunction with heating, ventilating, and air conditioning systems.

(c) Automatically or manually released gravity roof vent devices, such as skylights, relief dampers, or smoke vents.

(d) Combinations of (a), (b), and (c) or any other engineered system designed to accomplish the purpose of this section.

In recent years, covered mall shopping areas have increased in both number and size. Two approaches in addressing the life safety aspects of these complexes were developed. The first approach (described in the base paragraph of 24-4.4.1) treats the mall and the attached stores essentially as one large Class A store subject to all the provisions of Chapter 24. If viewed in this way, the covered mall would be treated as an aisle of a store. See Formal Interpretation 88-10, which follows the commentary associated with 24-1.4.2.1.

The second approach permits the mall to be considered as a pedestrian way through which occupants of the attached stores may egress during a fire. The phrase "pedestrian way" was intended to convey the meaning of the term exit access.

The Exception to 24-4.4.1 recognizes that, if the mall and all the buildings attached to the mall are protected by automatic sprinklers, occupants fleeing into the mall from a fire in a store are then moving into a space whose volume, size, and arrangement affords most of the benefits provided by an enclosed stair or a horizontal exit as well as providing many of the benefits of an outdoor area. The exception considers the mall to be a safe area

for the occupants of the tenant spaces attached to it, despite the fact that the mall is not separated from these attached spaces by the type of construction normally provided for an exit as required by 5-1.3.1.

Where a covered mall is considered as a pedestrian way, the maximum travel distance to an exit or to the covered mall from any point within a store attached to the covered mall is 200 ft (60 m). The reasoning behind this provision is that use of the covered mall for egress is as acceptable as use of an exit. An additional travel distance of up to 200 ft (60 m) is permitted within the covered mall [in addition to the 200 ft (60 m) allowed within the store] if all of the following conditions are met:

1. The covered mall building (i.e., the covered mall and all attached buildings) must be sprinklered. The sprinkler system must be electrically supervised. Note that, if the shopping complex is considered as one building rather than as a covered mall building with complying pedestrian way, sprinkler protection most likely is also required under the 12,000-sq ft (1,100-sq m) gross area criterion of 24-3.5.1(b).

2. The clear width of the mall must be at least 20 ft (6.1 m) or wider if mandated by the egress capacity. Note that, where the covered mall of a shopping center is considered as a pedestrian way, an occupant load is not calculated for the covered mall based on its area. The required capacity of the means of egress for the covered mall is calculated on the basis of aggregate gross leasable area of the attached stores (excluding anchor stores), including mid-mall kiosks and similar sales areas. (See the detailed commentary on this subject following A-24-1.7.1.)

3. At least 10 ft (3 m) of clear unobstructed space must be available for exit access in front of all store fronts. This requirement is designed to prohibit displays of merchandise, kiosks, or small sales stands from being placed within 10 ft (3 m) of the store fronts and ensures that the mall will have a minimum clear width of 20 ft (6.1 m).

4. Each exit access must terminate at an exit with a minimum width of 66 in. (168 cm).

5. Walls separating stores must run continuously from the floor slab to the roof slab or floor slab above, but not necessarily through the roof or floor. Walls need not

have any fire resistance rating. The intent of such separation is to resist the passage of smoke. The store front need not be separated from the mall by construction.

6. The covered mall, but not the stores, must have a smoke control system. Since the individual stores are open to the mall, this requirement is essential if the mall is to be used as a safe means of egress. For detailed guidance on the design, installation, and maintenance of smoke control systems, see NFPA 92B, *Guide for Smoke Management Systems in Malls, Atria, and Large Areas.*[5]

If these six conditions are not met, the covered mall may still be used as part of the exit access from the covered mall building, but the additional travel distance to an exit would not be allowed. Therefore, from any point within the overall covered mall building, which includes the stores and the covered mall, there would be a limit of 100 ft (30 m) of travel distance [200 ft (60 m) if the stores and covered mall are sprinklered]. In the majority of configurations, this restriction would preclude the use of the mall as an exit access.

Figure 24-14 illustrates many of the requirements necessary to qualify a mall as a pedestrian way.

The *Fire Protection Handbook*[6] contains a discussion of the hazards to life safety associated with covered mall buildings.

24-4.4.2 Exit Details.

24-4.4.2.1 Every floor of a covered mall shall have no less than two exits remotely located from each other.

Paragraph 24-4.4.2.1 reaffirms the fundamental *Code* requirement for providing at least two independent means of egress.

24-4.4.2.2 No less than one-half the required exit widths for each Class A or Class B store connected to a covered mall shall lead directly outside without passage through the mall.

Note that the larger stores (Class A and B mercantile occupancies) must still have 50 percent of their exits arranged to be independent of the covered mall. This is usually achieved by evacuating occupants directly from the store to the outside or directly into an exit passageway without entering the covered mall.

24-4.4.2.3* Each individual anchor store shall have means of egress independent of the covered mall.

A-24-4.4.2.3 It is not the intent of this paragraph to require that large stores be considered anchor stores. A store not considered in determining the occupant load of the mall must be arranged so that all of its means of egress will be independent of the covered mall.

24-4.4.2.4 Every covered mall shall be provided with unobstructed exit access parallel to and adjacent to the mall tenant fronts. This exit access shall extend to each mall exit.

Paragraph 24-4.4.2.4 repeats the provisions of item (b) of the Exception to 24-4.4.1 without stating that the exit access mall at the front of the stores within the covered mall must have a clear width of at least 10 ft (3 m).

Figure 24-14. A Covered Mall Used as a Pedestrian Way.

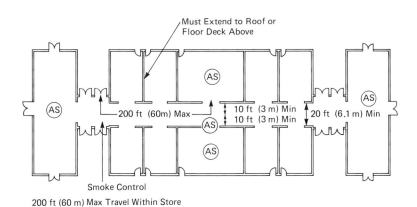

Must Extend to Roof or Floor Deck Above

200 ft (60m) Max

10 ft (3 m) Min
10 ft (3 m) Min

20 ft (6.1 m) Min

Smoke Control

200 ft (60 m) Max Travel Within Store

24-4.4.3 Detection, Alarm, and Communication Systems.

24-4.4.3.1 General. Covered malls shall be provided with a fire alarm system in accordance with Section 7-6.

Although the provisions of 24-4.4 address the overall covered mall building, the provisions of 24-4.4.3.1, which apply to alarm systems, require only that the alarm system be provided for the covered mall (i.e., the covered pedestrian way). In addition, the provisions of 24-3.4.1 require that any Class A mercantile occupancy within the covered mall building also be provided with an alarm system. Therefore, Class B and Class C mercantile occupancies within the covered mall building are not required to have alarm systems.

24-4.4.3.2 Initiation. Initiation of the required fire alarm system shall be by means of the approved automatic sprinkler system in accordance with 7-6.2.1(c).

Note that manual pull stations are not required but that the sprinkler system must have a water flow alarm that initiates the fire alarm system.

24-4.4.3.3 Notification. During all times that the covered mall is occupied (see 5-2.1.1.3), the required fire alarm system shall:

(a) Sound a general audible alarm throughout the covered mall, or

(b) Sound an audible alarm in a continuously attended location for the purpose of initiating emergency action.

Note that the *Code* provides a choice between two methods of notification. Many large shopping malls do have a continuously attended location, and item (b) can be used; if such a location is not provided or not considered reliable by the authority having jurisdiction, item (a) must be applied. In either case, the notification must be provided to the occupants of the covered mall and not to the occupants of the tenant stores within the covered mall building.

24-4.4.3.4 Occupant Notification. Occupant notification shall be by means of live voice public address system announcement originating from the attended location where the alarm signal is received. (*See 24-4.4.3.3.*) The system shall be permitted to be used for other announcements. (*See 7-6.3.9 Exception No. 2.*)

Exception: Any other occupant notification means allowed by 7-6.3 shall be permitted in lieu of live voice public address system announcement.

This exception allows a system that applies 24-4.4.3.3(a) to use an automatic voice alarm or regular alarm sounding device in lieu of the live voice alarm.

24-4.4.3.5 Emergency Forces Notification. Emergency forces notification shall include notifying:

(a) The fire department in accordance with 7-6.4, and

(b) The local fire brigade, if provided, via the attended location where the alarm signal is received. (*See 24-4.4.3.3.*)

Paragraph 7-6.4 allows for several different methods of automatically notifying the fire department.

24-4.4.3.6 Emergency Control. The fire alarm system shall be arranged to automatically actuate smoke management or smoke control systems in accordance with 7-6.5.2(c).

24-4.5 Operating Features. (*See Chapter 31.*)

SECTION 24-5   Building Services

24-5.1 Utilities. Utilities shall comply with the provisions of Section 7-1.

24-5.2 Heating, Ventilating, and Air Conditioning Equipment. Heating, ventilating, and air conditioning equipment shall comply with the provisions of Section 7-2.

24-5.3 Elevators, Escalators, and Conveyors. Elevators, escalators, and conveyors shall comply with the provisions of Section 7-4.

24-5.4 Rubbish Chutes, Incinerators, and Laundry Chutes. Rubbish chutes, incinerators, and laundry chutes shall comply with the provisions of Section 7-5.

References Cited in Commentary

[1]NFPA 13, *Standard for the Installation of Sprinkler Systems*, National Fire Protection Association, Quincy, MA, 1991.

[2]NFPA 13A, *Recommended Practice for the Inspection, Testing, and Maintenance of Sprinkler Systems*, National Fire Protection Association, Quincy, MA, 1987.

[3]NFPA 30, *Flammable and Combustible Liquids Code*, National Fire Protection Association, Quincy, MA, 1990.

[4]John L. Bryan, *Automatic Sprinkler and Standpipe Systems*, 2nd ed., National Fire Protection Association, Quincy, MA, 1990.

[5]NFPA 92B, *Guide for Smoke Management Systems in Malls, Atria, and Large Areas*, National Fire Protection Association, Quincy, MA, 1991.

[6]*Fire Protection Handbook*, 17th ed., National Fire Protection Association, Quincy, MA, 1991.

25

Existing Mercantile Occupancies

(See also Chapter 31.)

Mercantile occupancies include stores, markets, and other rooms, buildings, or structures used for the display and sale of merchandise. Included in this occupancy group are:

Supermarkets	24-hour convenience stores
Department stores	Video sales and rentals stores
Drugstores	Flea markets and crafts centers
Auction rooms	Building materials/supplies centers
Shopping centers/malls	Rental equipment centers
Hardware stores	Automobile sales showrooms

Minor merchandising operations in buildings consisting predominantly of other occupancies, such as a newsstand in an office building, must meet the *Life Safety Code* requirements of the predominant occupancy.

Documentation of fires that have occurred in occupancies that the *Life Safety Code* would classify as mercantile occupancies (*see 4-1.7*) are grouped and stored in the national fire incident data bases under the category of stores. Although this category covers more uses than those that the *Life Safety Code* would define as mercantile, including occupancies such as those used as vehicle repair facilities, the fire statistics applicable to stores provide a general guideline for the yearly death toll and fire incident frequency in mercantile occupancies. Stores accounted for 28,100 structure fires per year as reported to U.S. fire departments from 1984 to 1988, with an associated 25 civilian (i.e., nonfire-service personnel) deaths and 569 civilian injuries per year. Nearly half of those who died in store fires during the period from 1980 to 1988 were not in the room of fire origin when the fire began. In addition, the fire records indicate that most stores in which fires occurred did not have sprinkler systems or fire detection systems.

In the 1980s, only one store fire killed 10 or more people, and it occurred in a natural gas company repair facility, which likely would not have been classified as a mercantile occupancy by the *Life Safety Code*. Fires in service stations and vehicle repair facilities typically accounted for the largest share of fire deaths in stores.

SECTION 25-1 General Requirements

25-1.1 Application.

25-1.1.1 Existing mercantile occupancies shall comply with the provisions of Chapter 25. (*See Chapter 31 for operating features.*)

To understand the full intent and scope of 25-1.1.1, it is necessary to review it concurrently with Sections 1-5, 1-6, and 1-7. Although a building code may exclude existing buildings from coverage under some form of a "grandfather clause," the *Life Safety Code*, by virtue of its interest in safety to life, does not condone existing building arrangements that do not comply with the *Code* except within a very narrow and strict set of guidelines. These guidelines are contained in this chapter.

If a building complies with an earlier edition of the *Code*, it is not "grandfathered" and thereby exempted from compliance with a more current edition that has been adopted as law in that building's jurisdiction. The Committee on Safety to Life is especially careful to avoid adopting requirements for existing buildings that become more stringent from one edition of the *Code* to the next, unless the change is absolutely necessary to enhance the overall package of safety to life intended by the *Code*. Thus, the old adage of "once in compliance, always in compliance" does not hold.

25-1.1.2 This chapter establishes life safety requirements for existing buildings. Specific requirements for suboccupancy groups, such as Class A, B, and C stores and covered malls, are contained in paragraphs pertaining thereto.

For the definitions of Class A, B, and C stores, see 25-1.4.2 and its associated commentary, including Table 25-1.

25-1.1.3 Additions to existing buildings shall conform to the requirements for new construction. Existing portions of the structure need not be modified, provided that the new construction has not diminished the firesafety features of the facility. Existing portions shall be upgraded if the addition results in a change of mercantile subclassification. (*See 25-1.4.2.*)

Paragraph 25-1.1.3 specifies that additions to existing mercantile occupancies must conform to the requirements for new construction, but the existing portion of the occupancy may generally continue in use without an upgrade to meet the requirements for new construction if the facility complies with the provisions for existing mercantile occupancies contained in this chapter. However, if the addition results in a change in the mercantile occupancy subclassification (*see 25-1.4.2*), such as a change from Class C to Class B or from Class B to Class A, the existing portion of the enlarged overall facility, as well as the newly constructed portion, must be upgraded to meet the provisions applicable to new construction. The provisions of 25-1.1.3 are illustrated in the following paragraphs and in Figure 25-1, Parts a, b, and c.

In Figure 25-1a, the new construction, which includes 10,000 sq ft (930 sq m) of additional sales area and approximately 2,000 sq ft (186 sq m) of new storage area is added to an existing Class B mercantile occupancy with 5,000 sq ft (465 sq m) of existing sales area. The size and placement of the new addition neither change the Class B mercantile subclassification of the enlarged overall facility nor diminish the firesafety features of the existing portion of the facility. Therefore, the addition is constructed in accordance with the requirements of Chapter 24, "New Mercantile Occupancies," and the existing portion of the building is allowed to continue to be used, without upgrade, if it meets the requirements of Chapter 25, "Existing Mercantile Occupancies." If the existing portion of the building does not meet the requirements of Chapter 25, it must be upgraded to meet those requirements.

Figure 25-1b illustrates new construction identical to that described in the preceding paragraph, which is added to an existing Class B mercantile occupancy with 14,000 sq ft (1,300 sq m) of existing sales area. Although the size of the addition does not change the Class B mercantile subclassification of the overall facility, the placement of the new addition appears to have diminished the firesafety of the existing portion of the building with respect to travel distance. The broken line in Figure 25-1b represents what had previously been an exterior wall and exit door in the existing mercantile occupancy prior to construction of the addition. The door had allowed occupants in the upper left portion of the existing building to reach an exit within the allowable 150-ft (45-m) travel distance specified for nonsprinklered existing mercantile occupancies in accordance with 25-2.6. Without the exit door, occupants of the existing portion of the building must be able to reach an exit (i.e., one of the three doors in the perimeter of the enlarged facility) within the same 150-ft (45-m) travel distance limitation. If this is not possible, an additional exit within that distance must be constructed or the building must be sprinklered in order to increase the allowable travel distance to 200 ft (60 m). Since the new construction must meet the provisions of Chapter 24, the entire building (new and existing portions) must be sprinklered in accordance with 24-3.5.1, because the building exceeds 12,000 sq ft (1,100 sq m) in gross area. [*See 24-3.5.1(b).*]

Figure 25-1c illustrates new construction identical to that described in the two preceding paragraphs, which is added to an existing Class B mercantile occupancy with 21,000 sq ft (1,950 sq m) of existing sales area. The size of the new sales area, when added to that of the existing mercantile occupancy, exceeds 30,000 sq ft (2,800 sq m) and results in a change of mercantile subclassification from Class B to Class A [*see 25-1.4.2.1(a)*]. In accordance with the provisions of the first and last sentences of 25-1.1.3, the entire building (new and existing portions) must meet the requirements for new mercantile occupancies as detailed in Chapter 24.

25-1.2 Mixed Occupancies.

25-1.2.1 Mixed occupancies shall comply with 1-5.7.

25-1.2.2 Combined Mercantile and Residential Occupancies.

25-1.2.2.1 No dwelling unit shall have its sole means of egress through any mercantile occupancy in the same building.

25-1.2.2.2 No multiple dwelling occupancy shall be located above a mercantile occupancy.

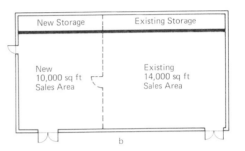

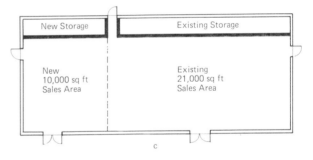

Figure 25-1a, b, and c. Examples of Additions to Existing Mercantile Occupancies. (See commentary associated with 25-1.1.3.) 1 sq ft = 0.093 sq m

Exception No. 1: Where the dwelling occupancy and exits therefrom are separated from the mercantile occupancy by construction having a fire resistance rating of at least 1 hour.

Exception No. 2: Where the mercantile occupancy is protected throughout by an approved automatic sprinkler system in accordance with Section 7-7.

Exception No. 3: As permitted in 25-1.2.2.3.

25-1.2.2.3 A building with not more than two dwelling units above a mercantile occupancy shall be permitted, provided that the mercantile occupancy is protected by an automatic fire detection system in accordance with Section 7-6.

The requirements for mixed occupancies were developed to address a once common (but now less prevalent) occupancy arrangement: the corner tavern, grocery store, or retail store that has one or two dwelling units located on the upper floors. The *Code* separates this type of combined occupancy into two classes.

Where there is a single dwelling unit located above or adjacent to the mercantile occupancy, the *Code* prohibits (*see 25-1.2.2.1*) the dwelling unit from having its sole means of egress pass through the mercantile occupancy in the same building. If the dwelling unit has a means of egress that passes through the mercantile occupancy, it must have access to a second means of egress that is independent of and does not pass through the mercantile occupancy.

The *Code* prohibits multiple dwelling units from being located above a mercantile occupancy unless one of the following conditions is met:

1. The dwelling units and their means of egress are separated from the mercantile occupancy by construction with a fire resistance rating of at least 1 hour, or
2. The mercantile occupancy is protected by an automatic sprinkler system. Sprinkler systems have proven to be an excellent alternative to 1-hour fire resistance rated construction under these circumstances (*see Section 7-7 of the Code, NFPA 13, Standard for the Installation of Sprinkler Systems,*[1] *and NFPA 13A, Recommended Practice for the Inspection, Testing, and Maintenance of Sprinkler Systems*),[2] or
3. There are no more than two dwelling units, and the mercantile occupancy is protected by an automatic fire detection system that must be capable of sounding an alarm in the dwelling units as required by Section 7-6.

The *Code* established these requirements because of the long historical record of deaths and injuries that have occurred where fire originated in mercantile occupancies and spread to dwelling units located above the mercantile occupancies.

25-1.2.3 **Combined Mercantile Occupancies and Parking Structures.** Walls separating parking structures from mercantile occupancies shall have a fire resistance rating of not less than 2 hours.

Exception: In enclosed parking structures that are protected throughout with an approved automatic sprinkler system in accordance with Section 7-7 or in open-air parking structures, nonrated glazing and opening protectives shall be permitted if all of the following conditions are met:

(a) The openings do not exceed 25 percent of the area of the wall in which they are located, and

(b) The openings are used for main entrance and associated sidelight functions, and

(c) The enclosed connecting mercantile building is protected throughout by an approved automatic sprinkler system in accordance with Section 7-7, and

(d) The floor elevation of the mercantile use is at least 4 in. (10.2 cm) above the floor level of the parking structure, and

(e) No vehicle is able to park or drive within 10 ft (3 m) of the openings, and

(f) The openings have a minimum of a glass membrane, and

(g) Any doors in the glass membrane are self-closing.

The provisions of 25-1.2.3 are new to this edition of the *Code* and, although they address combined mercantile occupancies and parking structures, are very similar to the new requirements of 27-1.2.2, which address combined business occupancies and parking structures. It is common for multistory mercantile occupancies (e.g., department stores and shopping mall buildings) and multistory business occupancies (e.g., office buildings) to be attached to multistory parking garages. Such garages provide access to the occupancy at multiple levels. In order to allow flexibility in the number and type of openings and in the degree of stringency required for opening protectives such as fire doors and fire windows, the Exception to 25-1.2.3 outlines a set of provisions that, when applied in total, will safely allow a reduction in the 2-hour fire resistance rating required by 25-1.2.3. The reduction allows the use of nonrated glazing and nonrated opening protectives. This permits the use of glass doors and glass sidelights in the barrier between the mercantile occupancy and the garage. Security in the garage is thereby increased, since customers can view the area through the glass doors or sidelights.

Note that all eight requirements mandated by the Exception to 25-1.2.3 [i.e., the sprinkler requirement for the garage in the base paragraph and the seven requirements of subparts (a) through (g)] must be met as a whole in order to apply the exception to the rule. Otherwise, a 2-hour fire resistance rated separation between the mercantile occupancy and the parking structure is required.

25-1.3 Special Definitions.

(a) **Anchor Store.** A department store or major merchandising center having direct access to the covered mall but having all required means of egress independent of the covered mall.

From a merchandising point of view, a shopping mall developer or operator may refer to any of the major tenants that have vast expanses of floor space and instant name recognition, and that are often positioned at the ends and corners of the covered mall building, as anchor stores. However, the *Code* reserves the use of this term for those stores having means of egress independent from the covered mall. (*See Figure 25-2.*)

(b) **Class A Stores.** [*See 25-1.4.2.1(a).*]
(c) **Class B Stores.** [*See 25-1.4.2.1(b).*]
(d) **Class C Stores.** [*See 25-1.4.2.1(c).*]
(e) **Covered Mall.** A covered or roofed interior area used as a pedestrian way and connected to a building(s) or portions of a building housing single or multiple tenants.

The definition of "covered mall" is differentiated from that of "covered mall building," since certain requirements apply only to the covered pedestrian way (i.e., the covered mall), while other requirements apply to the entire building, including all tenant spaces and common areas (i.e., the covered mall building). See the commentary

immediately following, which addresses 25-1.3(f) "Covered Mall Building." A portion of a building can be considered a covered mall even if it is open to the outside elements at one or more points.

(f) **Covered Mall Building.** A building, including the covered mall, enclosing a number of tenants and occupancies, such as retail stores, drinking and dining establishments, entertainment and amusement facilities, offices, and other similar uses, wherein two or more tenants have a main entrance into the covered mall.

The definition of "covered mall building" is differentiated from that of "covered mall," since certain requirements apply to the entire building, including all tenant spaces and common areas (i.e., the covered mall building), while other requirements apply only to the covered pedestrian way (i.e., the covered mall). For example, the provisions of 25-4.4 require automatic sprinkler protection throughout the entire covered mall building but require an alarm system and, under certain conditions, a smoke control system only within the covered mall.

(g) **Gross Leasable Area.** The total floor area designated for tenant occupancy and exclusive use, expressed in square feet (square meters), measured from centerlines of joining partitions and exteriors of outside walls.

The term gross leasable area is defined in order to provide a criterion under which an occupant load can be calculated for use in sizing the means of egress system for just the covered mall [*see 25-1.3(e)*]. [*See 25-1.7.1(g), Figure 25-1.7.1(g), and associated commentary.*]

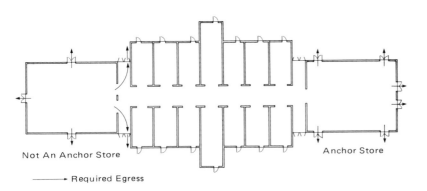

Not An Anchor Store

Anchor Store

——→ Required Egress

Figure 25-2. Anchor Store. This figure illustrates the difference between an anchor store and a store that, while large, is not an anchor store. Note that required egress from an anchor store cannot pass through the covered mall.

(h) **Open-Air Mercantile Operations.** Operations conducted outside of all structures with the operations area devoid of all walls and roofs except for small, individual, weather canopies.

See the provisions of 25-4.3 and the associated commentary applicable to open-air mercantile operations.

25-1.4 Classification of Occupancy.

25-1.4.1 Mercantile occupancies shall include all buildings and structures or parts thereof with occupancy as described in 4-1.7.

It is important to review the *Code's* definition (*see 4-1.7*) of a mercantile occupancy. Note that this definition does not include "minor merchandising operations in buildings predominantly of other occupancies, such as a newsstand in an office building... ." Paragraph 4-1.7 requires that such occupancies be subject to the requirements of the predominant (i.e., major) occupancy. For example, a newsstand that is located in an office building would be treated under the same business occupancy requirements (Chapter 26 or 27) as the office building.

25-1.4.2 Subclassification of Occupancy.

25-1.4.2.1 Mercantile occupancies shall be subclassified as follows:

(a) *Class A.* All stores having aggregate gross area of more than 30,000 sq ft (2,800 sq m), or utilizing more than three levels, excluding mezzanines, for sales purposes.

(b) *Class B.* All stores of more than 3,000 sq ft (280 sq m) but not more than 30,000 sq ft (2,800 sq m) aggregate gross area, or utilizing floors above or below the street floor level for sales purposes. Mezzanines are permitted. (*See 25-1.4.2.3.*)

Exception to (b): If more than three floors, excluding mezzanines, are utilized, the store shall be Class A, regardless of area.

(c) *Class C.* All stores of not more than 3,000 sq ft (280 sq m) gross area used for sales purposes on one story only, excluding mezzanines.

Mezzanines allowed by the one-half area rule of 25-1.4.2.3 do not constitute a story and, therefore, are not a factor in determining mercantile occupancy subclassification based on the number of stories used for sales purposes. The area of such mezzanines used for sales purposes (*see 25-1.4.2.2*) is, however, a factor in determining occupancy subclassification based on floor area devoted to sales. For example, a store with a 2,000-sq ft (186-sq m) main sales floor and a 1,000-sq ft (93-sq m) sales mezzanine is a Class C mercantile occupancy, while a store with a 2,400-sq ft (225-sq m) main sales floor and a 1,200-sq ft (112-sq m) sales mezzanine is a Class B mercantile occupancy. In each case, the mezzanine meets the maximum one-half area rule and is not treated as a story. In the second case, the area of the 1,200-sq ft (112-sq m) sales mezzanine, when added to the 2,400-sq ft (225-sq m) main sales floor, exceeds the maximum 3,000-sq ft (280-sq m) sales area for Class C mercantile occupancies and is, therefore, a Class B mercantile occupancy.

Mezzanines with areas in excess of the maximum one-half area rule constitute stories and, thus, sales levels. Therefore, they must be considered as such when determining mercantile occupancy subclassification. For example, a set of plans might show a proposed store with three floor levels of 8,000 sq ft (740 sq m) each that are used for sales purposes and a single 5,000-sq ft (465-sq m) sales "mezzanine." The store will actually use four stories for sales purposes, because the so-called "mezzanine" is not a mezzanine based on the maximum one-half area rule of 25-1.4.2.3. Although the 30,000-sq ft (2,800-sq m) sales area limitation associated with Class A mercantile occupancies is not exceeded, the four stories used for sales purposes result in a Class A mercantile occupancy subclassification in accordance with the definition contained in 25-1.4.2.1(a).

To qualify as a Class A, B, or C mercantile occupancy, a store must meet the requirements of 25-1.4.2.1 as summarized in Table 25-1. The classification process is important because specific life safety requirements vary for each mercantile class. The criteria vary in degree of stringency depending upon a store's classification, which, while based directly on the size of the sales areas, is indirectly a measure of the number of occupants at risk from any given fire.

Table 25-1. Subclassification of Mercantile Occupancies

Store Class	By Height		By Aggregate Gross Area† (sq ft)
A	>3 Stories‡	or	>30,000
B	≤3 Stories‡	and	>3,000 and ≤30,000
C	One Story Only§	and	≤3,000

† Sections of floors not used are not counted in the area classification.
‡ Stories not used for sales above or below sales floor are not counted in the height classification.
§ A mezzanine < ½ the area of the floor below is permitted.

Formal Interpretation: 88-10
Reference: Chapters 24 and 25

Question 1: Is it the intent of the *Code* to permit a store with more than 30,000 sq ft (2,800 sq m) used for sales purposes and many separate tenants or companies operating within it to be classified as a Class A store?

Answer: Yes.

Question 2: Is it the intent of the *Code* to permit a designer to select at his/her option if a building with more than 30,000 sq ft (2,800 sq m) used for sales purposes is to be classified as a Covered Mall Building or a Class A Mercantile Occupancy?

Answer: Yes.

Issue Edition: 1988
Reference: Chapters 24 and 25
Issue Date: June 11, 1990 ∎

25-1.4.2.2 For the purpose of the classification required in 25-1.4.2.1, the aggregate gross area shall be the total gross area of all floors used for mercantile purposes and, where a store is divided into sections, regardless of fire separation, shall include the area of all sections used for sales purposes. Areas of floors not used for sales purposes, such as an area used only for storage and not open to the public, shall not be counted for the purposes of the above classifications, but exits shall be provided for such nonsales areas in accordance with their occupancy as specified by other chapters of this *Code*.

Some mercantile occupancies locate their sales and storage areas together (e.g., furniture warehouse sales areas). In such cases, the mercantile occupancy subclassification should be determined using all aggregate gross area open to public use.

25-1.4.2.3 The floor area of a mezzanine or the aggregate floor area of multiple mezzanines shall not exceed one-half of the floor area of the room or story in which the mezzanines are located. A mezzanine or aggregated mezzanines in excess of the one-half area limitation shall be treated as floors.

The mezzanine measurement provisions of 25-1.4.2.3 for existing mercantile occupancies use a "one-half" area rule, whereas the provisions of 24-1.4.2.3 for new mercantile occupancies use a "one-third" area rule. The one-third rule for new mercantile occupancy mezzanines correlates with the definition of mezzanine in Chapter 3. Since the one-half area rule applied to mercantile occupancies long before the generalized definition of mezzanine was added to Chapter 3, it has been retained for existing (but not new) mercantile occupancies in order to prevent the abrupt noncompliance of existing buildings due to an issue that, itself, does not significantly lower the level of safety to life in an existing building. Therefore, mezzanines in existing mercantile occupancies continue to be judged based on the historical "one-half" area criteria.

Examples of mezzanine arrangements to which the maximum one-half area rule of 25-1.4.2.3 can be applied are illustrated in Figure 25-3(a) through (f). For purposes of illustration, it should be assumed that all the mezzanines as well as the entire main floor level are used for sales. Parts (a), (b), (c), and (d) of Figure 25-3 illustrate only a single story or single floor level with a mezzanine because the aggregate areas of the mezzanines [i.e., 5,000 sq ft (465 sq m)] do not exceed one-half of the floor area [i.e., 10,000 sq ft (930 sq m)] of the room or story in which the mezzanine is located.

In Part (e), the single 6,000-sq ft (560-sq m) intermediate level referred to by occupants as a mezzanine exceeds the one-half area rule. Therefore, it is not a mezzanine for *Life Safety Code* purposes but a story by itself. Part (e) of Figure 25-3, therefore, depicts a two-story mercantile occupancy.

In Part (f), one of the 4,000-sq ft (370-sq m) mezzanines fits within the maximum one-half area allowance and can be called a mezzanine without constituting a story. The other mezzanine, although of the same size and, thus, by itself not in excess of the one-half area rule, does create a story, because the sum of the areas of the two mezzanines [i.e., 8,000 sq ft (745 sq m)] exceeds one-half of the 10,000-sq ft (930-sq m) lower floor level. Thus, the figure shows a two-story mercantile occupancy with a mezzanine.

Although the mezzanines in Parts (a) through (d) of Figure 25-3 do not establish separate stories, their areas, because they are used for sales, are included in the total gross sales area against which the Class A, B, and C mercantile occupancy subclassification definitions of 25-1.4.2.1 are applied. Parts (a) through (d) each show 15,000 sq ft (1,400 sq m) of sales area and would be classified as Class B mercantile occupancies.

In addition to the maximum one-half area limitation of 25-1.4.2.3, the provisions of 6-2.5 (which are new to this edition of the *Code*) are also applicable to mezzanines. For example, a mezzanine used for sales purposes that meets the one-half area rule, although it would not affect the mercantile occupancy subclassification with respect to the number of stories used for sales purposes, would have to be sufficiently open in accordance with 6-2.5.3 to avoid treatment as a separate floor in terms of the number of means of egress (*see 25-2.4.1*) and other egress arrangement requirements applicable to floors or stories.

25-1.4.2.4 Where a number of stores under different management are located in the same building, the aggregate gross area of all such stores shall be used in determining classification per 25-1.4.2.1.

Exception No. 1: Where individual stores are separated by fire barriers with a 1-hour fire resistance rating.

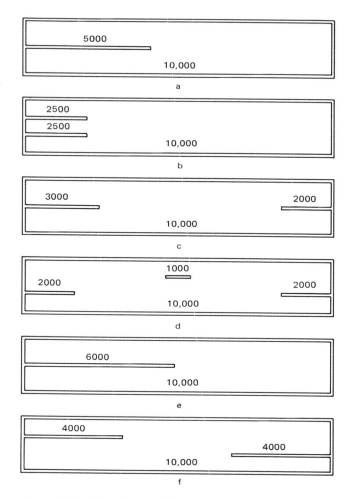

Figure 25-3 a, b, c, d, e, and f. *Examples of Mercantile Occupancy Mezzanine Arrangement Elevation Views (see commentary associated with 25-1.4.2.3). All values are expressed in square feet. For metric values, 1 sq ft = 0.093 sq m.*

Note that, for new mercantile occupancies (*see Exception No. 1 to 24-1.4.2.4*), the fire resistance rated separation required to waive aggregate gross area is 2-hour rather than the 1-hour rating of the basic rule.

Exception No. 2: Covered mall buildings. (See 25-4.4.)

Paragraphs 25-1.4.2.2 through 25-1.4.2.4 further clarify the subclassification of stores as Class A, B, or C. Most of these provisions are included in the footnotes to Table 25-1. The following should be noted for emphasis:

1. The aggregate gross area is the sum of the gross areas of all floors used for mercantile (sales) purposes.

2. If the store is divided so that some portions are not used for sales purposes, such as shipping/receiving/ storage areas, only the sales areas should be included in the aggregate gross area.

3. With the exception of covered mall buildings (*see 25-4.4*), where stores are contiguous to one another (even if under different ownership or management and occupying numerous buildings) or where there are sections or floors used for sales within any building that are considered as separate stores (because, for example, they are under different management), and these contiguous or intermixed stores are not separated from each other by at least 1-hour fire resistance rated fire barriers, the aggregate gross area of all such stores must be used in subclassifying the mercantile occupancy as Class A, B, or C.

25-1.5 **Classification of Hazard of Contents.** The contents of mercantile occupancies shall be classed as ordinary hazard in accordance with Section 4-2.

Exception: Mercantile occupancies shall be classified as high hazard if high hazard commodities are displayed or handled without protective wrappings or containers, in which case the following additional provisions shall apply:

(a) Exits shall be located so that not more than 75 ft (23 m) of travel from any point is required to reach the nearest exit.

(b) From every point there shall be at least two exits accessible by travel in different directions (no common path of travel).

(c) All vertical openings shall be enclosed.

Most occupancy chapters refer to Section 4-2 for classification of hazard of contents. However, the requirement of 25-1.5 emphasizes that, unless an extraordinarily hazardous situation exists, the contents of mercantile occupancies must be classed as ordinary hazard. This wording is intended to prevent the user from classifying the hazard of contents as high hazard unless a situation equivalent to dispensing explosives in bulk is present. Since the total package of life safety provided by the chapter's requirements anticipates the display of significant quan-

tities of combustibles, these requirements should provide an acceptable level of safety without making it necessary to classify the typical mercantile occupancy environment as highly hazardous. Specifically, the chapter's requirements should be adequate without imposing the stringent high hazard contents requirements of the Exception to 25-1.5 on all but the most hazardous of mercantile occupancies.

Some procedures that would require classification of a mercantile occupancy as highly hazardous include dispensing gunpowder or other explosives in bulk or dispensing gasoline or flammable solvents by pouring them into open containers. The sale of flammable liquids such as camp stove fuel and rubbing alcohol should be controlled by NFPA 30, *Flammable and Combustible Liquids Code,*[3] with regard to display configuration, total amount, and separation from ignition sources.

Figure 25-4 illustrates an arrangement of exits from a highly hazardous area of a mercantile occupancy that meets the requirements of subparts (a) and (b) of the Exception to 25-1.5, which address limited travel distance and the exclusion of common path of travel. Although mercantile occupancy requirements are generally lenient in allowing vertical openings (*see 25-3.1*), all vertical openings in high hazard mercantile occupancies are required to be fully enclosed (*see 6-2.4*) in accordance with subpart (c) of the Exception to 25-1.5.

25-1.6 **Minimum Construction Requirements.** No special requirements.

The phrase "minimum construction" is used in the *Code* to describe the construction of the building housing the occupancy. Some occupancy chapters such as Chapters 12 and 13, which address the life safety needs of nonambulatory occupants of health care occupancies, require a minimum building construction type to help ensure structural integrity for a prolonged evacuation or for safe refuge within the building. Because mercantile occupancies are characteristically used by ambulatory customers and employees and do not provide sleeping accommodations, there are no minimum construction requirements imposed. Since there are no special requirements, the provisions of a local or state building code, if applicable, would need to be met.

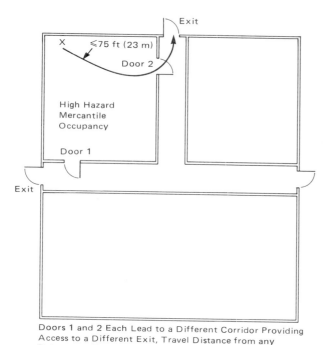

Doors 1 and 2 Each Lead to a Different Corridor Providing Access to a Different Exit, Travel Distance from any Point to an Exit Must not Exceed 75 ft (23 m)

Figure 25-4. Exit Arrangement from an Area of a Mercantile Occupancy Defined as Highly Hazardous by 25-1.5.

25-1.7 Occupant Load.

25-1.7.1* For purposes of determining required exits, the occupant load of mercantile buildings or parts of buildings used for mercantile purposes shall be not less than required in the following:

(a) Street floor: One person for each 30 sq ft (2.8 sq m) gross floor area of sales space. In stores with no street floor, as defined in Chapter 3, but with access directly from the street by stairs or escalators, the principal floor at the point of entrance to the store shall be considered the street floor.

Exception to (a): In stores where, due to differences in grade of streets on different sides, there are two or more floors directly accessible from streets (not including alleys or similar back streets), for the purpose of determining occupant load, each such floor shall be considered a street floor. The occupant load factor shall be one person for each 40 sq ft (3.7 sq m) gross floor area of sales space.

(b) Sales floors below the street floor: Same as street floor.

(c) Upper floors used for sales: One person for each 60 sq ft (5.6 sq m) gross floor area of sales space.

(d) Floors or portions of floors used only for offices: One person for each 100 sq ft (9.3 sq m) gross floor area of office space.

(e) Floors or portions of floors used only for storage, receiving, shipping and not open to the general public: One person per each 300 sq ft (27.9 sq m) gross area of storage, receiving, or shipping space.

(f) Floors or portions of floors used for assembly purposes: Occupant load determined in accordance with Chapter 9 for such assembly occupancies.

(g)* Covered mall buildings: Determined in accordance with 25-1.7.1(a) through (f).

Exception: The portions of the covered mall, where considered a pedestrian way (see Exception to 25-4.4.1) and not used as gross leasable area, shall not be assessed an occupant load. However, means of egress from a covered mall shall be provided for an occupant load determined by dividing the gross leasable area (not including anchor stores) by the appropriate lowest whole number occupant load factor from Figure 25-1.7.1(g) as shown on the following page.

Each individual tenant space shall have means of egress to the outside or to the covered mall based on occupant loads figured by using 25-1.7.1(a) through (f).

Each individual anchor store shall have means of egress independent of the covered mall.

A-25-1.7.1 These figures were established on the basis of counts of the population of typical store buildings during periods of maximum occupancy, such as before Christmas or during special sales. In some cases, the actual occupancy may be more dense than indicated by these figures, but it may reasonably be assumed that in any large mercantile building, all areas will not be similarly crowded at the same time, and the average occupant load should seldom exceed these figures.

In some types of stores, the occupant load will normally be much less than indicated: for example, in furniture stores. However, the character of mercantile operations is subject to such rapid changes that it is not prudent in designing exit facilities to assume that any store will never be crowded, and for this reason, the same load figures are used for all types of stores.

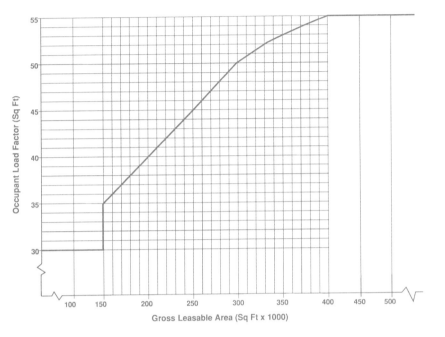

Figure 25-1.7.1(g)

A-25-1.7.1(g) The figure used in determining the occupancy load for covered mall shopping centers of varying sizes is arrived at empirically in surveying over 270 covered mall shopping centers, in studying mercantile occupancy parking requirements, and in observing the number of occupants per vehicle during peak seasons.

These studies show that with an increase in shopping center size, there is a decrease in the number of occupants per square foot of gross leasable area.

This phenomenon is explained when one considers that above a certain shopping center gross leasable area [approx. 600,000 sq ft (56,000 sq m)], a multiplicity of the same types of stores starts to occur: the purpose is to increase the choices available to a customer for any given type of merchandise. Therefore, when shopping center size increases, the occupant load increases as well, but at a declining rate. In using the figure, the occupant load factor is applied to only the gross leasable area utilizing the covered mall as a means of egress.

The occupant load factors specified for mercantile occupancies are based on the observation that, during normal use of a mercantile occupancy, the public will usually congregate on the street floor or in a basement sales area. In assigning a higher occupant load to the street floor, lowing 25-1.3(e) and (f)], the intent of 25-1.7.1(g) and the *Code* recognizes merchandising techniques that arrange merchandise to take advantage of the heavy flow of traffic on the street floor. Customers are attracted to merchandise displays as they walk through portions of the street floor to reach escalators, elevators, and stairs to other floors. Thus, larger numbers of occupants are expected to be present on the street floor.

The street floor, as distinguished from other sales floors, is any floor that has an entrance/exit that is directly accessible from the street with not more than three risers of ascent or descent (*see Section 3-2 for definition of street floor*). If differences in the ground level on different sides of a store create several floors of this nature, the *Code* treats them all as street floors; however, a slightly different occupant load factor is used in accordance with the Exception to 25-1.7.1(a). It is important to note that, if the only access to a store from the street is by means of stairs or escalators, the principal sales floor rather than the street level must be considered the street floor for the purpose of choosing an occupant load factor and calculating the occupant load.

Since the terms "covered mall" and "covered mall building" have different meanings [see commentary following 25-1.3(e) and (f)], the intent of 25-17.1(g) and its exception is that the egress capacity of the overall covered mall building be sized to handle a number of occupants. This is calculated in two steps. First, the occupant load is calculated individually for each store and tenant space using the occupant load factors of 25-1.7.1(a) through (f). Second, the required egress capacity for the covered mall itself (i.e., the covered pedestrian way) is calculated using the values shown in Figure 25-1.7.1(g). Each store or tenant space must have sufficient egress capacity for its occupant load. The covered mall must have egress capacity based on 24-1.7.1(g), which, in effect, automatically accounts for those persons who are in the covered mall (i.e., the covered pedestrian walkway) and those persons discharged from stores into the covered mall as part of the stores' means of egress.

For example, consider a covered mall building with 21 tenant stores, all located on the "street floor." Each has 6,000 sq ft (560 sq m) of sales area from the 7,500 sq ft (700 sq m) of gross leasable area [assume that the other 1,500 sq ft (140 sq m) is storage area]. Using an occupant load factor of 30 sq ft (2.8 sq m) per person for the sales areas in accordance with 25-1.7.1(a) and 300 sq ft (27.9 sq m) for the storage areas in accordance with 25-1.7.1(e), each store must size its means of egress system to handle 205 persons (6,000 ÷ 30 + 1,500 ÷ 300 = 200 + 5 = 205). Store occupants can be sent into the covered mall as part of the required means of egress from each store. Based on the 21 tenant stores, each with 7,500 sq ft (700 sq m) of gross leasable area, the covered mall has 21 × 7,500 sq ft (700 sq m) or 157,500 sq ft (14,700 sq m) of gross leasable area that forms the basis on which the means of egress from the covered mall must be sized. Using Figure 25-1.7.1(g), for a gross leasable area of 157,500 sq ft (14,700 sq m), an occupant load factor of 36 sq ft (3.3 sq m) per person is indicated by the graph. The covered mall must provide a means of egress system for 157,000 sq ft (14,700 sq m) ÷ 36 sq ft per person (3.3 sq m per person) or 4,375 persons.

SECTION 25-2   Means of Egress Requirements

25-2.1   General.

25-2.1.1 All means of egress shall be in accordance with Chapter 5 and this chapter.

25-2.1.2 No inside open stairway, escalator, or ramp may serve as a component of the required means of egress system for more than one floor.

This provision prohibits the use of unenclosed interior stairways, unenclosed interior escalators, or unenclosed interior ramps as exit access for more than one floor; it does not establish permission for the existence of an open stairway, escalator, or ramp. See 25-3.1, "Protection of Vertical Openings," to determine if the stairway, escalator, or ramp may remain unenclosed.

25-2.1.3 Where there are two or more floors below the street floor, the same stair or other exit may serve all floors, but all required exits from such areas shall be independent of any open stairways between the street floor and the floor below it.

25-2.1.4 Where a level, outside exit from upper floors is possible owing to hills, such outside exits may serve instead of horizontal exits. If, however, such outside exits from the upper floor also serve as an entrance from a principal street, the upper floor shall be classed as a street floor in accordance with the definition of Chapter 3 and is subject to the requirements of this section for street floors.

Paragraph 25-2.1.4 reconfirms the requirements of 25-1.7.1(a) for the classification of floors as street floors. Figure 25-5 illustrates a case where two floors qualify as street floors because each has one side located at a ground level. Note, however, that each floor has its other sides located either above or below the building's other ground level. As a result, these floors must have their exits arranged to allow horizontal travel to the exterior at one end of the floor and vertical travel (either up or down to ground level) at the other end of the floor. The exit capacity of the doors to the exterior on Floor 1 must accommodate that portion of the occupant load from an upper floor that is expected to travel down to and through the exits to the exterior from Floor 1 in addition to the portion of the Floor 1 occupant load assigned to that exit. The reverse is true for Floor 2, which must increase the size of its exterior exit capacity to accommodate occupants traveling up from Floor 1 as well as those traveling down to and through the exterior exits on Floor 2. Paragraphs 5-3.1.4, 5-3.1.5, and 25-2.3.2 explain how to add exit capacity based on the number of occupants expected to discharge from floors above and below the street floor. Figure 25-9 provides an example of how to calculate exit capacity for a street floor as illustrated by Floor 2 in Figure 25-5.

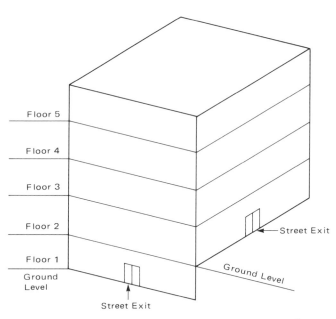

Figure 25-5. Mercantile Occupancy with Two Street Floors. The exit capacity of each street floor must comply with 25-2.3.2. (See also Figure 25-9.)

25-2.1.5 For special considerations with contents of high hazard, see 25-1.5.

25-2.2 Means of Egress Components.

25-2.2.1 Components of means of egress shall be limited to the types described in 24-2.2.2 through 24-2.2.11.

25-2.2.2 Doors.

25-2.2.2.1 Doors shall comply with 5-2.1.

25-2.2.2.2* Locks complying with 5-2.1.5.1 Exception No. 2 shall be permitted only on principal entrance/exit doors.

A-25-2.2.2.2 The term "principal entrance/exit doors" is intended to imply doors that the authority having jurisdiction can be reasonably assured will be unlocked in order for the facility to do business.

This provision permits only the principal entrance/exit doors of a mercantile occupancy to be equipped with the special key-operated dead bolt lock described by the provisions of Exception No. 2 to 5-2.1.5.1, which must be easily determined to be locked by means such as a flag indicator that can be seen at some distance from the door. Other doors along the perimeter of the building are prohibited from being equipped with a key-operated dead bolt, because it cannot be guaranteed that these locks will be disengaged simultaneously when the principal entrance/exit door is unlocked each day at the opening of business. *(See Figure 25-6.)*

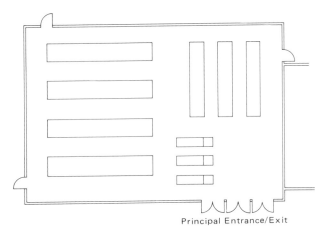

Figure 25-6. Principal Entrance/Exit. The concept of a principal entrance/exit as used in 25-2.2.2.2 is illustrated here.

25-2.2.2.3 The reentry provisions of 5-2.1.5.2 need not be met. *(See 5-2.1.5.2 Exception No. 3.)*

If the application of Exception No. 3 to 5-2.1.5.2 had not been specifically recognized by this paragraph, the basic requirements of 5-2.1.5.2 that provide for reentry from stairwells back onto all floors of the building would have applied. In recognition of Exception No. 3, existing mercantile occupancies are exempt from the reentry provisions.

25-2.2.2.4   Special locking arrangements in accordance with 5-2.1.6 are permitted.

Use of the delayed release locking device covered by 5-2.1.6 is allowed on any door in recognition of the security needs of a mercantile occupancy. The building must be protected throughout by an approved automatic sprinkler system or automatic fire detection system in order to apply the delayed release locking provisions. In effect, the allowable 15- or 30-second delay will be experienced only under nonfire conditions or very early in a fire's growth, since the door must be usable immediately upon sprinkler operation, smoke or heat detection, or upon loss of power that controls the locking mechanism.

25-2.2.2.5   Where horizontal or vertical security grilles or doors are used as a part of the required means of egress from a tenant space, such grilles or doors shall comply with 5-2.1.4.1 Exception No. 3.

Although Exception No. 3 to 5-2.1.4.1 establishes provisions for the arrangement and use of horizontal or vertical security grilles or doors, it requires that an occupancy chapter specifically recognize the use of such security grilles or doors. Paragraph 25-2.2.2.5 provides this recognition for mercantile occupancies.

25-2.2.2.6   All doors at the foot of stairs from upper floors or at the head of stairs leading to floors below the street floor shall swing with the exit travel.

This provision supplements the conditions of 5-2.1.4 by requiring doors that would otherwise not have to swing in the direction of egress travel to do so, based on their location. The queuing and accumulation of people at doors in locations such as at the foot of stairs from upper floors make it difficult for occupants to step back to allow the door to swing inward.

25-2.2.2.7   Revolving doors shall comply with 5-2.1.10.

Existing revolving doors may continue to be used without having to meet some of the more stringent requirements applicable to new revolving doors if such exemption is approved by the authority having jurisdiction. (*See the various exceptions to 5-2.1.10.1 and the commentary following 24-2.2.2.7.*)

25-2.2.2.8   In Class C mercantile occupancies, doors shall be permitted to swing inward where such doors serve only the street floor area.

25-2.2.3   **Stairs.**

25-2.2.3.1   Stairs shall comply with 5-2.2.

25-2.2.3.2   Spiral stairs complying with 5-2.2.2.7 are permitted.

Note that 5-2.2.2.7 permits spiral stairs to serve only an occupant load of five or fewer persons. Spiral stairs may be effectively used in mercantile occupancies in storage areas having a small occupant load.

25-2.2.3.3   Winders complying with 5-2.2.2.8 are permitted.

25-2.2.4   **Smokeproof Enclosures.**   Smokeproof enclosures shall comply with 5-2.3.

This paragraph does not mandate the use of smokeproof enclosures, but it does recognize a smokeproof enclosure as part of the means of egress system in a mercantile occupancy only if the smokeproof enclosure meets the requirements of 5-2.3. For an example of an occupancy requiring a smokeproof enclosure, see 19-2.11.1, in which nonsprinklered, existing, high rise apartment buildings are required to be provided with smokeproof enclosures in accordance with 5-2.3.

25-2.2.5   **Horizontal Exits.**   Horizontal exits shall comply with 5-2.4.

This paragraph does not mandate the use of horizontal exits, but it does recognize a horizontal exit as part of the means of egress system in a mercantile occupancy only if the horizontal exit meets the requirements of 5-2.4.

25-2.2.6 **Ramps.** Ramps shall comply with 5-2.5.

This paragraph does not mandate the use of ramps in mercantile occupancies, but it does recognize a ramp as part of the means of egress system only if the ramp meets the requirements of 5-2.5.

25-2.2.7 **Exit Passageways.** Exit passageways shall comply with 5-2.6.

Exit passageways are frequently used within the means of egress system of covered mall buildings as a way of meeting the travel distance limitations or as a method of avoiding numerous exit doors along exterior walls located at the rear of tenant spaces. In effect, the exit passageway labeled A in Figure 25-7 moves the exit closer to occupants to create a building arrangement that would otherwise require occupants to travel further than allowable in order to reach an exit door in an exterior wall. The exit passageway labeled B in Figure 25-7 runs along the rear of multiple tenant spaces and provides access to the exterior only at each end of the exit passageway for security reasons. In both cases, the exit passageway is a *Code*-complying exit in accordance with 5-2.6 and is considered to provide the same degree of safety that an exit stair enclosure would provide an occupant of an upper floor in a multistory building.

Exception*: In lieu of the provisions of 5-2.6.4, an exit passageway in a covered mall building shall be permitted to independently accommodate:

(a) Its assigned occupant load from only the covered mall/pedestrian way, and

(b) The largest occupant load assigned to it from a single tenant space/store.

A-25-2.2.7 **Exception.** To design exits from a covered mall building, the following steps should be used:

(1) The covered mall/pedestrian way has been assigned no occupant load, but it must be provided with means of egress sized to accommodate the total occupant load of the covered mall building based on the gross leasable area. The exits for the covered mall/pedestrian way can be provided by a combination of exterior exit doors and exit passageways.

(2) After completion of step (1), each tenant space (i.e., store) is to be judged individually for occupant load and exits. This step normally sends some portion of the store's occupant load into the covered mall and the remainder through the back of the store into an exit passageway that may serve multiple tenant stores and the covered mall.

(3) The exit passageway must be sized for the most restrictive of the following conditions:

(a) Minimum 66 in. per 25-4.4.1 Exception (b), or

(b) The portion of the exit capacity from the largest single tenant store being served by the exit passageway, or

(c) The portion of the exit capacity from the covered mall being provided by the exit passageway.

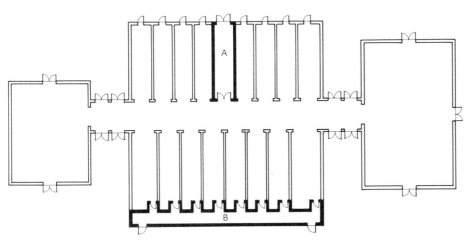

Figure 25-7. *Examples of Typical Uses of Exit Passageways in Covered Mall Buildings. (See 25-2.2.7.)*

The concepts used in the above steps include:

(1) After proper egress capacity is provided for the covered mall/pedestrian way, each store must then independently provide egress capacity for its occupants.

(2) The covered mall and the store's required exit passageway width need not be added together.

(3) The required exit passageway width for a tenant store need not be added to that of other stores using the same exit passageway.

Although the provisions of 5-2.6.4 require an exit passageway to be sized to accommodate the aggregate required capacity of all means of egress discharging through the exit passageway, the Exception to 25-2.2.7 allows some reduction in the required width of exit passageways in covered mall buildings. The exception recognizes that the sizing of the means of egress from the covered mall, calculated in accordance with the provisions of 25-1.7.1(g), provides egress capacity for occupants of the covered mall and occupants of the adjoining tenant spaces within the covered mall building. To require an exit passageway in a covered mall building to be of sufficient size to accommodate both the occupant load assigned to it from the covered mall and the occupant load of all tenant spaces discharging through the exit passageway would be the equivalent of counting a portion of the building's occupants twice, thereby oversizing the means of egress system.

25-2.2.8 Escalators and Moving Walks. Escalators and moving walks complying with 5-2.7 are permitted.

Note that to be permitted to remain within the required means of egress, existing escalators and moving walks must meet the requirements of 5-2.7. In order to qualify as exits, escalators and moving walks must also meet the requirements of 5-2.2.6 that address enclosure.

25-2.2.9 Fire Escape Stairs. Fire escape stairs complying with 5-2.8 are permitted.

Note that 5-2.8.1.4 allows only those occupancy chapters that apply to existing buildings to permit a fire escape stair within the required means of egress. Furthermore, 5-2.8.1.4 permits existing buildings to use or continue to use fire escape stairs for no more than 50 percent of the building's required exit capacity.

25-2.2.10 Fire Escape Ladders. Fire escape ladders complying with 5-2.9 are permitted.

25-2.2.11 Alternating Tread Devices. Alternating tread devices complying with 5-2.11 are permitted.

In accordance with the provisions of 25-2.2.10 and 25-2.2.11, both fire escape ladders and alternating tread devices are allowed within the means of egress of existing mercantile occupancies, but only as permitted by the relatively narrow provisions of 5-2.9 and 5-2.11. The provisions of 5-2.11, in effect, restrict the use of alternating tread devices to locations where the Code recognizes the use of fire escape ladders. (See 25-2.2.10 and 5-2.9.)

25-2.3 Capacity of Means of Egress.

25-2.3.1 The capacity of means of egress shall be in accordance with Section 5-3.

The mercantile occupancy chapters of prior editions of the Code specified requirements mandating that the occupant load of a mezzanine be added to that of the floor below the mezzanine for the purpose of determining the total size of the required means of egress system from the combined mezzanine and associated floor beneath. In the 1991 Edition, those requirements have been dropped from the mercantile occupancy chapters because a similar requirement now appears in 5-3.1.6. The new wording in Chapter 5 mandates that any required egress capacity from a mezzanine that passes through the room below must be added to the required egress capacity of that room through which the egress passes.

Figure 25-8 illustrates a case in which a mezzanine is open to the street floor. The exits from the street floor must accommodate (1) the occupant load of the street floor, (2) the occupant load of the mezzanine in accordance with 5-3.1.6, and (3) the required capacity provided by the stairs from other floors discharging through the street floor in accordance with 25-2.3.2.

To determine the exit capacity for the street floor, the occupant load of the mezzanine (1,000) is added to the occupant load of the street floor (2,000). In addition, because one-half of the exits from the upper floors discharge through the street floor, the exit capacity of the street floor must accommodate the capacity of the exit stair enclosure that discharges through that floor. The maximum

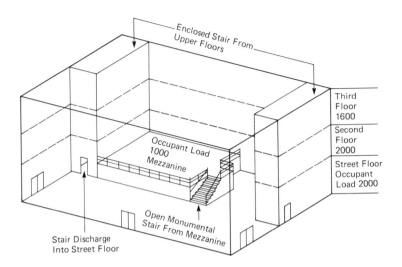

Figure 25-8.   Mercantile Occupancy with a Mezzanine Open to the Street Floor. (See second paragraph of commentary following 25-2.3.1.)

occupant load on any upper floor is 2,000 (second floor), and 25-2.7.2 permits a maximum one-half of the exits or the exit capacity to discharge through the street floor, provided that the building is sprinklered. Therefore, the street floor must be provided with egress capacity for 4,000 persons or 800 in. (2,030 cm) of exit width using the factor of 0.2 in. (0.5 cm) per person for level exit components found in 5-3.3.1 (2,000 for street floor + 1,000 for mezzanine + 1,000 for upper floors = 4,000).

25-2.3.2   In Class A and Class B stores, street floor exits shall be sufficient for the occupant load of the street floor plus the required capacity of stairs, ramps, escalators and moving walks discharging through the street floor.

Paragraph 25-2.3.2 requires that the exits for the street floor of a Class A or B mercantile occupancy have sufficient capacity to handle the occupant load of the street floor and the capacity of the exits discharging through the street floor, such as an enclosed exit stair that accommodates occupants who, when exiting the building during an emergency, must travel up from the basement sales area or down from the upper sales floors and mix with the customers already occupying the first or street floor.

Since people move more quickly in a horizontal direction than in a vertical direction, it is permissible to provide less door width than stair width. For example, in mercantile occupancies, in accordance with the egress capacity factors of 5-3.3.1, level components and ramps require only 0.2 in. (0.5 cm) of width per person, whereas stairs require 0.3 in. (0.8 cm) of width per person. As a rough approximation, for every 44 in. (112 cm) of stair discharging through the street floor, an additional 30 in. (76 cm) of door width opening to the outside must be added from the street floor. Figure 25-9 provides an example of the proper calculation method for determining the required exit capacity for the street floor.

Street floor occupant load alone	1000
plus maximum upper floor occupant load discharging back through street floor (500 ÷ 2)	250
plus basement occupant load discharging back through street floor (400 ÷ 2)	200

1450 persons × 0.2 in. (0.5 cm) per person for level exit components per 5-3.3.1 =290 in. (737 cm) of exit width required from the street floor egress system.

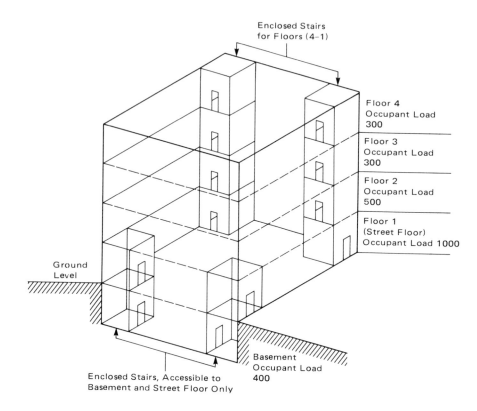

Enclosed Stairs
for Floors (4-1)

Floor 4
Occupant Load
300

Floor 3
Occupant Load
300

Floor 2
Occupant Load
500

Floor 1
(Street Floor)
Occupant Load 1000

Ground
Level

Basement
Occupant Load
400

Enclosed Stairs, Accessible to
Basement and Street Floor Only

Figure 25-9. Calculation of Exit Capacity Required for a Street Floor in Accordance with 25-2.3.2.

25-2.4 Number of Exits.

25-2.4.1 At least two separate exits shall:

(a) Be provided on every story, and

(b) Be accessible from every part of every story or mezzanine.

Exception to (b): Exit access travel shall be permitted to be common for the distances allowed as common path of travel by 25-2.5.3.

Exception No. 1: A single means of egress shall be permitted in a Class C mercantile occupancy provided that one of the following conditions is met:

(a) The travel distance does not exceed 75 ft (23 m) to the exit or to a covered mall (if it is considered a pedestrian way), or

(b) The travel distance does not exceed 100 ft (30 m) to the exit or to a covered mall (if it is considered a pedestrian way) and the story on which the occupancy is located and all

communicating levels that must be traversed to reach the exit or covered mall are protected throughout by an approved automatic sprinkler system in accordance with Section 7-7.

Exception No. 2: A single means of egress to an exit or to a covered mall (if it is considered a pedestrian way) shall be permitted from a mezzanine within any Class A, B, or C mercantile occupancy, provided that the common path of travel does not exceed 75 ft (23 m) or 100 ft (30 m) if protected throughout by an approved automatic sprinkler system in accordance with Section 7-7.

The provisions of 25-2.4, which apply to the required number of exits for mercantile occupancies, have been revised for this edition of the *Code* to clarify that any level that constitutes a story must have at least two exits located on that story. This means that the occupants of the story must be able to enter an exit (e.g., an enclosed exit stair on an upper floor of a multistory building) without having to travel to some other story to reach the entrance to the exit. Since a mezzanine that meets the maximum one-half area rule of 25-1.4.2.3 does not constitute a floor (*see the commentary following 25-1.4.2.3*), two exits are not required on the mezzanine, but (1) the criteria of 25-2.4.1(b) must be met with respect to providing access to two separate exits, or (2) the provisions of the Exception to (b) or Exception No. 2 must be met.

The Exception to (b) applies only to subpart (b) of 25-2.4.1, which requires access to two separate exits from every part of every level (i.e., story or mezzanine). The exception indicates that 25-2.5.3 allows the occupant to travel in one direction for a maximum distance (i.e., the common path allowance) before requiring access in two separate directions. Therefore, although the story or mezzanine must eventually provide access to two exits in accordance with 25-2.4.1(b), that access need only be available at the point where the allowable common path is expended.

Although the basic requirement of 25-2.4.1 mandates that a mercantile occupancy be provided with at least two remotely located exits, Exception No. 2 permits a single exit for small facilities, i.e., Class C mercantile stores, such as tobacco shops, newsstands, and small 24-hour convenience stores. If the travel distance from any point in such a store to an exit is 75 ft (23 m) or less, the likelihood that a fire might surprise and overcome the customers before they could escape is low (*see Figure 25-10*). Furthermore, by allowing a single exit in these small mercantile occupancies if there is no more than 100 ft (30 m) of travel to an exit (or to a covered mall that qualifies as a pedestrian way in accordance with the provisions of the Exception to 25-4.4.1, which include an automatic sprinkler system requirement for the entire covered mall building), the exception provides additional flexibility and a potential increase in security for those small stores protected by means of automatic sprinkler installations within the store and in those portions of the overall building that occupants must traverse to reach an exit or pedestrian way.

While the Exception to (b) allows common access to the two required means of egress for some limited distances, Exception No. 2 exempts the facility from providing a point where access to two exits is available if the single means of egress leads to an exit or to a covered mall that qualifies as a pedestrian way in accordance with

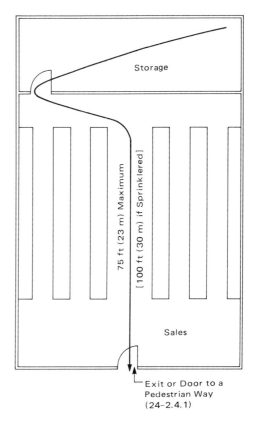

Figure 25-10. *Single Exit. A Class C mercantile occupancy may be provided with a single exit if travel distance is limited. (See Exception No. 1 to 25-2.4.1.)*

the provisions of the Exception to 25-4.4.1, which include an automatic sprinkler system requirement for the entire covered mall building. The exit or covered mall must be located within the same limited distances as those allowed for common path of travel. [*See the Exception to 25-2.4.1(b) and the exceptions to 25-2.5.3.*]

25-2.5 Arrangement of Means of Egress.

25-2.5.1 Exits shall be arranged in accordance with Section 5-5.

25-2.5.2* No dead-end corridor shall exceed 50 ft (15 m).

Exception*: Existing dead-end corridors exceeding 50 ft (15 m) may continue to be used subject to the approval of the authority having jurisdiction and the travel distance requirements of 25-2.6.

A-25-2.5.2 The purpose of this paragraph is to avoid pockets or dead ends of such size that they pose an undue danger of persons becoming trapped in case of fire.

A-25-2.5.2 Exception. It is recognized that excessive dead ends exist and, in some cases, are impractical to eliminate. The authority having jurisdiction may allow these to continue, taking into consideration any or all of the following:

Tenant arrangement.

Automatic sprinkler protection.

Smoke detection.

Exit remoteness.

25-2.5.3* No common path of travel shall exceed 75 ft (23 m).

Exception No. 1: A common path of travel shall be permitted for the first 100 ft (30 m) on a story protected throughout by an approved automatic sprinkler system in accordance with Section 7-7.

Exception No. 2*: Existing excessive common paths of travel may continue to be used subject to the approval of the authority having jurisdiction and the travel distance requirements of 25-2.6.

A-25-2.5.3 The common path of travel requirement permits small areas such as rooms or alcoves with only one way out where the distance is small enough so that there is little likelihood that a fire might develop to such proportions as to block escape before the occupants become aware of the fire and make their way out.

A-25-2.5.3 Exception No. 2. It is recognized that excessive common paths of travel exist and, in some cases, are impractical to eliminate. The authority having jurisdiction may allow these to continue, taking into consideration any or all of the following:

Tenant arrangement.

Automatic sprinkler protection.

Smoke detection.

Exit remoteness.

See the commentary following 5-5.1.6 for a detailed discussion on common path of travel. Also see the commentary following the Exception to 25-2.4.1(b), which allows a portion of the access to a single exit or multiple exits to be common.

Prior to 1988, the maximum common path of travel allowed by the *Code* in mercantile occupancies was 50 ft (15 m) [75 ft (23 m) if protected by smoke detectors or 100 ft (30 m) if sprinklered]. A special provision of Chapter 5 that specified the point where measurement of travel distance and common path begins for small rooms [i.e., distance within a room was not counted if there was a maximum occupant load of 6 and a maximum 50 ft (15 m) of travel within the room] was deleted from the *Code* in 1988. The allowable common path of travel was increased in 1988 without either reducing the level of safety to life or imposing a hardship on designers.

25-2.5.4 Aisles leading to each exit are required. The aggregate width of such aisles shall be equal to at least the required width of the exit.

These provisions are intended to prevent constrictions in the means of egress system that would delay egress of building occupants. The aggregate width of aisles leading to an exit are required to provide egress width equal to that required of the exit to which they lead. Without this provision, occupants could be forced to squeeze through a relatively narrow aisle or similar constriction before reaching, for example, an expansive bank of doors to the outside. The exit capacity at the doors, rather than providing simultaneous egress for the large number of occupants assigned to that exit, would not be fully utilized. Occupants would move through the doors a few at a time as they passed slowly through the constriction. This requirement is illustrated in Figure 25-11 in the upper left and right corners of the floor plan of the mercantile occupancy.

25-2.5.5 In no case shall any required aisle be less than 28 in. (71 cm) in clear width.

The minimum 28-in. (71-cm) aisle width requirement is illustrated in Figure 25-11 and is consistent with the minimum 28-in. (71-cm) exit access width allowed in existing buildings by Exception No. 2 to 5-3.4.1.

25-2.5.6 In Class A stores, at least one aisle of 5 ft (152 cm) minimum width shall lead directly to an exit.

The intent of 25-2.5.4 through 25-2.5.6 is to ensure that the interior arrangement of counters, racks, and displays of merchandise does not block or obscure accesses to an exit. Figure 25-11 illustrates an arrangement that meets the requirements for a Class A store. Essentially, the width of the exit determines the minimum width of the aisle, with the exception that one of the aisles must be at least 5 ft (152 cm) wide and lead directly to an exit.

25-2.5.7 If the only means of customer entrance is through one exterior wall of the building, two-thirds of the required exit width shall be located in this wall.

In establishing the requirement of 25-2.5.7, the *Code* demonstrates its concern regarding the arrangement of many discount and variety stores, which have one large main exit/entrance located in the front of the store and the other exits (which cannot be used as entrances) situated at points unfamiliar to the public. In such occupancies, the wall containing the main exit/entrance must be sized to handle two-thirds of the required exit capacity of the store, since, due to its familiarity, most of the customers will use this exit under emergency conditions. This requirement is illustrated in Figure 25-11.

25-2.5.8 At least one-half of the required exits shall be so located as to be reached without passing through checkout stands. In no case shall checkout stands or associated railings or barriers obstruct exits, required aisles, or approaches thereto.

This is one of the most frequently violated provisions of Chapter 25. It is necessary in many supermarkets and discount and variety stores to pass through checkout counters, around shopping carts, and through turnstiles in order to exit the facility. This causes congestion or blockage during an emergency. The *Code* requires at least one-half of all exits to be located so that occupants can avoid passing through or around these impediments to egress.

25-2.5.9* Where wheeled carts or buggies are used by customers, adequate provision shall be made for the transit and

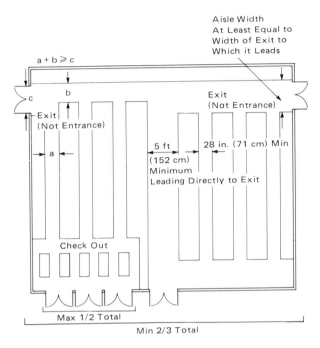

Figure 25-11. Means of Egress Arrangement in a Mercantile Occupancy. The conditions described in the commentary associated with the requirements of 25-2.5.4 through 25-2.5.8 are illustrated here.

parking of such carts to minimize the possibility that they may obstruct means of egress.

A-25-2.5.9 In order to eliminate the obstruction to the means of egress of the interior exit access and the exterior exit discharge, it is the intent to provide adequate area for transit and parking of wheeled carts or buggies used by customers. This includes corral areas adjacent to exits that are constructed to restrict the movement of wheeled carts or buggies therefrom.

In states where returnable beverage bottle legislation has been enacted, stores and markets have had to create space for the collection of empty bottles and the refund of deposit charges. The area most commonly used is located near the entrance/exit where wheeled shopping carts were formerly stored to be clear of the path of egress travel. The displaced carts are now often stored so that they obstruct the means of egress. This illustrates a situation where a properly designed, installed, and complying means of egress can be compromised abruptly by unexpected changes.

25-2.5.10 Exit access in Class A stores protected throughout with an approved supervised automatic sprinkler system in accordance with Section 7-7 and in all Class B or Class C stores shall be permitted to pass through storerooms provided the following conditions are met:

(a) Not more than 50 percent of exit access is provided through the storeroom.

(b) The storeroom is not subject to locking.

(c) The main aisle through the storeroom shall be not less than 44 in. (112 cm) wide.

(d) The path of travel, defined with fixed barriers, through the storeroom shall be direct and continuously maintained in an unobstructed condition.

In 25-2.5.10 (a) above, the storeroom is limited to providing a maximum of 50 percent of the store's exit access, either in number of exits or exit capacity. Therefore, since two exits are required, neither of the following limits can be exceeded:

1. Only one of the two required exits can be reached by exit access travel through the storeroom, and
2. A maximum of half of the store's occupant load is permitted to egress through the storeroom.

In addition to allowing exit access in all Class B and C stores to pass through storerooms, 25-2.5.10 allows exit access in some Class A stores to pass through storerooms where that store is protected throughout by an approved automatic sprinkler system. This is permitted in recognition of the increased safety to life that a sprinkler system provides.

Figures 25-12 and 25-13 illustrate the application of the provisions of 25-2.5.10.

25-2.6 **Travel Distance to Exits.** Travel distance to exits, measured in accordance with Section 5-6, shall be no more than 150 ft (45 m).

Exception: Travel distance shall not exceed 200 ft (60 m) in buildings protected throughout by an approved automatic sprinkler system in accordance with Section 7-7.

In accordance with Section 5-6, travel distance requirements apply to only the first (or nearest) exit from a given point in the building. In other words, the 150-ft (45-m) travel distance limit requires that at least one exit must

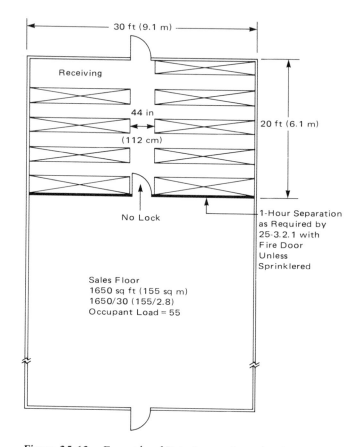

Figure 25-12. Example of Exit Access through a Storeroom as Permitted by 25-2.5.10. The aisle within the storeroom must be defined by fixed barriers, such as those formed by the ends of shelving. The aisle must be kept unobstructed.

be located within 150 ft (45 m) of a point in the building; it does not require that all exits must be within 150 ft (45 m) of that same point in the building.

Prior to 1988, the maximum travel distance allowed by the *Code* in mercantile occupancies was 100 ft (30 m) and, if the building was sprinklered, 150 ft (45 m). A special provision in Chapter 5 that specified the point where measurement of travel distance begins for small rooms [i.e., distance within a room was not counted if there was a maximum occupant load of 6 and a maximum 50 ft (15 m) of travel within the room] was deleted from the *Code* in 1988. The allowable travel distance for existing mercantile occupancies was increased in 1988 to 150 ft (45 m) or 200 ft (60 m) if the building is sprinklered. The allowable travel distance had to be increased, since mea-

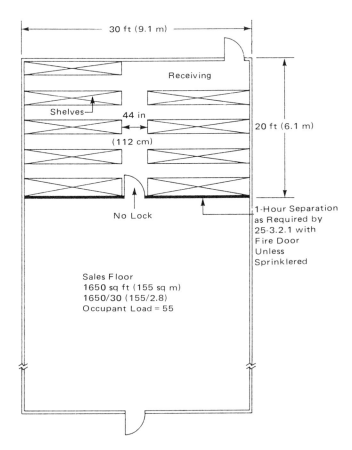

Figure 25-13. *Example of Exit Access through a Storeroom That Will Be Problematic Because of Its Relationship to the Receiving Area.*

surement of travel distance now always begins within the room. Many existing means of egress arrangements that had applied the exception for "small rooms" and complied with the *Code* prior to 1988 would otherwise be faced with noncompliance.

25-2.7 Discharge from Exits.

25-2.7.1 Exit discharge shall comply with Section 5-7 except as modified by 25-2.7.2.

25-2.7.2* Fifty percent of the exits shall be permitted to discharge through the level of exit discharge in accordance with 5-7.2 only where the building is protected throughout by an approved automatic sprinkler system in accordance with Sec-

tion 7-7, and the distance of travel from the termination of the exit enclosure to an outside street door shall not exceed 50 ft (15 m).

A-25-2.7.2 The basis for the exception to the general rule on complete enclosure of exits up to their point of discharge to the outside of the building is that, with the specified safeguards, reasonable safety is maintained.

A stairway is not considered to discharge through the street floor area if it leads to the street through a fire resistance rated enclosure (exit passageway) separating it from the main area, even though there are doors between the first floor stairway landing and the main area.

The provisions of 25-2.7.2 should not be confused with open stairways as permitted by 25-3.1 Exception No. 1.

This arrangement is restricted to prevent more than 50 percent of the exits from any floor from discharging through the street floor. Furthermore, it is permitted only where the building is sprinklered throughout. Also note that the path of travel on the first floor from the stair enclosure to the outside door cannot exceed 50 ft (15 m). The remaining 50 percent of the exits must discharge directly to the exterior.

The requirements of 25-2.7.2 are more stringent than those of 5-7.2, since they mandate automatic sprinkler protection throughout the building; set a 50-ft (15-m) travel limit on the street floor; and require that the street floor have an exit capacity that accommodates the street floor and the stairs discharging through the street floor. These requirements are not mandated by 5-7.2. The added requirements are imposed in recognition of the high combustible load of merchandise that may be on display, which is characteristic of mercantile occupancies.

25-2.8 Illumination of Means of Egress. Means of egress shall be illuminated in accordance with Section 5-8.

Note that illumination for the means of egress is not the same as emergency lighting; failure of the building power supply may cause failure of the means of egress illumination system, which is not required to have a back-up, auxiliary, or secondary power supply unless required by 25-2.9.

25-2.9   Emergency Lighting. Class A and Class B stores shall have emergency lighting facilities in accordance with Section 5-9.

Class C stores, due to their small size and small occupant load, are not required by the *Code* to have emergency lighting facilities.

25-2.10   Marking of Means of Egress. Means of egress shall have signs in accordance with Section 5-10.

Exception: Where an exit is immediately apparent from all portions of the sales area, the exit marking is not required.

The intent of the exception to the provision for marking the means of egress is to avoid requiring exit signs in small areas where the exit is readily apparent. For example, exit signs would not be required in the office of a service station, the purchase and eating areas of a small "fast food" restaurant, or in a Class C store whose size and arrangement comply with Exception No. 1 to 25-2.4.1.

25-2.11   Special Features. (Reserved.)

SECTION 25-3   Protection

25-3.1   Protection of Vertical Openings. Each stairway, elevator shaft, escalator opening, or other vertical opening shall be enclosed or protected in accordance with Section 6-2.

Exception No. 1: In Class A or Class B mercantile occupancies, unprotected openings shall be permitted between any two floors, such as between the street floor and the floor below, or between the street floor and mezzanine, or between the street floor and second floor.

Exception No. 2: In Class A or B mercantile occupancies protected throughout by an approved automatic sprinkler system in accordance with Section 7-7, unprotected vertical openings shall be permitted as follows:

(a) Between the street floor and floor below and to the floor above the street floor or to mezzanines above the street floor; or

(b) Between the street floor, street floor mezzanine and second floor, but not among more than three floor levels; or

(c) In accordance with 6-2.4.5; or

(d) Among all floors permitted in Class B mercantile occupancies; or

(e) One floor above those permitted may be open if such floor is not used for sales purposes.

Exception No. 3: In Class C mercantile occupancies, unprotected vertical openings shall be permitted as follows:

(a) Between the street floor and mezzanine; or

(b) Between the street floor and the floor below or the second floor if not used for sales purposes.

Exception No. 4: Atriums in accordance with 6-2.4.6 are permitted.

Follow the provisions of 25-1.7 to properly assess the occupant load in order to provide sufficient egress capacity for a store in which floors or mezzanines are open to the street floor. Exceptions No. 1 and No. 2 to 25-3.1 specify conditions under which such openings are permitted in Class A and B stores. Exception No. 3 allows certain unprotected vertical openings in Class C stores.

Exception No. 1 allows unprotected vertical openings between any two floors. Although the term "such as" is used and all the examples involve a street floor and a floor adjacent to that street floor, a two-story unprotected vertical opening could also be located between floors four and five of a multistory department store. If the exception were to be interpreted as requiring the street floor to be included as one of the levels involved in the two-story vertical opening, existing mercantile occupancies would have no option for a similar opening between upper floors of the building. Yet, if sprinklered, new mercantile occupancies are afforded the option in accordance with 24-3.1 Exception No. 1(a). It is the *Code's* intent to allow for the two-story unprotected opening to be located anywhere within an existing mercantile occupancy without meeting the sprinkler requirement that is imposed on new mercantile occupancies. However, mercantile occupancies of any appreciable size must be sprinklered by the requirements of 25-3.5.

As a condition of Exception No. 2, unprotected vertical openings, which are usually various forms of three-story openings, are allowed if the mercantile occupancy is protected throughout by automatic sprinklers. Subpart (c) permits the use of the provisions of 6-2.4.5. Subpart

(e) would allow an unprotected vertical opening of up to four stories in, for example, a four-story building where only the first three stories are used for sales purposes.

In Class C mercantile occupancies, Exception No. 3 allows certain unprotected vertical openings that, by definition, involve only a single sales floor or a sales floor and sales mezzanine that are all of limited sizes. Although it is most common to locate a Class C mercantile occupancy such that its main sales floor is a street floor, the Class C mercantile occupancy might, for example, occupy space on the third floor of a covered mall building (*see 25-4.4*). Therefore, it is not the intent to restrict the two-story opening between the main sales floor and the mezzanine of a Class C mercantile occupancy, as addressed by Exception No. 3(a) to 25-3.1, so that the main sales floor must be a street floor. Using the two-story vertical opening permitted in Class A and B mercantile occupancies by Exception No. 1 to 25-3.1 and its commentary as a guide, the opening could be located within a Class C mercantile occupancy located on any floor of a multistory covered mall building.

Exception No. 4 permits an atrium in accordance with 6-2.4.6.

25-3.2   Protection from Hazards.

25-3.2.1   Hazardous areas, including but not limited to areas used for general storage, boiler or furnace rooms, fuel storage, janitor closets, maintenance shops including woodworking and painting areas, shall:

(a) Be separated from other parts of the building by fire barriers having a fire resistance rating of not less than 1 hour with all openings therein protected by ¾-hour fire protection rated self-closing fire doors, or

(b) The area shall be protected by an automatic extinguishing system in accordance with Section 7-7.

Exception: In general storage and stock areas protected by an automatic extinguishing system in accordance with Section 7-7, an enclosure, if provided, is exempt from the provisions of 6-4.1.

Paragraph 6-4.1 has been revised in the 1991 Edition of the *Code* to include a concept that previously applied only to assembly and educational occupancies. Specifi-

cally, where a hazardous area was protected by automatic sprinklers, rather than by enclosure with fire barriers of 1-hour fire resistance rating and doors of 45-minute fire protection rating, the hazardous area had to be enclosed by walls and doors that were at least smoke resisting. The Exception to 25-3.2.1 now allows the hazardous areas comprised of general storage and stock areas in a mercantile occupancy to be protected by automatic sprinklers without the need for the smoke resisting enclosure.

25-3.2.2   Areas with high hazard contents as defined in Section 4-2 shall be provided with both fire-resistive separation and automatic sprinkler protection.

Paragraphs 25-3.2.1 and 25-3.2.2 reflect the intent of Section 6-4, which (1) requires separation of a hazardous area from the remainder of the occupancy by means of suitable construction, or (2) mandates the installation of an automatic sprinkler system in a hazardous area, or (3) requires both where the hazard is severe.

25-3.3   Interior Finish.

25-3.3.1   Interior finish on walls and ceilings shall be Class A or B in accordance with Section 6-5.

Exception: Existing Class C interior finish shall be permitted as follows:

(a) *On walls.*
(b) *Throughout Class C stores.*

Essentially, the Exception to 25-3.3.1 states that, in existing Class C stores only, all the interior finish (walls and ceilings) may be rated as Class C (flame spread as high as 200). All existing Class A and B stores may have Class C interior finish on the walls, but such finish is prohibited on the ceiling.

25-3.3.2   **Interior Floor Finish.** No requirements.

25-3.4   Detection, Alarm, and Communication Systems.

25-3.4.1   **General.** Class A mercantile occupancies shall be provided with a fire alarm system in accordance with Section 7-6.

Class B and C mercantile occupancies are not required to have a fire alarm system.

25-3.4.2 Initiation. Initiation of the required fire alarm system shall be by manual means per 7-6.2.1(a).

Exception No. 1: Initiation shall be permitted to be by means of an approved automatic fire detection system in accordance with 7-6.2.1(b) that provides protection throughout the building.

Exception No. 2: Initiation shall be permitted by means of an approved automatic sprinkler system in accordance with 7-6.2.1(c) that provides protection throughout the building.

Since most Class A stores will be sprinklered based on gross floor area (*see 25-3.5.1*), it is logical that the method described in Exception No. 2 will be most commonly used to activate the fire alarm system, because the requirement for manual pull stations is waived if the sprinkler water flow activates the fire alarm system. Nuisance alarms might be reduced by eliminating the manual pull stations and satisfying the initiation requirements by means of water flow through the sprinkler system.

25-3.4.3 Notification.

25-3.4.3.1 During all times that the store is occupied (*see 5-2.1.1.3*), the required fire alarm system shall:

(a) Sound a general audible alarm throughout the store, or
(b) Sound an audible alarm in a continuously attended location for purposes of initiating emergency action.

Note that the *Code* does provide a choice between two methods of notification. Many Class A stores do have a continuously attended location, and item (b) can be used; if such a location is not provided or not considered reliable by the authority having jurisdiction, item (a) must be applied.

25-3.4.3.2 Occupant Notification. Occupant notification shall be by means of live voice public address system announcement originating from the attended location where the alarm signal is received. (*See 25-3.4.3.1.*) The system shall be permitted to be used for other announcements. (*See 7-6.3.9 Exception No. 2.*)

Exception: Any other occupant notification means allowed by 7-6.3 shall be permitted in lieu of live voice public address system announcement.

This exception allows a system in accordance with 25-3.4.3.1(a) to use an automatic voice alarm or regular alarm sounding devices in lieu of the live voice alarm.

25-3.5 Extinguishment Requirements.

25-3.5.1 Mercantile occupancies shall be protected throughout by an approved automatic sprinkler system in accordance with Section 7-7 as follows:

(a) In all buildings with a story over 15,000 sq ft (1,400 sq m) in area.
(b) In all buildings exceeding 30,000 sq ft (2,800 sq m) in gross area.
(c) Throughout stories below the level of exit discharge where such stories have an area exceeding 2,500 sq ft (230 sq m) where used for the sale, storage, or handling of combustible goods and merchandise.

Exception: Single-story buildings that meet the requirements of a street floor.

For information on the proper criteria for an approved automatic sprinkler system, see NFPA 13, *Standard for the Installation of Sprinkler Systems,*[1] NFPA 13A, *Recommended Practice for the Inspection, Testing, and Maintenance of Sprinkler Systems,*[2] and *Automatic Sprinkler and Standpipe Systems.*[4]

Under the provisions of item (a), a building with a total gross area of not more than 30,000 sq ft (2,800 sq m) but with any one story (including the area of mezzanines) of more than 15,000 sq ft (1,400 sq m) would have to be protected with a complete automatic sprinkler system. A building with a total gross area of not more than 30,000 sq ft (2,800 sq m) would not be required to be sprinklered as long as the area of any story does not exceed 15,000 sq ft (1,400 sq m).

The intent of item (b) is to require that all buildings with a total gross area of more than 30,000 sq ft (2,800 sq m) be protected with a complete automatic sprinkler system.

Item (c) ensures that all basement areas larger than 2,500 sq ft (230 sq m) (regardless of whether the space is used for sales, storage, or the handling of combustible merchandise) be sprinklered to avoid the potential threat to occupants of the floors above. Studies have shown that there is a higher rate of fire incidence in basements than in other areas of stores. Because smoke and heat rise, a fire in a basement can quickly render exits and exit discharges located on the street floor unusable. This danger is especially acute in mercantile occupancies, where allowances for various vertical openings in accordance with the provisions of 25-3.1 and its exceptions are more lenient than those for other occupancies.

This exception appears only in Chapter 25 and applies to existing buildings only. It is believed that in existing, one-story, "street floor only" buildings that comply with all other provisions of the *Code*, including travel distance, adequate life safety is provided so that to require the building to be sprinklered retroactively is unnecessary. The term "street floor" is defined in 3-2 and includes a maximum of three risers of ascent or descent to reach the ground level.

25-3.5.2 Portable fire extinguishers shall be provided in all mercantile occupancies in accordance with 7-7.4.1.

Portable extinguishers are to be used by properly trained employees of the mercantile occupancy as required by 31-8.2.

25-3.6 **Corridors.** No special requirements.

There are no corridor separation requirements for existing mercantile occupancies, whereas such requirements appear in 24-3.6 for new mercantile occupancies.

25-3.7 **Subdivision of Building Spaces.** No special requirements.

25-3.8 **Special Features.**

25-3.8.1 Nonrated glazing and opening protectives per 25-1.2.3 Exception shall be permitted between mercantile occupancies and parking structures.

See the commentary following 25-1.2.3.

SECTION 25-4 Special Provisions

25-4.1 **Windowless or Underground Buildings.** (*See Section 30-7.*)

25-4.2 **High Rise Buildings.** No additional requirements.

The provisions of Section 30-8, "High Rise Buildings," whether applied singly, in various combinations, or in total, must be mandated by specific occupancy chapter requirements. In existing high rise mercantile occupancies, 25-4.2 does not require any of the provisions of Section 30-8. Rather, the sprinkler system mandated by 25-3.5.1, based on floor area, helps to provide adequate life safety in existing high rise mercantile occupancies.

25-4.3 **Open-Air Mercantile Operations.**

25-4.3.1 Open-air mercantile operations, such as open-air markets, gasoline filling stations, roadside stands for the sale of farm produce, and other outdoor mercantile operations shall be so arranged and conducted as to maintain free and unobstructed ways of travel at all times to permit prompt escape from any point of danger in case of fire or other emergency, with no dead ends in which persons might be trapped due to display stands, adjoining buildings, fences, vehicles, or other obstructions.

Paragraph 25-4.3.1 is virtually an open-ended provision that provides guidance for the arrangement, use, and display of merchandise for sale in open-air mercantile operations. The phrase "ways of travel" is purposely used to avoid confusion with "means of egress." "Means of egress" is strictly defined, and its use implies the application of the minimum requirements of Chapter 5. "Ways of travel" is not defined and implies no specific minimum *Code* provisions. Most open-air mercantile operations have unlimited means of entering and evacuating the areas used to display goods. For this reason, it is not necessary to provide specific *Code* requirements beyond the precautionary measures expressed in this paragraph.

25-4.3.2 If mercantile operations are conducted in roofed-over areas, they shall be treated as mercantile buildings, provided that canopies over individual small stands to protect merchandise from the weather shall not be construed to constitute buildings for the purpose of this *Code*.

The intent of 25-4.3.2 is to exempt small merchandise stands with canopies from classification as mercantile buildings. All other "roofed-over" areas should be treated as buildings, classified by area and height as Class A, B, or C mercantile occupancies, and subject to the appropriate provisions of Chapter 25.

25-4.4 Covered Mall Buildings.

25-4.4.1 The covered mall building shall be treated as a single building for the purpose of calculation of means of egress and shall be subject to the requirements for appropriate occupancies. The covered mall shall be at least of sufficient clear width to accommodate egress requirements as set forth in other sections of this *Code*.

Exception: The covered mall shall be permitted to be considered a pedestrian way, in which case the distance of travel within a tenant space to an exit or to the covered mall shall be a maximum of 200 ft (60 m) (see Exception to 25-2.6), or shall be the maximum for the appropriate occupancy; plus, an additional 200 ft (60 m) shall be permitted for travel through the covered mall space if all the following requirements are met:

(a) The covered mall shall be at least of sufficient clear width to accommodate egress requirements as set forth in other sections of this chapter, but in no case less than 20 ft (6.1 m) wide in its narrowest dimension.

(b)* On each side of the mall floor area, the covered mall shall be provided with an unobstructed exit access of not less than 10 ft (3 m) in clear width parallel to and adjacent to the mall tenant front. Such exit access shall lead to an exit having a minimum of 66 in. (168 cm) in width. (See 25-4.4.2.)

A-25-4.4.1 **Exception (b).** The minimum requirement for terminating mall exit access in not less than 66 in. (168 cm) of exit width relates to the minimum requirement for at least one aisle in Class A stores [30,000 sq ft (2,800 sq m) or greater] to be 5 ft (152 cm) in width.

(c) The covered mall and all buildings connected thereto shall be protected throughout by an approved electrically supervised automatic sprinkler system in accordance with Section 7-7.

(d) Walls dividing stores from each other shall extend from the floor to the underside of the roof deck or floor deck above. No separation is required between a tenant space and the covered mall.

(e)* The covered mall shall be provided with a smoke control system.

A-25-4.4.1 **Exception (e).** Fire experience in covered mall shopping centers indicates that the most likely place of fire origin is in the tenant space where the combustible fire loading is far greater than in the covered mall proper.

Furthermore, any fires resulting from the comparatively low fire loading in the covered mall proper are far more likely to be detected and extinguished in their incipient stages because of the nature of the covered mall proper as a high traffic pedestrian way, thus producing far less smoke development in a far greater volume of space than in the much more confined adjacent tenant space.

Smoke control systems that address the foregoing are necessary in order to:

(a) Assure the integrity of the covered mall as a pedestrian way by maintaining it reasonably free of the products of combustion for at least the duration required to evacuate the building,

(b) Confine the products of combustion to the area of fire origin, and

(c) Remove the products of combustion with a minimum of migration of such products of combustion from one tenant to another.

Systems or combinations of systems that can be engineered to accomplish this include:

(a) Separate or mechanical exhaust or control systems.

(b) Mechanical exhaust or control systems in conjunction with heating, ventilating, and air conditioning systems.

(c) Automatically or manually released gravity roof vent devices, such as skylights, relief dampers, or smoke vents.

(d) Combinations of (a), (b), and (c) or any other engineered system designed to accomplish the purpose of this section.

In recent years, covered mall shopping areas have increased in both number and size. Two approaches in addressing the life safety aspects of these complexes were developed. The first approach (described in the base paragraph of 25-4.4.1) treats the mall and the attached stores essentially as one large Class A store subject to all the provisions of Chapter 25. If viewed in this way, the covered mall would be treated as an aisle of a store. See Formal Interpretation 88-10, which follows the commentary associated with 25-1.4.2.1.

The second approach permits the mall to be considered as a pedestrian way through which occupants of the attached stores may egress during a fire. The phrase "pedestrian way" was intended to convey the meaning of the term exit access.

The Exception to 25-4.4.1 recognizes that, if the mall and all the buildings attached to the mall are protected by automatic sprinklers, occupants fleeing into the mall from a fire in a store are then moving into a space whose volume, size, and arrangement afford most of the benefits provided by an enclosed stair or a horizontal exit as well as many of the benefits of an outdoor area. The exception considers the mall to be a safe area for the occupants of the tenant spaces attached to it, despite the fact that the mall is not separated from these attached spaces by the type of construction normally provided for an exit as required by 5-1.3.1.

Where a covered mall is considered as a pedestrian way, the maximum travel distance to an exit or to the covered mall from any point within a store attached to the covered mall is 200 ft (60 m). The reasoning behind this provision is that use of the covered mall for egress is as acceptable as use of an exit. An additional travel distance of up to 200 ft (60 m) is permitted within the covered mall [in addition to the 200 ft (60 m) allowed within the store] if all of the following conditions are met:

1. The covered mall building, (i.e., the covered mall and all attached buildings) must be sprinklered. The sprinkler system must be electrically supervised. Note that if the shopping complex is considered as one building rather than as a covered mall building with complying pedestrian way, sprinkler protection is also most likely required under the 30,000-sq ft (2,800-sq m) gross area criterion of 25-3.5.1(b).

2. The clear width of the mall must be at least 20 ft (6.1 m) or wider if mandated by the egress capacity. Note that where the covered mall of a shopping center is considered as a pedestrian way, an occupant load is not calculated for the covered mall based on its area. The required capacity of the means of egress for the covered mall is calculated on the basis of aggregate gross leasable area of the attached stores (excluding anchor stores), including mid-mall kiosks and similar sales areas. (*See the detailed commentary on this subject following A-25-1.7.1.*)

3. At least 10 ft (3 m) of clear unobstructed space must be available for exit access in front of all store fronts. This requirement is designed to prohibit displays of merchandise, kiosks, or small sales stands from being placed within 10 ft (3 m) of the store fronts and ensures that the mall will have a minimum clear width of 20 ft (6.1 m).

4. Each exit access must terminate at an exit with a minimum width of 66 in. (168 cm).

5. Walls separating stores must run continuously from the floor slab to the roof slab or floor slab above, but not necessarily through the roof or floor. Walls need not have any fire resistance rating. The intent of such separation is to resist the passage of smoke. The store front need not be separated from the mall by construction.

6. The covered mall, but not the stores, must have a smoke control system. Since the individual stores are open to the mall, this requirement is essential if the mall is to be used as a safe means of egress. For detailed guidance on the design, installation, and maintenance of smoke control systems, see NFPA 92B, *Guide for Smoke Management Systems in Malls, Atria, and Large Areas.*[5]

If these six conditions are not met, the covered mall may still be used as part of the exit access from the covered mall building, but the additional travel distance to an exit would not be allowed. Therefore, from any point within the overall covered mall building, which includes the stores and the covered mall, there would be a limit of 150 ft (45 m) of travel distance [200 ft (60 m) if the store and covered mall are sprinklered]. In the majority

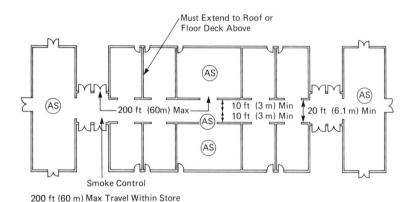

Figure 25-14. A Covered Mall Used as a Pedestrian Way.

of configurations, this restriction would preclude the use of the mall as an exit access.

Figure 25-14 illustrates many of the requirements necessary to qualify a covered mall as a pedestrian way.

The *Fire Protection Handbook*[6] contains a discussion of the hazards to life safety associated with covered mall buildings.

25-4.4.2 **Exit Details.**

25-4.4.2.1 Every floor of a covered mall shall have no less than two exits remotely located from each other.

Paragraph 25-4.4.2.1 reaffirms the fundamental *Code* requirement for providing at least two independent means of egress.

25-4.4.2.2 No less than one-half the required exit widths for each Class A or Class B store connected to a covered mall shall lead directly outside without passage through the mall.

Note that the larger stores (Class A and B mercantile occupancies) must still have 50 percent of their exits arranged to be independent of the covered mall. This is usually achieved by evacuating occupants directly from the store to the outside or directly into an exit passageway without entering the covered mall.

25-4.4.2.3* Each individual anchor store shall have means of egress independent of the covered mall.

A-25-4.4.2.3 It is not the intent of this paragraph to require that large stores be considered anchor stores. A store not considered in determining the occupant load of the mall must be arranged so that all of its means of egress will be independent of the covered mall.

25-4.4.2.4 Every covered mall shall be provided with unobstructed exit access parallel to and adjacent to the mall tenant fronts. This exit access shall extend to each mall exit.

Paragraph 25-4.4.2.4 repeats the provisions of item (b) of the Exception to 25-4.4.1 without stating that the exit access at the front of the stores within the covered mall must have a clear width of at least 10 ft (3 m).

25-4.4.3 **Detection, Alarm, and Communication Systems.**

25-4.4.3.1 **General.** Covered malls shall be provided with a fire alarm system in accordance with Section 7-6.

Although the provisions of 25-4.4 address the overall covered mall building, the provisions of 25-4.4.3.1, which apply to alarm systems, require only that the alarm system be provided for the covered mall (i.e., the covered pedestrian way). In addition, the provisions of 25-3.4.1 require that any Class A mercantile occupancy within the covered mall building also be provided with an alarm system. Therefore, Class B and Class C mercantile occupancies within the covered mall building are not required to have alarm systems.

25-4.4.3.2 **Initiation.** Initiation of the required fire alarm system shall be by means of the approved automatic sprinkler system in accordance with 7-6.2.1(c).

Note that manual pull stations are not required but that the sprinkler system must have a water flow alarm that initiates the fire alarm system.

25-4.4.3.3 **Notification.** During all times that the covered mall is occupied (*see 5-2.1.1.3*), the required fire alarm system shall:

(a) Sound a general audible alarm throughout the covered mall, or

(b) Sound an audible alarm in a continuously attended location for the purpose of initiating emergency action.

Note that the *Code* provides a choice between two methods of notification. Many large malls do have a continuously attended location, and item (b) can be used; if such a location is not provided or not considered reliable by the authority having jurisdiction, item (a) must be applied. In either case, the notification must be provided to the occupants of the covered mall and not to the occupants of the tenant stores within the covered mall building.

25-4.4.3.4 **Occupant Notification.** Occupant notification shall be by means of live voice public address system announcement originating from the attended location where the alarm signal is received. (*See 25-4.4.3.3.*) The system shall be permitted to be used for other announcements. (*See 7-6.3.9 Exception No. 2.*)

Exception: Any other occupant notification means allowed by 7-6.3 shall be permitted in lieu of live voice public address system announcement.

This exception allows a system that applies 25-4.3.3.3(a) to use an automatic voice alarm or regular alarm sounding device in lieu of the live voice alarm.

25-4.4.3.5 **Emergency Forces Notification.** Emergency forces notification shall include notifying:

(a) The fire department in accordance with 7-6.4, and

(b) The local fire brigade, if provided, via the attended location where the alarm signal is received. (*See 25-4.4.3.3.*)

Paragraph 7-6.4 allows for several different methods of automatically notifying the fire department.

25-4.4.3.6 **Emergency Control.** The fire alarm system shall be arranged to automatically actuate smoke management or smoke control systems in accordance with 7-6.5.2(c).

25-4.5 **Operating Features.** (*See Chapter 31.*)

SECTION 25-5   Building Services

25-5.1 **Utilities.** Utilities shall comply with the provisions of Section 7-1.

25-5.2 **Heating, Ventilating, and Air Conditioning Equipment.** Heating, ventilating, and air conditioning equipment shall comply with the provisions of Section 7-2.

25-5.3 **Elevators, Escalators, and Conveyors.** Elevators, escalators, and conveyors shall comply with the provisions of Section 7-4.

25-5.4 **Rubbish Chutes, Incinerators, and Laundry Chutes.** Rubbish chutes, incinerators, and laundry chutes shall comply with the provisions of Section 7-5.

References Cited in Commentary

[1]NFPA 13, *Standard for the Installation of Sprinkler Systems*, National Fire Protection Association, Quincy, MA, 1991.

[2]NFPA 13A, *Recommended Practice for the Inspection, Testing, and Maintenance of Sprinkler Systems*, National Fire Protection Association, Quincy, MA, 1987.

[3]NFPA 30, *Flammable and Combustible Liquids Code*, National Fire Protection Association, Quincy, MA, 1990.

[4]John L. Bryan, *Automatic Sprinkler and Standpipe Systems*, 2nd ed., National Fire Protection Association, Quincy, MA, 1990.

[5]NFPA 92B, *Guide for Smoke Management Systems in Malls, Atria, and Large Areas*, National Fire Protection Association, Quincy, MA, 1991.

[6]*Fire Protection Handbook*, 17th ed., National Fire Protection Association, Quincy, MA, 1991.

26

New Business Occupancies

(See also Chapter 31.)

Business occupancies are those used for the transaction of business, for the keeping of accounts and records, and similar purposes.

General offices is the most readily identifiable class of business properties found in the national fire incident data bases. This class accounted for 6,100 structure fires per year as reported to U.S. fire departments from 1984 to 1988, with an associated 4 civilian (i.e., nonfire-service personnel) deaths and 93 civilian injuries per year. Courthouse and legislative halls, which are normally classified with assembly properties for fire reporting purposes, accounted for fewer than 100 structure fires and 1 civilian injury per year from 1984 to 1988. College and university buildings, usually classified with educational properties for purposes of fire reporting, accounted for 1,100 structure fires, 1 civilian death, and 30 civilian injuries, while trade and business schools suffered a total of 600 structure fires and 9 civilian injuries per year. Laboratories, usually classified as industrial properties for fire reporting, accounted for 500 structure fires and 25 civilian injuries per year.

Medical and scientific offices (900 structure fires, 2 civilian deaths, and 10 civilian injuries per year) and clinics (200 structure fires and 1 civilian injury per year) are addressed in the commentary associated with health care occupancies in Chapters 12 and 13.

Other office buildings and unclassified office buildings (e.g., bank buildings, engineering or architectural offices) accounted for another 2,100 structure fires, 1 civilian death, and 31 civilian injuries per year.

Multiple-death fires are rare in the business occupancy properties mentioned above. For example, the 1989 Georgia office building fire that killed 5 people was the first office building fire in 17 years to cause 3 or more fatalities. Nearly half the victims of office fires from 1980 to 1988 were not occupying the room of fire origin when the fire began. The 1989 Georgia fire began in an electrical vault, yet four of the five victims were elsewhere on that floor when the fire began.

SECTION 26-1   General Requirements

26-1.1   Application.

26-1.1.1   New construction shall comply with the provisions of this chapter. (*See Chapter 31 for operating features.*)

Exception*: Facilities where the authority having jurisdiction has determined equivalent safety is provided in accordance with Section 1-6.

A-26-1.1.1   **Exception.** In determining equivalency for conversions, modernizations, renovations, or unusual design concepts of business occupancies, the authority having jurisdiction may use NFPA 101M, *Alternative Approaches to Life Safety*, Chapter 7, utilizing the parameters for new construction.

See Section 1-5 for application provisions.

Existing business occupancies must comply with Chapter 27 of the *Code*.

The exception emphasizes that Section 1-6, "Equivalency Concepts," permits alternatives to literal *Code* compliance in which a building design would still be considered as *Code* conforming. However, the authority having jurisdiction ultimately determines whether or not equivalent safety has been provided.

Paragraph 26-1.1.1 and its accompanying exception do not intend to limit the methods an authority having jurisdiction might use to determine equivalency. However, as noted in the Exception to A-26-1.1.1, Chapter 7 of NFPA 101M, *Alternative Approaches to Life Safety*,[1] provides an "equivalency system" that uses numerical values to analyze the firesafety effectiveness of a building design. This system is known as the Firesafety Evaluation System (FSES). The system provides a method by which alternative designs can be evaluated as options to literal *Code* compliance.

The 1992 Edition of NFPA 101M, *Alternative Approaches to Life Safety*, although published one year after this 1991 Edition of the *Life Safety Code*, is the proper edition of NFPA 101M to consult for one possible equivalency system for business occupancies. Its measurement system has been calibrated against the requirements of the 1991 Edition of the *Life Safety Code*, whereas the firesafety evaluation systems contained in the 1988 Edition of NFPA 101M were calibrated against the requirements of the 1988 Edition of the *Code*.

In providing the equivalency concept, the *Code* does not intend to limit equivalency evaluations to those based solely on the one system presented for business occupancies in NFPA 101M. The authority having jurisdiction retains the power to evaluate and approve alternative designs on the basis of appropriate supporting data. The FSES may be used to aid in this evaluation. This exception in no way mandates the use of the FSES, nor does it require the authority having jurisdiction to accept the results of an evaluation using the equivalency system.

Although the FSES was primarily developed to evaluate alternative designs in existing buildings, it is particularly useful for determining equivalency for conversions, modernizations, renovations, or unusual design concepts—all of which would be considered new construction. However, the FSES is a tool used to help determine equivalency, and it should not be used to circumvent *Code* requirements. *Code* requirements must be met in new construction, or equivalent safety must be provided by alternative means approved by the authority having jurisdiction.

26-1.1.2   This chapter establishes life safety requirements for all new business buildings. Specific requirements for high rise buildings [buildings over 75 ft (23 m) in height] are contained in paragraphs pertaining thereto.

Existing buildings are addressed in Chapter 27. Subsection 26-4.2 contains additional requirements for high rise buildings.

26-1.1.3   Additions to existing buildings shall conform to the requirements for new constructon. Existing portions of the structure need not be modified, provided that the new construction has not diminished the fire safety features of the facility.

Although construction of an addition generally does not require existing portions of the building to be modified, Figure 26-1 illustrates a case where the planned new construction would diminish the firesafety features of the existing building and, thus, necessitate corrective action within the existing portion of the building. The placement

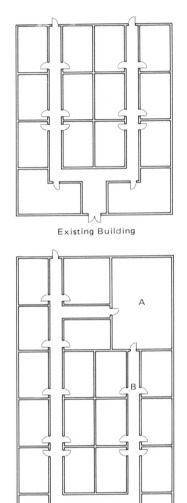

Existing Building

Existing Building And Planned Addition

Figure 26-1. The Placement of New Room A Creates an Excessively Long Dead-End Corridor B in the Existing Building, Which Must Be Corrected.

of new room A creates an excessively long dead-end corridor B, which must be corrected.

26-1.2 Mixed Occupancies.

26-1.2.1 Mixed occupancies shall comply with 1-5.7.

Minor office occupancies incidental to operations in another occupancy are considered as part of the predom-

inating occupancy, rather than creating a mixed occupancy, and are subject to the *Code* provisions that apply to the predominating occupancy. The commentary following 26-1.4 discusses classification of business occupancies in more detail.

The determination of those criteria that constitute a minor or incidental office area cannot be based solely on percentage of business area in comparison to overall building area. For example: a 200-sq ft (19-sq m) office area in a 4,000-sq ft (370-sq m) warehouse can reasonably be judged incidental to the storage operations and result in the building being classified as a storage occupancy. A 20,000-sq ft (1,860-sq m) office area in a 400,000-sq ft (37,200-sq m) distribution warehouse represents the same proportion of business use area as the 200-sq ft (19-sq m) office in the 4,000-sq ft (370-sq m) example but cannot be judged incidental (*see Figure 26-2*). The 20,000-sq ft (1,860-sq m) office area probably has an occupant load of approximately 200 persons. The *Code* requirements applicable to business occupancies, which are more stringent than those applicable to storage occupancies, are needed to protect the occupants of the office area adequately. The distribution warehouse is classified as a mixed occupancy that is part storage occupancy and part business occupancy. If packaging operations are present, it might also be classified as part industrial occupancy. Consequently, the requirements of 1-5.7 for mixed occupancies apply.

26-1.2.2 Combined Business and Residential Occupancies.

26-1.2.2.1 No dwelling shall have its sole means of egress through any business occupancy in the same building.

26-1.2.2.2 No multiple dwelling occupancy shall be located above a business occupancy.

Exception No. 1: Where the dwelling occupancy and exits therefrom are separated from the business occupancy by construction having a fire resistance rating of at least 1 hour.

Exception No. 2: Where the business occupancy is protected throughout by an approved automatic sprinkler system in accordance with Section 7-7.

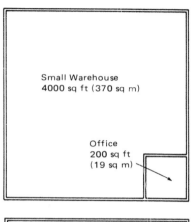

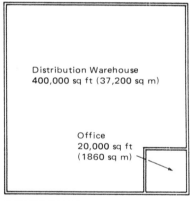

NOT TO SCALE

Figure 26-2. Determination of "Incidental" Office Use Cannot Be Based on Percentage of Overall Building Area. (See commentary associated with 26-1.2.1.)

The requirements for combined business and residential occupancies were developed to address an occupancy arrangement in which a dwelling unit is located, for example, on the floors above a ground-level real estate or insurance agent's office.

The *Code* prohibits the dwelling unit from having its sole means of egress pass through the business occupancy. It also prohibits multiple living units from being located above a business occupancy unless the business occupancy is completely sprinklered in accordance with Exception No. 2 or, where applying Exception No. 1, if the dwelling unit and its means of egress are separated from the business occupancy by construction having a minimum 1-hour fire resistance rating.

26-1.2.3 Combined Business Occupancies and Parking Structures. Walls separating parking structures from business occupancies shall have a fire resistance rating of not less than 2 hours.

Exception: In enclosed parking structures that are protected throughout with an approved automatic sprinkler system in accordance with Section 7-7 or in open-air parking structures, nonrated glazing and opening protectives shall be permitted if all of the following conditions are met:

(a) The openings do not exceed 25 percent of the area of the wall in which they are located, and

(b) The openings are used for main entrance and associated sidelites functions, and

(c) The enclosed connecting business building is protected throughout by an approved automatic sprinkler system in accordance with Section 7-7, and

(d) The floor elevation of the business use is at least 4 in. (10.2 cm) above the floor level of the parking structure, and

(e) No vehicle is able to park or drive within 10 ft (3 m) of the openings, and

(f) The openings have a minimum of a glass membrane, and

(g) Any doors in the glass membrane are self-closing.

The provisions of 26-1.2.3 are new to this edition of the *Code* and, although they address combined business occupancies and parking structures, are very similar to the new requirements of 24-1.2.3, which address combined mercantile occupancies and parking structures. It is very common for multistory business occupancies, such as office buildings, and multistory mercantile occupancies (e.g., department stores and shopping mall buildings) to be attached to multistory parking garages. Such garages provide access to the occupancy at multiple levels. In order to allow flexibility in the number and type of openings and considering the stringent requirements for opening protectives such as fire doors and fire windows, the Exception to 26-1.2.2 outlines a set a provisions that, when applied in total, will safely allow for the 2-hour fire resistance rated separation requirement of 26-1.2.2 to be reduced. The reduction allows the use of nonrated glazing and nonrated opening protectives. This permits the use of glass doors and glass sidelights in the barrier between the business occupancy and the garage. Security in the garage is thereby increased, since occupants can view the area through the glass doors or sidelights. This helps to meet the security concerns of office building managers.

Note that all eight requirements mandated by the Exception to 26-1.2.2 [i.e., the sprinkler requirement for the garage per the base paragraph of the exception and the other seven requirements of subparts (a) through (g) of the exception] must be met as a whole in order to apply the exception to the rule that would have otherwise required a 2-hour fire resistance rated separation between the business occupancy and the parking structure.

26-1.3 Special Definitions. None.

26-1.4 Classification of Occupancy.

26-1.4.1 Business occupancies shall include all buildings and structures or parts thereof with occupancy described in 4-1.8.

Note that the *Code's* definition of a business occupancy (*see 4-1.8*) does not include types of stores that, although considered "businesses," are covered under the provisions of Chapter 24, "New Mercantile Occupancies." These include, for example, supermarkets, department stores, and other occupancies that display and sell merchandise. Also not included are the assembly portions of city halls, town halls, and courthouses, which are covered by Chapter 8, "New Assembly Occupancies."

The following constitute business occupancies and are covered by the provisions of Chapter 26:

1. Those occupancies used for the transaction of business (other than those classified as mercantile occupancies).
2. Those occupancies used for keeping accounts and records and for similar purposes.

Items 1 and 2 include: doctors' offices, dentists' offices (*see Chapter 12 for ambulatory health care centers*), and general offices, as well as city halls, town halls, and courthouses, all of which have areas for keeping books and records and transacting public business. Other occupan-

cies included under the definition of business occupancies are service facilities common to office buildings, such as newsstands, lunch counters (serving fewer than 50 people), barber shops, and beauty parlors.

Also, by reference in Chapter 10, college classroom buildings are also considered business occupancies.

26-1.5 Classification of Hazard of Contents.

26-1.5.1 The contents of business occupancies shall be classified as ordinary hazard in accordance with Section 4-2.

Most occupancy chapters refer to Section 4-2 for classification of hazard of contents. However, the requirement of 26-1.5.1 emphasizes that, unless an extraordinarily hazardous situation exists, the contents of business occupancies must be classified as ordinary hazard. This wording is intended to prevent the user from classifying the hazard of contents as high hazard except where a combustible load far in excess of the usual, yet considerable, quantity of boxed records and paper files exists. Isolated hazardous areas within the overall ordinary hazard business occupancy, such as storage rooms, must be protected or separated in accordance with the requirements of 26-3.2.

26-1.5.2 For purposes of the design of an automatic sprinkler system, a business occupancy shall be classified as "light hazard occupancy," as identified by NFPA 13, *Standard for the Installation of Sprinkler Systems*.

The classification of hazard of contents listed and defined in Section 4-2 has little bearing on or relationship to the hazard classifications found in NFPA 13, *Standard for the Installation of Sprinkler Systems*.[2] Therefore, an ordinary hazard business occupancy might be protected by a light hazard sprinkler system.

Paragraph 26-1.5.2 was written to clarify that contents classified by the *Code* as "ordinary" for the purpose of life safety are not always classified as ordinary under NFPA 13, *Standard for the Installation of Sprinkler Systems*.[2] Paragraph 26-1.5.2 states that, for purposes of sprinkler design, the anticipated fuel load of business occupancies in Chapter 26 is classified as "light hazard."

26-1.6 Minimum Construction Requirements. No requirements.

The provisions of a local or state building code may apply.

Some occupancy chapters, such as Chapters 12 and 13, which address the life safety needs of nonambulatory health care occupants, require a minimum building construction type to help ensure the structural integrity required for a lengthy evacuation or for safe refuge within the building. Because business occupancies are normally occupied by those who are ambulatory, and since they do not provide sleeping accommodations, there are no minimum construction requirements imposed.

26-1.7 Occupant Load.

26-1.7.1* For purposes of determining required means of egress, the occupant load of business buildings or parts of buildings used for business purposes shall be no less than one person per 100 sq ft (9.3 sq m) of gross floor area. The occupant load for parts of buildings used for other purposes shall be calculated using occupant load factors associated with the use.

A-26-1.7.1 In calculating the occupant load of a business occupancy, it is important to base the calculation on the actual uses of the various building areas. For example, given that buildings having educational uses above grade 12 are for the most part business occupancies because they are exempted from being classed as educational occupancies under Chapters 10 and 11, occupant load factors of 20 sq ft (1.9 sq m) net for classroom areas and 50 sq ft (4.6 sq m) net for instructional laboratory areas should be used. Occupant load calculations for conference rooms should be based on 7 or 15 sq ft (0.65 or 1.4 sq m) net per person. For typical office areas, the occupant load calculation should be based on the 100 sq ft (9.3 sq m) gross factor.

Because the number of people expected to occupy certain types of office buildings can be determined with a great degree of accuracy (e.g., by means of a company's detailed account of its office space), it may prove beneficial to compare such a figure with one calculated on the basis of one person per 100 sq ft (9.3 sq m) of gross floor

area (*see 26-1.7.1*). In office occupancies where people work in highly concentrated groups (such as a bullpen or secretarial pool area often associated with government operations), the actual number of people occupying a space may exceed the figure calculated by gross area. As emphasized in Section 5-3, where this is the case, the exit capacity must be designed to accommodate the larger, actual occupant load. Note that the converse is not true; that is, if the actual occupant load is less than the gross area calculation, the *Code* still requires that the gross area calculation be used to determine the required exit capacity.

SECTION 26-2 Means of Egress Requirements

26-2.1 General.

26-2.1.1 All means of egress shall be in accordance with Chapter 5 and this chapter.

26-2.1.2 If, owing to differences in grade, any street floor exits are at points above or below the street or ground level, such exits shall comply with the provisions for exits from upper floors or floors below the street floor.

Figure 26-3 illustrates a case where two floors qualify as street floors, because each has one side located at a ground level. Note, however, that each floor has its other sides located either above or below the building's other ground level. As a result, these floors must have their exits arranged to allow horizontal travel to the exterior at one end of the floor and vertical travel (either up or down to ground level) at the other end of the floor. The exit capacity of the doors to the exterior on Floor 1 must accommodate that portion of the occupant load from an upper floor that is expected to travel down to and through the exits to the exterior from Floor 1 in addition to the portion of the Floor 1 occupant load assigned to that exit. The reverse is true for Floor 2, which must increase the size of its exterior exit capacity to accommodate occupants traveling up from Floor 1, as well as those traveling down to and through the exterior exits on Floor 2. Paragraphs 5-3.1.4, 5-3.1.5, and 26-2.3.3 explain how to add exit capacity based on the number of occupants expected to discharge from floors above and below the street floor. Figure 26-6 provides an example of how to calculate exit capacity for a street floor such as that illustrated by Floor 2 in Figure 26-3.

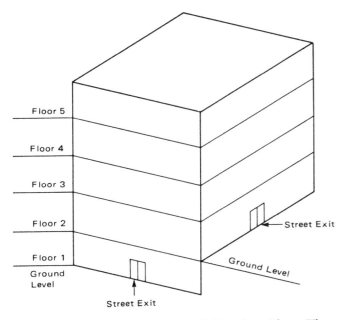

Figure 26-3. Business Occupancy with Two Street Floors. The exit capacity of each street floor must comply with 26-2.3.3. (See also Figure 26-6.)

26-2.1.3 Where two or more floors below the street floor are occupied for business use, the same stairs or ramps may serve each.

Exception: No inside open stairway or ramp shall serve as a required egress facility from more than one floor level.

This provision prohibits the use of unenclosed interior stairs or unenclosed interior ramps as exit access for more than one floor; it does not establish permission for the use of an open stairway or open ramp. See 26-3.1, which addresses the protection of business occupancy vertical openings, to determine if the stairway or ramp is permitted to be unenclosed. It is important to remember that the width of the stair or ramp is determined by the floor with the largest occupant load. This ensures that a stair

or other component of a means of egress will accommodate the population of any floor it serves.

26-2.1.4 Floor levels below the street floor used only for storage, heating, and other service equipment and not subject to business occupancy shall have exits in accordance with Chapter 29.

A significant reduction in the number and size of exits is allowed for floors located below the street floor that are used only for storage, heating and other service equipment, and that are not subject to business occupancy use. This is permitted because the expected population of such floors will be well below that of a floor used as a typical business occupancy. Also refer to Section 5-12, which now specifically governs boiler rooms and similar spaces.

26-2.2 Means of Egress Components.

26-2.2.1 Components of means of egress shall be limited to the types described in 26-2.2.2 through 26-2.2.9.

26-2.2.2 Doors.

26-2.2.2.1 Doors shall comply with 5-2.1.

26-2.2.2.2* Locks complying with 5-2.1.5.1 Exception No. 2 shall be permitted only on principal entrance/exit doors.

A-26-2.2.2.2 The term "principal entrance/exit doors" is intended to imply doors that the authority having jurisdiction can be reasonably assured will be unlocked in order for the facility to do business.

This provision permits only the principal entrance/exit doors of a business occupancy to be equipped with the special key-operated dead bolt lock described by the provisions of Exception No. 2 to 5-2.1.5.1, which must be easily determined to be locked by means such as a flag indicator that can be seen at some distance from the door. Other doors along the perimeter of the building are prohibited from being equipped with a key-operated dead bolt, because it cannot be guaranteed that these locks will be disengaged simultaneously when the principal entrance/

exit door is unlocked each day at the opening of business. (*See Figure 26-4.*)

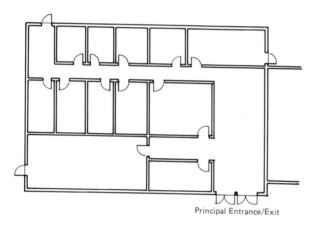

Principal Entrance/Exit

Figure 26-4. Principal Entrance/Exit. The concept of a principal entrance/exit as used in 26-2.2.2.2 is illustrated here.

26-2.2.2.3 Selected doors on stairwells shall be permitted to be equipped with hardware that prevents reentry in accordance with 5-2.1.5.2 Exception No. 1.

If the application of Exception No. 1 to 5-2.1.5.2 was not specifically recognized by this paragraph, the basic requirements of 5-2.1.5.2 would have been the only options offered for achieving reentry to the building from stairwells. This would have compelled new business occupancies to provide either reentry from the stairwell back onto all floors at anytime or similar reentry following automatic release of locking devices initiated by the building fire alarm system. Exception No. 1 to 5-2.1.5.2 allows some stairwell doors to remain locked from the stairwell side of the door to provide building security, while other doors must allow reentry. The location and number of reentry points provide the same overall level of life safety for this type of occupancy as that intended by the base provisions of 5-2.1.5.2.

26-2.2.2.4 Special locking arrangements in accordance with 5-2.1.6 are permitted.

Use of the delay release device covered by 5-2.1.6 is allowed on any door in recognition of the security needs of a business occupancy. The building must be protected throughout by an approved automatic sprinkler system or automatic fire detection system in order to apply the delayed release locking provisions. In effect, the allowable 15- or 30-second delay will be experienced only under nonfire conditions or very early in a fire's growth, since the door must be usable immediately upon sprinkler operation, smoke or heat detection, or loss of power that controls the locking mechanism.

26-2.2.2.5 Where horizontal or vertical security grilles or doors are used as part of the required means of egress from a tenant space, such grilles or doors shall comply with 5-2.1.4.1 Exception No. 3.

Although Exception No. 3 to 5-2.1.4.1 establishes provisions for the arrangement and use of horizontal or vertical security grilles or doors, it requires that an occupancy chapter specifically recognize the use of such security grilles or doors. Paragraph 26-2.2.2.5 provides this recognition for business occupancies.

26-2.2.2.6 Revolving doors shall comply with 5-2.1.10.

The provisions of 5-2.1.10 specify that the use of a revolving door, regardless of whether it is permitted as part of the required means of egress, requires a conforming side-hinged swinging door to be positioned and usable within the same wall as, and located within 10 ft (3 m) of, the revolving door. This helps to ensure that, once people move toward the door, if the collapsibility and other safety features of the door should fail and render it unusable, egress from the vicinity would still be possible without retracing steps and perhaps traveling toward the fire.

26-2.2.3 Stairs.

26-2.2.3.1 Stairs shall comply with 5-2.2.

26-2.2.3.2 Spiral stairs complying with 5-2.2.2.7 are permitted.

Note that 5-2.2.2.7 permits spiral stairs to serve only an occupant load of five or fewer persons. Spiral stairs may be effectively used in business occupancies to provide exit access from small mezzanines.

26-2.2.4 **Smokeproof Enclosures.** Smokeproof enclosures shall comply with 5-2.3.

This paragraph does not mandate the use of smokeproof enclosures but it does recognize a smokeproof enclosure as part of the means of egress system in a business occupancy only if the smokeproof enclosure meets the requirements of 5-2.3. For an example of an occupancy requiring a smokeproof enclosure, see 19-2.11.1, in which nonsprinklered, existing, high rise apartment buildings are required to be provided with smokeproof enclosures in accordance with 5-2.3.

26-2.2.5 **Horizontal Exits.** Horizontal exits shall comply with 5-2.4.

This paragraph does not mandate the use of horizontal exits, but it does recognize a horizontal exit as part of the means of egress system in a business occupancy only if the horizontal exit meets the requirements of 5-2.4.

26-2.2.6 **Ramps.** Ramps shall comply with 5-2.5.

This paragraph does not mandate the use of ramps in business occupancies, but it does recognize a ramp as part of the means of egress system only if the ramp meets the requirements of 5-2.5.

26-2.2.7 **Exit Passageways.** Exit passageways shall comply with 5-2.6.

This paragraph does not mandate the use of exit passageways in business occupancies, but it does recognize an exit passageway as part of the means of egress system only if the exit passageway meets the requirements of 5-2.6.

26-2.2.8 **Fire Escape Ladders.** Fire escape ladders complying with 5-2.9 are permitted.

26-2.2.9 **Alternating Tread Devices.** Alternating tread devices complying with 5-2.11 are permitted.

The provisions of 5-2.11, in effect, restrict the use of alternating tread devices to locations where the *Code* recognizes the use of fire escape ladders. (*See 26-2.2.8 and 5-2.9.*)

Note that escalators do not appear in the 26-2.2 listing of acceptable components for use within the required means of egress. Although they were once recognized, they are no longer allowed to be included in the means of egress. If escalators are present, they cannot be considered part of the egress system.

26-2.3 **Capacity of Means of Egress.**

26-2.3.1 The capacity of means of egress shall be in accordance with Section 5-3.

In the business occupancy chapters of prior editions of the *Code*, specified requirements mandating that the occupant load of a mezzanine be added to that of the floor below the mezzanine for the purpose of determining the total size of the required means of egress system from the combined mezzanine and associated floor beneath. In the 1991 Edition, those requirements have been dropped from the business occupancy chapters, because a similar requirement now appears in 5-3.1.6. The new wording in Chapter 5 mandates that any required egress capacity from a mezzanine that passes through the room below must be added to the required egress capacity of that room through which the egress passes.

Figure 26-5 illustrates a case in which a mezzanine is open to the street floor. The exits from the street floor must accommodate (1) the occupant load of the street floor, (2) the occupant load of the mezzanine in accordance with 5-3.1.6, and (3) the required capacity provided by the stairs from other floors discharging through the street floor in accordance with 26-2.3.3.

To determine the exit capacity for the street floor, the occupant load of the mezzanine (1,000) is added to the occupant load of the street floor (2,000). In addition, because one-half of the exits from the upper floors discharge through the street floor, the exit capacity of the street floor must accommodate the capacity of the exit stair enclosure that discharges through that floor. The maximum occupant load on any upper floor is 2,000 (second floor), and 26-2.7, in accordance with its reference to Section 5-7, permits a maximum of one-half of the exits or the exit capacity to discharge through the street floor, provided that the provisions of 5-7.2 are met, which most

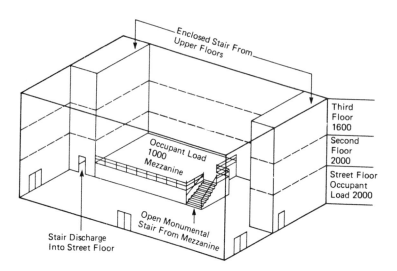

Figure 26-5. Business Occupancy with a Mezzanine Open to the Street Floor. (See commentary following 26-2.3.1.)

typically involve the sprinklering of the level of exit discharge. Therefore, the street floor must be provided with egress capacity for 4,000 persons or 800 in. (2,030 cm) of exit width using the factor of 0.2 in. (0.5 cm) per person for level exit components found in 5-3.3.1 (2,000 for street floor + 1,000 for mezzanine + 1,000 for upper floors = 4,000).

26-2.3.2* The minimum width of any corridor or passageway shall be 44 in. (112 cm) in the clear.

A-26-2.3.2 It is not the intent of this provision to apply to noncorridor or nonpassageway areas of exit access such as the spaces between rows of desks created by office layout or low height partitions. It is the intent of this provision to require that all corridors and passageways be at least 44 in. (112 cm) in width (wider if serving an occupant load of more than 220 persons) regardless of occupant load served (i.e., small number of persons).

A corridor with the minimum 44-in. (112-cm) width required by 26-2.3.2 has sufficient egress capacity, calculated using the 0.2 in. (0.5 cm) capacity factor of 5-3.3.1 for level components, for 220 persons [i.e., 44 in. ÷ 0.2 in. per person (approximately 112 cm ÷ 0.5 cm per person)]. For example, in a corridor that runs from one end of a building to the other end and has an exit stair located at each end, 220 persons can travel from the midpoint of that corridor to the exit enclosure at one end, and another 220 persons can travel to the exit enclosure

at the other end. Therefore, in this example, the occupant load of the floor would have to exceed 440 persons before the minimum 44-in. (112-cm) corridor width must be further increased.

26-2.3.3 Street floor exits shall be sufficient for the occupant load of the street floor plus the required capacity of stairs and ramps discharging through the street floor.

Paragraph 26-2.3.3 requires that the exits for the street floor of a business occupancy have sufficient capacity to handle the occupant load of the street floor and the capacity of the exits discharging through the street floor, such as an enclosed exit stair that accommodates occupants who, when exiting the building during an emergency, must travel up from the basement area or down from the upper floors and mix with the occupants already occupying the street floor.

Since people move more quickly in the horizontal direction than in the vertical direction, it is permissible to provide less door width than stair width. For example, in business occupancies, in accordance with the egress capacity factors of 5-3.3.1, level components and ramps require only 0.2 in. (0.5 cm) of width per person, whereas stairs require 0.3 in. (0.8 cm) of width per person. As a rough approximation, for every 44 in. (112 cm) of stair discharging through the street floor, an additional 30 in. (76 cm) of door width opening to the outside must be added from the street floor. Figure 26-6 provides an example of the proper calculation method for determining the required exit capacity for the street floor.

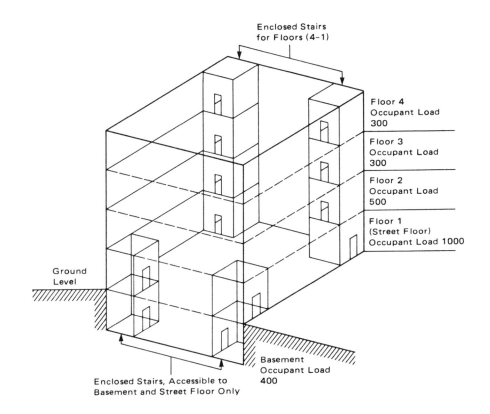

Enclosed Stairs
for Floors (4-1)

Floor 4
Occupant Load
300

Floor 3
Occupant Load
300

Floor 2
Occupant Load
500

Floor 1
(Street Floor)
Occupant Load 1000

Ground
Level

Basement
Occupant Load
400

Enclosed Stairs, Accessible to
Basement and Street Floor Only

Figure 26-6. Calculation of Exit Capacity Required for a Street Floor in Accordance with 26-2.3.3.

Street floor occupant
load alone   1000

plus maximum upper
floor occupant load
discharging back
through street floor
(500 ÷ 2)   250

plus basement occupant
load discharging back
through street floor
(400 ÷ 2)   200

1450 persons × 0.2 in.
(0.5 cm) per person for
level exit components per
5-3.3.1 =290 in. (737 cm)
of exit width required
from the street floor egress
system.

26-2.4 **Number of Exits.** At least two separate exits shall:

(a) Be provided on every story, and

(b) Be accessible from every part of every story and mezzanine.

Exception to (b): Exit access travel shall be permitted to be common for the distances allowed as common path of travel by 26-2.5.3.

Exception No. 1: For a room or area with a total occupant load of less than 100 persons having an exit that discharges directly to the outside at the level of exit discharge for the building, with a total distance of travel, including travel within the exit, from any point not over 100 ft (30 m), a single exit shall be permitted. Such travel shall be on the same floor level or, if traversing of stairs is required, such stairs shall not be more than 15 ft (4.5 m) in height, and they shall be provided with complete enclosures to separate them from any other part of the building, with no door openings therein. A single outside stairway in accordance with 5-2.2 shall be permitted to serve all floors allowed within the 15-ft (4.5-m) vertical travel limitation.

Exception No. 2: Any business occupancy not over three stories and not exceeding an occupant load of 30 people per floor shall be permitted with a single separate exit to each floor if the total travel distance to the outside of the building does not exceed 100 ft (30 m), and if such exit is enclosed in accordance with 5-1.3 and serves no other levels and discharges directly to the outside. A single outside stairway in accordance with 5-2.2 shall be permitted to serve all floors.

Exception No. 3: A single means of egress shall be permitted from a mezzanine within a business occupancy, provided that the common path of travel does not exceed 75 ft (23 m) or 100 ft (30 m) if protected throughout by an approved automatic sprinkler system in accordance with Section 7-7.

Exception No. 4: A single exit shall be permitted for a maximum two-story single tenant space or building that is protected throughout by an approved automatic sprinkler system in accordance with Section 7-7 if the total travel to the outside does not exceed 100 ft (30 m).

This paragraph requires a minimum number of exits. Refer to 5-4.1.2, which establishes a minimum number of means of egress, which can be as high as four, depending upon the occupant load.

The provisions of 26-2.4, which apply to the required number of exits for business occupancies, have been revised for this edition of the *Code* to clarify that any level that constitutes a story must have at least two exits located on that story. This means that the occupants of the story must be able to enter an exit (e.g., an enclosed exit stair on an upper floor of a multistory building) without having to travel to some other story to reach the entrance to the exit. Since a mezzanine that meets the maximum one-third area rule of 6-2.5 does not constitute a story (*see 6-2.5.1 and 6-2.5.2.1*), two exits are not required on the mezzanine, but (1) the criteria of 26-2.4(b) must be met with respect to providing access to two separate exits, or (2) the provisions of the Exception to (b) or Exception No. 3 must be met.

The Exception to (b) applies only to subpart (b) of 26-2.4, which requires access to two separate exits from every part of every level (i.e., story or mezzanine). The exception indicates that 26-2.5.3 allows the occupant to travel in one direction for a maximum distance (i.e., the common path allowance) before requiring access in two

separate directions. Therefore, although the story or mezzanine must eventually provide access to two exits in accordance with 26-2.4(b), that access need only be available at the point where the allowable common path is expended.

Figures 26-7 and 26-8 illustrate two cases where a single exit from a room or area in a business occupancy is allowed (*see Exception No. 1 to 26-2.4*). In the first case, the travel distance from the area is located on the same floor level as the exit. In the second case, stairs must be traversed.

The criteria for allowing the single exit are:

1. An occupant load less than 100 persons;
2. Direct exit to a street or to an open exterior area at ground level;
3. Total distance of no more than 100 ft (30 m) from any point in the room to the exterior. Note that this is total distance from any point to the exterior, not travel distance as measured in Section 5-6. Therefore, the total distance includes the distance traveled on enclosed stairs (exit);
4. Any stairs must be no more than 15 ft (4.5 m) in height; and
5. Any stairs must be completely enclosed with no door openings between the stair enclosure and the rest of the building, or stairs must meet the requirements applicable to outside stairs. (*See 5-2.2.6.3.*)

Failure to meet any of these conditions requires two exits from the floor in question.

Figure 26-9 illustrates a single exit from the third floor of a business occupancy in accordance with Exception No. 2. The criteria for allowing the single exit are:

1. The building is not more than three stories high;
2. Each floor has no more than 30 occupants;
3. Total distance from any point on any floor to the exterior at ground level is no more than 100 ft (30 m), including travel over stairs. Note that this is total distance from any point to the exterior, not travel distance as measured in Section 5-6;
4. The stair is not used by, nor has an opening to, any other floor; and
5. The stair is totally enclosed or meets the requirements applicable to outside stairs. (*See 5-2.2.6.3.*)

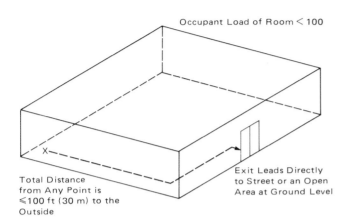

Occupant Load of Room < 100

Total Distance from Any Point is ⩽100 ft (30 m) to the Outside

X

Exit Leads Directly to Street or an Open Area at Ground Level

Figure 26-7.   Single Exit from an Area or Room in a Business Occupancy. Travel from area to exit is horizontal. (See Exception No. 1 to 26-2.4.)

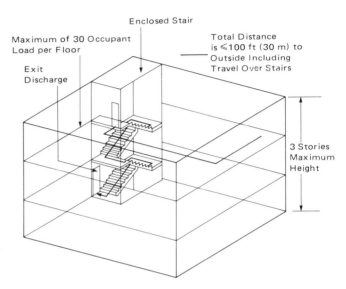

Enclosed Stair

Maximum of 30 Occupant Load per Floor

Exit Discharge

Total Distance is ⩽100 ft (30 m) to Outside Including Travel Over Stairs

3 Stories Maximum Height

Figure 26-9.   Single Exit from Third Floor of a Business Occupancy. Stair is totally enclosed, has opening onto a building floor only at third floor, and discharges directly to street with no communication at second and first floors. A similar, but separate, arrangement could be provided for the second floor of the same building.

Failure to meet any of these conditions requires two exits from the floor in question.

While the Exception to (b) allows common access to the two required means of egress for some limited distances, Exception No. 3 exempts a mezzanine in a business from providing a point where access to two exits is available if the single means of egress leads to an exit within the same limited distances as those allowed for common path of travel. [*See the Exception to 26-2.4(b) and 26-2.5.3 and its exceptions.*]

Exception No. 4 was developed to provide some relief from the requirement mandating two separate exits on every story that affects typical townhouse-type, sprinklered business occupancies. These townhouse-type business occupancies typically have two stories with an open interior stair and are of such limited size that, if a second stair were added, little usable space would remain, and the two stairs would, in effect, be located side by side. The exception offers any single tenant space in a fully sprinklered building with a maximum of two stories, or any sprinklered single tenant building with a maximum of two stories, the option of providing only one exit if the total travel distance to the outside does not exceed 100 ft (30 m).

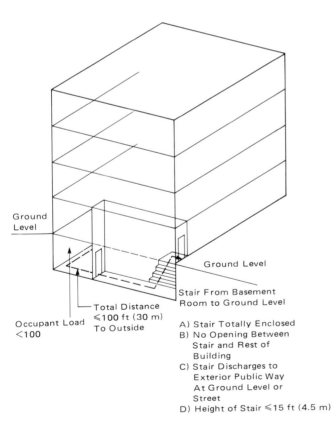

Ground Level

Ground Level

Stair From Basement Room to Ground Level

Total Distance ⩽100 ft (30 m) To Outside

Occupant Load <100

A) Stair Totally Enclosed
B) No Opening Between Stair and Rest of Building
C) Stair Discharges to Exterior Public Way At Ground Level or Street
D) Height of Stair ⩽15 ft (4.5 m)

Figure 26-8.   Single Exit from an Area or Room in a Business Occupancy Where Stairs Must Be Traversed. (See Exception No. 1 to 26-2.4.)

26-2.5 Arrangement of Means of Egress.

26-2.5.1 Exits shall be arranged in accordance with Section 5-5.

26-2.5.2 No dead-end corridor shall exceed 20 ft (6.1 m).

Exception: In buildings protected throughout by an approved supervised automatic sprinkler system, in accordance with Section 7-7, dead-end corridors shall not exceed 50 ft (15 m).

Because they have separate and distinct requirements, dead-end corridors and common path of travel are separated by the *Code* into two distinct and separate paragraphs. Dead-end corridors are limited to 20 ft (6.1 m) in buildings that are not protected throughout by an approved supervised automatic sprinkler system. The Exception to 26-2.5.2 recognizes the additional level of safety to life that a complete automatic sprinkler system provides. It also allows added flexibility when designing the location of corridors and exits in buildings where approved sprinkler systems are installed by allowing for the dead-end corridor pocket to be as deep as 50 ft (15 m).

Three typical dead-end corridors are illustrated in Figure 26-10.

26-2.5.3 No common path of travel shall exceed 75 ft (23 m).

Exception No. 1: A common path of travel shall be permitted for the first 100 ft (30 m) in a building protected throughout by an approved supervised automatic sprinkler system in accordance with Section 7-7.

Exception No. 2: A common path of travel shall be permitted for the first 100 ft (30 m) for single tenant spaces with an occupant load of not more than 30 persons.

The 1985 Edition of the *Code* limited common path of travel to 50 ft (15 m) or 75 ft (23 m) if the building was sprinklered. In the 1988 Edition, the provisions of Chapter 5 that applied to the point where measurement of travel distance and common path begins for small rooms were revised, and the allowable common path was increased without either reducing the level of safety to life or imposing a hardship on designers.

See the commentary following 5-5.1.6 for a detailed discussion on common path of travel. Also see the commentary following the Exception to 26-2.4(b), which allows a portion of the access to a single exit or multiple exits to be common.

Figure 26-10.   Illustration of Dead Ends and Common Path of Travel.

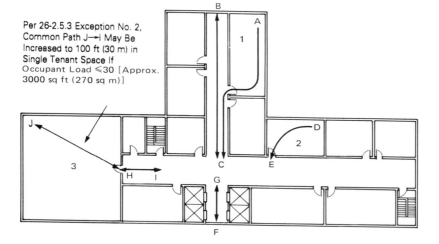

The restriction on common path of travel is separate and distinct from the restriction on dead-end corridors. Although a common path of travel may at times involve a dead-end corridor, and dead ends may involve common path of travel, this is not always the case. For an example, see the elevator lobby illustrated in Figure 26-10, which is a dead-end corridor but not a common path of travel.

Common path of travel is measured similarly to travel distance (*see Section 5-6*) with the exception that, instead of being terminated at the entrance to an exit, common path of travel measurement often ends before the exit entrance, because it is terminated at that point where the occupant has a choice of two distinct and separate paths to an exit (*see the definition of common path of travel in Chapter 3*). It should be noted that the starting point for measurement of common path of travel is the same as the starting point (*see 5-6.2*) for travel distance measurement. Specifically, the starting point is 1 ft (30.5 cm) from the most remote point. (*See rooms 1 and 2 in Figure 26-10.*)

Figure 26-11 provides an additional illustration of common path of travel in a business occupancy. (*Also see the commentary in Section 5-5 on arrangement of means of egress.*)

In Suite A, the travel from point X to point A is a common path of travel; although there are two routes to reach the corridor, they both merge at common point A. In Suite B, the travel from point X to point B is common path of travel, but it does not appear to exceed the 75-ft (23-m) maximum allowable common path; if it were in excess of 75 ft (23 m) but no more than 100 ft (30 m), it would be permitted by either Exception No. 1 (building sprinklered) or Exception No. 2 (maximum 30-person single

tenant space) to 26-2.5.3. Although Suites C and D do not have common paths of travel, the remoteness of the two exit access doors from each suite is questionable. (*See 5-5.1.4.*)

Questions are often asked concerning the conditions under which an office space or suite requires two exit access doors. The common path of travel restriction regulates where an office space requires two exit access doors. If the common path of travel is exceeded, a second door from the office space is required. It must be positioned so that any resulting common path of travel would comply with the allowable distances. In addition, the second door must be remotely located from the first door (*see 5-5.1.4*), and each door must lead to remote exits by means of remote paths. Therefore, in a single requirement, the *Code* not only regulates the number of exit access doors required from an office area, but also the arrangement of these doors.

Exception No. 1 allows the common path of travel to be extended to 100 ft (30 m) in buildings protected throughout by an approved supervised automatic sprinkler system. The exception recognizes the additional level of safety to life that a complete automatic sprinkler system provides and allows added flexibility when designing the location of corridors and exits in buildings where approved sprinkler systems are installed.

Exception No. 2 extends the common path allowance to 100 ft (30 m) in a single tenant space without requiring sprinklers if that space has a maximum occupant load of 30 people [normally, approximately 3,000 sq ft (270 sq m), based on the business occupant load factor of 100 sq ft (9.3 sq m) per 26-1.7.1]. (*See room 3 in Figure 26-10.*)

Figure 26-11.   Common Path of Travel.

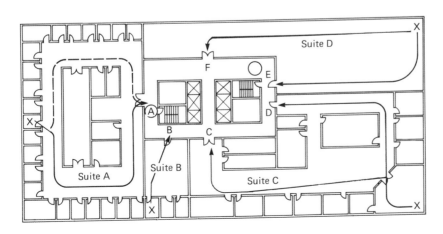

26-2.6 **Travel Distance to Exits.** Travel distance to exits, measured in accordance with Section 5-6, shall be no more than 200 ft (60 m).

Exception: Travel distance shall not exceed 300 ft (91 m) in buildings protected throughout by an approved supervised automatic sprinkler system in accordance with Section 7-7.

In accordance with Section 5-6, travel distance requirements apply to only the first (or nearest) exit from a given point in a building. In other words, the 200-ft (60-m) travel distance limit requires that at least one exit must be located within 200 ft (60 m) of any point in the building; it does not require that all exits must be within 200 ft (60 m) of that point in the building.

The exception allows for the travel distance to be increased to 300 ft (91 m) if the building is protected throughout by an approved automatic sprinkler system. It recognizes the additional level of safety to life that a complete automatic sprinkler system provides and allows added flexibility in the design and arrangement of the means of egress.

26-2.7 **Discharge from Exits.** Exit discharge shall comply with Section 5-7.

26-2.8 **Illumination of Means of Egress.** Means of egress shall be illuminated in accordance with Section 5-8.

26-2.9 **Emergency Lighting.**

26-2.9.1 Emergency lighting shall be provided in accordance with Section 5-9 in any building where:

(a) The building is two or more stories in height above the level of exit discharge, or

(b) The occupancy is subject to 100 or more occupants above or below the level of exit discharge, or

(c) The occupancy is subject to 1,000 or more total occupants.

If any of the three conditions of 26-2.9.1 exist, emergency lighting as specified in Section 5-9 is required for the building. Note that condition (a) specifically mentions

buildings that have two stories located above the level of exit discharge, or a minimum of three stories.

26-2.9.2 Emergency lighting in accordance with Section 5-9 shall be provided for all windowless or underground structures meeting the definition of 30-1.3.

26-2.10 **Marking of Means of Egress.** Means of egress shall have signs in accordance with Section 5-10.

26-2.11 **Special Features.** (Reserved.)

SECTION 26-3   Protection

26-3.1 **Protection of Vertical Openings.**

26-3.1.1 Every stairway, elevator shaft, escalator opening, and other vertical opening shall be enclosed or protected in accordance with Section 6-2.

Exception No. 1: Unprotected vertical openings connecting not more than three floors used for business occupancy only shall be permitted in accordance with 6-2.4.5.

Note that 6-2.4.5 requires that, if the communicating space (i.e., the vertical opening and all areas open to it) contains ordinary hazard contents, it must be protected by automatic sprinklers. In accordance with 26-1.5, business occupancies are classified as ordinary hazard.

Exception No. 2: A vertical opening enclosure shall not be required for a vertical opening where:

(a) The vertical opening connects only two adjacent floors, neither of which is a basement, and

(b) The vertical opening is not a required means of egress, and

(c) The vertical opening is not connected with corridors or other stairways.

Exception No. 2 to 26-3.1.1 permits, for example, a two-level office or reference library in an office building to have an unenclosed convenience stair. Item (a) restricts the application of this exception to two levels only. Item (b) requires that the stairs cannot be part of the means of egress; therefore, the space would have to have access to exits on both levels in order that occupants would not have to rely on the open stair as part of the required means of egress. Item (c) requires that the areas connected by the opening be separated from corridors and other stairways.

Exception No. 3: Atriums in accordance with 6-2.4.6 are permitted.

Exception No. 3 recognizes an atrium without mandating requirements other than those provided by 6-2.4.6.

Exception No. 4: Exit access stairs shall be permitted to be unenclosed in two-story single tenant spaces provided with a single exit in accordance with the provisions of Exception No. 4 to 26-2.4.

Exception No. 4 completes the single exit package for townhouse-type, and similarly arranged, business occupancies by allowing the single means of egress to include an unenclosed stair. (*See the commentary associated with Exception No. 4 to 26-2.4.*)

26-3.1.2 Floors below the street floor used for storage or other than business occupancy shall have no unprotected openings to business occupancy floors.

The requirement of 26-3.1.2 prevents the possibility that a fire in a hazardous area with a high fuel load (e.g., areas used for shops, repairs, or storage of maintenance supplies, files, and records) might directly expose the floor of exit discharge through a vertical opening that is unprotected. A fire in a basement can quickly cause exits and exit discharges located on the street floor to become unusable when smoke and heat rise.

26-3.2 **Protection from Hazards.**

26-3.2.1* Hazardous areas, including but not limited to areas used for general storage, boiler or furnace rooms, fuel storage, janitor closets, and maintenance shops including woodworking and painting areas shall:

(a) Be separated from other parts of the building by fire barriers having a fire resistance rating of not less than 1 hour with all openings therein protected by ¾-hour fire protection rated self-closing fire doors, or

(b) The area shall be protected by an automatic extinguishing system in accordance with Section 7-7.

A-26-3.2.1 It is not the intent of this provision to require that rooms inside individual tenant spaces, used to store routine office supplies for that tenant, be either separated or sprinklered.

26-3.2.2 High hazard content areas, as defined in Section 4-2, shall be protected by both fire resistance rated construction and automatic extinguishing equipment.

Paragraphs 26-3.2.1 and 26-3.2.2 reflect the intent of Section 6-4, which (1) requires separation of a hazardous area from the remainder of the occupancy by means of suitable construction, or (2) mandates the installation of an automatic extinguishing system in the hazardous area, or (3) requires both where the hazard is severe. For this edition of the *Code*, 6-4.1 has been revised to include a concept that applied to assembly and educational occupancies in previous editions; specifically, where a hazardous area is protected by automatic sprinklers, rather than enclosure with fire barriers of 1-hour fire resistance rating and doors of 45-minute fire protection rating, the hazardous area must be enclosed by walls and doors that are at least smoke resisting. (*See 6-4.1.*)

Section 6-4 contains two additional mandatory provisions. One is a reference to NFPA 30, *Flammable and Combustible Liquids Code,*[3] and the other is a reference to NFPA 45, *Standard on Fire Protection for Laboratories Using Chemicals.*[4] (*See 6-4.3 and 6-4.4.*)

26-3.2.3 Laboratories that use chemicals shall comply with NFPA 45, *Standard on Fire Protection for Laboratories Using Chemicals.*

26-3.3 **Interior Finish.**

26-3.3.1 Interior finish on walls and ceilings of exits and of enclosed corridors furnishing access thereto or ways of travel therefrom shall be Class A or Class B in accordance with Section 6-5.

26-3.3.2 In office areas, Class A, Class B, or Class C interior finish shall be provided in accordance with Section 6-5.

26-3.3.3 Interior floor finish in corridors and exits shall be Class I or Class II in accordance with Section 6-5.

Chapter 26, which addresses new business occupancies, is among the few occupancy chapters that regulate interior floor finish. The requirement that such finish be Class I or Class II (*see Section 6-5*) applies only to exits, such as enclosed stairs, and to corridors. The intent is that the interior floor finish materials used in corridors and exits resist the spread of fire should the interior floor finish in these areas be exposed to the radiant energy from a fully developed room fire by means of an open door. Section 6-5 contains a provision that allows a reduction of one class of interior floor finish (i.e., from Class I to Class II, or from Class II to no rating required) for sprinklered buildings. No rating is required for floor finish in sprinklered business occupancy buildings, since Chapter 26 specifies a Class II interior floor finish.

26-3.4 **Detection, Alarm, and Communication Systems.**

See Supplement 2.

26-3.4.1 **General.** A fire alarm system in accordance with Section 7-6 shall be provided in any business occupancy where:

(a) The building is two or more stories in height above the level of exit discharge, or

(b) The occupancy is subject to 100 or more occupants above or below the level of exit discharge, or

(c) The occupancy is subject to 1,000 or more total occupants.

A fire alarm system is required in a business occupancy under the same conditions as those under which emergency lighting is required (*see 26-2.9.1*). If any one of the three conditions listed above exists, a fire alarm system must be provided. Note that "two or more stories in height above the level of exit discharge" usually describes a building with three or more stories.

26-3.4.2 **Initiation.** Initiation of the required fire alarm system shall be by manual means per 7-6.2.1(a).

Exception No. 1: Initiation shall be permitted by means of an approved automatic fire detection system in accordance with 7-6.2.1(b) that provides protection throughout the building.

Exception No. 2: Initiation shall be permitted by means of an approved automatic sprinkler system in accordance with 7-6.2.1(c) that provides protection throughout the building.

This paragraph clearly states that a fire alarm system is required, but the requirement for manual pull stations is waived if the system is activated by either an automatic fire detection system providing protection throughout the building or an automatic sprinkler system providing protection throughout the building. This does not exempt the fire alarm system, but exempts only the manual pull stations.

26-3.4.3 **Notification.**

26-3.4.3.1 During all times that the building is occupied (*see 5-2.1.1.3*), the required fire alarm system shall:

(a) Sound a general audible alarm throughout the building, or

(b) Sound an audible alarm in a continuously attended location for purposes of initiating emergency action.

This paragraph requires that, when the fire alarm system is actuated (*see 26-3.4.2*), the system shall either automatically sound a general alarm throughout the building, or, if a continuously attended location is provided (as is often the case in high rise or other large office buildings), the alarm may sound at that location only, with initiation of the appropriate emergency action occurring at that location.

26-3.4.3.2 **Occupant Notification.** Occupant notification shall be by means of live voice public address system announcement originating from the attended location where the alarm signal is received. (*See 26-3.4.3.1.*) The system shall be permitted to be used for other announcements. (*See 7-6.3.9 Exception No. 2.*)

Exception: Any other occupant notification means allowed by 7-6.3 shall be permitted in lieu of live voice public address system announcement.

It is preferable for a voice alarm system to be controlled from the continuously attended location referred to in 26-3.4.3.1. The exception would be used primarily in buildings where a continuously attended location is not provided and would allow either a recorded voice system or a general audible alarm.

26-3.5 **Extinguishment Requirement.** Portable fire extinguishers shall be provided in every business occupancy in accordance with 7-7.4.1. (*See also Section 26-4.*)

Although no requirements for automatic sprinkler systems are provided in this paragraph, 26-4.2.2 requires new high rise office buildings to be protected by automatic sprinklers, and Exception No. 3 to 26-3.1.1, by referencing Chapter 6, requires a building containing an atrium to be sprinklered. Additional incentives are provided to encourage sprinkler installation in connection with the following features: nonrated openings to attached parking structures (26-1.2.2); delay release hardware (26-2.2.2.4); number of exits (26-2.4 exceptions); dead ends (26-2.5.2); common path of travel (26-2.5.3); travel distance (26-2.6); discharge of exits through the level of exit discharge (26-2.7 per Section 5-7); protection from hazards (26-3.2); interior finish (26-3.3 per Section 6-5); deletion of manual pull stations (26-3.4.2); and corridors (26-3.6.1).

26-3.6 **Corridors.**

26-3.6.1 Where access to exits is limited to corridors, such corridors shall be separated from use areas by fire barriers having a fire resistance rating of at least 1 hour.

Exception No. 1: Where exits are available from an open floor area.

A-26-3.6.1 **Exception No. 1.** Where exits are available from an open floor area, such as open plan buildings, corridors need not be separated. (An example of an open plan building is one in which the work spaces and accesses to exits are delineated by the use of tables, desks, bookcases, counters, or by partitions that are less than floor to ceiling height.)

Exception No. 2: Corridors need not have a fire resistance rating within a space occupied by a single tenant.

A-26-3.6.1 **Exception No. 2.** It is the intent of this paragraph that a single tenant be limited to an area occupied under a single management and work the same hours. The concept is that people under the same employ working the same hours would largely be familiar with their entire tenant space. It is not the intent to apply this just because tenants might be owned by the same organization. For example, in a government-owned office building, the offices of different federal agencies would be considered tenants since an employee normally works for one agency. The agencies may work various hours. Another example would be a classroom building of a university, since some classrooms may be in use at times when other classrooms are not being used.

Exception No. 3: Corridors need not have a fire resistance rating within buildings protected throughout by an approved automatic sprinkler system in accordance with Section 7-7.

The requirement of 26-3.6.1 is clear.

Exception No. 1 provides for the popular "office landscape" or "open office" arrangement. If there is direct access to exits from the open area, it is not necessary to require separated corridors. This exception recognizes that a fire in an open space is subject to more rapid observation and response than a fire in an enclosed room or office.

Exception No. 2 recognizes that, in areas occupied by a single tenant, there is a high level of familiarity with the area, and the partitioned offices or spaces are occupied by the same people on a regular basis. The appendix note to Exception No. 2 provides further discussion on this subject.

Exception No. 3 recognizes the value of automatic sprinklers as a life safety feature that helps to control fire growth and, thus, maintains the exit access usable for a longer period of time.

26-3.6.2 Openings in corridor partitions required to have a fire resistance rating by 26-3.6.1 shall be protected in accordance with 6-2.3.

Paragraph 6-2.3 has been revised for this edition of the *Code* so that, if referenced by another paragraph of the *Code*, such as 26-3.6.2, it provides a complete set of requirements with respect to doors and vision panels.

26-3.7 Subdivision of Building Spaces. (Reserved.)

26-3.8 Special Features. (Reserved.)

26-3.8.1 Nonrated glazing and opening protectives per 26-1.2.3 Exception shall be permitted between business occupancies and parking structures.

SECTION 26-4 Special Provisions

26-4.1 Windowless or Underground Buildings. (*See Section 30-7.*)

26-4.2* High Rise Buildings.

A-26-4.2 In the design of high rise buildings, special consideration should also be given to a life safety system including, among others, the following features:

Movement of occupants to safety.
Control of fire and smoke.
Psychological features.
Communications.
Elevators (*see A-7-4.1*).
Emergency planning.
Overall system reliability.

See the definition of high rise building in Chapter 3.

The problems posed by high rise buildings with respect to safety to life, fire fighting, and fire protection in general are covered in *High-Rise Building Fires and Fire Safety,*[5] *Fighting High-Rise Building Fires — Tactics and Logistics,*[6] *and Fires in High-Rise Buildings.*[7] All three publications contain extensive bibliographies on the subject.

26-4.2.1 General. In addition to the requirements of this section, all high rise buildings shall comply with all other applicable provisions of this *Code.*

Although 26-4.2.1 makes reference to "all other applicable provisions of this *Code*," it is not the intent of the paragraph to require compliance with Section 30-8, "High Rise Buildings."

The provisions of Section 30-8, singly, in various combinations, or in total, must be mandated by specific occu-

pancy chapter requirements. Chapter 26, which addresses new business occupancies, does not require any of the provisions of Section 30-8. Instead, 26-4.2.2, 26-4.2.3, 26-4.2.4, and 26-4.2.5 provide a self-contained set of requirements in which many of the concepts of Section 30-8 are reworded to be mandatory.

26-4.2.2 Extinguishment Requirements. High rise buildings shall be protected throughout by an approved electrically supervised automatic sprinkler system installed in accordance with Section 7-7. A sprinkler control valve and a water flow device shall be provided for each floor.

See Supplement 3.

26-4.2.3 Detection, Alarm, and Communication Systems.

26-4.2.3.1 General. Detection, alarm, and communications systems as specified by 26-4.2.3.2 and 26-4.2.3.3 shall be provided in all buildings with an occupied story 150 ft (45 m) or more in height, measured from the lowest level of fire department vehicle access.

The alarm system requirements for high rise business occupancy buildings are contained in 26-3.4 and 26-4.2.3.1 through 26-4.2.3.3 rather than Section 30-8. For example, new high rise business occupancy buildings are required to have a fire alarm system in accordance with 26-3.4.1.

The provisions of 26-4.2.3.2 and 26-4.2.3.3 are additional provisions required only for those high rise buildings that are 150 ft (45 m) or more in height.

26-4.2.3.2 A fire alarm system utilizing voice communication shall be installed in accordance with Section 7-6.

The additional voice communication requirement of 26-4.2.3.2 applies to buildings 150 ft (45 m) in height rather than 75 ft (23 m) in height in accordance with Section 30-8. The intent is to apply this requirement to buildings of approximately 12 stories or more and is based upon the belief that general building evacuation can be achieved in buildings that are 12 or fewer stories in height. Therefore, voice communication capability is not as necessary as it might be in buildings 12 or more stories in height, where general evacuation is not as feasible.

26-4.2.3.3 Two-way telephone communication service shall be provided for fire department use. This system shall be in accordance with NFPA 72, *Standard for the Installation, Maintenance, and Use of Protective Signaling Systems.* The communication system shall operate between the central control station and every elevator car, every elevator lobby, and each floor level of exit stairs.

Exception: Where the fire department radio system is approved as an equivalent system.

Two-way telephone communication requirements are specified for buildings 150 ft (45 m) or more in height, because the technology of portable two-way communication units has improved greatly, and thus, the equipment available to fire departments should be adequate to serve buildings that are 12 or fewer stories in height.

26-4.2.4 **Standby Power.** Standby power in accordance with Article 701 of NFPA 70, *National Electrical Code,* shall be provided. The standby power system shall have a capacity and rating sufficient to supply all required equipment. Selective load pickup and load shedding shall be permitted in accordance with NFPA 70, *National Electrical Code.* The standby power system shall be connected to the following:

(a) Emergency lighting system.

(b) Fire alarm system.

(c) Electric fire pump.

(d) Central control station equipment and lighting.

(e) At least one elevator serving all floors and be transferable to any elevator.

(f) Mechanical equipment for smokeproof enclosures.

26-4.2.5* **Central Control Station.** A central control station shall be provided in a location approved by the fire department. The control station shall contain:

(a) Voice fire alarm system panels and controls.

(b) Fire department two-way telephone communications service panels and controls.

(c) Fire detection and fire alarm system annunciation panels.

(d) Elevator floor location and operation annunciators.

(e) Sprinkler valve and water flow annunciators.

(f) Emergency generator status indicators.

(g) Controls for any automatic stairway door unlocking system.

(h) Fire pump status indicators.

(i) A telephone for fire department use with controlled access to the public telephone system.

A-26-4.2.5 It is not the intent of the paragraph to require any of the equipment in the list other than the telephone for fire department use, but only to provide the controls, panels, annunciators, and similar equipment at this location where the equipment is provided or required by another section of the *Code.*

26-4.3 **Operating Features.** (*See Chapter 31.*)

SECTION 26-5 Building Services

26-5.1 **Utilities.** Utilities shall comply with the provisions of Section 7-1.

26-5.2 **Heating, Ventilating, and Air Conditioning Equipment.** Heating, ventilating, and air conditioning equipment shall comply with the provisions of Section 7-2.

26-5.3 **Elevators, Escalators, and Conveyors.** Elevators, escalators, and conveyors shall comply with the provisions of Section 7-4.

Refer to Section 7-4 and its referenced document, ASME/ANSI A17.1, *Safety Code for Elevators and Escalators.*[8] It contains design criteria and specifications for the proper arrangement of an elevator control system that will provide both automatic recall during a fire and fire fighter service features that are exclusive of the normal automatic control mode of the elevator system.

26-5.4 **Rubbish Chutes, Incinerators, and Laundry Chutes.** Rubbish chutes, incinerators, and laundry chutes shall comply with the provisions of Section 7-5.

References Cited in Commentary

[1]NFPA 101M, *Alternative Approaches to Life Safety*, National Fire Protection Association, Quincy, MA.†

[2]NFPA 13, *Standard for the Installation of Sprinkler Systems*, National Fire Protection Association, Quincy, MA, 1991.

[3]NFPA 30, *Flammable and Combustible Liquids Code*, National Fire Protection Association, Quincy, MA, 1990.

[4]NFPA 45, *Standard on Fire Protection for Laboratories Using Chemicals*, National Fire Protection Association, Quincy, MA, 1991.

[5]*High-Rise Building Fires and Fire Safety*, NFPA SPP-18, National Fire Protection Association, Boston, MA, 1973.

[6]Robert F. Mendes, *Fighting High-Rise Building Fires— Tactics and Logistics*, NFPA FSP-44, National Fire Protection Association, Boston, MA, 1975.

[7]Fires in High-Rise Buildings, NFPA SPP-25, *National Fire Protection Association*, Boston, MA, 1974.

[8]ASME/ANSI A17.1, *Safety Code for Elevators and Escalators*, American Society of Mechanical Engineers, 345 East 47th Street, New York, NY, 10017, 1987.

† The edition of NFPA 101M that corresponds with the 1991 *Life Safety Code* will be published in 1992.

27

Existing Business Occupancies

(See also Chapter 31.)

Business occupancies are those used for the transaction of business, for the keeping of accounts and records, and similar purposes.

General offices is the most readily identifiable class of business properties found in the national fire incident data bases. This class accounted for 6,100 structure fires per year as reported to U.S. fire departments from 1984 to 1988, with an associated 4 civilian (i.e., nonfire-service personnel) deaths and 93 civilian injuries per year. Courthouse and legislative halls, which are normally classified with assembly properties for fire reporting purposes, accounted for fewer than 100 structure fires and 1 civilian injury per year from 1984 to 1988. College and university buildings, usually classified with educational properties for purposes of fire reporting, accounted for 1,100 structure fires, 1 civilian death, and 30 civilian injuries, while trade and business schools suffered a total of 600 structure fires and 9 civilian injuries per year. Laboratories, usually classified as industrial properties for fire reporting purposes, accounted for 500 structure fires and 25 civilian injuries per year.

Medical and scientific offices (900 structure fires, 2 civilian deaths, and 10 civilian injuries per year) and clinics (200 structure fires and 1 civilian injury per year) are addressed in the commentary associated with health care occupancies in Chapters 12 and 13.

Other office buildings and unclassified office buildings (e.g., bank buildings, engineering or architectural offices) accounted for another 2,100 structure fires, 1 civilian death, and 31 civilian injuries per year.

Multiple-death fires are rare in the business occupancy properties mentioned above. For example, the 1989 Georgia office building fire that killed 5 people was the first office building fire in 17 years to cause 3 or more fatalities. Nearly half the fatal victims of office fires from 1980 to 1988 were not occupying the room of fire origin when the fire began. The 1989 Georgia fire began in an electrical vault, yet four of the five victims were elsewhere on that floor when the fire began.

SECTION 27-1 General Requirements

27-1.1 Application.

27-1.1.1 Existing business occupancies shall comply with the provisions of this chapter. (*See Chapter 31 for operating features.*)

Exception*: Facilities where the authority having jurisdiction has determined equivalent safety is provided in accordance with Section 1-5.

A-27-1.1.1 **Exception.** In determining equivalency for business occupancies, the authority having jurisdiction may use NFPA 101M, *Alternative Approaches to Life Safety*, Chapter 7, utilizing the parameters for existing buildings.

See Section 1-5 for application provisions.

New business occupancies must comply with Chapter 26 of the *Code*.

To understand the full intent and scope of 27-1.1.1, it is necessary to review it concurrently with Sections 1-5, 1-6, and 1-7. Although a building code may exclude existing buildings from coverage under some form of a "grandfather clause," the *Life Safety Code*, by virtue of its interest in safety to life, does not condone existing building arrangements that do not comply with the *Code* except within a set of guidelines. These guidelines are contained in this chapter.

If a building complies with an earlier edition of the *Code*, it is not "grandfathered" and thereby exempted from compliance with a more current edition that has been adopted as law in that building's jurisdiction. The Committee on Safety to Life is especially careful to avoid adopting requirements for existing buildings that become more stringent from one edition of the *Code* to the next unless the change is absolutely necessary to enhance the overall package of safety to life intended by the *Code*. Thus, the old adage of "once in compliance, always in compliance" does not hold.

Chapter 27 has been prepared for application to existing buildings only. In those editions of the *Code* prior to 1973, the sections that addressed existing business occupancies made reference to provisions contained within the

section covering new construction. Since the 1973 Edition of the *Code*, the sections that cover existing facilities have been complete and are intended to be applied without reference to the requirements for new construction.

This chapter is to be applied retroactively. Due consideration has been given to the practical difficulties of making alterations in existing, functioning facilities. The specified provisions, viewed as a whole, establish minimum acceptable criteria for safety to life that reasonably minimize the likelihood of a life-threatening fire.

The requirements of Chapter 27 may be modified in instances of practical difficulty or where alternate, but equal, provisions are proposed. The modifications must provide a level of protection equivalent to that achieved by compliance with the corresponding *Code* provisions.

The exception emphasizes that Section 1-6, "Equivalency Concepts," permits alternatives to literal *Code* compliance in which a building design would still be considered as *Code* conforming. However, the authority having jurisdiction ultimately determines whether or not equivalent safety has been provided.

Paragraph 27-1.1.1 and its accompanying exception do not intend to limit the methods an authority having jurisdiction might use to determine equivalency. However, as noted in the Exception to A-27-1.1.1, Chapter 7 of NFPA 101M, *Alternative Approaches to Life Safety*,[1] provides an "equivalency system" that uses numerical values to analyze the firesafety effectiveness of a building design. This system is known as the Firesafety Evaluation System (FSES). The system provides a method by which alternative designs can be evaluated as options to literal *Code* compliance.

The 1992 Edition of NFPA 101M, *Alternative Approaches to Life Safety*, although published one year after this 1991 Edition of the *Life Safety Code*, is the proper edition of NFPA 101M to consult for one possible equivalency system for business occupancies. Its measurement system has been calibrated against the requirements of the 1991 Edition of the *Life Safety Code*, whereas the firesafety evaluation systems contained in the 1988 Edition of NFPA 101M were calibrated against the requirements of the 1988 Edition of the *Code*.

In providing the equivalency concept, the *Code* does not intend to limit equivalency evaluations to those based solely on the one system presented for business occupancies in NFPA 101M. The authority having jurisdiction retains the power to evaluate and approve alternative designs on the basis of appropriate supporting data. The FSES may be used to aid in this evaluation. This exception in no way mandates the use of the FSES, nor does it require the authority having jurisdiction to accept the results of an evaluation using the equivalency system.

Although the FSES was primarily developed to evaluate alternative designs in existing buildings, it is particularly useful for determining equivalency for conversions, modernizations, renovations, or unusual design concepts—all of which would be considered new construction. However, the FSES is a tool used to help determine equivalency, and it should not be used to circumvent *Code* requirements.

27-1.1.2 This chapter establishes life safety requirements for existing business buildings. Specific requirements for high rise buildings [buildings over 75 ft (23 m) in height] are contained in paragraphs pertaining thereto.

New buildings are addressed in Chapter 26. Subsection 27-4.2 contains additional requirements for high rise buildings.

The provisions of 26-1.1.3, which address new construction where additions are made to existing buildings, also affect existing buildings and warrant additional discussion. Although construction of an addition generally does not require existing portions of the building to be modified, Figure 27-1 illustrates a case where the planned new construction would diminish the firesafety features of the existing building and, thus, necessitate corrective action within the existing portion of the building. The placement of new room A creates an excessively long dead-end corridor B, which must be corrected.

27-1.2 Mixed Occupancies.

27-1.2.1 Mixed occupancies shall comply with 1-5.7.

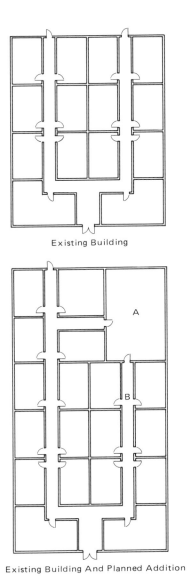

Existing Building

Existing Building And Planned Addition

Figure 27-1. The Placement of New Room A Creates an Excessively Long Dead-End Corridor B in the Existing Building, Which Must Be Corrected.

Minor office occupancies incidental to operations in another occupancy are considered as part of the predominating occupancy, rather than creating a mixed occupancy, and are subject to the *Code* provisions that apply to the predominating occupancy. The commentary following 27-1.4 discusses classification of business occupancies in more detail.

The determination of those criteria that constitute a minor or incidental office area cannot be based solely on percentage of business area in comparison to overall building area. For example: a 200-sq ft (19-sq m) office area in a 4,000-sq ft (370-sq m) warehouse can reasonably be judged incidental to the storage operations and result in the building being classified as a storage occupancy. A 20,000-sq ft (1,860-sq m) office area in a 400,000-sq ft (37,200-sq m) distribution warehouse represents the same proportion of business use area as the 200-sq ft (19-sq m) office in the 4,000-sq ft (370-sq m) example but cannot be judged incidental (*see Figure 27-2*). The 20,000-sq ft (1,860-sq m) office area probably has an occupant load of approximately 200 persons. The *Code* requirements applicable to business occupancies, which are more stringent than those applicable to storage occupancies, are needed to protect the occupants of the office area adequately. The distribution warehouse is classified as a mixed occupancy that is part storage occupancy and part business occupancy. If packaging operations are present, it might also be classified as part industrial occupancy. Consequently, the requirements of 1-5.7 for mixed occupancies apply.

27-1.2.2   (Reserved.)

27-1.2.3   Combined Business Occupancies and Parking Structures.
Walls separating parking structures from business occupancies shall have a fire resistance rating of not less than 2 hours.

Exception: In enclosed parking structures that are protected throughout with an approved automatic sprinkler system in accordance with Section 7-7 or in open-air parking structures, nonrated glazing and opening protectives shall be permitted if all of the following conditions are met:

(a) The openings do not exceed 25 percent of the area of the wall in which they are located, and

(b) The openings are used for main entrance and associated sidelight functions, and

(c) The enclosed connecting business building is protected throughout by an approved automatic sprinkler system in accordance with Section 7-7, and

(d) The floor elevation of the business use is at least 4 in. (10.2 cm) above the floor level of the parking structure, and

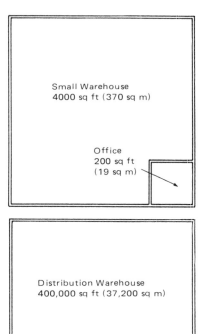

NOT TO SCALE

Figure 27-2.   Determination of "Incidental" Office Use Cannot Be Based on Percentage of Overall Building Area. (See commentary associated with 27-1.2.1.)

(e) No vehicle is able to park or drive within 10 ft (3 m) of the openings, and

(f) The openings have a minimum of a glass membrane, and

(g) Any doors in the glass membrane are self-closing.

The provisions of 27-1.2.3 are new to this edition of the *Code* and, although they address combined business occupancies and parking structures, are very similar to the new requirements of 25-1.2.3, which address existing combined mercantile occupancies and parking structures. It is very common for multistory business occupancies, such as office buildings and multistory mercantile occupancies (e.g., department stores and shopping mall buildings), to be attached to multistory parking garages with access between the two structures located at multiple levels. In order to allow some flexibility with respect to the number and type of these access openings and considering the stringent requirements for providing opening protectives such as fire doors and fire windows, the Exception to 27-1.2.2 outlines a set of provisions that, when incorporated in total, will safely allow for the 2-hour fire resistance rated separation requirement of 27-1.2.2 to be reduced. The reduction allows the use of nonrated glazing and nonrated opening protectives.

This permits the use of glass doors and glass sidelights in the barrier between the business occupancy and the garage. Security in the garage is thereby increased, since customers can view the area through the glass doors or sidelights.

Note that all eight requirements mandated by the Exception to 27-1.2.2 [i.e., the sprinkler requirement for the garage per the base paragraph of the exception and the other seven requirements of subparts (a) through (g) of the exception] must be met as a whole in order to apply the exception to the rule that would have otherwise required a 2-hour fire resistance rated separation between the business occupancy and the parking structure.

27-1.3 **Special Definitions.** None.

27-1.4 **Classification of Occupancy.**

27-1.4.1 Business occupancies shall include all buildings and structures or parts thereof with occupancy described in 4-1.8.

Note that the *Code's* definition of a business occupancy (*see 4-1.8*) does not include types of stores that, although considered "businesses," are covered under the provisions of Chapter 25, "Existing Mercantile Occupancies." These include, for example, supermarkets, department stores, and other occupancies that display and sell merchandise. Also not included are the assembly portions of city halls, town halls, and courthouses, which are covered by Chapter 9, "Existing Assembly Occupancies."

The following constitute business occupancies and are covered by the provisions of Chapter 27:

1. Those occupancies used for the transaction of business (other than those classified as mercantile occupancies).

2. Those occupancies used for keeping accounts and records and for similar purposes.

Items (1) and (2) include: doctors' offices, dentists' offices (*see Chapter 13 for ambulatory health care centers*), and general offices, as well as city halls, town halls, and courthouses, all of which have areas for keeping books and records and transacting public business. Other occupancies included under the definition of business occupancies are service facilities common to office buildings, such as newsstands, lunch counters (serving fewer than 50 people), barber shops, and beauty parlors.

Also, by reference in Chapter 11, college classroom buildings are considered office buildings.

27-1.5 **Classification of Hazard of Contents.**

27-1.5.1 The contents of business occupancies shall be classified as ordinary hazard in accordance with Section 4-2.

Most occupancy chapters refer to Section 4-2 for classification of hazard of contents. However, the requirement of 27-1.5.1 emphasizes that, unless an extraordinarily hazardous situation exists, the contents of business occupancies must be classified as ordinary hazard. This wording is intended to prevent the user from classifying the hazard of contents as high hazard except where a combustible load far in excess of the usual, yet considerable, quantity of boxed records and paper files exists. Isolated hazardous areas within the overall ordinary hazard business occupancy, such as storage rooms, must be protected or separated in accordance with the requirements of 27-3.2.

27-1.5.2 For purposes of the design of an automatic sprinkler system, a business occupancy shall be classified as "light hazard occupancy," as identified by NFPA 13, *Standard for the Installation of Sprinkler Systems.*

The classification of hazard of contents listed and defined in Section 4-2 has little bearing on or relationship to the hazard classification in NFPA 13, *Standard for the Installation of Sprinkler Systems.*[2] Therefore, an ordinary hazard business occupancy might be protected by a light hazard sprinkler system.

Paragraph 27-1.5.2 was written to clarify that contents classified by the *Code* as "ordinary" for the purpose of life safety are not always classified as ordinary under NFPA 13, *Standard for the Installation of Sprinkler Systems*. Paragraph 27-1.5.2 states that, for purposes of sprinkler design, the anticipated fuel load of business occupancies in Chapter 27 is classed as "light hazard."

27-1.6 Minimum Construction Requirements. No requirements.

The provisions of a local or state building code may apply.

Some occupancy chapters, such as Chapters 12 and 13, which address the life safety needs of nonambulatory health care occupants, require a minimum building construction type to help ensure the structural integrity required for a lengthy evacuation or for safe refuge within the building. Because business occupancies are normally occupied by those who are ambulatory, and since they do not provide sleeping accommodations, there are no minimum construction requirements imposed.

27-1.7 Occupant Load.

27-1.7.1* For purposes of determining required means of egress, the occupant load of business buildings or parts of buildings used for business purposes shall be no less than one person per 100 sq ft (9.3 sq m) of gross floor area. The occupant load for parts of buildings used for other purposes shall be calculated using occupant load factors associated with the use.

A-27-1.7.1 In calculating the occupant load of a business occupancy, it is important to base the calculation on the actual uses of the various building areas. For example, given that buildings having educational uses above grade 12 are for the most part business occupancies because they are exempted from being classed as educational occupancies under Chapters 10 and 11, occupant load factors of 20 sq ft (1.9 sq m) net for classroom areas and 50 sq ft (4.6 sq m) net for instructional laboratory areas should be used. Occupant load calculations for conference rooms should be based on 7 or 15 sq ft

(0.65 or 1.4 sq m) net per person. For typical office areas, the occupant load calculation should be based on the 100 sq ft (9.3 sq m) gross factor.

Because the number of people expected to occupy certain types of office buildings can be determined with a great degree of accuracy (e.g., by means of a company's detailed account of its office space), it may prove beneficial to compare such a figure with one calculated on the basis of one person per 100 sq ft (9.3 sq m) of gross floor area (*see 27-1.7.1*). In office occupancies where people work in highly concentrated groups (such as a bullpen or secretarial pool area often associated with government operations), the actual number of people occupying a space may exceed the figure calculated by gross area. As emphasized in Section 5-3, where this is the case, the exit capacity must be designed to accommodate the larger, actual occupant load. Note that the converse is not true; that is, if the actual occupant load is less than the gross area calculation, the *Code* still requires that the gross area calculation be used to determine the required exit capacity.

SECTION 27-2   Means of Egress Requirements

27-2.1 General.

27-2.1.1 All means of egress shall be in accordance with Chapter 5 and this chapter.

27-2.1.2 If, owing to differences in grade, any street floor exits are at points above or below the street or ground level, such exits shall comply with the provisions for exits from upper floors or floors below the street floor.

Figure 27-3 illustrates a case where two floors qualify as street floors, because each has one side located at a ground level. Note, however, that each floor has its other sides located either above or below the building's other ground level. As a result, these floors must have their exits arranged to allow horizontal travel to the exterior at one end of the floor and vertical travel (either up or down to ground level) at the other end of the floor.

The exit capacity of the doors to the exterior on Floor 1 must accommodate that portion of the occupant load from an upper floor that is expected to travel down to and through the exits to the exterior from Floor 1 in addition to the portion of the Floor 1 occupant load assigned to that exit. The reverse is true for Floor 2, which must increase the size of its exterior exit capacity to accommodate occupants traveling up from Floor 1, as well as those traveling down to and through the exterior exits on Floor 2. Paragraphs 5-3.1.4, 5-3.1.5, and 27-2.3.3 explain how to add exit capacity based on the number of occupants expected to discharge from floors above and below the street floor. Figure 27-6 provides an example of how to calculate exit capacity for a street floor such as that illustrated by Floor 2 in Figure 27-3.

27-2.1.3 Where two or more floors below the street floor are occupied for business use, the same stairs, escalators, or ramps may serve each.

Exception: No inside open stairway, escalator, or ramp shall serve as a required egress facility from more than one floor level.

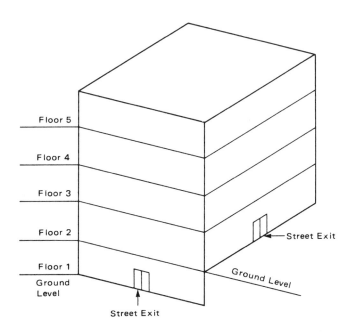

Figure 27-3. Business Occupancy with Two Street Floors. The exit capacity of each street floor must comply with 27-2.3.3. (See also Figure 27-6.)

This provision prohibits the use of unenclosed interior stairs, unenclosed interior escalators, or unenclosed interior ramps as exit access for more than one floor; it does not establish permission for the use of an open stairway, open escalator, or open ramp. See 27-3.1, which addresses the protection of business occupancy vertical openings, to determine if the stairway, escalator, or ramp is permitted to be unenclosed. It is important to remember that the width of the stair, escalator, or ramp is determined by the floor with the largest occupant load. This ensures that a stair or other component of a means of egress will accommodate the population of any floor it serves.

27-2.1.4 Floor levels below the street floor used only for storage, heating, and other service equipment and not subject to business occupancy shall have exits in accordance with Chapter 29.

A significant reduction in the number and size of exits is allowed for floors located below the street floor that are used only for storage, heating and other service equipment, and that are not subject to business occupancy use. This is permitted because the expected population of such floors will be well below that of a floor used as a typical business occupancy. Also refer to Section 5-12, which now specifically governs boiler rooms and similar spaces.

27-2.2 Means of Egress Components.

27-2.2.1 Components of means of egress shall be limited to the types described in 27-2.2.2 through 27-2.2.11.

27-2.2.2 Doors.

27-2.2.2.1 Doors shall comply with 5-2.1.

27-2.2.2.2* Locks complying with 5-2.1.5.1 Exception No. 2 shall be permitted only on principal entrance/exit doors.

A-27-2.2.2.2 The term "principal entrance/exit doors" is intended to imply doors that the authority having jurisdiction can be reasonably assured will be unlocked in order for the facility to do business.

This provision permits only the principal entrance/exit doors of a business occupancy to be equipped with the special key-operated dead bolt lock described by the provisions of Exception No. 2 to 5-2.1.5.1, which must be easily determined to be locked by means such as a flag indicator that can be seen at some distance from the door. Other doors along the perimeter of the building are prohibited from being equipped with a key-operated dead bolt, because it cannot be guaranteed that these locks will be disengaged simultaneously when the principal entrance/exit door is unlocked each day at the opening of business. (*See Figure 27-4.*)

27-2.2.2.3 The reentry provisions of 5-2.1.5.2 need not be met. (*See 5-2.1.5.2 Exception No. 3.*)

If the application of Exception No. 3 to 5-2.1.5.2 was not specifically recognized by this paragraph, the basic requirements of 5-2.1.5.2, which mandate reentry capabilities from stairwells back onto all floors of the building, would have applied. In recognizing Exception No. 3, the *Code* exempts existing business occupancies from the reentry provisions.

27-2.2.2.4 Special locking arrangements in accordance with 5-2.1.6 are permitted.

Use of the delay release device covered by 5-2.1.6 is allowed on any door in recognition of the security needs of a business occupancy. The building must be protected throughout by an approved automatic sprinkler system or automatic fire detection system in order to apply the delayed release locking provisions. In effect, the allowable 15- or 30-second delay will be experienced only under nonfire conditions or very early in a fire's growth, since the door must be usable immediately upon sprinkler operation, smoke or heat detection, or loss of power that controls the locking mechanism.

27-2.2.2.5 Where horizontal or vertical security grilles or doors are used as part of the required means of egress from a tenant space, such grilles or doors shall comply with 5-2.1.4.1 Exception No. 3.

Although Exception No. 3 to 5-2.1.4.1 establishes provisions for the arrangement and use of horizontal or vertical security grilles or doors, it requires that an occupancy chapter specifically recognize the use of such security grilles or doors. Paragraph 27-2.2.2.5 provides this recognition for business occupancies.

27-2.2.2.6 Revolving doors shall comply with 5-2.1.10.

The provisions of 5-2.1.10 specify that the use of a revolving door, regardless of whether it is permitted as part of the required means of egress, requires a conforming side-hinged swinging door to be positioned and usable within the same wall as, and located within 10 ft (3 m) of, the revolving door. This helps to ensure that, once people move toward the door, if the collapsibility and other safety features of the door should fail and render it unusable, egress from the vicinity would still be possible without retracing steps and perhaps traveling toward the fire.

Existing revolving doors may continue to be used without having to meet some of the more stringent requirements applicable to new revolving doors if such exemption is approved by the authority having jurisdiction. (*See 5-2.1.10.*)

27-2.2.3 Stairs.

27-2.2.3.1 Stairs shall comply with 5-2.2.

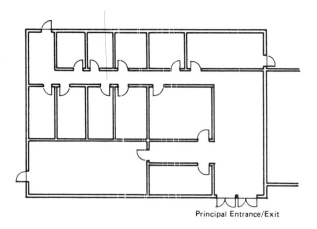

Principal Entrance/Exit

Figure 27-4. Principal Entrance/Exit. The concept of a principal entrance/exit as used in 27-2.2.2.2 is illustrated here.

27-2.2.3.2 Spiral stairs complying with 5-2.2.2.7 are permitted.

Note that 5-2.2.2.7 permits spiral stairs to serve only an occupant load of five or fewer persons. Spiral stairs may be effectively used in business occupancies to provide exit access from small mezzanines.

27-2.2.3.3 Winders complying with 5-2.2.2.8 are permitted.

27-2.2.4   Smokeproof Enclosures. Smokeproof enclosures shall comply with 5-2.3.

This paragraph does not mandate the use of smokeproof enclosures, but it does recognize a smokeproof enclosure as part of the means of egress system in a business occupancy only if the smokeproof enclosure meets the requirements of 5-2.3. For an example of an occupancy requiring a smokeproof enclosure, see 19-2.11.1, in which nonsprinklered, existing, high rise apartment buildings are required to be provided with smokeproof enclosures in accordance with 5-2.3.

27-2.2.5   Horizontal Exits. Horizontal exits shall comply with 5-2.4.

This paragraph does not mandate the use of horizontal exits, but it does recognize a horizontal exit as part of the means of egress system in a business occupancy only if the horizontal exit meets the requirements of 5-2.4.

27-2.2.6   Ramps. Ramps shall comply with 5-2.5.

This paragraph does not mandate the use of ramps in business occupancies, but it does recognize a ramp as part of the means of egress system only if the ramp meets the requirements of 5-2.5.

27-2.2.7   Exit Passageways. Exit passageways shall comply with 5-2.6.

This paragraph does not mandate the use of exit passageways in business occupancies, but it does recognize an exit passageway as part of the means of egress system only if the exit passageway meets the requirements of 5-2.6.

27-2.2.8   Escalators and Moving Walks. Escalators and moving walks complying with 5-2.7 are permitted.

Note that 5-2.7 allows escalators and moving walks to continue to be permitted within the required means of egress if an occupancy chapter so allows. In earlier editions of the *Code*, such escalators and moving walks may have been permitted by providing egress capacity for 75 persons. In order to qualify as exits, escalators and moving walks must also meet the requirements of 5-2.2.6, which addresses exit enclosures.

Note that escalators protected in accordance with the sprinkler-vent method, the spray nozzle method, the rolling shutter method, or the partial enclosure method do not constitute acceptable exits, but could continue to serve as exit access if previously approved as such.

27-2.2.9   Fire Escape Stairs. Fire escape stairs complying with 5-2.8 are permitted.

Note that 5-2.8.1.4 permits existing buildings to continue to use fire escape stairs for no more than 50 percent of their required exit capacity.

27-2.2.10   Fire Escape Ladders. Fire escape ladders complying with 5-2.9 are permitted.

27-2.2.11   Alternating Tread Devices. Alternating tread devices complying with 5-2.11 are permitted.

The provisions of 5-2.11, in effect, restrict the use of alternating tread devices to those locations where the *Code* recognizes the use of fire escape ladders. (*See 27-2.2.10 and 5-2.9.*)

27-2.3   Capacity of Means of Egress.

27-2.3.1 The capacity of means of egress shall be in accordance with Section 5-3.

In the business occupancy chapters of prior editions of the *Code*, specified requirements mandated that the occupant load of a mezzanine be added to that of the floor below the mezzanine for the purpose of determining the total size of the required means of egress system from the combined mezzanine and associated floor beneath. In the 1991 Edition, those requirements have been dropped from the business occupancy chapters, because a similar requirement now appears in 5-3.1.6. The new wording in Chapter 5 mandates that any required egress capacity from a mezzanine that passes through the room below must be added to the required egress capacity of that room through which the egress passes.

Figure 27-5 illustrates a case in which a mezzanine is open to the street floor. The exits from the street floor must accommodate (1) the occupant load of the street floor, (2) the occupant load of the mezzanine in accordance with 5-3.1.6, and (3) the required capacity provided by the stairs from other floors discharging through the street floor in accordance with 27-2.3.3.

To determine the exit capacity for the street floor, the occupant load of the mezzanine (1,000) is added to the occupant load of the street floor (2,000). In addition, because one-half of the exits from the upper floors discharge through the street floor, the exit capacity of the street floor must accommodate the capacity of the exit stair enclosure that discharges through that floor. The maximum occupant load on any upper floor is 2,000 (second floor), and 27-2.7, in accordance with its reference to Section 5-7, permits a maximum of one-half of the exits or the exit capacity to discharge through the street floor, provided that the provisions of 5-7.2 are met, which most typically involve the sprinklering of the level of exit discharge. Therefore, the street floor must be provided with

egress capacity for 4,000 persons or 800 in. (2,030 cm) of exit width using the factor of 0.2 in. (0.5 cm) per person for level exit components found in 5-3.3.1 (2,000 for street floor + 1,000 for mezzanine + 1,000 for upper floors = 4,000).

27-2.3.2 The minimum width of any corridor or passageway shall be 44 in. (112 cm) in the clear.

A corridor with the minimum 44-in. (112-cm) width required by 27-2.3.2 has sufficient egress capacity, calculated using the 0.2 in. (0.5 cm) capacity factor of 5-3.3.1 for level components, for 220 persons [i.e., 44 in. ÷ 0.2 in. per person (approximately 112 cm ÷ 0.5 cm per person)]. For example, in a corridor that runs from one end of a building to the other end and has an exit stair located at each end, 220 persons can travel from the midpoint of that corridor to the exit enclosure at one end, and another 220 persons can travel to the exit enclosure at the other end. Therefore, in this example, the occupant load of the floor would have to exceed 440 persons before the minimum 44-in. (112-cm) corridor width must be increased. (*Also see A-26-2.3.2.*)

27-2.3.3 Street floor exits shall be sufficient for the occupant load of the street floor plus the required capacity of stairs, ramps, escalators, and moving walks discharging through the street floor.

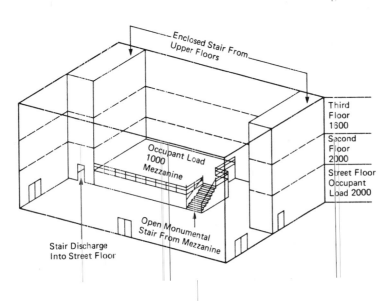

Figure 27-5. Business Occupancy with a Mezzanine Open to the Street Floor. (See second paragraph of commentary to 27.2.3.1.)

Enclosed Stair From Upper Floors

Occupant Load 1000 Mezzanine

Open Monumental Stair From Mezzanine

Stair Discharge Into Street Floor

Third Floor 1600

Second Floor 2000

Street Floor Occupant Load 2000

In 27-2.3.3, the *Code* requires that the exits for the street floor of a business occupancy have sufficient capacity to handle the occupant load of the street floor and the capacity of the exits discharging through the street floor, such as an enclosed exit stair that accommodates occupants who, when exiting the building during an emergency, must travel up from the basement area or down from the upper floors and mix with the occupants already occupying the street floor.

Since people move more quickly in the horizontal direction than in the vertical direction, it is permissible to provide less door width than stair width. For example, in business occupancies, in accordance with the egress capacity factors of 5-3.3.1, level components and ramps require only 0.2 in. (0.5 cm) of width per person, whereas stairs require 0.3 in. (0.8 cm) of width per person. As a rough approximation, for every 44 in. (112 cm) of stair discharging through the street floor, an additional 30 in. (76 cm) of door width opening to the outside from the street floor must be added. Figure 27-6 provides an example of the proper calculation method for determining the required exit capacity for the street floor.

Street floor occupant load alone	1000
plus maximum upper floor occupant load discharging back through street floor (500 ÷ 2)	250
plus basement occupant load discharging back through street floor (400 ÷ 2)	200

1450 persons × 0.2 in. (0.5 cm) per person for level exit components per 5-3.3.1 = 290 in. (737 cm) of exit width required from the street floor egress system.

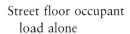

Figure 27-6. *Calculation of Exit Capacity Required for a Street Floor in Accordance with 27-2.3.3.*

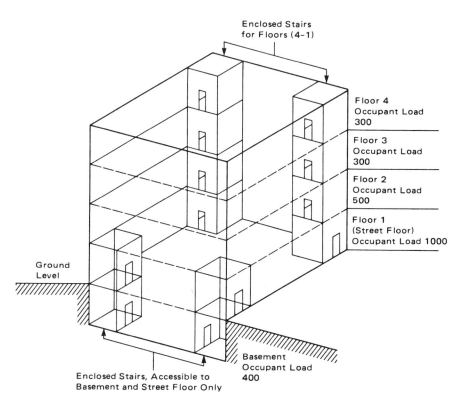

27-2.4 Number of Exits.

27-2.4.1 The number of exits shall be in accordance with 27-2.4.2. The requirements of 5-4.1.2 shall not apply.

27-2.4.2 At least two separate exits shall:

(a) Be provided on every story, and

(b) Be accessible from every part of every story and mezzanine.

Exception to (b): Exit access travel shall be permitted to be common for the distances allowed as common path of travel by 27-2.5.3.

Exception No. 1: For a room or area with a total occupant load of less than 100 persons having an exit that discharges directly to the outside at the level of exit discharge for the building, with a total distance of travel, including travel within the exit, from any point not over 100 ft (30 m), a single exit shall be permitted. Such travel shall be on the same floor level or, if traversing of stairs is required, such stairs shall not be more than 15 ft (4.5 m) in height, and they shall be provided with complete enclosures to separate them from any other part of the building, with no door openings therein. A single outside stairway in accordance with 5-2.2 shall be permitted to serve all floors allowed within the 15-ft (4.5-m) vertical travel limitation.

Exception No. 2: Any business occupancy not over three stories and not exceeding an occupant load of 30 people per floor shall be permitted with a single separate exit to each floor if the total travel distance to the outside of the building does not exceed 100 ft (30 m), and if such exit is enclosed in accordance with 5-1.3 and serves no other levels and discharges directly to the outside. A single outside stairway in accordance with 5-2.2 shall be permitted to serve all floors.

Exception No. 3: A single means of egress shall be permitted from a mezzanine within a business occupancy, provided that the common path of travel does not exceed 75 ft (23 m) or 100 ft (30 m) if protected throughout by an approved automatic sprinkler system in accordance with Section 7-7.

Exception No. 4: A single exit shall be permitted for a maximum two-story single tenant space or building that is protected throughout by an approved automatic sprinkler system in accordance with Section 7-7 if the total travel to the outside does not exceed 100 ft (30 m).

The provisions of 27-2.4.2, which apply to the required number of exits for business occupancies, have been revised for this edition of the *Code* to clarify that any level that constitutes a story must have at least two exits located on that story. This means that the occupants of the story must be able to enter an exit (e.g., an enclosed exit stair on an upper floor of a multistory building) without having to travel to some other story to reach the entrance to the exit. Since a mezzanine that meets the maximum one-third area rule of 6-2.5 does not constitute a story (*see 6-2.5.1 and 6-2.5.2.1*), two exits are not required on the mezzanine but (1) the criteria of 27-2.4.2(b) must be met with respect to providing access to two separate exits, or (2) the provisions of the Exception to (b) or Exception No. 3 must be met.

The Exception applies only to subpart (b) of 27-2.4.2, which requires access to two separate exits from every part of every level (i.e., story or mezzanine). The exception indicates that 27-2.5.3 allows the occupant to travel in one direction for a maximum distance (i.e., the common path allowance) before requiring access in two separate directions. Therefore, although the story or mezzanine must eventually provide access to two exits in accordance with 27-2.4.2(b), that access need be available only at the point where the allowable common path is expended.

Figures 27-7 and 27-8 illustrate two cases where a single exit from a room or area in a business occupancy is allowed (*see Exception No. 1 to 27-2.4.2*). In the first case, the travel distance from the area is located on the same floor level as the exit. In the second case, stairs must be traversed.

The criteria for allowing the single exit are:

1. An occupant load less than 100 persons;
2. Direct exit to a street or to an open exterior area at ground level;
3. Total distance of no more than 100 ft (30 m) from any point in the room to the exterior.

Note that this is total distance from any point to the exterior, not travel distance as measured in Section 5-6. Therefore, the total distance includes the distance traveled on enclosed stairs (exit);

4. Any stairs must be no more than 15 ft (4.5 m) in height; and

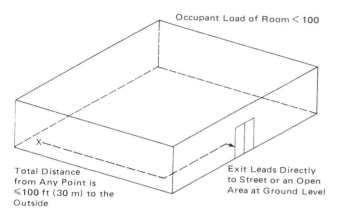

Figure 27-7. *Single Exit from an Area or Room in a Business Occupancy. Travel from area to exit is horizontal. (See Exception No. 1 to 27-2.4.2.)*

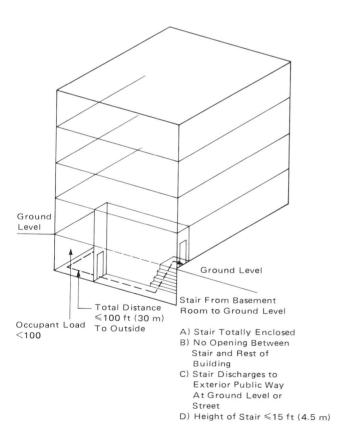

Figure 27-8. *Single Exit from an Area or Room in a Business Occupancy Where Stairs Must Be Traversed. (See Exception No. 1 to 27-2.4.2 .)*

5. Any stairs must be completely enclosed with no door openings between the stair enclosure and the rest of the building, or stairs must meet the requirements applicable to outside stairs. (*See 5-2.2.6.3.*)

Failure to meet any of these conditions requires two exits from the floor in question.

Figure 27-9 illustrates a single exit from the third floor of a business occupancy as permitted by Exception No.2. The criteria for allowing a single exit are:

1. The building is not more than three stories high;
2. Each floor has no more than 30 occupants;
3. Total distance from any point on any floor to the exterior at ground level is no more than 100 ft (30 m), including travel over stairs. Note that this is total distance from any point to the exterior, not travel distance as measured in Section 5-6;
4. The stair is not used by, nor does it have an opening to, any other floor; and
5. The stair is totally enclosed or meets the requirements applicable to outside stairs. (*See 5-2.2.6.3.*)

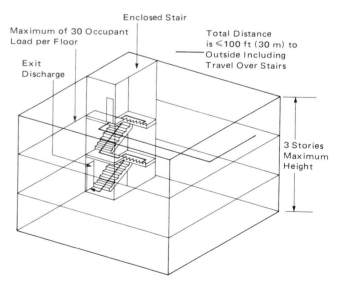

Figure 27-9. *Single Exit from Third Floor of a Business Occupancy. Stair is totally enclosed, has opening onto a building floor only at third floor, and discharges directly to street with no communication at second and first floors. A similar, but separate, arrangement could be provided for the second floor of the same building.*

Failure to meet any of these conditions requires two exits from the floor in question.

While the Exception to (b) allows common access to the two required means of egress for some limited distances, Exception No. 3 exempts a mezzanine in a business from providing a point where access to two exits is available if the single means of egress leads to an exit within the same limited distances as those allowed for common path of travel. [*See the Exception to 27-2.4.2(b) and 27-2.5.3 and its exceptions.*]

Exception No. 4 was developed to provide some relief from the requirement mandating two separate exits on every story that affects typical townhouse-type, sprinklered business occupancies. These townhouse-type business occupancies typically have two stories with an open interior stair and are of such limited size that, if a second stair were added, little usable space would remain, and the two stairs would, in effect, be located side by side. The exception offers any single tenant space in a fully sprinklered building with a maximum of two stories, or any sprinklered single tenant building with a maximum of two stories, the option of providing only one exit if the total travel distance to the outside does not exceed 100 ft (30 m).

27-2.5 Arrangement of Means of Egress.

27-2.5.1 Exits shall be arranged in accordance with Section 5-5.

27-2.5.2 No dead-end corridor shall exceed 50 ft (15 m).

Exception: Existing dead-end corridors exceeding 50 ft (15 m) may continue to be used subject to the approval of the authority having jurisdiction and the travel distance requirements of 27-2.6.

A-27-2.5.2 **Exception.** It is recognized that excessive dead ends exist and in some cases are impractical to eliminate. The authority having jurisdiction may allow these to continue, taking into consideration any or all of the following:

Tenant arrangement.
Automatic sprinkler protection.
Smoke detection.
Exit remoteness.

Because they have separate and distinct requirements, dead-end corridors and common path of travel are separated by the *Code* into two distinct and separate paragraphs.

Three typical dead-end corridors are illustrated in Figure 27-10.

27-2.5.3 No common path of travel shall exceed 75 ft (23 m).

Exception No. 1: A common path of travel shall be permitted for the first 100 ft (30 m) on a story protected throughout by an approved automatic sprinkler system in accordance with Section 7-7.

Exception No. 2: A single tenant space that does not exceed an occupant load of 30 people shall be permitted to have a single exit access, provided the corridor to which that exit access leads does not have a dead end in excess of 50 ft (15 m).

Exception No. 3*: Existing excessive common paths of travel may continue to be used subject to the approval of the authority having jurisdiction and the travel distance requirements of 27-2.6.

A-27-2.5.3 **Exception No. 3.** It is recognized that excessive common paths of travel exist and in some cases are impractical to eliminate. The authority having jurisdiction may allow these to continue, taking into consideration any or all of the following:

Tenant arrangement.
Automatic sprinkler protection.
Smoke detection.
Exit remoteness.

The 1985 Edition of the *Code* limited common path of travel to 50 ft (15 m) or 75 ft (23 m) or 100 ft (30 m) under various detector and sprinkler exceptions. In the 1988 Edition, the provisions of Chapter 5 that applied to the point where measurement of travel distance and common path begins for small rooms were revised, and the allowable common path was increased without either reducing the level of safety to life or imposing a hardship on existing buildings.

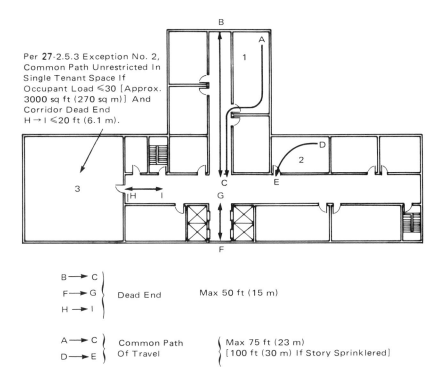

Per **27**-2.5.3 Exception No. 2, Common Path Unrestricted In Single Tenant Space If Occupant Load ≤30 [Approx. 3000 sq ft (270 sq m)] And Corridor Dead End H → I ≤20 ft (6.1 m).

Figure 27-10. *Illustration of Dead Ends and Common Path of Travel.*

B → C
F → G   } Dead End   Max 50 ft (15 m)
H → I

A → C } Common Path { Max 75 ft (23 m)
D → E } Of Travel   { [100 ft (30 m) If Story Sprinklered]

See the commentary following 5-5.1.6 for a detailed discussion on common path of travel. Also see the commentary following the Exception to 27-2.4.2(b), which allows a portion of the access to a single exit or multiple exits to be common.

The restriction on common path of travel is separate and distinct from the restriction on dead-end corridors. Although a common path of travel may at times involve a dead-end corridor, and dead ends may involve common path of travel, this is not always the case. For an example, see the elevator lobby illustrated in Figure 27-10, which is a dead-end corridor but not a common path of travel.

Common path of travel is measured similarly to travel distance (*see Section 5-6*), with the exception that, instead of being terminated at the entrance to an exit, common path of travel measurement often ends before the exit entrance, because it is terminated at that point where the occupant has a choice of two distinct and separate paths to an exit (*see definition of common path of travel in Chapter 3*). It should be noted that the starting point for

measurement of common path of travel is the same as the starting point (*see 5-6.2*) for travel distance measurement. Specifically, the starting point is 1 ft (30.5 cm) from the most remote point. (*See rooms 1 and 2 in Figure 27-10.*)

Figure 27-11 provides an additional illustration of common path of travel in a business occupancy. (*Also see the commentary in Section 5-5 on arrangement of means of egress.*)

Exception No. 1 allows the common path of travel to be extended to 100 ft (30 m) on stories protected throughout by an approved supervised automatic sprinkler system. The exception recognizes the additional level of safety to life that an automatic sprinkler system provides and allows added flexibility when designing the location of corridors and exits in buildings where approved sprinkler systems are installed.

Exception No. 2 exempts a single tenant space with a maximum occupant load of not more than 30 people [normally, approximately 3,000 sq ft (270 sq m), based on the business occupant load factor of 100 sq ft (9.3 sq m) per

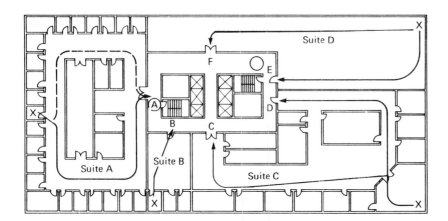

Figure 27-11.   Common Path of Travel.

26-1.7.1] from the common path of travel requirement, provided that the single door from that tenant space leads to a corridor that does not have a dead end in excess of 50 ft (15 m). (*See room 3 in Figure 27-10.*)

Questions are often asked concerning the conditions under which an office space or suite requires two exit access doors. The common path of travel restriction regulates where an office space requires two exit access doors. If the common path of travel is exceeded, a second door from the office space is required. It must be positioned so that any resulting common path of travel would comply with the allowable distances. In addition, the second door must be remotely located from the first door (*see 5-5.1.4*), and each door must lead to remote exits by means of remote paths. Therefore, in a single requirement, the *Code* not only regulates the number of exit access doors required from an office area, but also the arrangement of these doors.

In Suite A, as shown in Figure 27-11, the travel from point X to point A is a common path of travel; although there are two routes to reach the corridor, they both merge at common point A. In Suite B, the travel from point X to point B is a common path of travel, but it does not appear to exceed the 75-ft (23-m) maximum allowable common path; if it were in excess of 75 ft (23 m) but no more than 100 ft (30 m), it would be permitted by Exception No. 1 to 27-2.5.3 (story sprinklered); if it were in excess of 75 ft (23 m) and there were no more than 50 ft (15) of dead-end corridor outside the tenant space, it would be allowed under Exception No. 2 to 27-2.5.3 (maximum 30-person single tenant space).

Although Suites C and D do not have common paths of travel, the remoteness of the two exit access doors from each suite is questionable. (*See 5-5.1.4.*)

27-2.6 Travel Distance to Exits. Travel distance to exits, measured in accordance with Section 5-6, shall be no more than 200 ft (60 m).

Exception: Travel distance shall not exceed 300 ft (91 m) in buildings protected throughout by an approved automatic sprinkler system in accordance with Section 7-7.

In accordance with Section 5-6, travel distance requirements apply to only the first (or nearest) exit from a given point in a building. In other words, the 200-ft (60-m) travel distance limit requires that at least one exit must be located within 200 ft (60 m) of any point in the building; it does not require that all exits must be within 200 ft (60 m) of that point in the building.

The exception allows for the travel distance to be increased to 300 ft (91 m) if the building is protected throughout by an approved automatic sprinkler system. It recognizes the additional level of safety to life that a complete automatic sprinkler system provides and allows added flexibility in the design and arrangement of the means of egress.

27-2.7 Discharge from Exits. Exit discharge shall comply with Section 5-7.

27-2.8 Illumination of Means of Egress. Means of egress shall be illuminated in accordance with Section 5-8.

27-2.9   Emergency Lighting.

27-2.9.1   Emergency lighting shall be provided in accordance with Section 5-9 in any building where:

(a) The building is two or more stories in height above the level of exit discharge, or

(b) The occupancy is subject to 100 or more occupants above or below the level of exit discharge, or

(c) The occupancy is subject to 1,000 or more total occupants.

If any of the three conditions of 27-2.9.1 exist, emergency lighting as specified in Section 5-9 is required for the building. Note that condition (a) specifically mentions buildings that have two floors located above the level of exit discharge, or a minimum of three floors.

27-2.9.2   Emergency lighting in accordance with Section 5-9 shall be provided for all windowless or underground structures meeting the definition of 30-1.3.

27-2.10   **Marking of Means of Egress.**   Means of egress shall have signs in accordance with Section 5-10.

27-2.11   **Special Features.**   (Reserved.)

SECTION 27-3   Protection

27-3.1   Protection of Vertical Openings.

27-3.1.1   Every stairway, elevator shaft, escalator opening, and other vertical opening shall be enclosed or protected in accordance with Section 6-2.

Exception No. 1: Unprotected vertical openings connecting not more than three floors used for business occupancy only shall be permitted in accordance with 6-2.4.5.

Note that 6-2.4.5 requires that, if the communicating space (i.e., the vertical opening and all areas open to it) contains ordinary hazard contents, it must be protected by automatic sprinklers. In accordance with 27-1.5, business occupancies are considered ordinary hazard.

Exception No. 2: A vertical opening enclosure shall not be required for a vertical opening where:

(a) The vertical opening connects only two adjacent floors, neither of which is a basement, and

(b) The vertical opening is not a required means of egress, and

(c) The vertical opening is not connected with corridors or other stairways.

Exception No. 2 to 27-3.1.1 permits, for example, a two-level office or reference library in an office building to have an unenclosed convenience stair. Item (a) restricts the application of this exception to two levels only. Item (b) requires that the stairs cannot be part of the means of egress; therefore, the space would have to have access to exits on both levels in order that occupants would not have to rely on the open stair as part of the required means of egress. Item (c) requires that the areas connected by the opening be separated from corridors and other stairways.

Exception No. 3: Atriums in accordance with 6-2.4.6 are permitted.

Exception No. 3 recognizes an atrium without mandating requirements other than those provided by 6-2.4.6.

Exception No. 4: Exit access stairs shall be permitted to be unenclosed in two-story single tenant spaces provided with a single exit in accordance with the provisions of Exception No. 4 to 27-2.4.2.

Exception No. 4 completes the single exit package for townhouse-type, and similarly arranged, business occupancies by allowing the single means of egress to include an unenclosed stair. (*See the commentary associated with Exception No. 4 to 27-2.4.2.*)

Exception No. 5: In buildings protected throughout by an approved automatic sprinkler system in accordance with Section 7-7, vertical unprotected openings shall be permitted if no unprotected vertical opening serves as any part of any required exit facility, and all required exits consist of smokeproof enclosures in accordance with 5-2.3, outside stairs in accordance with 5-2.2, or horizontal exits in accordance with 5-2.4.

Application of Exception No. 5 to 27-3.1.1 requires not only that the building be protected with complete automatic sprinkler protection, but all building exits must be either smokeproof enclosures, outside stairs, horizontal exits, or doors leading directly to the outside at ground level. Otherwise, the unprotected vertical openings must be suitably enclosed.

27-3.1.2   Floors below the street floor used for storage or other than business occupancy shall have no unprotected openings to business occupancy floors.

The requirement of 27-3.1.2 prevents the possibility that a fire in a hazardous area with a high fuel load (e.g., areas used for shops, repairs, or storage of maintenance supplies, files, and records) might directly expose the floor of exit discharge through a vertical opening that is unprotected. A fire in a basement can quickly cause exits and exit discharges located on the street floor to become unusable when smoke and heat rise.

27-3.2   Protection from Hazards.

27-3.2.1*   Hazardous areas, including but not limited to areas used for general storage, boiler or furnace rooms, fuel storage, janitor closets, and maintenance shops including woodworking and painting areas shall:

(a) Be separated from other parts of the building by fire barriers having a fire resistance rating of not less than 1 hour with all openings therein protected by ¾-hour fire protection rated self-closing fire doors, or

(b) The area shall be protected by an automatic extinguishing system in accordance with Section 7-7.

A-27-3.2.1   It is not the intent of this provision to require that rooms inside individual tenant spaces, used to store routine office supplies for that tenant, be separated or sprinklered.

27-3.2.2   High hazard content areas, as defined in Section 4-2, shall be protected by both fire resistance rated construction and automatic extinguishing equipment.

Paragraphs 27-3.2.1 and 27-3.2.2 reflect the intent of Section 6-4, which (1) requires separation of a hazardous area from the remainder of the occupancy by means of suitable construction, or (2) mandates the installation

of an automatic extinguishing system in the hazardous area, or (3) requires both where the hazard is severe. For this edition of the *Code*, 6-4.1 has been revised to include a concept that applied to assembly and educational occupancies in previous editions; in the case of new construction or renovations of existing buildings, where a hazardous area is protected by automatic sprinklers, rather than by enclosure with fire barriers of 1-hour fire resistance rating and doors of 45-minute fire protection rating, the hazardous area must be enclosed by walls and doors that are at least smoke resisting. (*See 6-4.1.*)

Section 6-4 contains two additional mandatory provisions. One is a reference to NFPA 30, *Flammable and Combustible Liquids Code,*[3] and the other is a reference to NFPA 45, *Standard on Fire Protection for Laboratories Using Chemicals.*[4] (*See 6-4.3 and 6-4.4.*)

27-3.3   Interior Finish.

27-3.3.1   Interior finish on walls and ceilings of exits and of enclosed corridors furnishing access thereto or ways of travel therefrom shall be Class A or Class B in accordance with Section 6-5.

27-3.3.2   In office areas, Class A, Class B, or Class C interior finish shall be provided in accordance with Section 6-5.

27-3.3.3   Interior Floor Finish. No requirements.

Unlike Chapter 26, which addresses new business occupancies and regulates interior floor finish in corridors and exits, Chapter 27 has no interior floor finish requirements for existing installations. If floor finish materials in corridors and exits are replaced or added, 1-5.6 requires compliance with the provisions of 26-3.3.3. (*See the commentary following 26-3.3.3.*)

27-3.4   Detection, Alarm, and Communication Systems.

See Supplement 2.

27-3.4.1   General. A fire alarm system in accordance with Section 7-6 shall be provided in any business occupancy where:

(a) The building is two or more stories in height above the level of exit discharge, or

(b) The occupancy is subject to 100 or more occupants above or below the level of exit discharge, or

(c) The occupancy is subject to 1,000 or more total occupants.

A fire alarm system is required in a business occupancy under the same conditions as those under which emergency lighting is required (*see 27-2.9.1*). If any one of the three conditions listed above exists, a fire alarm system must be provided. Note that "two or more stories in height above the level of exit discharge" usually describes a building with three or more stories.

27-3.4.2 Initiation. Initiation of the required fire alarm system shall be by manual means per 7-6.2.1(a).

Exception No. 1: Initiation shall be permitted by means of an approved automatic fire detection system in accordance with 7-6.2.1(b) that provides protection throughout the building.

Exception No. 2: Initiation shall be permitted by means of an approved automatic sprinkler system in accordance with 7-6.2.1(c) that provides protection throughout the building.

This paragraph clearly states that a fire alarm system is required, but the requirement for manual pull stations is waived if the system is activated by either an automatic fire detection system providing protection throughout the building or an automatic sprinkler system providing protection throughout the building. This does not exempt the fire alarm system, but exempts only the manual pull stations.

27-3.4.3 Notification.

27-3.4.3.1 During all times that the building is occupied (*see 5-2.1.1.3*), the required fire alarm system shall:

(a) Sound a general audible alarm throughout the building, or

(b) Sound an audible alarm in a continuously attended location for purposes of initiating emergency action.

This paragraph requires that, when the fire alarm system is actuated (*see 27-3.4.2*), the system shall either automatically sound a general alarm throughout the building, or, if a continuously attended location is provided (as is often the case in high rise or other large office buildings), the alarm may sound at that location only, with initiation of the appropriate emergency action occurring at that location.

27-3.4.3.2 Occupant Notification. Occupant notification shall be by means of live voice public address system announcement originating from the attended location where the alarm signal is received. (*See 27-3.4.3.1.*) The system shall be permitted to be used for other announcements. (*See 7-6.3.9 Exception No. 2.*)

Exception: Any other occupant notification means allowed by 7-6.3 shall be permitted in lieu of live voice public address system announcement.

It is preferable for a voice alarm system to be controlled from the continuously attended location referred to in 27-3.4.3.1. The exception would be used primarily in buildings where a continuously attended location is not provided and would allow either a recorded voice system or a general audible alarm.

27-3.5 Extinguishment Requirements. Portable fire extinguishers shall be provided in every business occupancy in accordance with 7-4.4.1. (*See also Section 27-4.*)

Although no requirements for automatic sprinkler systems are provided in this paragraph, 27-4.2.1 requires high rise office buildings to be protected by automatic sprinklers, or the equivalent, and Exception No. 3 to 27-3.1.1, by referencing Chapter 6, requires a building containing an atrium to be sprinklered. Additional incentives are provided to encourage sprinkler installation in connection with the following features: nonrated openings to attached parking structures (27-1.2.2); delay release hardware (27-2.2.2.4); number of exits (27-2.4.2 exceptions); common path of travel (27-2.5.3); travel distance (27-2.6); discharge of exits through the level of exit discharge (27-2.7 per Section 5-7); protection from hazards (27-3.2); interior finish (27-3.3 per Section 6-5); and deletion of manual pull stations (27-3.4.2).

27-3.6 Corridors. (Reserved.)

27-3.7 Subdivision of Building Spaces. (Reserved.)

27-3.8 **Special Features.** (Reserved.)

27-3.8.1 Nonrated glazing and opening protectives per 27-1.2.3 Exception shall be permitted between business occupancies and parking structures.

SECTION 27-4 Special Provisions

27-4.1 **Windowless or Underground Buildings.** (*See Section 30-7.*)

27-4.2 **High Rise Buildings.**

See the definition of high rise building in Chapter 3.

27-4.2.1 All high rise business occupancy buildings shall be provided with a reasonable degree of safety from fire that shall be accomplished by the installation of a complete approved automatic sprinkler system in accordance with Section 7-7 or an engineered life safety system approved by the authority having jurisdiction, which may consist of a combination of any or all of the following systems:

Partial automatic sprinkler protection.
Smoke detection alarms.
Smoke control.
Compartmentation and/or other approved systems.

The problems posed by high rise buildings with respect to safety to life, fire fighting, and fire protection in general are covered in *High-Rise Building Fires and Fire Safety*,[5] *Fighting High-Rise Building Fires — Tactics and Logistics*,[6] *and Fires in High-Rise Buildings*.[7] All three publications contain extensive bibliographies on the subject.

27-4.2.2* A limited but reasonable time shall be allowed for compliance with any part of this section commensurate with the magnitude of expenditure and the disruption of services.

A-27-4.2.2 In some cases, appreciable cost may be involved in bringing an existing occupancy into compliance. Where this is true, it would be appropriate for the authority having jurisdiction to prescribe a schedule determined jointly with the facility, allowing suitable periods of time for the correction of the various deficiencies and giving due weight to the ability of the owner to secure the necessary funds.

27-4.2.3 In addition to the above requirements, all buildings, regardless of height, shall comply with all other applicable provisions of this chapter.

Paragraph 27-4.2.3 emphasizes that the provision for the installation of automatic sprinkler protection does not preclude the need for meeting the other requirements in the *Code* unless specific exceptions for the presence of automatic sprinklers are granted in the *Code's* text.

27-4.3 **Operating Features.** (*See Chapter 31.*)

SECTION 27-5 Building Services

27-5.1 **Utilities.** Utilities shall comply with the provisions of Section 7-1.

27-5.2 **Heating, Ventilating, and Air Conditioning Equipment.** Heating, ventilating, and air conditioning equipment shall comply with the provisions of Section 7-2.

27-5.3 **Elevators, Escalators, and Conveyors.** Elevators, escalators, and conveyors shall comply with the provisions of Section 7-4.

Refer to Section 7-4 and its referenced document, ASME/ANSI A17.3, *Safety Code for Existing Elevators and Escalators*.[8] It contains design criteria and specifications for the proper arrangement of an elevator control system that will provide both automatic recall during a fire and fire fighter service features that are exclusive of the normal automatic control mode of the elevator system.

27-5.4 **Rubbish Chutes, Incinerators, and Laundry Chutes.** Rubbish chutes, incinerators, and laundry chutes shall comply with the provisions of Section 7-5.

References Cited in Commentary

[1]NFPA 101M, *Alternative Approaches to Life Safety*, National Fire Protection Association, Quincy, MA.†

[2]NFPA 13, *Standard for the Installation of Sprinkler Systems*, National Fire Protection Association, Quincy, MA, 1991.

[3]NFPA 30, *Flammable and Combustible Liquids Code*, National Fire Protection Association, Quincy, MA, 1990.

[4]NFPA 45, *Standard on Fire Protection for Laboratories Using Chemicals*, National Fire Protection Association, Quincy, MA, 1991.

[5]*High-Rise Building Fires and Fire Safety*, NFPA SPP-18, National Fire Protection Association, Boston, MA, 1973.

[6]Robert F. Mendes, *Fighting High-Rise Building Fires—Tactics and Logistics*, NFPA FSP-44, National Fire Protection Association, Boston, MA, 1975.

[7]*Fires in High-Rise Buildings*, NFPA SPP-25, National Fire Protection Association, Boston, MA, 1974.

[8]ASME/ANSI A17.3, *Safety Code for Existing Elevators and Escalators*, American Society of Mechanical Engineers, 345 East 47th Street, New York, NY, 10017, 1987.

† The edition of NFPA 101M that corresponds with the 1991 *Life Safety Code* will be published in 1992.

28

Industrial Occupancies

(See also Chapter 31.)

Industrial occupancies is a broad classification. The following are examples of industrial occupancies:

Factories of all kinds	Gas plants
Laboratories	Refineries
Dry cleaning plants	Sawmills
Power plants	Postal central sorting facilities
Pumping stations	Telephone exchanges
Laundries	Recycling plants
Food processing plants	Autobody and repair shops
Hangers (for servicing/maintenance)	

The national fire incident data bases indicate that the classifications of industrial and manufacturing properties accounted for 27,500 structure fires per year as reported to U.S. fire departments from 1984 to 1988. These fires led to 45 civilian (i.e., nonfire-service personnel) deaths and 858 civilian injuries a year as well. Only one-fourth of the people killed by fire in those properties from 1980 to 1988 were outside the room of fire origin when the fire began.

Many industrial properties pose the particular hazard of rapid fire development as a result of explosion or flash fire. This fact is underscored each year in the detailed descriptions of multiple-death and large-loss fires. In the 1980s, eight industrial fires killed 10 or more people, although three of those fires took place in coal mines, which are addressed as special structures by the *Life Safety Code.* The other five consisted of two fireworks manufacturing plant incidents, one in Oklahoma in 1985 and one in Tennessee in 1983; a 1980 metal manufacturing plant incident in New York; a 1984 refinery incident in Illinois, where the 17 dead included many employees who acted as fire fighters; and a 1989 polyolefin plant incident in Texas, which also ranks as the fourth highest property loss from fire in U.S. history, after adjusting for inflation, and the highest loss to involve only one property.

SECTION 28-1   General Requirements

28-1.1   Application. The requirements of this chapter apply to both new and existing industrial occupancies. Industrial occupancies include factories making products of all kinds and properties used for operations such as processing, assembling, mixing, packaging, finishing or decorating, repairing, and similar operations.

Unlike most occupancies covered in the *Code*, both new and existing industrial occupancies are covered in one chapter. Where the requirements vary, it is common for exceptions that apply to existing industrial occupancies to appear or for additional requirements that are limited to new industrial occupancies to be included.

The statistics provided by the national fire incident data bases demonstrate that the potential loss of life from fire in an industrial occupancy is directly related to the hazard of the industrial operation or process. The majority of multiple-death industrial fires is the result of flash fires caused by highly combustible material or explosions involving combustible dusts, flammable liquids, or gases.

Although industrial fire losses constitute a high percentage of the annual property loss from fire, such fires have not, as a general rule, resulted in extensive loss of life. A number of operating features common to industrial occupancies have contributed to this favorable record. Continued emphasis on proper exit design and maintenance and day-to-day attention to industrial safety and training programs can help to perpetuate this trend.

One of the major features to be considered in the design of an industrial building's life safety system is the widespread utilization of automatic sprinkler protection. Originally developed for industrial property protection, the automatic sprinkler has also been largely responsible for an excellent life safety record in industrial occupancies. This record has been recognized by the fire protection community, as evidenced by the widespread use of automatic sprinkler systems for life safety protection in buildings with significant hazards to life. Automatic sprinkler protection in industrial occupancies has been a principal factor in ensuring safety to life through the control of fire spread. Limiting the size of a fire by means of sprinklers provides sufficient time for the safe evacuation of occupants exposed to fire. The contribution of the automatic sprinkler to safety to life can be fully appreciated only when the wide range of fire risks associated with the many processes used in an industrial facility is recognized.

Employees and other occupants of industrial buildings are generally ambulatory and capable of quick response to fires. They are also able to exit rapidly once properly alerted. In order to capitalize on this employee capability, many industrial facilities include life safety measures in their emergency preplanning. A well-conceived plan provides a valuable tool in preventing loss of life. Provisions that should be part of the emergency preplan include measures for alerting employees, identification and posting of exit access routes, establishment of group assembly areas for occupants once they have evacuated the building, and procedures for determining that all employees have safely evacuated. Responsibilities are usually established and assigned in the preplan to ensure that the tasks necessary to facilitate safe evacuation of the building are performed. The preplan should routinely be evaluated through simulated fire exercises and fire drills. Only through the execution of such drills can flaws in the preplan be recognized and modified.

Although the life safety record in industry has been relatively good, a major problem may be emerging in the trend toward constructing large industrial plants that house hazardous operations. The introduction of new materials, such as extensive quantities of plastics, has increased the need for additional measures to help protect employees from fire. Compared with industrial buildings of the early twentieth century, the modern industrial complex has placed a larger number of employees in a more complex and increasingly hazardous environment. This trend has increased the need for industrial management to concentrate on life safety principles, not only during the design stage, but also during day-to-day plant operations.

As part of their employee training programs, most industrial firms include education in the use of first aid fire fighting equipment, such as in-plant standpipes, hose, and portable fire extinguishers. Industrial training of this type, where fully utilized, has resulted in a major reduction in property loss and loss of life. Although first aid fire fighting measures are primarily a property protection measure, there is also a significant life safety benefit. In any situation where the spread of a fire is checked through effective employee action, employee life safety is also provided. If fire spread is restricted to the incipient stages, there is no significant threat to life safety.

28-1.2 **Mixed Occupancies.** In any building occupied for both industrial and other purposes, means of egress shall comply with 1-5.7.

In addition to requiring that means of egress complies with 1-5.7, which covers mixed occupancies, the intent of this paragraph is that the other life safety features addressed by the *Code* comply with 1-5.7.

28-1.3 **Special Definitions.** None.

Although no special definitions are listed in 28-1.3, industrial occupancies are subclassified and defined in 28-1.4.1 (a), (b), and (c) under the labels "general," "special purpose," and "high hazard" industrial occupancy.

28-1.4 **Classification of Occupancy.** (*See 4-1.9.*)

The method for determining the degree of hazard to life safety posed by an industrial occupancy is at best a result of personal judgment and not an exact science. The authority having jurisdiction must use judgment based on past experience, a review of reference materials, and full discussion with third parties to evaluate the life safety measures in an industrial occupancy. The *Code* establishes broad categories of occupancy classification so that the relative risks to life safety posed by various types of buildings can be assessed.

A common error made when classifying industrial occupancies is the use of risk categories for automatic sprinklers contained in NFPA 13, *Standard for the Installation of Sprinkler Systems*,[1] to determine the hazard to life safety. While the guidelines in NFPA 13 may not differ greatly from those of the *Life Safety Code* when classifying high hazard occupancies, the remaining categories in NFPA 13 are usually not suitable for the general industrial occupancy classification of the *Code*. This is particularly true when classifying low hazard occupancies, which are classified differently by NFPA 13 (i.e., light hazard) than by the *Life Safety Code*. The distinction is that the life safety industrial occupancy classification is concerned with determining the overall hazard to occupants in a manufacturing building in order to implement an adequate means of egress system, while the NFPA 13 classification system is concerned with defining the hazard

so that a sprinkler system can be designed to meet the challenge of the hazard.

To examine the conflicts between life safety occupancy classification and classifications in other fire codes, consider a metalworking plant using a flammable solvent in a dip tank coating operation. From a life safety standpoint, the normally low hazard classification of the metalworking plant should not be changed to high hazard solely because of the presence of a dip tank coater. Adequate means of safe egress that leads away from the coater is needed to ensure the safety of the occupants, but additional exits and a reduction in travel distance to an exit, as specified for a high hazard occupancy, are not required. However, if the coater is the principal piece of equipment in a separately enclosed area, that area should be considered as a high hazard industrial occupancy.

When determining the life safety hazard classification for an industrial occupancy, the authority having jurisdiction should carefully analyze the nature of that industrial operation to ensure an accurate evaluation of the hazard to occupants. A number of resources are available as aids to properly determine the degree of risk to life safety. One aid that should not be overlooked is the expertise of the industrial plant operator. The operator has available a wealth of hazard information. However, the information may be treated as confidential material to prevent competitors from learning the details of an industrial process. An enforcing authority should earn the trust of the operator by carefully handling such material. It is vital that process data be kept confidential, because once an enforcing authority is known to be a source of data on industrial secrets, further cooperation will be difficult to obtain.

Another resource is the engineering department of the company responsible for a facility's insurance coverage. In addition, discussions with officials who oversee jurisdictions where similar facilities exist and a review of NFPA literature will provide further information on a particular process and its associated hazards.

To assess the risk to life safety in an industrial occupancy, a number of factors should be considered. It should be determined if the manufacturing process includes the handling of flammable, reactive, or explosive materials in quantities that could expose occupants to an initial fire or explosion. If so, the occupancy is a strong candidate for a high hazard classification.

It should also be determined whether the manufacturing process requires a large number of people or whether it is basically a large collection of machines or equipment occasionally attended by operators. In some instances, the operators may be clustered in one location, such as a control room. If a building is predominantly occupied by machinery or equipment and is used by few employees, the building can be classified as a special purpose industrial occupancy. [See 28-1.4.1(b).]

If an industrial building is used mostly for storage of materials (such as preparatory stock for assembly or finished goods), it may meet the requirements for classification as a storage occupancy. (See Chapter 29.)

Occupancy classification is dependent on the burning and explosive characteristics of the materials contained in a building, not on the quantity of combustibles. For example, there is no reason to classify a building as high hazard simply because it is associated with a manufacturing process that requires extensive quantities of ordinary combustible materials distributed in such a manner that the process would involve a high combustible load.

The classification of an industrial occupancy for life safety purposes does not depend on the type of structure housing the industrial process. The basic purpose of the hazard classification in Chapter 4 is to evaluate the risk of contents (see Section 4-2). The classification is determined by an evaluation of the contents and other factors in a fire's development that affect the time available to safely evacuate the occupants. Once employees are evacuated to a safe location, the extent of fire spread in the structure becomes a threat to property. As long as life safety measures are met, the threat of heavy fire damage to a building is beyond the scope of the *Life Safety Code*. [*See also commentary following 28-1.4.1(b) and 28-1.4.1(c).*]

28-1.4.1 Subclassification of Industrial Occupancies. Each industrial occupancy shall be subclassified according to its use as follows:

(a) *General Industrial Occupancy.* Ordinary and low hazard manufacturing operations conducted in buildings of conventional design suitable for various types of manufacture.

Included are multistory buildings where floors are occupied by different tenants or buildings suitable for such occupancy and, therefore, subject to possible use for types of manufacturing with a high density of employee population.

(b) *Special Purpose Industrial Occupancy.* Includes ordinary and low hazard manufacturing operations in buildings designed for and suitable only for particular types of operations, characterized by a relatively low density of employee population, with much of the area occupied by machinery or equipment.

It can be difficult to determine if a building qualifies as a special purpose industrial occupancy. For example, a structure is often erected to protect a large machine or equipment from weather. Once constructed, authorities may try to impose exit requirements applicable to a general industrial occupancy, despite the fact that there is to be only a handful of personnel occupying the building. Steel mills, paper plants, generating plants, and other operations with large machines are examples of the types of industrial occupancies requiring massive structures for process control and weather protection. These structures often represent minimum hazards to life safety and should be classed as special purpose industrial occupancies. In many of the more modern operations, all process control is conducted from a control room by remote means, which further reduces the number of occupants likely to be exposed to a fire.

However, the special purpose industrial occupancy classification cannot be applied to a building simply to reduce exit requirements. Economic considerations, or staffing limitations that result in occupancy by fewer employees than usual, cannot be used as justification for reducing life safety features; the full number and arrangement of exits required for a general industrial occupancy should be maintained. A reduction in aisles, doors, stairways, and other components of the means of egress cannot be justified by the temporary classification of a building as a special purpose industrial occupancy.

(c)* *High Hazard Industrial Occupancy.* Includes those buildings having high hazard materials, processes, or contents. Incidental high hazard operations in low or ordinary occupancies and protected in accordance with Section 4-2 and 28-3.2 shall not be the basis for overall occupancy classification.

A-28-1.4.1(c) High hazard occupancy may include occupancies where gasoline and other flammable liquids are handled, used, or are stored under such conditions as to involve possible release of flammable vapors; where grain dust, wood flour or plastic dusts, aluminum or magnesium dust, or other explosive dusts may be produced; where hazardous chemicals or explosives are manufactured, stored, or handled; where cotton or other combustible fibers are processed or handled under conditions such as to produce flammable flyings, and other situations of similar hazard.

Chapter 28, "Industrial Occupancies," and Chapter 29, "Storage Occupancies," include detailed provisions on high hazard occupancy.

A high hazard occupancy classification is limited to those industrial buildings housing extremely hazardous operations. Incidental use of restricted quantities of flammable liquids in a building does not constitute a high hazard, although some additional life safety precautions may be required during the limited period of use. Refer to NFPA 30, *Flammable and Combustible Liquids Code*,[2] for guidance. Storage of flammable liquids, such as paint, in sealed containers does not require a high hazard occupancy classification unless the operation includes mixing or blending operations that require the containers to be opened. Mixing and blending of flammable liquids can be conducted in a separate room with a fire barrier between the storage and mixing areas. In such an operation, the mixing and blending room would be considered a high hazard industrial occupancy, while the adjacent, fire-separated storage area would be considered a general purpose industrial occupancy or possibly a storage occupancy subject to the requirements of Chapter 29.

Combustible dusts released from an industrial or manufacturing process constitute a significant threat to life safety and often require a high hazard classification. Major loss of life has occurred in industrial occupancies that release extensive quantities of combustible dusts. Every opportunity for the quick escape of employees who work in operations releasing combustible dust should be provided to prevent injury or loss of life if a dust explosion occurs. In high hazard occupancies that are subject to explosions, the provisions of 28-3.2 require special consideration of the techniques for explosion suppression or venting to ensure the life safety of occupants. Full utilization of fire protection engineering techniques should be employed in such occupancies to minimize the risk to life safety.

The industrial occupancies that clearly require classification as a high hazard are those associated with the production of explosives or highly reactive chemicals. In some especially hazardous operations, additional exits will be necessary to ensure rapid egress in order to prevent loss of life in the event of an explosion or fire. Where installation of the preventive or protective measures specified in 28-3.2 is not possible due to the nature of the industrial operation, consideration should be given to operating procedures that restrict access to a limited number of people during the hazardous portion of the operation. The operating procedures would limit the potential threat to those trained personnel who are fully aware of the extent of the hazard. Procedures should also include a record of personnel who have signed in or out to ensure prompt determination of the number of personnel exposed to a hazardous operation and, thus, the number who may require rescue.

28-1.5 **Classification of Hazard of Contents.** Classification of hazard of contents shall be as defined in Section 4-2.

28-1.6 **Minimum Construction Requirements.** No occupancy requirement.

Some occupancy chapters, such as Chapters 12 and 13, which address the life safety needs of nonambulatory health care occupants, specify minimum building construction type requirements to help ensure structural integrity for the time period needed for a lengthy evacuation or for safe refuge within the building. There are no minimum construction requirements imposed because industrial occupancies characteristically have ambulatory occupants and do not provide sleeping accommodations.

28-1.7* **Occupant Load.** The occupant load of industrial occupancies for determination of means of egress shall be one person per 100 sq ft (9.3 sq m) of gross floor area.

Exception: In a special purpose industrial occupancy, the occupant load shall be the maximum number of persons to occupy the area under any probable conditions.

A-28-1.7 In most cases, the requirements for maximum travel distance to exits will be the determining factor rather than numbers of occupants, as exits provided to satisfy travel distance requirements will be sufficient to provide exit capacity for all occupants, except in cases of unusual arrangement of buildings or high occupant load of a general manufacturing occupancy.

The occupant load of an industrial building is based on an average of 100 sq ft (9.3 sq m) of gross floor area per occupant. Many industrial users of the *Code* confuse this concept with the actual number of employees who use the facility. The usual complaint is that the number of potential employees calculated for exit purposes in accordance with the 100-sq ft (9.3-sq m) criterion far exceeds the anticipated or actual number of employees. Many industrial managers argue that using the larger number as a basis for exit design requires more exits, wider doors, and more passageways than are needed for exit purposes, reducing productive work space and resulting in increased cost.

The concept of determining occupant load by using an occupant load factor is useful, although it does not necessarily relate directly to the actual number of building occupants. It is a means of calculating the minimum egress requirements based on the needs of an average industrial occupancy. While actual conditions may vary in an individual location, the amount of egress width determined by the occupant load calculation will normally provide the necessary, adequate, and required means of egress for a typical industrial building with little or no penalty to the building's owner/operator.

See Figure 28-1 for examples of occupant load determination using the occupant load factor for a general industrial occupancy and using the probable number of occupants for a special purpose industrial occupancy.

In A, the general industrial occupancy must provide a means of egress for at least 2,000 persons based on use of an occupant load factor of 1 person per 100 sq ft (9.3 sq m).

In B, a special purpose industrial occupancy can size its means of egress for the maximum 20 persons who are apt to occupy the facility under any probable condition.

In C, the 200-person tour groups that visit this special purpose industrial occupancy on the first Monday of each

A   200,000 sq ft (18,600 sq m)
Electronics Assembly Plant

B   200,000 sq ft (18,600 sq m)
Fully-Automated,
High-Security Missile Assembly Plant

C   200,000 sq ft (18,600 sq m)
Steel Rolling Mill with
Tour Group Viewing Gallery

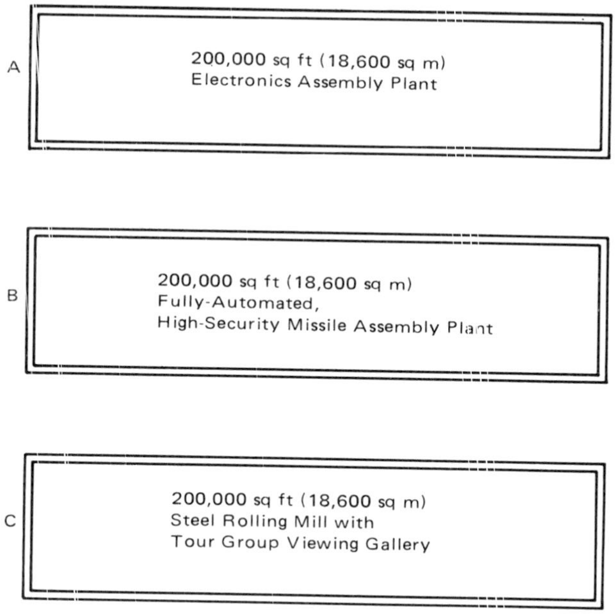

Figure 28-1.   Determination of Occupant Load of Industrial Occupancies.

month must be added to the 45 employees who are normally present, for a total occupant load of 245 persons.

SECTION 28-2   Means of Egress Requirements

28-2.1 General.

28-2.1.1 Each required means of egress shall be in accordance with the applicable portions of Chapter 5.

28-2.2 Means of Egress Components.

28-2.2.1 Components of means of egress shall be limited to the types described in 28-2.2.2 through 28-2.2.12.

28-2.2.2 Doors.

28-2.2.2.1 Doors shall comply with 5-2.1.

Since doors are required to comply with 5-2.1 and since Exception No. 1 and Exception No. 3 to 5-2.1.5.2, which provide exemptions from the stairwell door reentry requirements, are not specifically recognized by Chapter 28, the basic reentry provisions of 5-2.1.5.2 apply to stairs serving more than four stories (*see Exception No. 5 to 5-2.1.5.2*) in both new and existing industrial occupancies. Paragraph 5-2.1.5.2 requires that stairwell doors must either allow reentry from the stairwell to the interior of the building (i.e., no stairwell doors are permitted to be locked from the stair side) or locked doors must automatically unlock upon initiation of the building fire alarm system to allow reentry. (*See 5-2.1.5.2.*)

28-2.2.2.2 Special locking arrangements complying with 5-2.1.6 are permitted.

Use of the delayed release locking device covered by 5-2.1.6 is allowed on any door in recognition of the security needs of some industrial occupancies. In effect, the allowable 15- or 30-second delay will be experienced only under nonfire conditions or very early in a fire's growth, since the door must be usable immediately upon sprinkler operation or smoke or heat detection and upon loss of power that controls the locking mechanism. The building must be protected throughout by an approved automatic sprinkler system or automatic fire detection system.

28-2.2.2.3 In low and ordinary hazard general and special purpose industrial occupancies, horizontal sliding doors shall be permitted in a means of egress serving an occupant load of less than 50 in accordance with 5-2.1.14.

28-2.2.2.4 In low and ordinary hazard general and special purpose industrial occupancies, horizontal sliding doors shall be permitted in horizontal exits and smoke barriers in accordance with 5-2.1.14. (See 28-2.2.5.2.)

Both 28-2.2.2.3 and 28-2.2.2.4 recognize limited use of horizontal sliding doors in other than high hazard industrial occupancies, including special purpose industrial occupancies; the *Code* would normally require a side-hinged swinging door. Exception No. 4 to 5-2.1.4.1 addresses horizontal sliding doors that meet all the special requirements of 5-2.1.14. (*See 5-2.1.14.*)

28-2.2.3 Stairs.

28-2.2.3.1 Stairs shall comply with 5-2.2.

Exception: Noncombustible grated stair treads and landing floors.

The Exception to 28-2.2.3.1 exempts stair treads and landings in industrial occupancies from the provisions of 5-2.2.3.5, which would otherwise require that all stair treads and stair landing floors be solid. Although the requirement for solid treads and landing floors is intended to prevent occupants from avoiding use of the stair because they become afraid when they are able to see through the openings to the floor or ground below, occupants of industrial occupancies are usually more familiar, and thus more comfortable, with grated or expanded metal treads and landings. The grated walking surfaces provide slip resistance in what can sometimes be greasy and slippery surroundings. For consistency, an exception has been added to 5-2.2.3.5 to alert the user that industrial occupancies, in accordance with Chapter 28, are exempt from the solid tread and landing provisions.

28-2.2.3.2 Spiral stairs complying with 5-2.2.2.7 are permitted.

Note that 5-2.2.2.7 only permits spiral stairs to serve an occupant load of five or fewer persons. They may be effectively used in industrial occupancies to provide exit access from small mezzanines, platforms, and equipment.

28-2.2.3.3 In existing buildings, winders complying with 5-2.2.2.8 are permitted.

28-2.2.4 Smokeproof Enclosures. Smokeproof enclosures shall comply with 5-2.3.

This paragraph does not mandate the use of smokeproof enclosures, but it does recognize a smokeproof enclosure as part of the means of egress system in an industrial occupancy only if the smokeproof enclosure meets the requirements of 5-2.3. For an example of an occupancy requiring a smokeproof enclosure, see 19-2.11.1 in which nonsprinklered, existing, high rise apartment buildings are required to be provided with smokeproof enclosures in accordance with 5-2.3.

28-2.2.5   Horizontal Exits.

28-2.2.5.1   Horizontal exits shall comply with 5-2.4.

This paragraph does not mandate the use of horizontal exits, but it does recognize a horizontal exit as part of the means of egress system in an industrial occupancy only if the horizontal exit meets the requirements of 5-2.4, as modified by 28-2.2.5.2.

28-2.2.5.2*   In horizontal exits where the doorway is protected by a fire door on each side of the wall in which it is located, one fire door shall be of the swinging type as provided in 5-2.4.3.6, and the other shall be permitted to be an automatic sliding fire door that shall be kept open whenever the building is occupied.

A-28-2.2.5.2   The customary building code requirement for fire doors on both sides of an opening in a fire wall may be met by having an automatic-sliding fire door on one side, and self-closing fire door swinging out from the other side of the wall. This arrangement qualifies only as a horizontal exit from the side of the sliding door. (*For further information, see A-5-2.4.3.8.*)

The intent of 28-2.2.5.2 is to recognize the common practice of combining a horizontal exit used for life safety with a fire barrier of significant fire resistance rating used for property protection. Opening protectives for such a fire barrier can require the use of a set of doors in order to achieve the required fire protection rating. It is impractical for both doors to swing in the same direction without interfering with each other; yet operation of two doors that swing in opposite directions is cumbersome for daily or common usage. One swinging and one sliding door, as shown in Figure 28-2, provide an acceptable arrangement for day-to-day functioning of the building. The open sliding door does not compromise life safety, because, by the time its fusible link mechanism releases the door and allows it to close, temperatures in the vicinity of the door opening render use of the door impractical.

28-2.2.6   Ramps. Ramps shall comply with 5-2.5.

This paragraph does not mandate the use of ramps in industrial occupancies, but it does recognize a ramp as

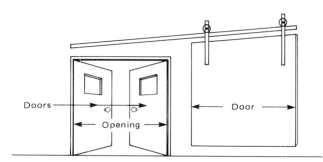

Figure 28-2.   Example of Combination Swinging and Sliding Doors Allowed by 28-2.2.5.2.

part of the means of egress system only if the ramp meets the requirements of 5-2.5.

28-2.2.7   Exit Passageways. Exit passageways shall comply with 5-2.6.

This paragraph does not mandate the use of exit passageways in industrial occupancies, but it does recognize an exit passageway as part of the means of egress system only if the exit passageway meets the requirements of 5-2.6.

28-2.2.8   Escalators and Moving Walks. In existing buildings, previously approved escalators and moving walks complying with 5-2.7 shall be permitted to be continued in use.

Note that 5-2.7 allows existing escalators and moving walks to continue to be recognized within the required means of egress if an occupancy chapter so allows. In earlier editions of the *Code*, such escalators and moving walks may have been recognized by providing egress capacity for 75 persons. In order to qualify as exits, escalators and moving walks must also meet the requirements of 5-1.3.1, which addresses exit enclosures.

Note that escalators protected in accordance with the sprinkler-vent method, the spray nozzle method, the rolling shutter method, or the partial enclosure method do not constitute acceptable exits, but can continue to serve as exit access if previously approved as such.

28-2.2.9   Fire Escape Stairs. Existing fire escape stairs complying with 5-2.8 are permitted.

28-2.2.10 **Fire Escape Ladders.** Fire escape ladders complying with 5-2.9 are permitted.

28-2.2.11 **Slide Escapes.** Approved slide escapes complying with 5-2.10 shall be permitted as components in the means of egress for both new and existing high hazard industrial occupancies. Slide escapes shall be counted as exits only when regularly used in drills or for normal exit so that occupants are familiar with their use through practice.

The intent of 28-2.2.11 is to allow the use of slide escapes, which are a common means of egress from areas housing explosives or other highly hazardous materials in chemical industry buildings. This provision allows consideration of slide escapes as part of the required means of egress from both new and existing high hazard industrial occupancies. In many high hazard industrial occupancies, slide escapes are the only practical means of ensuring safe egress prior to an explosion or flash fire.

28-2.2.12 **Alternating Tread Devices.** Alternating tread devices complying with 5-2.11 are permitted.

The provisions of 5-2.11, in effect, limit the use of alternating tread devices to those locations where the *Code* recognizes the use of fire escape ladders. (*See 28-2.2.10 and 5-2.9.*)

28-2.3 **Capacity of Means of Egress.**

Prior editions of the *Code* required a minimum 44-in. (112-cm) width for corridors and passageways within the required means of egress of industrial occupancies. A corridor or passageway of that minimum width would provide egress capacity for 220 persons [i.e., 44 in. ÷ 0.2 in. per person (approximately 112 cm ÷ 0.5 cm per person) in accordance with 5-3.3.1 for level travel components]. The prior requirement produced artificially large egress systems, when compared to the occupant load, for many industrial occupancies. The requirement was dropped, and the minimum 36-in. (91-cm) width requirement of 5-3.4.1, which addresses the width of any exit access, was made applicable to industrial occupancies. Exit access is required to be wider than 36 in. (91 cm) only if a corridor or passageway in an industrial occupancy is to provide capacity for more than 180 persons

[i.e., 36 in. ÷ 0.2 in. per person (approximately 91 cm ÷ 0.5 cm per person)].

28-2.3.1 The capacity of means of egress shall be in accordance with Section 5-3.

Exception: In special purpose industrial occupancies, means of egress shall be provided at least for the persons actually employed; spaces not subject to human occupancy because of the presence of machinery or equipment are excluded from consideration.

The Exception to 28-2.3.1 places practical limits on the number of required exits and on the arrangement of the means of egress in a special purpose industrial occupancy. There is no life safety purpose served by providing exits from the center of a large machine or equipment installation that is unoccupied under normal operating conditions. A number of industries provide weather shelter for large processes and equipment. Typical examples include steel rolling mills, paper extruders, and metalworking machines, all of which occupy a majority of the floor space in the sheltered building. In many of the more sophisticated operations, full process control is conducted from a remotely located control room. Personnel normally occupy the building only for maintenance and adjustment purposes and, then, only on a limited basis. To provide exits from such special purpose industrial occupancies would serve no useful purpose and could unjustly impose an economic penalty in the name of safety.

The large areas normally enclosed by special purpose structures would require excessive egress width if the occupant load were calculated on the basis of 100 sq ft (9.3 sq m) per person. If provisions for the capacity of the means of egress in a special purpose industrial occupancy were based on the requirements specified for general industrial occupancies, the result would be extensive egress facilities for nonexistent occupants. Such arrangements might actually result in the requirement of exits from the interior of machinery and equipment installations, which would be incompatible with the equipment's design. In many cases, these exits would originate from locations that, even under normal operating conditions, would be considered dangerous for humans. Poorly conceived exit facilities serve no life safety purpose and detract from an otherwise well-designed exit system.

28-2.4 **Number of Means of Egress.** (*See also Section 5-4.*)

28-2.4.1 There shall be not less than two means of egress from every story or section, and at least one exit must be reached without traversing another story.

The provisions of 28-2.4.1, which apply to the minimum required number of means of egress for industrial occupancies, have been revised for this edition of the *Code* to clarify that, in addition to providing every story or section with access to at least two means of egress, one of the exits must be located on each floor so that the entrance to that exit (e.g., a door that opens into an enclosed exit stair) can be reached without having to travel to another floor.

Exception: In low and ordinary hazard industrial occupancies, a single means of egress shall be permitted from any story or section, provided that the exit can be reached within the distance allowed as common path of travel. (See 28-2.5.1 Exception.)

This exception recognizes that there are small floors or areas in low and ordinary hazard industrial occupancies that, if provided with access to only a single exit, are no less safe than larger areas of a building that have access to two exits where an occupant must first travel through the maximum allowable common path. Where a single exit is provided, the occupant travels the 50 ft (15 m) of common path allowed by the Exception to 28-2.5.1, enters the exit (*see Figure 28-3*), and is judged to have reached a point of safety. In larger buildings and larger building areas that do not meet the limited travel distance for a single exit, a minimum of two exits must be provided. By traveling to the nearer of the two exits, the occupant is permitted to travel the same 50 ft (15 m) of common path that the occupant of the single exit building traveled to reach the one exit, before reaching the point where travel to the two exits in different directions is possible. Although the occupant of the single exit building has reached an exit by this point, the occupant of the multiple-exit building is then allowed an additional 150 ft (45 m) [200 ft (60 m) if building is sprinklered] of exit access travel before the safety of an exit is reached. Therefore, the exception for the single exit provides a level of

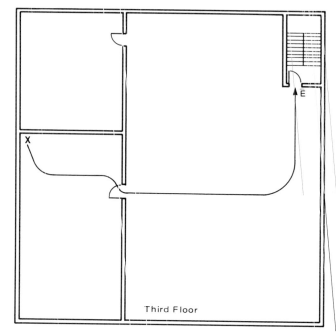

Figure 28-3. *Example of Single Means of Egress from a Story of a Low or Ordinary Hazard Industrial Occupancy. This is permitted, provided the distance to the single exit (X to E) does not exceed the allowable common path of travel [i.e., 50 ft (15 m) in accordance with the Exception to 28-2.5.1].*

life safety at least equivalent to that of the multiple-exit building.

28-2.4.2 Floors or portions thereof with an occupant load of more than 500 shall have the minimum number of separate and remote means of egress specified by 5-4.1.2.

Exception: Existing buildings.

Historically, the *Code* has required more than two exits based on occupant load for assembly occupancies only. Third, fourth, and subsequent exits were provided in industrial occupancies in order to meet travel distance requirements or as a convenience for day-to-day use. Paragraph 5-4.1.2 was added to the *Code* in 1988 and extends the concept of requiring three or four exits based on occupant load to all occupancies. The Exception to 28-2.4.2, in compliance with the option offered by the Exception to 5-4.1.2, exempts existing buildings from the requirement for third and fourth exits to avoid forcing existing, previously complying means of egress systems into non-compliance.

28-2.4.3 High hazard areas shall comply with Section 5-11.

Section 5-11, "Special Provisions for Occupancies with High Hazard Contents," includes an adequate set of provisions for high hazard areas and is referenced by this chapter to provide commensurate protection to industrial occupancies that contain high hazard areas. The provisions of Section 5-11 are vital to life safety in high hazard occupancies. The requirement for two means of egress for all high hazard occupancies recognizes that there is always the possibility that a fire or explosion could block or destroy one of the two exits. Two separate and equal means of egress from high hazard areas provide a necessary redundancy to ensure the evacuation of occupants under fire or explosion conditions and to minimize the potential for injury or loss of life. The Exception to 5-11.3 recognizes that it is not necessary to require two means of egress from very small high hazard areas [maximum 200 sq ft (18.6 sq m)], with limited occupant load (maximum 3 persons), if the room door can be reached within 25 ft (7.6 m) of travel.

28-2.5 Arrangement of Means of Egress. (*See also Section 5-5.*)

28-2.5.1* Where two or more means of egress are required, they shall be so arranged as to be reached by different paths of travel in different directions.

Exception: A common path of travel shall be permitted for the first 50 ft (15 m) from any point in low and ordinary hazard occupancies.

A-28-2.5.1 Unless exits are suitably located, this requirement may interfere with the practice in multiple tenant manufacturing buildings of renting a wing or large section to a single tenant who closes the corridor with a door subject to locking and treats the corridor inside the door as part of that tenant's manufacturing space. No required exit may be blocked by a door subject to locking against the exit travel.

The requirements of 28-2.5.1 must be considered by designers, inspectors, and authorities having jurisdiction, particularly where sections of a building are occupied by more than one tenant. Uncontrolled access between areas of different ownership is clearly not desirable from a tenant's point of view. However, security provisions between separate facilities must never be allowed to restrict the use of a required means of egress. Where multiple tenants occupy the same building and use common exit facilities, careful consideration is required to ensure continued use of the means of egress over the life of a building. A tenant will often close off an exit access corridor with a door subject to locking and treat the corridor on that side of the door as part of that tenant's manufacturing space. If such a practice eliminates another tenant's access to an exit, alternate exits must be provided.

28-2.5.2 No dead end may be more than 50 ft (15 m) deep. Dead ends are not permitted in high hazard occupancies.

See the discussion of dead ends and common path of travel in Chapter 5. A common path of travel cannot be permitted in high hazard occupancies. (*See commentary in Chapters 26 and 27 for a discussion on dead ends and common path of travel in office areas. See definition of common path of travel in Chapter 3.*)

28-2.6 Travel Distance to Exits.

28-2.6.1 Travel distance limitations shall be in accordance with 5-6.4.

Exception No. 1: As permitted by 28-2.6.2.

Exception No. 2: As permitted by 28-2.6.3.

Exception No. 3: Travel distance to exits in high hazard industrial occupancies shall not exceed 75 ft (23 m).

Paragraph 5-6.4 establishes travel distance limitations of 200 ft (60 m) in nonsprinklered buildings and 250 ft (76 m) in sprinklered buildings. Exception No. 1 to 5-6.4 allows occupancies to set different limits as necessary. Paragraph 28-2.6.1 recognizes the travel distance limitations of 5-6.4 and subsequently establishes additional allowances in accordance with Exception Nos. 1 through 3.

28-2.6.2 In low or ordinary hazard general industrial occupancies, travel distance shall not exceed 400 ft (122 m) if the following additional provisions are met in full:

(a) Application shall be limited to one-story buildings.

(b)* Smoke and heat venting shall be provided by engineered means or by building configuration to ensure that occupants shall not be overtaken by spread of fire or smoke within 6 ft (183 cm) of floor level before they have time to reach exits.

A-28-2.6.2(b) Smoke and heating venting should be in accordance with NFPA 204M, *Guide for Smoke and Heat Venting.* (*See Appendix B.*)

(c) Automatic sprinkler or other automatic fire extinguishing systems in accordance with Section 7-7 shall be provided. The extinguishing system shall be supervised.

The provisions of 28-2.6.2 are meant to provide flexibility in determining the layout of the means of egress system in a single-story industrial building with a large floor area that houses a low or ordinary hazard general industrial occupancy.

The construction of tunnels and elevated means of egress that originate from the center of an industrial building with an extensive floor area is rarely attempted. Only a handful of buildings have ever been provided with such egress facilities, and most were World War II airframe manufacturing buildings of massive size. In most industrial buildings, it is not practicable or economical to construct exit tunnels or overhead passageways. These special types of means of egress are not easily altered if modifications are necessary to adjust to changes in the layout of an industrial facility. In addition, the construction costs for tunnels and elevated passageways are high due to the special design features required to ensure their safety, including fire resistance rated supports for the elevated passageways, waterproofing, and other features necessary to maintain the integrity of underground tunnels. Another negative factor in such construction is the confining nature of a tunnel or elevated passage, which tends to divert employees from such means of egress.

The use of horizontal exits that pass through firewalls is common in many industrial occupancies. Full consideration of the provisions in Chapter 5 is required to ensure the safe use of these types of exits. A common violation of the provisions of Chapter 5 is the failure to provide the proper type of door in a fire wall. A roll-up type of fire door cannot be considered as an acceptable element of a means of egress. Because a horizontal exit may be used from both sides of a fire wall, careful consideration of the direction of door swing is necessary to ensure that the *Code* will recognize this use. In many instances, two doors swinging in opposite directions will be required so that the exit may be used as a means of egress from both sides of the fire wall. (*See 5-2.1.4, 5-2.4.2.3, and 28-2.2.5.*)

The increase in allowable travel distance to 400 ft (122 m) is often applied to exits in a general purpose industrial occupancy that is classified as a low or ordinary hazard, in accordance with the requirements of items (a) through (c) of 28-2.6.2.

Item (a) limits use of the increased travel distance provisions to one-story buildings in order to permit horizontal movement of the occupants through the means of egress. Any stairs or other impediments to the rapid movement of occupants would result in slower evacuation of the building and increase the possibility of exposure to smoke or fire.

To satisfy the intent of item (b), a great deal of judgment must be exercised in the design of systems for smoke and heat venting. The provisions of Appendix A of the *Code* that recommend utilization of the guidelines of NFPA 204M, *Guide for Smoke and Heat Venting,*[3] should be sufficient in most instances. In addition, in accordance with the recommendations of A-7-3.1, NFPA 92B, *Guide for Smoke Management Systems in Malls, Atria, and Large Areas,*[4] can be consulted when designing buildings with ceilings of heights approximating those of covered mall buildings and atria.

The limitation on smoke accumulation in item (b) is a key factor in the design of the smoke removal system. The average evacuation speed of a person who is walking is normally considered to be 250 ft (76 m) per minute, or a little over 4 ft (122 cm) per second. Where this evacuation speed is applied to the 400-ft (122-m) travel distance allowed by the *Code*, the maximum time required to reach an exit should not exceed 2 min. It is an extremely rare situation in which the smoke that accumulates in an industrial building is so extensive that it fills the structure and descends to less than 6 ft (183 cm) above the floor level in 2 min. The added benefit of a properly designed system for smoke and heat venting ensures that there will be little possibility that the means of egress will be blocked by smoke.

The use of available computerized smoke-filling and evacuation time models can provide documentation that permits a designer to meet the smoke and heat venting requirements in some buildings by providing only a high ceiling and no mechanical smoke removal equipment.

The installation of a complete automatic extinguishing system as required by item (c) is intended to ensure control and extinguishment of incipient fires and ultimately minimize exposure of the occupants to a fire. It is not the intent of this paragraph to allow only an automatic sprinkler system to provide the required protection, because a number of equally effective extinguishing agents and systems may be utilized for specific fire hazards. The importance of this provision is the requirement for automatic initiation of the fire control and extinguishing system to minimize the extent of the occupants' exposure to fire. The installed system is required to be fully supervised to ensure that it will operate when a fire occurs. Adequate procedures must be provided by the building's owner or tenant to ensure the prompt correction of any impairments to the extinguishing systems. In some facilities, the degree of fire risk during the impairment period may require limitations on hazardous operations and the number of occupants so that the level of safety to life will be equivalent to that provided when the extinguishing system is operational.

28-2.6.3 In low or ordinary hazard special purpose industrial occupancies, travel distance shall not exceed 300 ft (91 m), or if the building is protected throughout by an automatic sprinkler system in accordance with Section 7-7, travel distance shall not exceed 400 ft (122 m).

Low and ordinary hazard special purpose industrial occupancies, which are characterized by large, specialized equipment and low occupant load, are allowed an increase in travel distance over that allowed low and ordinary general industrial occupancies. Paragraph 28-2.6.3 permits an increase to 300 ft (91 m) if nonsprinklered and to 400 ft (122 m) if sprinklered, without mandating the additional requirements of 28-2.6.2.

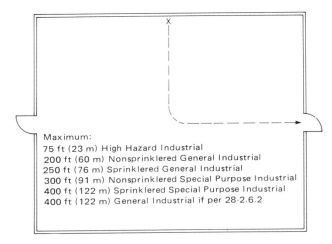

Figure 28-4. Summary of Travel Distance Options Allowed by 28-2.6.1 through 28-2.6.3.

For a summary of the various travel distance allowances for industrial occupancies, see Figure 28-4.

28-2.7 Discharge from Exits. Discharge from exits shall be in accordance with Section 5-7.

The purpose of 5-7.2 is to control the arrangement of exits from upper stories that discharge to the outside through the level of exit discharge. The basis for this exception to the general rule for complete enclosure of exits up to their point of discharge to the outside of the building is that the use of the safeguards specified in 5-7.2 (especially automatic sprinkler protection for the level of exit discharge) maintains reasonable safety. When the arrangement of exits is evaluated, a stairway is not considered as discharging through the level of discharge if it leads to the outside through an exit passageway in accordance with 5-2.6; this is true despite the fact that there are doors between the base of the enclosed stairway and the door to the outside on the level of exit discharge.

28-2.8 Illumination of Means of Egress.

28-2.8.1 Illumination of means of egress shall be provided in accordance with Section 5-8.

Exception: In structures occupied only during daylight hours, with skylights or windows arranged to provide the required level of illumination on all portions of the means of egress during these hours.

Paragraph 28-2.8.1 is not meant to require the installation of extensive and unneeded illumination systems in industrial occupancies. Illumination is required for the exit access, which is limited to designated aisles, corridors, and passageways that lead to an exit. There is no requirement for the provision of illumination throughout the building, which in many industrial occupancies would involve lighting an extensive floor area. The purpose of the lighting system is to ensure that occupants are able to see the means of egress; the purpose is not to illuminate the operation of production facilities.

In addition, the *Code* does not require illumination of the means of egress if the building is occupied during the daylight hours only. To meet the requirements of the Exception to 28-2.8.1, the building, including stairways, must have sufficient windows and skylights to ensure natural illumination. The authority having jurisdiction should make certain that the building is not occupied during the night.

28-2.9 Emergency Lighting.

28-2.9.1 All industrial occupancies shall have emergency lighting in accordance with Section 5-9.

Exception No. 1: Special purpose industrial occupancies where routine human habitation is not the case.

Exception No. 2: Structures occupied only during daylight hours, with skylights or windows arranged to provide the required level of illumination on all portions of the means of egress during these hours.

Exceptions to the requirement for emergency lighting are included in the *Code* for the same reasons that illumination of the means of egress is not required (*see 28-2.8.1*). An additional exception has been made for special purpose industrial occupancies, which are not routinely occupied; there is no need to install an extensive and costly emergency lighting system in an unoccupied building.

28-2.10 Marking of Means of Egress.

28-2.10.1 Signs designating exits or ways of travel thereto shall be provided in accordance with Section 5-10.

28-2.11 Special Features. (Reserved.)

SECTION 28-3   Protection

28-3.1 Protection of Vertical Openings.

28-3.1.1 Every stairway, elevator shaft, escalator opening, and other vertical opening shall be enclosed or protected in accordance with Chapter 5 and Section 6-2.

Exception No. 1: Unprotected vertical openings connecting not more than three floors shall be permitted in accordance with 6-2.4.5.

Exception No. 2: An atrium shall be permitted in accordance with 6-2.4.6.

Exception No. 1 and Exception No. 2 to 28-3.1.1 recognize the provisions of Chapter 6, which sanction limited vertical openings and atriums for industrial occupancies.

Exception No. 3: In special purpose and high hazard occupancies where unprotected vertical openings are in new or existing buildings and are necessary to manufacturing operations, they shall be permitted beyond the specified limits, provided every floor level has direct access to one or more enclosed stairways or other exits protected against obstruction by any fire or smoke in the open areas connected by the unprotected vertical openings.

Exception No. 3 to 28-3.1.1 strictly limits the use of unprotected vertical openings in high hazard and special purpose industrial occupancies. Direct access to one or more enclosed stairways or to other exits is required from any areas connected by unprotected vertical openings. This provision recognizes that many high hazard and special purpose industrial occupancies require openings between floor levels to accommodate piping, conveyors, and other devices and equipment essential to the orderly operation of the facility. In most of these situations, full enclosure is not practical or feasible. In high hazard occupancies, the provision of two means of egress will, in most situations, be sufficient to comply with this exception. In special purpose occupancies, additional exits or other special arrangements will normally be required in order to comply with the provision that stairways and exits be protected against obstruction from fire and smoke in open areas connected by unprotected vertical openings.

Exception No. 4: Existing open stairways, existing open ramps, and existing escalators shall be permitted where connecting only two floor levels.

Exception No. 4 to 28-3.1.1 limits existing open stairways, existing open ramps, and existing escalators that are unenclosed or unprotected by permitting them to connect only two floors. An existing open stairway connecting three floors would have to be enclosed, protected, or permitted by another of the exceptions to 28-3.1.1.

Exception No. 5: In existing buildings with low or ordinary hazard contents and protected throughout by an approved automatic sprinkler system in accordance with Section 7-7, unprotected vertical openings shall be permitted provided the vertical opening does not serve as a required exit. All required exits under such conditions shall consist of smokeproof enclosures in accordance with 5-2.3, outside stairs in accordance with 5-2.2, or horizontal exits in accordance with 5-2.4.

Exception No. 5 to 28-3.1.1 recognizes that an existing industrial occupancy may contain unprotected vertical openings and still provide a reasonable level of safety to life if the building contains only low or ordinary hazards and is protected by a complete automatic sprinkler system. Smokeproof enclosures and outside stairways (the only types of vertical exits allowed by this exception) must be fully enclosed or protected against vertical fire spread and meet the requirements of Chapter 5. The unenclosed vertical openings may not serve as part of the means of egress, although they can remain as convenience openings and stairways to be used for normal operations.

While the major reason for allowing this provision is economic, since the cost of enclosing all vertical openings in existing buildings is high, there is actually little effect on the life safety of occupants where the building houses low or ordinary hazards. However, some difficulties in fire control are created, since unprotected vertical

openings can contribute to fire spread in buildings and result in extensive property damage and potential impact on occupants prior to evacuation; therefore, a complete automatic sprinkler system is required.

28-3.2* **Protection from Hazards.** Every high hazard industrial occupancy, operation, or process shall have automatic extinguishing systems or such other protection appropriate to the particular hazard, such as explosion venting or suppression, protecting any area subject to an explosion hazard for the purpose of minimizing danger to occupants in case of fire or other emergency before they have time to utilize exits to escape. Hazardous areas in industrial occupancies protected by automatic extinguishing systems shall be exempt from the smoke resisting enclosure requirement of 6-4.1.2.

A-28-3.2 Emergency lighting should be considered where operations require lighting to perform orderly manual emergency operation or shutdown, maintain critical services, or provide safe start-up after a power failure.

The intent of 28-3.2 is to provide for the life safety of the occupants of industrial buildings through control of the risk associated with hazardous operations. The alternatives offered in the paragraph are not meant to be inclusive, and a proper fire protection engineering solution might not incorporate the listed provisions. The *Code* intends to allow for engineering judgment in a wide range of potentially hazardous situations, including some where protection may be limited. The intent of the paragraph is also broad in application, since, in many highly hazardous operations, an explosion may be immediately preceded by a fire or other emergency, such as an overheated reactor vessel, an exothermic reaction, or increased pressure. Because such conditions may initiate an explosion, depending upon the process and arrangement of the equipment, immediate egress from the facility may be necessary. If fire or other emergencies are likely to develop rapidly into an explosion, adequate precautions are necessary for life safety.

In many modern facilities, provisions that prove adequate for the life safety of occupants may already be included for process control and property protection, and any additional measures will not increase the life safety of operators to an appreciable degree.

Section 12, Chapter 11, of the NFPA *Fire Protection Handbook*[5] discusses the basic principles of explosion prevention, venting, and suppression. This section also contains an extensive bibliography on the subject. Recommendations for the design and utilization of vents to limit pressures developed by explosions are contained in NFPA 68, *Guide for Venting of Deflagrations*.[6] Standards for explosion prevention systems are found in NFPA 69, *Standard on Explosion Prevention Systems*.[7] (*See also the NFPA Industrial Fire Hazards Handbook*.)[8]

In this edition of the *Code*, 6-4.1 has been revised to include a concept that applied to assembly and educational occupancies in previous editions; i.e., where a hazardous area is protected by automatic sprinklers, rather than by enclosure with fire barriers of 1-hour fire resistance rating and doors of 45-minute fire protection rating, the hazardous area must be enclosed by walls and doors that are, at minimum, smoke resisting. The last sentence of 28-3.2 exempts hazardous areas in industrial occupancies from the requirement for smoke resisting enclosures if those areas are protected by automatic sprinklers. For consistency, similar wording appears in Exception No. 2 to 6-4.1.2.

28-3.3   Interior Finish.

28-3.3.1   Interior wall and ceiling finish shall be Class A, B, or C in accordance with Section 6-5 in operating areas and shall be as required by 5-1.4 in exit enclosures.

28-3.3.2   Interior Floor Finish. No occupancy requirements.

28-3.4   Detection, Alarm, and Communication Systems.

28-3.4.1   General. Industrial occupancies shall be provided with a fire alarm system in accordance with Section 7-6.

Exception: If the total capacity of the building is under 100 persons and fewer than 25 persons are above or below the level of exit discharge.

28-3.4.2   Initiation. Initiation of the required fire alarm system shall be by either manual or automatic means in accordance with 7-6.2.

28-3.4.3   Notification.

28-3.4.3.1   The required fire alarm system shall sound an audible alarm in a continuously attended location for purposes of initiating emergency action.

28-3.4.3.2   In high hazard industrial occupancies (*see 28-1.4*), the required fire alarm system shall automatically initiate an occupant evacuation alarm signal per 7-6.3.

The requirements of 28-3.4.3 contain two separate and distinct provisions for audible alarms activated by the fire alarm system required by 28-3.4.1. In low and ordinary hazard occupancies, the system is not required to activate an evacuation alarm but is required to sound an alarm in a continuously attended location for the purpose of initiating emergency action. The intent of this provision is to allow an interface between the alarm system and the plant's emergency organization. The alarm system may be controlled from a central security console or a similar location. The key feature is that the location from which the alarm sounds must be continuously staffed. This requirement need not be interpreted as mandating installation of supervisory service, such as that connected to a central station, but the location must be fully attended at all times when the building is occupied.

In high hazard occupancies, the alarm must be arranged to sound an evacuation signal, since the safety of the occupants of these areas depends on their immediate notification of a fire.

28-3.5   Extinguishing Requirements. None.

28-3.6   Corridors. The provisions of 5-1.3.4 shall not apply.

Without the exemption to the requirements of 5-1.3.4 provided by 28-3.6, all new industrial occupancy corridors serving more than 30 persons would be required to have a 1-hour fire resistance rating, with openings protected by 20-minute fire protection rated door assemblies. The exemption to 5-1.3.4 was adopted due to the ambulatory nature of occupants of industrial occupancies and the operational need for openings, even where corridors are provided.

SECTION 28-4 Special Provisions

28-4.1 Operating Features. (*See Chapter 31.*)

28-4.2 High Rise Buildings. High rise industrial occupancies shall comply with the automatic sprinkler requirements of 30-8.2.1.

The provisions of 28-4.2, which apply to high rise industrial occupancy buildings, are new to this edition of the *Code*. This paragraph references a portion of the high rise building provisions of Section 30-8 available to an occupancy chapter for mandatory purposes. High rise general purpose industrial occupancy buildings classified as ordinary hazard and high rise industrial occupancy buildings classified as high hazard are required to be protected throughout by an approved, supervised automatic sprinkler system in accordance with 30-8.2.1. The remainder of Section 30-8 is not mandated in high rise industrial occupancy buildings.

Exception No. 1: Low hazard industrial occupancies.

Exception No. 2: Special purpose industrial occupancies.

Exception No. 3: Existing industrial occupancies.

SECTION 28-5 Building Services

28-5.1 Utilities. Utilities shall comply with the provisions of Section 7-1.

28-5.2 Heating, Ventilating, and Air Conditioning Equipment. Heating, ventilating, and air conditioning equipment shall comply with the provisions of Section 7-2.

28-5.3 Elevators, Escalators, and Conveyors. Elevators, escalators, and conveyors shall comply with the provisions of Section 7-4.

28-5.4 Rubbish Chutes, Incinerators, and Laundry Chutes. Rubbish chutes, incinerators, and laundry chutes shall comply with the provisions of Section 7-5.

SECTION 28-6* Special Provisions for Aircraft Servicing Hangars

Although new to this edition of the *Code*, Section 28-6, "Special Provisions for Aircraft Servicing Hangars," is nearly identical to Section 29-6, "Special Provisions for Aircraft Storage Hangars," which has been part of the *Code* for numerous editions. Since aircraft hangars are used for both storage and repair, corresponding requirements can be found in both Chapters 28 and 29.

A-28-6 For further information on aircraft hangars, see NFPA 409, *Standard on Aircraft Hangars*. (*See Appendix B.*)

28-6.1 The requirements of Sections 28-1 through 28-5 shall be met, except as modified by 28-6.2 through 28-6.4.

28-6.2 Exits from aircraft servicing areas shall be provided at intervals of not more than 150 ft (45 m) on all exterior walls. There shall be a minimum of two means of egress from each aircraft servicing area. Horizontal exits through interior fire walls shall be provided at intervals of not more than 100 ft (30 m) along the wall.

Exception: Dwarf or "smash" doors in doors used for accommodating aircraft shall be permitted to be used for compliance with these requirements.

28-6.3 Means of egress from mezzanine floors in aircraft servicing areas shall be so arranged that the maximum travel distance to reach the nearest exit from any point on the mezzanine shall not exceed 75 ft (23 m). Such means of egress shall lead directly to a properly enclosed stair that discharges directly to the exterior, to a suitable cutoff area, or to outside stairs.

28-6.4 No dead end may be more than 50 ft (15 m) deep.

Exception: No dead end shall be allowed for high hazard areas.

References Cited in Commentary

[1]NFPA 13, *Standard for the Installation of Sprinkler Systems*, National Fire Protection Association, Quincy, MA, 1991.

[2]NFPA 30, *Flammable and Combustible Liquids Code*, National Fire Protection Association, Quincy, MA, 1990.

[3]NFPA 204M, *Guide for Smoke and Heat Venting*, National Fire Protection Association, Quincy, MA, 1991.

[4]NFPA 92B, *Guide for Smoke Management Systems in Malls, Atria, and Large Areas*, National Fire Protection Association, Quincy, MA, 1991.

[5]NFPA *Fire Protection Handbook*, 17th ed., National Fire Protection Association, Quincy, MA, 1991.

[6]NFPA 68, *Guide for Venting of Deflagrations*, National Fire Protection Association, Quincy, MA, 1988.

[7]NFPA 69, *Standard on Explosion Prevention Systems*, National Fire Protection Association, Quincy, MA, 1986.

[8]*Industrial Fire Hazards Handbook*, 3rd ed., National Fire Protection Association, Quincy, MA, 1990.

29

Storage Occupancies

(See also Chapter 31.)

Storage occupancies include all buildings or structures utilized primarily for the storage or sheltering of goods, merchandise, products, vehicles, or animals. Included in this occupancy group are:

Barns	Hangars (for storage only)
Bulk oil storage	Parking garages
Cold storage	Stables
Freight terminals	Truck and marine terminals
Grain elevators	Warehouses

The national fire incident data bases indicate that storage properties accounted for 57,700 structure fires per year as reported to U.S. fire departments from 1984 to 1988. These fires led to 46 civilian (i.e., nonfire-service personnel) deaths and 622 civilian injuries per year. However, of these, garages associated with private dwellings (which are classified by the *Life Safety Code* as incidental to a one- and two-family dwelling occupancy rather than as a storage occupancy) accounted for 24,700 structure fires per year, with an associated 17 civilian deaths and 310 civilian injuries per year. Other types of storage properties frequently reported in the fire statistics included barns and stables (7,500 fires, 2 civilian deaths, and 44 civilian injuries per year) and tool sheds (4,400 fires, 5 civilian deaths, and 31 civilian injuries per year). Large, commercial storage facilities accounted for less than half the storage property fires.

About 5 percent of the storage properties that experience fires are equipped with automatic fire detectors, and about 5 percent are equipped with automatic suppression equipment. Even when fires in general warehouses are separately grouped for statistical purposes, it appears that most general warehouses are not protected by automatic sprinkler systems. Approximately one-third of victims of storage property fires (excluding dwelling garages) from 1980 to 1988 were outside the room of fire origin when the fire began.

There were 18 multiple-death storage property fires in the 1980s (i.e., fires that killed at least three people), excluding vacant or idle properties. Half of these fires took place in grain elevators or grain silos, which also account for the two most recent storage property fires that killed 10 or more persons. These two 1977 grain elevator fires in Louisiana and Texas killed a total of 54 persons. Of the other 9 multiple-death storage property fires that took place during the 1980s, two occurred in parking garages; a tool shed, a petroleum products storage facility, a barn, an LP-gas bulk plant, an explosives bunker, a paper products storage facility, and a warehouse complex each accounted for one fire.

SECTION 29-1   General Requirements

29-1.1 **Application.** The requirements of this chapter apply to both new and existing storage occupancies. Storage occupancies include all buildings or structures used primarily for the storage or sheltering of goods, merchandise, products, vehicles, or animals.

Note that this chapter applies to both new and existing facilities. Where the requirements vary, it is common for exceptions that apply to existing storage occupancies to appear or for additional requirements to be provided that apply only to new storage occupancies.

Minor storage that is incidental to another occupancy is treated as part of that other occupancy.

29-1.2 **Mixed Occupancies.** (*See 1-5.7 and 29-1.4.*)

29-1.3 **Special Definitions.** None.

29-1.4 **Classification of Occupancy.** Storage occupancies shall include all occupancies defined in 4-1.10. Incidental storage in another occupancy shall not be the basis for overall occupancy classification.

Exception: Storage occupancies or areas of storage occupancies that are used for the purpose of packaging, labeling, sorting, special handling, or other operations requiring an occupant load greater than that normally contemplated for storage shall be classified as industrial occupancies. (See Chapter 28.)

Life safety provisions for storage locations are not extensive, since the number of occupants is generally low and many of those who occupy such a structure are present for only short periods of time. Furthermore, employees of storage occupancies normally do not remain in one location; instead, their assignments require that they move about and perform activities of a short term nature.

Fire records indicate a minimum of life safety problems in storage occupancies. (*See the above summary of storage occupancy fire incidents for 1984 to 1988.*)

Due to the special characteristics of storage occupancies, a number of provisions have been included in the *Code* to modify, as required, those provisions normally applicable to occupancies with larger populations.

The purpose of the Exception to 29-1.4 is to provide suitable egress facilities for storage occupancies, or portions of storage occupancies, where a storage building has a population greater than normally expected. It is common practice to use large numbers of people in a storage building for the purpose of conducting an industrial type of operation, such as labeling, sorting, or packaging; this requires additional egress facilities in accordance with the provisions of Chapter 28 for industrial occupancies.

29-1.5 **Classification of Hazard of Contents.** Contents of storage occupancies shall be classified as low hazard, ordinary hazard, or high hazard, in accordance with Section 4-2, depending upon the character of the materials stored, their packaging, and other factors.

In recent years, a great deal of fire protection literature has focused on the risk associated with rack storage facilities. Although NFPA 231C, *Standard for Rack Storage of Materials*,[1] was developed because of increased awareness of the fire potential inherent in rack storage methods, there is no basis for comparison between the hazard categories in NFPA 231C and those of the *Life Safety Code*. The hazard categories contained in NFPA 231C are established for the design of automatic sprinkler systems. All commodity classifications in NFPA 231C can be considered as low or ordinary hazard of contents as defined in Section 4-2 when determining hazards to life safety.

There is a strong inclination to use the potential for rapid fire growth associated with high-piled or racked storage as justification for establishing strict life safety provisions. However, the arrangement of buildings typical for this type of storage is adequate to allow safe and rapid egress at the first notification or discovery of fire. If a building is not protected by automatic sprinklers, the *Code* then provides adequate provisions (such as those for travel distance to an exit) to help ensure the survival of the occupants.

29-1.6 **Minimum Construction Requirements.** No occupancy requirements.

Some occupancy chapters, such as Chapters 12 and 13, which address the life safety needs of nonambulatory health care occupants, specify minimum building construction type requirements to ensure structural integrity for the time period needed for a lengthy evacuation or for safe refuge within the building. There are no minimum construction requirements imposed, because storage occupancies characteristically have few occupants and those few occupants are ambulatory.

29-1.7 **Occupant Load.** No requirements.

Although 29-1.7 does provide a required occupant load factor for use in calculating a minimum occupant load for which a means of egress system must be sized, a storage occupancy does have an established occupant load. The occupant load is determined on the basis of the maximum number of persons expected to occupy the storage occupancy under any anticipated facility operation. Due to the low occupant load characteristic of storage occupancies, compliance with other *Code* provisions, such as (1) minimum widths for doors, corridors, or passageways, (2) minimum numbers of exits, and (3) travel distance allowances, generally provides a means of egress system capable of handling the actual occupant load without specifically considering the occupant load when the means of egress is designed.

SECTION 29-2 Means of Egress Requirements

29-2.1 **General.** Every required means of egress shall be in accordance with the applicable portions of Chapter 5.

29-2.2 **Means of Egress Components.**

29-2.2.1 Components of means of egress shall be limited to the types described in 29-2.2.2 through 29-2.2.11.

29-2.2.2 **Doors.**

29-2.2.2.1 Doors shall comply with 5-2.1.

29-2.2.2.2 Special locking arrangements complying with 5-2.1.6 are permitted.

This paragraph permits the delayed release lock described in 5-2.1.6, which requires that the building be protected by either a complete automatic sprinkler system or an automatic fire detection system.

29-2.2.2.3 Horizontal sliding doors shall be permitted in a means of egress serving an occupant load of less than 50 in accordance with 5-2.1.14.

For a discussion of specifications for the occupant load of a storage occupancy, see the commentary following 29-1.7.

29-2.2.2.4 Horizontal sliding doors shall be permitted in horizontal exits and smoke barriers in accordance with 5-2.1.14. (*See 29-2.2.5.2.*)

Both 29-2.2.2.3 and 29-2.2.2.4 recognize limited use of horizontal sliding doors in storage occupancies in locations where the *Code* normally requires a side-hinged swinging door. Exception No. 4 to 5-2.1.4.1 addresses horizontal sliding doors by referring to the special requirements in 5-2.1.14. (*See 5-2.1.14.*)

29-2.2.3 **Stairs.**

29-2.2.3.1 Stairs shall comply with 5-2.2.

29-2.2.3.2 Spiral stairs complying with 5-2.2.2.7 are permitted.

Note that, in accordance with Chapter 5, spiral stairs can serve an occupant load of five or fewer persons only.

29-2.2.3.3 In existing buildings, winders complying with 5-2.2.2.8 are permitted.

29-2.2.4 **Smokeproof Enclosures.** Smokeproof enclosures shall comply with 5-2.3.

This paragraph does not mandate the use of smoke-proof enclosures, but it does recognize a smokeproof enclosure as part of the means of egress system in a storage occupancy only if the smokeproof enclosure meets the requirements of 5-2.3. For an example of an occupancy requiring a smokeproof enclosure, see 19-2.11.1, in which nonsprinklered, existing, high rise apartment buildings are required to be provided with smokeproof enclosures in accordance with 5-2.3.

29-2.2.5 Horizontal Exits.

29-2.2.5.1 Horizontal exits shall comply with 5-2.4.

This paragraph does not mandate the use of horizontal exits, but it does recognize a horizontal exit as part of the means of egress system in a storage occupancy only if the horizontal exit meets the requirements of 5-2.4 as modified by 29-2.2.5.2.

29-2.2.5.2* In horizontal exits where the doorway is protected by a fire door on each side of the wall in which it exists, one fire door shall be of the swinging type as provided in 5-2.4.3.6, and the other shall be permitted to be an automatic sliding fire door that shall be kept open whenever the building is occupied.

A-29-2.2.5.2 The customary requirement of building codes for fire doors on both sides of an opening in a fire wall may be met by having an automatic-sliding fire door on one side, and a self-closing fire door swinging out from the other side of the wall. This arrangement qualifies only as a horizontal exit from the side of the sliding door. (*For further information, see A-5-2.4.3.8.*)

The intent of 29-2.2.5.2 and its appendix item is to recognize the common practice of combining a horizontal exit used for life safety with a fire barrier of significant fire resistance rating used for property protection. Opening protectives for such a fire barrier can require the use of a set of two doors in order to achieve the required fire protection rating. It is impractical for both doors to swing in the same direction without interfering with each other, yet operation of two doors that swing in opposite directions is cumbersome for daily or common usage. One swinging and one sliding door provide an acceptable

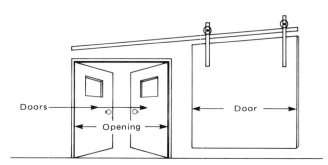

Figure 29-1. *Example of Combination Swinging and Sliding Doors Allowed by 29-2.2.5.2.*

arrangement for day-to-day functioning of the building as shown in Figure 29-1. The open sliding door does not compromise life safety, because, by the time its fusible link mechanism releases the door and allows it to close, temperatures in the vicinity of the door opening render use of the door impractical.

29-2.2.6 Ramps. Ramps shall comply with 5-2.5.

This paragraph does not mandate the use of ramps in storage occupancies, but it does recognize a ramp as part of the means of egress system only if the ramp meets the requirements of 5-2.5.

29-2.2.7 Exit Passageways. Exit passageways shall comply with 5-2.6.

This paragraph does not mandate the use of exit passageways in storage occupancies, but it does recognize an exit passageway as part of the means of egress system only if the exit passageway meets the requirements of 5-2.6.

29-2.2.8 Fire Escape Stairs. Existing fire escape stairs complying with 5-2.8 are permitted.

29-2.2.9 Fire Escape Ladders. Fire escape ladders complying with 5-2.9 are permitted.

29-2.2.10 Slide Escapes. Existing slide escapes complying with 5-2.10 are permitted.

The intent of 29-2.2.10 is to allow the continued use of existing slide escapes, which are a common means of egress from areas that house explosives or other highly hazardous materials in warehouses associated with the chemical industry. The provision allows slide escapes to be considered as part of the required means of egress from existing storage occupancies only if the slide escape meets the requirements of 5-2.10.

29-2.2.11 Alternating Tread Devices. Alternating tread devices complying with 5-2.11 are permitted.

The provisions of 5-2.11, in effect, limit the use of alternating tread devices to those locations where the *Code* recognizes the use of fire escape ladders. (*See 29-2.2.9 and 5-2.9.*)

29-2.3 Capacity of Means of Egress.

Prior editions of the *Code* required a minimum 44-in. (112-cm) width for corridors and passageways within the required means of egress of storage occupancies. A corridor or passageway of that minimum width would provide egress capacity for 220 persons [i.e., 44 in. ÷ 0.2 in. per person (approximately 112 cm ÷ 0.5 cm per person) in accordance with 5-3.3.1 for level travel components]. The prior requirement produced artificially large egress systems, when compared to the occupant load, for many storage occupancies. The requirement was dropped, and the minimum 36-in. (91-cm) width requirement of 5-3.4.1, which addresses the minimum width of any exit access, was made applicable to storage occupancies. Exit access is required to be wider than 36 in. (91 cm) only if a corridor or passageway in a storage occupancy is to provide capacity for more than 180 persons [i.e., 36 in. ÷ 0.2 in. per person (approximately 91 cm ÷ 0.5 cm per person)].

29-2.3.1 The capacity of a means of egress shall be in accordance with Section 5-3.

See commentary following 29-1.7.

29-2.4 Number of Means of Egress. (*See also Section 5-4.*)

29-2.4.1 Every building or structure used for storage and every section thereof considered separately shall have at least two separate means of egress as remotely located from each other as practicable.

Exception No. 1: In low hazard storage occupancies, a single means of egress shall be permitted from any story or section.

Exception No. 2: In ordinary hazard storage occupancies, a single means of egress shall be permitted from any story or section, provided that the exit can be reached within the distance allowed as common path of travel. (See 29-2.5.1 Exception No. 3.)

Exception Nos. 1 and 2 modify the requirement for two, separate, remotely located means of egress due, in part, to the small number of employees typically found in a storage occupancy and the exemplary life safety fire record of such facilities. Exception No. 1 recognizes that a low hazard storage occupancy is not subject to a self-propagating fire, and, therefore, a single means of egress is considered to be safe. Exception No. 2 allows a single means of egress in an ordinary hazard storage occupancy if the total travel distance to the single exit does not exceed the 50-ft (15-m) or 100-ft (30-m) common path of travel allowance for nonsprinklered and sprinklered buildings, respectively (*see Exception No. 3 to 29-2.5.1*). This allowance is made because such a single-exit arrangement is equivalent or superior to a two-exit arrangement that applies the maximum common path of travel allowance and subsequently requires additional travel distance to reach an exit. (*See Figures 29-2a and b.*)

29-2.4.2 Floors or portions thereof with an occupant load of more than 500 shall have the minimum number of separate and remote means of egress specified by 5-4.1.2.

Exception: Existing buildings.

29-2.5 Arrangement of Means of Egress. (*See also Section 5-5.*)

29-2.5.1 Where two or more means of egress are required, they shall be arranged so as to be reached by different paths of travel in different directions.

X1–C1 Common Path Of Travel
X1–E1 Total Travel Distance
X2–E2 Total Travel To Single Exit
    Within Allowable Common Path

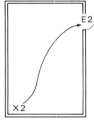

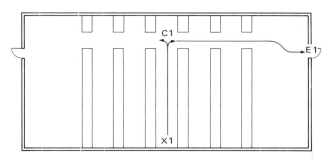

Figures 29-2a and b. *A Single Exit Is Illustrated in Figure 29-2a. It is located within the distance allowed as common path of travel, as addressed by Exception No. 2 to 29-2.4.1 for ordinary hazard storage occupancies, and creates a situation no worse than the common path of travel shown as X1-C1 in Figure 29-2b.*

Exception No. 1: Existing buildings.

Exception No. 2: Low hazard storage occupancies.

See 29-2.4.1 Exception No. 1.

Exception No. 3: Common paths of travel and dead ends shall be allowed in ordinary hazard storage occupancies, provided that they do not exceed 50 ft (15 m) in an unsprinklered building and 100 ft (30 m) in a building protected throughout by an approved automatic sprinkler system in accordance with Section 7-7.

A storage occupancy, despite its characteristically low occupant load, is not permitted to contain a common path of travel that forces an occupant to travel in one direction only for more than 50 ft (15 m) [100 ft (30 m) in a sprinklered building] without providing a route to a second remotely located exit. Therefore, both common path of travel and dead-end corridor limitations are established by Exception No. 3.

29-2.5.2 Travel from all locations in a storage occupancy of high hazard contents shall be via at least two separate means of egress.

29-2.5.3 No dead ends are permitted in high hazard occupancies.

29-2.6 **Travel Distance to Exits.** (*See also Section 5-6.*)

29-2.6.1* Travel to exits shall not exceed 200 ft (60 m) from any point to reach the nearest exit.

Exception No. 1: In a building protected throughout by an approved automatic sprinkler system in accordance with Section 7-7, travel distance shall not exceed 400 ft (122 m).

Exception No. 2: There shall be no limitations on travel to exits for low hazard storage occupancy.

Exception No. 3: Every area used for the storage of high hazard commodities shall have an exit within 75 ft (23 m) of any point in the area where persons may be present. Travel distance shall be measured in accordance with Section 5-6.

Exception No. 4: In areas used for the storage of high hazard commodities and protected throughout by an approved automatic sprinkler system in accordance with Section 7-7, travel distances to an exit shall be within 100 ft (30 m) of any point in the area where persons may be present.

A-29-2.6.1 The travel distance to exits specified contemplate a low population density. Consideration should be given to locating areas that have a relatively high population, such as lunchrooms, meeting rooms, packaging areas, and offices near the outside wall of the building, to keep the travel distance to a minimum.

Paragraph 29-2.6.1 and its exceptions establish limitations on travel distance for storage occupancies. Note that the provisions create a direct relationship between the level of hazard of contents housed by a building and its life safety requirements. Therefore, in low hazard storage occupancies, there is no limitation on travel distance. As the level of hazard of contents increases, travel limitations are required. Storage buildings housing ordinary hazards and lacking protection are limited to 200 ft (60 m) of travel distance to an exit. A distance of 400 ft

(122 m) is permissible if complete automatic sprinkler protection is provided. In high hazard storage occupancies, travel distance is restricted to a maximum of 75 ft (23 m) if nonsprinklered and 100 ft (30 m) if the building is equipped with a complete automatic sprinkler system.

The absence of travel distance restrictions for low hazard storage occupancies is reasonable, since the small fire risk posed by low hazard materials, coupled with the low occupant population, provides a minimal risk to life safety. The imposition of restrictive provisions would not be consistent with good fire protection and reasonable life safety requirements, since the possibility of fire is very low and little difficulty is expected to be experienced by occupants when evacuating the building. (*See Section 4-2 for the definition of low hazard contents.*)

29-2.7 Discharge from Exits. Discharge from exits shall be in accordance with Section 5-7.

29-2.8 Illumination of Means of Egress.

29-2.8.1 Illumination of means of egress shall be provided in accordance with Section 5-8.

Exception: In structures occupied only during daylight hours, with windows arranged to provide the required level of illumination of all portions of the means of egress during these hours, illumination requirements may be waived by special permission of the authority having jurisdiction.

The provisions of 29-2.8.1 are not intended to require the installation of extensive and unneeded exit illumination systems in storage occupancies. Illumination is required for the exit and for the exit access, which is limited to designated aisles, corridors, and passageways that lead to an exit. Limiting the extent of the lighting system to egress areas eliminates the necessity for installing specialized lighting systems throughout storage areas, a practice that would be extremely costly while providing little or no return in safety to life.

The exception waives the requirement for illumination systems if a building, including stairways, is sufficiently lit during periods of occupancy by means of natural lighting. The term "windows," as used in the text of the excep-

tion, should not be interpreted literally. The term is meant to include skylights, open wall sections, and similar means of illumination by natural sources. The provisions are based on the fact that there is no need for a lighting system if the building is unoccupied during non-daylight hours.

29-2.9 Emergency Lighting.

29-2.9.1 All storage occupancies shall have emergency lighting in accordance with Section 5-9.

Exception No. 1: Storage occupancies do not require emergency lighting when not normally occupied.

Exception No. 2: In structures occupied only during daylight hours, with skylights or windows arranged to provide the required level of illumination of all portions of the means of egress during these hours, emergency lighting is not required.

Exceptions to the requirement for emergency lighting are included for the reasons stated in the commentary following 29-2.8.1. Exception No. 1 allows circuit arrangements that disconnect power from emergency lighting systems when the building is unoccupied. In many warehouses, power is turned off during periods when the building is unoccupied. This power disconnection serves fire prevention, energy conservation, and security purposes.

29-2.10 Marking of Means of Egress. Signs designating exits or ways of travel thereto shall be provided in accordance with Section 5-10.

29-2.11 Special Features. (Reserved.)

SECTION 29-3 Protection

29-3.1 Protection of Vertical Openings.

29-3.1.1 Every stairway, elevator shaft, escalator opening, manlift opening, and other vertical opening shall be enclosed or protected in accordance with Section 6-2.

Exception No. 1: Unprotected vertical openings connecting not more than three floors shall be permitted in accordance with the conditions of 6-2.4.5.

Exception No. 2: An atrium in accordance with 6-2.4.6 shall be permitted.

Exceptions No. 1 and No. 2 to 29-3.1.1 recognize the provisions of Chapter 6 for limited vertical openings and atriums as adequate for storage occupancies.

Exception No. 3: In existing buildings with low or ordinary hazard contents and protected throughout by an approved automatic sprinkler system in accordance with Section 7-7, unprotected vertical openings shall be permitted where they do not serve as required exits. All required exits under such conditions shall consist of smokeproof enclosures in accordance with 5-2.3, outside stairs in accordance with 5-2.2, or horizontal exits in accordance with 5-2.4.

Exception No. 3 to 29-3.1.1 recognizes that an existing storage occupancy may contain unprotected vertical openings and still provide a reasonable level of safety to life if the building houses only low or ordinary hazard contents and is protected by a complete automatic sprinkler system. Smokeproof enclosures and outside stairways (the only types of vertical exits allowed by this exception) must be fully enclosed or protected against vertical fire spread and meet the requirements of Chapter 5. The unenclosed vertical openings must not be used in any manner as a means of egress, although they can be used as convenience openings for normal operations.

While the major reason for allowing this provision is the high cost of enclosing all vertical openings in existing buildings, there is actually little effect on the life safety of occupants where the building houses low or ordinary hazard contents. However, some difficulties in fire control are created, since unprotected vertical openings can contribute to fire spread in buildings and result in extensive property damage and potential impact on occupants prior to evacuation. Therefore, a complete automatic sprinkler system is required.

29-3.2 **Protection from Hazards.** No occupancy requirements.

29-3.3 **Interior Finish.**

29-3.3.1 Interior wall and ceiling finish shall be Class A, B, or C in accordance with Section 6-5 in the storage areas and shall be as required by 5-1.4 in exit enclosures.

29-3.3.2 **Interior Floor Finish.** No occupancy requirements.

29-3.4 **Detection, Alarm, and Communication Systems.**

29-3.4.1 **General.** Storage occupancies shall be provided with a fire alarm system in accordance with Section 7-6.

Exception No. 1: Storage occupancies limited to low hazard contents.

Exception No. 2: Storage occupancies with ordinary or high hazard contents not exceeding an aggregate floor area of 100,000 sq ft (9,300 sq m).

Exception No. 3: Storage occupancies with complete automatic extinguishment protection.

29-3.4.2 **Initiation.** Initiation of the required fire alarm system shall be by either manual or automatic means in accordance with 7-6.2.

29-3.4.3 **Notification.** The required fire alarm system shall sound an audible alarm in a continuously attended location for purposes of initiating emergency action.

Subsection 29-3.4 requires the installation of a fire alarm system in nonsprinklered storage occupancies with an aggregate floor area of over 100,000 sq ft (9,300 sq m). An alarm system is not required in a storage occupancy limited to housing low hazard contents, regardless of its size, nor is one required in a sprinklered storage occupancy, regardless of size. Storage placement limits visibility in buildings with large floor areas. As a result, personnel who work in storage areas may be unaware of the occurrence of fire for a long period of time. If fire spreads, which is highly possible in an unprotected storage building, means of exit access could be blocked. An alarm system provides a means of alerting all occupants to the presence of fire and allows for timely egress. The alarm is required to sound in a continuously attended location as a precaution in case it is necessary to alert additional fire fighting personnel or initiate search and rescue procedures. The *Code* does not specify an alarm system as a property protection requirement, although the probability of property loss is reduced in any occupancy where an alarm system is installed. In buildings provided with an automatic sprinkler system, it is assumed that an alarm will sound in a continuously attended location upon operation of the sprinkler system.

29-3.4.4 In high hazard storage occupancies, the required fire alarm system shall automatically initiate an occupant evacuation alarm signal in accordance with 7-6.3.

29-3.5 Extinguishing Requirements. None.

29-3.6 Corridors. The provisions of 5-1.3.4 shall not apply.

If the provisions of 5-1.3.4 were not specifically exempted, they would require 1-hour fire resistance rated corridors where corridors serve more than 30 persons. The life safety fire record of storage occupancies and the functional need served by open floor areas makes separation of corridors unnecessary.

SECTION 29-4   Special Provisions

29-4.1 Operating Features. (*See Chapter 31.*)

29-4.2 High Rise Buildings. High rise storage occupancies shall comply with the automatic sprinkler requirements of 30-8.2.1.

Exception No. 1: Low hazard storage occupancies.

Exception No. 2: Existing storage occupancies.

The provisions of 29-4.2, which apply to high rise storage occupancy buildings, are new to this edition of the *Code*. This paragraph references a portion of the high rise building provisions of Section 30-8 available to an occupancy chapter for mandatory purposes. New high rise buildings classified as ordinary hazard and new high rise storage occupancy buildings classified as high hazard are required to be protected throughout by an approved, supervised automatic sprinkler system in accordance with 30-8.2.1. The remainder of Section 30-8 is not mandated in high rise storage occupancy buildings.

SECTION 29-5   Building Services

29-5.1 Utilities. Utilities shall comply with the provisions of Section 7-1.

29-5.2 Heating, Ventilating, and Air Conditioning Equipment. Heating, ventilating, and air conditioning equipment shall comply with the provisions of Section 7-2.

29-5.3 Elevators, Escalators, and Conveyors. Elevators, escalators, and conveyors shall comply with the provisions of Section 7-4.

29-5.4 Rubbish Chutes, Incinerators, and Laundry Chutes. Rubbish chutes, incinerators, and laundry chutes shall comply with the provisions of Section 7-5.

SECTION 29-6*   Special Provisions for Aircraft Storage Hangars

Section 29-6, which addressed aircraft hangars used for both storage and servicing in previous editions of the *Code*, has been retitled and revised so as to apply only to aircraft storage hangars. For those provisions applicable to aircraft servicing hangars see Section 28-6, "Special Provisions for Aircraft Servicing Hangars."

A-29-6 For further information on aircraft hangars, see NFPA 409, *Standard on Aircraft Hangars.* (*See Appendix B.*)

29-6.1 The requirements of Sections 29-1 through 29-5 shall be met, except as modified by 29-6.2 through 29-6.4.

29-6.2 Exits from aircraft storage areas shall be provided at intervals of not more than 150 ft (45 m) on all exterior walls. There shall be a minimum of two exits serving each aircraft storage area. Horizontal exits through interior fire walls shall be provided at intervals of not more than 100 ft (30 m) along the wall.

Exception: Dwarf or "smash" doors in doors used for accommodating aircraft shall be permitted to comply with these requirements.

Paragraph 29-6.2 specifies two alternate methods of providing egress from aircraft storage hangars. Where egress is possible through the outside wall, a space of 150 ft (45 m) between exit doors is adequate. In larger hangars, the servicing bay may have offices and shops located along one or more sides, with the walls constructed of fire resistance rated materials. In those cases where the wall has a fire resistance rating, exit spacing of up to 100 ft (30 m) is specified. If the wall is nonrated, access to the outside is required. During inclement weather, large hangar doors cannot be left open to provide a means of egress, so it is common procedure to provide small access doors for personnel in the larger aircraft hangar door. The small door can be considered a normal means of egress from an aircraft hangar. If possible, the door should swing in the direction of egress; however, this may not be possible due to the design of the aircraft door. (*For further information on aircraft hangars, see NFPA 409, Standard on Aircraft Hangars.*)[2]

29-6.3 Means of egress from mezzanine floors in aircraft storage areas shall be so arranged that the maximum travel distance to reach the nearest exit from any point on the mezzanine shall not exceed 75 ft (23 m). Such means of egress shall lead directly to a properly enclosed stairwell discharging directly to the exterior, to a suitable cutoff area, or to outside stairs.

29-6.4 No dead end may be more than 50 ft (15 m) deep.

Exception: No dead end shall be allowed for high hazard areas.

SECTION 29-7*   Special Provisions for Grain or Other Bulk Storage Elevators

A-29-7 For further information, see NFPA 61B, *Standard for the Prevention of Fires and Explosions in Grain Elevators and Facilities Handling Bulk Raw Agricultural Commodities (see*

Appendix B). The exit requirements for storage elevators are based upon the possibility of fire and are not based upon the possibility of grain dust explosions.

29-7.1 The requirements of Sections 29-1 through 29-5 shall be met, except as modified in 29-7.2 through 29-7.4.

29-7.2 There shall be at least two means of egress from all working levels of the head house. One of these means of egress shall be a stair to the level of exit discharge that is enclosed by a dust-resistant 1-hour fire resistance rated enclosure in accordance with 5-1.3. The second means of egress shall be either:

(a) An exterior stair or basket ladder-type fire escape accessible from all working levels of the head house that provides a passage to ground level, or

(b) An exterior stair or basket ladder-type fire escape accessible from all working levels of the head house that provides access to the top of adjoining structures that provide a continuous path to the means of egress described in 29-7.3.

Exception: Stair enclosures in existing structures shall be permitted to have non-fire-rated dust-resistant enclosures.

It is not the intent of 29-7.2 to require a fully dust-tight shaft, since the door will allow passage of limited amounts of dust during the normal course of daily operations. However, the shaft should be separated from the operating areas by fire resistance rated construction and be as free of dust as possible.

29-7.3 There shall be an exterior stair or basket ladder-type fire escape that provides passage to ground level from the top of the end of an adjoining structure, such as a silo, conveyor, gallery, or gantry.

29-7.4 **Underground Spaces.**

29-7.4.1 Underground spaces shall have at least two means of egress, one of which may be a means of escape. The means of escape shall be arranged to eliminate dead ends.

29-7.4.2 Travel distance to means of escape or exit shall not exceed 200 ft (60 m).

Exception No. 1: Existing facilities.

Exception No. 2: In a building protected throughout by an approved automatic sprinkler system in accordance with Section 7-7, travel distance shall not exceed 400 ft (122 m).

Section 29-7 provides three basic requirements:

1. Two means of egress from all working levels of the head house.
2. A means of egress at the end of all galleries and similar spaces, thereby eliminating dead ends.
3. A means of escape provided to eliminate dead ends in underground areas.

Paragraph 29-7.2 requires that one means of egress from the head house must be an enclosed stair. The alternate means of egress can be either an outside stair or a basket ladder-type fire escape connecting all working levels and leading to either the ground or the top of an adjoining structure that complies with 29-7.3.

The principal hazard of elevator storage structures that handle combustible materials is dust explosion. A dust explosion can be violent enough to damage or destroy the primary means of egress required in 29-7.2.

SECTION 29-8   Special Provisions for Parking Structures

29-8.1   General Requirements.

29-8.1.1*   Application. The following provisions apply to parking structures of closed or open type, above or below ground, but not to mechanical or exclusively attendant-type parking facilities, which are not occupied by customers and thus require a minimum of exits. The requirements of Sections 29-1 through 29-7 shall not apply.

A-29-8.1.1   For further information on garages, including a definition of "open garage," see NFPA 88A, *Standard for Parking Structures. (See Appendix B.)*

The intent of the special provisions for garages is to provide adequate life safety for the patrons of parking facilities, who will probably be unfamiliar with the garage and its arrangement. Where parking attendants are the only occupants that enter the parking area, the *Code's* intent is to provide exits in accordance with the previous sections of Chapter 29. In such instances, the provisions for ordinary hazard occupancies apply.

Paragraph 29-8.1.1 has been reworded and additional provisions have been added to Section 29-8 to allow the section to be self-contained and, therefore, independent of Sections 29-1 through 29-7, which are applicable to other storage occupancies. However, Section 29-8 does reference other portions of the *Code*, mainly Chapters 1 through 7.

For further information on garages, see NFPA 88A, *Standard for Parking Structures.*[3]

29-8.1.2   Mixed Occupancies.

29-8.1.2.1   Where both parking and repair operations are conducted in the same building, the entire building shall comply with Chapter 28.

Exception: If the parking and repair sections are separated by a minimum of 1-hour fire-rated construction, the parking and repair sections shall be permitted to be treated separately.

The Exception to 29-8.1.2.1 allows a building to house parking and repair operations simultaneously and to be treated independently if they are separated by 1-hour fire resistance rated construction. The repair operation would be governed by the provisions of Chapter 28 and the parking facilities by those of Section 29-8. Guidelines for the rating of construction assemblies can be found in NFPA 220, *Standard on Types of Building Construction.*[4] Special requirements for repair garages can be found in NFPA 88B, *Standard for Repair Garages.*[5]

29-8.1.2.2   In areas where repair operations are conducted, the means of egress shall comply with Chapter 28, "Industrial Occupancies."

29-8.1.3   Special Definitions.

Open-Air Parking Structure.   Buildings, structures, or portions thereof used for parking motor vehicles and having at least 25 percent of the total wall area open to atmosphere at each level, utilizing at least two sides of the structure.

29-8.1.4 **Classification of Occupancy.** Incidental vehicle parking in another occupancy shall not be the basis for overall occupancy classification.

29-8.1.5 **Classification of Hazard of Contents.** Parking structures used only for the storage of vehicles shall be classified as ordinary hazard in accordance with Section 4-2.

Paragraph 29-8.1.5 appropriately classifies the hazard of contents as ordinary hazard for garages used only for the storage of vehicles. With the increased use of plastic materials in vehicle bodies and interiors, a garage presents a hazard greater than that of low hazard contents in accordance with the definitions of the hazard of contents classifications specified by Section 4-2.

29-8.1.6 **Minimum Construction Requirements.** No requirements.

29-8.1.7 **Occupant Load.** No requirements.

See commentary following 29-1.7.

29-8.2 **Means of Egress Requirements.**

29-8.2.1 **General.** Means of egress shall be in accordance with Chapter 5 and this section.

29-8.2.2 **Means of Egress Components.**

29-8.2.2.1 Components of means of egress shall be limited to the types described in 29-8.2.2.2 through 29-8.2.2.8.

29-8.2.2.2 **Doors.**

(a) Doors shall comply with 5-2.1.
(b) Special locking arrangements complying with 5-2.1.6 are permitted.

This item permits the delayed release lock described in 5-2.1.6, which requires that the building be protected throughout by automatic sprinklers or a complete fire detection system.

(c) Horizontal sliding doors shall be permitted in a means of egress serving an occupant load of less than 50 in accordance with 5-2.1.14.

For a discussion of specifications for the occupant load of a storage occupancy, see the commentary following 29-1.7.

(d) Horizontal sliding doors shall be permitted in horizontal exits and smoke barriers in accordance with 5-2.1.14.

See commentary following 29-2.2.2.4.

(e) An opening for the passage of automobiles shall be permitted to serve as an exit from a street floor, provided no door or shutter is installed therein.

29-8.2.2.3 **Stairs.**

(a) Stairs shall comply with 5-2.2.
(b) In existing buildings, winders in accordance with 5-2.2.2.8 are permitted.

29-8.2.2.4 **Smokeproof Enclosures.** Smokeproof enclosures shall comply with 5-2.3.

29-8.2.2.5 **Horizontal Exits.** Horizontal exits shall comply with 5-2.4.

29-8.2.2.6 **Ramps.** Ramps shall comply with 5-2.5 and shall not be subject to normal vehicular traffic where used as an exit.

Exception No. 1: In a ramp-type open-air parking structure with open vehicle ramps not subject to closure, the ramp shall be permitted to serve in lieu of the second exit from floors above the level of exit discharge, provided the ramp discharges directly outside at the street level.

Exception No. 2: For parking structures extending only one floor level below the level of exit discharge, a vehicle ramp leading directly to the outside shall be permitted to serve in lieu of the second exit, provided no door or shutter is installed therein.

The Exception Nos. 1 and 2 to 29-8.2.2.6 allow the designer to use garage ramps as part of the means of egress. Properly arranged ramps can facilitate safe egress to a degree well in excess of that required for the given number of occupants.

Exception No. 1 allows consideration of ramps as an alternate secondary means of egress from floors located above the street level where they are arranged so that discharge to the street level is clear and unobstructed. Ramps from floors located above the street level are required to be open and must not be enclosed by walls or other means that will confine smoke and heat in the ramp structure. Exception No. 1 permits a ramp as part of the exit design only if the parking garage is an open-type structure. Ramps located in closed garages cannot be considered as part of the egress system, and normal means of egress (specified in 29-8.2.2) should be provided.

Exception No. 2 allows a ramp to be used as an alternate secondary means of egress in a closed or open garage that extends not more than one floor level below the level of exit discharge. The ramp must not have a door or a shutter and must lead directly outside.

29-8.2.2.7 **Exit Passageways.** Exit passageways shall comply with 5-2.6.

29-8.2.2.8 **Fire Escape Stairs.** Fire escape stairs complying with 5-2.8 are permitted for existing parking structures only.

29-8.2.3 **Capacity of Means of Egress.** (*See also 29-8.2.4 and 29-8.2.5.*)

See commentary following 29-1.7.

29-8.2.4 **Number of Means of Egress.** (*See also Section 5-4.*)

29-8.2.4.1 Every floor of every parking structure shall have access to at least two separate exits.

Note that there is no exception to the two-exit rule for parking garages.

29-8.2.4.2 Floors or portions thereof with an occupant load of more than 500 shall have the minimum number of separate and remote means of egress specified by 5-4.1.2.

Exception: Existing buildings.

29-8.2.5 **Arrangement of Means of Egress.** (*See also Section 5-5.*)

29-8.2.5.1 Exits shall be so arranged that from any point in the parking structure the paths of travel to the two exits will be in different directions.

Exception: A common path of travel shall be permitted for the first 50 ft (15 m) from any point.

29-8.2.5.2 No dead end shall exceed 50 ft (15 m).

29-8.2.5.3 If fuel dispensing devices are located within a parking structure, travel away from the fuel dispensing device in any direction shall lead to an exit with no dead end in which occupants might be trapped by fire. Within closed parking structures, exits shall be arranged and located to meet the following additional requirements:

(a) Exits shall lead to the outside of the building on the same level or to stairs; no upward travel shall be permitted unless direct outside exits are available from that floor.

(b) Any story below that story at which fuel is being dispensed shall have exits leading directly to the outside via outside stairs or doors at ground level.

Paragraph 29-8.2.5.3 specifies the conditions required for protection of the occupants of parking garages from fires that may be caused by gasoline-dispensing operations located inside the building. Additional items apply when this is done in closed parking structures. Item (b) requires that direct access to the outside be provided from floors located below those on which gasoline is dispensed. This prevents the possibility of gasoline vapors, which are heavier than air, accumulating in enclosed portions of a means of egress, such as inside exit stairways.

The hazards associated with dispensing gasoline inside buildings are avoided by dispensing fuel outdoors, as in the case of ordinary gasoline filling stations. See NFPA 30A, *Automotive and Marine Service Station Code,*[6] for requirements on dispensing gasoline indoors.

29-8.2.6 **Travel Distance to Exits.** Exits in parking structures shall be so arranged that no point will be more than 150 ft (45 m), measured in accordance with Section 5-6, from the nearest exit.

Exception No. 1: Travel distance shall not exceed 200 ft (60 m) for open floors of nonsprinklered, open-air parking structures and 300 ft (91 m) in open-air parking structures protected throughout by an approved automatic sprinkler system.

Exception No. 2: Travel distance shall not exceed 200 ft (60 m) for enclosed parking structures protected throughout by an approved automatic sprinkler system in accordance with Section 7-7.

29-8.2.7 **Discharge from Exits.** Exit discharge shall comply with Section 5-7.

29-8.2.8 **Illumination of Means of Egress.** Every public space, hall, stair enclosure, and other means of egress shall have illumination in accordance with Section 5-8.

Exception: Structures occupied only during daylight hours, arranged to provide the required level of illumination of all portions of the means of egress by natural means, may have the requirement for artificial illumination waived by the authority having jurisdiction.

29-8.2.9 **Emergency Lighting.** Every public space, hall, and stair enclosure shall have emergency lighting in accordance with Section 5-9.

Exception: In structures occupied only during daylight hours, arranged to provide the required level of illumination of all portions of the means of egress by natural means, emergency lighting is not required.

29-8.2.10 **Marking of Means of Egress.** Signs designating exits or ways of travel thereto shall be provided in accordance with Section 5-10.

29-8.2.11 **Special Features.** (Reserved.)

29-8.3 **Protection.**

29-8.3.1 **Protection of Vertical Openings.** No requirements.

29-8.3.2 **Protection from Hazards.** No requirements. (*See 29-8.1.2.1.*)

29-8.3.3 **Interior Finish.**

29-8.3.3.1 **Interior Wall and Ceiling Finish.** Interior wall and ceiling finish shall be Class A, B, or C in accordance with Section 6-5 in parking structures, and shall be as required by 5-1.4 in exit enclosures.

29-8.3.3.2 **Interior Floor Finish.** No requirements.

29-8.3.4 **Detection, Alarm, and Communication Systems.**

29-8.3.4.1 **General.** Parking structures exceeding an aggregate floor area of 100,000 sq ft (9,300 sq m) shall be provided with a fire alarm system in accordance with Section 7-6.

Exception No. 1: Open-air parking structures.

Exception No. 2: Parking structures protected throughout by an approved automatic sprinkler system in accordance with Section 7-7.

29-8.3.4.2 **Initiation.** Initiation of the required fire alarm system shall be by either manual or automatic means in accordance with 7-6.2.

29-8.3.4.3 **Notification.** The required fire alarm system shall sound an audible alarm in a continuously attended location for purposes of initiating emergency action.

29-8.3.5 **Extinguishing Requirements.** None.

29-8.3.6 **Corridors.** The provisions of 5-1.3.4 shall not apply.

See commentary following 29-3.6.

29-8.4 **Special Provisions.**

29-8.4.1 **Operating Features.** (*See Chapter 31.*)

29-8.4.2 **High Rise Buildings.** No requirements.

29-8.5 **Building Services.**

29-8.5.1 **Utilities.** Utilities shall comply with the provisions of Section 7-1.

29-8.5.2 **Heating, Ventilating, and Air Conditioning Equipment.** Heating, ventilating, and air conditioning equipment shall comply with the provisions of Section 7-2 except as otherwise required in Section 29-8.

29-8.5.3 **Elevators, Escalators, and Conveyors.** Elevators, escalators, and conveyors shall comply with the provisions of Section 7-4.

29-8.5.4 **Rubbish Chutes, Incinerators, and Laundry Chutes.** Rubbish chutes, incinerators, and laundry chutes shall comply with the provisions of Section 7-5.

References Cited in Commentary

[1]NFPA 231C, *Standard for Rack Storage of Materials*, National Fire Protection Association, Quincy, MA, 1991.

[2]NFPA 409, *Standard on Aircraft Hangars*, National Fire Protection Association, Quincy, MA, 1990.

[3]NFPA 88A, *Standard for Parking Structures*, National Fire Protection Association, Quincy, MA, 1991.

[4]NFPA 220, *Standard on Types of Building Construction*, National Fire Protection Association, Quincy, MA, 1985.

[5]NFPA 88B, *Standard for Repair Garages*, National Fire Protection Association, Quincy, MA, 1991.

[6]NFPA 30A, *Automotive and Marine Service Station Code*, National Fire Protection Association, Quincy, MA, 1990.

30

Special Structures and High Rise Buildings

(See also Chapter 31.)

A "usual" occupancy might be housed in an "unusual" or special structure. Two examples would be a large convention center (Class A assembly occupancy) located on a pier so that the facility is surrounded by water on three sides or a moderate size restaurant (Class C assembly occupancy) located on an upper level of an air-traffic control tower. An authority having jurisdiction should ensure that any engineered solutions to the special structure's inherent egress deficiencies must provide an overall level of safety to life equivalent to that specified by the requirements of the occupancy chapter applicable to the structure's use.

Occupancies housed in unusual or special structures also include any building or structure that cannot be properly classified under any of the other occupancy groups, due to the performance of a function not covered by the provisions of those groups or to an unusual combination of functions inherent to the purpose of the building or structure. Such miscellaneous buildings and structures must conform to the fundamental principles stated in Chapter 2, as well as to the provisions of this chapter.

SECTION 30-1   General Requirements

30-1.1 **Application.** The requirements of this chapter apply to both new and existing occupancies in special structures and to those occupancies regulated by Chapters 8 through 29 that are in a special structure or building.

Exception: Any building, tower, or vessel surrounded by water and under the jurisdiction of the U.S. Coast Guard, such as a lighthouse, offshore oil platform, or vessel mooring point, and designed and arranged in accordance with Coast Guard regulations is exempt from the requirements of this chapter.

Occupancies in special structures pose a special challenge to life safety. Many of the structures covered by the provisions of Chapter 30 are also governed by provisions in other chapters of the *Code*. The provisions for specific occupancies contained in Chapters 8 through 29 take precedence over the provisions in Chapter 30. However, all occupancies housed in windowless and underground buildings must comply with the additional provisions of

Section 30-7 for complete automatic sprinkler protection, emergency lighting, smoke venting, and directional indicator signs for egress paths.

Although the *Code* is essentially complete, the provision of adequate means of egress from many special structures requires unique solutions. In many instances, engineered solutions will clearly exceed the minimum provisions of Chapter 30. However, the unique character of a structure should not become an excuse for reducing safety to life. The *Code* user is cautioned to exercise judgment when determining the egress requirements for special structures that are not specifically addressed in Chapter 30.

30-1.2 Mixed Occupancies. *(See 1-5.7.)*

30-1.3 Special Definitions.

30-1.3.1 Tower. Independent structure or portion of a building occupied for observation, signaling, or similar limited use and not open to general use.

30-1.3.2 Vehicle. Any trailer, railroad car, street car, bus, or similar conveyance that is not mobile or is attached to a building or is permanently fixed to a foundation.

30-1.3.3 Vessel. Any ship, barge, or other vessel permanently fixed to a foundation or mooring or unable to get under way by means of its own power and occupied for purposes other than navigation.

30-1.3.4* Underground Structure. A structure or portions of a structure in which the story is below the level of exit discharge.

Exception: A structure or portions of a structure shall not be considered an underground structure if:

(a) The story is provided on at least two sides with at least 20 sq ft (1.9 sq m) of opening entirely above the adjoining grade level in each 50 lineal ft (15 m) of exterior enclosing wall area, and

(b) The openings have minimum dimensions of not less than 22 in. (55.9 cm) in width and 24 in. (61 cm) in height and are unobstructed to allow for ventilation and rescue operations from the exterior, and

(c) The bottom of the openings are not more than 44 in. (112 cm) above the floor, and

(d) The openings are readily identifiable from both the exterior and interior of the story, and

(e) The openings are readily openable from both the exterior and interior of the story.

A-30-1.3.4 In determining openings in exterior walls, doors or access panels may be included. Windows may also be included if they are openable or provide a breakable glazed area.

The exception to the definition of underground structures establishes the criteria by which the provision of openings for ventilation and rescue exempts stories below the level of exit discharge from classification as underground. The basement in Figure 30-1 is not considered underground if:

1. Openings are provided on at least two sides, and
2. Openings are located entirely above the adjoining grade level, and
3. Openings comprise a minimum of 20 sq ft (1.9 sq m) of area per 50 lineal ft (15 lineal m) of walls, and
4. X = a minimum width of 22 in. (55.9 cm) of unobstructed opening
   Y = a minimum height of 24 in. (60 cm) of unobstructed opening
   Z = a maximum of 44 in. (112 cm) from floor to bottom of opening, and
5. Openings are readily identified, and
6. Openings are readily openable.

Openings are permitted in the form of a window or an access panel.

30-1.3.5 Windowless Structure. A structure or portions of a structure lacking means for direct access to the outside from the enclosing walls or lacking outside openings for ventilation or rescue through windows.

Exception No. 1: A one-story structure or portion thereof shall not be considered a windowless structure if:

(a) The story is provided with grade level doors, access panels, or windows on two sides of the building, spaced not more than 125 ft (38 m) apart in the exterior walls, and

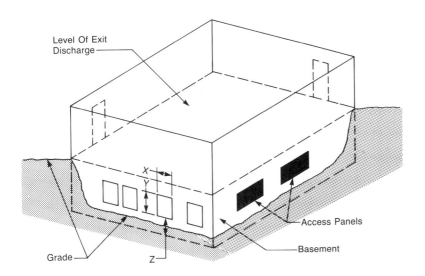

Level Of Exit
Discharge

X
Y

Access Panels

Grade

Z

Basement

Figure 30-1. *Underground Structures. If the conditions of the exception to the definition of underground structures (see 30-1.3.4) are met, the basement is not considered to be underground and, therefore, is not subject to the requirements of Section 30-7.*

(b) The access panels or windows have a minimum dimension of not less than 22 in. (55.9 cm) in width and 24 in. (61 cm) in height and are unobstructed to allow for ventilation and rescue operations, and

(c) The bottom of the openings are not more than 44 in. (112 cm) above the floor, and

(d) The openings are readily identifiable from both the exterior and interior of the story, and

(e) The openings are readily openable from both the exterior and interior of the story.

Exception No. 2: A structure or portion thereof more than one story in height shall not be considered a windowless structure if:

(a) Access openings are provided for the first story as required in Exception No. 1 above, and

(b) Every story above the first floor is provided with access openings or windows on two sides of the building, spaced not more than 30 ft (9.1 m) apart, and

(c) The openings have minimum dimensions of not less than 22 in. (55.9 cm) in width and 24 in. (61 cm) in height and are unobstructed to allow for ventilation and rescue operations, and

(d) The bottoms of the openings are not more than 44 in. (112 cm) above the floor, and

(e) The openings are readily identifiable from both the exterior and interior of the story, and

(f) The openings are readily openable from both the exterior and interior of the story.

Note that a structure is not considered windowless if certain provisions are made for openings for ventilation and rescue. The provisions are more stringent for multistory structures than for single-story structures. (*In connection with the above discussion on windowless structures, see the commentary associated with the definition of an underground structure contained in 30-1.3.4.*)

30-1.3.6 **Water Surrounded Structure.** A structure fully surrounded by water.

30-1.3.7 **Open Structure.** Operations and equipment conducted in open air and not enclosed within buildings, such as found in oil refining and chemical processing plants. Roofs or canopies providing shelter without enclosing walls may be provided and shall not be considered an enclosure.

Subsection 30-1.3 defines the special structures addressed in Chapter 30. If an occupancy housed in one of these structures is regulated by Chapters 8 through 29, the provisions of the appropriate chapter also apply. An arrangement that frequently causes confusion is an assembly occupancy, such as a restaurant or sightseeing lookout point, located in a tower structure. A number of towers have been constructed for promotional purposes in cities and amusement centers, and many are as high as 500 ft (150 m). Despite such unusual arrangements, the placement of an assembly occupancy in a tower requires consideration of the provisions of Chapters 8 and 9 in addition to the requirements of Chapter 30 (*see 30-1.4*). However, towers that serve special purposes, such as fire observation, radio or television transmission, or some other similar function, must meet only the requirements of Chapter 30.

30-1.4   **Classification of Occupancy.** Occupancies regulated by Chapters 8 through 29 that are in special structures or buildings shall meet the requirements of those chapters, except as modified by Chapter 30.

30-1.5   Classification of hazard of contents shall be as defined in Section 4-2.

30-1.6   **Minimum Construction Requirements.** No requirements.

30-1.7   **Occupant Load.** The occupant load of special structures shall be as determined by the maximum actual design occupant load.

Exception: Any special structure or part of a special structure utilized for an occupancy regulated by Chapters 8 through 29, in which case the requirements of the appropriate chapter shall apply.

SECTION 30-2   Means of Egress Requirements

30-2.1   **General.** Each required means of egress shall be in accordance with the applicable portions of Chapter 5.

30-2.2*   **Means of Egress Components.**

A-30-2.2   Escape chutes, controlled descent devices, and elevators may provide escape routes in special structures; however, they should not be substituted for the provisions of this *Code*.

30-2.2.1   Components of means of egress shall be limited to the types described in 30-2.2.2 through 30-2.2.11.

Special structures housing occupancies regulated by Chapters 8 through 30 must also meet the requirements of Chapters 8 through 30 as discussed in the commentary to 30-1.3.7. Therefore, acceptable components will often be further restricted by the applicable occupancy chapter.

30-2.2.2   **Doors.**

30-2.2.2.1   Doors shall comply with 5-2.1.

30-2.2.2.2   Horizontal sliding doors shall be permitted in a means of egress serving an occupant load of less than 50 in accordance with 5-2.1.14.

30-2.2.2.3   Horizontal sliding doors shall be permitted in horizontal exits and smoke barriers in accordance with 5-2.1.14.

Both 30-2.2.2.2 and 30-2.2.2.3 recognize limited use of horizontal sliding doors in special structures where the *Code* normally requires a side-hinged swinging door. Before horizontal sliding doors are used in a usual occupancy housed in a special structure, the appropriate occupancy chapter should be referenced to determine if application of 5-2.1.14 is permitted for that occupancy. (*See the commentary following 30-1.3.7 and 30-2.2.1. Also see 5-2.1.14.*)

30-2.2.3   **Stairs.**

30-2.2.3.1   Stairs shall comply with 5-2.2.

30-2.2.3.2   Spiral stairs complying with 5-2.2.2.7 are permitted.

Note that 5-2.2.2.7 permits spiral stairs to serve an occupant load of five or fewer persons only. (*Also see commentary following 30-2.2.1.*)

30-2.2.3.3   In existing buildings, winders complying with 5-2.2.2.8 are permitted.

30-2.2.4 Smokeproof Enclosures. Smokeproof enclosures shall comply with 5-2.3.

This paragraph does not mandate the use of smokeproof enclosures, but it does recognize a smokeproof enclosure as part of the means of egress system in some special structures (*see the commentary following 30-2.2.1*) only if the smokeproof enclosure meets the requirements of 5-2.3. For an example of an occupancy requiring a smokeproof enclosure, see 19-2.11.1 in which non-sprinklered, existing, high rise apartment buildings are required to be provided with smokeproof enclosures in accordance with 5-2.3.

30-2.2.5 Horizontal Exits. Horizontal exits shall comply with 5-2.4.

This paragraph does not mandate the use of horizontal exits, but it does recognize a horizontal exit as part of the means of egress system in some special structures (*see the commentary following 30-2.2.1*) only if the horizontal exit meets the requirements of 5-2.4.

30-2.2.6 Ramps. Ramps shall comply with 5-2.5.

This paragraph does not mandate the use of ramps, but it does recognize a ramp as part of the means of egress system in some special structures (*see the commentary following 30-2.2.1*) only if the ramp meets the requirements of 5-2.5.

30-2.2.7 Exit Passageways. Exit passageways shall comply with 5-2.6.

This paragraph does not mandate the use of exit passageways, but it does recognize an exit passageway as part of the means of egress system in some special structures (*see the commentary following 30-2.2.1*) only if the exit passageway meets the requirements of 5-2.6.

30-2.2.8 Escalators and Moving Walks. In existing buildings, previously approved escalators and moving walks complying with 5-2.7 shall be permitted to be continued in use.

Note that 5-2.7 allows existing escalators and moving walks to continue to be recognized as part of the required means of egress if permitted by an occupancy chapter.

In earlier editions of the *Code*, such escalators and moving walks may have been recognized by providing egress capacity for 75 persons. In order to qualify as exits, escalators and moving walks must also meet the requirements of 5-2.2.6, which address exit enclosure.

Note that escalators protected in accordance with the sprinkler-vent method, the spray nozzle method, the rolling shutter method, or the partial enclosure method do not constitute acceptable exits, but may continue to serve as exit access if previously approved as such. (*Also see commentary following 30-2.2.1.*)

30-2.2.9 Fire Escape Stairs. Fire escape stairs complying with 5-2.8 are permitted for existing buildings. (*Also see commentary following 30-2.2.1.*)

30-2.2.10 Fire Escape Ladders.

30-2.2.10.1 Fire escape ladders complying with 5-2.9 are permitted.

30-2.2.10.2 Towers and open structures such as a forest fire observation or railroad signal tower that are designed for occupancy by not more than three persons employed therein shall be permitted to be served by ladders instead of stairs.

30-2.2.11 Alternating Tread Devices. Alternating tread devices complying with 5-2.11 are permitted.

The provisions of 5-2.11, in effect, limit the use of alternating tread devices to those locations where the *Code* recognizes the use of fire escape ladders. (*See 30-2.2.1 and 5-2.9.*)

30-2.3 Capacity of Means of Egress.

30-2.3.1 The width and capacity of a means of egress shall be in accordance with Chapter 5.

Exception No. 1: The means of egress for towers shall be provided for the persons expected to occupy the space.

Exception No. 2: Open structures.

Exception No. 3: Spaces not subject to human occupancy because of machinery or equipment are excluded from consideration.

Exception No. 2 to 30-2.3.1 recognizes the multiple means of egress available in open structures, such as those found in petrochemical and process industries. An open structure is actually an access platform to the equipment that it surrounds or supports. Normal occupancy is very limited in number and occasional in frequency. If a fire should block one means of egress, a number of alternate means of egress remain accessible. An escape route is provided by the fixed means of egress, and rescue is possible from any portion of the structure by use of the emergency procedures of fire fighting personnel. The potential for exposure of portions of the structure not involved in a fire is minimal, since, in open platforms, flames, heat, and smoke are safely dispersed directly into the atmosphere, and not into the uninvolved portions of the structure.

30-2.3.2 The minimum width of any component of the means of egress shall be in accordance with 5-3.4.

Exception: Where ladders are permitted by 30-2.2.

Prior editions of the *Code* required a minimum 44-in. (112-cm) width for corridors and passageways within the required means of egress of special structures. A corridor or passageway of that minimum width would provide egress capacity for 220 persons [i.e., 44 in. ÷ 0.2 in. per person (approximately 112 cm ÷ 0.5 cm per person) in accordance with 5-3.3.1 for level travel components in all but high hazard areas and nonsprinklered health care occupancies]. The prior requirement produced artificially large egress systems, when compared to the occupant load, for many occupancies. The requirement was dropped, and the minimum 36-in. (91-cm) width requirement of 5-3.4.1, which addresses the width of any exit access, was made applicable to special structures. Exit access is required to be wider than 36 in. (91 cm) only if a corridor or passageway in a special structure is to provide capacity for more than 180 persons [i.e., 36 in. ÷ 0.2 in. per person (approximately 91 cm ÷ 0.5 cm per person)].

30-2.4 **Number of Means of Egress.** *(See also Section 5-4.)*

30-2.4.1 There shall be not less than two means of egress from every story or section and at least one exit must be reached without traversing another story.

Exception No. 1: Piers used exclusively to moor cargo vessels and to store materials, where provided with proper means of egress from structures thereon to the pier and a single means of access to the mainland as appropriate with the pier's arrangement.

Exception No. 2: The grade level of open structures which by their very nature contain an infinite number of exits.

Exception No. 3: Towers shall be permitted to have a single exit if the following conditions are met:*

(a) The tower is subject to occupancy by less than 25 persons.

(b) The tower is not used for living or sleeping purposes and is subject to occupancy by only able-bodied persons.

(c) The tower is of Type I, II, or IV construction. (See 6-2.1.)

(d) The tower interior finish is Class A or B.

(e) The tower has no combustible materials in, under, or in the immediate vicinity, except necessary furniture.

(f) There are no high hazard occupancies in the tower or immediate vicinity.

Exception No. 4: Open structures occupied by not more than three people with travel distance to exit not more than 200 ft (60 m).

The provisions of 30-2.4.1, which apply to the minimum number of means of egress required for special structures, have been revised for this edition of the *Code* in order to clarify that, in addition to providing every story or section with access to at least two means of egress, one exit must be located on each floor so that the entrance to that exit (e.g., a door opening into an enclosed exit stair) can be reached without requiring travel to another floor.

The intent of Exception No. 1 to 30-2.4.1 is to recognize the open nature of a pier and to equate a pier with a public way for purposes of exit arrangement. Note that the exception applies mainly to cargo and storage piers, which are occupied by a limited number of people, the majority of whom are accustomed to the arrangement of piers. The risk to life safety is considered minimal under these conditions, and one exit is acceptable.

Exception No. 3 to 30-2.4.1 restricts the provisions for a single means of egress from a tower. Calculation of the total occupancy of a tower [*see item (a) of this exception*] should be based on the actual number expected to occupy the facility. This method of calculation is valid, since the tower is not subject to the provisions for calculating occupant load specified in Chapters 8 through 29. Limitations on the combustibility and interior finish of the structure are established so that the potential exposure of the tower occupants to fire is minimal. Types I, II, and IV construction [*see item (c) of Exception No. 3*] are defined in NFPA 220, *Standard on Types of Building Construction*.[1]

One difficulty associated with the requirements for exits in towers is acurate determination of the level of exposure of the tower to combustible materials under or in the immediate vicinity of the structure. Judgment should be used by the authority having jurisdiction and other users of the *Code* to ensure that arbitrary limitations are not established that restrict the use of the tower too severely. For example, a forest fire tower is usually located in a clearing in a large forest. The proximity of trees to the tower could be interpreted as constituting combustible materials in the "immediate" vicinity of the tower. Reasonable clearances [such as a clear space of 50 ft (15 m) to 100 ft (30 m)] between the tower and forest could be considered adequate separation for the life safety of the tower's occupants. Similar judgment is required where evaluating the clearance between high hazard occupancies and towers.

A-30-2.4.1 **Exception No. 3.** The Washington Monument, Washington, D.C., is an example of a tower where it would not be practicable to provide a second stairway.

30-2.4.2 Floors or portions thereof with an occupant load of more than 500 shall have the minimum number of separate and remote means of egress specified by 5-4.1.2.

Exception: Existing buildings.

30-2.5 **Arrangement of Means of Egress.** (*See also Section 5-5.*)

30-2.5.1 Where two or more means of egress are required, they shall be arranged so as to be reached by different paths of travel in different directions.

Exception: A common path of travel shall be permitted for the first 50 ft (15 m) from any point.

30-2.5.2 No dead end shall exceed 50 ft (15 m).

30-2.5.3* **Piers.**

A-30-2.5.3 For further information on pier fire protection, see NFPA 307, *Standard for the Construction and Fire Protection of Marine Terminals, Piers, and Wharves.* (*See Appendix B.*)

30-2.5.3.1 Piers not meeting requirements of 30-2.4.1 Exception No. 1 and occupied for other than cargo handling and storage shall have means of egress arranged in accordance with Chapters 8 through 29. (*See 30-1.4.*) In addition, one of the following measures shall be provided on piers extending over 150 ft (45 m) from shore to minimize the possibility that fire under or on the pier may block escape of occupants to shore.

(a) The pier shall be arranged to provide two separate ways of travel to shore, such as by two well separated walkways or independent structures, or

(b) The pier deck shall be open and fire resistive, set on noncombustible supports, or

(c) The pier shall be open and unobstructed and shall be 50 ft (15 m) or more in width if less than 500 ft (150 m) long, or its width shall be not less than 10 percent of its length if over 500 ft (150 m) long, or

(d) The pier deck shall be provided with automatic sprinkler protection for combustible substructure and all superstructures, if any.

The provisions of 30-2.5.3.1 apply to all pier structures except those structures waived by Exception No. 1 to 30-2.4.1. Note that these provisions must be applied in addition to those contained in Chapters 8 through 29 for those piers exceeding 150 ft (45 m) in length. The provisions of 30-2.5.3.1(a) through (d) are not required to be applied in total; in other words, the pier is required to comply with only one of the four subparts.

30-2.6 **Travel Distance to Exits.** Travel to exits, where not regulated by Chapters 8 through 29, shall not exceed 100 ft (30 m).

Exception No. 1: In a building or structure protected throughout by an approved automatic sprinkler system in accordance with Section 7-7, travel distance shall not exceed 150 ft (45 m).

Exception No. 2: Where ladders are permitted in 30-2.2.10.2.

Exception No. 3: Open structures.

30-2.7 **Discharge from Exits.** Discharge from exits shall be in accordance with Section 5-7.

Exception: Towers or other structures provided with one exit, as permitted by 30-2.4 and arranged in accordance with 30-2.5, shall be permitted to have 100 percent of the exit discharge through areas on the level of discharge.

30-2.8 **Illumination of Means of Egress.** Illumination of means of egress shall be provided in accordance with Section 5-8.

Exception No. 1: Open structures.

Exception No. 2: Towers with ladders for exits as permitted by 30-2.2.10.2.

30-2.9 **Emergency Lighting.** Emergency lighting shall be provided in accordance with Section 5-9.

Exception No. 1: Open structures.

Exception No. 2: Towers with ladders for exits as permitted by 30-2.2.10.2.

Exception No. 3: Locations not routinely inhabited by humans.

Exception No. 4: Structures occupied only during daylight hours, with windows arranged to provide the required level of illumination of all portions of the means of egress during these hours, upon special approval of the authority having jurisdiction.

30-2.10 **Marking of Means of Egress.** Signs designating exits or ways of travel thereto shall be provided in accordance with Section 5-10.

Exception No. 1: Towers with ladders for exits as permitted by 30-2.2.10.2.

Exception No. 2: Open structures.

Exception No. 3: Locations where routine human habitation is not provided.

30-2.11 **Special Features.** (Reserved.)

SECTION 30-3 Protection

30-3.1 **Protection of Vertical Openings.** Every stairway, elevator shaft, escalator opening, and other vertical opening shall be enclosed or protected in accordance with Chapter 5 and Section 6-2.

Exception No. 1: In towers where there is no occupancy below the top floor level, stairs shall be permitted to be open with no enclosure required or fire escape stairs shall be permitted to be used where the structure is entirely open.

Exception No. 2: Towers with ladders for exits as permitted by 30-2.2.10.2.

Exception No. 3: Open structures.

30-3.2 **Protection from Hazards.** Every special structure shall have automatic, manual, or such other protection as may be appropriate to the particular hazard that is designed to minimize danger to occupants in case of fire or other emergency before they have time to utilize exits to escape.

Exception: Special structures, such as open structures, with only occasional occupancy.

The provisions of 30-3.2 require careful analysis to ensure that fire protection required for life safety is provided. The key element of the requirement is that protection must be adequate to safeguard occupants during the time needed to reach exits. Fire protection systems that may be needed for property protection or for control of fire losses in a process or in an occupancy will, in many cases, provide superflous features for the life safety of occupants and are beyond the scope of this *Code.*

30-3.3 **Interior Finish.**

30-3.3.1 Interior wall and ceiling finish shall be Class A, B, or C in accordance with Section 6-5 and as required by 5-1.4 in exit enclosures.

30-3.3.2 **Interior Floor Finish.** No requirements.

30-3.4 Detection, Alarm, and Communication Systems.

30-3.4.1 General. A fire alarm system shall be provided in accordance with Section 7-6.

Exception No. 1: Towers designed for occupancy by not more than three persons.

Exception No. 2: Open structures.

30-3.4.2 Initiation. Initiation of the required fire alarm system shall be by either manual or automatic means in accordance with 7-6.2.

30-3.4.3 Notification. The required fire alarm system shall sound an audible alarm in a continuously attended location for purposes of initiating emergency action.

30-3.5 Extinguishing Requirements. None.

30-3.6 Corridors. The corridor provisions for the occupancy involved within the special structure shall apply.

SECTION 30-4 Special Provisions

30-4.1 Operating Features. (*See Chapter 31.*)

30-4.2 High Rise Buildings. The high rise building provisions for the occupancy involved within the special structure shall apply. (*See Chapters 8 through 29.*)

Exception: Existing buildings.

SECTION 30-5 Building Services

30-5.1 Utilities. Utilities shall comply with the provisions of Section 7-1.

30-5.2 Heating, Ventilating, and Air Conditioning Equipment. Heating, ventilating, and air conditioning equipment shall comply with the provisions of Section 7-2.

30-5.3 Elevators, Escalators, and Conveyors. Elevators, escalators, and conveyors shall comply with the provisions of Section 7-4.

30-5.4 Rubbish Chutes, Incinerators, and Laundry Chutes. Rubbish chutes, incinerators, and laundry chutes shall comply with the provisions of Section 7-5.

SECTION 30-6* Special Provisions for Vehicles and Vessels

A-30-6 Firesafety information for manufactured home parks will be found in NFPA 501A, *Standard for Firesafety Criteria for Manufactured Home Installations, Sites, and Communities.* (*See Appendix B.*)

30-6.1 Any vehicle as defined by 30-1.3.2 that is subject to human occupancy shall comply with the requirements of this *Code* that are appropriate to buildings of similar occupancy. (*See 30-1.4.*)

30-6.2 Any ship, barge, or other vessel permanently fixed to a foundation or mooring, or unable to get under way by means of its own power, and occupied for purposes other than navigation shall be subject to the requirements of this *Code* applicable to buildings of similar occupancy.

SECTION 30-7 Special Provisions for Underground Structures and Windowless Buildings

See the definitions of underground structures and windowless structures in 30-1.3.

30-7.1 General.

30-7.1.1 In addition to meeting the applicable requirements of this section, occupancies in underground structures and windowless buildings meeting the purposes regulated by Chapters 8 through 29 shall meet the requirements of those chapters. (*See 30-1.4.*)

30-7.1.2 Windowless or underground structures with an occupant load of more than 50 persons shall be protected throughout by an approved automatic sprinkler system in accordance with Section 7-7.

Exception: Existing structures with an occupant load not greater than 100.

30-7.1.3 Windlowless or underground structures shall be provided with emergency lighting in accordance with Section 5-9.

Exception: One- and two-family dwellings.

30-7.2 Underground Structures.

30-7.2.1 Exits from underground structures having an occupant load greater than 50 shall be cut off from the level of exit discharge per Section 5-1 and shall be provided with outside smoke venting facilities or other means to prevent the exits from becoming charged with smoke from any fire in the area served by the exits.

Exception No. 1: Existing structures with an occupant load not greater than 100.

Exception No. 2: As modified by Chapters 8 through 29.

30-7.2.2 Underground structures with an occupant load greater than 100 having combustible contents, interior finish, or construction shall have automatic smoke venting facilities in accordance with Chapter 7 in addition to automatic sprinkler protection.

Exception: Existing structures.

30-7.2.3 Exit stair enclosures shall be provided with a sign at each floor level landing in accordance with 5-2.2.6.6 and shall include a chevron-shaped indicator to show direction to exit discharge.

The provisions contained in 30-7.1.1 through 30-7.2.3 that regulate life safety deficiencies in windowless or underground buildings are minimal and are considered to be in addition to those contained in Chapters 8 through 29. It is not the intent of these paragraphs to provide a means of circumventing the life safety provisions contained in other chapters of the *Code*. If the building under consideration is windowless or located underground and, due to its occupancy classification, subject to stricter requirements than those contained in Chapter 30, those stricter provisions of the *Code* must be applied. For example, the provisions of 8-4.1, which apply to new assembly occupancies located in underground buildings or underground areas of buildings, require that each level located more than 30 ft (9.1 m) below the level of exit discharge must be equipped with a mechanical means of moving occupants vertically, such as an elevator or escalator.

Windowless and underground structures pose special risks to life safety, since the buildings cannot be easily vented of products of combustion. In an area from which there is no direct access to the outside and where there are no windows to permit outside fire department rescue operations and ventilation, fire or smoke may tend to produce panic. Therefore, additional corrective measures, such as complete automatic sprinkler protection and automatic smoke venting systems, must be provided where necessary to ensure an adequate level of safety to life.

The provisions of 30-7.2.3 are new to this edition of the *Code* and address the need for cues to guide occupants toward the exit and level of exit discharge. Traveling upward in an exit stair may appear illogical, since most egress from buildings involves downward travel within an exit stair enclosure. However, the direction of travel chosen by an occupant can depend upon how that occupant entered the building. Paragraph 30-7.2.3 requires that a sign be provided within the exit stair enclosure to direct occupants to the exit discharge. The indicator must be of the same chevron-design as required by 5-10.4.1 for directional exit signs.

"Fire Hazards of Windowless Buildings"[2] addresses the life safety problems encountered in windowless buildings. "Underground Buildings"[3] contains a detailed review of the fire experience in underground structures.

SECTION 30-8   High Rise Buildings

Section 30-8 was added to the *Code* in the 1988 Edition and does not itself require that any special provisions be applied to high rise buildings. Instead, it is intended to provide a menu of options for high rise buildings that can be wholly or partially mandated by other *Code* sections. For example, Chapters 8, 10, 16, and 18 (which apply to new assembly occupancies, new educational occupancies, new hotels and dormitories, and new apartment buildings, respectively) require high rise buildings to comply with the entire package of requirements contained in Section 30-8. Chapters 12 and 14 (applicable to new health care occupancies and new detention and correctional occupancies) require high rise buildings to comply with the provisions of 30-8.2 that cover extinguishment, which require sprinklers and standpipes. Chapters 24, 28, and 29 (which address new mercantile, new industrial, and new storage occupancies) require that high rise buildings be sprinklered in accordance with 30-8.2.1. Chapter 26 requires that new high rise business occupancies provide protection approximately equivalent to that of Section 30-8 by incorporating a section within Chapter 26 that is nearly identical to Section 30-8. The distinction is that some of the requirements in Chapter 26 apply to buildings 150 ft (45 m) or more in height, as opposed to the 75-ft (23-m) height criterion of Section 30-8. (*See the commentary associated with the requirements of 26-4.2.*)

30-8.1 General.

30-8.1.1 Where required by Chapters 8 through 30, the provisions of this section shall apply to high rise buildings as defined in Chapter 3.

Exception: As modified by Chapters 8 through 30.

30-8.1.2 In addition to the requirements of this section, compliance with all other applicable provisions of this *Code* shall be required.

30-8.2 Extinguishment Requirements.

30-8.2.1* High rise buildings shall be protected throughout by an approved supervised automatic sprinkler system installed in accordance with Section 7-7. A sprinkler control valve and a water flow device shall be provided for each floor.

A-30-8.2.1 Where an occupancy chapter permits the omission of sprinklers in specific spaces, such as small bathrooms and closets in residential occupancies, the building is

still considered to be "protected throughout" for the purposes of this section.

30-8.2.2 High rise buildings shall be protected throughout by a Class I standpipe system installed in accordance with Section 7-7 as follows:

(a) For buildings less than 150 ft (45 m) in height, the standpipe system shall be of any system type defined in Section 1-7 of NFPA 14, *Standard for the Installation of Standpipe and Hose Systems*.

(b) For buildings 150 ft (45 m) or more in height, the standpipe system shall be a wet system as defined in Section 1-7 of NFPA 14, *Standard for the Installation of Standpipe and Hose Systems*.

The requirements of 30-8.2.2 are new to this edition of the *Code* and expand the menu of provisions that can be mandated for high rise buildings in accordance with the various occupancy chapters to include standpipes. Although the *Life Safety Code* has traditionally considered standpipes mainly as property protection devices, limited mandatory standpipe requirements for life safety purposes have been included for many editions of the *Code*. Standpipes are required on stages in assembly occupancies and in resident housing areas of detention and correctional occupancies (*see 8-3.2.1.12, 9-3.2.1.12, 14-3.5.5 and 15-3.5.5*); this is based on the belief that (1) occupants will not be able to leave the fire area immediately, either due to the presence of large numbers of people, as is characteristic of an assembly occupancy, or because doors to the outside will not be unlocked, as might be expected in a detention and correctional occupancy, and (2) that trained persons will be present early in the fire development to make effective use of the standpipe and hose.

Standpipes can serve to increase life safety, as well as property protection, in high rise buildings because of the lengthy evacuation times associated with tall buildings. In many cases, fire emergency plans advise occupants who are not in immediate danger of exposure to fire to remain within the building to allow responding fire service personnel better access to the standpipes within the exit stair enclosures. Use of standpipes at that time supplements the operation of the required automatic sprinkler system.

30-8.3 Detection, Alarm, and Communication Systems.

30-8.3.1* A fire alarm system utilizing an approved emergency voice/alarm communication system shall be installed in accordance with Section 7-6.

A-30-8.3.1 The need for voice communication can be based on a decision regarding staged or partial evacuation versus total evacuation of all floors. The determination of need is a function of occupancy classification and building height.

30-8.3.2 Two-way telephone communication service shall be provided for fire department use. This system shall be in accordance with NFPA 72, *Standard for the Installation, Maintenance, and Use of Protective Signaling Systems*. The communication system shall operate between the central control station and every elevator car, every elevator lobby, and each floor level of exit stairs.

Exception: Where the fire department radio system is approved as an equivalent system.

30-8.4 Emergency Lighting and Standby Power.

30-8.4.1 Emergency lighting in accordance with Section 5-9 shall be provided.

30-8.4.2 Standby power in accordance with NFPA 70, *National Electrical Code*, and NFPA 110, *Standard for Emergency and Standby Power Systems*, Class I, Type 60 shall be provided. The standby power system shall have a capacity and rating sufficient to supply all required equipment. Selective load pickup and load shedding shall be permitted in accordance with NFPA 70, *National Electrical Code*. The standby power system shall be connected to the following:

(a) Emergency lighting system.
(b) Fire alarm system.
(c) Electric fire pump.
(d) Central control station equipment and lighting.

(e) At least one elevator serving all floors and shall be transferable to any elevator.
(f) Mechanical equipment for smokeproof enclosures.

30-8.5 Central Control Station.

30-8.5.1* A central control station shall be provided in a location approved by the fire department. The control station shall contain:

(a) Voice fire alarm system panels and controls.
(b) Fire department two-way telephone communications service panels and controls.
(c) Fire detection and fire alarm system annunciation panels.
(d) Elevator floor location and operation annunciators.
(e) Sprinkler valve and water flow annunciators.
(f) Emergency generator status indicators.
(g) Controls for any automatic stairway door unlocking system.
(h) Fire pump status indicators.
(i) A telephone for fire department use with controlled access to the public telephone system.

A-30-8.5.1 It is not the intent of the paragraph to require any of the equipment in the list, other than the telephone for fire department use, but only to provide the controls, panels, annunciators, and similar equipment at this location where the equipment is provided or required by another section of the Code.

References Cited in Commentary

[1]NFPA 220, *Standard on Types of Building Construction*, National Fire Protection Association, Quincy, MA 1985.

[2]E. E. Juillerat, "Fire Hazards of Windowless Buildings," *NFPA Quarterly*, Vol. 58, No. 1, pp. 22-30, July 1964.

[3]Horatio Bond, "Underground Buildings," *Fire Journal*, Vol. 59, No. 4, pp. 52-55, July 1965.

31

Operating Features

(See also Section 31-2 through 31-9 for special occupancy requirements.)

Chapter 31 serves a unique purpose in the *Life Safety Code*. It's provisions complement the structural features mandated by the earlier chapters of the *Code*. These complete the package of requirements that ensure a minimum acceptable level of safety to life. As a rule, codes and standards are confined to the subject of proper building arrangements, without emphasis or advice on issues such as maintenance, inspections, drills, or the regulation of building contents (i.e., furniture and furnishings).

These issues are germane to the scope and content of the *Code*, because, as stated in Section 2-1, "the design of exits and other safeguards shall be such that reliance for safety to life in case of fire or other emergency will not depend solely on any single safeguard; additional safeguards shall be provided for life safety in case any single safeguard is ineffective due to some human or mechanical failure."

Prevention of "human or mechanical failure" involves the *Code* in the areas of care, operation, maintenance, and inspection of equipment. Furthermore, because life safety depends upon proper action by occupants during an emergency, the importance of drills and checklists of emergency procedures is critical. Because the protection safeguards built into a structure may be rendered ineffective by the introduction of hazardous material, it is necessary to address those characteristics of a building's contents (such as arrangement, flammability, or rate of heat release under combustion) that have a bearing on safety to life.

Chapter 31 addresses these factors for all occupancies in general and covers them specifically for each occupancy individually. Most of Section 31-1 applies to all occupancies. Some provisions, such as those of 31-1.4.1, which address flame resistance of draperies, and 31-1.4.2 through 31-1.4.4, which address ignition resistance and rate of heat release limitations for upholstered furniture and mattresses, apply only where specifically required by provisions of Sections 31-2 through 31-9, which cover individual occupancies.

Chapter 31 focuses on how individuals (occupants, owners, tenants, and maintenance personnel) can augment the fixed, active life safety systems and other passive building features required by the *Code*. This allows people to be involved in providing for their own safety and that of others. If such personal involvement is properly addressed, the enthusiasm and commitment generated will help to ensure compliance with all *Code* requirements.

SECTION 31-1 General Requirements

31-1.1 Construction, Repair, Improvement Operations.

31-1.1.1 In buildings under construction, adequate escape facilities shall be maintained at all times for the use of construction workers. Escape facilities shall consist of doors, walkways, stairs, ramps, fire escapes, ladders, or other approved means or devices arranged in accordance with the general principles of the *Code* insofar as they can reasonably be applied to buildings under construction. See also NFPA 241, *Standard for Safeguarding Construction, Alteration, and Demolition Operations*.

31-1.1.2 Flammable or explosive substances or equipment for repairs or alterations shall be permitted in a building of normally low or ordinary hazard classification while the building is occupied only if the condition of use and safeguards provided are such as not to create any additional danger or handicap to egress beyond the normally permissible conditions in the building.

The threat of fire during construction, alteration, or demolition operations is ever-present. The potential for fire is inherently greater during these procedures than after they are completed due to previous occupancy hazard, the presence of large quantities of combustible materials and debris, and ignition sources such as temporary heating devices, cutting/welding/plumber's torch operations, open fires, and smoking. The threat of arson is also greater during construction and demolition operations due to the on-site availability of combustible materials and the open access. NFPA 241, *Standard for Safeguarding Construction, Alteration, and Demolition Operations*,[1] provides measures for preventing or minimizing worker fire injuries, life loss, and other fire damage during construction, alteration, and demolition operations.

31-1.2 Means of Egress Reliability.

31-1.2.1 Every required exit, exit access, or exit discharge shall be continuously maintained free of all obstructions or impediments to full instant use in the case of fire or other emergency.

For a given occupancy, the combination of requirements contained in Chapters 5 and 6 and in the corresponding occupancy chapter provide for an adequately-sized and protected means of egress system. This provision of Chapter 31 emphasizes the importance of maintaining that egress system usable at all times. In the case of a Class A mercantile occupancy, the minimum 5-ft (152-cm) aisle width required by 24-2.5.6 and 25-2.5.6 cannot, subsequent to receipt of the store's occupancy permit, be filled with mid-aisle displays that reduce the exit access aisle width to less than 5 ft (152 cm). Similarly, in a business occupancy with an exit stair of the minimum 44-in. (112-cm) width required by 5-2.2.2.1, the stair width cannot be reduced by the introduction of a mechanized chair lift that is installed, for example, to comply with legislation mandating accessibility by the mobility impaired. In an apartment building complex, the required width of the outside exit discharge sidewalk that runs along the side of the building cannot be reduced by the presence of a trash dumpster on either a temporary or permanent basis.

Paragraph 31-1.2.1 does not designate responsibility for keeping the means of egress (i.e., exit accesses, exits, and exit discharges) free and clear of obstructions. The individuals responsible for each facility, whether they are managers, owners, or operators, must make certain that required egress components are maintained in usable condition. The authority having jurisdiction has the power to ensure that this is done.

31-1.2.2 Furnishings and Decorations in Means of Egress.

31-1.2.2.1 No furnishings, decorations, or other objects shall be so placed as to obstruct exits, access thereto, egress therefrom, or visibility thereof.

31-1.2.2.2 Hangings or draperies shall not be placed over exit doors or otherwise be located to conceal or obscure any exit. Mirrors shall not be placed on exit doors. Mirrors shall not be placed in or adjacent to any exit in such a manner as to confuse the direction of exit.

Paragraphs 31-1.2.2.1 and 31-1.2.2.2 provide guidance for the interior decoration and maintenance of buildings that serve as restaurants and theaters, where excessive decoration used to establish a style or theme often camouflages, and in some cases obstructs, exits. For such occupancies, care must be taken to ensure that the required, standard, well-marked exit access that leads to an unobstructed exit is not obscured in the pursuit of period or style authenticity. For example, a restaurant that is heavily decorated with red wall coverings might use a green exit sign to help meet the requirements of these paragraphs, despite the fact that Chapter 5 does not require exit signs to be of a certain color.

31-1.2.2.3 There shall be no obstruction by railings, barriers, or gates that divide the open space into sections appurtenant to individual rooms, apartments, or other uses. Where the authority having jurisdiction finds the required path of travel to be obstructed by furniture or other movable objects, the authority may require that they be fastened out of the way or may require that railings or other permanent barriers be installed to protect the path of travel against encroachment.

Paragraph 31-1.2.2.3 relates to the arrangement of furniture, as well as the arrangement of railings, gates, or barriers, that is found in lobbies, foyers, waiting spaces, or staging areas of businesses, hospitals, health care clinics, hotels, and apartments. Because these large spaces are often subdivided by furniture (chairs, tables, and plants) or by railings and gates, furnishings must be prevented from blocking access to exits. This paragraph recommends fastening furnishings so that they are clear of access to exits or placing railings around them to ensure that they will be held in a fixed position and cannot be easily moved or rearranged. This will prevent obstruction of an access to an exit. The *Code* recognizes the problem created by storage that is placed within the exit access aisles of storage rooms in mercantile occupancies, which is a violation of *Code* requirements. Both Chapters 24 and 25, in accordance with the provisions of 24-2.5.10(d) and

25-2.5.10(d), require fixed barriers to define such exit access as a specific condition that must be met in order to allow exit access to pass through storerooms.

31-1.3 Equipment Maintenance and Testing.

31-1.3.1 Whenever or wherever any device, equipment, system, condition, arrangement, level of protection, or any other feature is required for compliance with the provisions of this *Code*, such device, equipment, system, condition, arrangement, level of protection, or other feature shall thereafter be permanently maintained unless the *Code* exempts such maintenance.

Because the *Code* requires the specific device or system, such equipment is necessary to provide the minimum level of safety to life mandated by the *Code*. Therefore, the device or system must be maintained in usable condition. Without such maintenance, the overall level of safety to life would fall below that required by the *Code*.

31-1.3.2 Every required automatic sprinkler system, fire detection and alarm system, smoke control system, exit lighting, fire door, and other item of equipment required by this *Code* shall be continuously maintained in proper operating condition.

31-1.3.3 Any equipment requiring test or periodic operation to assure its maintenance shall be tested or operated as specified elsewhere in this *Code* or as directed by the authority having jurisdiction.

31-1.3.4 Systems shall be under the supervision of a responsible person who shall ensure that proper tests are made at specified intervals and have general charge of all alterations and additions.

31-1.3.5 Systems shall be tested at intervals required by the appropriate standards listed in Chapter 32.

31-1.3.6* **Automatic Sprinkler Systems.** All automatic sprinkler systems required by this *Code* shall be continuously maintained in reliable operating condition at all times, and such periodic inspections and tests shall be made as are necessary to ensure proper maintenance. When a required automatic sprinkler system is out of service for more than four hours within a 24-hour period, the building shall be evacuated, or an approved fire watch shall be provided for all portions left unprotected by the sprinkler system shutdown until the sprinkler system has been returned to service.

A-31-1.3.6 NFPA 13A, *Recommended Practice for the Inspection, Testing, and Maintenance of Sprinkler Systems (see Appendix B)*, gives detailed information on maintenance procedures.

During the life cycle of any building, the sprinkler system will have to be shut down at times for legitimate reasons. When periodic testing and maintenance are performed, the downtime should be relatively short. When areas of a building and its mechanical systems are renovated, the downtime might be more excessive if advance planning has not been done to help ensure that the system, or most of the system, can be restored to service despite the scope of the renovation or the extent of an unexpected impairment. If the automatic sprinkler system was required by the *Code* or was installed in order to make use of one of the alternatives offered by the *Code*, it must be in good, operable condition in order for the building to be considered to be in compliance with the *Code*.

Instead of designating a building with an inoperative sprinkler system as a noncomplying and prohibiting occupancy under all conditions in accordance with the provisions of 1-7.1, 31-1.3.6 differentiates between those sprinkler system impairments with a duration of less than 4 hours within a 24-hour period and those impairments in excess of that time. Continued occupancy of a building that has a sprinkler system impairment of more than 4 hours within any 24-hour period (i.e., either a single period of more than 4 hours or the aggregate of multiple periods that, in total, exceed 4 hours within any 24-hour period) can be tolerated only if a fire watch acceptable to the authority having jurisdiction is provided. Such lengthy impairments generally indicate a situation that involves a problem more serious in nature than typical system maintenance or testing.

31-1.3.7* **Alarm and Fire Detection Systems.** Fire alarm signaling equipment shall be restored to service as promptly as possible after each test or alarm and shall be kept in normal condition for operation. Equipment requiring rewinding or replenishing shall be rewound or replenished as promptly as possible after each test or alarm.

A-31-1.3.7 NFPA 72H, *Guide for Testing Procedures for Local, Auxiliary, Remote Station, and Proprietary Protective Signaling Systems*, gives detailed information on testing procedures.

31-1.3.8 **Periodic Testing of Emergency Lighting Equipment.** A functional test shall be conducted on every required emergency lighting system at 30-day intervals for a minimum of 30 seconds. An annual test shall be conducted for the 1½-hour duration. Equipment shall be fully operational for the duration of the test. Written records of testing shall be kept by the owner for inspection by the authority having jurisdiction.

31-1.3.9 **Emergency Generators.** Emergency generators used to provide power to emergency lighting systems shall be installed, tested, and maintained in accordance with NFPA 110, *Standard for Emergency and Standby Power Systems*.

Paragraphs 31-1.3.1 through 31-1.3.9 emphasize that any system or mechanical device installed to ensure life safety must be maintained in working condition. Maintenance should be performed according to a set schedule established either by code (this *Code* or other referenced codes and standards) or by the authority having jurisdiction. If this maintenance is not performed, failure of these systems is a possibility. Therefore, failure to provide maintenance results in a noncomplying facility, if the system in question is required by the *Code* or has been installed to provide an equivalency to the *Code's* requirements.

31-1.3.10 **Elevator Testing.** Elevators shall be subject to routine and periodic inspections and test as specified in ASME/ANSI A17.1, *Safety Code for Elevators and Escalators*, Part X. All elevators equipped with fire fighter service in accordance with Paragraph 7-4.4 shall be subject to a monthly operation with a written record of the findings made and kept on the premises as required by ASME/ANSI/ A17.1, *Safety Code for Elevators and Escalators*, Rule 1206.7.

Although elevators traditionally have not been recognized as part of the means of egress from a building, the new provisions of 5-2.12 that address areas of refuge for the mobility impaired require that an area of refuge provide access to either an exit or a fire fighter service elevator. Similarly, the provisions of Section 7-4 require that elevators meet the fire fighters service requirements of ASME/ANSI A17.1, *Safety Code for Elevators and Escalators,*[2] or ASME/ANSI A17.3, *Safety Code for Existing Elevators and Escalators,*[3] because, in part, it is fire fighters who will be responding to the needs of the mobility impaired who are temporarily within the area of refuge. Because of the new emphasis placed on elevators by the *Code,* it is important that 31-1.3.10 requires a commensurate level of elevator testing in order to help ensure that the elevator can be used by trained personnel under fire emergency conditions.

31-1.3.11 Smokeproof Enclosures and Pressurized Stairs. Before mechanical equipment is accepted by the authority having jurisdiction, it shall be tested to confirm that such equipment is operating in compliance with the *Code.* All operating parts of the system shall be tested semiannually by approved personnel, and a log shall be kept of the results.

For additional guidance on stairwell pressurization system design, acceptance testing, periodic testing, and maintenance, see NFPA 92A, *Recommended Practice for Smoke Control Systems.*[4] Note Section 2-3, 3-4.4, and 4-3.4 of NFPA 92A in particular.

31-1.4 Furnishings, Contents, Decorations, and Treated Finishes. *(See also 31-1.2.2.)*

Subsection 31-1.4 has been completely rewritten and greatly expanded for this edition of the *Code* to provide a detailed menu of provisions that are applicable to furnishings and contents such as draperies, upholstered furniture, and mattresses and that can be adopted singly, in various combinations, or in their entirety in accordance with an occupancy's individual operating features requirements. These requirements appear in Sections 31-2 through 31-9. For example, provisions for detention and correctional occupancies, found in 31-5.4, make extensive mandatory use of all provisions outlined in the 31-1.4 menu; provisions for health care occupancies, found in 31-4.5 and A-31-4.5, and residential board and care occupancies, found in 31-7.5 and A-31-7.5, make partial mandatory and partial advisory use of the menu items.

31-1.4.1* Where required by the applicable provisions of this chapter, draperies, curtains, and other similar loosely hanging furnishings and decorations shall be flame resistant as demonstrated by passing both the small- and large-scale tests of NFPA 701, *Standard Methods of Fire Tests for Flame-Resistant Textiles and Films.*

Exception: For materials that show excessive melting or shrinkage or ongoing combustion at the junction of the specimen and its holder in the small-scale test, the large-scale test shall be considered applicable in accordance with the test selection provisions of 1-4.2 of NFPA 701.

A-31-1.4.1 Testing per NFPA 701, *Standard Methods of Fire Tests for Flame-Resistant Textiles and Films,* is applicable to textiles and films used in a hanging configuration. If the textiles and films are to be applied to surfaces of buildings or backing materials as interior finishes for use in buildings, they should be treated as interior wall and ceiling finishes in accordance with Section 6-5 of this *Code* and tested for flame spread ratings and smoke development values in accordance with NFPA 255, *Standard Method of Test of Surface Burning Characteristics of Building Materials.*

The testing requirements of NFPA 701, *Standard Methods of Fire Tests for Flame-Resistant Textiles and Films,*[5] measure the level of hazard posed by draperies and other loosely hanging fabrics and films. However, the requirements of NFPA 701 may not adequately address the hazards associated with multilayered fabrics or assemblies of fabrics. Limited experience has shown that multilayered fabrics may burn in a manner that differs from that of individual components. Many materials may meet the test criteria of the standard because they shrink away from the flame, melt, ablate, or otherwise fail to support upward flames when heated. Yet, when such materials are in contact with a material that meets the test criteria of the standard and do not shrink away from the flame but, instead, char and maintain a degree of structural integrity, the martertial in question may fail to evade the flame and can support upward burning. Therefore, two materials that individually pass the test criteria of NFPA 701 may, in combination (e.g., a drapery consisting of a decorative fabric in contact with a lining material or a single layer drapery with a sheer sun-screening curtain in close proximity), support upward burning that creates a level of hazard greater than that expected of materials that have successfully passsed NFPA 701 testing. The development of test criteria that adequately address multilayered fabrics is currently being undertaken by the NFPA Fire Tests Committee. Should a revision to NFPA 701 be published prior to the next edition of the *Life Safety Code*, the concept stated in A-1-6.1 should encourage the *Code* user to be guided by the revised fire test procedure.

31-1.4.2*   Where required by the applicable provisions of this chapter, upholstered furniture and mattresses shall be resistant to a cigarette (i.e., smoldering) ignition in accordance with the following:

(a) Where required by the applicable provisions of this chapter, the components of the upholstered furniture shall meet the requirements for Class I when tested in accordance with NFPA 260, *Standard Methods of Tests and Classification System for Cigarette Ignition Resistance of Components of Upholstered Furniture.*

Exception: Upholstered furniture in rooms or spaces protected by an approved automatic sprinkler system.

(b) Where required by the applicable provisions of this chapter, mocked-up composites of the upholstered furniture shall have a char length not exceeding 1.5 in. (3.8 cm) when tested in accordance with NFPA 261, *Standard Method of Test for Determining Resistance of Mock-Up Upholstered Furniture Material Assemblies to Ignition by Smoldering Cigarettes.*

Exception: Upholstered furniture in rooms or spaces protected by an approved automatic sprinkler system.

(c) Where required by the applicable provisions of this chapter, mattresses shall have a char length not exceeding 2 in. (5.1 cm) when tested in accordance with Part 1632 of the *Code of Federal Regulations 16.*

Exception: Mattresses in rooms or spaces protected by an approved automatic sprinkler system.

A-31-1.4.2   The Class I requirement associated with testing per NFPA 260, *Standard Methods of Tests and Classification*

System for Cigarette Ignition Resistance of Components of Upholstered Furniture, the maximum 1.5-in. (3.8-cm) char length requirement associated with testing per NFPA 261, *Standard Method of Test for Determining Resistance of Mock-Up Upholstered Furniture Material Assemblies to Ignition by Smoldering Cigarettes*, and the maximum 2-in. (5.1-cm) char length requirement of FF4-72, *Standard for the Flammability of Mattresses*, are indicators that the furniture item or mattress is resistant to a cigarette ignition. Although rooms or spaces protected by an approved automatic sprinkler system are exempt from cigarette ignition resistance testing, a fire that smolders for an excessive period of time without flaming can reduce the tenability within the room or area of fire origin without developing the temperatures necessary to operate automatic sprinklers.

In an attempt to reduce the incidence of fires involving upholstered furniture and mattresses, the provisions of 31-1.4.2 address a key problem area, i.e., ignition by cigarettes or other smoldering sources. Such ignition sources can smolder for considerable periods of time before producing flaming ignition.

Two NFPA fire test methods address the cigarette ignition resistance of upholstered furniture: NFPA 260, *Standard Methods of Tests and Classification System for Cigarette Ignition Resistance of Components of Upholstered Furniture*,[6] and NFPA 261, *Standard Method of Test for Determining Resistance of Mock-Up Upholstered Furniture Material Assemblies to Ignition by Smoldering Cigarettes.*[7] One federal test method is specified for judging the cigarette ignition resistance of mattresses: 16 CFR 1632, *Standard for the Flammability of Mattresses and Mattress Pads.*[8]

NFPA 260 tests individual components of upholstered furniture such as cover fabric, interior fabric, welt cord, filling/padding, decking materials, and barrier materials. Specimens of the component to be tested are assembled with specimens of standardized materials to create a miniature horizontal base panel and vertical panel tester that mocks up an arrangement that simulates the junction and surrounding area of a seat cushion and back cushion in a piece of upholstered furniture. By standardizing all the components of the mocked-up tester excepting the component being tested, the test measures the ignition resistance of that component. Components that meet the test criteria are designated as Class I materials. Components that do not meet the test criteria are designated as Class II materials. Upholstered furniture constructed from components that individually received a Class I designation is judged to be resistant to cigarette ignition without the need to test the actual combination of materials.

NFPA 261 tests a mocked-up assembly consisting of all the actual components that will be used to construct the piece of upholstered furniture, rather than testing the components individually. The test procedure specifies that a char length be measured and reported. There are no pass/fail criteria within the document, so 31-1.4.2 specifies that the char length not exceed 1.5 in. (3.8 cm) in order to be considered resistant to cigarette ignition.

Whereas NFPA 260 and 261 address the cigarette ignition resistance of upholstered furniture, so 16 CFR 1632 does the same for mattresses. In this test method, a char length of 2 in. (5.1 cm) establishes that the mattress is resistant to cigarette ignition.

31-1.4.3*   Where required by the applicable provisions of this chapter, upholstered furniture shall have limited rates of heat release as follows:

(a) The peak rate of heat release for the single upholstered furniture item shall not exceed 250 kW.

Exception No. 1: Upholstered furniture in rooms or spaces protected by approved smoke detectors that initiate, without delay, an alarm that is audible in that room or space.

Exception No. 2: Upholstered furniture in rooms or spaces protected by an approved automatic sprinkler system.

(b) The peak rate of heat release for the single upholstered furniture item shall not exceed 500 kW.

Exception: Upholstered furniture in rooms or spaces protected by an approved automatic sprinkler system.

(c) The total energy released by the single upholstered furniture item during the first five minutes of the test shall not exceed 75 MJ.

Exception: Upholstered furniture in rooms or spaces protected by an approved automatic sprinkler system.

A-31-1.4.3   The intent of the provisions of 31-1.4.3 is as follows:

(a) The maximum 250 kW peak rate of heat release for a single upholstered furniture item was chosen based on maintaining a tenable environment within the room of fire origin. The smoke detector exception was developed because the smoke detector will give early warning so as to allow the occupant sufficient time to leave the room of fire origin. The sprinkler exception was developed because the sprinkler system will help to maintain tenable conditions even if the single upholstered furniture item were to have a peak rate of heat release in excess of 250 kW.

(b) The maximum 500 kW peak rate of heat release established for a single upholstered furniture item was chosen to help avoid flashover within the room of fire origin. Whereas (a) above is intended to protect the person within the room of fire origin, avoiding flashover will help to protect occupants outside the room of fire origin. Only a sprinkler exception was developed because the sprinkler system will help to prevent flashover within the room of fire origin, thus protecting occupants outside the room.

(c) The maximum 75 MJ total energy release by the single upholstered furniture item during the first five minutes of the test was established as an additional safeguard to protect against the adverse conditions that would be created by an upholstered furniture item that released its heat in other than the usual measured scenario. During the test for measurement of rate of heat release, the instantaneous heat release value usually peaks quickly and then quickly falls off so as to create a triangle-shaped curve. In the a typical case, if the heat release were to peak and remain steady at that elevated level, as opposed to quickly falling off, the maximum 250 kW and 500 kW limits would not assure safety. Again, only a sprinkler exception is allowed in lieu of the test because of the ability of the sprinkler system to control the fire.

The provisions of 31-1.4.2 address only one important property of upholstered furniture and mattresses, i.e., their resistance to cigarette ignition. The provisions of 31-1.4.3 and 31-1.4.4 supplement those provisions by addressing rates of heat release. Different combustible materials vary in their potential to produce heat. Some plastic materials, for example, have twice as much potential heat per weight of material as wood. However, if the material with twice the potential heat were to burn only half as fast as the material with the lower potential, the two materials would liberate about the same amount of heat during any given time period and create approximately eqivalent hazards. If one material with a heat potential approximately equal to another material were to burn twice as fast as the other, it would liberate about twice as much heat during any given time period and, thus, create a greater hazard than the slower burning material. Therefore, the property of a material or group of materials expressed by a rate of heat release classification is important in regulating the combustibility of upholstered furniture and mattresses.

The above appendix material adequately describes the intent of the rates of heat release provisions, which is to prevent any single furniture item from causing room flashover. The appendix material also explains how automatic sprinklers, in certain cases, can serve in lieu of a low rate of heat release. However, although maximum rate of heat release and total energy release values are specified, neither the *Code's* mandatory text nor its advisory appendix text specifies the test procedure to be used to measure such values. Both California Technical Bulletin 133, *Flammability Test Procedure for Seating Furniture for Use in High Risk and Public Occupancies*,[9] and UL 1056, *Standard for Fire Test of Upholstered Furniture*,[10] are currently being used to measure heat release for upholstered furniture. Mattresses can be tested by UL 1895, *Standard for Fire Test of Mattresses*.[11] It is expected that additional test methods will become available before publication of the next edition of the *Code*.

31-1.4.4 Where required by the applicable provisions of this chapter, mattresses shall have limited rates of heat release as follows:

(a) The peak rate of heat release for the mattress shall not exceed 250 kW.

Exception No. 1: Mattresses in rooms or spaces protected by approved smoke detectors that initiate, without delay, an alarm that is audible in that room or space.

Exception No. 2: Mattresses in rooms or spaces protected by an approved automatic sprinkler system.

(b) The peak rate of heat release for the mattress shall not exceed 500 kW.

Exception: Mattresses in rooms or spaces protected by an approved automatic sprinkler system.

(c) The total energy released by the mattress during the first five minutes of the test shall not exceed 75 MJ.

Exception: Mattresses in rooms or spaces protected by an approved automatic sprinkler system.

See the commentary following A-31-1.4.3.

31-1.4.5* Furnishings or decorations of an explosive or highly flammable character shall not be used.

A-31-1.4.5 Christmas trees not effectively flame-retardant treated, ordinary crepe paper decorations, and pyroxylin plastic decorations may be classed as highly flammable.

The *Code* relies on the authority having jurisdiction to exercise judgment in enforcing 31-1.4.5.

31-1.4.6 Fire retardant coatings shall be maintained so as to retain the effectiveness of the treatment under service conditions encountered in actual use.

See NFPA 703, *Standard for Fire Retardant Impregnated Wood and Fire Retardant Coatings for Building Materials*.[12]

31-1.5*   Fire Exit Drills.

A-31-1.5 The term "fire exit drill" is used to avoid confusion between drills held for the purpose of rapid evacuation of buildings and drills of fire fighting practice that from a technical viewpoint are correctly designated as "fire drills," although this term is by common usage applied to egress drills in schools, etc.

The purpose of fire exit drills is to ensure the efficient and safe use of the exit facilities available. Proper drills ensure orderly exit under control and prevent the panic that has been responsible for the greater part of the loss of life in the major fire disasters of history. Order and control are the primary purposes of the drill. Speed in emptying buildings, while desirable, is not in itself an object, and should be made secondary to the maintenance of proper order and discipline.

The usefulness of a fire exit drill and the extent to which it can be carried depends upon the character of the occupancy, it being most effective in occupancies where the occupant load of the building is under discipline and subject to habitual control. For example, schools offer possibilities of more highly developed and valuable fire exit drills than other types of occupancy.

In buildings where the occupant load is of a changing character and not under discipline, such as hotels or department stores, no regularly organized fire exit drill, such as that which may be conducted in schools, is possible. In such cases, the fire exit drills must be limited to the regular employees, who can, however, be thoroughly schooled in the proper procedure and can be trained to properly direct other occupants of the building in case of fire. In occupancies such as hospitals, regular employees can be rehearsed in the proper procedure in case of fire; such training always is advisable in all occupancies whether or not regular fire exit drills can be held.

Paragraphs 31-1.5.1 through 31-1.5.6 serve as a primer on how to conduct a fire exit drill. Sections 31-2 through 31-9 provide specific details that directly correlate a drill with the characteristics of the occupancy in question.

31-1.5.1 Fire exit drills conforming to the provisions of this chapter shall be regularly conducted in occupancies where specified by the provisions of this chapter, or by appropriate action of the authority having jurisdiction. Drills shall be designed in cooperation with the local authorities.

31-1.5.2 Fire exit drills, where required by the authority having jurisdiction, shall be held with sufficient frequency to familiarize all occupants with the drill procedure and to have the conduct of the drill a matter of established routine.

31-1.5.3 Responsibility for the planning and conduct of drills shall be assigned only to competent persons qualified to exercise leadership.

31-1.5.4 In the conduct of drills, emphasis shall be placed upon orderly evacuation under proper discipline rather than upon speed.

31-1.5.5* Drills shall include suitable procedures to ensure that all persons in the building or all persons subject to the drill actually participate.

A-31-1.5.5 If a fire exit drill is considered merely as a routine exercise from which some persons may be excused, there is a grave danger that in an actual fire the drill will fail in its intended purpose.

31-1.5.6* Drills shall be held at unexpected times and under varying conditions to simulate the unusual conditions that occur in the case of fire.

A-31-1.5.6 Fire is always unexpected. If the drill is always held in the same way at the same time it loses much of its value, and when for some reason in actual fire it is not possible to follow the usual routine of the fire exit drill to which occupants have become accustomed, confusion and panic may ensue. Drills should be carefully planned to simulate actual fire conditions. Not only should they be held at varying times, but different means of exit should be used based upon an assumption that, for example, some given stairway is unavailable by reason of fire or smoke, and all the occupants must be led out by some other route. Fire exit drills should be designed to familiarize the occupants with all available means of exits, particularly emergency exits that are not habitually used during the normal occupancy of the building.

31-1.6 **Flammable Liquids and Gases.**

31-1.6.1 The storage and the handling of flammable liquids or gases shall be in accordance with the applicable standards listed below:

    (a) NFPA 30, *Flammable and Combustible Liquids Code*
    (b) NFPA 54, *National Fuel Gas Code*
    (c) NFPA 58, *Standard for the Storage and Handling of Liquefied Petroleum Gases*.

31-1.6.2 No storage or handling of flammable liquids or gases shall be permitted in any location where it would jeopardize egress from the structure.

31-1.6.3 Refueling of equipment with liquids with flashpoints below 100°F (38°C) shall not be permitted within the structure.

31-1.7 **Laboratories.** Laboratories that use chemicals shall comply with NFPA 45, *Standard on Fire Protection for Laboratories Using Chemicals*, unless otherwise modified by other provisions of this *Code*.

31-1.8 **Maintenance.** Whenever or wherever any device, equipment, system, condition, arrangement, level of protection, or any other feature is required for compliance with the provisions of this *Code*, such device, equipment, system, condition, arrangement, level of protection, or other feature shall thereafter be permanently maintained unless the *Code* exempts such maintenance.

See commentary following 31-1.3.1.

SECTION 31-2   Assembly Occupancies

31-2.1* **Crowd Managers.** In Class A assembly occupancies, there shall be trained crowd managers or crowd manager supervisors at a ratio of 1 crowd manager/supervisor for every 250 occupants who shall have received approved training in crowd management techniques.

Exception No. 1: Assembly occupancies used exclusively for religious worship with an occupant load not greater than 2000.

Exception No. 2: Where in the opinion of the authority having jurisdiction the existence of an approved supervised sprinkler system and the nature of the event warrant, the ratio of trained crowd managers to occupants may be reduced.

A-31-2.1 The training program in crowd management should develop a clear appreciation of factors of space, energy, time, and information, as well as specific crowd management techniques such as metering. Published guidelines on these factors and techniques are found in the SFPE *Handbook of Fire Protection Engineering*, Section 1, Chapter 15.

The referenced material contained in Section 1 of Chapter 15 in the SFPE *Handbook of Fire Protection Engineering*[13] makes a distinction between the required "crowd management" and the more extreme, but nonmandatory, "crowd control." Crowd management meshes the design features of a facility, the established operating features of that facility, and an understanding of the occupants' expected natural behavior in that facility for a specific type of event. That chapter further offers the Disney amusement complexes as examples of good crowd management. Crowd control, on the other hand, is often necessitated when crowd management fails.

31-2.2* **Drills.**

A-31-2.2 Attention is directed to the importance of having an adequate number of competent attendants on duty at all times when the assembly occupancy is occupied.

31-2.2.1 The employees or attendants of places of public assembly shall be schooled and drilled in the duties they are to perform in case of fire, panic, or other emergency in order to be of greatest service in effecting orderly exiting.

31-2.2.2 Employees or attendants of assembly occupancies shall be instructed in the proper use of portable fire extinguishers and other manual fire suppression equipment if provided.

The *Code* does not require fire extinguishers for life safety in an assembly occupancy. However, the Committee feels that, if fire extinguishers are provided, the staff must be trained in their use to prevent a false sense of security and possible injury. The extent of this training (e.g., instruction only, instruction and hands-on use) is determined by the authority having jurisdiction.

31-2.2.3* In theaters, motion picture theaters, auditoriums, and other similar Class A and B assembly occupancies where there are noncontinuous programs, an audible announcement shall be made prior to the start of each program to notify occupants of the location of the exits to be used in case of a fire or other emergency.

Exception: Assembly occupancies in schools when used for nonpublic events.

A-31-2.2.3 It is not the intent of this provision to require an announcement in bowling alleys, cocktail lounges, restaurants, or places of worship.

The relatively simple requirement for notifying occupants of the location of exits can make a significant difference during an emergency. Note that the requirement does not apply to assembly occupancies where the flow of people is constantly changing, such as in a restaurant. Movie theatres commonly meet the provisions of 31-2.2.3 through means of sound and screen projection that are presented prior to the main feature, during the same period that notifications of restroom, trash container, and snack bar locations are made and previews are shown. The same complete message is thereby delivered to each audience without the need for human intervention.

31-2.3 **Open Flame Devices.** No open flame devices nor pyrotechnic device shall be used in any assembly occupancy.

Exception No. 1: *When necessary for ceremonial or religious purposes, the authority having jurisdiction may permit open flame or pyrotechnic devices under such restrictions as are necessary to avoid danger of ignition of combustible materials or injury to occupants.*

A-31-2.3 **Exception No. 1.** Securely supported altar candles in churches, well separated from any combustible material, may be permitted. On the other hand, lighted candles carried by children wearing cotton robes present a hazard too great to be permitted even for the most worthy cause. There are many other situations of intermediate hazard where the authority having jurisdiction will have to exercise judgment.

Exception No. 2: *Open flame or pyrotechnic devices may be used on stages and platforms when a necessary part of a performance, provided adequate precautions satisfactory to the authority having jurisdiction are taken to prevent ignition of any combustible materials.*

Exception No. 3: *Gas lights may be permitted provided adequate precautions satisfactory to the authority having jurisdiction are taken to prevent ignition of any combustible materials.*

Exception No. 4: *Candles may be used on tables if securely supported on substantial noncombustible bases so located as to avoid danger of ignition of combustible materials and only if approved by the authority having jurisdiction. Candle flames shall be protected.*

Exception No. 5: *As permitted in 31-2.4.*

Exception No. 6: *Demonstrations of open-flame or pyrotechnic devices in exhibits may be allowed provided adequate precautions satisfactory to the authority having jurisdiction are taken to prevent ignition of any materials.*

Exception No. 7: *Heat-producing equipment complying with 7-2.2.*

The list of tragic fires in assembly occupancies caused by "friendly" fire (e.g., alcohol or solid alcohol fires in

restaurants, flames used for dramatic effects in theaters.) is well-documented. Paragraph 31-2.3 and its exceptions provide a fundamental exercise in fire prevention, whereby the use of these open flame devices is tightly controlled. The first step in fire prevention is prevention of ignition, which is addressed by 31-2.3 and 31-2.4. Exception Nos. 1 and 2 to 31-2.3 have been revised and Exception No. 6 has been added to recognize and, thus, regulate pyrotechnic devices such as those commonly used for visual effects at rock concerts. At the time that this edition of the *Code* was released, the NFPA Technical Committee on Pyrotechnics had prepared its Technical Committee Report proposing a new document, NFPA 1126, *Code for the Use of Pyrotechnics in the Performing Arts.*[14] This new document is intended to provide reasonable protection where pyrotechnic special effects are used in the entertainment industry in conjunction with theatrical, musical, or any similar productions that involve a proximate audience, performers, or support personnel.

31-2.4 **Special Food Service Devices.** Portable cooking equipment that is not flue-connected shall be permitted only as follows:

(a) Equipment fueled by small heat sources that can be readily extinguished by water, such as candles or alcohol-burning equipment (including "solid alcohol"), may be used provided adequate precautions satisfactory to the authority having jurisdiction are taken to prevent ignition of any combustible materials.

(b) Candles may be used on tables used for food service if securely supported on substantial noncombustible bases so located as to avoid danger of ignition of combustible materials and only if approved by the authority having jurisdiction. Candle flames shall be protected.

(c) "Flaming Sword" or other equipment involving open flames and flamed dishes, such as cherries jubilee, crepes suzette, etc., may be permitted provided that necessary precautions are taken and subject to the approval of the authority having jurisdiction.

31-2.5 **Smoking.**

31-2.5.1 Smoking in assembly occupancies shall be regulated by the authority having jurisdiction.

31-2.5.2 In rooms or areas where smoking is prohibited, plainly visible "NO SMOKING" signs shall be posted.

31-2.5.3 No person shall smoke in prohibited areas that are so posted.

Exception: The authority having jurisdiction may permit smoking on a stage only when it is a necessary and rehearsed part of a performance and only when the smoker is a regular performing member of the cast.

31-2.5.4 Where smoking is permitted, suitable ashtrays or receptacles shall be provided in convenient locations.

31-2.6 Furnishings, Decorations, and Stage Scenery.

31-2.6.1 Fabrics and films used for decorative purposes, all draperies and curtains, and similar furnishings shall be in accordance with the provisions of 31-1.4.1.

31-2.6.2 The authority having jurisdiction shall impose controls on the amount and arrangement of combustible contents in assembly occupancies to provide an adequate level of safety to life from fire.

31-2.6.3* Exposed foamed plastic materials and unprotected materials containing foamed plastic used for decorative purposes or stage scenery shall have a maximum heat release rate of 100 kW when tested in accordance with UL 1975, *Standard for Fire Tests for Foamed Plastics Used for Decorative Purposes.*

Exception: Individual foamed plastic items or items containing foamed plastic where the foamed plastic does not exceed 1 lb (.45 kg) in weight.

A-31-2.6.3 The term "unprotected materials containing foamed plastic" is meant to include foamed plastic items covered by "thermally-thin" combustible fabrics or paint. *(See A-6-5.3.1.)*

The scenery stored in the fly sections of a stage, in addition to that used in a stage production, represents a sizable (and usually highly combustible) fuel load. Classic theater fires (for example, the Iroquois Theater, Chicago, 1903) involve ignition of the scenery on stage and sub-

sequent exposure to the audience caused by this sizable amount of burning fuel. Chapters 8 and 9 provide for a curtain of noncombustible or noncombustible-based materials to drop, which separates the fuel from the audience, and for the installation of extinguishing systems (both automatic and manual) on or around the stage. In 31-2.6.1 through 31-2.6.3, the *Code* controls the hazard level of fuel stored or placed outside the proscenium arch and attempts to limit the flammability of all the scenery, thus minimizing the level of exposure (hazard) to the audience. Ignition sources are controlled by 31-2.3.

For additional information on the importance of limiting the rate of heat release of furnishings and contents, see the commentary following A-31-1.4.3.

31-2.7 Seating.

31-2.7.1 Seats in assembly occupancies accommodating more than 200 persons shall be securely fastened to the floor except where fastened together in groups of not less than three nor more than seven and as permitted by 31-2.7.2. All seats in balconies and galleries shall be securely fastened to the floor, except in places of worship.

31-2.7.2 Seats not secured to the floor shall be permitted in restaurants, night clubs, and other occupancies where the fastening of seats to the floor may be impracticable, provided that in the area used for seating (excluding dance floor, stage, etc.), there shall be not more than one seat for each 15 sq ft (1.4 sq m) of net floor area and adequate aisles to reach exits shall be maintained at all times.

Exception: Seating diagrams shall be submitted for approval of the authority having jurisdiction to allow increase in occupant load per 8-1.7.2 and 9-1.7.2.

The function of 31-2.7.1 and 31-2.7.2 is to prevent the movement of seats so that aisles, rows, and access to the exits do not become blocked in an assembly occupancy during the jostling that occurs when people flee from a fire.

31-2.7.3 Every room constituting an assembly occupancy and not having fixed seats shall have the occupant load of the room posted in a conspicuous place near the main exit from the room. Approved signs shall be maintained in a legible manner by the owner or authorized agent. Signs shall be durable and shall indicate the number of occupants permitted for each room use.

31-2.8 **Projection Room.** Unless the projection room is constructed in accordance with NFPA 40, *Standard for the Storage and Handling of Cellulose Nitrate Motion Picture Film*, there shall be posted on the outside of each projection room door, and within the projection room proper, a conspicuous sign with 1-in. (2.5-cm) block letters stating "SAFETY FILM ONLY PERMITTED IN THIS ROOM."

31-2.9 **Coat Racks.** Clothing and personal effects shall not be stored in corridors and lobbies.

Clothing hung on hooks along corridor walls or on racks in lobbies greatly increases the combustible load and will generally allow flame to spread quickly. Since Chapters 8 and 9 regulate corridor and lobby interior wall finish, surfaces covered by combustible clothing should not be created that would allow flame to spread more quickly than is permitted by wall surfaces.

31-2.10 **Proscenium Curtain.** All proscenium curtains shall be in the closed position except during performances, rehearsals, or similar activities.

The 1903 Iroquois Theater fire in Chicago demonstrated that a proscenium curtain may fail to close fully if it is not operated on a regular basis or if it is obstructed either temporarily by scenery or props or permanently by alterations to the building. Requiring fire curtains to be closed on a regular basis helps to ensure that the curtain will fully close when needed.

SECTION 31-3 Educational Occupancies

Firesafety, including an approved fire evacuation plan, should be included in the curriculum of all educational occupancies. This part of the curriculum should be approved by the authority having jurisdiction. The NFPA *Learn Not to Burn Curriculum*[15] is a proven system of firesafety education in schools.

31-3.1 **Drills.**

31-3.1.1* Fire exit drills shall be conducted regularly in accordance with the applicable provisions of the following paragraphs.

A-31-3.1.1 The requirements are of necessity general in scope, as it is appreciated that they must apply to all types of schools as well as conditions of occupancies, such as truant schools, schools for mentally handicapped, the vision impaired, hearing and speech impaired, and public schools. It is fully recognized that no one code can meet all the conditions of the various buildings involved, and it will be necessary for some school authorities to issue supplements to these requirements, but all supplements should be consistent with these requirements.

Drills for educational occupancies, particularly those at the grade school level, are essential to ensure an orderly response during a fire. Unfortunately, the predictability of such drills often leads to their ineffectiveness. When an alarm bell sounds and a fire department monitor appears in a corridor, some teachers ignore the bell, assuming that it is a false alarm; if the bell sounds and a fire department monitor is not seen, teachers opt to either "all go" or "all stay." This decision is made in the hallway. While the bell continues to ring, the students remain in their classrooms. Therefore, when a bell sounds, primary emphasis should be placed on evacuation, regardless of who is or is not present in the hallways, or whether or not fire equipment is parked in front of the school. Essentially, the fire department and the school should vary the timing and arrangement of the drills but not the required response, which is orderly evacuation. (*See also 31-1.5.*)

31-3.1.2* There shall be at least two fire exit drills held during the first two weeks of a school term and eight additional fire exit drills during the year. In climates where the weather is severe during the winter months, at least six drills should be held at the beginning of the school term and four drills held after the winter months to complete the ten required drills.

A-31-3.1.2 "Practice drills" may be held during inclement weather. Such drills would be held at the regular dismissal time, when the pupils are fully clothed, by using the exit drill alarm signal. With such drills there would be no necessity of a return signal.

31-3.1.3*   Drills shall be executed at different hours of the day or evening; during the changing of classes; when the school is at assembly; during the recess or gymnastic periods; or during other times to avoid distinction between drills and actual fires. If a drill is called while pupils are going up and down the stairways, such as during the time classes are changing, the pupils shall be instructed to form in file and immediately proceed to the nearest available exit in an orderly manner.

A-31-3.1.3   Cards of instruction should be conspicuously posted describing the procedure of the drills.

31-3.1.4*   Every fire exit drill shall be an exercise in school management for principal and teachers with the chief purpose of every drill being the complete control of the class so that the teacher can form its ranks quickly and silently, and may halt, turn, or direct the class as desired. Great emphasis shall be put upon the execution of each drill in a brisk, quiet, and orderly manner. Running shall be prohibited. In case there are pupils incapable of holding their places in a line moving at a reasonable speed, provisions shall be made to have them taken care of by the more capable pupils, who will keep them from moving independently of the regular line of march.

A-31-3.1.4   If for any reason a line becomes blocked, some of the pupils should be countermarched to another exit in order to prevent panic conditions arising as a result of inactivity.

31-3.1.5   Monitors shall be appointed from among the more mature pupils to assist in the proper execution of all drills. They shall be instructed to hold doors open in the line of march or to close doors where necessary to prevent spread of fire or smoke in accordance with 5-2.1.8. There shall be at least two substitutes for each appointment so as to provide for proper performance in case of the absence of the regular monitors. The searching of toilet or other rooms shall be the duty of the teachers or other members of the staff. If the teachers are to search, this should be done after they have joined their classes to the preceding lines.

31-3.1.6   As all drills simulate an actual fire condition, pupils shall not be allowed to obtain clothing after the alarm is sounded, even when in home rooms, due to the confusion that would result in forming the lines and the danger of tripping over dragging apparel.

31-3.1.7   Each class or group shall proceed to a predetermined point outside the building and remain there while a check is made to see that all are accounted for, leaving only when a recall signal is given to return to the building or when dismissed. Such points shall be sufficiently far away from the building and from each other as to avoid danger from any fire in the building, interference with fire department operations, or confusion among different classes or groups.

31-3.1.8*   Where necessary for drill lines to cross roadways, signs reading "STOP! SCHOOL FIRE DRILL," or the equivalent, shall be carried by monitors to the traffic intersecting points in order to stop traffic during the period of the drill.

A-31-3.1.8   Wherever possible, drill lines should not cross a street or highway, especially where the traffic is heavy. It is recommended that, where drill lines must cross roadways, a police officer, school janitor, or a teacher acting as a traffic officer be on duty to control traffic during drills.

31-3.1.9*   Fire exit drills in schools shall not include any fire extinguishing operations.

A-31-3.1.9   Instructors and employees should be trained in the function and use of such equipment to meet an emergency.

As indicated in the appendix note, instructors and employees should be trained in the function and use of fire extinguishing equipment for the purpose of meeting an emergency; however, their primary responsibility is to lead students to safety.

31-3.2   Signals.

31-3.2.1   All fire exit drill alarms shall be sounded on the fire alarm system.

31-3.2.2   Whenever any of the school authorities determine that an actual fire exists, they shall immediately call the local fire department using the public fire alarm system or such other facilities as are available.

31-3.2.3 In order to prevent pupils from being returned to a building that is burning, the recall signal shall be one that is separate and distinct from, and cannot be mistaken for, any other signals. Such signal may be given by use of distinctively colored flags or banners. If the recall signal is electrical, the push buttons or other controls shall be kept under lock, the key for which shall be in the possession of the principal or some other designated person in order to prevent a recall at a time when there is an actual fire. Regardless of the method of recall, the means of giving the signal shall be kept under a lock.

31-3.3 Inspection.

31-3.3.1* It shall be the duty of principals and teachers to inspect all exit facilities daily in order to make sure that all stairways, doors, and other exits are in proper condition.

A-31-3.3.1 Particular attention should be given to keeping all doors unlocked, having doors closed that serve to protect the safety of paths of egress, such as doors on stairway enclosures, closed and under no conditions blocked open, keeping outside stairs and fire escape stairs free from all obstructions and clear of snow and ice, and allowing no accumulation of snow or ice or materials of any kind outside exit doors that might prevent the opening of the door or interfere with rapid escape from the building.

Any condition likely to interfere with safe exit should be immediately corrected if possible or otherwise should be reported at once to the appropriate authorities.

31-3.3.2 Open-plan buildings require extra surveillance to ensure that exit paths are maintained clear of obstruction and are obvious.

31-3.4 Day-Care Centers.

31-3.4.1 Fire prevention inspections shall be conducted monthly by a trained senior member of the staff. A copy of the latest inspection form shall be posted in a conspicuous place in the day-care facility.

Paragraph 31-3.4.1 does not intend to eliminate inspections by the personnel of fire prevention bureaus where they exist but, instead, intends to supplement such inspections. Where no fire department inspections are made or where they are made infrequently, monthly inspections must be made by a senior staff member who has been trained to make such inspections by the authority having jurisdiction.

31-3.4.2* An approved fire evacuation plan shall be executed not less than once per month.

A-31-3.4.2 It is recommended that firesafety be a part of the educational program of the center.

Firesafety, including an approved fire evacuation plan, should be included in the curriculum of all day-care centers, group day-care homes, and family day-care homes. This part of the curriculum should be approved by the authority having jurisdiction. The NFPA *Learn Not to Burn Curriculum*[15] is a proven system of firesafety education in schools that can be easily used in day-care occupancies.

31-3.4.3 Flammable and combustible liquids shall be stored in areas accessible only to designated individuals and as required in 31-1.6.

To ensure that only designated individuals have access to flammable or combustible liquids, such materials should be kept in locked areas.

31-3.4.4 Wastebaskets and other waste containers shall be made of noncombustible materials.

31-3.5 Group Day-Care Homes. At least one operable flashlight shall be provided for each staff member in a location accessible to the staff for use in the event of a power failure.

31-3.6 Family Day-Care Homes. At least one operable flashlight shall be provided in a location accessible to the staff for use in the event of a power failure.

31-3.7 Day-Care Staff. Adequate adult staff shall be on duty, alert, awake, and in the facility at all times when clients are present.

31-3.8 Furnishings and Decorations.

31-3.8.1 Draperies, curtains, and other similar furnishings and decorations in educational occupancies shall be in accordance with the provisions of 31-1.4.1.

31-3.8.2 Clothing and personal effects shall not be stored in corridors and lobbies.

Exception: Metal lockers shall be permitted in corridors for storage of clothing and personal effects provided the corridor width is maintained.

See commentary following 31-2.9.

31-3.9 Child-Prepared Artwork. Child-prepared artwork and teaching materials shall be permitted to be attached directly to the walls and shall not exceed 20 percent of the wall area.

It is advantageous not only to limit the quantity of child-prepared materials displayed but also to avoid placing such materials near the exit access doors of a room. Since the combustibility of the artwork cannot be effectively controlled, the quantity, in terms of the percentage of the overall wall area covered, is regulated to avoid creating a continuous combustible surface that will spread flame across the room.

31-3.10 Unvented Fuel-Fired Heating Equipment. Unvented fuel-fired heating equipment shall be prohibited in educational occupancies and in all categories of day-care facilities.

SECTION 31-4* Health Care Occupancies

A-31-4 Health care occupants have, in large part, varied degrees of physical disability, and their removal to the outside or even disturbance by moving is inexpedient or impractical in many cases, except as a last resort. Similarly recognizing that there may be an operating necessity for the restraint of the mentally ill, often by use of barred windows and locked doors, exit drills are usually extremely disturbing, detrimental, and frequently impracticable.

In most cases, fire and exit drills as ordinarily practiced in other occupancies cannot be conducted in health care occupancies. Fundamentally, superior construction, early discovery and extinguishment of incipient fires, and prompt notification must be relied upon to reduce the occasion for evacuation of buildings of this class to a minimum.

31-4.1 Attendants, Evacuation Plan, Fire Exit Drills.

31-4.1.1 The administration of every hospital, nursing home, and limited care facility shall have, in effect and available to all supervisory personnel, written copies of a plan for the protection of all persons in the event of fire and for their evacuation to areas of refuge and for evacuation from the building when necessary. All employees shall be periodically instructed and kept informed with respect to their duties under the plan. A copy of the plan shall be readily available at all times in the telephone operator's position or at the security center.

The provisions of 31-4.1.2 to 31-4.2.3 inclusive shall apply.

The former requirement for movable beds on wheels or casters was deleted from this edition of the *Code*. Ordinary practice in health care occupancies is to move patients through the hospital on narrow carts or in wheelchairs. Thus, hospitals have little or no experience in moving patients in large beds. In addition, the furniture in rooms (chairs, nightstands, food trays/tables) must be moved out of the way to allow beds to be turned and moved out. This requires extra staff time that is usually unavailable during a fire. Emphasis should be placed on moving patients who are in the room of fire origin, as well as others who are directly exposed to the fire. This is often achieved by moving occupants on bedding, as opposed to using beds.

31-4.1.2* Fire exit drills in health care occupancies shall include the transmission of a fire alarm signal and simulation of emergency fire conditions except that the movement of infirm or bedridden patients to safe areas or to the exterior of the building is not required. Drills shall be conducted quarterly on each shift to familiarize facility personnel (nurses, interns, maintenance engineers, and administrative staff) with signals and emergency action required under varied conditions. At least twelve drills shall be held every year. When drills are conducted between 9:00 p.m. (2100 hours) and 6:00 a.m. (0600 hours), a coded announcement may be used instead of audible alarms.

A-31-4.1.2 Many hospitals conduct fire exit drills without disturbing patients by advance planning in the choice of location of the simulated emergency and by closing doors to patients' rooms or wards in the vicinity prior to the initiation of the drill. The purpose of a fire drill is to test the efficiency, knowledge, and response of institutional personnel. Its purpose is not to disturb or excite patients.

Convalescent patients should be removed from involved zones lest their curiosity or anxiety hamper fire brigade activity or cause themselves injury. All sections should be assured of a necessary complement of doctors, nurses, attendants, and other employees in reserve in readiness to assist in the transfer of bed patients to less exposed areas or sections.

See also 31-1.5.

Formal Interpretation 73-38
Reference: 31-4.1.2

Question: In a multibuilding hospital complex, is it a requirement to conduct a fire exit drill quarterly on each shift in each hospital building that houses or is frequented by patients?

Answer: Yes.

Question: In a multibuilding hospital complex, is it a requirement to conduct a fire exit drill quarterly on each shift in each hospital building that houses patients?

Answer: Yes.

Question: In a multibuilding hospital complex, is it a requirement to conduct a fire exit drill quarterly on each shift in only one of the patient-occupied buildings?

Answer: No.

Issue Edition: 1973
Reference: 17-4113
Date: May 1977 ∎

31-4.1.3 Employees of health care facilities shall be instructed in life safety procedures and devices.

31-4.2 Procedure in Case of Fire.

31-4.2.1* For health care occupancies, the proper protection of patients requires the prompt and effective response of health care personnel. The basic response required of staff shall include the removal of all occupants directly involved with the fire emergency, transmission of an appropriate fire alarm signal to warn other building occupants, confinement of the effects of the fire by closing doors to isolate the fire area, and the execution of those evacuation duties as detailed in the Facility Firesafety Plan. See Appendix A for a more detailed suggested emergency plan.

A-31-4.2.1 Each facility has specific characteristics that may vary from other facilities sufficiently to prevent the specification of a universal emergency procedure. The following recommendations, however, contain many of the elements that should be considered and adapted as appropriate to the individual facility.

Upon discovery of fire, personnel should immediately take the following action:

(a) If any person is involved in the fire, the discoverer should go to the aid of that person, calling aloud an established code phrase. The use of a code provides for both the immediate aid of any endangered person and the transmission of an alarm. Any person in the area, upon hearing the code called aloud, should activate the building fire alarm using the nearest manual alarm station.

(b) If a person is not involved in the fire, the discoverer should activate the building fire alarm using the nearest manual alarm station.

(c) Personnel, upon hearing the alarm signal, should immediately execute their duties as outlined in the facility firesafety plan.

(d) The telephone operator should determine the location of the fire as indicated by the audible signal. In a building equipped with an uncoded alarm system, a person on the floor of fire origin should be responsible for promptly notifying the facility telephone operator of the fire location.

(e) If the telephone operator receives a telephone alarm reporting a fire from a floor, the operator should regard that alarm in the same fashion as an alarm received over the fire alarm system. The operator should immediately notify the fire department and alert all facility personnel of the place of fire and its origin.

(f) If the building fire alarm system is out of order, any person discovering a fire should immediately notify the telephone operator by telephone. The operator should then transmit this information to the fire department and alert the building occupants.

31-4.2.2 A written facility firesafety plan shall provide for:

(a) Use of alarms.
(b) Transmission of alarm to fire department.
(c) Response to alarms.
(d) Isolation of fire.
(e) Evacuation of area.
(f) Preparation of building for evacuation.
(g) Extinguishment of fire.

31-4.2.3 All facility personnel shall be instructed in the use of and response to fire alarms; and, in addition, they shall be instructed in the use of the code phrase to ensure transmission of an alarm under the following conditions:

(a) When the individual who discovers a fire must immediately go to the aid of an endangered person.
(b) During a malfunction of the building fire alarm system.

Personnel hearing the code announced shall first activate the building fire alarm using the nearest manual alarm station and shall then immediately execute their duties as outlined in the firesafety plan.

In addition to the requirements of 31-4.2, evacuation plans should stress that the doors of as many patient rooms as possible be closed in order to block smoke spreading from a fire and, if possible, to confine the fire in a room. This single action taken by the staff (i.e., manually closing the doors) achieves the level of safety to life mandated by the *Code* in Chapters 12 and 13. In studies of fires in health care institutions in which the staff closed doors, the fire spread was readily confined, and there was either no loss of life or life loss was low.

In many recent serious loss-of-life fires in health care facilities, staff either did not close doors or they reopened them. The fire spread was sizable, and the life loss was high. Emphasis must be placed on training staff to sound an alarm, to rescue patients (as needed), and, then, to close all doors. The closing of doors has historically had the most significant effect on limiting the spread of fire and smoke.

31-4.3 **Maintenance of Exits.** Proper maintenance shall be provided to ensure the dependability of the method of evacuation selected. Facilities that find it necessary to lock exits shall at all times maintain an adequate staff qualified to release and conduct occupants from the immediate danger area to a place of safety in case of fire or other emergency.

31-4.4* **Smoking.** Smoking regulations shall be adopted and shall include the following minimal provisions:

(a) Smoking shall be prohibited in any room, ward, or compartment where flammable liquids, combustible gases, or oxygen is used or stored and in any other hazardous location. Such areas shall be posted with "NO SMOKING" signs.

(b) Smoking by patients classified as not responsible shall be prohibited.

Exception to (b): When the patient is under direct supervision.

(c) Ashtrays of noncombustible material and safe design shall be provided in all areas where smoking is permitted.

(d) Metal containers with self-closing cover devices into which ashtrays may be emptied shall be readily available to all areas where smoking is permitted.

A-31-4.4 The most rigid discipline with regard to prohibition of smoking may not be nearly so effective in reducing incipient fires from surreptitious smoking as the open recognition of smoking, with provision of suitable facilities for smoking. Proper education and training of the staff and attendants in the ordinary fire hazards and their abatement is unquestionably essential. The problem is a broad one, variable with different types and arrangement of buildings; the effectiveness of rules of procedure, necessarily flexible, depends in large part upon the management.

Smoking in bed or discarding smoking materials into ordinary waste containers not designed to hold them leads the list of causes of fires in health care occupancies. The requirements of 31-4.4 must be met in order to minimize the chance of ignition.

31-4.5 Furnishings, Bedding, and Decorations.

31-4.5.1* Draperies, curtains, including cubicle curtains, and other loosely hanging fabrics and films serving as furnishings or decorations in health care occupancies shall be in accordance with the provisions of 31-1.4.1.

A-31-4.5.1 In addition to the provisions of 31-1.4.1 dealing with ignition resistance, additional requirements with respect to the location of cubicle curtains relative to sprinkler placement are included in NFPA 13, *Standard for the Installation of Sprinkler Systems*.

Formal Interpretation 81-40
Reference: 31-4.5.1

Question: Is it the Committee's intent that shower curtains in health care facilities fall under the requirements of 31-4.5.1?

Answer: No.

Issue Edition: 1981
Reference: 31-4.5
Date: February 1984 ■

See also commentary following A-31-1.4.1.

31-4.5.2* Newly introduced upholstered furniture within health care occupancies shall be tested in accordance with the provisions of 31-1.4.2(b).

This requirement, which applies to newly introduced upholstered furniture in nonsprinklered health care occupancies, regulates in accordance with test results from NFPA 261, *Standard Method of Test for Determining Resistance of Mock-Up Upholstered Furniture Material Assemblies to Ignition by Smoldering Cigarettes*.[7] (*See commentary following A-31-1.4.2.*)

A-31-4.5.2 Newly introduced upholstered furniture within health care occupancies should be tested for rate of heat release in accordance with 31-1.4.3.

Rate of heat release testing, as addressed by 31-1.4.3, A-31-1.4.3 and the associated handbook commentary, is suggested, but not mandated, for newly introduced upholstered furniture in health care occupancies.

31-4.5.3* Newly introduced mattresses within health care occupancies shall be tested in accordance with the provisions of 31-1.4.2(c).

For the same reasons that it is important to regulate furniture for protection against cigarette ignition, it is also important to regulate mattress ignition resistance in nonsprinklered facilities. The reference to 31-1.4.2(c) mandates testing by 16 CFR 1632, *Standard for the Flammability of Mattresses and Mattress Pads*.[8] (*See commentary following A-31-1.4.2.*)

A-31-4.5.3 Newly introduced mattresses within a health care occupancy should be tested for rate of heat release in accordance with 31-1.4.4.

Rate of heat release testing, as addressed by 31-1.4.3, A-31-1.4.3 and the associated handbook commentary, is suggested, but not mandated, for newly introduced mattresses in health care occupancies.

31-4.5.4 Combustible decorations are prohibited in any health care occupancy unless flame-retardant.

Exception: Combustible decorations of such limited quantities that a hazard of fire development or spread is not present, such as photographs and paintings.

31-4.5.5* Wastebaskets and other waste containers shall be of noncombustible or other approved materials.

A-31-4.5.5 It is not the intent of the *Code* that small wall or cart mounted waste type containers be required to comply with this section of the *Code*.

The purpose of 31-4.5.5 is to contain any fire that may start in a waste container. A combustible container or container that collapses during fire exposure will help

Formal Interpretation 88-1 (supersedes 85-4)
Reference: 31-4.5.5

Question No. 1: Is it the intent of 31-4.5.5 to regulate clean-linen carts for fire retardancy?

Answer: No.

Question No. 2: Is it the intent of 31-4.5.5 to regulate soiled-linen carts for fire retardancy?

Answer: No.

Question No. 3: Is it the intent of 31-4.5.5 to regulate trash carts for fire retardancy?

Answer: Yes.

Question No. 4: Is it a literal interpretation of the *Code* that 31-4.5.5 regulates mobile trash carts?

Answer: Yes.

Issue Edition: 1988
Reference: 31-4.5.4
Date: January 1988 ■

spread the fire. If the trash container is adjacent to a bed, there is a high probability that the bed linens will ignite, regardless of whether the container is approved. This fire spread scenerio is very common in health care facilities.

Appendix item A-31-4.5.5 was added to this edition of the *Code* to offer relief to facilities using small disposal containers attached to walls or carts. Such units are common for receiving used sharps (hypodermic needles and syringes) or chemotherapy waste and do not present the same hazard as trash receptacles.

31-4.6* **Engineered Smoke Control Systems.** Existing engineered smoke control systems, unless specifically exempted by the authority having jurisdiction, shall be tested in accordance with established engineering principles. Systems not meeting the performance requirements of such testing shall be continued in operation only with the specific approval of the authority having jurisdiction. New engineered smoke control systems shall be tested in accordance with established engineering principles and shall meet the performance requirements of such testing prior to acceptance. Following accep-

tance, all engineered smoke control systems shall be tested periodically in accordance with recognized engineering principles. Test documentation shall be maintained on the premises at all times.

A-31-4.6 Two documents that provide recognized engineering principles for the testing of smoke control systems are NFPA 92A, *Recommended Practice for Smoke Control Systems,* and NFPA 92B, *Guide for Smoke Management Systems in Malls, Atria, and Large Areas.*

31-4.7 **Portable Space Heating Devices.** Portable space heating devices are prohibited in all health care and ambulatory health care occupancies.

Exception: Portable space heating devices shall be permitted to be used in nonsleeping staff and employee areas when the heating elements of such devices are limited to not more than 212°F (100°C).

31-4.8 **Construction, Repair, and Improvement Operations.**

31-4.8.1 Construction, repair, and improvement operations shall comply with 31-1.1.

31-4.8.2 The means of egress in any area undergoing construction, repair, or improvements shall be inspected daily. (*See 31-1.2.1.*)

SECTION 31-5   Detention and Correctional Occupancies

31-5.1 **Attendants, Evacuation Plan, Fire Exit Drills.**

31-5.1.1 Detention and correctional facilities or those portions of facilities having such occupancy must be provided with 24-hour staffing. Staff must be within three floors or 300 ft (91 m) horizontal distance of the access door of each resident housing area.

In addition, for Use Conditions III, IV, and V, the arrangement shall be such that the staff involved can start release of locks necessary for emergency evacuation or rescue and initiate other necessary emergency actions within two minutes of alarm.

31-5.1.2*   Provisions shall be made so that residents in Use Conditions III, IV, and V can readily notify staff of an emergency.

A-31-5.1.2   This can be met by electronic or oral monitoring systems, visual monitoring, call signals, or other means.

Use Conditions III, IV, and V rely on staff action to protect residents; therefore, the staff needs to be made aware of conditions immediately, as residents may discover a fire before automatic detection devices react.

31-5.1.3*   The administration of every detention or correctional facility shall have in effect, and provide to all supervisory personnel, written copies of a plan for the protection of all persons in the event of fire and for their evacuation to areas of refuge and for evacuation from the building when necessary. All employees shall be instructed and drilled with respect to their duties under the plan. The plan shall be coordinated with and reviewed by the fire department legally committed to serve the facility.

A-31-5.1.3   There should be periodic coordinated training involving detention/correctional facility personnel and personnel of the fire department legally committed to serving the facility.

A properly designed and well-tested plan is of great importance, especially in a detention and correctional occupancy, where residents depend heavily on staff performance in order to survive a fire.

31-5.1.4   Employees of detention and correctional occupancies shall be instructed in the proper use of portable fire extinguishers and other manual fire suppression equipment that they may be called upon to use. With respect to new staff, such training shall be provided promptly upon commencement of duty. With respect to existing staff, refresher training shall be provided at least annually.

31-5.2   Books, clothing, and other combustible personal property allowed in sleeping rooms shall be stored in closable metal lockers or a fire resistant container.

31-5.3   The number of heat-producing appliances, such as toasters and hot plates, and the overall use of electrical power within a sleeping room shall be controlled by facility administration.

31-5.4*   Furnishings, Bedding, and Decorations.

A-31-5.4   Personal property provides combustible contents for fire development. Therefore, adequate controls are needed to limit the quantity and combustibility of fuels available to burn to reduce the probability of room flashover. The provisions of 31-5.4 will not, by themselves, prevent room flashover if personal property controls are not provided.

The provisions of 31-5.4 make extensive use of the menu of provisions in 31-1.4 that apply to furnishings and contents, particularly those that address upholstered furniture and mattresses (*see 31-5.4.2 and 31-5.4.3*). Nevertheless, to prevent the occurrence of room flashover in the small room spaces characteristic of detention and correctional occupancies, the control of combustible personal property is also very important.

31-5.4.1   Draperies and curtains, including privacy curtains, in detention and correctional occupancies shall be in accordance with the provisions of 31-1.4.1.

31-5.4.2   Newly introduced upholstered furniture within detention and correctional occupancies shall be tested in accordance with the provisions of 31-1.4.2(b) and 31-1.4.3. Exception No. 1 to 31-1.4.3(a) shall not apply to Use Conditions IV and V.

31-5.4.3   Newly introduced mattresses within detention and correctional occupancies shall be tested in accordance with the provisions of 31-1.4.2(c) and 31-1.4.4. The provisions of 31-1.4.4(a) shall not apply to Use Conditions II and III. Exception No. 1 to 31-1.4.4(a) shall not apply to Use Conditions IV and V.

The provisions of 31-5.4.1 through 31-5.4.3 present the most vigorous regulation of contents and furnishings by this *Code*. It is appropriate that this be done for detention and correctional occupancies in consideration of the protect-in-place strategy required of this occupancy by the *Code* and the unwillingness of staff to unlock doors to allow residents to move to the outside.

Draperies and curtains must be flame resistant. Newly introduced upholstered furniture and mattresses must be resistant to cigarette ignition and must also have limited rates of heat release.

Use of the exemptions applicable to sprinklered building spaces, as addressed by the exceptions to 31-1.4.2 (a), (b), and (c), 31-1.4.3 (a), (b), and (c), and 31-1.4.4(a), (b), and (c), is not prohibited. Therefore, in spaces protected by smoke detectors, there is a relaxation in the allowable peak rate of heat release of upholstered furniture and mattresses in accordance with the provisions of Exception No. 1 to 31-1.4.3 and Exception No. 1 to 31-1.4.4. Similarly, in a sprinklered detention and correctional occupancy space, neither upholstered furniture nor mattresses are regulated on the assumption that the sprinklers will prevent room flashover.

31-5.4.4 Combustible decorations are prohibited in any detention or correctional occupancy unless flame-retardant.

31-5.4.5 Wastebaskets and other waste containers shall be of noncombustible or other approved materials.

31-5.5 **Keys.** All keys necessary for unlocking doors installed in means of egress shall be individually identified by both touch and sight.

31-5.6 **Portable Space Heating Devices.** Portable space heating devices are prohibited.

Loss of keys, broken keys, and incorrect keys have played a major role in several multiple-death detention and correctional occupancy fires.

SECTION 31-6   Residential Occupancies

31-6.1 **Hotel Emergency Organization.**

31-6.1.1* All employees of hotels shall be instructed and drilled in the duties they are to perform in the event of fire, panic, or other emergency.

A-31-6.1.1 The exact nature of this emergency organization must of necessity be governed by such factors as the number of available employees, the structural conditions, the degree of compliance with this *Code*, and other elements pertinent to the individual situation.

In order to be efficient, any such organization must depend upon:

(a) A definite working plan.
(b) Competent leadership.
(c) Rigid discipline.
(d) Maintenance of necessary apparatus.
(e) A schedule of sufficient training under discipline with such apparatus.

It will be found advisable to secure the cooperation of local fire department officials in developing and training such an organization of employees.

31-6.1.2* Drills of the emergency organization shall be held at monthly intervals, covering such points as the operation and maintenance of the available first aid fire appliances, the testing of devices to alert guests, and a study of instructions for emergency duties.

A-31-6.1.2 It is recommended that emergencies be assumed to have arisen at various locations in the occupancy in order to train employees in logical procedures.

31-6.2 **Emergency Duties.**

31-6.2.1 Upon discovery of fire, performance of some or all of these duties will become immediately imperative, the number and sequence depending upon the exact situation encountered:

Alarms
   Notify office.
   Notify public fire department.
   Notify private fire brigade.
Guests
   Warn guests or others who are or may become endangered.
   Assist occupants to safety, with special attention to aged, infirm, or otherwise incapacitated persons.
   Search rooms to ensure all occupants have escaped.
   Staff all elevators, including those of automatic type, with competent operators.
Extinguishment
   Extinguish or control the fire using available first aid equipment.

Send messenger to meet public fire department upon arrival in order to direct latter to exact location of fire. (The public fire department is in full command upon arrival.)

Special Equipment

Fire Pumps — stand by for instant operation.

Ventilating Equipment — in case of dense smoke, stand by, operate under proper instructions to clear area affected.

Refrigerating Equipment — if machines are definitely endangered, shut them down and blow refrigerant to sewer or atmosphere to prevent explosion.

Generators and Motors — protect against water damage with tarpaulins — shut down motors not needed — keep generators operating to furnish lights, elevator power, etc.

Boilers — if necessary to abandon boiler room, extinguish or dump fire and lower steam pressure by blowing to sewer or atmosphere to prevent possible explosion.

31-6.3 Dormitories.

31-6.3.1 Drills. Fire exit drills shall be regularly conducted in accordance with 31-1.5.

31-6.4 Emergency Instructions for Residents or Guests.

31-6.4.1* A floor diagram reflecting the actual floor arrangement, exit locations, and room identification shall be posted in a location and manner acceptable to the authority having jurisdiction on or immediately adjacent to every guest room door in hotels and in every resident room in dormitories.

A-31-6.4.1 Floor diagrams should reflect the actual floor arrangement and should be oriented with the actual direction to the exits.

Note that the manner in which the information is to be posted and the nature of its contents are at the discretion of the authority having jurisdiction. This will vary depending on the building, its layout, and the protection provided.

31-6.4.2* Firesafety information shall be provided to allow guests to make a decision to either: evacuate to the outside; evacuate to an area of refuge; remain in place; or any combination of the three.

A-31-6.4.2 Factors for developing the firesafety information include construction type, suppression systems, alarm and detection systems, building layout, and building HVAC systems, etc.

31-6.5 Emergency Instructions for Residents of Apartment Buildings.

31-6.5.1 Emergency instructions shall be provided to each living unit on a yearly basis indicating the location of alarms, exiting paths, and actions to be taken, both in response to a fire in the living unit and in response to the sounding of the alarm system.

31-6.6* Furnishings and Decorations.

A-31-6.6 In nonsprinklered hotels, dormitories, or apartment buildings, new upholstered furniture located in corridors or areas not separated from corridors by corridor walls as specified in the *Code* should be tested in accordance with NFPA 261, *Standard Method of Test for Determining Resistance of Mock-up Upholstered Furniture Material Assemblies to Ignition by Smoldering Cigarettes* (*see Appendix B*), with a char length not exceeding 1.5 in. (3.8 cm), and should be labeled indicating such compliance.

Although there are no mandatory references to the upholstered furniture and mattress provisions of 31-1.4.2 through 31-1.4.4, most new hotels, dormitories, and apartment buildings will be sprinklered in accordance with the requirements of Chapters 16 and 18. In accordance with the exceptions to the 31-1.4 upholstered furniture and mattress provisions, sprinklered building spaces are exempted from regulation on the assumption that the sprinklers will prevent room flashover. For nonsprinklered hotels, dormitories, and apartment buildings, the appendix note suggests that, as a minimum, cigarette ignition resistance be proven by testing.

31-6.6.1 New draperies, curtains, and other similar loosely hanging furnishings and decorations in hotels and dormitories shall be in accordance with the provisions of 31-1.4.1.

31-6.7 Unvented fuel-fired heaters shall not be used in residential occupancies.

Exception: Listed and approved unvented fuel-fired heaters in one- and two-family dwellings.

SECTION 31-7   Board and Care Homes

31-7.1 **Emergency Plan.** The administration of every residential board and care facility shall have, in effect and available to all supervisory personnel, written copies of a plan for protecting all persons in the event of fire and for keeping persons in place, and for their evacuation to areas of refuge and from the building when necessary. The plan shall include special staff response, including fire protection procedures needed to ensure the safety of any resident, and shall be amended or revised for use upon admission to the home of any resident with unusual needs. All employees shall be periodically instructed and kept informed with respect to their duties and responsibilities under the plan. Such instruction shall be reviewed by the staff at least every two months. A copy of the plan shall be readily available at all times within the facility.

31-7.2 **Resident Training.** All residents participating in the emergency plan shall be trained in the proper actions to be taken in the event of fire. This training shall include actions to be taken if the primary escape route is blocked. If the resident is given rehabilitation or habilitation training, training in fire prevention and actions to be taken in the event of a fire shall be a part of the rehabilitation training program. Residents shall be trained to assist each other in case of fire to the extent their physical and mental abilities permit them to do so without additional personal risk.

31-7.3 **Fire Exit Drills.** Fire exit drills shall be conducted at least twelve times per year, four times a year on each shift. The drills may be announced in advance to the residents. The drills shall involve the actual evacuation of all residents to an assembly point as specified in the emergency plan and shall provide residents with experience in exiting through all exits required by the *Code.* Exits not used in any fire drill shall not be credited in meeting the requirements of this *Code* for board and care homes.

Exception No. 1: Actual exiting from windows shall not be required to meet the requirements of this section; opening the window and signaling for help shall be an acceptable alternative.

Exception No. 2: If the board and care home has an evacuation capability rating of "Impractical," those residents who cannot meaningfully assist in their own evacuation or who have special health problems need not actively participate in the drill. Section 31-4 applies in such instances.

See also 31-1.5.

31-7.4 **Smoking.**

31-7.4.1 Where smoking is permitted, noncombustible safety-type ashtrays or receptacles shall be provided in convenient locations.

31-7.5* **Furnishings, Bedding, and Decorations.**

A-31-7.5 The requirements applicable to draperies/curtains, upholstered furniture, and mattresses apply only to "new" draperies/curtains, "new" upholstered furniture, and "new" mattresses. The word "new" means unused, normally via procurement from the marketplace, either by purchase or donation, of items not previously used. Many board and care facilities allow the residents to bring into the board and care home upholstered furniture items from that resident's previous place of residence. Such an item is not "new" and thus will not be regulated. On the other hand, some of the larger board and care homes purchase "contract furniture" much the same way as is done in hotels. Such new, unused furniture, whether purchased or received as a donation, is regulated by the requirements of 31-7.5.2. By federal law, mattresses manufactured and sold within the United States must pass testing per FF4-72, *Standard for the Flammability of Mattresses.*

The provisions of 31-7.5 are new to this edition of the *Code* and extend the level of life safety provided to a residential board and care facility by further attempting to prevent room flashover. However, rather than impose these requirements retroactively, the requirement is applicable to new upholstered furniture and new mattresses. The appendix note sufficiently details the definition of the word "new" in this context. Where the appendix note references in accordance with FF4-72, *Standard for the Flammability of Mattresses,*[16] testing, this test is the same as that designated in 31-1.4.2(c) as 16 CFR 1632, *Standard for the Flammability of Mattresses and Mattress Pads.*[8]

31-7.5.1 New draperies, curtains, and other similar loosely hanging furnishings and decorations in board and care homes shall be in accordance with the provisions of 31-1.4.1.

31-7.5.2* New upholstered furniture within board and care homes shall be tested in accordance with the provisions of 31-1.4.2(a).

A-31-7.5.2 New upholstered furniture within board and care homes should be tested for rates of heat release in accordance with 31-1.4.3.

31-7.5.3* New mattresses within board and care homes shall be tested in accordance with the provisions of 31-1.4.2(c).

A-31-7.5.3 New mattresses within board and care homes should be tested for rates of heat release in accordance with 31-1.4.4.

Draperies must be flame resistant in accordance with 31-7.5.1. New upholstered furniture and mattresses must be resistant to cigarette ignition in accordance with 31-7.5.2 and 31-7.5.3. New upholstered furniture and mattresses should have limited rates of heat release, as recommended by A-31-7.5.2 and A-31-7.5.3. (*See commentary on 31-1.4.*)

SECTION 31-8   Mercantile Occupancies

31-8.1 **Drills.** In every Class A or B store, employees shall be regularly trained in fire exit drill procedures in general conformance with 31-1.5.

31-8.2 Employees of mercantile occupancies shall be instructed in the proper use of portable fire extinguishers.

The extent of this training (e.g., instruction only, instruction and hands-on use) is determined by the authority having jurisdiction.

SECTION 31-9   Business Occupancies

31-9.1 **Drills.** In any building subject to occupancy by more than 500 persons or more than 100 persons above or below the street level, employees and supervisory personnel shall be instructed in fire exit drill procedures in accordance with 31-1.5 and shall hold practice drills periodically where practicable.

31-9.2 Employees of business occupancies shall be instructed in the proper use of portable fire extinguishers.

The extent of this training (e.g., instruction only, instruction and hands-on use) is determined by the authority having jurisdiction.

References Cited in Commentary

[1]NFPA 241, *Standard for Safeguarding Construction, Alteration, and Demolition Operations,* National Fire Protection Association, Quincy, MA, 1989.

[2]ASME/ANSI A17.1, *Safety Code for Elevators and Escalators,* American Society of Mechanical Engineers, 345 East 47th Street, New York, NY, 1990.

[3]ASME/ANSI A17.3, *Safety Code for Existing Elevators and Escalators,* American Society of Mechanical Engineers, 345 East 47th Street, New York, NY, 1990.

[4]NFPA 92A, *Recommended Practice for Smoke Control Systems,* National Fire Protection Association, Quincy, MA, 1988.

[5]NFPA 701, *Standard Methods of Fire Tests for Flame-Resistant Textiles and Films,* National Fire Protection Association, Quincy, MA, 1989.

[6]NFPA 260, *Standard Methods of Tests and Classification System for Cigarette Ignition Resistance of Components of Upholstered Furniture,* National Fire Protection Association, Quincy, MA, 1989.

[7]NFPA 261, *Standard Method of Test for Determining Resistance of Mock-Up Upholstered Furniture Material Assemblies to Ignition by Smoldering Cigarettes,* National Fire Protection Association, Quincy, MA, 1989.

[8]16 CFR 1632, *Standard for the Flammability of Mattresses and Mattress Pads*, Code of Federal Regulations, Volume 16, Part 1632, U.S. Government Printing Office, Washington, DC, published annually.

[9]CAL 133, *Flammability Test Procedure for Seating Furniture for Use in High Risk and Public Occupancies*, California Technical Bulletin 133, California Bureau of Home Furnishings, Department of Consumer Affairs, North Highlands, CA, 1991.

[10]UL 1056, *Standard for Fire Test of Upholstered Furniture*, Underwriters Laboratories Inc., Northbrook, IL, 1989.

[11]UL 1895, *Standard for Fire Test of Mattresses*, Underwriters Laboratories Inc., Northbrook, IL, 1990.

[12]NFPA 703, *Standard for Fire Retardant Impregnated Wood and Fire Retardant Coatings for Building Materials*, National Fire Protection Association, Quincy, MA, 1985.

[13]The SFPE *Handbook of Fire Protection Engineering*, National Fire Protection Association, Quincy, MA, 1988.

[14]NFPA 1126, *(Proposed) Code for the Use of Pyrotechnics in the Performing Arts*, as contained in the *1991 Fall Meeting Technical Committee Reports*, National Fire Protection Association, Quincy, MA, 1991.

[15]NFPA *Learn Not to Burn Curriculum*, Firesafety Program for Grades Kindergarten through Eight, National Fire Protection Association, Quincy, MA, 1981.

[16]FF4-72, *Standard for the Flammability of Mattresses*, U.S. Government Printing Office, Washington, D.C.

32

Referenced Publications

This chapter contains the mandatory referenced publications that, prior to the 1985 Edition of the *Code*, were found in Appendix B-1 of the *Code*. Appendix B now contains only nonmandatory referenced publications.

(See Appendix B for other referenced publications that are advisory and thus do not constitute part of the requirements of this Code.)

32-1 The following documents or portions thereof are referenced within this *Code* and shall be considered part of the requirements of this document to the extent called for by the *Code*. The edition indicated for each reference is the current edition as of the date of the NFPA issuance of this document.

The numbers in parentheses represent the paragraph numbers from chapters of this *Code* that reference the given publication in a mandatory way.

The Committee on Safety to Life recognizes that it is sometimes not practical to continually upgrade existing buildings or installations to comply with all the requirements of the following referenced publications. Existing buildings or installations that do not comply with the provisions of the following referenced publications may be continued in service, subject to approval by the authority having jurisdiction and provided the lack of conformity with these standards does not present a serious hazard to the occupants.

There are two important points to be made regarding Section 31-1. First, the listed documents are mandatory only to the extent called for in the *Code*. For example, although NFPA 13, *Standard for the Installation of Sprinkler Systems*, is listed here, this does not mean that *all* buildings must be sprinklered, but rather that, where the *Code* requires them to be sprinklered, NFPA 13 is to be used for sprinkler installation. Second, the Committee recognizes that existing installations need not be continuously upgraded as new editions of the referenced standards are adopted, provided the authority having jurisdiction agrees that no serious life safety hazard is present.

32-1.1 **NFPA Publications.** The following publications are available from the National Fire Protection Association, 1 Batterymarch Park, P.O. Box 9101, Quincy, MA 02269-9101.

NFPA 10-1990, *Standard for Portable Fire Extinguishers* (7-7.4.1, 31-1.3.5)

NFPA 11-1988, *Standard for Low Expansion Foam and Combined Agent Systems* (7-7.3, 31-1.3.5)

NFPA 11A-1988, *Standard for Medium- and High-Expansion Foam Systems* (7-7.3, 31-1.3.5)

NFPA 12-1989, *Standard on Carbon Dioxide Extinguishing Systems* (7-7.3, 31-1.3.5)

NFPA 12A-1989, *Standard on Halon 1301 Fire Extinguishing Systems* (7-7.3, 31-1.3.5)

NFPA 12B-1990, *Standard on Halon 1211 Fire Extinguishing Systems* (7-7.3, 31-1.3.5)

NFPA 13-1989, *Standard for the Installation of Sprinkler Systems* (6-2.4.8, 7-7.1.1, 8-4.4.3.7, 9-4.4.3.7, 16-1.5.1, 17-1.5.1, 22-2.3.5.1, 23-2.3.5.1, 26-1.5.2, 27-1.5.2, 31-1.3.5)

NFPA 13D-1989, *Standard for the Installation of Sprinkler Systems in One- and Two-Family Dwellings and Mobile Homes* (7-7.1.1, 21-2.2.3, 22-2.3.5.1, 23-2.3.5.1, 31-1.3.5)

NFPA 13R-1989, *Standard for the Installation of Sprinkler Systems in Residential Occupancies up to Four Stories in Height* (7-7.1.1, 16-3.5.1, 17-3.5.1, 18-3.5.1, 19-3.5.1, 21-2.2.3, 22-3.3.5.1, 23-3.3.5.1, 31-1.3.5)

NFPA 14-1990, *Standard for the Installation of Standpipe and Hose Systems* (7-7.4.2, 30-8.2.2, 31-1.3.5)

NFPA 15-1990, *Standard for Water Spray Fixed Systems for Fire Protection* (7-7.3, 31-1.3.5)

NFPA 16-1991, *Standard on the Installation of Deluge Foam-Water Sprinkler and Foam-Water Spray Systems* (7-7.3, 31-1.3.5)

NFPA 17-1990, *Standard for Dry Chemical Extinguishing Systems* (7-7.3, 31-1.3.5)

NFPA 17A-1990, *Standard for Wet Chemical Extinguishing Systems* (7-7.3, 31-1.3.5)

NFPA 20-1990, *Standard for the Installation of Centrifugal Fire Pumps* (7-7.3, 31-1.3.5)

NFPA 22-1987, *Standard for Water Tanks for Private Fire Protection* (31-1.3.5)

NFPA 30-1990, *Flammable and Combustible Liquids Code* (6-4.3, 31-1.6.1)

NFPA 31-1987, *Standard for the Installation of Oil Burning Equipment* (7-2.2)

NFPA 40-1988, *Standard for the Storage and Handling of Cellulose Nitrate Motion Picture Film* (8-3.2.2.1, 9-3.2.2.1, 31-2.8)

NFPA 45-1986, *Standard on Fire Protection for Laboratories Using Chemicals* (6-4.4, 7-2.4, 10-3.2.4, 11-3.2.4, 26-3.2.3, 31-1.7)

NFPA 54-1988, *National Fuel Gas Code* (7-1.1, 7-2.2, 31-1.6.1)

NFPA 58-1989, *Standard for the Storage and Handling of Liquefied Petroleum Gases* (7-1.1, 31-1.6.1)

NFPA 70-1990, *National Electrical Code* (5-9.2.4, 6-2.4.8, 7-1.2, 7-2.2, 7-6.1.4, 8-4.1.4, 10-4.1.5, 14-5.1.2, 15-5.1.2, 26-4.2.4, 30-8.4.2)

NFPA 71-1989, *Standard for the Installation, Maintenance, and Use of Signaling Systems for Central Station Service* (7-6.1.4, 7-6.4, 31-1.3.5)

NFPA 72-1990, *Standard for the Installation, Maintenance, and Use of Protective Signaling Systems* (7-6.1.4, 7-6.3.3, 7-6.3.8, 7-6.4, 14-3.4.1.3, 15-3.4.1.3, 26-4.2.3.3, 30-8.3.2, 31-1.3.5)

NFPA 72E-1990, *Standard on Automatic Fire Detectors* (5-2.1.8, 6-3.5.2, 6-3.5.3, 7-6.1.4, 7-6.2.7, 7-6.2.8, 19-3.4.4.2, 22-3.3.4.8, 23-3.3.4.6, 31-1.3.5)

NFPA 74-1989, *Standard for the Installation, Maintenance, and Use of Household Fire Warning Equipment* (7-6.1.4, 7-6.2.9, 31-1.3.5)

NFPA 80-1990, *Standard for Fire Doors and Windows* (5-2.1.14.2, 6-2.3.3, 6-2.3.4, 12-3.6.3.4, 13-3.6.3.6, 31-1.3.5)

NFPA 82-1990, *Standard on Incinerators, Waste, and Linen Handling Systems and Equipment* (7-5.2)

NFPA 88A-1985, *Standard for Parking Structures* (16-3.5.3, 18-3.5.4)

NFPA 90A-1989, *Standard for the Installation of Air Conditioning and Ventilating Systems* (6-2.6.1, 7-2.1, 12-3.1.1)

NFPA 90B-1989, *Standard for the Installation of Warm Air Heating and Air Conditioning Systems* (7-2.1)

NFPA 91-1990, *Standard for the Installation of Blower and Exhaust Systems for Dust, Stock, and Vapor Removal or Conveying* (7-2.2)

NFPA 96-1991, *Standard for the Installation of Equipment for the Removal of Smoke and Grease-Laden Vapors from Commercial Cooking Equipment* (7-2.3, 31-1.3.5)

NFPA 99-1990, *Standard for Health Care Facilities* (6-4.4, 7-2.4, 12-2.9.2, 12-2.10.2, 12-3.2.1, 12-3.2.2, 12-3.2.3, 12-3.2.4, 12-5.1.2, 12-5.1.3, 12-6.2.9.2, 12-6.3.2.1, 12-6.3.2.2, 13-3.2.2, 13-3.2.3, 13-3.2.4, 13-6.2.9.2, 13-6.3.2.1, 13-6.3.2.2, 31-1.3.5)

NFPA 101M, *Manual on Alternative Approaches to Life Safety* (22-2.1.3.2, 23-2.1.3.2, 23-2.3.6.1)†

The point values assigned to the various parameters in the FSESs of the 1988 Edition of NFPA 101M were calibrated for use with the 1988 Edition of the *Life Safety Code* and should not be used with the 1991 Edition of the *Life Safety Code*. At the time this *Handbook* went to press, the Committee on Safety to Life was preparing a version of NFPA 101M calibrated to the 1991 *Life Safety Code*. This should result in a 1992 Edition of NFPA 101M.

NFPA 102-1986, *Standard for Assembly Seating, Tents, and Membrane Structures* (8-2.5.6.6, 8-2.5.8.5, 8-4.3.1, 9-2.5.6.6, 9-2.5.8.5, 9-4.3.1)

NFPA 110-1988, *Standard for Emergency and Standby Power Systems* (5-9.2.3, 30-8.4.2, 31-1.3.9)

NFPA 211-1988, *Standard for Chimneys, Fireplaces, Vents, and Solid Fuel Burning Appliances* (7-2.2, 12-5.2.2, 13-5.2.2)

NFPA 220-1985, *Standard on Types of Building Construction* (6-2.1, 6-5.3.4)

NFPA 241-1989, *Standard for Safeguarding Construction, Alteration, and Demolition Operations* (31-1.1.1)

NFPA 251-1990, *Standard Methods of Fire Tests of Building Construction and Materials* (Section 3-2, 6-2.3.1, 8-3.2.1.7, 13-3.6.2.1, 22-1.3, 23-1.3)

NFPA 252-1990, *Standard Methods of Fire Tests of Door Assemblies* (6-2.3.3, 6-2.3.5, 6-3.4.2, 13-3.6.3.4)

NFPA 253-1990, *Standard Method of Test for Critical Radiant Flux of Floor Covering Systems Using a Radiant Heat Energy Source* (Section 3-2, 6-5.4.1)

NFPA 255-1990, *Standard Method of Test of Surface Burning Characteristics of Building Materials* (6-5.3.1, 8-3.2.1.7)

NFPA 256-1987, *Standard Methods of Fire Tests of Roof Coverings* (12-1.6.2, 13-1.6.2, 15-1.6.3, 22-3.1.3.3, 23-3.1.3.3)

NFPA 257-1990, *Standard for Fire Tests of Window Assemblies* (6-2.3.4)

NFPA 260-1989, *Standard Methods of Tests and Classification System for Cigarette Ignition Resistance of Components of Upholstered Furniture* (31-1.4.2)

NFPA 261-1989, *Standard Method of Test for Determining Resistance of Mock-Up Upholstered Furniture Material Assemblies to Ignition by Smoldering Cigarettes* (31-1.4.2)

NFPA 701-1989, *Standard Methods of Fire Tests for Flame-Resistant Textiles and Films* (8-3.2.1.11, 8-4.4.3.4, 9-3.2.1.11, 9-4.4.3.4, 31-1.4.1)

NFPA 703-1985, *Standard for Fire Retardant Impregnated Wood and Fire Retardant Coatings for Building Materials* (6-5.6.1, 8-4.4.3.4, 9-4.4.3.4)

NFPA 1221-1988, *Standard for the Installation, Maintenance, and Use of Public Fire Service Communication Systems* (7-6.1.4, 31-1.3.5)

32-1.2 Other Publications.

ANSI A14.3-1984, *Safety Code for Fixed Ladders*, American National Standards Institute, 1430 Broadway, New York, NY 10018 (5-2.9.2)

ANSI A117.1-1986, *Standard for Buildings and Facilities—Providing Accessibility and Usability for Physically Handicapped People*, American National Standards Institute, 1430 Broadway, New York, NY 10018 (5-1.2.1)

ASME/ANSI A17.1-1990, *Safety Code for Elevators and Escalators*, American Society of Mechanical Engineers, 345 East 47th Street, New York, NY 10017 (5-2.12.2.4, 7-4.2, 7-4.4, 31-1.3.10)

ASME/ANSI A17.3-1990, *Safety Code for Existing Elevators and Escalators*, American Society of Mechanical Engineers, 345 East 47th Street, New York, NY 10017 (7-4.3, 7-4.5)

ASTM E136-1982, *Standard Test Method for Behavior of Materials in a Vertical Tube Furnace at 750°F*, American Society for Testing and Materials, 1916 Race Street, Philadelphia, PA 19103 (Section 3-2)

ASTM F851-1983, *Standard Test Method for Self-Rising Seat Mechanisms*, American Society for Testing and Materials, 1916 Race Street, Philadelphia, PA 19103 (8-2.5.6.1, 9-2.5.6.1)

Code of Federal Regulations 16, Part 1632 (31-1.4.2)

UL 1975, *Standard for Fire Tests for Foamed Plastic Used for Decorative Purposes* (8-3.2.1.11, 8-4.4.3.4, 8-4.4.3.6, 9-4.4.3.4, 9-4.4.3.6, 31-2.6.3)

---

† The edition of NFPA 101M that corresponds with the 1991 *Life Safety Code* will be published in 1992.

This chapter contains mandatory references to other documents. As noted in the commentary to 32-1, the extent to which these documents are mandatory is specified within the *Code*. Note that, after each entry in 32-1-1, there is a paragraph or series of paragraph numbers located within parentheses. These numbers indicate the paragraphs that contain references to the specific document in question. The reasons for locating all the mandatory references in one chapter are, first, to simplify the *Code* and, second, to make it easier for adopting jurisdictions to update the references when they adopt the *Code*. When adopting the *Code*, the adopting authority can review Chapter 32 and, if desired, update referenced documents in only one location rather than throughout the *Code*. It should be noted that, between the time the *Code* was adopted in the fall of 1990 and the time this *Handbook* was written in the spring of 1991, several NFPA documents were updated at the NFPA Annual Meeting in May of 1991. Therefore, in some cases, references in the commentary to various standards, such as NFPA 13, carry a different edition date from those listed in Chapter 32. The editions of the *Code* listed in Chapter 32 are the legally referenced editions unless the jurisdiction, when adopting the *Code*, has updated the list of codes and standards.

The material contained in Appendix A of the 1991 *Life Safety Code* is included within this *Handbook* and, therefore, Appendix A is not repeated here.

B

Referenced Publications

B-1 The following documents or portions thereof are referenced within this *Code* for informational purposes only and thus are not considered part of the requirements of this *Code*. The edition indicated for each reference is the current edition as of the date of the NFPA issuance of this document.

The numbers in parentheses represent the paragraph numbers from the appendices of this *Code* that reference, in an advisory manner, the given publication.

Note that the mandatory referenced publications are now listed in Chapter 32. Many of the documents listed here are also listed in Chapter 32 and, although not mandatory here, they remain mandatory in Chapter 32.

B-1.1 **NFPA Publications.** National Fire Protection Association, 1 Batterymarch Park, P.O. Box 9101, Quincy, MA 02269-9101.

NFPA 10-1990, *Standard for Portable Fire Extinguishers* (A-7-7.4.1)

NFPA 11-1988, *Standard for Low Expansion Foam and Combined Agent Systems* (A-7-7.3)

NFPA 12-1989, *Standard on Carbon Dioxide Extinguishing Systems* (A-7-7.3)

NFPA 12A-1989, *Standard on Halon 1301 Fire Extinguishing Systems* (A-7-7.3)

NFPA 12B-1990, *Standard on Halon 1211 Fire Extinguishing Systems* (A-7-7.3)

NFPA 13-1989, *Standard for the Installation of Sprinkler Systems* (A-4-2.2.1, A-6-2.4.8 Exception No. 1, A-12-3.5.1, A-12-3.5.2, A-31-4.5.1)

NFPA 13A-1987, *Recommended Practice for the Inspection, Testing, and Maintenance of Sprinkler Systems* (A-31-1.3.6)

NFPA 13D-1989, *Standard for the Installation of Sprinkler Systems in One- and Two-Family Dwellings and Mobile Homes* (A-20-3.5.1, A-22-2.3.5.1, A-23-2.3.5.1)

NFPA 15-1990, *Standard for Water Spray Fixed Systems for Fire Protection* (A-7-7.3)

NFPA 17-1990, *Standard for Dry Chemical Extinguishing Systems* (A-7-7.3)

NFPA 22-1987, *Standard for Water Tanks for Private Fire Protection* (A-12-3.5.1)

NFPA 61B-1989, *Standard for the Prevention of Fires and Explosions in Grain Elevators and Facilities Handling Bulk Raw Agricultural Commodities* (A-29-7)

NFPA 68-1988, *Guide for Venting of Deflagrations* (A-6-4.2)

NFPA 70-1990, *National Electrical Code* (A-5-9.2.2, A-5-9.2.4, A-16-5.3)

NFPA 71-1989, *Standard for the Installation, Maintenance, and Use of Signaling Systems for Central Station Service* (A-7-7.2.1)

NFPA 72-1990, *Standard for the Installation, Maintenance, and Use of Local Protective Signaling Systems* (A-7-6.1.3, A-7-7.2.1)

NFPA 72G-1989, *Guide for the Installation, Maintenance, and Use of Notification Appliances for Protective Signaling Systems* (A-7-6.1.4, A-7-6.1.7)

NFPA 72H-1988, *Guide for Testing Procedures for Local, Auxiliary, Remote Station, and Proprietary Protective Signaling Systems* (A-7-6.1.4, A-7-6.1.7, A-31-1.3.7)

NFPA 80-1990, *Standard for Fire Doors and Windows* (A-5-1.3.4, A-6-2.3.5)

NFPA 88A-1985, *Standard for Parking Structures* (A-29-8.1.1)

NFPA 90A-1989, *Standard for the Installation of Air Conditioning and Ventilating Systems* (A-6-2.3.5.2, A-7-3.1)

NFPA 92A-1988, *Recommended Practice for Smoke Control Systems* (A-5-2.12.2.2)

NFPA 92B-1991, *Guide for Smoke Management Systems in Malls, Atria, and Large Areas* (A-7-3.1, A-31.4.6)

NFPA 99-1990, *Standard for Health Care Facilities* (A-12-3.2.1)

NFPA 101M, *Manual on Alternative Approaches to Life Safety* (A-5-3.2, A-12-1.1.1.1, A-13-1.1.1.1, A-14-1.1.2, A-15-1.1.2, A-22-1.3, A-22-2.1.2.1, A-22-3.1.2.1, A-22-3.1.2.2, A-22-4.1.3.1, A-23-1.3, A-23-2.1.2.1, A-23-3.1.2.1, A-23-3.1.2.2, A-23-4.1.3.1, A-26-1.1.1, A-27-1.1.1)†

The point values assigned to the various parameters in the FSESs of the 1988 Edition of NFPA 101M were calibrated for use with the 1988 Edition of the *Life Safety Code* and should not be used with the 1991 Edition of the *Life Safety Code*. At the time this *Handbook* went to press, the Committee on Safety to Life was preparing a version of NFPA 101M calibrated to the 1991 *Life Safety Code*. This should result in a 1992 Edition of NFPA 101M.

NFPA 105-1989, *Recommended Practice for the Installation of Smoke- Control Door Assemblies* (A-5-1.3.4, A-5-2.3.2, A-5-2.4.3.7, A-5-2.12.2.2, A-5-2.12.2.5, A-6-3.4.1)

---

† The edition of NFPA 101M that corresponds with the 1991 *Life Safety Code* will be published in 1992.

NFPA 204M-1991, *Guide for Smoke and Heat Venting* [A-28-2.6.2(b)]

NFPA 211-1988, *Standard for Chimneys, Fireplaces, Vents, and Solid Fuel Burning Appliances* (A-12-5.2.2, A-13-5.2.2)

NFPA 220-1985, *Standard on Types of Building Construction* (A-3-2, A-6-2.1, A-10-3.3.1, A-11-3.3.1)

NFPA 251-1990, *Standard Methods of Fire Tests of Building Construction and Materials* (A-6-2.3.6.2, A-6-2.4.2)

NFPA 253-1990, *Standard Method of Test for Critical Radiant Flux of Floor Covering Systems Using a Radiant Heat Energy Source* (A-12-3.3.2)

NFPA 255-1990, *Standard Method of Test of Surface Burning Characteristics of Building Materials* (A-6-5.2.3, A-6-5.3.1, A-6-5.3.2, A-31-1.4.1)

NFPA 259-1987, *Standard Test Method for Potential Heat of Building Materials* (A-3-2)

NFPA 260-1989, *Standard Methods of Tests and Classification System for Cigarette Ignition Resistance of Components of Upholstered Furniture* (A-31-1.4.2)

NFPA 261-1989, *Standard Method of Test for Determining Resistance of Mock-Up Upholstered Furniture Material Assemblies to Ignition by Smoldering Cigarettes* (A-31-1.4.2, A-31-6.6)

NFPA 307-1990, *Standard for the Construction and Fire Protection of Marine Terminals, Piers, and Wharves* (A-30-2.5.3)

NFPA 409-1990, *Standard on Aircraft Hangars* (A-29-6)

NFPA 501A-1987, *Standard for Firesafety Criteria for Manufactured Home Installations, Sites, and Communities* (A-30-6)

NFPA 701-1989, *Standard Methods of Fire Tests for Flame-Resistant Textiles and Films* (A-6-5.3.1, A-8-4.4.3.4(c), A-9-4.4.3.4(c), A-31-1.4.1, A-31-4.5.3, A-31-5.4.2)

NFPA 1221-1988, *Standard for the Installation, Maintenance, and Use of Public Fire Service Communication Systems* (A-7-7.2.1)

NFPA FPH1791, *NFPA Fire Protection Handbook*, 17th Edition, 1991 (A-7-7.1.1, A-12-3.2.2, A-13-3.2.2, A-13-3.6.1)

NFPA SPP-53, *Butcher and Parnell, Smoke Control in Fire Safety Design* (A-7-3.1)

B-1.2   Other Publications.

ASHRAE *Handbook and Product Directory* — 1985 Fundamentals, American Society of Heating, Refrigerating, and Air Conditioning Engineers, 1791 Tullie Circle, N.E., Atlanta, GA 30329 (A-5-2.3.2, A-5-2.12.2.2, A-7-3.1)

ANSI A117.1-1986, *Standard for Buildings and Facilities— Providing Accessibility and Usability for Physically Handicapped People,* American National Standards Institute, 1430 Broadway, New York, NY 10018 (A-2-10, A-3-2, A-5-1.2.2, A-5-1.2.3, A-5-2.2.3.4, A-8-2.5.9.2, A-8-4.5, A-9-2.5.9.2, A-10-1.1.2)

ASME/ANSI A17.1-1990, *Safety Code for Elevators and Escalators,* American Society of Mechanical Engineers, 345 East 47th St., New York, NY 10017 (A-5-2.12.2.3, A-7-4.1)

ASME/ANSI A17.3-1990, *Safety Code for Existing Elevators and Escalators,* American Society of Mechanical Engineers, 345 East 47th Street, New York, NY 10017 (A-7-4.1)

ASTM E-814-83, *Methods for Fire Tests of Through-Penetration Fire Stops* (A-6-2.3.6.2, A-6-2.4.2)

FF1-70, *Standard for the Surface Flammability of Carpets and Rugs (Pill Test)* (A-6-5.4.1)

FF4-72, *Standard for Flammability of Mattresses* (A-31-1.4.2, A-31-7.5)

SFPE *Handbook of Fire Protection Engineering,* (A-5-2.12.2.2, A-8-2.3.2, A-9-2.3.2, A-31-2.1)

Fisher, F., MacCracken, B., and Williamson, R. Brady, *Room Fire Experiments of Textile Wall Coverings,* ES-7853 for American Textile Manufacturers Institute, University of California Fire Research Laboratory, Berkeley, CA 94720, March, 1986 (A-6-5.2.3)

Klote and Fothergill, *Design of Smoke Control Systems for Buildings,* ASHRAE, 345 East 47th Street, New York, NY 10017 (A-5-2.3.2, A-5-2.12.2.2, A-7-3.1)

Templer, J., Mullet, G., Archea, J., and Margulis, S., *An Analysis of the Behavior of Stair Users,* National Bureau of Standards NBS BSS 120. Available from National Technical Information Service (NTIS), Springfield, VA 22151 (A-5-2.2.3.4)

PART 2

Supplements

The following six supplements are included in this *Handbook* to provide background information for *Code* users not familiar with the specialties addressed in them. Since they are not part of the *Code*, they are printed in black.

1. Case Histories: Fires Influencing the *Life Safety Code*
2. Fire Alarm Systems for *Life Safety Code* Users
3. Sprinkler Systems for *Life Safety Code* Users
4. Extracts from ASME A17.1, *Safety Code for Elevators and Escalators*
5. Fire Tests for *Life Safety Code* Users
6. How to Adopt the *Life Safety Code* into Law

1

Case Histories: Fires Influencing the Life Safety Code

Paul E. Teague, M.A.

Codes and standards are living documents. Born of the efforts of men and women to make their environment safer, they grow into maturity based on fire experience and the observations and research of those responsible for them. The best codes and standards, such as those produced by the NFPA, never age, since they are continually updated with new information that allows them to adapt to an ever changing world.

Such is the case with NFPA 101, *The Life Safety Code*. Originally known as *The Building Exits Code*, it had its origins in the effort to make factories safer for workers in the early days of this century. Its first focus was on the hazards of stairways and fire escapes, the need for fire drills in various occupancies, and the construction and arrangement of exits.

However, as American society changed, technology blossomed, and fire experience accumulated, the *Code* grew in scope. It began to include provisions for sprinklers, alarm and detection systems, protection of interior finish, and other important features. Of the thousands of fires whose lessons are reflected in this latest edition of the *Code,* probably none has had a bigger impact than the Triangle Shirtwaiste fire of March 25, 1911. It was that fire that prompted creation of the NFPA's Committee on Safety to Life and, ultimately, development of the *Code* itself.

The Triangle Fire

Since its founding in 1896, the NFPA has always placed special importance on its life safety work. The NFPA's original objectives, "establishing proper safeguards against loss of life and property by fire," placed life safety ahead of property protection. Yet, until the Triangle fire there was no one technical committee devoted exclusively to life safety concerns.

The Triangle Shirtwaiste Company was located on the eighth, ninth, and tenth floors of the Asch Building at the intersection of Washington Place and Green Street in New York City's Washington Square. The building was a "loft," typical of many in its day. The Triangle company, with more than 500 employees, was reportedly the largest business of its kind in the city. Most of the employees were young women, many of them recent immigrants, who worked six days a week in cramped and dirty quarters.

Numerous Fire Hazards

New York City law at the time required buildings 11 stories and higher to have stone floors and metal window frames. The Asch Building was only ten stories high and was constructed with wood floors, wood trim, and wood window frames. Unsafe as they were, these features of the building's construction were only part of the fire danger that workers unwittingly faced every day.

Buildings with 10,000 square feet of floor space per floor were required to have three staircases per floor. The Asch Building had two. The building's architect had pleaded for approval of two staircases, because there was also an outside fire escape that could be reached by windows on each floor. The fire escape terminated at the second floor, not at the ground.

Labor laws in effect at the time required that factory doors open outward, *if practical*. The architect claimed it was not practical in the Asch Building, because each landing was only one stair width from the door. All doors had to open inward.

Those same labor laws required that factory doors be kept unlocked during the workday. Doors at the Triangle company reportedly were usually locked during the workday to keep track of the workers and prevent them from stealing material.

Rags consisting of cutaway cloth materials regularly accumulated on the floors of the Triangle company. At the time of the fire, the rags had not been removed for about two months. When last collected, an accumulation of 2,252 pounds of rags had been removed.

The Triangle workers were crowded together on the top three floors of the Asch Building. Aisles leading to exits were narrow and obstructed. Partitions were placed in front of doors and elevators. A fire insurance inspector had recommended in 1909 that the company keep the doors unlocked during the workday and conduct fire drills. The Triangle owners took no action on those recommendations.

Fire Begins in the Rags

No NFPA investigative report was written on the Triangle fire, but two books describe the horror that took place. One book, *The Triangle Shirtwaist Fire* (Franklin Watts, Inc., 1971), was written by Corinne Naden. The other book, *The Triangle Fire*, was written by Leon Stein (J. B. Lippencott, 1962). The descriptions of the building and the fire reported here are summarized from these books.

It was near quitting time on March 25, 1911, when one of the workers on the eighth floor noticed smoke coming from one of the rag bins. A fire in a rag bin was reportedly not unusual, but this fire spread with astonishing speed, despite the attempts of supervisors to extinguish it using pails of water. The fire spread from the rags to cutting tables and then to cloth patterns hanging on wire above the tables. In no time, flames consumed the wood floor trim, the sewing tables, and partitions and then spread to the ceiling.

Workers on the eighth floor rushed for the doors. One door was locked. When workers finally got it unlocked, it opened inward. The panicked workers piled up against the door, making it difficult for those who arrived first to open it. Eventually, they were able to open the door, and workers rushed into the stairway. However, some fell at the seventh floor level, and those behind piled up until there was no more room in the stairway. A policeman, who had seen the fire from the street, saw the pile-up as he ran up the stairs to help. He untangled the pile-up, and about 125 workers escaped down that stairway.

Other workers frantically rang for the elevators. However, the elevators had been summoned to the tenth floor, where the executive offices were located, so, at first, they didn't stop on the eighth floor. When they did stop, workers crowded into them, one on top of another. The elevators made so many trips to save workers on the eighth and tenth floors that the operators were overcome by smoke and exhaustion.

Some workers on the eighth floor climbed out the windows to the narrow fire escape. At least one worker fell down the fire escape to the courtyard below. Others climbed down to the sixth floor, went back into the building through a window, and walked down the inside staircase.

There was a telephone on the eighth floor that was connected to the executive offices on the tenth floor. One of the workers called the tenth floor to report the fire. Someone on the tenth floor rang for the elevators, which at first bypassed the eighth and ninth floors to rescue people on the tenth floor. Many of the workers on the tenth floor escaped to the roof of the building, where they were rescued by law students from an adjacent building. Of the approximately

70 workers on that floor, only one died. That death occurred because the victim jumped from a window.

The only telephone communication to the ninth floor was through the tenth-floor switchboard. No one on the tenth floor notified the ninth-floor workers of the fire.

The Ninth-Floor Workers Were the Last to Be Informed

There were about 260 workers on the ninth floor. There were also eight double rows of sewing machines on 75-foot-long tables that took up nearly the entire floor. The only way to leave the tables was to walk to the north end of the building. Workers sitting at the south end had to walk the entire length of the rows of tables to reach the area where the exits were located. Along the way, they had to negotiate around chairs, wicker baskets, and other items that obstructed the passageways.

When the quitting bell rang, one worker walked down one of the stairways to go home. When he reached the eighth floor, he saw it was in flames. He was the first ninth-floor worker to learn of the fire. Confused, he simply continued moving. By the time he thought of running back up the stairs to warn his coworkers, it was too late. He was unable to get back up the stairway.

The rest of the workers on the ninth floor learned of the fire when flames leaped through the windows. About 150 workers raced for the Green Street exit, and more than 100 of them made it down to the sidewalk. Other workers ran to the Washington Place exit, but it was locked. Some rushed for the fire escape. Jammed with people and hot from the fire, the fire escape pulled away from the building and partially collapsed, sending bodies flying to the courtyard below.

Many workers, including those who found the Washington Place exit locked, congregated at the elevators and summoned them. However, the elevators were already packed with people from the eighth and tenth floors. Some of the workers jumped or were pushed into the elevator shafts. A few slid down the cables, some landing on the roofs of the elevators.

To escape the searing heat and suffocating smoke, many of the workers climbed out to the window ledge and jumped to their death. The impact of their bodies was so great that it not only broke the fire department nets, but also smashed holes in the concrete and glass pavement.

The fire department arrived at the scene early but could do little except cool the exterior of the building. Its equipment was good for fighting fires only up to seven stories. In total, about 147 people died in the Triangle Shirtwaist fire.

The Spark for Reform

The Asch Building was a fire trap, but it was not the worst one in the city. In 1910, a public agency investigated conditions in 1,243 coat and suit shops. Nine days before the Triangle fire, a local New York City newspaper published excerpts from the agency's report. The report stated that 99 percent of the shops were deficient in safety. Many had only one exit, many others had locked doors during the workday, and 94 percent had doors that opened inward rather than outward.

Whether that report by itself would have generated remedial action is open to question. The dismal record of previous attempts by unions and others to mobilize action indicates that improvements would not likely have been made. The Triangle fire, however, illustrated more than a report ever could the dangers lurking in loft and other types of buildings.

In fact, the Triangle Shirtwaist fire aroused the nation and eventually revolutionized an industry. Unions, particularly the garment workers' union, intensified their activities to bring about improvements in working conditions for their members. Citizens of all economic classes in New York City banded together to work for safer factories, and politicians passed new laws to protect workers.

Almost immediately after the fire, New York City residents formed the Committee on Safety. Among its members was Frances Perkins, who later became U.S. Secretary of Labor. The chairman was Henry Stimson, who soon left that position to become Secretary of War. He was succeeded as chairman by Henry Morgenthau. The committee became a focus for efforts to pass laws mandating improvements in factories and other buildings.

In June of 1911, New York Governor John Alden Dix created the New York State Factory Investigating Commission to look into conditions in all factories and allocated the commission a $10,000 budget. Chairman of the commission was Robert Wagner, Sr., then a state senator. Samuel Gompers was also on the commission.

In October of the same year, the Sullivan-Hoey Law was passed, which established the New York City Fire Prevention Bureau, the first in the country, and expanded the powers of the fire commissioner.

NFPA Broadens Its Focus To Include Life Safety

NFPA members were shocked but not surprised by the fire. For years, they had warned of many of the dangers present in buildings like the Asch Building. In particular, they had warned about the problems of fire escapes. The April 1911 NFPA *Quarterly* stated that it had long been recognized that fire escapes were a "delusion." For a quarter of a century, fire escapes have "contributed the principal element of tragedy to all fires where panic resulted. Iron is quickly heated ... and expansion of the bolts, stays, and fastenings soon pulls the frame loose so that the weight of a single body may precipitate it into a street or alley."

At the NFPA Annual Meeting in May of 1911, R. H. Newbern presented a paper on private fire departments and fire drills and referred to the value of drills in educating factory workers in procedures that help avoid panic and promote survival. A year later, Mr. Newbern's recommendations were published in a pamphlet titled "Exit Drills in Factories, Schools, Department Stores, and Theatres." This was the first safety-to-life publication produced by NFPA. However, there was still no specific NFPA committee devoted exclusively to life safety.

Formation of the Safety to Life Committee

At the 1913 NFPA Annual Meeting, President H. L. Phillips suggested to members that they could include "a section or committee having for its object the consideration of safety of life against accidents of every description." Later during that meeting, members listened to a speech titled "The Social and Human Cost of Fire" by Frances Perkins of the New York Committee on Safety. She urged them to study hazardous industries, publish the results, and publish rules that would make people in factories safe.

Perkins had witnessed the Triangle fire. She saw workers leap from the ninth floor to the street below, and she was horrified. She told NFPA members that when she counted the social, human, and economic cost of that fire,

she found it was enormous. "We lost not only those workers in the Triangle fire," she said, "we lost their valuable services to society as economic factors. ... It is because that social and human loss is to the entire community that this problem of fire deserves the closest attention of all people who are interested in the general progress and welfare of humanity. ... Nothing is so important as human health and happiness ... and if it costs dollars and cents to procure ... then we must pay ... and if it reduces profits we must reduce those profits. ... You who are more or less technical ... must help us by giving ... the correct information ... which we will be only too glad to use."

On June 23, 1913, the NFPA's Executive Committee formed the Committee on Safety to Life and left it to the new committee itself to suggest the scope of its work. The July 1913 *Quarterly* stated that the formation of the committee was "the crystalization of a latent feeling which has for some time existed in the membership" for focusing attention on life safety.

The new committee, headed by H. W. Forster, spent the first few years studying fires involving loss of life and attempting to analyze the cause of that loss of life. At the 1914 Annual Meeting, the Committee delivered its first report, which included a special section on egress, a statement that sprinklers can save lives, and preliminary specifications for outside fire escapes.

The Committee said its studies showed that existing laws "are exceedingly deficient in this very important matter of egress. A number of states report frankly that they have no real legislation upon the subject."

The preliminary specifications for outside fire escapes were controversial and received a great deal of attention from the membership. The committee members did not like outside fire escapes, and many felt they were a delusion as stated in the 1911 *Quarterly*. Nevertheless, the Committee felt they had to face the fact that fire escapes existed and would be used.

"Admitting ... that a fire escape on a building is usually an admission that life is not safe in it, the fact remains that the outside fire escape is the commonest special provision for escape ... [and] this Association should determine upon proper precautions for such escapes, and use its influence to have them adopted and enforced," the Committee wrote.

At the 1915 Annual Meeting, the NFPA adopted revised specifications for fire escapes. In 1916, the Committee's work was published in a pamphlet, "Outside Stairs for Fire Exits." In 1918, another committee report was published in a pamphlet titled "Safeguarding Factory Workers from Fire." The pamphlets were widely circulated, put into general use, and, with other documents, form the basis of the present *Life Safety Code.*

In 1921, the Committee on Safety to Life was enlarged to include representation from interested groups not previously participating in its work. Work was started on the further development and integration of previous Committee publications to provide a comprehensive guide to exits and related features of life safety from fires in all classes of occupancy. The work resulted in the publication in 1927 of the first edition of the NFPA's *Building Exits Code.*

As anyone involved in any safety endeavor will attest, it often takes a tragedy to alert society to dangers that must be addressed. The Triangle fire moved the nation toward the prevention of many fire hazards. However, as time passes, the public forgets the lessons it learned and is forced to learn them once again through another tragedy.

Thirty-one years after the Triangle fire, in which locked exits trapped and doomed many workers, the U.S. witnessed another major fire in a building with locked exits. The fire occurred at the Cocoanut Grove in Boston.

The Cocoanut Grove Fire

There are many differences between the fires at the Triangle Shirtwaist Company and the Cocoanut Grove. One building was a high-rise factory, while the other was a single-story nightclub. The biggest difference lies in the state of the art of fire protection at the time. In 1911, when the Triangle fire erupted, there were no universally recognized standards for exits. In 1942, when the Cocoanut Grove burned, those standards existed and were part of the NFPA's *Building Exits Code.* Evidently, they were ignored.

Virtually all the hazards at the Cocoanut Grove were covered by the 1942 Edition of *The Building Exits Code.* The main problems appear to have been the chaotic condition of Boston's building regulations and lax enforcement.

Four hundred and ninety-two people died in the fire. As the *Christian Science Monitor* said in an editorial after the fire, "action will be taken to prevent another Cocoanut Grove, and somebody could have taken action to prevent this one."

The late Robert S. Moulton, long-time NFPA Technical Secretary and Secretary to the Committee on Safety to Life, wrote a report on the fire that was widely circulated. Much of the information that follows comes from that report.

A Popular Night Spot

The Cocoanut Grove was one of the most popular night clubs in Boston. It was a one-story-and-basement structure originally built in 1916. The original property was of reinforced concrete construction. Several additions had been made to the building, and a rolling roof had been installed over the dance floor.

In 1942, the Broadway Cocktail Lounge was added to the building. It was installed in a group of old brick-joisted buildings varying in height from two stories to three and one-half stories and was connected to the main property by a passageway and doorways leading to dressing rooms for entertainers.

The basement of the original structure contained the Melody Lounge, another cocktail area. The Melody Lounge had false walls made of light wooden frame covered with light wallboard. Decorations in the lounge included colorful fabrics, artificial leather on the walls, and cloth on the ceiling. In addition, there were imitation coconut palm trees in the lounge and in the main dining/dance hall. Light fixtures were made from coconut shells, with the wiring concealed in the "foliage." These decorations had reportedly been flame-proofed.

No Easy Way Out

There was only one obvious exit from the Melody Lounge. It was a door at the top of the stairway that led to a narrow hallway on the first floor, and then to a foyer and the main entrance. Another door, which led to an outside alley, was concealed behind the false walls of the lounge. It was locked. A door leading to the street from the narrow hallway at the head of the stairs to the Melody Lounge was equipped with panic hardware. This door was locked, however.

According to writer Paul Benzaquin in his book, *Holocaust* (Henry Holt and Company, 1959), there was also a passageway from the Melody Lounge to the kitchen, but it seems that only employees knew of this passageway. That door was painted and draped and unlikely to be seen by those who didn't know it was there. Nevertheless, it was counted as an exit by the city's fire commissioner in his post-fire report.

There were many other doors that were locked as well, and there were some that opened inward. Many of the windows were obscured by the false walls, and the main doorway of the Cocoanut Grove was blocked by a revolving door.

A Capacity Crowd That Kept Getting Bigger

The official seating capacity of the nightclub was about 600 persons. No one knows exactly how many patrons were there the night of November 28, but unofficial estimates indicate that there were about 1000 people. Benzaquin reports that waiters were setting up more tables to accommodate additional patrons.

Overcrowding was not (and probably is not) unusual in nightclubs. They are businesses established to make a profit, and the more patrons served, the greater the profit. Moulton said he was told the club was often congested, particularly on Saturday evenings.

According to Benzaquin, the club's application for a new license requested permission to install an additional 30 fixed stools for the new cocktail lounge. He writes that the stools were installed *before* permission was granted on the assumption that there would be no objection.

That was probably a reasonable assumption. A member of the city's licensing board testified at the fire commissioner's hearing that the Cocoanut Grove got its original license and several renewals without any hearings to determine whether it complied with regulations.

The 12-Minute Fire

Benzaquin states in his book that the fire lasted about 12 minutes. It started in the Melody Lounge and was possibly ignited accidentally by a match held by a bus boy who was replacing a light bulb in one of the fake palm trees. As Moulton reported, however, the exact source of ignition was of less importance than the inadequacy of the exits and the extensive use of combustible decorations.

According to the fire commissioner's report, the fire immediately spread throughout the Melody Lounge along the underside of the false ceiling. Feeding on the combustible decorations, the fire reached and ascended the stairway and passed through the connecting passageway into the foyer, past the main entrance, and into the dining room and other areas of the club.

When the fire began to spread rapidly, panic ensued. Most of the patrons in the Melody Lounge raced for the stairway, their only obvious exit. Many died on those stairs. Those who escaped the basement lounge through the stairway piled up in the corridor while attempting to reach the main entrance. If the door from that corridor to the outside had been unlocked, many may have been saved.

Led by a few quick-thinking employees, a few patrons made their escape from the lounge by going through the concealed door to the kitchen area, and some of those escaped through a door to an alley outside. Others tried to get to the main floor but could not because of the heat. A few escaped through a basement window into a courtyard, and a few others survived the fire by seeking refuge in a large refrigerator.

Moulton wrote that about 100 people died at the Broadway entrance to the club, more than 190 feet from the stairway leading from the Melody Lounge, where the fire started. He reported that about 200 were trapped behind the revolving door at the main entrance. That revolving door, which under the best of conditions would slow exit travel, jammed and blocked the exit.

Lessons Learned

There were few "new" lessons to be learned from the Cocoanut Grove fire. Even before the Triangle fire in 1911, the danger of locked, blocked, and concealed exits was known. The NFPA had publicized its views on exits and means of egress in pamphlet form after the Triangle fire.

The 1942 *Building Exits Code* prohibited revolving doors as exits in places of assembly and required that, in other occupancies where revolving doors were used, they must have swinging doors immediately adjacent or within 20 feet.

That same edition of the *Code* required that "decorations of theatres and assembly halls shall be of fire-resistive or non-flammable materials. Fabrics and papers used for such purposes shall be treated with an effective flame-proofing material." There was a cautionary note that warned, "paper and cloth decorative materials should be kept to a minimum in places of assembly since such flimsy materials increase the hazard of the kindling and spread of fire."

The decorative materials in the Cocoanut Grove were supposedly flameproofed, but, if this was true, the flameproofing was ineffective. The fire did demonstrate, once again, that "fireproof" buildings, which was the status of the Cocoanut Grove when first erected, can still be death traps due to their contents. It also proved that fire inspections should be conducted when facilities are in operation. According to Moulton, the Boston building inspector reported that he had inspected the building and found the exits adequate. This may have been true when the building was not crowded with 1000 people and the doors were unlocked.

"There is a real danger in attempting to remedy conditions such as were responsible for the Cocoanut Grove tragedy by the enactment of more laws," wrote Moulton. "In our opinion, building and fire officials can now do practically everything that is necessary to assure public safety from fire without any more laws."

Six months after the fire, at the 1943 NFPA Annual Meeting, Moulton reported to the membership that, due to the war, the Safety to Life Committee had been unable to meet. The committee members did exchange correspondence, however, and Moulton said they believed "our existing recommendations, that date back to 1913, are adequate."

There was one change involving the *Building Exits Code* that did come about immediately after and as a direct result of the Cocoanut Grove fire: the *Code* was adopted by many more jurisdictions across the country, due in large part to the efforts of the fire service. The Committee on Safety to Life reported on that increased usage at the 1945 NFPA Annual Meeting.

During the 1945 NFPA Annual Meeting, the Committee recommended a change in the method of exit measurement, clarification of the need for stairway enclosure, provisions covering loose chairs in nightclubs, and changes in lighting and signs. Those changes were incorporated into the 1946 Edition of the *Code*, as was a special note on interior finish.

Interior Finish

While combustible decorations were a factor in the Cocoanut Grove fire, interior finish was becoming more and more of a fire problem in the 1940s. In 1946, the nation witnessed the LaSalle and Winecoff hotel fires. The latter, with 119 fatalities, was the largest multiple-death hotel fire that had occurred up to that time during the twentieth century.

The Committee on Safety to Life was concerned about the dangers of combustible interior finish. Therefore, it recommended, and the full membership approved, a caution in the 1946 *Code*, which stated that, "where interior finish materials are used having a higher combustibility, greater rate of fire spread, or potentialities of greater generation of smoke or fumes than wood, the exits specified in the *Code* may not be sufficient to provide adequate life safety from fire."

The lack of a standard way to measure the combustibility of interior finish hampered the Committee. In the July 1943 *Quarterly*, A. J. Steiner of Underwriters Laboratories described a new method he was developing to test the combustibility of interior finish. The Steiner Tunnel Test was recommended for adoption at the 1953 NFPA Annual Meeting by the NFPA Building Construction Committee. It was eventually incorporated into the *Building Exits Code*.

The Our Lady of Angels School Fire

Combustible interior finish was one of the factors that led to fire spread at the Our Lady of Angels School in Chicago in December 1958. Wood trim in one corridor and combustible ceiling tile in classrooms in one wing (and perhaps in other areas of the building) provided fuel for this fire.

However, the primary cause of loss of life, according to the NFPA investigative report of the fire, was *the inadequacy of the exit facilities*. As a result of this completely avoidable problem, 90 pupils and 3 nuns died.

Adequacy of exits, as determined by proper enclosure, provision of at least two exits that are remote from each other, and sufficient exit capacity were well-established fundamentals of fire protection by 1958. The Triangle fire, the Cocoanut Grove fire, and hundreds of other fires had demonstrated the consequences of exits that are neglected. The 1958 Editition of the *Building Exits Code* specified exact requirements for adequate exits and for other elements of school firesafety.

Chester I. Babcock, then Manager of the NFPA Fire Records Department, and Rex Wilson, then an NFPA engineer and currently a consultant, investigated the fire for the NFPA. A year later, Babcock wrote, "We know now and have known since before most of today's schools were built how to design and protect a school so that the lives of the pupils and teachers will be safe from fire. Refinements and improvements are needed and undoubtedly will come, but this does not mean that fire protection engineering has been groping for an answer. Practical methods of assuring life safety from fire that have stood the test of time and are based on sound fire protection engineering principles have been available for years."

One Fire Area

In 1953, the two-story school building was connected to another old, two-story, brick, wood-joisted building by a two-story, brick-joisted annex. The NFPA report of the fire stated that the building constituted one fire area, due to open stairways and the fact that the masonry division wall between the north wing and the annex had substandard doorway protection.

The stairways in the school were open except for two located in the front of the north wing. Those stairs were enclosed at the second-story level by substandard doors that were held open at the time of the fire. Because the three stairways from the second floor corridor of the north wing were connected through a common corridor, pupils in second-story classrooms, in effect, had no way out.

Origin Of the Fire

About 2:25 p.m., one half-hour before school was normally dismissed, fire broke out in combustible materials at the bottom of the rear stairway of the north wing. Pupils from one of the second-floor classrooms had taken trash to the boiler room incinerator, as was their routine, returned to the classroom at 2:30 p.m., and reported that they had smelled smoke. Their teacher informed a teacher in a nearby room, who went to find the principal. When the principal could not be found, both teachers led their classes out of the building to the parish church. Smoke was already at head level in the second-floor corridor. Only after they had their classes settled in the church did one of the teachers run back to the school and operate the fire alarm signal.

The school's janitor noticed smoke and ran to the parish house to tell the housekeeper to call the fire department. Apparently, the housekeeper waited a few minutes before placing the call. The fire department reported that it received the first of some 15 calls reporting the fire at about 2:42 pm.

Hot fire gases and smoke billowed up the chimney-like stairwell and mushroomed through the second-story corridor. Eventually the hot gases and combustible interior finish in the corridor ignited. The heat broke the large glass transoms over the classroom doors, and the hot gases and flames entered the rooms.

Those Who Escaped, and Those Who Did Not

As soon as the fire alarm rang, occupants of the first floor left the building by means of the five available stairways, according to the NFPA report. The evacuation of pupils in the second-floor annex and south wing was hampered by smoke that came through an open door in the division wall at that level. Either the janitor or a fire fighter closed the door.

Pupils in the second-floor north wing did not escape as easily. Their travel through the corridor to the stairways was blocked by heavy smoke and heat. Some jumped from their classroom windows. Others were taken down fire department ladders. Many died in their classrooms, some at their desks.

Aftermath of the Fire

One immediate effect of the Our Lady of Angels fire was a public awakening to the hazards in the nation's schools. According to Babcock's follow-up report a year after the fire, hazardous conditions had been eliminated in thousands of schools across the country.

Throughout this country's history, major improvements in safety have been made after terrible fires. The Iroquois Theater fire brought about improvements in theater safety; the Triangle fire brought about improvements in factories;

the Cocoanut Grove fire resulted in improvements in night-clubs; and the LaSalle, Winecoff, MGM Grand, Stouffer's, and DuPont Plaza fires resulted in improvements in hotels.

In 1959, the NFPA sampled more than 2,000 fire departments to analyze the level of improvement made in school safety. Many had been made. Nearly every community had acted on such issues as frequent and improved exit drills, tighter control of waste disposal, inspections, and proper storage of combustible supplies. However, that same survey revealed that needed improvements had not been made in about 30,000 schools.

The NFPA conducted another informal telephone survey in 1978, twenty years after the fire. The consensus from that informal survey was that schools were safer. (Indeed, one respondent said they couldn't help but be safer than they were in 1958, when they were the "lousiest-constructed buildings in existence!") Unfortunately, they were not as safe as fire professionals had hoped. The passage of time and the growing concern with vandalism and security had blocked out the memories of the Our Lady of Angels tragedy.

The LA School Fire Tests

The most publicized result of the fire was the fire test program conducted by the Los Angeles Fire Department. The tests, conducted under the direction of then Los Angeles Fire Marshal Raymond M. Hill, were designed to investigate methods of protecting multistory, open-stairway school buildings.

The tests were conducted in 1959 and 1960. One of the conclusions drawn from the tests was the fact that complete automatic sprinkler protection offered the best chance for escape.

The 1958 Edition of the *Building Exits Code* provided for sprinklers in schools. The 1960 edition retained those provisions and totally reorganized the section of the *Code* covering educational occupancies. That edition classified schools as follows:

Group A: one-story buildings with exterior or interior access, or multistory buildings with access only by exterior balconies and outside stairs.

Group B: buildings of two stories or more with egress through corridors and interior stairways.

Group C: sprinklered buildings.

Group D: open-plan schools.

Group E: existing buildings.

There were somewhat different requirements for each group.

There was a great deal of discussion among members of the Committee on Safety to Life in 1960 regarding whether they should recommend permitting open stairways in two-story sprinklered schools. The Committee decided not to make this recommendation that year. The 1961 Edition of the *Code*, however, did permit open stairs in sprinklered two-story schools. One reason for this decision was that committee members noted that, in two-story buildings, pupils constantly pass through the doors anyway.

In 1966, the year the *Building Exits Code* was reorganized and renamed *The Life Safety Code*, a provision was added that required all parts of school buildings below grade to be sprinklered. In addition, the allowable travel distance to the nearest exit was increased from 100 feet to 150 feet, under normal conditions, and up to 200 feet in sprinklered school buildings.

The Beverly Hills Supper Club Fire

Those who study fires can't help but have a feeling of *déja vu*. It seems that the same fire problems return to haunt us time and again. Inadequate means of egress, lack of employee preparedness and training, and a general noncompliance with proven provisions of the *Life Safety Code* were all factors in the Triangle, Cocoanut Grove, and Our Lady of Angels fires, as well as in countless others.

These problems were critical factors again on May 28, 1977 at the Beverly Hills Supper Club. One hundred and sixty-four people died in the fire at the club, a public assembly occupancy that billed itself as "The Showplace of the Nation." The NFPA conducted an in-depth investigation of the fire, and much of what follows was taken from the investigative report prepared by Richard L. Best.

The Beverly Hills was a glamorous nightclub in Southgate, Kentucky, just outside Cincinnati, Ohio. Banquets, dinner dances, balls, floor shows, fashion shows, weddings, wedding receptions, and business meetings were all held in the club's "18" function rooms.

The quotation marks around the number 18 represent the advertised number of function rooms. There were actually five main dining rooms, the large "Cabaret Room," a small function room called the "Zebra Room," and the main bar. Three of the large dining rooms could be subdivided into smaller rooms by the use of folding partitions.

There had been a wedding reception in the Zebra Room on the day of the fire. The wedding party had left at approximately 8:00 p.m. Performers were scheduled to entertain guests in the Cabaret Room around 8:30 p.m. There were an estimated 1,200 to 1,300 guests in the Cabaret Room, about triple the number that could be accommodated safely. Numerous patrons later said that tables were squeezed together, and the narrow aisles were obstructed with chairs. There were about 2,400 to 2,800 patrons in the club altogether.

Delayed Notification

The fire was discovered by employees between 8:45 p.m. and 8:50 p.m. in the empty Zebra Room. It had begun in a concealed space, and the origin was presumed by investigators to have been electrical in nature.

Employees alerted the club's hostess, while other employees ran around looking for the management. Two managers tried to fight the fire with portable fire extinguishers. Busboys and waiters helped them, but their efforts were to no avail. One of the managers eventually ran to the hostess and told her to evacuate the patrons. By that time, it was about 9:00 p.m. Someone notified the fire department about a minute later.

As this general description of events indicates, about 15 minutes may have elapsed between discovery of the fire and notification of employees. That delay was a critical factor in evacuation efforts. Also, it seems that there was some degree of staff confusion regarding evacuation procedures, since employees had not been trained.

Once notification of patrons was begun, an interesting phenomenon took place. According to interviews conducted by the Kentucky State Police after the fire, waiters and waitresses instinctively took responsibility for the safety of the patrons they were serving. They went directly to those guests and to other guests in those rooms and told them to leave. They did not, however, necessarily take responsibility for guests they were not serving who were in different parts of the building.

The Cabaret Room was isolated from the rest of the club once the show was in progress. There were no waiters, waitresses, busboys, or hostesses traveling to and from the kitchen or standing in the service halls between dining room seatings. This indicates that employees serving the Cabaret Room did not see other employees rushing around notifying patrons and the management of the fire, so they were totally unaware of the danger. However, one busboy, who had just left the Cabaret Room to work in another room, learned of the fire and decided to take action.

Quick Thinking

In a display of courage, calmness, and good sense, the busboy took upon himself the responsibility of evacuating patrons in the Cabaret Room. He was walking down one of the main corridors from the Cabaret Room to the Viennese Room when he learned of the fire. He looked toward the Zebra Room and saw smoke coming through the top edge of the closed doors. He quickly told a bartender to leave, then spun around and ran back to the Cabaret Room.

When he arrived there, he told the host to open the doors of the room. The host also moved the rope divider and reservations stand from the corridor and instructed people waiting in line to walk toward the Garden Room area in another part of the building.

The busboy then walked into the Cabaret Room, calmly climbed up onto the stage where a performance was taking place, took the microphone, and spoke to the guests in the room. This is what he told the post-fire investigators:

"The first thing I did was . . . ask them to look at the exit sign . . . 'I want you to all notice that exit sign and I want you to look at the other corner of the room and there will be another exit sign . . . I want the left side of my room to go out of the exit sign behind that I'm pointing to now . . . I want my right half of the room to go out of the other exit sign. . . . There is a fire in the small room on the other side of the building . . . I don't think there is any reason to panic or rush . . . you should leave.' "

Although he later said that some people looked at him as if he were crazy, people did begin to leave. Of the 164 fatalities in the fire, most occurred in the Cabaret Room. There is no way of knowing how many more would have died if the busboy had not taken charge.

Once he was back in the hallway, the busboy saw smoke billowing toward him, so he went to an exit. "There were just three doors, and one was locked," he said. "I tried to bang it open with my shoulder [but] I couldn't."

The Human Factor

Post-fire interviews showed, not surprisingly, that people, in general, did not take the fire threat too seriously at first. Much of the evacuation in the early stages of the fire was without difficulty, partly because people proceeded calmly and deliberately, some perhaps not even believing there was a serious fire in the making.

When heavy smoke and intense heat descended on patrons trying to leave the Cabaret Room, those people suddenly did realize the seriousness of the situation. Some began to rush and push, and some stumbled and fell, blocking exits with their bodies. One fire fighter reported seeing people stacked two and three high.

One bartender told of a young woman who had fallen near an exit. Other people fell on top of her. The bartender and one of his coworkers tried to pull her out, but they were unable to move her. "And there was a man that was on top," the bartender said. "He was a heavy guy and he was reaching up his arms and so I thought he was all right . . . the first thought was to get him off the top so you can do something with the bottom ones . . . I had him wrap his arms around my neck and I pushed up against this door as hard as I could . . . and I didn't have enough strength to lift him and he just looked at me and shook his head . . . there was nothing I could do."

Familiar Factors Contributed to Deaths

The rapid fire spread along the main corridor of the club, delay in notifying patrons in the Cabaret Room, insufficient exit capacity, and an excessive number of people in the Cabaret Room were all major factors that resulted in employees and guests having insufficient time to escape this fire. Virtually all of these factors were covered in the *Life Safety Code* that was in existence at that time. Some specific factors are examined below.

Construction

Class A places of assembly have a capacity of 1,000 people or more. The Beverly Hills Supper Club's total occupant load was 2,375. Unprotected, noncombustible construction such as that of the Beverly Hills Supper Club was not permitted for Class A. That construction was permitted for Class C occupancies, which have capacity for 300 people or less. (It is now permitted, but only if the building is fully sprinklered.)

Number of exits

The number of exits, based on 100 persons per unit of exit width and on square footage, should have been 27.5 exit units. The actual number was 16.5. The second floor had no exits with components permitted by the *Code*. (The Melody Lounge at the Cocoanut Grove was also overcrowded.)

The Cabaret Room should have had four exits, since it was itself a Class A place of assembly. It had only three. (The Cocoanut Grove's Melody Lounge had only one obvious exit.)

There was evidence of locked doors and chains and locks on panic hardware. (The same was true at the Cocoanut Grove.)

Exits were not well marked. A door to the corridor, for example, appeared to be part of the wall paneling, and it was not marked as an exit. (In the Cocoanut Grove's Melody Lounge, there was a door that was painted and draped and not likely to be seen by patrons. In addition, some windows were concealed by false walls.)

Obstructions

There was seating in the aisles in the Cabaret Room. Tables were placed too close together, and there were too many chairs and other items restricting the aisles. There also were chairs and tables stored on the platform outside the Viennese Room that led to steps to double doors. (Chairs and tables also blocked aisles at the Cocoanut Grove.)

Enclosures

Vertical openings should be enclosed. The curved stairway in the club's "Hallway of Mirrors" was neither enclosed nor protected.

Interior Finish

The 1976 *Code* required interior finish in all means of egress in all places of assembly to be Class A, i.e., with a flame spread rating of 0-25. The interior finish in the Hallway of Mirrors and the main north-south corridor had a flame spread rating of greater than 25. It is interesting to note how many of these factors were present in the Cocoanut Grove fire 35 years before.

Alarm Systems

One of the factors that made it difficult for patrons to escape was a delay in notification of the fire. An alarm system would have avoided that delay. The *Code* required alarm systems in all occupancies except storage facilities and places of assembly. Committee members had discussed the importance of alarm systems for a long time, but many felt an alarm system could cause panic. The Beverly Hills fire demonstrated the need for an alarm system, however, and so the requirement was added for public assembly occupancies in the next edition of the *Code,* which was published in 1981. Still concerned with the potential for panic and aware of tests showing the value of voice alarms, the Committee added an interesting note to its alarm requirements.

Manual pull stations were required to alert occupants. The pull stations send an alarm to a central office or other location on the property that is continuously staffed while the occupancy is in use. The central office must have a way of then notifying occupants, either through a voice alarm over a public address system or a vocal fire alarm system. The alarm notification requirement was made retroactive to apply to new and existing buildings.

Sprinklers

Historically, the *Code* had required sprinklers in assembly occupancies used as exhibit halls. Cost was a perceived prohibitive factor in efforts to spread that requirement to other public assembly occupancies. After the Beverly Hills fire, however, the Committee said, in effect, that cost is important, but lives are more important.

The Committee approached sprinkler requirements in the following two ways:

Members reassessed construction requirements for all classes of assembly occupancies, consolidated them, and required sprinklers based on construction type and location of assembly occupancy within the building. It was decided that even fire-resistive buildings having four or more stories above the exit discharge should be sprinklered. These provisions applied to new buildings, and some were made retroactive for existing buildings.

In addition, every Class A and B occupancy was required to be sprinklered throughout. This requirement applied only to new construction. There were some exceptions, but none applied to facilities such as the Beverly Hills Supper Club.

There had long been much discussion of the value of sprinklering all places of assembly. Numerous fires, including the Gulliver's Discotheque fire in New York and the Upstairs Lounge fire in New Orleans, both of which took place during the 1970s, highlighted problems similar to those found at the Beverly Hills Supper Club and emphasized the need for sprinklers. (In the incidents at the Upstairs Lounge and Gulliver's Discotheque, fire blocked a means of egress.)

The story of fire protection is one that continues. Fire protection professionals study history and conduct research to determine code requirements that are needed to protect lives. They continuously use their influence to ensure that those requirements are adopted and enforced.

Unfortunately, it often takes a tragedy to bolster their efforts, and, even then, if action isn't taken immediately, people forget. In Nevada, momentum toward tighter codes had slowed down a year after the 1980 MGM Grand fire. Subsequent fires brought back memories of that tragedy. Today, the Bally Las Vegas (formerly the MGM) has installed about 30,000 sprinklers, 8,000 loud speakers, and other fire protection equipment. In addition, the American Automobile Association now includes fire protection among the factors they consider when rating hotels in their travel guides.

Sometimes fires demonstrate the wisdom of committee members. For example, the 1987 DuPont Plaza Hotel fire illustrated that the Committee on Life Safety was correct in requiring corridors and lobbies to be separated from assembly areas by 1-hour walls, unless the building is sprinklered or unless 50 percent of the egress is independent of the lobby.

The Las Vegas Hilton fire illustrated that committee members were correct in restricting carpeting on walls. That fire saw flames leap-frogging up the side of the building, entering windows, and spreading along carpeting on the walls and ceilings. The Committee had been convinced of the dangers of carpeting on walls by fire tests sponsored by the carpeting industry, which had pushed for regulation of its own products.

The Positive Side — and the Challenge

It is always tempting to concentrate on the tragedies, because they are so obvious. However, there are positive results to consider even if they are not as well documented.

It is impossible to know the number of lives saved because vertical openings were enclosed, exits were adequate and unlocked, and alarm, detection, and sprinkler systems were in place, since fires in such buildings don't get out of hand.

The key, once requirements are put into codes and the codes are adopted, is enforcement. The challenge for everyone who reads this *Handbook* is to make certain that the codes, which contain the accumulated fire protection knowledge of generations, are enforced. To paraphrase Frances Perkins' speech to the 1913 NFPA Annual Meeting: People are not always their own masters. "It is necessary for organizations like yours . . . to insist on safety for them." That is our job.

2

Fire Alarm Systems for Life Safety Code Users

Robert P. Schifiliti, P.E.

Introduction

This supplement is an introduction to fire detection and signaling systems. Various types of systems contemplated by the *Life Safety Code* are discussed along with detailed discussion of their components.

Different types of fire detection devices are reviewed with an emphasis on proper selection to meet firesafety goals and to reduce the likelihood of false and nuisance alarms. Also, methods for occupant notification and off-premises signaling of alarms are summarized. Included is a discussion of circuit types and allowable wiring methods, with references to other NFPA codes, standards, and guides. A review of testing and maintenance needs for fire detection and signaling systems provides the reader with an understanding of how to extend a system's life, reduce nuisance alarms, and ensure system operation during a fire emergency.

Specific requirements and designs for various occupancies are not discussed in this section. The occupancy chapters of the *Life Safety Code* should be consulted for specific requirements. The additional commentary contained in other chapters of this *Handbook* provides a good explanation of the requirements and the philosophy behind their intent. This supplement provides an introduction to the operation of required devices and systems. Designers, owners, installers, and inspectors will find useful information to assist them in choosing among options not specifically addressed within the *Code*. For example, a choice might need to be made between using photoelectric or ionization smoke detectors, or information might be required on how to reduce the likelihood of false and nuisance alarms.

Overview of Protective Signaling Systems

There are four principal types of fire detection and signaling systems required or recommended by various chapters of the *Life Safety Code*:

- Household fire warning equipment
- Manual fire alarm systems
- Automatic fire alarm systems
- Extinguishing system supervisory systems

Each of these categories may be viewed as consisting of three components as shown in Figure 1. Detection and initiating devices are either manual or automatic, as shown in the figure, and are referred to as input devices. Manual initiating devices, such as pull stations, are operated by people and, in turn, signal the control system. Automatic detection devices sense a change in the environment or equipment that is monitored and signal the control portion of the system. The control or processing section receives the incoming signals and initiates output signals. The control system may also supply power and supervise the various components and circuits of the system and provide output signals when there is a fault or when maintenance is needed. The control or processor interfaces with people and other systems through output signals.

The simplest form of system described in Figure 1 is a self-contained smoke alarm. It contains a smoke sensor and a control system that includes a power source and a signaling system, usually a horn, used for occupant notification. In more complex systems, initiating devices and signaling devices are separate, self-contained units connected to a control panel by electrical circuits or radio waves. In these component systems, power is usually provided to the input and output devices through the control panel. However, it is also possible for power to be provided directly to those units that require it. Each of these three principal components is discussed in more detail in later sections of this supplement.

Each occupancy chapter of the *Life Safety Code* specifies fire detection and signaling requirements where appropriate. Those that do contain requirements include subsections that provide the requirements for initiation and notification. Where initiation is addressed, the occupancy chapter refers to either a complete system or a partial system. In addition, the system will be described as manual, automatic, or both. Chapter 7, "Building Service and Fire Equipment," defines complete, partial, manual, and automatic systems. Where automatic detection is required, most chapters of the *Code* specify smoke detection, either partial or complete. Where an automatic detection system is required but the type of detection is not specified, any units that comply with NFPA 72E, *Standard on Automatic Fire Detectors*, may be used interchangeably. An occupancy chapter may also require separate smoke detection within dwelling units in addition to any required partial or complete system.

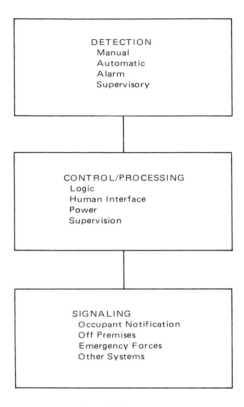

Figure 1.   Overview Block Diagram.

Household fire warning equipment is intended for use within living units such as apartments, hotel rooms, dormitory rooms, and one- or two-family residences. These devices or systems are intended to detect smoke conditions and alert the occupants of the living unit. In occupancies such as hotels, apartment buildings, and dormitories, they are not intended to be connected to the overall building fire alarm system.

Within the dwelling unit, household fire warning equipment may be self-contained smoke alarms, or it may be a small system with detectors, a control panel, and notification appliances such as bells or horns. The building system may consist of manual and automatic initiating devices, extinguishing system supervisory devices, and signaling devices that are all connected to a control panel or console. Therefore, there are two categories of detection and signaling: one that is located within the family dwelling unit and one that is intended to protect the entire building.

In some cases, an occupancy chapter of the *Code* may require a partial automatic detection system that covers all common spaces. In addition, household fire warning equipment may be required in dwelling units. For purposes of occupant notification, the building system would cover all occupiable spaces, including the dwelling units. The household equipment is required to signal only within the dwelling unit.

In other cases, a complete automatic detection system may be required in addition to the requirements for the dwelling unit. The building system must then provide detection within all spaces, including the dwelling units. This is not redundant detection for the dwelling units. The intent is for the household fire warning equipment to provide an alarm of smoke conditions to the occupants of the dwelling unit. The additional detectors connected to the building system would be heat detectors, which would notify the other occupants of the building before a fire in the unit became a threat. This design concept is described thoroughly in the commentary of the occupancy chapters in which it is required.

NFPA standards contain mandatory requirements indicated by the use of the word "shall," while guides contain recommendations and good practices and use the word "should." NFPA 74, *Standard for the Installation, Maintenance, and Use of Household Fire Warning Equipment*, contains detailed requirements for devices and systems used within the dwelling unit. Building systems and systems for off-premises monitoring of building systems are addressed by several other NFPA standards and guides.

NFPA 72, *Standard for the Installation, Maintenance, and Use of Protective Signaling Systems*, covers local, auxiliary, remote station, proprietary, and emergency voice/alarm protective signaling systems.

A local system is that part of a system serving the protected premises. This standard provides requirements and recommendations for installation and performance of systems located within the protected premises. Acceptance testing and periodic testing requirements are also discussed. Local, or protected premise systems, include one or more of the following services:

1. Manual fire alarm service
2. Automatic fire alarm service
3. Automatic detection of alarm and supervisory conditions in fire extinguishing systems such as sprinkler systems, halon systems, and carbon dioxide systems
4. Guard's tour supervisory service
5. Supervision of industrial processes

Local protective signaling systems can combine the services listed above. The principal goal of a local system is to provide for the protection of life. This is achieved by requiring occupant notification and evacuation signals.

An emergency voice/alarm signaling system is often combined with a local system to provide voice and two-way communications within a building, rather than using only horns, bells, or other devices that provide limited information. The remaining system types in NFPA 72 are used for off-premises signaling of alarm, trouble, and supervisory conditions.

NFPA 72 is a new document, issued in 1990, and is a combination of the former NFPA 72A, 72B, 72C, 72D, and 72F. A chapter is now devoted to each of the former standards in this new document. The recombination of these documents eliminated redundant and conflicting material. The combination of signaling standards continues with the following documents, which will be added to NFPA 72 in the 1993 code cycle: NFPA 71, 72E, 72G, and 72H.

NFPA 71, *Standard for the Installation, Maintenance, and Use of Signaling Systems for Central Station Service*, is commonly referred to as the "central station standard." The equipment covered by NFPA 71 includes that located in the central station as well as the transmitting equipment located at the protected premises. The standard also addresses the communication channels between the protected premises and the central station, as well as any satellite stations or repeating facilities used in the transmission of signals. The document includes stringent requirements for the operation and performance of the central station systems and staff.

The fundamental intent of NFPA 72E, *Standard on Automatic Fire Detectors*, is to provide basic requirements for the performance of automatic fire detectors. Items covered include: minimum performance, location, mounting requirements, testing, and maintenance. The detectors covered by this standard do not stand alone but are intended to be used with circuits and control equipment covered by other NFPA standards. These detectors are commonly referred to as initiating devices in the other standards. When combined with control equipment, signaling devices, and indicating appliances, they form a complete automatic fire detection and alarm system.

NFPA 72G, *Guide for the Installation, Maintenance, and Use of Notification Appliances for Protective Signaling Systems*, provides performance recommendations for audible and visual notification appliances. These appliances are intended to provide information for initiating emergency actions and procedures. Audible devices are appliances such as horns, bells, chimes, and speakers. Visual appliances include direct and indirect viewing appliances such as strobe lights, incandescent lights, and annunciators.

Note that these devices are referred to as notification appliances and not signaling devices. While horns, lights, and other such devices do provide a form a signaling, the words "signal" and "signaling" have other, specific meanings in the NFPA signaling standards and guides. These other definitions refer primarily to circuits where multiple pieces of information are transmitted and received. These are discussed in more detail in the sections on signaling and wiring.

NFPA 72H, *Testing Procedures for Local, Auxiliary, Remote Station, and Proprietary Protective Signaling Systems*, contains recommended procedures for acceptance testing and periodic testing of the signaling systems listed in the title. Testing of central station system equipment is addressed in NFPA 71. The guide also lists the frequency with which certain devices and systems should be periodically tested. Much of the test frequency information has been summarized from the former NFPA 72A, B, C, D, and F.

Fire Signatures

Fire signatures are changes in the normal environment caused by a fire. Understanding fire signatures is important, as it affects the choice of fire detector to be used in an area. The objective is to choose a fire detector that will respond to an expected fire signature without responding to similar signatures that are normally present in the area. At the same time, the response time of the detector in reaction to the range of expected fires must meet the firesafety goals and objectives of the system.

Fire signatures can be placed in two categories, as shown in Figure 2. The first group is categorized by the energy produced by the fire, which is transferred in three ways: conduction, convection and radiation. The second signature group is categorized by the physical/chemical changes that take place. This group is comprised of solids, liquids, and gases produced by the fire. The solid and liquid particles are grouped together and called smoke or aerosols.

Conduction occurs when, during the combustion process, some of the energy released is conducted through the fuel to further the combustion process. Any time the temperature of one part of a material differs from another part, heat energy is conducted from the hotter portion to the cooler portion.

Convection occurs when heat is transferred by fluid motion. During combustion, hot fire gases rise, entraining fresh air, which then heats and also rises until the mixture either collects at the ceiling or cools to approximately room temperature. The energy carried away by the hot gases is referred to as convected energy.

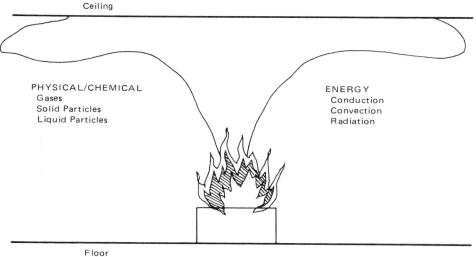

Figure 2. Fire Signatures.

Electromagnetic radiation is the third mode of energy transfer that occurs during the combustion process. Thermal radiation is one form of electromagnetic radiation and is proportional to an object's temperature. Light is another form of electromagnetic radiation produced during the combustion process. Unlike conduction and convection, a solid, liquid, or gaseous material is not needed to transfer energy by radiation. Electromagnetic radiation can travel through a vacuum, such as space. Radiation travels in all directions and in straight lines. Thermal radiation behaves in the same way as visible light radiation; if you turn your back to it, you can't "see" it. Therefore, when you stand in front of a fire, your face is warmed by thermal radiation, but your back is not heated.

Smoke and gases are produced by all fires in varying quantities. Perfect combustion of most fuels (hydrocarbon based) produces only carbon dioxide and water, in addition to the energy released. Other materials are produced when combustion is not 100 percent efficient. These include gases such as carbon monoxide and liquids and solids such as tar, carbon soot, and more complex hydrocarbon particles.

The solid and liquid particles, which together are called smoke, are produced in a wide range of sizes. Some are small and invisible to the human eye, and others are large and obscure our vision. Some particle sizes are produced in larger quantities than others. The color of the smoke also varies. Many of these factors depend on the fuel and also on how efficient the combustion process is. For instance, well-ventilated, hot, efficient fires produce mostly small, invisible, grayish-colored particles in large quantities. Compared to flaming fires, inefficient smoldering combustion produces mainly a smaller number of large black particles.

Initiating Devices

Manual Pull Stations

Manual pull stations are either coded or noncoded. Noncoded pull stations are the most common in use on new systems. When a noncoded pull station is operated, a switch closes. All noncoded devices produce the same single bit of information — a switch closure. Therefore, where there is more than one switch on a circuit, the circuit does not know which switch operated.

Coded manual pull stations have a mechanical code wheel located inside them. When operated, the wheel turns, and teeth on the wheel tap out a coded signal on a circuit. These coded wheels are essentially automatic telegraph keys. When each station has a different code, information is transmitted when the device is operated. This code might be transferred to a bell circuit to notify the occupants of a building which station has been operated.

Manual pull stations, coded or noncoded, can be single action or double action. When operating a single action station, the hand is used to pull it. When operating a double action station, two actions are required: either the door is opened and the station is pulled, or the glass is broken and a button is pushed. Double action manual stations tend to reduce false alarms caused by accidental operation. They also reduce nuisance alarms to some degree.

Pull station protectors are clear plastic covers that can be mounted over manual stations. These can provide protection from weather, dust, dirt and mechanical damage. They also serve to make a single action station into a double action station. Where placed over a double action station, three actions are then required to initiate an alarm signal: the protector is lifted, the cover is opened, and the station is pulled.

Some versions of pull station protectors are available with an internal battery-operated buzzer. These have been shown to greatly reduce nuisance alarms in public areas such as schools and shopping centers. When the cover is lifted, the local buzzer sounds, which tends to scare away vandals before they can operate the station. In locations such as schools or other crowded public areas, someone is likely to see or catch a vandal before the station is operated. When the cover is removed and the local buzzer sounds, a person may think the building's fire alarm system has been initiated. For this reason, it is important that pull station protectors be properly labeled and that the usual occupants of the area be instructed in their use.

Where an occupancy chapter of the *Life Safety Code* requires manual stations, Chapter 7 describes the quantity and location. NFPA 72 also contains requirements concerning the location and operation of manual pull stations. Essentially, manual stations are located at each required exit in the natural path of egress.

Therefore, in a corridor arranged with exits at each end, the pull stations are located at the door to each exit. The station should be located on the same side as the door handle so that it is easily seen when someone is exiting from the space. In most cases, it is best to locate the station within the corridor, and not on the other side of the door. The pull station is then located in the space that it serves. If the pull stations were located on the other side of the door, for instance, in the stair tower, an occupant from the fifth floor might pull the station on the second floor, possibly slowing discovery of the fire's location.

In addition to those located at required exits, additional pull stations are required to ensure that there is less than a 200-foot travel distance to a station. Pull stations should also be provided near the telephone operator's area of a hotel or hospital and, for example, near portable extinguishers placed adjacent to hazardous operations in a factory. NFPA 72 requires mounting height to be between $3\frac{1}{2}$ feet and 5 feet, although some locally adopted codes for the disabled may limit the height to no more than $4\frac{1}{2}$ feet.

Automatic Fire Detectors—General

NFPA 72E classifies automatic fire detectors as either spot type, line type, or air sampling type. Spot type detectors include conventional smoke and heat detectors. When using spot type detectors, other factors being equal, the farther a fire is from the detector, the slower its response time. In addition, if a circle is drawn with the detector placed at the center, a given fire anywhere along the perimeter of the circle results in the same response time. Therefore, sensitivity of a detector to a given fire varies with radial distance from the detector.

Projected-beam smoke detectors and heat-sensitive cable are examples of line type detectors. The response time is about the same when a particular fire is burning anywhere directly under the line, except where close to the ends. As that same fire is moved farther away, to a position perpendicular to the line type detector, response time increases. Similarly, response time anywhere along a line parallel to the line detector, except at the ends, would be about the same for a given fire.

Air-sampling detectors draw air from the protected area back to a remotely located detector. The tube or pipe may have several holes or sampling ports, or it may have only one. In any case, NFPA 72E treats the sampling port like a spot type detector with respect to its location and spacing.

Spot and line type detectors can be restorable or nonrestorable. Restorable detectors reset themselves after the fire signature is no longer present, provided they are not severely exposed to a fire. For instance, some heat detectors will heat until they respond, cool off, and then return to their original state. Self-contained household smoke alarms automatically reset after the smoke has cleared from their chamber (there may be a slight time delay built into the detector). Nonrestorable detectors are destroyed with use and must be replaced after exposure to the fire signature for which they were designed.

There are advantages and disadvantages to both restorable and nonrestorable detectors. Nonrestorable detectors generally provide a positive visual indication of operation, while a restorable detector may not have any visual cue that it is, or has been, in the alarm state. This is true of most heat detectors, but not smoke detectors, which have visual alarm indicators. Restorable heat detectors can also be provided with visual indicators, although this greatly increases the cost of a relatively inexpensive detector. One key advantage to restorable detectors is their ability to test the units with the same signature for which they are designed to respond.

Heat Detection

There are three basic types of commercially available heat detectors: fixed temperature, rate-of-rise, and rate compensation. The *Life Safety Code* allows any of these units to be used interchangeably wherever heat detection is required.

Heat detectors respond to hot smoke and fire gases, i.e., convected energy. Because it takes time for a heat detector to absorb heat, the air and fire gases surrounding a detector may be much hotter than the detector element. This is called thermal lag. Thermal lag can be illustrated by imagining a fixed temperature heat detector, such as a 165°F sprinkler, that is dropped into a pan of boiling water. Although the water is 212°F, there is a time delay before the sprinkler link melts. The longer the delay, the greater the thermal lag. The smaller the mass of the link or detector element, the shorter the thermal lag. Thermal lag is a measure of detector sensitivity. The shorter the thermal lag, the greater the sensitivity of the unit.

Thermal lag makes it possible for a detector with a fixed temperature of 200°F to respond to the same fire faster than a sprinkler with a fixed temperature of 165°F. It is only necessary to use a detector with a more sensitive element (shorter thermal lag) than the sprinkler. It is detector sensitivity that determines the number of detectors needed for a particular application.

There are several ways to measure detector sensitivity. The term Response Time Index (RTI) is used for sprinklers. The smaller the RTI, the more sensitive the unit. The RTI of a unit can be used in calculations to determine when that unit will respond to a given fire scenario. For heat detectors, the current measurement of sensitivity is the UL listed or F.M. approved spacing. The higher the spacing rating, the more sensitive the detector. For instance, a detector with a listed spacing of 50 feet is more sensitive than one with a listed spacing of 30 feet. The listed spacing of a detector is determined by fire testing and cannot be directly used as part of any engineering calculations.

Where heat detectors are used, NFPA 72E requires that they be spaced on smooth ceilings less than 10 feet high, in accordance with their listed spacing. The installed spacing is equal to the listed or approved spacing. For higher ceilings, NFPA 72E contains reduction factors to be applied to the listed spacing. Therefore, as ceiling height increases, the installed spacing becomes less than the listed spacing. There are also reduction factors for joisted, beamed, and sloped ceilings contained in the standard. The beams or joists must be 4 inches deep or more before reductions are required for heat detectors. Each of these factors (high ceilings, ceilings that are not smooth, etc.) affects detector response. The reduction and correction factors contained in NFPA 72E are intended to provide some adjustments for these effects.

Rather than list all of the various correction factors here, it is best to reference NFPA 72E. Spacing reductions are often missed by designers, installers, and inspectors; yet they can have a dramatic effect on detector response time during a fire. The NFPA two-day workshop on fire detection and alarm systems presents a series of examples that demonstrate how these factors work. In one example, changing from a low, smooth ceiling to a high, joisted ceiling requires over four times as many detectors for compliance.

Fixed temperature heat detectors respond when the temperature of their element reaches a preset level. To reduce the likelihood of false alarms, the temperature rating selected for an application should be at least 20°F above the maximum expected ambient temperature. These detectors are available in a wide range of temperature ratings. The most common ranges are 135°F to 140°F and 190°F to 200°F. Fixed temperature detectors are available as spot type and as line type.

Fixed temperature heat detectors available in the market use several different methods of operation. The two most common use a fusible element or a bimetal element. Fusible elements melt at a preset temperature and are spring-loaded to close or open a set of electrical contacts. Bimetal units use two or more metals that expand at different rates causing the element to change shape and initiate operation of a set of electrical contacts. Line type fixed temperature heat detectors generally operate either when insulation melts, allowing two conductors to short circuit, or when heat causes a decrease in electrical resistance and an increase in conductivity between two conductors.

NFPA 72E contains basic operational descriptions of these and other detection principals. For a more detailed discussion of the many different types of heat detectors available, consult the NFPA *Fire Protection Handbook* or the *Fire Alarm Signaling Systems Handbook*.

Rate-of-rise heat detectors respond when their temperature or the temperature of the air surrounding them rises faster than some preset rate — regardless of their actual fixed temperature. Units are available with various alarm rates, a common one being 15°F/min. The speed with which a detector responds depends on how hot the fire gases are compared to the detector's starting temperature and also on the detector's sensitivity. Therefore, if a rate-of-rise detector is initially monitoring a room temperature of 65°F and a fire causes the temperature around the detector to rise quickly, it will respond in a given time, *t*. If the detector is in a freezer at –20°F and the temperature rises at the same rate, the response time would be about the same.

Depending on environmental conditions, detector sensitivity, and the fire growth rate, rate-of-rise detectors can respond much faster than fixed temperature units. However, there are also many situations, as in the case of slow fires, where a rate-of-rise detector will not respond to a real fire. For this reason, testing laboratories, codes, and standards require these detectors to be backed up with fixed temperature elements.

As with fixed temperature detectors, rate-of-rise heat detectors are available in many different configurations. The most common spot type unit works on a pneumatic principal. As the detector is heated, air inside a chamber is heated and expands. The air escapes through a vent hole when heated slowly. However, when heated faster than its preset rate, the air cannot escape quickly enough, and pressure builds up in the detector. As the pressure increases, a diaphragm moves and activates a set of electrical contacts. Line type rate-of-rise detectors are also available using this pneumatic principal. Other rate-of-rise detectors use bimetal elements or electrical conductivity to detect rapid temperature changes.

It is important when using rate-of-rise heat detectors to ensure that they will not be subjected to changes in ambient conditions that might cause false alarms. For instance, they should not be located too close to air supply vents or directly over heat sources such as ovens, radiators, or large sinks where hot steam might set them off. They can be used in high temperature areas, but caution should be used in situations where the temperature may cool rapidly and then rise again fast enough to set off the rate-of-rise units. A large boiler house is such an example. The temperature at the ceiling might be 100°F to 150°F under normal circumstances. As long as the fixed temperature backup to the rate-of-rise detector is at least 170°F, there should be no false actuation. However, if a large door is opened in the winter, the temperature could drop quickly. When the door is closed, the temperature at the ceiling could rise fast enough to set off the rate-of-rise portion of the detector.

Rate compensation heat detectors are more complex in operation than either fixed or rate-of-rise devices. In short, they combine the principals of both in order to compensate for thermal lag. When the air temperature is rising at a rate of about 40°F/min or less, the unit is designed to respond almost exactly at the point when the air temperature reaches the unit's rated temperature; it does not lag while it absorbs the heat and rises to that temperature. At faster rates of temperature rise, the unit will respond more quickly than most fixed temperature detectors, even though some thermal lag will still occur. In addition, with these very fast temperature rises, rate-of-rise detectors will generally respond more quickly than either fixed or rate compensation detectors.

Because of the precision associated with their operation, rate compensation heat detectors are well-suited for use in areas where thermal lag must be minimized to provide fast response when temperatures exceed a certain level. At the same time, they are stable even in areas where temperatures fluctuate but do not exceed the preset alarm level. There-fore, they respond more quickly to most fires than fixed temperature detectors without producing false alarms due to moderate temperature fluctuations, which can occur with the use of rate-of-rise units. They are also suitable where precise temperature actuation is needed.

Smoke Detection
General

There are four principal types of smoke detection equipment currently on the market: (1) spot type ionization detectors, (2) spot type light scattering photoelectric detectors, (3) line type projected beam light obscuration detectors, and (4) air sampling detectors. The *Life Safety Code* allows each of these types to be used interchangeably wherever smoke detection is required.

By definition and by design, smoke detectors respond to the solid and liquid aerosols produced by a fire. Each type responds differently to different types of smoke. Also, because they respond to aerosols from nonfire sources, an understanding of their operating characteristics is helpful in their correct selection and placement to reduce the chances of false and nuisance alarms. Therefore, selection of a smoke detection principal should be based on the type of fire and fuel expected, as well as on environmental characteristics.

At some point, the smoke detector transmits an alarm signal either by sounding an internal alarm or by signaling a control panel. With newer digital and analog/digital systems, the detector may send information on the amount of smoke in the chamber back to the control panel, where a decision is made to perform some function, such as sounding an alarm. Such units are often called "smart" or "intelligent" devices. Because they send all information back to a control panel or processor and do not make alarm decisions, these units are often referred to as "sensors" rather than detectors. In the case of conventional detectors, a decision to alarm is made internally. The conventional detector then signals an alarm with either an internal audible or visual device or by signaling the control panel. More information on how conventional and digital smoke detectors signal a control panel is contained in the section on wiring.

Where required by an occupancy chapter, household smoke detectors, often called single or multiple station smoke detectors, must be located and installed in accordance with NFPA 74. The location and placement of required smoke detectors for local protective systems is governed by NFPA 72E. All requirements and recommendations for smoke detector spacing contained in NFPA 72E apply equally to ionization or photoelectric spot type smoke detectors, to projected beam detectors, and to the sampling ports or heads of a sampling type system.

For general area coverage with smoke detectors, NFPA 72E requires that spacing be based upon manufacturer's recommendations. NFPA 72E also recommends an installed spacing of 30 feet between detectors. This recommendation applies to smooth, flat ceilings and is also in agreement with the recommendation of most manufacturers. Therefore, in many cases, the installed spacing is the manufacturer's recommended spacing, which is usually 30 feet, center to center. There is no listed or approved spacing of smoke detectors as is provided for heat detectors. Also, there is no specific requirement for changing detector spacing, depending on the sensitivity of the unit.

NFPA 72E requires detector spacing to be reduced for ceilings with beams or joists. Where using smoke detectors, the beams or joists must be 8 inches deep or more before reductions are required. Spacing adjustment is also required when airflow in the space is greater than about 8 minutes per air change.

Unlike its provisions for heat detectors, NFPA 72E does not contain specific spacing reductions for smoke detectors where ceilings are over 10 feet high. Instead, it advises use of the manufacturers' recommendations and good engineering judgment. Other factors that must be considered are discussed in the section below on detector selection and placement.

Spot type smoke detector sensitivity is generally based on the percentage of light obscuration per foot required for the unit to signal an alarm. The alarm threshold may also be expressed in optical density per foot or per meter, which can be directly converted to obscuration per foot.

The *Life Safety Code* does not require detectors to have any minimum or maximum sensitivity. It only requires compliance with either NFPA 72E or NFPA 74. These documents also do not contain any explicit requirements regarding detector sensitivity. NFPA 72E only requires the detector to be tested and listed for its intended use. It is the listing company, acceptable to the authority having jurisdiction, that determines the range of acceptable smoke detector sensitivity for a given application.

NFPA 74 also requires detectors to be tested and listed. It also specifically requires testing and listing in compliance with ANSI/UL 217 or 268 standards. ANSI/UL 217 is the *Standard for Single and Multiple Station Smoke Detectors.* ANSI/UL 268 is the *Standard for Smoke Detectors for Fire Protective Signaling Systems.* Both of these ANSI/UL standards contain requirements for minimum and maximum detector sensitivity to grey and black smoke.

The range of possible sensitivities for spot type detectors is generally between 1.0 and 4.0 percent per foot obscuration due to grey smoke. This provides the designer of a smoke detection system some choice with regard to sensitivity. This is covered more in the section on "Selection and Placement."

Ionization

Figure 3 shows a schematic diagram of an ionization smoke detector. Ionization smoke detectors have two parallel electrically charged plates separated by an air gap. A small, low-strength radioactive source causes the air between the plates to be ionized. Because of the voltage between the plates, the positive ions travel to the negative plate and the negative ions travel to the positive plate. This creates a small electrical current. As smoke particles enter the detector, they slow down the movement of the ionized air between the plates. The corresponding change in electrical current is measurable by the detector and is proportional to the number and size of the smoke particles between the plates. In the case of ionization smoke detectors, the strongest signal is obtained when there are a large number of small particles in the chamber.

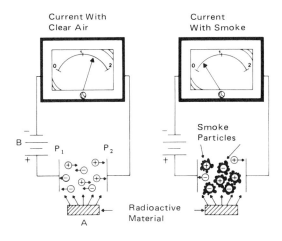

Figure 3. Ionization Smoke Detector.

Photoelectric

Figure 4 shows a schematic diagram of a photoelectric smoke detector. Spot type photoelectric smoke detectors operate on the light-scattering principle. A small light source, usually an infrared LED, shines a beam into the detector chamber. A light sensitive receiver is located so that it normally sees only a very small amount of light from the source reflected from the detector chamber. When smoke enters the detector chamber, additional light is scattered within the chamber, some of which reaches the photosensitive receiver and changes the detector signal. As with ionization detectors, the magnitude of the signal is related to the number and size of the smoke particles.

There are many other factors that also affect the signal from a light-scattering smoke detector. The color of the smoke affects the amount of light that is scattered. Dark smoke, such as that from some plastics and hydrocarbon fuels, absorbs more light than it reflects, so more light is required before the signal reaches the alarm threshold. Light-colored particles reflect a lot of light, so smaller quantities can produce strong signals. Particle shape also affects the amount of light reflected, as does the wavelength of the light source and the angle between the source and receiver. However, in general, in the case of a particular scattering type photoelectric detector design, the strongest signal is obtained when there are large, light-colored smoke particles in the chamber.

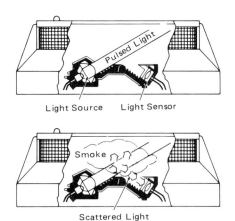

Figure 4. Photoelectric Smoke Detector.

Projected Beam

Projected beam smoke detectors, as illustrated in Figure 5, operate on the light obscuration principal. These detec-

tors consist of a source that projects a light beam across a space to a receiver. As smoke enters the beam path, some of the light is absorbed and some is scattered, reducing the total amount reaching the receiver. The color and shape of the smoke particles is not as important as it is where using spot type photoelectric detectors. In the case of projected beam smoke detectors, it is the size and quantity of smoke particles in the path that has the greatest effect on the detector's signal.

Projected beam smoke detectors respond to the total amount of light obscuration in their paths. When the percentage of light obscured reaches a given threshold, the unit alarms. Typically, the units are available with adjustable sensitivities between 20 percent and 70 percent total obscuration. If the light beam is suddenly and totally obscured, the unit should not alarm, but should give a trouble signal after a short time period. Fires do not suddenly and totally obscure a light beam. Similarly, a very slow, gradual loss of light is probably not indicative of a fire either; it is more likely an accumulation of dust or a misalignment of the beam. This situation should also produce a trouble signal and not an alarm signal.

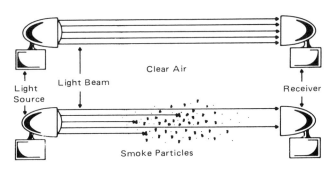

Figure 5. Projected Beam Smoke Detector.

Sampling Detectors

Sampling type smoke detection devices are designed to draw air samples from the protected space to a separate detection chamber. The sampling portion may consist of a combination of air pumps, filters, and tubing or piping fitted with sampling heads or perforated to draw room air samples. The detection device may be self-contained or may be part of, or served by, a control panel.

Air sampling detectors should not be confused with duct smoke detectors. Sampling detectors use positive ventilation methods to draw an air sample. Duct smoke detectors are usually only spot type photoelectric or ionization detectors in special housings. Duct smoke detectors might use a sampling tube that penetrates the duct to allow natural pressure differences to draw air into the detector housing.

There are two principal types of air sampling smoke detection systems. One type uses a cloud chamber to detect very small particles in the air from the protected space. In a cloud chamber, humidity is added to the air sample, and the pressure is reduced to lower its temperature. This causes water to condense on small particles present in the sample. The resulting cloud is measured by an LED light source and a phototransistor light receiver. These units are very sensitive to very small- (submicron-) sized particles.

The second principal type of air sampling smoke detection system uses a very sensitive photoelectric light scattering detector. Unlike a spot type light scattering smoke detector, this uses a high power strobe light or a laser beam rather than an infrared LED. Where combined with a sensitive light receiver, the unit can detect submicron-sized particles in very small concentrations. Other sampling type smoke detectors may use other detection principles such as an ionization chamber.

Other Detection Principles

Radiant Energy Detectors

The selection, location, and placement of radiant energy detectors is addressed by NFPA 72E. Often, these detectors are called flame detectors. However, the broader name, "radiant energy detectors," includes units designed to sense smoldering and glowing ember combustion.

The radiant energy emitted during combustion of a fuel falls predominantly into three categories, distinguished by the wavelength of the radiation. The three categories are:

1. Ultraviolet: Wavelength smaller than visible radiation — smaller than about 0.35 microns.
2. Visible: Wavelength larger than ultraviolet radiation but smaller than infrared radiation — between about 0.35 microns and 0.75 microns.
3. Infrared: Wavelength larger than visible radiation — more than about 0.75 microns.

The two most common wavelengths used by radiant energy detectors are the ultraviolet and infrared band widths. Except in very special applications, visible light comes from so many normal sources that it cannot effectively be used as a fire signature.

The application of radiant energy sensing detectors is beyond the scope of this supplement. The selection and use of flame detectors is complex and requires thorough knowledge of fuel behavior, environmental conditions, and specific detector characteristics. Generally, these detectors are used in special applications such as in aircraft hangars and areas where flammable and combustible solids, liquids, and gases are handled, used, or conveyed. Subject to the approval of the authority having jurisdiction, these detectors may be used as part of an automatic fire detection system required by the *Life Safety Code* where specific detection, such as smoke, is not mentioned in the occupancy chapter.

NFPA 72E has descriptions of these radiant energy detection principles. For a more detailed discussion concerning these detectors and their applications, consult the *Fire Protection Handbook*, the *Fire Alarm Signaling Systems Handbook*, and manufacturers' literature.

Fire Gas Detectors

Fire gas detectors are another type of automatic detector covered by NFPA 72E. These detectors are designed to detect the gases produced by a burning fuel. There is a difference between these detectors and those designed to respond to combustible gases that might lead to a fire or explosion.

Fire gas detection is a special subject and is beyond the scope of this supplement. As with radiant energy detectors, fire gas detectors are not directly addressed within the *Life Safety Code*. Nevertheless, they may be used as part of an automatic fire detection system required by an occupancy chapter of the *Code* where allowed by the authority having jurisdiction and where specific detection, such as for smoke, is not mentioned.

Other Fire Detectors

NFPA 72E recognizes that there are, or may someday be, detectors suitable for use as automatic fire detectors other than those discussed above. As with any detector, their selection, application, and use is governed by their principle of operation, their testing and/or listing, if any, and their manufacturers' recommendations.

Any fire detector listed or approved for its specific intended purpose may be used where the *Life Safety Code* requires automatic fire detection but does not specify the type. The selection must be approved by the authority having jurisdiction.

Monitoring Other Fire Protection Systems

Fire detection and alarm systems may be interconnected to receive signals from other fire prevention and protection systems. These systems may or may not be required by parts of the *Life Safety Code* and include:

- Sprinkler systems
- Fire pumps
- Other extinguishing systems
  (CO2, halon, dry chemical, wet chemical, foam, etc.)
- Heating, ventilating, and air conditioning systems
- Smoke control systems
- Elevator control systems
- Emergency lighting systems

The signals received from systems or devices such as those listed above may be fire alarm, supervisory, or some other signal indicating the status of the system or device. Detailed discussion of these systems is not possible in this brief introduction to detection and alarm signaling. However, some discussion of sprinklers, the most common of these systems, is warranted.

Where an occupancy chapter of the *Life Safety Code* requires an automatic sprinkler system, the requirement will indicate if the system must be supervised. Section 7-7 defines a supervised sprinkler system. Under "Extinguishment Requirements," the occupancy chapter may also state that the system is required to be connected to the fire alarm system. Under "Detection, Alarm, and Communications Systems" of the same occupancy chapter, the section titled "Initiation" will indicate whether alarm signals must be activated by the sprinkler system.

Where a supervised automatic sprinkler system is required, it must produce a distinct signal to indicate conditions that might impair the satisfactory operation of the sprinkler system. This requires monitoring of such features as the opening and closing of control valves and fire pump operation and water tank level. The chapter also requires supervisory signals to terminate within the protected premises at a constantly attended location or in an approved remote receiving facility. In Appendix A, reference is made to other NFPA standards for provisions on these supervisory functions. These standards, which include NFPA 71 and NFPA 72, contain detailed requirements for monitoring of supervisory signals.

Chapter 7 also requires waterflow alarm signals from required supervised sprinkler systems to be transmitted to an approved auxiliary, remote station, proprietary, or central station facility. These systems are introduced in the section on signaling. Where the occupancy chapter requires a sprinkler system to be monitored by and to produce an alarm on the protected premise system, NFPA 72 contains requirements for its connection.

At the local protected premise, NFPA 72 has specific definitions of alarm, trouble, and supervisory signals. Alarm signals indicate an emergency requiring immediate action. A supervisory signal indicates the need to initiate a specific action regarding some type of protective service or equipment, such as guard tour or extinguishing systems. For example, a closed-valve signal on a sprinkler system is a supervisory signal indicating the need to investigate the signal and take corrective action (i.e., open the valve) when appropriate. A trouble signal, on the other hand, indicates a fault or problem with a protective signaling system. Trouble signals occur because of faults in the protective signaling system while supervisory signals are signals initiated in conjunction with other systems or services.

The three different signals must each be distinct from one another. In the case of trouble and supervisory signals at the protected premise, these may have the same audible signal as long as they have separate and distinct visual signals. Therefore, it is clear that the common practice of wiring a valve tamper switch to open the waterflow alarm circuit and cause a trouble signal is not acceptable. The valve tamper switch would break the circuit just as a broken wire would. Both would result in a trouble condition at the control panel. Correct and incorrect methods for monitoring supervisory devices are addressed in the section on wiring.

Selection and Placement

Within the context of the *Life Safety Code*, some degree of decision making is necessary concerning the type of detector to be used in a given situation. For instance, where the *Code* requires a supervised fire alarm system with initiation by smoke detection, it does not specify what type of smoke detection may be used. In such a case, the *Code* intends that life safety fire detection goals for this particular occupancy will be met by smoke detection designed, installed, maintained, and tested in accordance with NFPA 72E. The same is true for a required household fire warning smoke detector in a dwelling unit. The opportunity to choose a smoke detection method allows design flexibility for performance and economy.

The majority of detectors used to meet the intent of this *Code* are spot type ionization, spot type photoelectric, or projected beam. Air sampling type smoke detectors are very sensitive and cost more than systems using spot and beam type detectors. Their use is generally limited to clean, high-value areas such as computer rooms and industrial clean rooms for manufacturing semiconductors. They have also found use in telecommunications facilities and power plant control rooms. Because of their cost and sensitivity, these detectors are not a common choice for meeting requirements of the *Life Safety Code*, despite the fact that they are allowed. Design considerations for these systems are complex and beyond the scope of this supplement.

The first step in selecting a smoke detector is to consider the type of fire that is likely to occur in the area. Is the fire likely to smolder for some time? Photoelectric or projected beam detectors would provide faster response because of the large particles produced during smoldering combustion. If the fire is most likely to be fast and hot with open flames, the larger quantity of small smoke particles will set off an ionization smoke detector faster than either photoelectric or projected beam.

The expected color of smoke should also be considered. Color is important to photoelectric light-scattering detectors but not to projected beam and ionization detectors. If black smoke is expected, projected beam or ionization detectors will give the best response. If the smoke is expected to be mostly large black particles, the ionization detector falls further down the list of choices. The projected beam detector would probably respond first, followed by either photoelectric or ionization.

Ambient environmental conditions must also be considered when selecting a smoke detection method. Smoke detectors cannot be used where the temperature is above or below the manufacturer's stated range. This range is usually 32°F to 120°F, although lower and higher temperature units may be found.

Cooking odors are blamed for a large number of nuisance alarms. The odors that are produced by cooking contain a large number of small invisible particles. A smoke detector's response to this is not a false alarm; it is a response to a valid fire signature. An ionization smoke detector would probably nuisance alarm in response to cooking odors, while a photoelectric smoke detector would probably not alarm unless the food was well burnt and producing visible smoke. Therefore, unless the detector can be located far enough from the kitchen to avoid odors, the better choice is a photoelectric detector.

Steam from showers and large sinks contains lots of small water drops and has much the same effect as cooking odors in causing nuisance alarms from smoke detectors. The heavier the steam, the more likely it is to also cause photoelectric smoke detectors to alarm. Detectors can often be located to avoid these sources of false fire signatures.

Insects can set off either type of spot smoke detector. They are not likely to cause an alarm from a projected beam smoke detector because of the small amount of light they obscure. Detectors with good bug screens stop most insects, but some still manage to get into the detector chamber. Ionization smoke detectors are less prone to nuisance alarms from insects than spot type photoelectric smoke detectors. Another solution that has been reported as successful is to place an insecticide strip on or near the detector. The detector manufacturer should be consulted before taking this action. Some insecticides may produce enough fumes to set off ionization detectors or harm electronic components. Never spray an insecticide in or near a functioning detector. It will probably set off the alarm, as would any aerosol spray, and it may harm the detector.

Cigarette smoke causes nuisance alarms from ionization and photoelectric smoke detectors. When the smoke dissipates to a light cloud, the ionization detector is likely to alarm first. When the smoke is heavy and thick, either type will alarm. Often, detectors can be placed to avoid such conditions. For instance, in elevator lobbies, smoke detectors should not be placed directly in front of the doors where people stand and where drafts from the shaft may bring dust into contact with the detector. In office areas, smoke detectors should not be placed directly over a smoker's desk or too close to a break room or cafeteria room, where smokers may congregate or where cooking may take place. Incidental cigarette smoke is not likely to set off projected beam smoke detectors. As a smoker passes near the beam, a cloud of smoke 3 to 10 feet wide might be produced, but it would not be thick enough to alarm the detector.

Detectors of the ionization or photoelectric type may be purchased with different sensitivities. Detector sensitivity is usually labeled on the detector and on its specification sheet. The sensitivity is typically between 1.0 and 4.0 percent per foot obscuration. This is the amount of light obscuration measured immediately outside the detector when it alarms during tests with grey smoke. Comparing labels on a photoelectric and an ionization smoke detector usually indicates the ionization unit to be more sensitive. Typically, ionization smoke detectors have labeled sensitivities on the order of 1.0 to 2.0 percent per foot. Photoelectric detectors may range from 1.0 to 4.0 percent per foot. This does not mean that ionization detectors are always more sensitive than photoelectric detectors. It means only that they may be more sensitive to fires that produce smoke similar to the grey smoke used in the test. A true comparison of detector sensitivity must include consideration of the type of smoke expected, as discussed in the previous paragraphs and in the section on fire signatures.

Sensitivity comparison is made more difficult by the fact that light obscuration is not comparable to those factors that set off either spot detector type. For photoelectric detectors, it is the light scattered, not the light obscured, that is important. For ionization units, it is the quantity and size of the particle. The amount of light obscured across a given distance is only partly related to these factors. The published numbers are useful only as a relative comparison between detectors of a given type as they react to a given type of smoke. A photoelectric detector having an alarm threshold of 2 percent per foot obscuration is more sensitive than one with a threshold of 3 percent per foot. Similarly, an ionization detector with an alarm threshold of 1 percent per foot is more sensitive than one with a threshold of 2 percent per foot. However, one cannot say that a photoelectric detector with a 2 percent per foot threshold is as sensitive as an ionization detector with a 2 percent per foot threshold. It might possibly be equally sensitive to the same grey smoke used to evaluate the units. In a real fire, many factors, including smoke color and size, will cause one detector to respond before the other.

By nature of their design, projected beam smoke detectors are a good choice for large open spaces. The source and the receiver of commercially available units may be placed as far as 300 feet apart, with 30 or more feet between adjacent beams. Therefore, there may be considerably fewer units to install, although each unit is more expensive. The sensitivity of projected beam smoke detectors is stated in total percent obscuration required to alarm the unit, not percent per foot, as is the case with spot type detectors. The sensitivity is usually adjustable, between about 20 percent and 70 percent total obscuration. This allows adjustment for different distances between the source and the receiver.

Because projected beam detectors total all the accumulated smoke in their path, they are very sensitive to real fires, while remaining insensitive to many environmental factors that would alarm a spot type detector. For instance, insects in the light path are not likely to block 20 percent of the beam. Similarly, a cigarette smoker might create a cloud of 1 to 2 percent per foot smoke, which would be 5 or 10 feet in diameter. If this cloud were under a spot type smoke detector, it would probably alarm unless a less sensitive unit were installed. However, the same cloud produces between 5 and 20 percent total obscuration of a beam projected through the cloud, which projected beam detectors can be set to disregard. Nevertheless, in a real fire scenario, a 20- to 30-foot cloud of smoke, which is 1 to 2 percent per foot on average, is likely by the time a spot type detector is activated and goes into alarm. A beam projected through this cloud would be obscured about 20 to 60 percent, which could set off a beam detector. The projected beam detector could be set for 30 percent total obscuration to respond sooner to a real fire while still disregarding small sources of activation such as tobacco smokers, sinks, and kitchenettes.

There are many other factors to consider in selecting smoke detectors. For instance, in a room with moderate to high air movement, smoke from a fire that would normally set off a spot type detector may be dissipated to form a thin haze. The fire must grow larger before there is enough smoke present to set off a spot type detector. Use of either projected beam or air sampling type detectors would overcome this delayed response. For more discussion of this and other factors affecting detector selection, consult NFPA 72E as well as the *Fire Protection Handbook* or the *Fire Alarm Signaling Systems Handbook*. A review of manufacturers' specification sheets and the standards used by testing laboratories for listing or approval will also provide some insight on detector selection.

There are other choices contained in the *Code* concerning detector selection. There are cases where heat detectors may be required or where smoke detection simply cannot be used due to normal ambient conditions. In some locations, the authority having jurisdiction may require the area to be made suitable for smoke detectors. In other cases, it might be judged that heat detectors could be used, and the life safety intent of the *Code* would still be met. These situations demand that a choice be made between the various types of heat detectors.

If the area has no friendly sources that produce rapid temperature changes, rate compensation or combination rate-of-rise/fixed temperature heat detectors will provide good results. If a fast fire occurs, they will respond before a fixed temperature heat detector. If a fire is slow, they will respond in about the same time as a fixed temperature heat detector. Where rapid temperature changes are expected during normal conditions, fixed temperature detectors should be chosen.

Detectors installed as household fire warning equipment must be installed in accordance with NFPA 74. This includes single and multiple station self-contained smoke alarms and also small systems installed to meet the requirements within the dwelling unit. (The distinction among single, multiple, and system detectors is explained in the section on wiring.) Application of the *Life Safety Code*, combined with NFPA 74, usually results in the installation of smoke detectors on each level of a dwelling unit, outside of the bedrooms, and at the base of any stairs leading to upper levels.

However, where the smoke detectors also contain the alarm sounder to alert occupants, additional units may be needed to achieve audibility in all spaces of the dwelling unit. In some cases, smoke detectors may be required in each bedroom. Additional detectors may also be warranted to provide longer escape times for some occupants or to provide faster response when complex floor plans are involved and smoke must travel a good distance to reach a required detector.

Where the *Code* requires an automatic fire alarm system initiated by smoke detection or heat detection, the spacing and placement of the chosen detectors is governed by NFPA 72E. The first step is to place detectors as close as possible to known hazards and as far away as possible from nuisance alarm sources. Any remaining space is then covered with evenly spaced detectors. This approach may result in a few more detectors than are required but will provide better fire detection and reduced chances of false and nuisance alarms.

For example, in a hall of a college dormitory, conditions might allow smoke detectors to be spaced 35 feet on center. However, if this results in a detector immediately outside a shower room, it might be best to use a different increment of spacing, such as 28 feet, and put detectors no closer to the shower room door than 14 feet.

The maximum spacing between detectors and the maximum distance from any point on the ceiling to a detector is determined by the many factors previously discussed for each detector type. For heat detectors, begin with the listed or approved spacing, then make corrections for ceiling height, beams, joists, and slopes. Where using smoke detectors, start with the manufacturer's recommended spacing, usually 30 feet, and make adjustments for ceiling height, beams, joists, slopes, and high airflow. Note that the actual correction factors in NFPA 72E for smoke detectors are different from the factors for heat detectors. Consult NFPA 72E for the exact correction factors to be used.

Once a detector spacing has been determined, detectors must be located in accordance with other requirements of NFPA 72E. Figure 6, reproduced from 72E, shows that ceiling-mounted detectors must be installed at least 4 inches away from walls. If the detector is to be wall-mounted, it should be installed at least 4 inches, but no more than 12 inches, from the top of the wall. The 4 inch × 4 inch space is called the dead air space. Detectors in that space will respond more slowly, since smoke and heat from a small fire tend to circumvent the wall/ceiling intersection.

When all correction factors have been applied to determine a required spacing for detectors, area coverage begins by locating the first detectors at one-half that distance from a wall. Figure 7, reproduced from NFPA 72E, demonstrates this concept. One part of the figure illustrates how spot type detectors would be spaced and the other half indicates how line type detectors would be evenly located. In the diagram, "S" is the corrected, or installed, spacing. These examples assume that the corrected spacing results in a square, such as 30 feet × 30 feet or 25 feet × 25 feet. In the case of beams or joists, the corrected spacing would create a rectangle such as 15 feet × 30 feet, the shorter distance being measured perpendicular to the joists or beams. Note in Figure 7 that no point on the ceiling can be farther from a detector than 0.7 times the installed spacing. This maximum distance applies to all points on a ceiling and is useful in lay-

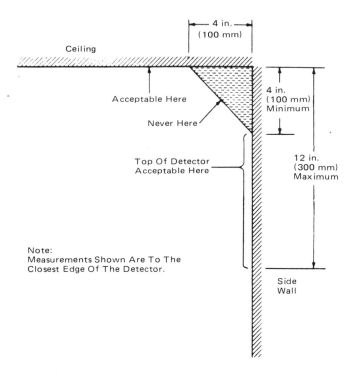

Figure 6. *Dead Air Space.*

ing out systems in irregularly shaped spaces. This concept is discussed in detail in NFPA 72E.

If a ceiling has beams or joists, it must be decided whether the detector should be located on the bottom of the beams or joists or in the ceiling pocket. In the case of joists, NFPA 72E always requires the detector, whether smoke or heat, to be located on the bottom of the joists. Joists are defined as more than 4 inches deep and 3 feet or less apart. Beams are more than 4 inches deep and more than 3 feet apart. In the case of beamed ceilings, the detector may be located on the bottom of the beams or on the ceiling in the pocket, depending on the beam depth, beam spacing, and ceiling height. The reader should refer to NFPA 72E for specific requirements.

Detectors must also be located for ease of testing and maintenance. A smoke detector located over the open part of a stair tower probably cannot be reached very easily once scaffolding is removed. As a result, smoke detectors are often not tested or cleaned and may fail in a fire or may cause false or nuisance alarms. They should be located over a landing or where a ladder can be placed to reach them. There is no need to place the detector in the middle of the space. The space is considered to be adequately covered as long

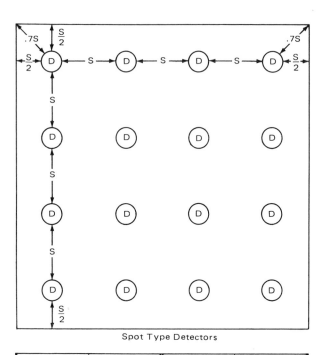

Spot Type Detectors

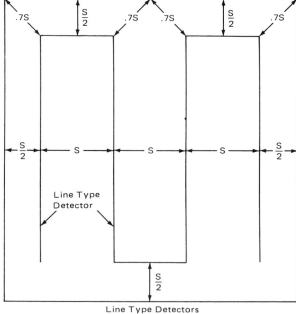

Line Type Detectors

Heat Detectors–Spacing Layouts–Smooth Ceiling
S–Listed Spacing
D–Detector

Figure 7. *Spot and Line Type Detector Spacing.*

as all points on the ceiling are within the detector's protection radius (0.7 times the installed spacing).

Construction dust is one of the largest causes of false and nuisance alarms from smoke detectors. When smoke detectors are installed before all construction work is complete, they collect dust in their chambers. The dust can cause immediate alarms, or it can bring the detector close to alarming. As a result, the slightest physical disturbance, such as air movement or people walking, might set it off. Where dust has caused a detector to become more sensitive, even small amounts of cigarette smoke or other aerosols will set it off. Plaster and sheetrock dust are very difficult to clear from a detector without disassembly and recalibration after cleaning by factory-trained service personnel.

Early installation of detectors must be resisted despite demands for a certificate of occupancy. This will only lead to future problems. If acceptable to the authority having jurisdiction, the detectors might be installed covered with bags or part of their original packaging. However, it should be noted that covering will render the smoke detectors unable to respond to smoke during a fire. The remainder of the system will be operational. Nevertheless, the life safety aspects of the system will have been compromised until the smoke detectors are uncovered.

In an open office area with a 20-foot ceiling, spot type detectors might be used. However, once the area is occupied, maneuvering a 20-foot high ladder for the purpose of testing is nearly impossible. This constitutes the perfect application for a projected beam smoke detector. The sender and receiver can be located on opposite walls where a ladder can be leaned to reach the units for cleaning and testing.

There are many factors other than those discussed here that have an effect on the selection and placement of fire detectors. Temperature stratifications might prevent smoke from reaching the ceiling; airflow might speed response of properly located detectors and slow the response of poorly located detectors; the height and width of fire and smoke doors might require additional smoke detectors for door release; machinery vibrations or radio frequency interference might result in the relocation of detectors to avoid false alarms. Complete familiarity with NFPA 72E is the source of a reliable system. The reference list following this supplement contains other valuable references to assist designers, installers, inspectors, and owners in achieving reliable fire detection while minimizing the chance of false or nuisance alarms.

Power Sources and System Wiring Methods

Household Fire Warning Equipment

Dwelling units are most often equipped with either single station or multiple station smoke detectors. In some cases, small systems designed as household fire warning equipment, with detectors, a control panel, and some notification appliances, are used. Often, the control panel also serves as part of a security system.

Single station smoke detectors are stand-alone units that detect smoke and provide occupant notification. Multiple station units are actually single station detectors that can be interconnected so that if one is activated, all units sound an alarm. Most single and multiple station smoke detectors contain only an internal horn, though some contain flashing lights as well. Units are also available with internal relays that can be used to control other functions, such as door release, a nurse call signaling system, activation of a bed vibrator to alert a hearing-impaired person, or operation of a light outside the dwelling unit.

The detectors may be powered by a battery or by commercial light and power (usually 120 volts AC). NFPA 74 requires detectors used in new construction to be AC-powered by a dependable commercial light and power service. In existing households, AC power is preferred. However, where not practical, NFPA 74 allows the use of a monitored battery as the power source. Within the *Life Safety Code*, there are occupancy chapters that require AC power, even in existing facilities, where NFPA 74 would allow battery-operated units.

One reason AC-powered detectors are preferred is that the detector is less likely to be subject to tampering. Battery-powered units are often disabled when the battery is "borrowed" for a toy or other device. Also, when batteries die, they are often not replaced for some time, leaving part or all of the dwelling unit without smoke detection.

Some people argue that battery power is superior, since, during a power outage, people resort to candles for light, and they heat with fireplaces, stoves, or portable heaters, which all increase the possibility of fire. However, the increased chance of fire does not offset the fact that, over time, loss of commercial power is less likely and shorter in duration than loss of battery power. NFPA 74 reflects the belief that the chance of fire during a power outage is smaller than the chance of fire occurring when a detector is rendered useless because it has no battery.

Single station smoke detectors are now available with integral battery backup. These units are allowed, but not required, by both the *Life Safety Code* and NFPA 74. Local codes, ordinances, or authorities may, however, require their use.

NFPA 74 requires that AC power not be controlled by a switch and that the circuit not have a ground-fault interrupter. Direct wiring to a power circuit is preferred. However, if a plug-in electrical cord is used, the standard requires some restraining method to make certain the unit is not accidentally unplugged. It is preferred that AC-powered detectors be connected to an often-used light circuit, such as one feeding kitchen or hallway lights. Therefore, if a fault occurs, such as a blown fuse or circuit breaker, it is likely to receive immediate attention. If the detectors were connected to their own circuit or one infrequently used, loss of power might go unnoticed until the units were tested. AC-powered units must also have a visual "power on" indicator.

NFPA 74 contains requirements for units that use batteries for primary power. Basically, they must be designed so the battery will last for at least one year of normal use, including weekly testing. Also, they must provide an audible trouble signal when the battery is low, well before the unit fails to operate. The unit must be capable of sounding a trouble condition at least once a minute for seven days and still have enough battery power to operate the alarm sounder for 4 minutes. Because of this requirement, it is very important that only battery types recommended by the manufacturer be used. Also, the smoke detectors must visually indicate when the battery has been removed.

Mechanically powered devices are allowed by NFPA 74 and by the *Life Safety Code*, unless otherwise stated in the occupancy chapter. Though not very common, these devices might be powered by compressed gas, a wind-up spring, or some other means. As with any equipment, they must be tested and listed or approved for the intended purpose. One reason mechanical devices are not very common is that electrical power is required by commercially available smoke detection devices. The sound portion of the self-contained unit is permitted to be mechanical, as long as it meets the requirement for 4 minutes of alarm power and visually indicates when sufficient power is not available.

Where multiple station units are used, they most often are connected to the same power circuit and also have a trip wire that interconnects them. It is very important where using multiple station detectors to follow the manufacturer's wiring diagrams and instructions closely. There is a limit on how many units may be interconnected. Some models allow only five or six to be interconnected, while others allow up to thirty in a chain. Detectors from different manufacturers cannot be interconnected. Different models from the same manufacturer may or may not be compatible for interconnection. Compatibility between different models allows both ionization and photoelectric detectors to be used on the same circuit where each is advantageous and also allows various sensitivities to be used in different areas of the dwelling unit.

The *Life Safety Code* and NFPA 74 both allow the use of component systems within a dwelling unit rather than single or multiple station units. The system must be listed or approved for use as household fire warning equipment. NFPA 74 contains requirements for the performance of component systems used within the dwelling unit. The requirements include supervision of detector circuits. The supervision requirement is excepted when occurrence of fault still allows the required detectors to perform as single station units. Another exception allows the use of wireless radio as the signal transmission medium, provided each detector has its own transmitter and the unit automatically sends a test signal at least once every 24 hours. The installation of hard wiring for component systems is required to meet Article 760 of NFPA 70, the *National Electrical Code*.

The use of combination systems is allowed by NFPA 74, provided the fire detection and alarm portion takes precedence over all other functions. Also, alarm signals for fire and any other function, such as burglary, must be distinctive.

NFPA 72 Systems

Power

Systems intended to meet the requirements of NFPA 72 are required to have three power sources: (1) primary power, (2) secondary power, and (3) trouble power. Primary power must come from a reliable source and is usually taken from a commercial light and power source, although NFPA 72 allows other sources, such as engine-driven generators. Primary power must come from a dedicated branch circuit.

Access to the circuit disconnecting means must be restricted and clearly marked "FIRE ALARM CIRCUIT CONTROL."

Secondary power is intended to operate all functions of the system in the event that primary power is lost. Most often, secondary power is provided by standby batteries. Engine-driven generators may also be used. The capacity of secondary power sources depends on the type of signaling system. Local, central station, and proprietary systems must be provided with secondary power capable of operating the system for 24 hours under normal loading conditions. Auxiliary and remote station systems must have 60 hours of supervisory power. At the end of the normal supervisory period, each system must have five minutes of alarm power available.

The trouble power supply provides power to a trouble indicator when primary power is lost. Usually the trouble power supply is the same as the secondary power supply. However, NFPA 72 does contain exceptions where a secondary power source would not be required when primary power comes from reliable sources meeting certain requirements. In such cases, a trouble power supply may still be required to indicate loss of the primary power. Refer Chapter 5 of NFPA 72 for more information.

NFPA 72 Circuit Classifications

In addition to power supply circuits, there are three principal types of circuits used in fire protective signaling systems:

1. Initiating device circuits (IDCs)
2. Signaling line circuits (SLCs)
3. Indicating appliance circuits (IACs)

An initiating device circuit (IDC) connects manual and automatic devices to a control panel or system. The main characteristic of the initiating device circuits is that the signal received at the control panel does not identify the device that operated. These circuits are called initiating zones of the fire detection panel. Because the devices are not readily identified at the panel, the quantity of devices on a circuit and the area served by the circuit must be limited to make identification of the source a bit easier.

In addition, since the control panel cannot recognize the individual devices on the circuit, alarm devices cannot be mixed with supervisory devices on the same circuit. Figure 8 shows one version of incorrect and correct methods for monitoring waterflow and valve tamper switches where using initiating device circuits.

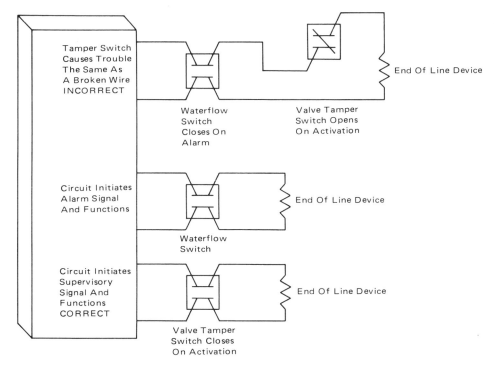

Figure 8. Incorrect and Correct Wiring of Valve Tamper Switch.

A signaling line circuit (SLC) may connect initiating devices to a control panel or system or may interconnect various pieces of control equipment. An SLC is characterized by its ability to carry multiple signals, often in two directions. For instance, multiplex systems, often called "smart" systems, communicate with initiating and control devices. Each device or group of devices might have a unique address. The panel signals to a specific address and asks for the status of that "point." The device responds by repeating its address and its current status, such as "alarm" or "trouble." Therefore, the circuit is carrying multiple pieces of information, and there is two-way communication.

Where signaling line circuits are used, it is possible to combine alarm and supervisory devices on the same circuit or data pathway. Since each device or group of devices is recognized at the control equipment, different output signals can be programmed for each.

The third type of circuit, the indicating appliance circuit (IAC), serves appliances such as horns, bells, lights, and other notification appliances. IACs are often called signal circuits, because they connect to devices intended to signal the occupants of a fire emergency. Even though occupant notification appliances generate a signal, care must be exercised not to confuse the circuit designations within the scope of NFPA 72. There are requirements for signaling line circuits that are different from those for indicating appliance circuits.

Circuit Supervision

NFPA 72 requires all means for interconnecting equipment and devices to be monitored for integrity. This is commonly referred to as circuit supervision. The standard also contains requirements for monitoring power supplies as well as the circuits to detectors and notification appliances. Monitoring power sources is primarily a function of the control equipment. Compliance with NFPA 72 requirements is checked during testing and listing or approval of the system. See Chapter 5 of NFPA 72 for performance and installation requirements.

The performance of IDCs, SLCs, and IACs is a function of the equipment and the installation of the circuits. Tables in NFPA 72 describe the performance of each type of circuit during various faults, including open circuits, ground faults, and short circuits. Because of the many different combinations of these faults and the different performance levels of the system, there are several different circuit styles for

each of the circuit types. For example, there are seven different styles of initiating device circuits, ten different styles of signaling line circuits, and four different styles of indicating appliance circuits.

In the past, circuits were designated as either Class A or Class B, which described their performance during open circuit conditions. However, with various performance levels during shorts and grounds, circuit styles have replaced circuit classes. Initiating device circuits, formerly called Class B, are now designated as Style A, B, or C, depending on their performance during ground or short circuit faults. IDCs, formerly called Class A, are now designated either Style D or E, depending on their performance during ground or short circuit faults.

The tables for initiating device circuits and signaling line circuits in NFPA 72 contain maximum quantities of devices and equipment to be connected on each style of circuit. A circuit style that performs better during a variety of faults is permitted to serve more devices. The tables are designed so that, if the circuit loadings are followed for each style, their statistical performance is approximately equal. For instance, circuits that continue to work at or near 100 percent during certain faults are allowed to have a greater number of devices on them. Though failure of the circuit is less likely, if failure does occur, more devices are affected. A circuit style that is more prone to failure during a fault would have fewer devices that would be affected. If the probability of failure is multiplied by the magnitude of the failure, the result is about the same for each circuit style. On the other hand, if a circuit is to have a specific number of devices connected to it, the higher the circuit style, the better the statistical performance of that circuit.

Unlike IDCs and SLCs, indicating appliance circuits do not have restrictions on the quantities of devices connected to them. Instead, the limits are a function of the power source, equipment design, wiring method, and area that is protected.

Neither the *Life Safety Code* nor NFPA 72 specify the styles of circuit that must be used for a given application. Unless the authority having jurisdiction specifies a certain style, it is up to the designer to make a selection. Once the quantity of devices and equipment for a given area have been determined, the designer can use the tables in NFPA 72 to select the appropriate circuit styles. For instance, initiating device circuits are designated as Styles A through E. The quantity of devices on a given floor might be such that NFPA 72 requires a Style D or E if all the devices are to be on the same circuit. Alternatively, the designer could choose to use two circuits meeting the performance requirements of Style B.

Some systems use emergency voice/alarm communication systems for occupant notification and fire department communication during a fire. These are often part of a local protective signaling system, forming what is called a "combination system." The circuits connected to speakers and lights are still referred to as indicating appliance circuits. Since these systems are most often used in high rise buildings or in areas subject to levels of hazard that are higher than normal, NFPA 72 contains requirements for survivability of the circuits during certain faults. By requiring the system to survive an attack by fire in certain locations, the standard narrows the choice of circuit styles and the methods of installation. For more information on these requirements, consult Chapter 10 of NFPA 72.

The discussion of circuits for controlling auxiliary functions, such as door release, fan control, and elevator recall, is beyond the scope of this supplement. Note, however, that the *Life Safety Code* may require these circuits to be supervised to within 3 feet of the device being controlled. See Chapter 7 of the *Life Safety Code* for more information on these circuits. NFPA 72, Chapter 3, also contains discussion of such ancillary functions.

Device Compatibility

Initiating devices and indicating appliances must be compatible with the control equipment to which they are connected. Where addressable, multiplex type equipment is used, there is no doubt that the equipment must be compatible and must be specifically designed to work together. However, with indicating appliances and conventional initiating devices, there is more flexibility in choice.

In the case of indicating appliances, compatibility is primarily a function of voltage and power consumption. Therefore, it is easy to match devices from one source with control equipment from another source. For initiating devices, compatibility depends on whether or not the device requires operating power. Mechanical devices such as manual pull stations, most heat detectors, and waterflow switches do not require power to operate. When they go into alarm, they close a set of contacts, as a light switch does, to signal the control panel. There is no compatibility issue here; these

devices can be mixed and matched among various manufacturers.

If a device does require operating power, as a smoke detector does, compatibility depends on whether its source of operating power comes from the initiating device circuit (often called the detection zone) or from a separate, external power circuit. Where power comes from a circuit other than the one used to signal the control panel, there is no compatibility issue. As in the case of indicating appliances, compatibility is then only a function of voltage and power consumption from the external power circuit. When the detector alarms, it closes a set of contacts to signal the control panel via the initiating device circuit in the same way a mechanical pull station does.

However, where a device such as a smoke detector obtains its operating power from the same circuit it uses to signal an alarm, compatibility is very important. These devices are often referred to as two-wire or zone-powered detectors. The electrical characteristics of the control panel and the detectors, including supervisory currents and alarm currents, must be carefully matched to ensure proper operation. Detector compatibility is a very complex issue. For more information on this subject, consult manufacturers' data sheets, NFPA 72E, the *Fire Alarm Signaling Systems Handbook*, and the approval or test agency's performance standards.

To check system compatibility, it is necessary to know the specific model of control panel as well as the model and quantity of the initiating device in question. Compatibility should be checked by consulting each manufacturer and the testing or approval agency acceptable to the authority having jurisdiction.

Wiring Methods

Article 760 of NFPA 70, the *National Electrical Code*, covers the installation of wiring for fire protective signaling systems operating at 600 volts or less. Two types of wiring methods are allowed by Article 760: Power-Limited and Nonpower-Limited. In order for a circuit to be designated as power-limited, it must meet certain voltage and power limitations. These are checked by the listing or approval agency. Where a circuit is designated as power-limited, the requirements for the wiring type and installation are less restrictive than if the circuit is nonpower-limited.

In addition to defining power-limited and nonpower-limited circuits, Article 760 provides detailed requirements for the wiring methods that can be used. Included are requirements for wire gages, insulation requirements, minimum requirements for stranded wires, overcurrent protection, circuit identification, and wiring raceways. Also included are restrictions on combining the use of power-limited and nonpower-limited circuits and other non-fire circuits in the same raceway or enclosure.

The *National Electrical Code* should be consulted for details on wiring requirements. Additional discussion of Article 760 is contained in the *National Electrical Code Handbook*, which provides explanation of the reasoning and intent behind specific code paragraphs.

Signaling

The subject of this section is output signaling, as opposed to the type of signaling discussed in the section on wiring, which occurs between detectors and control equipment. The principal signaling functions of a system are off-premises signaling to emergency forces and occupant notification.

Off-premises signaling may be transmitted to a central station in accordance with NFPA 71 or to systems such as an auxiliary system, a remote station system, or a proprietary signaling system in accordance with NFPA 72. Where off-premises signaling is required or desirable, NFPA 71 and NFPA 72 should be consulted concerning installation and performance requirements for the system. These standards contain requirements for both the protected premises system and the receiving system. The standards allow only certain signaling methods that have shown themselves to be reliable. Telephone tape dialers, for example, and digital communicators with only one phone line are not recognized by any of the standards.

Each occupancy chapter of the *Life Safety Code* clearly states where occupant notification and/or emergency forces signaling is required. The chapter may also require specific occupant notification systems, such as emergency voice communications systems in high rise hotels and dormitories. Each occupancy chapter should be carefully reviewed to determine which initiating devices are required to activate occupant notification signals and off-premises signaling. In most cases, all initiating devices operate as general alarm devices and activate all output functions. However, there are cases where detectors in specific areas of a building may not be required to sound evacuation signals.

Where occupant notification is required, it must be distinct and clearly audible in all occupiable spaces. NFPA 72G, *Guide for the Installation, Maintenance, and Use of Notification Appliances for Protective Signaling Systems*, and the appendix of NFPA 72 contain criteria for the definition of "audible." The recommended noise level from an alarm system is at least 15 dBA above the 24-hour average ambient level or at least 5 dBA above any peak background noise that lasts one minute or more; dBA stands for decibels, A-weighted. This is a way of measuring sound pressure levels and adjusting for the way the human ear hears.

The use of inexpensive meters (under $40.00) allows background levels in existing areas to be checked and systems to be installed appropriately. Ambient and fire alarm noise levels should be measured with all intervening doors closed and with common equipment such as air conditioners turned on. For new construction, NFPA 72G provides examples of ambient noise levels in a variety of occupancies.

Once background levels have been determined, design methods can be used to determine where notification appliances should be located. One such procedure is presented and discussed in the *SFPE Handbook of Fire Protection Engineering*, published by NFPA.

Calculations are not needed for existing construction. Portable appliances can be tried in a variety of locations before final mounting.

In most new construction, due to minimum insulation requirements and privacy laws, it is not possible to place alarm devices in common hallways and expect them to meet audibility requirements in adjacent spaces. Tests show that, in most cases, an audible device may be loud enough in only one or two adjacent spaces. Therefore, a large number of units would be required in the common halls of occupancies such as apartment or dormitories. Cost estimates often indicate that it is less expensive to put smaller devices in each space, rather than to provide the required number of larger devices in common spaces.

In addition to audible devices, the *Code* may require visual appliances for occupant notification. These are usually incandescent lights or strobe lights mounted with each audible device. Where audible devices are placed in dwelling units, visual devices may be required only in the common spaces. These visual devices are not intended to directly inform hearing impaired persons of the emergency. They are intended solely to provide visual verification to persons alerted by the audible signals. Where notification and alerting of hearing impaired persons is necessary, special devices and methods are available, but will not be discussed here.

The signal produced must also convey the information: FIRE EMERGENCY. This is where the requirement for distinct signals is applied. For instance, in a school, bells should not be used on a fire alarm system if bells are also used to signal class changes and recess. Similarly, in buildings equipped with earthquake warning systems, the fire signal needs to be distinct and recognizable by the occupants.

NFPA 72 does have a recommendation in the appendix for a standard evacuation signal. The signal, referred to as a temporal coded three signal, can be produced on a variety of appliances such as bells, horns, lights, speakers, chimes, etc. A coded three signal is recognized internationally as a distress signal. Thus, it would be the pattern of the signal, and not the particular sound, that would convey the information that there is a fire emergency. Some chapters of the *Life Safety Code* may require rather than simply recommend use of this signal for occupant notification.

Other types of signaling that might be required include:

1. Fan and damper control
2. Heating, ventilating, and air conditioning systems
3. Smoke control systems
4. Elevator control systems
5. Emergency lighting systems
6. Process control systems

The design, installation, testing, and maintenance of these systems should be performed by qualified fire protection engineers, technicians, and inspection professionals. Where activation of these or other emergency control systems is required by a chapter of the *Life Safety Code*, specific requirements are found in Chapter 7. One requirement is that any relay used for emergency control must be located and supervised to within 3 feet of the device being controlled. Additional requirements for the control equipment may be found in NFPA 72, and requirements for associated automatic fire detectors are found in NFPA 72E.

System Testing and Maintenance

Surveys and general field experience continue to demonstrate the importance of continued testing and maintenance of fire detection and signaling systems. Testing identifies problems before they impair a system's ability to perform during an emergency. Maintenance reduces false and nuisance alarms and keeps systems in service.

The *Life Safety Code* requires all fire detection and signaling equipment to be maintained and tested in accordance with the appropriate signaling standard. In the case of household fire warning equipment, NFPA 74 is the governing standard. For other systems, NFPA 72 contains requirements for acceptance and periodic tests and maintenance. Testing and maintenance requirements for automatic fire detectors are contained in NFPA 72E, which is referenced by NFPA 72. Central station systems are covered by NFPA 71.

NFPA 72H, *Guide for Testing Procedures for Local, Auxiliary, Remote Station, and Proprietary Protective Signaling Systems*, summarizes requirements from NFPA 72 and NFPA 72E and also contains recommended procedures for conducting acceptance tests and periodic tests. The guide is formatted to include a description of the device, equipment, or appliance; the test frequency (monthly, quarterly, annually, etc.); the recommended test procedure; and references to the appropriate source standard for the requirement. The appendix includes comments and descriptions of tests and test procedures for a variety of equipment types and circuit styles.

Whenever a system or device is to be tested, it is important to notify those who might hear or receive a signal from the system. Usually, this means several days of advance notice to authorities and regular occupants of the area. In addition, when testing or working on systems under NFPA 72, the authority having jurisdiction must be notified, even for periodic tests that they may not witness. Other trades or specialists may require notice in order to participate in the tests. For instance, testing of smoke detectors used for elevator recall may require elevator technicians to be present. Similarly, HVAC mechanics or electricians may be required to reset air-moving equipment or dampers after the system is tested. In addition, it is usually advisable to post notices at entrances to the premises to alert people as they arrive. Notices should include phone numbers or brief procedures for reporting emergencies while the system is being tested or serviced.

Household Fire Warning Equipment

The requirements for testing and maintenance of equipment in accordance with NFPA 74 are kept simple so that, in most cases, the work can be done by the homeowner. The standard recommends that the homeowner consider a testing and maintenance agreement if the homeowner is unable or unwilling to perform the necessary procedures.

The standard requires that battery-operated units get new batteries in accordance with the manufacturers' recommendations. In most but not all cases, manufacturers recommend replacement of batteries at least once a year. Recent educational and awareness programs have promoted battery changing at the same time that clocks are changed from daylight savings time to standard time in the fall of each year. Scheduled replacement tends to increase confidence that the detector will work when needed, rather than waiting for the signal that indicates the need for replacement. Facilities with large numbers of battery-operated detectors save time and labor by replacing all batteries at the same time, whether or not it is necessary.

Units with batteries are required to be tested at least once a week. Units with other power sources must be tested at least once per month. The lower frequency for nonbattery units reflects a higher confidence level in the availability of power.

All tests, inspections, and maintenance recommended by the manufacturer must be performed in accordance with its instructions. This emphasizes the importance of providing the owner, member of the household, or occupant with the manufacturer's instruction booklet(s). Without the proper documentation, the individuals performing the test may not be aware of their responsibilities or the correct methods for testing and maintenance. NFPA 74 requires the installer or supplier to provide this and other information to the owner. In addition to the instructions, the owner must receive information on how to establish an evacuation plan and information on parts that require regular replacement, such as batteries. The owner must also receive written information on where to obtain repair and replacement service.

Each smoke detector for use in an NFPA 74 application is required to have an integral test method to permit testing of the system and sensitivity. This is usually a test button or switch. Unless otherwise recommended by the manufacturer, this test button is the best way for the occupant to test the detector. By using the test button, the detector is checked for operation at the limit of sensitivity allowed by the ANSI/UL test standards for the detector. Using unmeasured aerosols such as cigarette smoke or canned smoke does not measure sensitivity. This might prove that a detector is operational, but the sensitivity may be so low that the amount of smoke required to alarm it is enough to have already caused harm or a delay in detector response to a real fire.

Cleaning of smoke detectors is necessary to prevent false and nuisance alarms and to ensure detector operation during a fire. NFPA 74 leaves the methods and frequency of cleaning up to each manufacturer. Most manufacturers recommend cleaning once or twice a year by vacuuming around the outside of the detector. Some detectors are now available that can be washed in a soap/water solution. Most manufacturers do not recommend disassembly of detectors for cleaning except by qualified technicians. If the detector is cleaned and properly maintained from the time it is new, the need for factory cleaning and calibration is almost eliminated.

Acceptance Testing

NFPA 72 requires 100 percent testing of the entire system upon completion of any installation or alteration. The test must include all devices and equipment and must test the system in all modes, including alarm, trouble, and supervisory. Satisfactory tests must be made in the presence of the authority having jurisdiction or a designated representative. NFPA 72H recognizes reacceptance tests on parts of systems affected by alterations or repairs, while NFPA 72 requires complete acceptance testing following any such work on a system. Commentary in the appendix of NFPA 72 refers the reader to NFPA 72H for information on how to conduct an acceptance test. The particular requirements are too numerous and detailed to be repeated here. Nevertheless, several key features of acceptance testing will be discussed.

A preliminary certificate of compliance is required to be issued to the owner and, if requested, to the authority having jurisdiction prior to the final acceptance test. The preliminary certificate is issued after installation and wiring tests have been completed. A final version is to be issued and distributed after all operational acceptance tests have been completed. A sample copy of a certificate of compliance is included in NFPA 72.

Following final acceptance of the system, the installer or supplier must provide the owner with an owner's manual or manufacturer's installation instruction as well as final "as-built" drawings. The definitions section of the standard describes in detail the information required on the custom, as-built drawings. During acceptance or reacceptance testing, the certificate of compliance and as-built drawings must be verified for accuracy and completeness. If necessary, corrections should be made to the master documents, and any old copies should be replaced or updated.

Installation testing includes checking the entire system for stray voltages, ground faults, short circuits, and open circuits. Ground fault testing includes testing all conductors not intentionally connected to ground. The test must check for isolation from ground in a way that will not damage any equipment connected to the circuit. This usually means that smoke detectors, indicating appliances, and other power-consuming devices must be removed from the circuit to prevent electrical damage and allow valid testing. Where removal of a detector or appliance from its base or from the circuit results in an open circuit, appropriate jumper wires should be installed to complete the circuit for testing. Conventional contact type devices, such as most heat detectors, pull stations, and waterflow switches can usually be left on the circuit during ground testing. However, it is important to check the electrical ratings of the contacts to ensure that test voltages do not damage the units. To prevent electrical damage, unless otherwise recommended by the manufacturer, circuit insulation testing should be completed before addressable or multiplex type devices are connected.

The loop resistance of initiating and indicating circuits must be measured and recorded. The measured value should be checked against the maximum allowable loop resistance indicated by the manufacturer of the control equipment. Signaling line circuits should also be tested in accordance with the manufacturer's recommendations. This will usually include measurement of circuit capacitance in addition to resistance.

System testing is done after all installation tests have been performed. After replacing any equipment removed during testing of the circuits, the control unit and all devices should be verified as being in the normal supervisory mode. Each circuit should be checked for proper supervision and integrity. This includes testing open circuit trouble indication as well as ground fault and short circuit fault indicators where provided. Where the style of circuit allows alarm receipt during specific faults, correct operation should be checked by

testing devices electrically before and after the location of the test fault. It is useful during the testing to use a copy of the wiring style tables from NFPA 72 as a checklist.

Every initiating device and indicating appliance must be checked for correct alarm operation. This verifies correct operation of the device, the circuit, and the control equipment. For systems that respond differently and result in different outputs depending on the device or devices in alarm, a programming matrix should be prepared and checked. The matrix, or system description, should explain what occurs when each particular device or group of devices is operated. For instance, an alarm from any first floor detector might cause bells to ring, doors to release, and a connection to the fire department to be activated. On the other hand, perhaps only certain smoke detectors will activate a smoke management system. The use of a table or matrix describing these options will speed testing and future work on the system.

Power supplies must also be tested during acceptance and reacceptance tests. This includes testing the switchover from primary to secondary power by disconnecting the primary supply. While the system is powered by the secondary supply, the standby current should be measured in accordance with the manufacturer's recommendations. The required standby capacity can then be calculated and compared to that which was provided. While on secondary power, the system should be tested for full alarm performance for at least five minutes. This test should be repeated with the system on primary power and with any secondary supply disconnected. Supervision of power supplies should also be tested.

Smoke detectors must be tested in accordance with NFPA 72E. During an acceptance test, it is no longer necessary to measure the detector's sensitivity (1990 Edition versus previous 1987 Edition). A pass/fail or go/no-go test using smoke or another unmeasured aerosol is acceptable, as is use of the detector's test mechanism. All smoke detectors, including duct and air sampling types, must be checked to ensure that smoke is entering the detector's chamber. In all cases, the manufacturer's directions should be followed.

NFPA 72E requires records of all testing and maintenance to be retained for at least five years. The NFPA 72 requirement is two years. All equipment should be tested in accordance with the requirements of the standards and the manufacturer's recommendations.

Periodic Testing

In addition to provisions for acceptance testing, NFPA 72 contains requirements for periodic tests and maintenance, while requirements for automatic fire detectors are contained in NFPA 72E. Essentially, the standards require all testing to be performed by qualified persons who understand the equipment. Ultimately, the owner of the system is responsible for ensuring that all required tests are done on time. Owners may rely on a written maintenance agreement with others rather than develop and use their own specialists.

The required frequency for testing a device varies. NFPA 72 contains the required frequencies for all devices except automatic fire detectors. As an example, waterflow devices must be tested every two months, while alarm indicating appliances must be tested only once per year. NFPA 72E requires smoke detectors to be tested at least annually. At least one restorable type heat detector must be tested on each initiating circuit every six months. Different heat detectors must be used during each test so that all are tested at least every five years.

In addition, some portion of the total system must be tested every month. Therefore, despite the fact that some tests are required only every year or more, the intent of the standard is best met by arranging for some portion of each device to be tested each month. For instance, if there were 100 smoke detectors on the system, 9 or 10 could be tested each month so that all are tested every year as required. Similarly, the devices being tested at each inspection should be on different circuits so that all or most circuits are checked at each monthly test. Consult NFPA 72, NFPA 72E, and NFPA 72H for specific test frequencies and recommended procedures. Additional requirements for central station systems are found in NFPA 71.

NFPA 72E requires the sensitivity of all smoke detectors to be checked within one year of the acceptance test, and then every other year. During the years when sensitivity tests are not required, a pass/fail test using smoke or another unmeasured aerosol is acceptable, as is use of the detector's test mechanism. The intent of the sensitivity test is to ensure that the detector is within its listed and marked sensitivity range. Detectors that are more than 0.25 percent per foot obscuration out of range must be recalibrated or replaced.

The standard lists acceptable methods for checking a smoke detector's operating sensitivity. The most common methods use either control panels that can check detector

sensitivity remotely or meters that plug into the detector for testing. In some cases, the meters are common volt-amp meters, and in other cases they are factory-supplied devices. There are also test instruments that generate measured smoke clouds that can be used to test any brand of detector. Using unmeasured aerosols such as cigarette smoke or canned smoke does not measure sensitivity. It might prove that a detector is operational, but the sensitivity might be so low that the amount of smoke required to cause an alarm is enough to have already caused harm or a delay in detector response to a real fire. On the other side of the issue, a detector might alarm when tested with cigarette smoke but be so sensitive that it would also nuisance alarm due to small amounts of friendly smoke.

In terms of smoke detector cleaning, the standard simply states that the frequency of service should be based on the ambient conditions. If the area is very clean, one to two years between cleaning may be possible. In very dusty or dirty areas, or areas with high airflow, cleaning might be required every three to six months. In most residential, business, and institutional type occupancies, yearly cleaning is usually sufficient. A sensitivity test must be performed on any detector that has been washed or disassembled for any reason, including cleaning.

Once a year, air duct smoke detectors must be checked to verify that they are properly sampling the air stream. The manufacturer's recommendations for testing should be followed. This may involve measuring the pressure difference between the sampling and air return tubes.

In addition to the NFPA 72 certification requirements, 72E lists minimum information that must be recorded and maintained whenever a system is tested or serviced.

Conclusions

Fire detection, alarm, and signaling systems range from very simple units to large complex systems. This supplement has only briefly introduced the reader to the many requirements and good practices associated with their design, installation, testing, and use.

The *Life Safety Code* and the NFPA standards that have been referenced and discussed contain a wealth of information for persons involved with any phase of a signaling system's life. By drawing on the expertise of hundreds of professionals and specialists, users of these NFPA documents benefit from years of combined experience, which no one person or company could hope to attain.

Bibliography

For additional information concerning the design, installation, testing, maintenance, and use of protective signaling systems, consult these references:

1. Bukowski, Richard W., O'Laughlin, Robert J., and Zimmerman, Charles E., ed., *Fire Alarm Signaling Systems Handbook*, National Fire Protection Association, Quincy, MA, 1987.
2. *Fire Protection Handbook*, 17th ed., National Fire Protection Association, Quincy, MA, 1991.
3. The *SFPE Handbook of Fire Protection Engineering*, National Fire Protection Association, Quincy, MA, 1988.
4. *Training Manual on Fire Alarm Systems*, National Electrical Manufacturers Association, 2101 L Street, Washington, D.C. 20037, 1985.
5. *Guide for Proper Use of System Smoke Detectors*, National Electrical Manufacturers Association, 2101 L Street, Washington, D.C. 20037, 1985.
6. *Guide for Proper Use of Smoke Detectors in Duct Applications*, National Electrical Manufacturers Association, 2101 L Street, Washington, D.C. 20037, 1985.
7. NFPA 71, *Standard for the Installation, Maintenance and Use of Signaling Systems for Central Station Service*, National Fire Protection Association, Quincy, MA, 1989.
8. NFPA 72, *Standard for the Installation, Maintenance, and Use of Protective Signaling Systems*, National Fire Protection Association, Quincy, MA, 1990.
9. NFPA 72E, *Standard on Automatic Fire Detectors*, National Fire Protection Association, Quincy, MA, 1990.
10. NFPA 72G, *Guide for the Installation, Maintenance, and Use of Notification Appliances for Protective Signaling Systems*, National Fire Protection Association, Quincy, MA, 1989.
11. NFPA 72H, *Guide for Testing Procedures for Local, Auxiliary, Remote Station, and Proprietary Protective Signaling Systems*, National Fire Protection Association, Quincy, MA, 1988.
12. NFPA 74, *Standard for the Installation, Maintenance and Use of Household Fire Warning Equipment*, National Fire Protection Association, Quincy, MA, 1989.
13. NFPA 90A, *Standard for the Installation of Air Conditioning and Ventilating Systems*, National Fire Protection Association, Quincy, MA, 1989.

In addition to the publications listed above and state and local authorities, the following organizations are sources for information on fire detection and signaling systems:

Automatic Fire Alarm Association, P.O. Box 1652, Barrington, IL 60011.

Factory Mutual System, P.O. Box 9102, Norwood, MA 02062.

National Fire Protection Association, 1 Batterymarch Park, Quincy, MA 02269-9101.

National Institute for Certification in Engineering Technologies, 1420 King Street, Alexandria, VA 22314-2715.

Underwriters Laboratories, Inc., 333 Pfingsten Road, Northbrook, IL 60062-2096.

3

Sprinkler Systems for Life Safety Code Users

Robert E. Solomon, P.E.

The very first edition of the *Life Safety Code*, which was published in 1927, addressed the use of sprinklers. During that period in history, it was widely believed that sprinklers were useful only in minimizing property damage. This assumption is not surprising since, in 1896, insurance companies were concerned with property protection issues when they agreed on the first set of rules for sprinkler installations. This first meeting of the newly formed organization, NFPA, was for the exclusive purpose of trying to standardize rules for sprinkler systems and the new technology called electricity.

NFPA 13, *Standard for the Installation of Sprinkler Systems*, was first published in 1896 by the NFPA. Many of the same underlying principles considered in that first edition are still important in 1991. Specifically, systems must be designed with an adequate, reliable water supply; the systems must be limited in size to make certain that protection impairments have minimal effect on the building; the systems must have auxiliary connections to permit the fire department to supplement the automatic water supply.

Since the first edition of NFPA 13 was published, the technology associated with the design and installation of an automatic sprinkler system has resulted in systems that are more reliable, easier to design, easier to install, and reasonable in cost for the building owner. No other fire protection system, active or passive, required by NFPA 101 results in a higher level of protection to the building occupants. The effectiveness of a sprinkler system is further enhanced where used as part of a "package" of fire protection features, such as detection and compartmentation.

The NFPA Sprinkler Standards

The NFPA currently publishes three sprinkler standards that are required by certain provisions of this *Code*. The most commonly used standard is NFPA 13, *Standard for the Installation of Sprinkler Systems*. This document should be considered as the commercial building standard, since its use normally addresses public domain buildings.

NFPA 13 is the oldest of the sprinkler standards and is generally used to design and install sprinklers in occupancies such as public assembly, educational, detention, health care, residential exceeding four stories in height, business, mercantile, and most industrial occupancies.

This standard requires the installation of sprinklers throughout a building or structure. There are some areas (e.g., bathrooms 55 square feet and less, with noncombustible plumbing fixtures in hotels, and certain concealed combustible spaces) where the standard specifically exempts the requirement for sprinklers. Users of the *Life Safety Code* are aware of certain situations in which partial- or limited-area sprinkler systems are permitted.

An example of such a situation involves the Option 3 protection scheme for existing apartment buildings (*see 19-3.5*). This concept is not considered in NFPA 13 because of the dual goals of NFPA 13: to protect life and to protect property. The differences between NFPA 13 and NFPA 101 with respect to sprinkler requirements can best be explained by the need to protect property as well as human life, as expressed in NFPA 13. Areas exempted from requiring sprinklers in this *Code* are those in which sprinklers would not be expected to have an impact on the number of injuries or fatalities from a fire. That same fire, however, might result in significant property damage; therefore, NFPA 13 contains no similar exemptions.

NFPA 13R, *Standard for the Installation of Sprinkler Systems in Residential Occupancies up to and Including Four Stories in Height*, is a relatively new document, the first edition having been published in 1989. The scope of this standard is limited to apartments, hotels, motels, select board and care facilities, and rooming houses. This standard is intended to provide a high but not absolute level of life safety to building occupants and a lesser degree of property protection.

NFPA 13R was developed in response to the changing threshold value for sprinkler protection in many of the state and model codes used in the United States. Many codes are being revised to require sprinklers in multifamily residential occupancies. While NFPA 13 would be acceptable for application in such properties, it was determined that a different set of requirements would be created to provide additional life safety to occupants and to provide some level of property protection.

NFPA 13R considers the economics of sprinkler protection by allowing omission of sprinklers from numerous areas. Such omissions result in the need for less hardware and therefore less labor to install the systems. This results in reduced cost to the building owner. By virtue of several exceptions in NFPA 13R, sprinklers may be omitted from select bathrooms, closets, porches, balconies, carports, garages, and concealed spaces that contain combustible construction material. A significant area from which sprinklers are excepted is the attic. In most parts of the U.S., an attic would require the use of a dry pipe system or an antifreeze system.

The primary distinction between NFPA 13 and NFPA 13R is the designation of those areas where sprinklers are required and are not required. Other differences are minimal, since features such as water supply, materials, and design rules are identical. NFPA 13R is specified for use in numerous occupancies by this *Code*, including those discussed in Chapters 16 through 23.

NFPA 13D, *Standard for the Installation of Sprinkler Systems in One- and Two-Family Dwellings*, is also a relatively new standard. The first edition of this document was released by the Technical Committee on Automatic Sprinklers in 1975 and was prepared in response to "America Burning: The Report of the Commission on Fire Prevention and Control," which was released in 1973. This report revealed that, of the estimated 12,000 fire deaths occurring in the U.S. each year, a disproportionate number of these fatalities take place in the home. The commission recommended that research be carried forward to determine the feasibility of a low cost fire protection system for the home.

The first edition of NFPA 13D was an attempt to fulfill this broad-based goal and involved the use of the same technology used to protect commercial properties, with exceptions to sprinkler protection in select areas. In order to help achieve the low cost objective established by the commission, the first edition also permitted a 10-minute water supply. Shortly after this first edition was published, the United States Fire Administration announced a program to make an NFPA 13D system a true life safety system.

Automatic sprinkler systems have been very beneficial in reducing loss of life due to fire, primarily by providing protection to occupants of areas adjacent to the room of fire origin. The aim of the research program conducted under the guidance of the USFA was to develop a sprinkler device that would control a fire in time to permit an occupant in that room to escape. The combination of response time, discharge characteristics, and duration of discharge were some of the attributes used to develop the residential sprinkler, the first of the fast response sprinklers. The 1980 Edition of NFPA 13D incorporated this new technology.

System Components and Hardware

The design and installation of any sprinkler system involves the use of many similar components and concepts. For example, all systems must utilize a series of pipe networks to allow delivery of water to the sprinklers in the system; this pipe network must be supported with hangers; a set of control valves must be used to permit the system or portions of the system to be isolated for any reason; and the system must be equipped with some type of alarm mechanism to notify building occupants or others that water is flowing in the system. All of these features must be considered together to ensure reliable system performance.

The types of material permitted for use in sprinkler systems have, in many instances, both changed dramatically and remained unchanged during the last 100 years. For example, steel pipe has been the prominent material used in these systems for many years. Beginning in the 1950s, copper tubing was introduced as an acceptable material, but its use was not fully recognized by NFPA 13 until 1965. The standard currently allows three different types of copper tubing to be used.

Selection of acceptable pipe materials is based upon several factors. An advantage of one material may be a liability for another material. For example, the advantage of using a lighter material such as copper or nonmetallic pipe may be negated by the need to follow very specific manufacturer's technical data sheets to ensure correct installation. Traditional steel pipe (schedule 40 pipe) may be more forgiving when threading or cut grooving the ends. In this instance, the tradeoff involves greater weight per foot of pipe.

Some sprinkler contractors prefer the use of copper tube or nonmetallic pipe for the installation of new systems in existing buildings. The advantage of lightweight features plus the flexibility associated with these materials should be considered. These combined features can result in reduced labor costs. Each material permitted has distinct advantages and disadvantages. In most cases, the material used for a sprinkler system is determined by the capabilities and comfort level of the installing contractor.

In 1984, the Shell Oil Company made a significant breakthrough in sprinkler system component technology when it introduced the first nonmetallic pipe for sprinkler systems. This material, polybutylene pipe, was initially permitted only for use in systems designed under the requirements of NFPA

13D. In 1985, permission for its use was extended to all light hazard occupancies as defined by NFPA 13. This material continues to be acceptable for use in these categories as well as those in NFPA 13R.

Another nonmetallic product was placed on the market in 1986. The Goodrich Tire and Rubber Company developed a resin and licensed several manufacturers to produce chlorinated polyvinyl chloride (CPVC) pipe. This pipe is fully recognized as an acceptable component in sprinkler system design in 1991. Its use is also limited to light hazard occupancies as defined by NFPA 13 and to systems designed using NFPA 13D and NFPA 13R.

While both nonmetallic pipes are acceptable, each has a unique set of installation restrictions and rules. These include but are not limited to: use only in wetpipe systems; mandatory installation behind a protective barrier, such as a ceiling (note: the CPVC product may be installed exposed under special conditions); and support in accordance with the manufacturer's instructions.

As previously mentioned, the use of steel pipe is still quite common. The fabrication of steel pipe has also changed significantly in the last 100 years. Thin wall steel pipe and light wall steel pipe have been made available for use in sprinkler systems. These materials result in somewhat better hydraulic characteristics and are easier to handle due to their lighter weight.

In addition to the advent of these special materials, a myriad of special fittings have accompanied the development of these materials. These fittings usually make the fabrication of a system easier, but they sometimes result in the introduction of higher than normal friction loss characteristics. Such features require the designer to follow the listing instructions and the manufacturer's instructions for proper use.

A number of specially listed fittings are available for use. These materials are evaluated for their compatibility with specific types of pipe and their ability to be installed in a relatively effortless manner. Grooved end fittings, for example, are only listed for use with specific types of listed rubber gaskets. In most cases, both the fitting and the gasket are made by the same manufacturer. The availability of such fittings permits the installation of the system to proceed on course, but it requires additional vigilance of the authority having jurisdiction to verify the compatibility of the assemblies.

Any sprinkler system must rely on several key components in order to ensure proper system response to a fire event.

Of these components, perhaps none is as singularly important as the automatic sprinkler itself. Sprinklers vary in shape and form. They also differ according to their use or purpose. When the first "conventional" sprinkler was developed in the 1870s, it was primarily intended for use in industrial and warehouse environments. After 120 years of experience with this device in the U.S., the technology for sprinklers has advanced farther than any other sprinkler system component.

The biggest advances in sprinkler technology have evolved in further pursuing the basic goals of a sprinkler system. Since 1896, sprinklers have been designed to control fire growth rather than to suppress or extinguish the fire. This concept was especially evident when the residential sprinkler program was undertaken in the mid 1970s. The program focused on and resulted in the production of listed residential sprinklers. These particular devices are designed to provide a tenable environment for the occupants in the room of fire origin. It is not intended to protect an occupant in the room of fire origin who is intimate with the ignition source.

While residential sprinklers were specifically developed for use in NFPA 13D systems, they are now acceptable for use in any of the residential occupancies that are governed by NFPA 13R and NFPA 13. These devices are currently listed using Underwriters Laboratories 1626, *Standard for Residential Sprinklers*. This standard provides evaluation criteria that determine the device's ability to minimize the air temperature at a level 5 feet above the floor and to minimize the carbon monoxide level in the fire room. In addition, the operation of the device is also tested its for ability to respond to a fire at a very early stage.

During its use over the course of approximately 11 years, this device has been responsible for several "saves," which have been documented by "Operation Life Safety," a program conducted by the International Association of Fire Chiefs. The devices performed as intended in fires characterized by a wide range of circumstances.

A direct result of the residential sprinkler program was the development of the listed quick response sprinkler (QR). Listed QR sprinklers, while having the same fast response characteristics as a listed residential sprinkler, are permitted to be used in both residential and nonresidential occupancies. This device has a somewhat different discharge geometry than a residential sprinkler. Therefore, it is not specifically designed to protect occupants in the room of fire origin, although it will likely provide a somewhat higher level of protection to occupants than a standard response sprinkler.

The QR sprinkler is evaluated under UL 199, *Standard for Automatic Sprinklers for Fire Protection Service*. This standard is used to evaluate the effectiveness of QR as well as other nonresidential sprinklers. There is a tendency to use the terms "residential sprinkler" and "quick response sprinkler" interchangeably. These two devices are completely different in terms of their intended use, discharge characteristics, and positioning requirements. In some cases, this *Code* mandates the use of one of these types of sprinklers. For example, see Section 3-5 in the chapters dealing with residential and health care occupancies.

In order to distinguish between listed residential and listed QR sprinklers, they should be considered as falling into a general category of "fast response" sprinklers. The following table serves as a reference to the fast response sprinkler category.

Fast Response Sprinklers

Residential Sprinklers	Quick Response Sprinklers
Tested by the UL 1626, *Standard for Residential Sprinklers*. Installed in accordance with NFPA 13, 13D, and 13R.	Tested by the UL 199, *Standard for Automatic Sprinklers for Fire Protection Service*. Installed in accordance with NFPA 13 and NFPA 13R under special conditions.

A total of 23 different types of sprinklers have been developed for use. Sprinklers have literally become a speciality item, considering the form and function of sprinklers in today's market. For example, sprinklers are now available with custom color finishes that can be used to help camouflage the sprinkler. Other devices have been developed that are low profile and streamlined to the point where they are very difficult to notice. Other sprinklers can be installed behind special concealed plates that are coated to match the ceiling background. It is important to note that these color schemes are limited to a small number of colors and that such coatings can be applied only by the sprinkler manufacturer.

Another category of sprinkler is the "extended coverage" (EC) sprinkler. As its name implies, this device is tested and listed to cover very large areas. For example, some of these sprinklers are capable of covering a 20 ft × 20 ft area. The tradeoff for this coverage is a rather demanding pressure and flow rate. In addition, an extended coverage sprinkler must also have a more sensitive operating element, since the sprinkler can be located at a distance farther from a fire. In addition, some EC sprinklers are equipped with a fast response sprinkler element. These are quick response extended coverage (QREC) sprinklers.

Because of the number of specially listed sprinklers available today and because of the device-dependent design concept used for so many systems, all sprinklers are required to have an identification code consisting of two, three, or four letters stamped on the device. In addition, other characteristics of the sprinkler might also be imprinted on the device. These additional items can include the temperature rating and the orifice diameter. A sampling of the letter codes that can be found on a particular sprinkler include the following:

Standard Spray Pendent ....SSP

Standard Spray Upright ....SSU

Extended Coverage...EC

Quick Response..QR

Quick Response Extended Coverage..................QREC

Residential ....RES

It is important to look closely at a sprinkler to determine its type, since type will not be immediately apparent through casual observation.

The following photos show four types of sprinklers as referenced above. None is equipped with an obvious feature that permits immediate identification to be made.

Figure 1 shows a Grinnell Standard Spray Pendent Sprinkler. The use of this type of device is quite common, and it is the oldest of the current generation of sprinklers.

Figure 2 shows a Viking Model M Pendent Mounted Extended Coverage Sprinkler. This device would be selected to provide sprinkler protection for areas up to 400 square feet using a single sprinkler. This device requires that special design provisions be followed, such as a higher than normal operating pressure.

A Viking Upright Mounted Quick Response Sprinkler is shown in Figure 3. This device offers the option of the fast response operating element. It does not, however, require any unusual design or installation parameters.

Figure 4 shows a Viking Horizontal Sidewall Residential Sprinkler. This device is tested in accordance with UL 1626, which was previously discussed. This sprinkler requires specific design criteria depending on the nature of the residential occupancy in which it is being installed. In general, the total flow rate is determined by installation in accordance with NFPA 13, 13D, or 13R, as appropriate, and the listing restrictions of a given device. The location of the device is governed by the appropriate standard, while the position and spacing are governed solely by NFPA 13D.

These special sprinklers are, in one respect or another, derived from the first sprinkler developed in 1870. The three basic forms of sprinklers are the upright, pendent, and sidewall types. The special sprinklers discussed above exist in these three basic forms. A major exception is the lack of a listed, upright residential sprinkler.

In the case of high challenge fires, such as those found in warehouses, large drop and early suppression fast response (ESFR) sprinklers are offered as an alternative to the standard sprinkler. These devices apply the technology of fire dynamics and the interface of water on that process.

The large drop sprinkler program was managed by the Factory Mutual Corporation. The purpose of this program was to develop a device that could produce a water droplet of sufficient size and mass to penetrate the fire plume that accompanies warehouse type fires.

In 1988, Factory Mutual granted approval for the ESFR sprinkler. This device is designed to deliver a large quantity of water to the surface of the burning material. The ability of this sprinkler to suppress the fire, as opposed to controlling it, is dependent on the combination of fast response features, the discharge of sufficient quantities of water from the sprinkler (100 gallons per minute from each sprinkler), and the ability of the water to penetrate the upward momentum of the fire plume and reach the surface of the burning commodity.

While both of these devices are intended for use in select high challenge fire scenarios, they are not specified for use in this *Code*. In any case, regardless of which type of sprinkler is intended for use in any type of occupancy, it is imperative that the appropriate NFPA sprinkler standard be used for designing and installing these systems.

Figure 1. *Grinnell Standard Spray Pendent Sprinkler.*

Figure 3. *Viking Upright Mounted Quick Response Sprinkler.*

Figure 2. *Viking Model M Pendent Mounted Extended Coverage Sprinkler.*

Figure 4. *Viking Horizontal Sidewall Residential Sprinkler.*

NFPA 13 Occupancy Hazards

The use of the term "occupancy hazards" as associated with the design of a sprinkler system is sometimes confused with the "hazard of occupancy" concept used in the *Life Safety Code*. The use of these similar terms is intentional, but their meanings connote separate and distinct ideas. "Hazard of occupancy," as used in this *Code*, refers to the relative threat to building occupants from the contents of that building.

When a sprinkler design is being considered, the hazard category is used to determine the relative challenge to the sprinkler system's ability to control the fire. The 1989 Edition of NFPA 13 discusses six categories of occupancy hazard. These categories range from the least severe (light hazard) to the most severe (extra hazard). Fundamentally, the less severe the fire potential, the smaller the total amount of water necessary to control the fire. Likewise, the more severe the fire potential, the larger the total amount of water necessary to control the fire.

NFPA 13 provides a comprehensive list of occupancy hazards, which can be used to determine the design parameters for a given system. In the same way that Chapter 4 of this *Code* provides a listing of occupancies and hazard of contents, the appendix to NFPA 13 provides a list of occupancies. Examples of how these occupancy categories compare with one another are shown in Table 1.

NFPA 13/101 Occupancies

Occupancy	NFPA 13	NFPA 101
Assembly	Light Hazard	Ordinary Hazard
Health Care	Light Hazard	Ordinary Hazard
Mercantile	Ordinary Hazard	Ordinary Hazard
Storage	Ordinary Hazard	Ordinary Hazard
Industrial	Extra Hazard	High Hazard
(using flammable and combustible liquids)		

This table lists a small percentage of occupancy types and is subject to change. The contents of any building are typically not a pure commodity. For example, an educational facility would typically be treated as a light hazard occupancy for purposes of the sprinkler system design. This holds true for the classrooms, offices, and seating areas in the cafeteria. If the facility is equipped with a wood shop area, lab-oratory, and food preparation area, light hazard classification is no longer valid. Since these areas would be expected to contain more hazardous materials with a higher heat release rate, the sprinkler system design features must be adjusted for these areas. The other areas mentioned would be treated as ordinary hazard occupancies.

The more severe the hazard, the greater the amount of water to be delivered by the sprinkler system. The total water demand that must be available to the sprinkler system includes an allowance for the use of exterior hose streams by the fire department. The quantity of water necessary for this purpose is directly dependent upon the occupancy hazard as determined by NFPA 13.

This hose stream allowance is absolutely critical because of the nature of sprinkler system design. As previously noted in this supplement, sprinkler systems are designed to control rather than extinguish the fire. The hose allowance is necessary to permit ultimate extinguishment of the fire.

Summary

The history and effectiveness of automatic sprinkler systems has been well documented over the last 100 years. This effectiveness is best summed up in the NFPA statement on sprinklers:

"NFPA has no record of a fire killing more than two people in a completely sprinklered building where the system was properly operating, except in an explosion or flash fire or where industrial or fire brigade members or employees were killed during fire suppression operations."

This statement is impressive because it refers back to the turn of the century, when the use of sprinkler systems was considered as an emerging technology. Changes to NFPA 13 in terms of the options available to the designer and the installer have made these systems more economical and, at the same time, more efficient. As sprinkler technology evolves, the time is near when the option of designing a sprinkler system to suppress fire, as opposed to controlling fire, is at hand.

Through the combined efforts of the National Fire Protection Research Foundation and the numerous organizations that support it, new breakthroughs occur each year that improve the effectiveness of sprinkler systems. These research endeavors result in devices and components that further enhance the already proven record of sprinkler systems.

For those interested in further information on sprinkler system design and theory, the following texts are recommended:

1. John L. Bryan, *Automatic Sprinkler and Standpipe Systems*, 2nd ed., National Fire Protection Association, Quincy, MA, 1990.
2. *Automatic Sprinkler Systems Handbook*, 4th ed., National Fire Protection Association, Quincy, MA, 1989.

3. *SFPE Handbook of Fire Protection Engineering*, 1st ed., Society of Fire Protection Engineers, National Fire Protection Association, Quincy, MA, 1988.

The following report from NFPA discusses the effectiveness of automatic sprinklers:

4. John Hall, Jr., *U.S. Experience with Sprinklers: Who Has Them? How Well Do They Work?*, National Fire Protection Association, Quincy, MA, 1990.

4

Extracts from ASME Elevator Code and Handbook

Extracts from ASME A17.1, *Safety Code for Elevators and Escalators**

Section 211 Emergency Operation and Signaling Devices

Rule 211.3 Firefighters' Service — Automatic Elevators

All automatic (non-designated attendant) elevators having a travel of 25 ft (7.62 m) or more shall conform to the requirements of this Rule.

211.3a Phase I Emergency Recall Operation.

A three-position key-operated switch shall be provided only at the designated level for each single elevator or for each group of elevators. The three-position switch shall be marked "ON," "OFF," and "BYPASS" with the "OFF" position as the center position. The three-position switch shall be located in the lobby within sight of the elevator or all elevators in that group and shall not be located behind a locked door or cover. An additional two-position ("OFF" and "ON") key-operated switch may be provided at any location. All keys shall be removable only in the "OFF" and "ON" positions.

No device, other than the Phase I switch(es) or the smoke detectors in the elevator lobbies, machine room or hoistway (Rule 211.3b), shall initiate Phase I operation.

Normal elevator service shall be provided and the operation from the smoke detectors required by Rule 211.3b shall be functional when all Phase I switches are in the "OFF" position, except as specified in Rule 211.3a(10).

When the designated-level three-position switch is in the "BYPASS" position, normal elevator service shall be restored regardless of the status of the smoke detectors required by Rule 211.3b.

When a switch is in the "ON" position:
(1) All cars controlled by this switch which are on automatic service shall return nonstop to the designated level and power-operated doors shall open and remain open.

*Reprinted with permission from the American Society of Mechanical Engineers, 345 E. 47th St., New York, New York 10017.

(2) A car traveling away from the designated level shall reverse at or before the next available landing without opening its doors.

(3) A car stopped at a landing shall have the in-car emergency stop switch or in-car stop switch rendered inoperative as soon as the car moves away from the landing. A moving car shall have the in-car emergency stop switch or in-car stop switch rendered inoperative without delay. Once the in-car emergency stop switch or in-car stop switch has been rendered inoperative, it shall remain inoperative while the car is on Phase I operation. All other stop switches required by Rule 210.2 shall remain operative.

(4) A car standing at a landing other than the designated level, with the doors open and the in-car emergency stop switch or in-car stop switch in the run position, shall conform to the following:

(a) Elevators having automatic power-operated horizontally sliding doors shall close the doors without delay and proceed to the designated level.

(b) Elevators having power-operated vertically sliding doors provided with automatic or momentary pressure closing operation per Rule 112.3d shall have the closing sequence initiated without delay in accordance with Rule 112.3d(1), (2), (3), and (5), and the car shall proceed to the designated level.

(c) Elevators having power-operated doors provided with continuous pressure closing operation per Rule 112.3b or elevators having manual doors, shall be provided with a visual and audible signal system to alert an operator to close the doors and shall, when the doors are closed, conform to the requirements of Rule 211.3a. Sequence operation, if provided, shall remain effective.

(5) Door reopening devices for power-operated doors which are sensitive to smoke or flame shall be rendered inoperative without delay. Door reopening devices not sensitive to smoke or flame (e.g., mechanically actuated devices) are permitted to remain operative. Door closing for power-operated doors shall conform to the requirements of Rule 112.5.

(6) All car and corridor call buttons shall be rendered inoperative. All car registered lights and directional lanterns shall be extinguished and remain inoperative. Position indicators, where provided, shall remain in service.

(7) Where provided on installations with vertical slide doors, corridor door open and corridor door close buttons shall remain operative.

(8) All cars shall be provided with an illuminated visual and audible signal system which shall be activated to alert the passengers that the car is returning nonstop to the designated level. The visual graphic shall be as shown in Fig. 211.3a. The signals shall remain activated until the car has returned to the designated level.

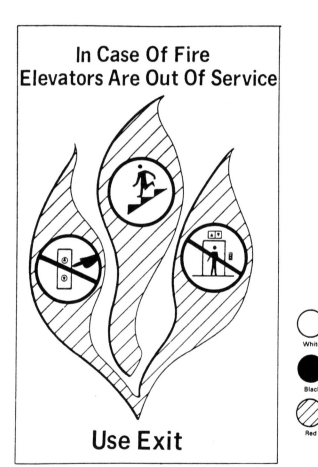

Figure 211.3a. Visual Signal.

(9) A car stopped at a landing shall have the in-car door open button rendered inoperative as soon as the car moves away from the landing. A moving car shall have the in-car door open button rendered inoperative without delay. Once the in-car door open button has been rendered inoperative, it shall remain inoperative until the car has returned to the designated level.

(10) If an additional two-position Phase I switch is provided, it shall not affect Phase I operation if the designated-level smoke detector [Rule 211.3b(2)] has been activated.

(11) The "BYPASS" position on the three-position Phase I switch shall not restore the elevator to normal service if the two-position Phase I switch is in the "ON" position.

211.3b Smoke Detectors.

Smoke detectors shall be installed in each elevator lobby at each landing and associated machine room in accordance with NFPA 72E, Chapter 4. Smoke detectors are not required in elevator lobbies at unenclosed landings. Smoke detectors may be installed in any hoistway and shall be installed in hoistways which are sprinklered (see Rule 102.2).

(1) The activation of a smoke detector in any elevator lobby, other than at the designated level, shall cause all cars that serve that lobby to return nonstop to the designated level. The activation of a smoke detector in any elevator machine room shall cause all elevators having any equipment located in that machine room, and any associated elevators of a group automatic operation, to return nonstop to the designated level. The activation of a smoke detector in any elevator hoistway shall cause all elevators having any equipment located in the hoistway, and any associated elevators of a group automatic operation, to return nonstop to the designated level. The operation shall conform to the requirements of Rule 211.3a.

(2) If the smoke detector at the designated level is activated, the operation shall conform to the requirements of Rule 211.3a, except that the cars shall return to an alternate level approved by the enforcing authority, unless the designated-level three-position Phase I switch (Rule 211.3a) is in the "ON" position.

(3) Elevators shall only react to the first smoke detector zone which is activated for that group.

(4) Phase I operation, when initiated by a smoke detector, shall be maintained until cancelled by moving the Phase I Switch to the "BYPASS" position [also see Rule 211.3a(10)]. Smoke detectors and/or smoke detector systems shall not be self-resetting.

NOTE (Rule 211.3b):   In buildings with fire alarm systems, see NFPA 72A for additional information.

211.3c Phase II Emergency In-Car Operation.

A three-position ("OFF," "HOLD," and "ON," in that order) key-operated switch shall be provided in an operating panel in each car. It shall become effective only when the designated level Phase I switch (Rule 211.3a) is in the "ON" position or a smoke detector (Rule 211.3b) has been activated, and the car has returned to the designated or alternate level by Phase I operation.

The key shall be removable in each position. The "OFF," "HOLD," and "ON" positions shall not change the operation until the car is at a landing with the doors in the normal open position.

(1) When the Phase II switch is in the "ON" position, the elevator shall be on Phase II operation, for use by trained emergency service personnel only, and the elevator shall operate as follows:

(a) The elevator shall be operable only by a person in the car.

(b) All corridor call buttons and directional lanterns shall remain inoperative.

(c) The opening of power-operated doors shall be controlled only by a continuous pressure door open button. If the button is released prior to the doors reaching the normal open position, the doors shall automatically reclose. Rules 112.4(a), 112.3c, and 112.3d do not apply. On cars with two entrances, if both entrances can be opened at the same landing, separate door-open buttons shall be provided for each entrance.

(d) Open power-operated doors shall be closed only by continuous pressure on the door close button. If the button is released prior to the doors reaching the fully closed position, horizontally sliding doors shall automatically reopen and vertically sliding doors shall automatically stop or stop and reopen. On cars with two entrances, if both entrances can be opened at the same landing, a separate door-close button shall be provided for each entrance.

(e) Opening and closing of power operated car doors or gates which are opposite manual swing or manual slide hoistway doors shall conform to the requirements of Rules 211.3c(1)(c) and (d). Door opening and closing buttons shall be provided in the car operating panel.

(f) All door reopening devices shall be rendered inoperative. Full speed closing is permitted. Corridor door opening and closing buttons, if provided, shall be rendered inoperative.

(g) Every car shall be provided with a button marked "CALL CANCEL," located in the same car operating panel as the Phase II switch, which shall be effective during Phase II operation. When activated, all registered calls shall be cancelled and a traveling car shall stop at or before the next available landing.

(h) Floor selection buttons shall be provided in the car to permit travel to all landings served by the car. Means which prevent the operation of the floor selection buttons or door operating buttons shall be rendered inoperative.

(i) A traveling car shall stop at the next available landing for which a car call was registered. When a car stops at a landing, all registered car calls shall be cancelled.

(2) When the Phase II switch is in the "HOLD" position, the elevator shall be on Phase II operation. The car shall remain at the landing with its doors open. The door close buttons shall be inoperative.

(3) When the Phase II switch is in the "OFF" position, the elevator is not at the designated level, and Phase I operation is in effect, the car shall revert to Phase I operation (Rule 211.3a) upon completion of door closing. Vertically sliding doors are not required to conform to the requirements of Rules 112.3d(3) and 112.5 when the doors can only be closed by continuous pressure means.

(4) When the Phase II switch is in the "OFF" position and the car is not at the designated level, and Phase I is not in effect, the car shall remain at the landing with the doors open and door-close buttons inoperative.

(5) Elevators shall only be removed from Phase II operation when:

(a) the Phase II switch is in the "OFF" position and the car is at the designated level with the doors in the normal open position; or

(b) the Phase II switch is in the "OFF" position when Phase I is in effect [Rule 211.3c(3)].

211.3d Interruption of Power.

Upon the resumption of power (normal, emergency, or standby), the car may move to reestablish absolute car position. Restoration of electrical power following a power interruption shall not cause any elevator to be removed from Phase I or Phase II operation.

211.3e Multideck Elevators.

Multideck elevators shall also conform to the following requirements:
(1) The Phase I switch (Rule 211.3a) shall be located at the designated level served by the upper deck.
(2) The Phase II switch (Rule 211.3c) shall be located in the upper compartment. The elevator shall be provided with a means for placing the lower deck out of service, located in that deck or adjacent to the entrance at the lower lobby landing.

Rule 211.4 Firefighters' Service — Non-Automatic Elevators

All non-automatic elevators having a travel of 25 ft (7.62 m) or more shall conform to the requirements of this Rule.

211.4a Phase I Emergency Recall Operation.

A three-position key-operated switch shall be provided only at the designated level for each single elevator or for each group of elevators. The three-position switch shall be marked "ON," "OFF," and "BYPASS" with the "OFF" position as the center position. An additional two-position ("OFF" and "ON") key-operated switch may be provided at any location; however, it shall not affect Phase I operation if the designated-level smoke detector (Rule 211.4b) has been activated. All keys shall be removable only in the "OFF" and "ON" positions.

No device, other than the Phase I switch(es) or the smoke detectors in the elevator lobbies, machine room, or hoistway shall initiate Phase I operation.

When all switches are in the "OFF" position, normal elevator service shall be retained and operation from the smoke detectors required by Rule 211.4b shall be functional.

When the designated-level three-position switch is in the "BYPASS" position, normal elevator service shall be restored independent of the smoke detectors required by Rule 211.4b.

A visual and audible signal shall be provided to alert the attendant to return nonstop to the designated or alternate level. The visual signal shall read "FIRE RECALL — RETURN TO [insert level to which the car should be returned (the designated or alternate level)]." The signal system shall be activated when Phase I is in effect.

If an additional two-position Phase I switch is provided, it shall not affect the visual signal if the designated-level smoke detector [Rule 211.3b(2)] has been activated.

The "BYPASS" position on the three-position Phase I switch shall not restore the elevator to normal service if the two-position Phase I switch is in the "ON" position.

Rule 211.4b Smoke Detectors.

Smoke detectors shall be installed in each elevator lobby at each floor and associated machine room in accordance with NFPA 72E, Chapter 4. Smoke detectors are not required in elevator lobbies at unenclosed landings. Smoke detectors may be installed in any hoistway and shall be installed in hoistways which are sprinklered (see Rule 102.2).

Phase I operation, conforming to Rule 211.4a, shall be initiated when any smoke detector in the elevator lobbies, machine room, or hoistway is activated.

Phase I operation, when initiated by a smoke detector, shall be maintained until cancelled by moving the Phase I Switch to the "BYPASS" position. Smoke detectors and/or smoke detector systems shall not be self-resetting.

Rule 211.5 Firefighters' Service — Automatic Elevators With Designated Attendant Operation

(a) When on without-designated-attendant operation, elevators shall conform to the requirements of Rule 211.3.

(b) When operated by a designated attendant in the car (except hospital service):
(1) elevators parked at a floor shall conform to the requirements of Rule 211.3a(8). At the completion of a time delay of not less than 15 sec nor more than 60 sec, elevators shall conform to the requirements of Rule 211.3.
(2) a moving car shall conform to the requirements of Rule 211.3.

(c) When operated by a designated attendant in the car on hospital service, the visual and audible signal shall activate while Phase I is in effect.

Rule 211.6 Firefighters' Service — Inspection Operation

When an elevator which is provided with firefighters' service is on inspection operation, a continuous audible signal which is audible on top of the car shall sound when the Phase I switch(es) (Rule 211.3a) is in the "ON" position or when the smoke detector (Rule 211.3b) is activated to alert the operator of an emergency. Car shall remain under the control of the operator until removed from inspection operation or hoistway access operation. The top of car operating device (Rule 210.1d) shall take precedence over Phase I and Phase II operations.

Rule 211.7 Firefighters' Service Operating Procedures

(a) Instructions for operation of elevators under Phase I shall be incorporated with or adjacent to the Phase I switch at the designated level. They shall include the wording shown in Fig. 211.7(a).

(b) Instructions for operation of elevators under Phase II shall be incorporated with or adjacent to the switch, in or adjacent to the operating panel in each car. They shall include the wording shown in Fig. 211.7(b).

(c) Instructions shall be in letters not less than $1/8$ in. (3.2 mm) in height and shall be permanently installed and protected against removal or defacement.

FIREFIGHTERS' OPERATION
To recall elevators
Insert fire key and turn to "ON"

Figure 211.7(a)   Phase I Instructions

FIREFIGHTERS' OPERATION

To operate car	Insert fire key and turn to "ON"
	Press desired floor button
To cancel floor selection	Press "CALL CANCEL" button
To close door	Press and hold "DOOR CLOSE" button
To open door	Press and hold "DOOR OPEN" button
To hold car at floor	With doors open, turn key to "HOLD"
To return car to recall floor	With doors open, turn key to "OFF"

Figure 211.7(b)   Phase II Instructions

Extracts from *Handbook on A17.1 Safety Code for Elevators and Escalators* *

Rule 211.3 Firefighters' Service — Automatic Elevators

In 1969, the National Fire Protection Association reported 12,100 fire fatalities in the United States. Not a single fire loss occurred in a high-rise building. The next year, however, five fire deaths occurred in high-rise office buildings in New York City. Although this number was relatively small, it did trigger serious concern about safety in high-rise buildings. A firefighter's nightmare is an out-of-control fire in a high-rise building during office hours. A major catastrophe, resulting in hundreds of deaths, could become a reality rather than a nightmare. The potential for this catastrophe does exist. Skyscrapers of 40 or 50 years ago contained steel desks, steel files, steel partitions, and masonry enclosed stock rooms. In contrast, today they contain an unbelievable amount of paper that is generated and stored in, and on, desks, cardboard boxes, open racks, computer printouts and libraries, as well as non-fire-resistive furnishings. Thus, the modern high-rise is a veritable container of a tremendous fire load, and this fire load is increasing yearly. In the past decade, it is estimated that over 4000 buildings seven stories and higher have been built in this country. High-rise buildings are usually defined as buildings which are more than 75 ft (22.9 m) high, which is generally as high as fire department equipment can reach from the street.

High-rise buildings present new and different problems to fire suppression forces, yet the cause of fires in high-rise buildings and the materials used, including furniture and fixtures, are not any different from that used in conventional low-rise buildings. However, if a fire breaks out in the top story of a megastructure, firefighters have to lug their equipment up the stairs or risk riding the elevator. Evacuation of this type of building also presents a special problem. It is estimated that it would take over an hour to evacuate a 50 story building even if all went well.

Let's review some of the reasons why elevators are unsafe in a fire and what led to the Code requirements for firefighters' operation of elevators. Elevators are unsafe in a fire because:

(a) persons may push a corridor button and have to wait for an elevator that may never respond; valuable time in which to escape is lost.

(b) elevators respond to car and corridor calls; one of these calls may be at the fire floor.

(c) elevators cannot start until the car and hoistway doors are closed. A panic could lead to overcrowding of an elevator and the blockage of the doors, thus preventing closing.

(d) power failure during a fire can happen at any time and thus lead to entrapment.

Fatal delivery of the elevator to the fire floor can be caused by any of the following:

(a) an elevator passenger pressing the car button for the fire floor;

(b) one or both of the corridor call buttons may be pushed on the fire floor;

(c) heat may melt or deform the corridor push button or its wiring at the fire floor; or

(d) normal functioning of the elevator, such as high or low call reversal, may occur at the fire floor.

The A17.1 Code recognized all of this and reacted by mandating elevator recall, more commonly referred to as Phase I Firefighters' Service.

The features discussed in Rule 211.3 are known as firefighters' service or special emergency service (SES) features. The Code committee is striving to standardize the operation to assure that there are no variations to confuse firefighters or other operators of the elevator during an emergency. The automatic or manual return of elevators to the designated level (see Section 3 for definition) is what is referred to as Phase I operation. The provision to allow emergency personnel to operate the elevator from within the car on emergency in-car operation is commonly referred to as Phase II. See Diagram 211.3.

211.3a Phase I Emergency Recall Operation.

The requirement was changed in Supplement A17.1b — 1989 from elevators with a travel of 25 ft above or below the designated landing to any elevator with a travel of 25 ft or more. Under the previous Rule, an elevator could have nearly 50 ft of travel (24 ft 11 in. above the designated landing, and 24 ft 11 in. below the designated landing), and still not be required to have Phase I and Phase II operations.

---

*Reprinted with permission from the American Society of Mechanical Engineers, 345 E. 47th St., New York, New York 10017. Handbook authored by Edward A. Donoghue.

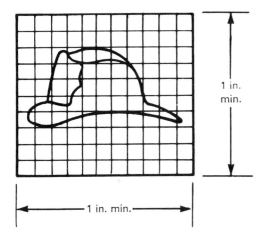

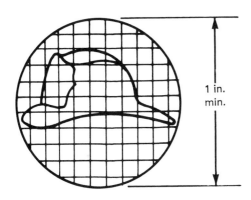

Diagram 211.3. *Elevator Corridor Call Station Pictograph.*

The Committee feels that an elevator with this amount of travel needs firefighters' service.

The term "designated level" refers to the main floor or other level that best serves the needs of emergency personnel for firefighting or rescue purposes. A three-position key-operated switch must be provided in the designated level lobby for each single elevator or for a group of elevators. The location of the three position Phase I switch has been specified for standardization and to make sure that it is located where all of the elevators will be within sight. The key should be removable only in the ON and OFF positions. The bypass position allows the restoration of normal elevator service when a lobby smoke detector is malfunctioning. The requirement that the key not be removable in the bypass position encourages building owners to repair a mal-

functioning smoke detector. An unattended key left in the lobby key switch could soon be in the possession of unauthorized personnel. An additional Phase I key switch is permitted and often is used at fire control centers. This second key switch is not allowed to have the bypass position. It was felt that a key switch with a bypass position in a locked room would encourage elevator operation without repairing smoke detectors.

Phase I operation assures that the elevator is not available to the general public during a fire emergency. When an elevator is out of service during a fire, the public is unable to use it as a means of exit from the building. Earlier versions of the Code addressed only automatic door operation. The 1981 and later editions of the Code cover the operation of vertically sliding doors, doors controlled by push buttons, and manual doors. The only time an automatic elevator will not return upon activation of Phase I is when that car is at a landing with its door(s) open and the in-car stop switch, emergency stop switch or some other electrical protective device, is activated, or if on inspection or designated attendant operation. This Rule recognizes that an elevator at a landing with the emergency stop switch in the STOP position should not be captured, as this is not a normal condition. The stop switch may have been activated to facilitate an inspection or maintenance and capturing the elevator could be a hazard to the inspection or maintenance personnel. The in-car stop switch should be disabled, just like the emergency stop button, so that the car cannot be inadvertently taken off of recall operation. A person with access to the key for the in-car stop switch, such as a building cleaning person, might be inclined to activate the switch while the elevator is being recalled. This would be unsafe.

For passenger safety, Rule 211.3a(5) requires elevators to close their doors at a slower speed when a door reopening device is rendered inoperative. This Rule also recognizes that mechanically actuated door reopening devices are not sensitive to smoke or flame, and can remain operative. Flame is the glowing gaseous part of a fire. Smoke or flame can register a signal whereas a fire will destroy. The reference to Rule 112.5 recognized "nudging" and, therefore, it is not unsafe to disconnect mechanically actuated door reopening devices.

Rules 211.3a(6) and (7) allow full control of those doors that may have to be closed from the corridor. Also, the automatic closing of vertical slide doors requires an active open or stop button on the corridor. The corridor door-open button must be operative to cover the case where a manual gate is open with the hoistway door closed. A firefighter may need the door-open button to open the door to see if anyone is inside the car.

The requirement for position indicators to remain operative is intended to assist emergency personnel in locating the elevator if it does not return to the designated level.

Unless the car is at the fire floor, it is safer to keep the doors open for inspection by firefighting personnel. The open hoistway door at the main floor or other designated level will admit air to the hoistway. If the fire is on a floor below the neutral pressure plane, the additional air will reduce the amount of smoke that can enter the hoistway from the fire floor, a beneficial side effect. If the fire is above the neutral pressure plane, there will be an increased flow of air from the hoistway to the floor, which is also beneficial.

Visual and audible signals alert passengers in an automatically operated elevator of the emergency and can minimize any apprehension that the passengers have when the elevator is returning to the main floor. In an attendant operated elevator, this signal alerts the attendant of the emergency and warns him to return immediately to the designated level. When on inspection operation, the inspector or maintenance personnel are also alerted to the emergency by this signal.

Rule 211.3a(10) recognized that if the smoke detector at the designated level is activated, turning the additional Phase I switch to the "ON" position will not override the smoke detector sending the car to the designated level, since this switch may be at a location where the condition of the designated level lobby cannot be determined.

211.3b Smoke Detectors.

Some systems are improperly-designed by initiating recall from smoke detectors that are a considerable distance from the elevator lobby. The action of the distant smoke detector does not warrant elevator recall. For instance, a waste paper basket fire some distance from the elevator may trigger a smoke detector in the immediate area. This in itself is not cause for elevator recall. Accordingly, only the activation of the smoke detector in the elevator lobby, hoistway, or machine room is now permitted to initiate elevator recall. There is no problem in isolating the elevator lobby, hoistway, or machine room detectors from the balance of smoke detectors on the floor. If sprinklers are placed in the hoistway,

a smoke detector must be provided in the vicinity of the sprinkler head. It is anticipated that this smoke detector will activate Phase I recall before the sprinkler is activated. See commentary on Rule 102.2.

A requirement added in the 1981 edition of the Code requires a smoke detector to be installed at the designated level elevator lobby which will cause the elevators to return to an alternate level in the event of a fire at the main floor. A requirement was also added in the 1981 edition for a smoke detector in the associated machine room which would also activate Phase I, as a fire in the machine room could seriously affect the safe operation of the elevator. These changes put the A17.1 Code in harmony with the requirements of the model building codes.

211.3b(3) This requirement specifically states that the elevator only responds to the first detector which was activated. The likelihood of two simultaneous fires is infinitesimal. It is assumed that the smoke detector at the fire floor will be the first one that is activated. Subsequent alarms would most likely be due to smoke migration and should not affect the choice of the recall floor.

211.3b(4) This requirement establishes a standard means of canceling Phase I once activated by a smoke detector and prohibits the cancellation of Phase I operation by automatic means, a short in the smoke detector circuit, or by loss of power.

The Note to Rule 211.3b makes reference to NFPA 72A which gives guidance on the installation of smoke detectors for elevator recall in buildings with fire alarm systems. This standard coordinates the requirements for smoke detectors used for elevator recall with other devices utilized in fire alarm systems (i.e., building smoke detectors, heat detectors, sprinkler flow valves, pull stations, etc.).

211.3c Phase II Emergency In-Car Operation.

Phase II firefighters' operation is for the benefit of firefighters. Some of the input received from firefighters are as follows:

(1) Hoistway doors of elevators at the recall floor should remain open. Upon arrival, firefighters cannot afford the luxury of the time required to ascertain if all elevators are present and accounted for, or if an elevator is somewhere else in the building. A glance will reveal what elevators have been recalled and what elevators have to be located to assure that there are no trapped passengers.

(2) Firefighters want the elevator for their use. They take command during a fire, and they will determine whether the elevators are to be used. They are willing to accept the risks that are associated with running elevators during a fire. It is standard operating procedure for the firefighters to use the elevators not only to carry equipment or for firefighting or evacuation purposes, but to also dispense fire personnel to non-fire floors. The presence of a firefighter reduces occupant panic, and firefighters can direct occupant movement strategy since they are in constant communication with the fire command post.

Many firefighters stated that there are times when they cannot afford the luxury of using personnel to operate an elevator on a return trip to the main floor. They requested that placing the Phase II switch in the elevator to the OFF position would automatically cause the elevator to return to the main floor for use by later arriving firefighters.

There also is a requirement that when the car is on Phase II operation, turning the switch in the car to the HOLD position at a floor will permit the firefighter to remove the key, and leave the car without the danger of someone taking the car to another floor.

The Phase II key must be removable in all positions because the shortage of available emergency service keys could prevent the required number of cars from being put into Phase II service if the key were not removable in the ON position as well as other positions. Also, the door open button is active in the ON and OFF positions of the in-car key switch. If the switch is turned to OFF and the doors start to close automatically, the door open button can be pushed to fully reopen the doors and then the switch setting can be changed to HOLD or ON.

Requirements for Phase II operation [Rule 211.3a(2)] were made more stringent in the 1981 edition. The previous edition of the Code required Phase II operation at 70 ft (21.3 m) above or below the main floor. The 1981 edition calls for Phase II operation whenever Phase I operation is required. The old requirement was predicated on the needs of emergency personnel only. The Rule considers the need for evacuating the handicapped during an emergency by emergency personnel. Handicapped persons are always a concern, but the term "handicapped" in the normal context is no longer applicable; under fire conditions, even a firefighter can be considered handicapped, especially when he is near

exhaustion or if his oxygen supply is gone. Further, able-bodied occupants can become handicapped from smoke, from walking up or down steps, or from hysteria. Therefore, when you hear that provisions must be made for the handicapped during a fire, expand your overall picture, because even normal ambulatory persons can suddenly become non-ambulatory.

Rules 211.3c(1)(c) and (d) recognize that compliance with Rule 112.4 is not necessary since constant pressure door controls are required. These Rules also establish appropriate requirements for cars with more than one entrance.

Rule 211.3c(1)(d) recognizes that on large vertically sliding doors with continuous pressure closing, reopening is impractical and could introduce a delay factor that may impair safety.

Rule 211.3c(1)(f) recognizes that door reopening devices are not necessary since constant pressure operation is required.

For standardization, Rule 211.3c(4) defines Phase II operation in the OFF position when Phase I is not in effect and the car is not at the designated level.

211.3d Interruption of Power.

This Rule clarifies that even in the case of power interruption upon restoration of power, Phase I or II would continue to remain in effect.

Rule 211.4 Firefighters' Service — Non-Automatic Elevators

This Rule establishes the operation requirements of elevators which are not covered by Rule 211.3. A standard sign is required to alert the operator as to which floor the elevator should be returned to. See commentary on Rule 211.3.

Rule 211.5 Firefighters' Service — Automatic Elevators with Designated Attendant Operation

A car could be left at the fire floor, exposing the hoistway to fire, when it could be recalled. The delay is to give ample warning prior to recall. Hospital service has been excluded, since there may be valid reasons for not returning the car.

Rule 211.7 Firefighters' Service Operating Procedures

Operating procedures must be incorporated with or be adjacent to the Phase I and Phase II key-operated switches to assure that during an emergency, emergency personnel have quick access to available instructions for their use.

Since firefighters' service is now standardized, the Code specifies signs with simple and clear wording which explain the operation of the elevators.

An explanation of the BYPASS position is not necessary on the Phase I sign because this is a building function, not a firefighter operation.

5

Fire Tests for Life Safety Code Users

Joseph M. Jardin, P.E.

This supplement, new to the 1991 Edition of the *Handbook*, explains the often misunderstood and misinterpreted role of fire testing as it relates to the *Life Safety Code*. In order to judge the level of safety offered by tested materials or assemblies for end-use application, one must understand not only the mechanics of the test but also its limitations. Many of the tests referenced by the *Code* have equivalent counterparts administered by other organizations. In concert with the equivalency concepts expressed in Section 1-6, it would be appropriate to consider products or devices tested in accordance with the equivalent test counterparts as satisfying *Life Safety Code* provisions. Where recognized, equivalent test methods are provided in this supplement.

Fire Barriers and Opening Protection

Fire Barriers

There are many locations in buildings where the *Code* considers compartmentation of the building spaces important to life safety. In these cases, the *Code* requires the segregation of these spaces by fire barriers.

Where fire compartments are required, such as for exit enclosures, vertical opening protection, and hazardous area separation, the *Code* specifies that such spaces shall be formed by fire barriers. Fire barriers specified by the *Code* are classified in accordance with their *fire resistance rating*. The *Life Safety Code*, depending upon the use of the fire barrier, specifies varying time periods of fire resistance, including 2-hour, 1-hour, 3/4-hour, 1/2-hour, and 20-minutes.

Fire resistance ratings are performance-based and are established by test in accordance with NFPA 251, *Standard Methods of Fire Tests of Building Construction and Materials* [American Society of Testing and Materials (ASTM) E-119, Underwriters Laboratories UL 263]. This test provides for a sample assembly to be exposed to a standard fire exposure when mounted to a furnace. Furnace temperatures are achieved by accurately following the Standard Time-Temperature Curve as depicted in Figure 1. Temperatures both inside the furnace and on the unexposed side of the test assembly are monitored. No fewer than nine thermocouples are placed on the unexposed surface to measure unexposed surface temperatures. Cotton waste is placed against the unexposed surface of the test assembly and observed for flaming. Temperature rise on the unexposed surface must be below that which would permit the ignition of combustibles on the unexposed side. For load-bearing assemblies, the sample is loaded in the same manner as would be expected when installed.

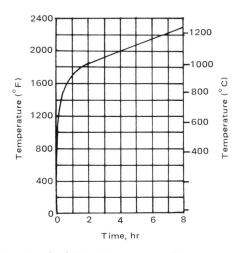

Figure 1.   Standard Time-Temperature Curve.

For an assembly to achieve a desired rating, it must exhibit the following behavior for at least the desired period of time:

– Cotton waste on unexposed surface shall not ignite.

– Temperature rise on the unexposed side cannot exceed 325°F at any point or an average of 250°F.

– Load-bearing assemblies must sustain the anticipated maximum load.

– Assemblies rated 1 hour or greater shall be subjected to and successfully withstand the effects of a hose stream test.

To further ensure the ability of the tested construction to resist disintegration under adverse conditions, NFPA 251 requires all walls and partitions with a fire endurance rating of 1 hour or more to be subjected to the cooling impact and erosion effects of water discharging through a hose with a standard playpipe nozzle. A duplicate specimen of the assembly to be rated is tested in the furnace for one-half the time period indicated as the fire resistance rating during the fire endurance test. The specimen is then removed from the furnace and immediately subjected to the hose stream test. If an opening develops that permits the projection of water beyond the unexposed surface, the assembly is considered to have failed.

Although rated for a specified time period, it must be recognized that, under actual field conditions, an assembly may fail in a shorter time period or may stay in place for a longer duration. The test exposure, as defined by the Standard Time-Temperature Curve, represents only one level of fire severity, which is based on an assumed fuel loading. When established circa 1920, that fuel load was chosen to represent the contents of a "typical office building." Hence, varying fuel loads result in varying challenges to building assemblies.

This potential variation between tested endurance and actual field performance is recognized by the *Code*. Fire resistance testing is valuable to the *Code*, because it does provide a *relative* measure of fire performance under specified conditions.

Opening Protection

Where the *Code* permits openings in fire barriers, the appropriate protection of those openings is of paramount importance to ensure the integrity of the protected barrier. The degree of fire resistance required of the opening protective depends upon the rating and use of the barrier for which it is intended. Generally, the fire protection ratings for the opening protectives required by the *Life Safety Code* are as follows:

Barrier Fire Resistance Rating	Opening Protective Fire Protection Rating
2 hr	1½ hr
1 hr for vertical opening protection or exit enclosure	1 hr
1 hr for hazardous area protection	¾ hr
1 hr for corridor walls or smoke barriers	20 min.
¾ hr or less	20 min.

The difference between required time period ratings for fire barriers and their associated opening protection is a recognition of the function of the opening protective. As openings are necessary for normal use of buildings and represent only a relatively small percentage of the overall fire barrier area, opening protectives are provided to preserve the integrity of the fire barrier (i.e., plug the openings). It is recognized that, for door openings to be usable, there must be a clear space on either side of the door to permit travel. Hence, concern over temperature transmission through the door is not as critical as transmission through the fire barrier assembly, since there should be no combustibles located near the door. If, however, the opening is not used and combustibles are permitted to be stored adjacent to the door, the assumed enclosure protection may be deficient.

Fire Doors

Where the *Code* uses the term "door," it includes the doorway, frame, and any needed hardware including latch and self-closer, as well as the door leaf. Fire doors needed to satisfy fire protection rating requirements are required to be tested in accordance with NFPA 252, *Standard Methods of Fire Tests of Door Assemblies* (ASTM E-152). The objective of this test is to ensure that the fire door remains in place for the period of exposure and, thus, plugs the opening.

The procedures of NFPA 252 are similar to those of NFPA 251. Fire door assembly specimens are mounted to a furnace and exposed to the Standard Time-Temperature fire exposure. In recognition of their function, fire doors must exhibit the following response for the desired time period to be considered acceptable:

- The test assembly shall withstand the fire endurance test without developing any openings through the assembly.
- The test assembly shall withstand the impact, cooling, and erosion effects of the hose stream test without developing any openings. (The standard does permit minor gaps in some circumstances.)
- No flaming shall occur on the unexposed surface of the assembly for the first 30 minutes of the classification period. (Intermittent light flaming is permitted after 30 minutes.)
- Hardware to be evaluated for use on fire doors shall secure the door in place for a period of 3 hours, and the latch bolt shall remain projected and shall be intact after the test. The hardware need not be operable after the test.

Once tested, the *Code* requires fire doors to be installed in accordance with NFPA 80, *Standard for Fire Doors and Windows*.

Fire Windows

Permitted by the *Code* in fire barriers having a required fire resistance rating of 1 hour or less, fire windows must be tested for acceptance in accordance with NFPA 257, *Standard for Fire Tests of Window Assemblies*. Fire windows, like fire doors, must remain in place during the period of exposure. Therefore, NFPA 257 evaluates the ability of windows or other glazing materials to remain in an opening during a predetermined 45-minute test exposure period.

In a closed position, the window assembly is exposed to a fire exposure defined by a Standard Time-Temperature Curve for this test method (*see Figure 2*). During the predetermined 45-minute period of exposure, the window must remain in place with no openings between the glass edges and the frame, and the window assembly cannot be loosened from its fastenings. Immediately following the fire exposure period, the fire-exposed side of the window assembly is subjected to the impact, cooling, and erosion effects of the hose stream test. During the hose stream test, the standard limits the "number" and "size" of openings in an acceptable assembly. Figures 3a and 3b represent two views of an assembly that has been exposed to both the fire endurance test and the hose stream test.

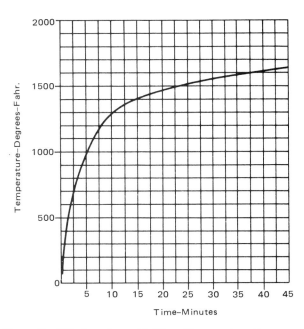

Figure 2.   Window Assembly Time-Temperature Curve.

Figure 3a.   Unexposed Side of Window Assembly after Fire Exposure and Hose Stream Application.

Figure 3b.   Exposed Side of Window Assembly after Fire Exposure and Hose Stream Application.

Minimum Construction Requirements

Several occupancy chapters provide minimum construction requirements in consideration of an occupant's ability to egress. Based on the location of an occupancy within a building (e.g., type of building, number of stories), these requirements dictate the degree of fire resistance associated with the various elements of construction (*see Table 1*). Listed in each column of Table 1 are the required fire resistance ratings of each of the elements. These ratings are derived in accordance with NFPA 251, *Standard Method of Fire Tests of Building Construction and Materials*. Both interior and exterior bearing walls are evaluated as described in the section on fire barriers (see page 1003).

Once loaded to the maximum anticipated loading, beams and columns are exposed to the Standard Time-Temperature Exposure. Unlike the function served by walls and partitions, however, which limit temperature transmission and flaming on the unexposed surface, beams and columns must sustain the applied load for a period equal to that for which classification is desired.

Fire endurance of floor and roof assemblies is also evaluated in accordance with NFPA 251 and exposed to the Standard Time-Temperature Exposure. Conditions of acceptance for floor and roof assemblies include:

- The ability to sustain applied load throughout the desired classification period.
- Cotton waste shall not ignite on the unexposed surface.
- The average temperature transmission through the test assembly shall not raise the temperature on the unexposed surface more than 250°F from its initial temperature (this condition may be modified based on the material and type of construction used).

Table 1. Fire Resistance Requirements for Type I Through Type V Construction[†]

	Type 1		Type II			Type III		Type IV	Type V	
	443	332	222	111	000	211	200	2HH	111	000
EXTERIOR BEARING WALLS—										
Supporting more than one floor, columns or other bearing walls	4	3	2	1	0[1]	2	2	2	1	0[1]
Supporting one floor only	4	3	2	1	0[1]	2	2	2	1	0[1]
Supporting a roof only	4	3	1	1	0[1]	2	2	2	1	0[1]
INTERIOR BEARING WALLS—										
Supporting more than one floor, columns or other bearing walls	4	3	2	1	0	1	0	2	1	0
Supporting one floor only	3	2	2	1	0	1	0	1	1	0
Supporting a roof only	3	2	1	1	0	1	0	1	1	0
COLUMNS—										
Supporting more than one floor, bearing walls or other columns	4	3	2	1	0	1	0	H[2]	1	0
Supporting one floor only	3	2	2	1	0	1	0	H[2]	1	0
Supporting a roof only	3	2	1	1	0	1	0	H[2]	1	0
BEAMS, GIRDERS, TRUSSES, and ARCHES—										
Supporting more than one floor, bearing walls or columns	4	3	2	1	0	1	0	H[2]	1	0
Supporting one floor only	3	2	2	1	0	1	0	H[2]	1	0
Supporting a roof only	3	2	1	1	0	1	0	H[2]	1	0
FLOOR CONSTRUCTION	3	2	2	1	0	1	0	H[2]	1	0
ROOF CONSTRUCTION	2	1½	1	1	0	1	0	H[2]	1	0
EXTERIOR NONBEARING WALLS.....	0[1]	0[1]	0[1]	0[1]	0[1]	0[1]	0[1]	0[1]	0[1]	0[1]

☐ Those members listed that are permitted to be of approved combustible material.

[1] Requirements for fire resistance of exterior walls, the provision of spandrel wall sections, and the limitation or protection of wall openings are not related to construction type. They need to be specified in other standards and codes, where appropriate, and may be required in addition to the requirements of this Standard for the construction type.

[2] "H" indicates heavy timber members; see text for requirements.

[†] This table is an extract from NFPA 220, *Standard on Types of Building Construction*.

Interior Finish

Although often confused with each other, fire resistance and the concept of fire resistance ratings have no relationship to the characteristics of interior finish. While fire resistance is necessary for ensuring a degree of structural integrity and compartmentation, the *Code* regulates the hazard of interior finish items to reduce their contribution to fire growth and spread. Interior finish, as it relates to the *Life Safety Code*, refers to exposed interior wall surfaces, exposed interior ceiling surfaces, and exposed interior floor surfaces. (*Also see detailed commentary in Chapter 6.*)

Interior Wall and Ceiling Finish

To ensure sufficient time for egress, the *Code*, depending upon occupancy use and location within the building, attempts to limit the relative rate of flame propagation across wall and ceiling surfaces. For the purpose of applying flame spread limitations, the *Code* groups finish items into three classes based upon the Flame Spread Index (FSI) and the Smoke Developed Index (SDI):

Class A	FSI 0-25	SDI 0-450
Class B	FSI 26-75	SDI 0-450
Class C	FSI 76-200	SDI 0-450

The Flame Spread Index reflects the *relative* rate at which flame will spread across the surface of a material as compared with inorganic-reinforced cement board, which has a FSI of 0, and red-oak, which has a FSI of 100. FSI is a dimensionless figure and does not represent flame speed or velocity. As discussed, flame spread is not an indication of the material's fire resistance; it is very possible that a material with a very low ability to spread flame may exhibit very little fire resistance when exposed to the NFPA 251 test (i.e., bare sheet metal).

NFPA 255, *Standard Method of Test of Surface Burning Characteristics of Building Materials* (ASTM E-84, UL 273), often referred to as the "Tunnel Test" or "Steiner Tunnel Test," is the test necessary to obtain both the FSI and SDI information. A 20-inch wide by 24-foot long sample is placed in the 25-foot long test chamber of the tunnel test assembly. A gas flame is applied at one end, and a regulated constant draft is applied through the tunnel from the flame end. Flame front progress is observed through side windows for a 10-minute time period. Figures 4 and 5 illustrate the design of the test apparatus. Once charted, the area under a time-distance curve is used to calculate the FSI.

The Smoke Developed Index represents the relative degree to which a material can obscure visibility within the means of egress (i.e., smoke density). Materials of all three interior finish classes acceptable to the *Code* must exhibit SDI values within the range of 0-450. If the SDI exceeds 450, the material receives no rating. The degree of smoke obscuration is measured by a photoelectric cell mounted in the tunnel vent pipe opposite a light source. Reduction in light due to passing smoke, particulate, and other effluent read by the photoelectric cell is recorded and used to calculate the SDI.

When specific materials or products are considered for use or reviewed for *Code* compliance, it is critical to ensure that the intended or actual use corresponds with the tested configuration. If the material or product differs in form or is mounted or applied in a manner that deviates from the tested sample, it cannot be relied upon to perform as tested. Appendix A to NFPA 255 provides a guide to mounting typical types of building materials and end-use products.

Therefore, it becomes important to follow manufacturers' or listing instructions when installing or applying interior finish items. Components demanding close review include size and spacing of fasteners, type and application of adhesives, and number of coats and application rate of fire retardant coatings.

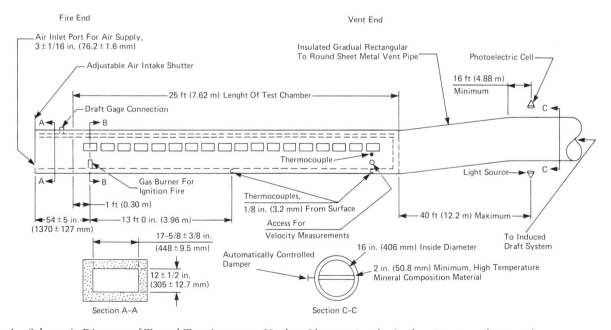

Figure 4. *Schematic Diagram of Tunnel Test Apparatus Used to Characterize the Surface Burning of Materials.*

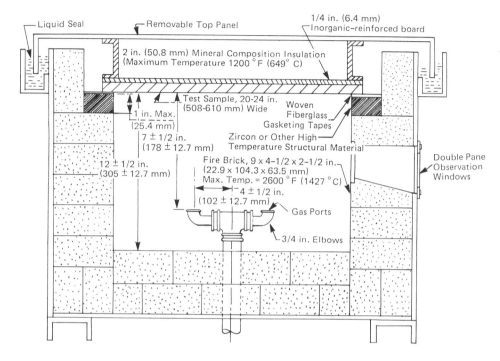

Figure 5. *A Cross-Sectional View of the Tunnel Test Apparatus.*

Room Corner Testing

See commentary following A-6-5.2.3 for a discussion of room-corner testing.

Interior Floor Finish

Where required by the *Code* or where, in the judgment of the authority having jurisdiction, regulation of floor finish materials is dictated (*see Chapter 6*), reference is made to NFPA 253, *Standard Method of Test for Critical Radiant Flux of Floor Covering Systems Using a Radiant Heat Energy Source* (ASTM E-648). Specifically developed to address floor finish concerns, NFPA 253 evaluates the tendency of a floor-covering material to propagate flame across its surface.

The specimen to be tested is installed flat in the bottom of the apparatus. A gas-fired panel serving as a radiant heat energy source is installed at one end of the chamber on an incline so that it extends over the test specimen. A pilot burner is located at the edge of the test specimen to provide ignition. (*See Figures 6a, 6b, and 7.*)

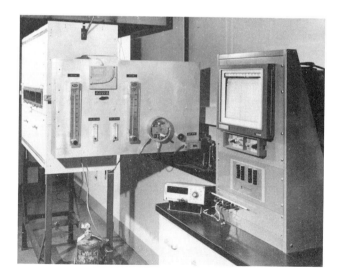

Figure 6a. *Flooring Radiant Panel Tester Apparatus.*

Critical Radiant Flux (CRF) is determined by measuring the distance burned from the gas-piloted ignition to the point of flameout. Converting the distance burned to a CRF is performed using the Standard Radiant Heat Energy Flux

Figure 6b. *Flooring Radiant Panel Test Showing Carpet Specimen and Gas-Fueled Panel.*

Curtains and Draperies

Not only do curtains, draperies, and other similar loosely hanging decorations present a concern because they contribute fuel to aid in fire growth, but they also provide a mechanism for rapidly propagating fire beyond the point of ignition or area of origin. NFPA 701, *Standard Method of Tests for Flame Resistance of Textiles and Films*, is the Code-mandated evaluation method of ensuring satisfactory performance of such materials. Although NFPA 701 offers two test alternatives, the small-scale test and the large-scale test, the *Life Safety Code* requires that, where regulated, draperies, curtains, and other similar loosely hanging furnishings and decorations pass *both* the small- and large-scale tests.

Both the large-scale and small-scale tests require that a hanging test sample be exposed to a gas burner flame for a specific period of time (12 seconds for the small-scale test and 2 minutes for the large-scale test). Pass/fail criteria for both tests are based on the duration of flaming after removal of the burner and the length of char on the sample.

To ensure the durability of the fire retardant treatment, NFPA 701 requires that the fabric to be tested be subjected to conditions that apply to its intended use. Procedures for accelerated dry cleaning, accelerated laundering, accelerated water leaching, and accelerated weathering are included in this test standard.

Chapter 10 of NFPA 701 contains guidance for performance of the match flame field test. One must recognize that this field test is to be used by the authority having jurisdiction only as a verification tool in the field when adequate documentation is not available for review or when there is concern regarding the effects of weathering or laundering. The field test is not a substitute for either the small- or large-scale tests and cannot be used to demonstrate *Code* compliance.

As cautioned by A-31-1.4.1 of the *Code*, if textiles or films are intended to be applied to interior surfaces of buildings or backing materials as interior finishes for use in buildings, they should be treated as interior wall and ceiling finishes and tested for flame spread ratings and smoke developed ratings in accordance with NFPA 255, *Standard Method of Test of Surface Burning Characteristics of Building Materials*.

Profile (*see Figure 8*). Therefore, CRF (measured in watts per square centimeter) is the minimum level of incident radiant heat energy necessary for continued flaming of the surface of the floor-covering material.

Where regulated, the *Code* accepts two classes of interior floor finish:

Class I	Minimum CRF:	0.45 W/cm²
Class II	Minimum CRF:	0.22 W/cm²

Materials with high CRF are more resistant to the radiant exposure and subsequent flame propagation across the surface than materials with lower CRF values. Therefore, Class I materials are better from a fire safety perspective than are Class II floor finish items.

Furnishings and Decorations

As in the case of interior finish, the *Code* addresses the flammability threat posed by certain articles of furniture and decorative furnishings to ensure that the means of egress is usable for a sufficient period of time. Chapter 31, "Operating Features," specifies the applicable flammability limitations based upon occupancy use.

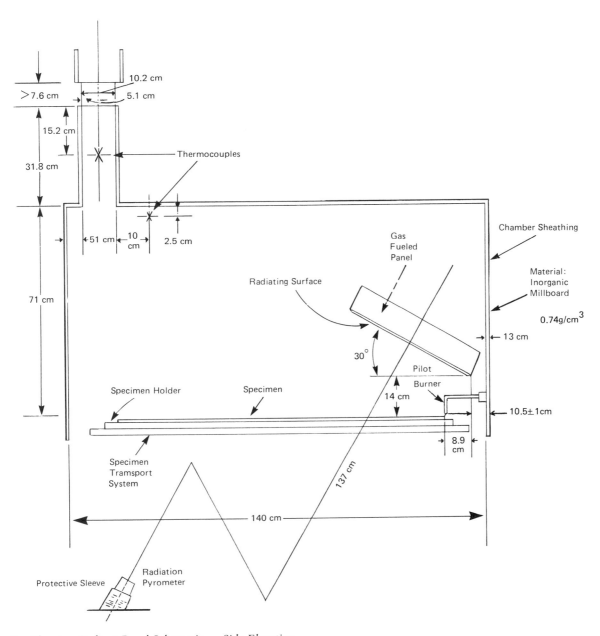

Figure 7. *Flooring Radiant Panel Schematic — Side Elevation.*

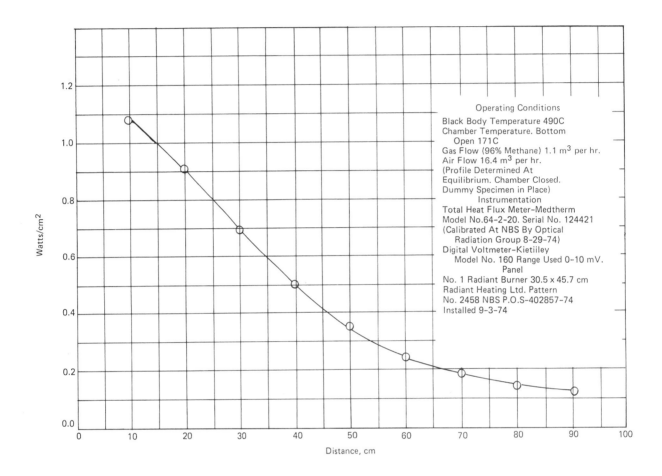

Operating Conditions

Black Body Temperature 490C
Chamber Temperature. Bottom
    Open 171C
Gas Flow (96% Methane) 1.1 m^3 per hr.
Air Flow 16.4 m^3 per hr.
(Profile Determined At
Equilibrium. Chamber Closed.
Dummy Specimen in Place)
        Instrumentation
Total Heat Flux Meter-Medtherm
Model No.64-2-20. Serial No. 124421
(Calibrated At NBS By Optical
    Radiation Group 8-29-74)
Digital Voltmeter-Kietiiley
    Model No. 160 Range Used 0-10 mV.
        Panel
No. 1 Radiant Burner 30.5 x 45.7 cm
Radiant Heating Ltd. Pattern
No. 2458 NBS P.O.S-402857-74
Installed 9-3-74

Figure 8. Standard Radiant Heat Energy Flux Profile.

Upholstered Furniture and Mattresses

Standards referenced to address the flammability hazard of upholstered furniture and mattresses include:

NFPA 260, *Standard Method of Tests and Classification System for Cigarette Ignition Resistance of Components of Upholstered Furniture* (UFAC Test Method - Upholstered Furniture Action Council).

NFPA 261, *Standard Method of Test for Determining Resistance of Mock-Up Upholstered Furniture Material Assemblies to Ignition by Smoldering Cigarettes.*

Code of Federal Regulations (CFR) 16, Part 1632.

For a discussion of upholstered furniture testing and regulation, see commentary to A-31-1.4.2 and A-31-1.4.3.

Who Can Perform Fire Tests?

It is not the *Code's* intent either to require the *Code* user or limit the *Code* user to the use of any specific testing laboratory. However, the *Code* leaves judgment of acceptability to the authority having jurisdiction. This applies to testing laboratories. Although NFPA publishes the *Life Safety Code* and many of the referenced test standards, the NFPA does not approve, inspect, or certify any installations, procedures, material, or equipment; nor does it approve or evaluate testing laboratories.

The "Yellow Pages" telephone directory of some larger cities or metropolitan areas contain listings of testing laboratories. However obtaining access to a fire testing lab may not be so simple. In addition to the better known testing laboratories, such as Underwriters Laboratories, Southwest Research Institute, Omega Point Laboratories, United States Testing Company, and Factory Mutual Research Corporation, many independent labs perform tests referenced by the *Code*. The following directories include some of these laboratories:

ASTM *Directory of Testing Laboratories*, American Society of Testing and Materials, 1916 Race St., Philadelphia, PA 19103-1187.

American Council of Independent Laboratories Directory, American Council of Independent Laboratories, Inc., 1725 K Street N.W., Washington, DC 20006.

Where Can Rating Information be Found?

Although not all-inclusive, the following list of references may prove useful in a search for rating and listing information.

1. NFPA *Fire Protection Handbook*
   National Fire Protection Association
   1 Batterymarch Park
   P.O. Box 9101
   Quincy, MA 02269-9101
   ATTN: Customer Service
   1-800 344-3555

2. UL *Fire Resistance Directory*
   Underwriters Laboratories Inc.
   Publications Stock
   333 Pfingsten Road
   Northbrook, IL 60062-2096

3. UL *Building Materials Directory*
   Underwriters Laboratories Inc.
   Publications Stock
   333 Pfingsten Road
   Northbrook, IL 60062-2096

4. FM *Approval Guide*
   Factory Mutual Engineering and Research Corp.
   P.O. Box 9102
   Norwood, MA 02062-9957

5. FM *Specification Tested Products Guide*
   Factory Mutual Engineering and Research Corp.
   P.O. Box 9102
   Norwood, MA 02062-9957

6. Gypsum Association *Fire Resistance Design Manual*
   Gypsum Association
   1603 Orrington Avenue
   Evanston, IL 60201

7. *Listings*
   Warnock Hersey
   3210 American Drive
   Mississauga, Ontario
   L4V 1B3

8. Rehabilitation Guidelines
   Volume 8, *Guidelines on Fire Ratings of Archaic Materials and Assemblies*. Published by the U.S. Department of Housing and Urban Development. Available from the Superintendent of Documents, U.S. Government Printing Office, Washington, DC 20402.

6

How to Adopt the Life Safety Code into Law

Dennis J. Berry, Esq.

Introduction

Due to the importance and wide industry acceptance of the *Life Safety Code*, it is often adopted into the law or regulations of a jurisdiction. This supplement to the *Handbook* addresses the recommended and most popular methods by which the *Life Safety Code*, or any model code, can be adopted into the law of a state, city, or town. The purpose is to assist those who are considering the adoption of the *Code* for their jurisdiction.

There are, generally speaking, two methods by which this adoption can be accomplished: either adoption by transcription or adoption by reference. The former method requires that the adopting ordinance reproduce, in full, the code or standard being adopted. The latter method requires only that the adopted code or standard be referenced in the laws of the jurisdiction by means of a full and adequate description.

Adoption by reference of a technical standard or code is a widely accepted (see appendix) and often preferable procedure for a legislative or regulatory body to follow in establishing fire and building regulations. There are many reasons why this particular procedure can be advantageous for governing authorities. First, adoption by reference avoids the necessity of printing in full a highly technical code that will often be several hundred pages in length. Thus, a reference statute or ordinance minimizes the ever-increasing bulk of official statute books and avoids the often prohibitive cost of reprinting and successive publication. Second, technical codes and standards are constantly improved and updated by the issuing organization. Such updated standards are easily adopted by the appropriate authority simply by adopting a new provision with an updated reference. Third, there is less opportunity for a lobbying influence to weaken the provisions of a code when the principle thrust is to adopt the entire work by reference.

The fundamental constitutionality of adoption by reference is not in doubt, nor, generally speaking, is its legality as long as the adoption is properly executed. Legal authorities appear to be in agreement that, "In the absence of statutory or charter provisions to the *contrary*, adoption of documents in municipal ordinance by incorporation by reference is valid where the document adopted is sufficiently identified and is made a part of the public record" [*see C. J. Antieu, Municipal Corporation Law, Vol. 1, § 4.17, pp. 4-34 (emphasis added)*]. There are numerous cases reported that have addressed and enforced regulations adopted by reference. Furthermore, the federal government, almost every state, and the District of Columbia have, to some extent, used this method of legislation (see appendix). On the local level, adoption by reference is even more widely used in recognition of the advantages mentioned above. In more than thirty states, statutes specifically enable local governmental bodies to adopt technical codes and standards by reference (see appendix).

In those states that have specific statutory procedures for adopting an ordinance, those procedures must generally be followed closely. However, the legal position stated previously makes clear that even in those states where there is no specific statute enabling municipal governments to adopt standards by reference, that procedure is nonetheless available unless specifically prohibited.

There have been cases in which adopted standards or regulations have been denied enforcement. In some cases, they have been struck down completely, while, in others, they have simply not been enforced in the case before the court. However, such cases are usually due to failure to follow all procedural requirements in the adoption and filing processes, rather than due to a basic flaw in the concept of adoption by reference.

Courts have, in some instances, drawn a distinction between requirements for adoption that are mandatory and those that are directory. Failure to meet those requirements that are mandatory can be fatal to adoption, while failure to meet a requirement that is directory may not cause the entire ordinance to be unenforceable. Careful attention to state requirements should prevent any flaws, mandatory or directory, from preventing full enforcement.

It should be noted that enforcement of adopted codes and standards is usually sought by a municipal official in a proceding where a court is being asked to assess fines or impose other penalties against individuals who allegedly failed to meet the standards. In such a case, particularly if it is deemed by state law to be a criminal proceding, the court is likely to resolve all doubts concerning both the facts and the law in favor of the defendant. Thus, counsel for the defendant will thoroughly review the entire record of the adoption, as well as the statutory conditions under which the adoption took place, in order to uncover any possible flaws. If able to find procedural flaws that have arguable validity, the defendant may well prevail and, thereby, cause doubt regarding the enforceability of the whole statute. In such situations, the basic concept behind adoption of the code is not in question as much as the procedural steps by which it was accomplished. Adherence to the statutory procedure of the jurisdiction is thus of vital importance.

Therefore, it falls on counsel for a municipality, rule-making body, or legislature seeking to adopt a particular standard by reference to ensure that the adoption process is properly followed in every respect. Procedural flaws that might be overlooked when a standard is adopted by transcription may lead to invalidation when adoption is by reference.

Methods of Adopting and Using Privately Developed Standards

This section presents a description of adoption by reference plus a description of the two other common methods of adopting or using fire and building codes or standards. It also presents model state and local legislation designed to implement each of these methods (see the appendix for a survey of the status of the adoption by reference method in the United States). The basic intent of this section is to present and explain means by which jurisdictions may adopt the *Life Safety Code* and other privately developed standards into local laws, ordinances, or regulations without incurring the often prohibitive costs of development and separate publication.

The model drafts included herein are typical methods and offer only broad guidelines. The constitution or charter of the subject jurisdiction, as well as enabling legislation and any applicable court decisions, should be reviewed in preparation for the adoption process. The focus is on the adoption of the *Life Safety Code* and other privately developed standards. It has become increasingly popular to adopt by reference standards promulgated by the state or federal government or agencies thereof. Standards promulgated by another level of government may appear to have an inherent credibility not shared by privately developed standards. In fact, there is little difference in the adoption or ultimate credibility of privately developed standards as opposed to those promulgated by another unit of government. The principles involved in such adoption will not change.

Like all forms, these present only a basis from which counsel for the group seeking adoption or municipal counsel can work to propose the actual legislation.

Adoption by Reference

This is the most economical procedure for adopting privately developed codes and standards. An act or ordinance simply references the applicable standard by title, edition, and date. The date of the standard is important. To adopt the standard without reference to a particular edition or date may cause the adoption to be struck down. It may seem logical to simply adopt the *Life Safety Code* and allow it to be changed as the NFPA adopts each new edition. The flaw in this logic is that to do so would, in effect, give the NFPA the right to change the law of a jurisdiction. This could be considered an improper delegation of legislative authority.

If a standard is adopted by reference, usually only the referencing legislation, not the entire standard, need be published. The legislation must generally indicate where the standard is available for public inspection, where copies of the standard may be purchased, and what penalties are provided for violation of the standards. In most cases, it is mandatory that all penalty provisions be published.

Different jurisdictions will have different filing and availability requirements. These should be addressed during the adoption process or be contained in the adoption legislation itself. Adherence to these requirements is important. A popular method of attack consists of arguing that a defendant did not have reasonable opportunity to know the law that has been broken.

The adopting authority may want to amend or delete certain provisions of the referenced standard. *All* such changes must also be published in the legislation, and they *must* be identified as changes.

Adoption by Transcription

This procedure involves transcribing the privately developed code or standard into a statute or ordinance. One section of the published act must acknowledge the originating group as the copyright owner of the provision transcribed. Adoption by transcription obviously lacks some of the simplicity of adoption by reference, since the entire code must be published in full. This method may discourage desired updating of the standard, because this would involve complete republication. In addition to the code or standard, penalty provisions should be specifically set out.

Prima Facie* Evidence Method

This is not a procedure for adopting a standard into law. Instead, it is a rule of law regarding the admissability of a standard. It is mentioned here only because it may prove helpful to those in authority who may be attempting to enforce the provisions of the *Life Safety Code*. The applicable legislation simply defines the legal standard to be a "reasonable standard of safety," and provides that a particular edition of the *Life Safety Code* or another standard shall be prima facie evidence of what is "reasonable." Thus, any condition that meets the requirements of the cited standard will be considered legally "reasonable" within the meaning of the act. The published legislation must indicate where a copy of the standard may be obtained. It is possible that other standards or even an ad hoc activity could be also found to be reasonable.

This method may appear to be the simplest of all, but its inherent lack of certainty with regard to the requirements of the law makes prospective regulatory enforcement difficult. The rule of law actually comes into play only after the fact. It would be difficult to enforce regulations against an individual who chose to ignore the appropriate standard and take the chance that injury would not occur.

Model Legislation: State

Model State Act to Incorporate a Privately Developed Code or Standard by Reference

The state of . . . does ordain as follows:

Section 1. In the interest of public safety, the standards as set forth in . . . (*identify the standard*) . . . are hereby adopted, as if set forth herein, as safety standards for . . . (*subject matter*).

---

* Prima facie: Presumed to be true unless disproved by evidence to the contrary.

Section 2. The following sections of the said . . . (*identify the standard*) . . . are amended to read as indicated: (a) Section . . . is amended to read: (*insert new language*) (b) Section . . . is deleted. (c) Section . . . (etc).

Section 3. Any person who shall violate any provisions of this Act, or who shall fail to comply with any of the requirements thereof, shall be guilty of a misdemeanor punishable by a fine of not more than . . . dollars or by imprisonment not exceeding . . . year(s), or by both.

Section 4. The Office of the . . . (*appropriate state official*) . . . shall keep (*required number*) copies of the said . . . (*identify the standard*) . . . additional copies are available from the . . . (*name and address of the originating group*).

Model State Statute to Adopt a Privately Developed Standard by Transcription

The state of . . . does ordain as follows:

Section 1. In the interest of public safety, the following standards shall govern . . . (*subject matter*) . . . .

Section 2. The . . . (*promulgating authority*) . . . recognizes the copyright owner to be the . . . (*name and address of originating group*).

Section 3. The following sections of the . . . (*identify the standard*) . . ., herein called . . . (*official name of state code*) . . ., have been added, amended, or deleted: (*List section numbers of all changes.*)

Section 4. . . (*the standard transcribed with indicated changes*).

Section 5. . . . (*indicate penalties for violations*) . . .

Model State Statute Using a Privately Developed Standard as Prima Facie Evidence

The state of . . . does hereby ordain as follows:

Section 1. In the interest of public safety, the . . . (*name of state code or act*) . . . is created to read and provide as follows:

Section 2. All . . . (*equipment named*) . . . hereafter installed, sold, or offered for sale shall be reasonably safe to persons and property.

(a) Installation, etc., of . . . (*equipment*) . . . that complies with the standards recommended by the . . . (*name of originating group*) . . . in the . . . (*identify the standard*) . . . shall be considered prima facie evidence of providing reasonable safety to persons and property in compliance with the intent of this Act.

Section 3. Copies of the . . . (*identify the standard*) . . . may be obtained from the . . . (*name and address of originating group*) . . . .

Section 4. . . . (*indicate penalties for violations*) . . . .

Model State Statute Enabling Municipal Governments to Adopt Privately Developed Standards by Reference

The state of . . . does ordain as follows:

Section 1. As used in this Act, unless the context otherwise requires:

(a) Municipality means . . . (*applicable state subdivisions*) . . .

(b) Code means a published "Code" or "Standard" as prepared and published by the . . . (*originating group*) . . .

(c) Related Document means those provisions of a published document that are adopted by reference in a code directly or indirectly by successive adoptions by reference through other printed documents.

(d) Adoption by Reference includes references making provisions of another document applicable.

(e) Published, as used in this Act, means printed, lithographed, multigraphed, mimeographed, or issued in other similar form.

Section 2. An ordinance of any municipality may adopt by reference a code, or any parts thereof, without setting forth the provisions of the code, or parts thereof, provided that copies of the code, or the pertinent parts thereof, and any related documents are filed in accordance with Section 3 of this Act. The title and date of publication shall be set forth in the ordinance. The requirements of law regarding the publication and posting of ordinances shall apply to the ordinance but not to the provisions that it adopts by reference, or any parts thereof, without setting forth the provisions of the related documents.

Section 3. Not less than three (3) copies of the code, or the pertinent parts thereof, and the related document shall be filed with the . . . (*appropriate official*) . . . and shall be available for public examination during regular business hours.

Section 4. The procedure authorized by this act for the enactment of ordinances shall apply to the amendment of ordinances enacted hereunder and to the amendment of all other ordinances prescribing standards or regulations with respect to the matters referred to in subsection (b) of Section 1 of this Act.

Section 5. This act may be cited as the Adoption by Reference Act.

Model Legislation: Local

Note: Local legislation follows the same basic pattern as the state legislation above; therefore, only one example of a local ordinance is included herein.

Model Municipal Ordinance to Adopt a Privately Developed Standard by Reference

Section 1. An ordinance to provide for the city of . . . rules and regulations to improve safety of the public by promoting the control of fire hazards; regulating the installation, use, and maintenance of equipment; the use of structures, premises, and open areas; providing for the abatement of fire hazards; and setting forth standards for compliance to achieve these objectives. (See NOTE below.)

[NOTE: A preamble of this type may be altered or amended as appropriate to include the hazard meant to be regulated. It is permissible to be comprehensive and nonspecific and to include hazards other than those that are to be specifically addressed by the adopted standard, but at least the general nature of the hazard should be included in the preamble list.]

Section 2. It shall be unlawful for any person to violate this ordinance, to permit or maintain such violation, to refuse to obey any provision thereof, or to fail or refuse to comply with any such provision or regulation except as variation may be allowed by action of the . . . (*title of enforcing official*) . . . in writing. Proof of such unlawful act or failure to act shall be deemed prima facie evidence that such act is that of the owner. Prosecution or lack thereof of either the owner or the occupant shall not be deemed to relieve the other.

Section 3. The provision shall apply equally to both public and private property. It shall apply to all new structures and their occupancies, including buildings, structures, equipment, etc., and, except as otherwise specified within its own terms, to existing structures and their occupancies, including buildings, structures, equipment, etc., that constitute a clear and present hazard to life or to property.

Section 4. The standard for . . . (*subject matter*) . . . shall be the standards set forth in . . . (*identify the standard*) . . . , and said code shall be part of this ordinance as though set out herein.

Section 5. The following sections of . . . (*identify the standard*) . . . are amended to read as indicated:

(*List any sections changed along with the changes made.*)

Section 6. . . . (*indicate penalties for violations*) . . .

Section 7. The Office of the . . . (*appropriate official*) . . . shall keep three (3) copies of the . . . (*identify the standard*) . . . on file and accessible to the public during regular business hours.

Section 8. Copies of the . . . (*identify the standard*) . . . are available from the . . . (*name and address of originating group*).

Retroactivity and Variances

Among the most popular additions to adopted codes are provisions regarding retroactivity and variances. Certain of the "model drafts" included herein may, if desired, be modified to include further language on "retroactivity" and on "variances." The decision to do so will depend on local needs, the legal terms of the enforcing authority, and whether the particular standard being incorporated into law contains such provisions. It should be noted that the *Life Safety Code* contains a provision on retroactivity. Therefore, in the adoption of the *Code*, there is no reason to provide a special section addressing the subject.

The following are suggested sections that may be included in any adopted statute or ordinance to provide language to cover these situations when they are determined to be necessary. These should be considered in light of the practices and intent of the authority having jurisdiction.

Section — (number of section) Retroactivity: Existing structures, facilities, and installations, as may be covered by regulations promulgated under the authority of this Act in service or under construction as of the effective date of this Act and which are not in strict compliance with the terms of this Act, may be continued or placed in use provided these do not constitute a distinct hazard to life or adjoining property. Where (*name appropriate board or committee*) deems that the continued use will constitute a distinct hazard to life or adjoining property, it shall notify the owner or operator and specify reason in writing.

Section — (number of section) Variances: The (*name appropriate board or committee*) shall have the power to grant exemption of application from specific requirements of regulations promulgated pursuant to this Act upon request in writing so to do when such request shows that the enforcement of the specific requirement will cause unnecessary hardship to the petitioner or in order to take advantage of new methods or equipment of recognized adequacy, provided that such request shall not be granted unless the requested equipment or use will, in the opinion of the (*name appropriate board or committee*), conform with all the fundamental requirements for safety. The particulars of such exemptions, when granted, shall be entered upon the approval granted. A copy thereof shall be retained by the (*name appropriate board, committee, or official*).

Appendix to Supplement 6

Examples of State Level Adoption by Reference	State Statutes Enabling Local Governments to Adopt by Reference
Federal Government: ex: 29 CFR § 1910.108 (g) (1)	
Alabama Code of Alabama Title 24-5-32	CA Title 11 § 45-8(c)
	Alaska AS § 29.25.040
Arizona City of Tuscan v. Stewart, 45 Ariz. 36;40 P2d 72 (1935) Case discusses an example of prima facie method of adoption and the larger right to adopt by reference. Uses the National Electrical Code.	Arizona Revised Statutes § 9-802
	California Annotated California Codes Government § 50022.2; Banks v. Civil Service Commissioner, 10 CA 2d 435; 74 P2d 741 (1937)
Colorado Colorado Revised Stats. Title 12-23-104 (3) (a)	CRS Title 31-16-201-208 or seq.
Connecticut Power of Fire Marshal to adopt Title 29 § 313	

Examples of State Level Adoption by Reference	State Statutes Enabling Local Governments to Adopt by Reference
Delaware (See Title 16 §6603 giving power to adopt regulations "in accordance with standard safe practices.")	
District of Columbia Title 5 D.C. § 1301-1303 (Rules and Regulations of the Fire Department)	
Florida Florida Statutes Annotated Title 23 § 320.822	
	Georgia Friedman v. Goodman 219 Ga. 152; 132 SE2d 60 (1963)
Hawaii Hawaii Revised Statutes Title 10 §132-3	Hawaii revised statutes Title 6 § 62-39
Idaho Idaho Code Title 41 Ch. 2 § 41-253	Idaho code Title 31 Ch. 7 § 31-714
Illinois ILL. Annot. Stats Ch.67½ § 502(g)	ILL. as Ch.24 § 1-3-2 and 1-3-3
Indiana Burns Ind. Stats. Annot. Title 22-8-1.1-13.1 22-8-1.1-15	BISA Title 36-1-5-4
Iowa Iowa Code 101A.5 Iowa Code Annotated Sec. 101A.5	Iowa Code Annotated § 380.10
Kansas Kan. Stats. Annot. 75-1220	Kansas Stats. Annot. Article 33 12-3301 et seq.
Kentucky Kentucky Revised Statutes 227.570	
Louisiana La. Revised Stats. ch.51 § 911.23	LA Rev. Stats. ch.33 § 1363
Maine Me. Revised Stats. Annot. Title 32 § 2313	MSRA Title 30 § 2156
	Maryland Annotated Codes of Maryland Art. 23A § 6
Massachusetts Ma. Gen. Laws Annot. ch.148 § 26A	
Michigan Mich. Compiled Laws Annot. Sec. 125.1504 (5); See also Michigan Statutes Annotated § 5.2949(4)	
Minnesota Minn. Stat. Annot. § 327.31 and .32	MSA § 471.62
Missouri Vernon's Annot. Mo. Stats. § 700.010	Different powers for different classes of cities. There is some language contrary to the general rule allowing adoption by reference.
Mississippi Miss. Code Annot. § 75-57-35	Mississippi Code Annotated § 21-19-25

Examples of State Level Adoption by Reference	State Statutes Enabling Local Governments to Adopt by Reference
Montana Montana Code Annotated 50-60-401	Montana Code Annotated 7-15-4121
Nebraska Revised Stats. of Neb. § 81-502	Revised Statutes of Nebraska § 18-132
Nevada Nevada Revised Stats. 278.583	Nevada Revised Statutes 266.115
New Hampshire N.H. Revised Stat. Annot. § 155-28156-A:10	
	New Jersey N.J.S.A. § 40:49-5.1
New Mexico N.M. Stats. Ann. 60-14-4	N.M. Stats. Annot. ch. 3-17-6
New York State Building Construction Code Vol. 9 Executive (B), Official Compilation of Codes, Rules and Regulations of the State of New York § 802.2 (example of use as prima facie evidence)	City of Syracuse v. Penny 59 Misc. 2d 818; 300 NYS2d 679 (1969)
North Carolina GSNC § 143-138(c)	GSNC § 160A-76(b)
North Dakota N.D. Century Code Annot. 54-21.3-03, 54-21.3-04	NDCCA 40-05-01
Ohio Baldwin's Ohio Revised Code Annot. Title 37 3737.17	BORCA Title 7 731.231
Oklahoma Okla. Stats. Annot. Title 75 § 251 (Actually an enabling statute)	
Oregon	Oregon Revised Stat. 215.605 and 221.330

Examples of State Level Adoption by Reference	State Statutes Enabling Local Governments to Adopt by Reference
Pennsylvania Purdon's Pa. Stats. Annot. Title 35 § 1655.3 (Repealed in 1982. Reference is now made to a Federal Government standard, National Manufactured Home Construction and Safety Standards Act of 1974).	PPSA Title 53 § 36014
Rhode Island Gen. Laws of R.I. 23-28.31-3,23-28.31-9	
South Carolina	Code or Laws of South Carolina § 6-9-60
South Dakota S.D. Compiled Laws § 34-38-14	SDCL § 9-33-4.1
Tennessee Tenn. Code Annot. § 68-18-101	TCA § 6-54-502
Texas Vernon's Civil Stats. of Tex. Annot. Art. 6066d § 3B	
	Virginia Code of Virginia § 27-5.1
Washington Revised Code of Wash. Title 19 § 27.030	RCW Title 35. § 27-5.1
West Virginia W.Va. Code § 21-3-3a	W.Va. C. § 8-11-4
Wisconsin Wisc. Stats. Annot. 101.94	
Wyoming Wyoming Stats. Annot. § 35-9-106	Wyoming Statutes Annotated § 15-1-119

Index

Tentative Interim Amendment

NFPA 101

Life Safety Code

1991 Edition

Reference: 20-3.5.1, 22-2.3.5.1, 23-2.3.5.1
T.I.A. 91-1

Pursuant to Section 15 of the NFPA Regulations Governing Committee Projects, the National Fire Protection Association has issued the following Tentative Interim Amendment to NFPA 101, *Life Safety Code*, 1991 edition. The TIA was processed by the Safety to Life Committee and was issued by the Standards Council on July 19, 1991.

A Tentative Interim Amendment is tentative because it has not been processed through the entire standards-making procedures. It is interim because it is effective only between editions of the standard. A TIA automatically becomes a Proposal of the proponent for the next edition of the standard; as such, it then is subject to all of the procedures of the standards making process.

1. Add a new exception to 20-3.5.1:

Exception No. 3:   In buildings up to and including four stories in height, systems installed in accordance with NFPA 13R, Standard for the Installation of Sprinkler Systems in Residential Occupancies up to and Including Four Stories in Height, 1991 edition, shall be permitted.

2. Add two new exceptions to 22-2.3.5.1:

Exception No. 4:   In prompt and slow facilities up to and including four stories in height, systems installed in accordance with NFPA 13R, Standard for the Installation of Sprinkler Systems in Residential Occupancies up to and Including Four Stories in Height, 1991 edition, shall be permitted.

Exception No. 5:   In impractical facilities up to and including four stories in height, systems installed in accordance with NFPA 13R, Standard for the Installation of Sprinkler Systems in Residential Occupancies up to and Including Four Stories in Height, 1991 edition, shall be permitted. All habitable areas and closets shall be sprinklered.

3. Add two new exceptions to 23-2.3.5.1:

Exception No. 4:   In prompt and slow facilities up to and including four stories in height, systems installed in accordance with NFPA 13R, Standard for the Installation of Sprinkler Systems in Residential Occupancies up to and Including Four Stories in Height, 1991 edition, shall be permitted.

(Continued)

Exception No. 5:   In impractical facilities up to and including four stories in height, systems installed in accordance with NFPA 13R, Standard for the Installation of Sprinkler Systems in Residential Occupancies up to and Including Four Stories in Height, 1991 edition, shall be permitted. All habitable areas and closets shall be sprinklered. Automatic sprinklers are not required in bathrooms not exceeding 55 sq ft (5.1 sq m) provided such spaces are finished with lath and plaster or material providing a 15-minute thermal barrier.

NEW! 1991 Life Safety Code Changes Video